COLLEGE PHYSICS

by

FRANCIS WESTON SEARS
Professor of Physics
Dartmouth College

and

MARK W. ZEMANSKY
Professor of Physics
The City College of New York

THIRD EDITION

ADDISON-WESLEY PUBLISHING COMPANY, INC.

Reading, Massachusetts · Menlo Park, California · London · Sydney · Manila

COLLEGE PHYSICS

PREFACE

College Physics is available in one complete volume or as two separate parts: Part 1 covers the subjects of mechanics, heat, and sound; Part 2 includes electricity and magnetism, light, and atomic physics. The total number of topics is small enough so that the complete text may be taught in two semesters.

The text consists exclusively of material suitable for students whose mathematical preparation goes no further than algebra and the elements of trigonometry; no calculus is used. The emphasis is on physical principles; historical background and practical applications have been given a place of secondary importance.

Three systems of units are used: the British gravitational system because it is the one used in engineering work throughout the country; the cgs system because some familiarity with it is essential for any intelligent reading of the literature of physics; and the mks system because of its increasing use in electricity and magnetism, as well as because it seems destined eventually to supplant the cgs system. The symbols and terminology, with few exceptions, are those recommended by the Committee on Letter Symbols and Abbreviations of the American Association of Physics Teachers as listed in the American Standard, ASA-Z10, published in 1947.

The main features of the preceding editions have been retained in the third. The supplementary problems that appeared at the end of the second edition have been incorporated with the problems that follow each chapter. Many figures have been redrawn to achieve greater uniformity and clarity, and many of the optical ray diagrams have been reproduced in white on black. Numerous illustrative problems are worked out in the body of the text; in each of them, all physical quantities are expressed by numerics along with the appropriate units.

The following new material has been incorporated in the third edition: Reynolds number, extension of Bernoulli's equation to include friction, thermoelectricity, Ampere's law, a simple derivation of the expression for the speed of an electromagnetic wave, and the Galilean telescope. Projectile motion and circular motion have been brought into the same chapter, entitled "Motion in a Plane." A new sign convention in geometrical optics allows the same formulas to be used for both mirrors and lenses. The chapter on energy has been completely rewritten from a simple point of view that prepares the student for later, more sophisticated treatments. In the interests of simplicity and clarity, much of the material from earlier editions has been rewritten.

In preparing this revision the authors have referred constantly to the many letters and reviews sent to the publishers by colleagues and friends. We have tried to incorporate most of the suggestions based upon actual teaching experience and have rejected only those which would have required too much space or would have involved too great a departure from normal practice. It is with a feeling of sincere gratitude that we acknowledge the help we have received from the following teachers of physics: C. Adler, R. S. Anderson, B. Bederson and S. Borowitz, C. J. Brasefield, A. Capecelatro, H. Conrad, F. S. C., L. H. Fisher, S. Freeman, Jr., N. S. Gingrich, S. Goodwin, L. E. Hammitt, C. D. Hodgman, M. Iona, R. Katz, S. W. Leifson, M. S. Livingston, R. J. Maurer, L. O. Olsen, R. Pinkston, J. G. Potter, R. Resnick, F. A. Scott, C. P. Slichter, F. W. Thiele, F. Verbrugge, A. E. Werbrouck, L. Wolfenstein, and R. E. Worley.

F. W. S.
M. W. Z.

July 1959

CONTENTS

MECHANICS

xi

SOUND

ELECTRICITY AND MAGNETISM

LIGHT

ATOMIC PHYSICS

CHAPTER 1

COMPOSITION AND RESOLUTION OF VECTORS

1–1 The fundamental indefinables of mechanics. Physics has been called the science of measurement. To quote from Lord Kelvin (1824–1907), "I often say that when you can measure what you are speaking about, and express it in numbers, you know something about it; but when you cannot express it in numbers, your knowledge is of a meagre and unsatisfactory kind; it may be the beginning of knowledge, but you have scarcely, in your thoughts, advanced to the stage of *Science*, whatever the matter may be."

A definition of a quantity in physics must provide a set of rules for calculating it in terms of other quantities that can be measured. Thus, when momentum is defined as the product of "mass" and "velocity," the rule for calculating momentum is contained within the definition, and all that is necessary is to know how to measure mass and velocity. The definition of velocity is given in terms of length and time, but there are no simpler or more fundamental quantities in terms of which length and time may be expressed. *Length and time are two of the indefinables of mechanics.* It has been found possible to express all the quantities of mechanics in terms of only three indefinables. The third may be taken to be "mass" or "force" with equal justification. *We shall choose mass as the third indefinable of mechanics.*

In geometry, the fundamental indefinable is the "point." The geometer asks his disciple to build any picture of a point in his mind, provided the picture is consistent with what the geometer *says* about the point. In physics, the situation is not so subtle. Physicists from all over the world have international committees at whose meetings the rules of measurement of the indefinables are· adopted. The rule for measuring an indefinable takes the place of a definition.

1–2 Standards and units. The measurement of any indefinable of physics involves the application of a simple set of rules. Instead of referring to these rules in the abstract, let us employ them in connection with the quantity "length." The first step is to choose an arbitrary *standard* of length, in the form of an inanimate, solid, durable material. The international standard of length is a bar of platinum-iridium alloy of X-shaped cross section (see Fig. 1–1) called the *standard meter*, which is kept at the International Bureau of Weights and Measures at Sevres, near Paris.

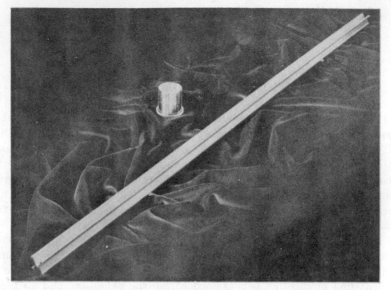

FIG. 1–1. The standard meter and the standard kilogram.

The distance between two lines engraved on gold plugs near the ends of the bar, when the bar is at the temperature of melting ice, is called *one meter*. The meter was originally intended to represent one ten-millionth of the earth's quadrant through Paris, but later, more accurate measurements, have shown that it differs from its intended value by a small amount. This is unimportant. There is no reason why a standard of length should have any connection with the earth's quadrant or with any other length. *A standard is arbitrary, and its virtue lies in the fact that all the scientists of the world accept it.*

The next step is to adopt, also by international agreement, a device or a method by which other lengths may be made equal to the standard, or any multiple or any fraction of the standard. The device for this purpose is a *dividing engine* in which a microscope, mounted on a movable stand, advances along a helical screw when the screw is rotated. With this device two lengths are said to be equal when they both require the same number of rotations of the screw. If one requires one-half the number, it is regarded as half the length, etc. Nowadays, the number of rotations of the screw is replaced by the number of wavelengths of cadmium red light. This requires the addition of an optical interferometer to the dividing engine.

Any multiple or fraction of the standard, and sometimes the standard itself, may be chosen as a convenient *unit* for some specific purpose. Thus, to measure the dimensions of objects like books or tables, a unit called the *centimeter* is often used, where

$$1 \text{ centimeter} = 10^{-2} \text{ meter.}$$

For atomic dimensions, however, a unit called the *angstrom unit* is found more convenient, where

$$1 \text{ angstrom unit} = 10^{-10} \text{ meter.}$$

In astronomy, a convenient unit of length is the distance light travels in a year, or

$$1 \text{ light year} = 9.45 \times 10^{15} \text{ meters.}$$

The *yard*, originally embodied by a physical standard like the meter, is now defined as

$$1 \text{ yard} = 0.9144 \text{ meter (exactly),}$$

so that the same physical standard serves for both the yard and the meter. The *foot* is defined as one-third of a yard.

The standard of time is our rotating earth and the standard time interval is called the *mean solar day*, the average time interval between successive appearances of the sun overhead. The device for determining whether two time intervals are equal, and also for subdividing the standard time interval into any number of equal subintervals, has been chosen to be the pendulum. The pendulum will be discussed fully in Chapter 11. It is sufficient at this time to know that two time intervals are equal when the same number of pendulum swings occur in each interval. If a pendulum makes 86,400 swings ($60 \times 60 \times 24$) in one mean solar day, the time interval for each swing is said to be one *second*. The second is the most convenient unit of time for most purposes.

The international standard of mass is a cylinder of platinum-iridium (see Fig. 1–1) called the standard *kilogram* (abbreviated kgm). It was originally intended to have a mass equal to that of 1000 cm^3 of pure water at a temperature of 4°C but, as with the standard meter, more precise measurements have shown that this is not exactly true. It is important to emphasize again that the standard kilogram does not have to correspond to a mass of water or of anything else. Whatever it is, it must be accepted by all scientists over the world. The device for determining whether two masses are equal, and also for subdividing the standard kilogram into any number of equal parts or of defining any multiple of the kilogram, is an *equal-arm balance*. The concept of mass as well as the operation of an equal-arm balance will be fully discussed in Chapter 5. It suffices at this time to know that two masses are said to be equal if they balance on an equal-arm balance. If two equal masses that are placed on the left pan balance the standard kilogram on the right pan, then each of the two masses on the left pan is equal to one-half a kilogram. A convenient unit of mass for many purposes is provided by one-one thousandth of a kilogram, or one gram (1 gm).

The pound mass, like the yard, was formerly embodied by a physical standard of its own, but the *standard avoirdupois pound* is now defined in the U.S. as a body of mass 0.4535924277 kgm.

1–3 Symbols for physical quantities. We shall adopt the convention that an algebraic symbol representing a physical quantity, such as F, p, or v, stands for both a *number* and a *unit*. For example, F might represent a force of 10 lb, p a pressure of 15 lb/ft^2, and v a velocity of 15 ft/sec.

When we write

$$x = v_0 t + \tfrac{1}{2}at^2,$$

if x is in feet then the terms $v_0 t$ and $\tfrac{1}{2}at^2$ must be in feet also. Suppose t is in seconds. Then the units of v_0 must be ft/sec and those of a must be ft/sec^2. (The factor $\tfrac{1}{2}$ is a *pure number*, without units.) As a numerical example, let $v_0 = 10$ ft/sec, $a = 4$ ft/sec^2, $t = 10$ sec. Then the preceding equation would be written

$$x = 10\,\frac{\text{ft}}{\text{sec}} \times 10\ \text{sec} + \tfrac{1}{2} \times 4\,\frac{\text{ft}}{\text{sec}^2} \times 100\ \text{sec}^2.$$

The units can now be treated like algebraic symbols. The sec's cancel in the first term and the sec^2's in the second, and

$$x = 100\ \text{ft} + 200\ \text{ft} = 300\ \text{ft}.$$

The beginning student will do well to include the units of all physical quantities, as well as their magnitudes, in all his calculations. This will be done consistently in the numerical examples throughout the book.

1–4 Force. Mechanics is the branch of physics which deals with the motion of material bodies and with the forces that bring about the motion. We shall postpone a discussion of motion until Chapter 4, and start with a study of forces.

When we push or pull on a body, we are said to exert a *force* on it. Forces can also be exerted by inanimate objects; a stretched spring exerts forces on the bodies to which its ends are attached, compressed air exerts a force on the walls of its container, a locomotive exerts a force on the train it is drawing. The force of which we are most aware in our daily lives is the force of gravitational attraction exerted on every body by the earth and called the *weight* of the body. Gravitational forces (and electrical and magnetic forces also) can act through empty space without contact. In this respect they differ from the forces mentioned above, where the body doing the pushing or pulling must make contact with the body being pushed or pulled.

We are not yet in a position to show how a unit of force can be defined in terms of the units of mass, length, and time. This will be done in Chapter 5. For the present, a unit of force can be defined as follows. We select as a standard body the standard pound, defined in the preceding section as a certain fraction (approximately 0.454) of a standard kilogram. The force with which the earth attracts this body, at some specified point on the earth's surface, is then a perfectly definite, reproducible force and is called a force of *one pound* (avoirdupois). A particular point on the earth's surface must be specified, since the attraction of the earth for a given body varies slightly from one point to another. If great precision is not required it suffices to take any point at sea level and 45° latitude. A more precise specification is given in Section 5–3.

In order that an unknown force can be compared with the force unit, and thereby measured, some measurable effect produced by a force must be used. One such effect is to alter the dimensions or shape of a body on which the force is exerted; another is to alter the state of motion of the body. Both of these effects are used in the measurement of forces. In this chapter we shall consider only the former; the latter will be discussed in Chapter 5.

The instrument most commonly used to measure forces is the spring balance, which consists of a coil spring enclosed in a case for protection and carrying at one end a pointer that moves over a scale. A force exerted on the balance changes the length of the spring. The balance can be calibrated as follows. The standard pound is first suspended from the balance at sea level and 45° latitude and the position of the pointer is marked 1 lb. Any number of duplicates of the standard can then be prepared by suspending a body from the balance and adding or removing material until the index again stands at 1 lb. Then when two, three, or more of these are suspended simultaneously from the balance the force stretching it is 2 lb, 3 lb, etc., and the corresponding positions of the pointer can be labeled 2 lb, 3 lb, etc. This procedure makes no assumption about the elastic properties of the spring except that the force exerted on it is always the same when the pointer stands at the same position. The calibrated balance can then be used to measure any unknown force.

1–5 Graphical representation of forces. Vectors. Suppose we are to slide a box along the floor by pulling it with a string or pushing it with a stick, as in Fig. 1–2. That is, we are to slide it by exerting a force on it. The point of view which we now adopt is that the motion of the box is caused not by the *objects* which push or pull on it, but by the *forces* which

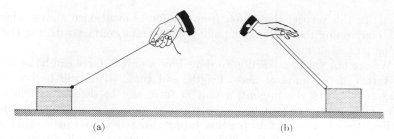

FIGURE 1-2

these exert. For concreteness, assume the magnitude of the push or pull to be 10 lb. It is clear that simply to write "10 lb" on the diagram would not completely describe the force, since it would not indicate the direction in which the force was acting. One might write "10 lb, 30° above horizontal to the right," or "10 lb, 45° below horizontal to the right," but all the above information may be conveyed more briefly if we adopt the convention of representing a force by an arrow. The length of the arrow, to some chosen scale, indicates the size or magnitude of the force, and the direction in which the arrow points indicates the direction of the force. Thus Fig. 1-3 is the force diagram corresponding to Fig. 1-2. (There are other forces acting on the box, but these are not shown in the figure.)

Force is not the only physical quantity which requires the specification of direction as well as magnitude. For example, the velocity of an aircraft is not completely specified by stating that it is 300 miles per hour; we need to know the direction also. The concept of volume, on the other hand, has no direction associated with it.

Quantities like volume, which involve a magnitude only, are called *scalars*. Those like force and velocity, which involve both magnitude and direction, are called *vector quantities*. A vector quantity is represented mathematically by a letter printed in boldface (heavy) type. When this letter appears in an equation, it is understood that both the magnitude and

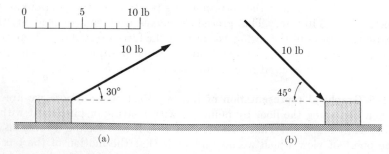

FIGURE 1-3

the direction of the vector quantity are included within the one symbol. The same letter in ordinary (lightface) type represents the magnitude only. Thus, the magnitude of the vector $\mathbf{F}$ is represented by F. In writing the symbol for a vector quantity on paper or on the blackboard it is often convenient to double one of the vertical lines of the letter, like $\mathbf{F}$. When a vector quantity is represented graphically by an arrow, the arrow is called a vector (or if a more specific statement is needed, a force vector or a velocity vector).

Some vector quantities, of which force is one, are not *completely* specified by their magnitude and direction alone. Thus the effect of a force depends also on its *line of action* and its *point of application*. (The line of action is a line of indefinite length, of which the force vector is a segment.) For example, if one is pushing horizontally against a door, the effectiveness of a force of given magnitude and direction depends on the distance of its line of action from the hinges. If a body is deformable, as all bodies are to a greater or lesser extent, the deformation depends on the point of application of the force. However, since many actual objects are deformed only very slightly by the forces acting on them, we shall assume for the present that all objects considered are perfectly rigid. The point of application of a given force acting on a rigid body may be transferred to any other point on the line of action without altering the effect of the force. Thus *a force applied to a rigid body may be regarded as acting anywhere along its line of action.*

1–6 Components of a vector. When a box is pulled or pushed along the floor by an inclined force as in Fig. 1–2, the effectiveness of the force in moving the box along the floor depends upon the direction in which the force acts. Furthermore, each of the forces in Fig. 1–2 is producing another effect in addition to moving the box ahead. That is, the pull of the cord is in part tending to lift the box off the floor, and the push of the stick is in part forcing the box down against the floor. We are thus led to the idea of the *components* of a force, that is, the effective values of a force in directions other than that of the force itself.

The component of a force in any direction can be found by a simple graphical method. Let a given force be represented by the vector $\mathbf{F}$ in Fig. 1–4, from O to A. To find the component of $\mathbf{F}$ in the direction of the line Ob, drop a perpendicular from A to this line, intersecting it at point B. The vector $\mathbf{F}_b$, from O to B, to the same scale as that used for the vector $\mathbf{F}$, then represents the component of $\mathbf{F}$ in the direction Ob, or the effective value of the force in this direction.

Similarly, the vector $\mathbf{F}_c$ from O to C represents the component of $\mathbf{F}$ in the direction Oc. The component along Od, at right angles to $\mathbf{F}$, is zero, and the component along Oa is equal to $\mathbf{F}$.

The magnitude of a component of a vector in any direction can be calculated as follows. Referring to Fig. 1–4, we have from the right triangle OAB,

$$\cos \theta_b = \frac{OB}{OA} = \frac{F_b}{F},$$

$$F_b = F \cos \theta_b.$$

If $F = 10$ lb and $\theta_b = 60°$, $\cos \theta_b = 0.500$ and

$$F_b = 10 \text{ lb} \times 0.500 = 5.00 \text{ lb}.$$

In the same way,

$$\cos \theta_c = \frac{OC}{OA} = \frac{F_c}{F},$$

$$F_c = F \cos \theta_c.$$

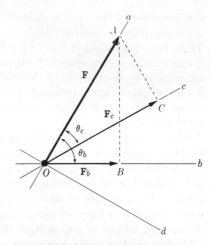

FIG. 1–4. Vectors F_b and F_c are the components of F in the directions Ob and Oc. The component along Od, perpendicular to F, is zero.

If $\theta_c = 30°$, $\cos \theta_c = 0.866$ and $F_c = 10 \text{ lb} \times 0.866 = 8.66$ lb.

In general, then, the magnitude of the component of a vector F in any direction making an angle θ with that of the vector is equal to $F \cos \theta$. If $\theta = 90°$, $\cos \theta = 0$ and the component at right angles to the vector is zero. If $\theta = 0$, $\cos \theta = 1$ and the component is equal to F.

Figure 1–5 shows the same box as in Figs. 1–2(a) and 1–3(a). The vectors F_x and F_y are the components of F in the mutually perpendicular directions Ox and Oy, and are called the *rectangular components* of F in these two directions. But since a vector has no component at right angles

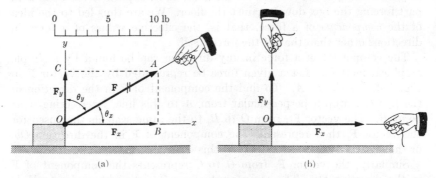

FIG. 1–5. The inclined force F may be replaced by its rectangular components F_x and F_y. $F_x = F \cos \theta_x$, $F_y = F \cos \theta_y$.

to its own direction, $\mathbf{F}_x$ has no component along Oy and $\mathbf{F}_y$ has no component along Ox. No further resolution of the force into x- and y-components is therefore possible. Physically, this means that the two forces $\mathbf{F}_x$ and $\mathbf{F}_y$, acting simultaneously as in Fig. 1–5(b), are equivalent in all respects to the original force $\mathbf{F}$. *Any force may be replaced by its rectangular components.*

As a numerical example, let the force $\mathbf{F}$ in Fig. 1–5 have a magnitude of 10 lb, and let $\theta_x = 30°$, $\theta_y = 60°$. Then $F_x = 8.66$ lb, $F_y = 5.00$ lb, and these two forces applied simultaneously as in part (b) are found to produce exactly the same effect as the single force of 10 lb in part (a).

It is often convenient to express both the x- and y-components of a vector in terms of the angle between the vector and the x-axis. We see from Fig. 1–5(a) that

$$\sin \theta_x = \frac{BA}{OA} = \frac{OC}{OA} = \frac{F_y}{F},$$

$$F_y = F \sin \theta_x.$$

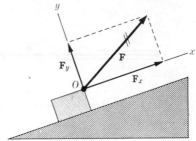

Hence with the understanding that θ refers to the angle between a vector $\mathbf{F}$ and the x-axis, we can say, in general, that

$$F_x = F \cos \theta,$$

$$F_y = F \sin \theta.$$

Fig. 1–6. $\mathbf{F}_x$ and $\mathbf{F}_y$ are the rectangular components of $\mathbf{F}$, parallel and perpendicular to the sloping surface of the inclined plane.

The directions in which the rectangular components of a vector may be desired are not necessarily horizontal and vertical. For example, Fig. 1–6 shows a block being dragged up an inclined plane by a force $\mathbf{F}$. The vectors $\mathbf{F}_x$ and $\mathbf{F}_y$ are the components of $\mathbf{F}$ parallel and perpendicular to the sloping surface of the plane.

1–7 Resultant or vector sum. Ordinarily a body is acted on simultaneously by a number of forces having different magnitudes, directions, and points of application. To begin with, we shall consider only sets of forces which lie in the same plane (*coplanar* forces) and which have the same point of application (*concurrent* forces). It is found by experiment that any set of coplanar, concurrent forces can be replaced by a single force whose effect is the same as that of the given forces and which is called their *resultant*.

In Fig. 1–7, a body is acted on by the two forces $\mathbf{F}_1$ and $\mathbf{F}_2$, both applied at point O. To find their resultant, construct the parallelogram $OACB$, of which the vectors $\mathbf{F}_1$ and $\mathbf{F}_2$ form two adjacent sides. The concurrent

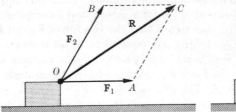

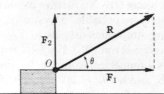

FIG. 1–7. Force **R**, the resultant of **F**$_1$ and **F**$_2$, is obtained by the parallelogram method.

FIG. 1–8. Resultant of two forces at right angles to each other.

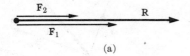

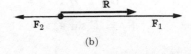

(a)   (b)

FIG. 1–9. Resultant of (a) two parallel forces, (b) two antiparallel forces.

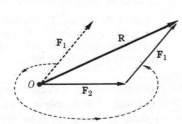

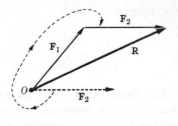

FIG. 1–10. The triangle method for finding the resultant of two forces.

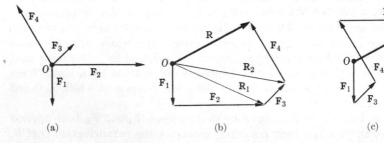

(a)   (b)   (c)

FIG. 1–11. Polygon method.

diagonal of the parallelogram, that is, the vector $\mathbf{R}$ from O to C, is called the *vector sum* of the vectors $\mathbf{F}_1$ and $\mathbf{F}_2$, and we find by experiment that it represents the resultant force in magnitude and direction.

In the special case in which the forces $\mathbf{F}_1$ and $\mathbf{F}_2$ are at right angles to each other, as in Fig. 1–8, the triangle OAC is a right triangle whose sides are the forces $\mathbf{F}_1$ and $\mathbf{F}_2$. The magnitude and direction of the resultant are then given by

$$R = \sqrt{F_1^2 + F_2^2}, \qquad \tan \theta = \frac{F_2}{F_1}.$$

Another special case is that in which two forces having the same line of action are parallel, as in Fig. 1–9(a), or antiparallel, as in Fig. 1–9(b). If they are parallel, the magnitude of the resultant $\mathbf{R}$ equals the sum of the magnitudes of $\mathbf{F}_1$ and $\mathbf{F}_2$. If they are antiparallel the magnitude of the resultant equals the difference between the magnitudes of $\mathbf{F}_1$ and $\mathbf{F}_2$.

The construction in Fig. 1–7 is called the *parallelogram* method of finding the resultant of two vectors. The *triangle* method, shown in Fig. 1–10, consists of displacing either vector parallel to itself until its tail coincides with the head of the other vector. The resultant $\mathbf{R}$ is then represented by the closing side of the triangle.

When more than two forces are to be combined, one may first find the resultant of any two, then combine this resultant with a third, and so on. The process is illustrated in Fig. 1–11, which shows the four forces $\mathbf{F}_1$, $\mathbf{F}_2$, $\mathbf{F}_3$, and $\mathbf{F}_4$ acting simultaneously at the point O. In Fig. 1–11(b), forces $\mathbf{F}_1$ and $\mathbf{F}_2$ are first combined by the triangle method, giving a resultant $\mathbf{R}_1$; force $\mathbf{R}_1$ is then combined by the same process with $\mathbf{F}_3$, giving a resultant $\mathbf{R}_2$; finally $\mathbf{R}_2$ and $\mathbf{F}_4$ are combined to obtain the resultant $\mathbf{R}$. Evidently the vectors $\mathbf{R}_1$ and $\mathbf{R}_2$ need not have been drawn—one need only draw the given vectors in succession, with the tail of each at the head of the one preceding it, and complete the polygon by a vector $\mathbf{R}$ from the tail of the first to the head of the last vector. The order in which the vectors are drawn makes no difference, as shown in Fig. 1–11(c).

1–8 Resultant by rectangular resolution. While the polygon method is a satisfactory graphical one for finding the resultant of a number of forces, it is awkward for computation because one must, in general, solve a number of oblique triangles. Therefore the usual analytical method of finding the resultant is first to resolve all forces into rectangular components along any convenient pair of axes and then combine these into a single resultant. This makes it possible to work with right triangles only.

Figure 1–12(a) shows three concurrent forces $\mathbf{F}_1$, $\mathbf{F}_2$, and $\mathbf{F}_3$, whose resultant we wish to find. Let a pair of rectangular axes be constructed in any arbitrary direction. Simplification results if one axis coincides with

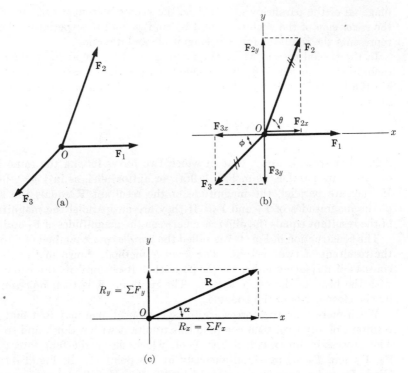

FIG. 1–12.   Vector **R**, the resultant of F_1, F_2, and F_3, is obtained by the method of rectangular resolution.   The rectangular components of **R** have the magnitudes $R_x = \sum F_x$, $R_y = \sum F_y$.

one of the forces, which is always possible.   In Fig. 1–12(b), the x-axis coincides with F_1.   Let us first resolve each of the given forces into x- and y-components.   According to the usual conventions of analytic geometry, x-components toward the right are considered positive and those toward the left, negative.   Upward y-components are positive and downward y-components are negative.

Force F_1 lies along the x-axis and need not be resolved.   The magnitudes of the components of F_2 are $F_{2x} = F_2 \cos \theta$, $F_{2y} = F_2 \sin \theta$.   Both of these are positive, and F_{2x} has been slightly displaced upward to show it more clearly.   The components of F_3 are $F_{3x} = F_3 \cos \phi$, $F_{3y} = F_3 \sin \phi$. Both of these are negative.

We now imagine F_2 and F_3 to be removed and replaced by their rectangular components.   To indicate this, the vectors F_2 and F_3 are crossed out lightly.   All the x-components can now be combined into a single force R_x whose magnitude equals the algebraic sum of the x-components, or ΣF_x, and all the y-components can be combined into a single force $\mathbf{R}_y$ of magnitude ΣF_y.

$$R_x = \Sigma F_x, \qquad R_y = \Sigma F_y.$$

Finally, these can be combined as in part (c) of the figure to form the resultant $\mathbf{R}$ whose magnitude, since R_x and R_y are perpendicular to each other, is

$$R = \sqrt{R_x^2 + R_y^2}.$$

The angle α between $\mathbf{R}$ and the x-axis can now be found from any one of its trigonometric functions. For example,

$$\tan \alpha = \frac{R_y}{R_x}.$$

EXAMPLE. In Fig. 1–12, let $F_1 = 120$ lb, $F_2 = 200$ lb, $F_3 = 150$ lb, $\theta = 60°$, $\phi = 45°$. The computations can be arranged systematically as follows:

Force	Angle	x-component	y-component
$F_1 = 120$ lb	0	$+120$ lb	0
$F_2 = 200$ lb	60°	$+100$ lb	$+173$ lb
$F_3 = 150$ lb	45°	-106 lb	-106 lb
		$\Sigma F_x =$ $+114$ lb	$\Sigma F_y =$ $+67$ lb

$$R = \sqrt{(114 \text{ lb})^2 + (67 \text{ lb})^2} = 132 \text{ lb},$$

$$\alpha = \tan^{-1} \frac{67 \text{ lb}}{114 \text{ lb}} = \tan^{-1} 0.588 = 30.4°.$$

1–9 Vector difference. It is sometimes necessary to subtract one vector from another. The process of subtracting one *algebraic* quantity from another is equivalent to adding the negative of the quantity to be subtracted. That is,

$$a - b = a + (-b).$$

Similarly, the process of subtracting one *vector* quantity from another is equivalent to adding (vectorially) the negative of the vector to be subtracted, where the negative of a given vector is defined as a vector of the same magnitude but in the opposite direction. That is, if $\mathbf{A}$ and $\mathbf{B}$ are two vectors,

$$\mathbf{A} - \mathbf{B} = \mathbf{A} + (-\mathbf{B}).$$

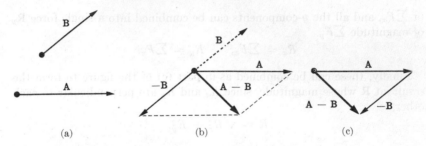

(a)   (b)   (c)

FIG. 1–13. The vector difference **A** — **B** is found in part (b) by the parallelo-gram method and in part (c) by the triangle method.

Vector subtraction is illustrated in Fig. 1–13. The given vectors are shown in part (a). In part (b), the vector sum of **A** and —**B**, or the vector difference **A** — **B**, is found by the parallelogram method. In part (c), the triangle method has been used.

Vector differences may also be found by the method of rectangular resolution. Both vectors are resolved into x- and y-components. The difference between the x-components is the x-component of the desired vector difference, and the difference between the y-components is the y-component of the vector difference.

Vector subtraction is not often used when dealing with forces, but we shall use it frequently in connection with velocities and accelerations.

PROBLEMS

1-1. (a) Find graphically the horizontal and vertical components of a 40-lb force the direction of which is 50° above the horizontal to the right. Let 1/16 in. = 1 lb. (b) Check your results by calculating the components.

1-2. A box is pushed along the floor as in Fig. 1-2 by a force of 40 lb making an angle of 30° with the horizontal. Using a scale of 1 in. = 10 lb, find the horizontal and vertical components of the force by the graphical method. Check your results by calculating the components.

1-3. A block is dragged up an inclined plane of slope angle 20° by a force **F** making an angle of 30° with the plane, as in Fig. 1-6. (a) How large a force **F** is necessary in order that the component F_x parallel to the plane shall be 16 lb? (b) How large will the component F_y then be? Solve graphically, letting 1 in. = 8 lb.

1-4. The three forces shown in Fig. 1-14 act on a body located at the origin. (a) Find the x- and y-components of each of the three forces. (b) Use the method of rectangular resolution to find the resultant of the forces. (c) Find the magnitude and direction of a fourth force which must be added to make the resultant force zero. Indicate the fourth force by a diagram.

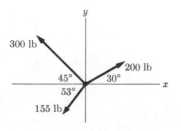

FIGURE 1-14

1-5. Find graphically the magnitude and direction of the resultant of the three forces in Fig. 1-14. Use the polygon method.

1-6. Two men and a boy want to push a crate in the direction marked x in Fig. 1-15. The two men push with forces **F₁** and **F₂** whose magnitudes and directions are indicated in the figure. Find the magnitude and direction of the smallest force which the boy should exert.

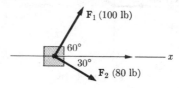

FIGURE 1-15

1-7. Find graphically the resultant of two 10-lb forces applied at the same point: (a) when the angle between the forces is 30°; (b) when the angle between them is 130°. Use any convenient scale.

1-8. Two men pull horizontally on ropes attached to a post, the angle between the ropes being 45°. If man A exerts a force of 150 lb and man B a force of 100 lb, find the magnitude of the resultant force and the angle it makes with A's pull. Solve: (a) graphically, by the parallelogram method; (b) graphically, by the triangle method; (c) analytically, by the method of rectangular resolution. Let 1 in. = 50 lb in (a) and (b).

1-9. Use the method of rectangular resolution to find the resultant of the following set of forces and the angle it makes with the horizontal: 200 lb, along the x-axis toward the right; 300 lb, 60° above the x-axis to the right;

100 lb, 45° above the x-axis to the left; 200 lb, vertically down.

1–10. (a) Find graphically the vector sum $\mathbf{A} + \mathbf{B}$ and the vector difference $\mathbf{A} - \mathbf{B}$ in Fig. 1–16. (b) Use the method of rectangular resolution to find the magnitude and direction of the vector sum and the vector difference.

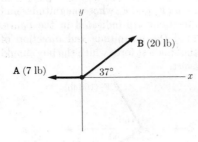

FIGURE 1–16

1–11. Vector $\mathbf{A}$ is 2 inches long and is 60° above the x-axis in the first quadrant. Vector $\mathbf{B}$ is 2 inches long and is 60° below the x-axis in the fourth quadrant. Find graphically (a) the vector sum $\mathbf{A} + \mathbf{B}$, and (b) the vector differences $\mathbf{A} - \mathbf{B}$ and $\mathbf{B} - \mathbf{A}$.

1–12. A vector $\mathbf{A}$ of length 10 units makes an angle of 30° with a vector $\mathbf{B}$ of length 6 units. Find the magnitude of the vector difference $\mathbf{A} - \mathbf{B}$ and the angle it makes with vector $\mathbf{A}$: (a) by the parallelogram method; (b) by the triangle method; (c) by the method of rectangular resolution.

1–13. Two forces, $\mathbf{F}_1$ and $\mathbf{F}_2$, act at a point. The magnitude of $\mathbf{F}_1$ is 8 lb and its direction is 60° above the x-axis in the first quadrant. The magnitude of $\mathbf{F}_2$ is 5 lb and its direction is 53° below the x-axis in the fourth quadrant. (a) What are the horizontal and vertical components of the resultant force? (b) What is the magnitude of the resultant? (c) What is the magnitude of the vector difference $\mathbf{F}_1 - \mathbf{F}_2$?

1–14. Two forces, $\mathbf{F}_1$ and $\mathbf{F}_2$, act upon a body in such a manner that the resultant force $\mathbf{R}$ has a magnitude equal to that of $\mathbf{F}_1$ and makes an angle of 90° with $\mathbf{F}_1$. Let $F_1 = R = 10$ lb. Find the magnitude of the second force, and its direction (relative to $\mathbf{F}_1$).

1–15. Find the resultant of the following set of forces by the method of rectangular resolution: 80 lb, vertically down; 100 lb, 53° above horizontal to the right; 60 lb, horizontal to the left. Check by the polygon method.

CHAPTER 2

EQUILIBRIUM

2-1 Introduction. The science of mechanics is based on three natural laws which were clearly stated for the first time by Sir Isaac Newton (1643–1727) and were published in 1686 in his *Philosophiae Naturalis Principia Mathematica* ("The Mathematical Principles of Natural Science"). It should not be inferred, however, that the science of mechanics began with Newton. Many men had preceded him in this field, the most outstanding being Galileo Galilei (1564–1642), who in his studies of accelerated motion had laid much of the groundwork of Newton's three laws.

In this chapter we shall make use of only two of Newton's laws, the first and the third. Newton's second law will be discussed in Chapter 5.

2-2 Equilibrium. Newton's first law. One effect of a force is to alter the dimensions or shape of a body on which the force acts; another is to alter the state of motion of the body.

The motion of a body can be considered as made up of its motion as a whole, or its *translational* motion, together with any *rotational* motion the body may have. In the most general case, a single force acting on a body produces a change in both its translational and rotational motion. However, when several forces act on a body simultaneously, their effects can compensate one another, with the result that there is no change in either the translational or rotational motion. When this is the case, the body is said to be in *equilibrium*. This means that (1) the body as a whole either remains at rest or moves in a straight line with constant speed, and (2) that the body is either not rotating at all or is rotating at a constant rate.

Let us consider some (idealized) experiments from which the laws of equilibrium can be deduced. Figure 2–1 represents a flat, rigid object of arbitrary shape on a level surface having negligible friction. If a single force F_1 acts on the body, as in Fig. 2–1(a), and if the body is originally at rest, it at once starts to move and to rotate clockwise. If originally in motion, the effect of the force is to change the translational motion of the body in magnitude or direction (or both) and to increase or decrease its rate of rotation. In either case, the body does not remain in equilibrium.

Equilibrium can be maintained, however, by the application of a second force F_2 as in Fig. 2–1(b), provided that F_2 is equal in magnitude to F_1,

17

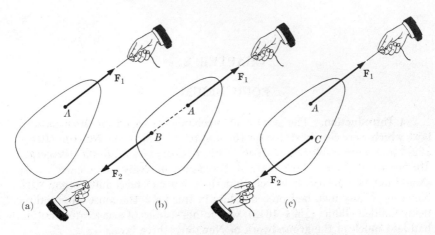

FIG. 2–1. A rigid body acted on by two forces is in equilibrium if the forces are equal in magnitude, opposite in direction, and have the same line of action, as in part (b).

is opposite in direction to F_1, and has the same line of action as F_1. The resultant of F_1 and F_2 is then zero. If the lines of action of the two forces are not the same, as in Fig. 2–1(c), the body will be in translational but not in rotational equilibrium.

In Fig. 2–2(a), a body is acted on by three nonparallel coplanar forces F_1, F_2, and F_3. Any force applied to a rigid body may be regarded as acting anywhere along its line of action. Therefore, let any two of the force vectors, say F_1 and F_2, be transferred to the point of intersection of their lines of action and their resultant R obtained, as in Fig. 2–2(b). The forces are now reduced to two, R and F_3, and for equilibrium these must (1) be equal in magnitude, (2) be opposite in direction, and (3) have the same line of action. It follows from the first two conditions that the resultant of the three forces is zero. The third condition can be fulfilled only if the line of action of F_3 passes through the point of intersection of the lines of action of F_1 and F_2. In other words, the three forces must be *concurrent.*

Problems involving more than three forces are usually best treated with the help of the concept of the *moment* of a force, which we shall postpone until the next chapter. This concept will also enable us to find the resultant of parallel forces, a problem we have not yet considered.

The construction in Fig. 2–2 provides a satisfactory graphical method for the solution of problems in equilibrium. For an analytical solution, it is usually simpler to deal with the rectangular components of the forces. We have shown that the magnitudes of the rectangular components of the

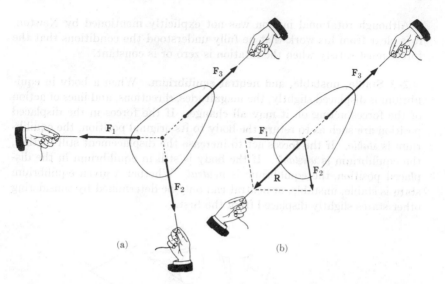

FIG. 2–2. When a body acted on by three nonparallel coplanar forces is in equilibrium, the forces are concurrent and the resultant of any two is equal and opposite to the third.

resultant **R** of any set of coplanar forces are

$$R_x = \sum F_x, \qquad R_y = \sum F_y.$$

When a body is in equilibrium, the resultant of all of the forces acting on it is zero. Both rectangular components are then zero and hence, for a body in equilibrium,

$$\boxed{\sum F_x = 0, \qquad \sum F_y = 0.}$$

These equations are called the *first condition of equilibrium*.

The *second condition of equilibrium* is that two forces in equilibrium must have the same line of action, or that three forces in equilibrium must be concurrent.

The first condition of equilibrium ensures that a body shall be in translational equilibrium; the second, that it be in rotational equilibrium. The statement that a body is in complete equilibrium when both conditions are satisfied is the essence of *Newton's first law of motion*. Newton did not state his first law in exactly these words. His original statement (translated from the Latin in which the *Principia* was written) reads: *"Every body continues in its state of rest, or of uniform motion in a straight line, unless it is compelled to change that state by forces impressed on it."*

Although rotational motion was not explicitly mentioned by Newton, it is clear from his work that he fully understood the conditions that the forces must satisfy when the rotation is zero or is constant.

2–3 Stable, unstable, and neutral equilibrium. When a body in equilibrium is displaced slightly, the magnitudes, directions, and lines of action of the forces acting on it may all change. If the forces in the displaced position are such as to return the body to its original position, the equilibrium is *stable*. If the forces act to increase the displacement still further, the equilibrium is *unstable*. If the body is still in equilibrium in the displaced position, the equilibrium is *neutral*. Whether a given equilibrium state is stable, unstable, or neutral can only be determined by considering other states slightly displaced from the first.

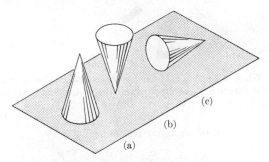

FIG. 2–3. (a) Stable, (b) unstable, and (c) neutral equilibrium.

A right circular cone on a level surface affords an example of the three types of equilibrium. When the cone rests on its base, as in Fig. 2–3(a), the equilibrium is stable. When balanced on its apex, as in part (b), the equilibrium is unstable. When resting on its side, as in part (c), the equilibrium is neutral.

2–4 Newton's third law of motion. Any given force is but one aspect of a mutual interaction between *two* bodies. It is found that *whenever one body exerts a force on another, the second always exerts on the first a force which is equal in magnitude, opposite in direction, and has the same line of action.* A single, isolated force is therefore an impossibility.

The two forces involved in every interaction between two bodies are often called an "action" and a "reaction," but this does not imply any difference in their nature, or that one force is the "cause" and the other its "effect." *Either* force may be considered the "action," and the other the "reaction" to it.

This property of forces was stated by Newton in his *third law of motion*. In his own words, *"To every action there is always opposed an equal reaction:*

or, the mutual actions of two bodies upon each other are always equal, and directed to contrary parts."

As an example, suppose that a man pulls on one end of a rope attached to a block as in Fig. 2–4. The weight of the block, and the force exerted on it by the surface, are not shown. The block may or may not be in equilibrium. The resulting action-reaction pairs of forces are indicated in the figure. (Actually, the lines of action of all the forces lie along the rope. The force vectors have been offset from this line to show them more clearly.) Vector $\mathbf{F}_1$ represents the force exerted on the rope by the man. Its reaction is the equal and opposite force $\mathbf{F}_1'$ exerted on the man by the rope. Vector $\mathbf{F}_2$ represents the force exerted on the block by the rope. The reaction to it is the equal and opposite force $\mathbf{F}_2'$, exerted on the rope by the block.

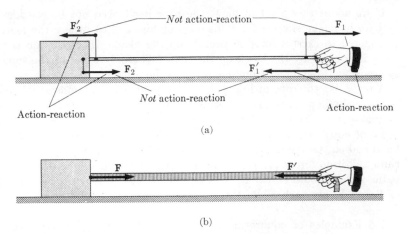

Fig. 2–4. (a) Forces $\mathbf{F}_1$ and $\mathbf{F}_1'$ form one action-reaction pair, and forces $\mathbf{F}_2$ and $\mathbf{F}_2'$ another. $\mathbf{F}_1$ is *always* equal to $\mathbf{F}_1'$, $\mathbf{F}_2$ is *always* equal to $\mathbf{F}_2'$. $\mathbf{F}_1$ and $\mathbf{F}_2'$ are equal only if the rope is in equilibrium, and force $\mathbf{F}_2'$ is *not* the reaction to $\mathbf{F}_1$. (Actually, all forces lie along the rope.)   (b) If the rope is in equilibrium it can be considered to transmit a force from the man to the block, and vice versa.

It is very important to realize that the forces $\mathbf{F}_1$ and $\mathbf{F}_2'$, although they are opposite in direction and have the same line of action, do *not* constitute an action-reaction pair. For one thing, both of these forces act on the *same* body (the rope), while an action and its reaction necessarily act on *different* bodies. Furthermore, the forces $\mathbf{F}_1$ and $\mathbf{F}_2'$ are not *necessarily* equal in magnitude. If the block and rope are moving to the right with increasing speed, the rope is not in equilibrium and F_1 is greater than F_2'. Only in the special case when the rope remains at rest or moves with constant speed are the forces $\mathbf{F}_1$ and $\mathbf{F}_2'$ equal in magnitude, but this is an example of Newton's *first* law, not his *third*. Even when the speed of the rope is changing, however, the action-reaction forces $\mathbf{F}_1$ and $\mathbf{F}_1'$ are equal to *each other*, and the action-reaction forces F_2 and F_2' are equal to *each other*, although then F_1 is not equal to F_2'.

In the special case when the rope is in equilibrium, and when no forces act on it except those at its ends, F_2' equals F_1 by Newton's *first* law. Since F_2 *always* equals F_2', by Newton's *third* law, then in this special case F_2 also equals F_1 and the force exerted on the block by the rope is equal to the force exerted on the rope by the man. The rope can therefore be considered to "transmit" to the block, without change, the force exerted on it by the man. This point of view is often useful, but it is important to remember that it applies only under the restricted conditions above.

If we adopt this point of view, the rope itself need not be considered and we have the simpler force diagram of Fig. 2–4(b), where the man is considered to exert a force $\mathbf{F}$ directly on the block. The reaction is the force $\mathbf{F}'$ exerted by the block on the man. The only effect of the rope is to transmit these forces from one body to the other.

A body like the rope in Fig. 2–4, which is subjected to pulls at its ends, is said to be in *tension*. The tension at any point equals the force exerted at that point. Thus in Fig. 2–4(a) the tension at the right-hand end of the rope equals the magnitude of $\mathbf{F}_1$ (or of $\mathbf{F}_1'$) and the tension at the left-hand end equals the magnitude of $\mathbf{F}_2$ (or of $\mathbf{F}_2'$). If the rope is in equilibrium and if no forces act except at its ends, as in Fig. 2–4(b), the tension is the same at both ends. If, for example, in Fig. 2–4(b) the magnitudes of $\mathbf{F}$ and $\mathbf{F}'$ are each 50 lb, the tension in the rope is 50 lb (*not* 100 lb).

2–5 Examples of equilibrium. The conditions of equilibrium express certain relations among the forces acting *on* a body in equilibrium. A carefully drawn diagram, in which each force exerted on a body is represented by a vector, is essential in the solution of problems of this sort. The standard procedure is as follows: First, make a neat sketch of the apparatus or structure. Second, choose some one body which is in equilibrium and show *all* the forces exerted *on* it. This is called "isolating" the chosen body, and the diagram is called a *force diagram* or a *free-body* diagram. On the diagram, which should be sufficiently large to avoid crowding, write the numerical values of all given forces, angles, and dimensions, and assign letters to all unknown quantities. When a structure is composed of several members, a separate force diagram must be constructed for each. Third, construct a set of rectangular axes and indicate on each force diagram the rectangular components of any inclined forces. Cross out lightly those forces which have been resolved. Fourth, obtain the necessary algebraic or trigonometric equations from the condition of equilibrium,

$$\sum F_x = 0, \qquad \sum F_y = 0.$$

A force which will be encountered in many problems is the *weight* of a body, that is, the force of gravitational attraction exerted on the body by the earth. We shall show in the next chapter that the line of action of this force always passes through a point called the *center of gravity* of the body.

EXAMPLE 1. To begin with a simple example, consider the body in Fig. 2–5, hanging at rest from the ceiling by a vertical cord. Part (b) of the figure is the free-body diagram for the body. The forces on it are its weight $\mathbf{w}_1$ and the upward force $\mathbf{T}_1$ exerted on it by the cord. If we take the x-axis horizontal and the y-axis vertical, there are no x-components of force, and the y-components are the forces $\mathbf{w}_1$ and $\mathbf{T}_1$. Then from the condition that $\sum F_y = 0$, we have

$$\sum F_y = T_1 - w_1 = 0,$$

$$T_1 = w_1. \quad \text{(1st law)}$$

In order that both forces have the same line of action, the center of gravity of the body must lie vertically below the point of attachment of the cord.

Let us emphasize again that the forces $\mathbf{w}_1$ and $\mathbf{T}_1$ are *not* an action-reaction pair, although they are equal in magnitude, opposite in direction, and have the same line of action. The weight $\mathbf{w}_1$ is a force of attraction exerted on the body by the earth. Its reaction is an equal and opposite force of attraction exerted on the earth by the body. This reaction is one of the set of forces acting *on the earth*, and therefore it does not appear in the free-body diagram of the suspended block.

The reaction to the force $\mathbf{T}_1$ is an equal downward force, $\mathbf{T}_1'$, exerted *on the cord* by the suspended body.

$$T_1 = T_1'. \quad \text{(3rd law)}$$

The force $\mathbf{T}_1'$ is shown in part (c), which is the free-body diagram of the

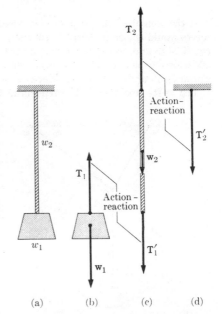

(a)　　　　(b)　　　　(c)　　　　(d)

FIG. 2–5. (a) Block hanging at rest from vertical cord. (b) The block is isolated and *all* forces acting *on* it are shown. (c) Forces on the cord. (d) Downward force on the ceiling. Lines connect action-reaction pairs.

cord. The other forces on the cord are its own weight w_2 and the upward force T_2 exerted on its upper end by the ceiling. Since the cord is also in equilibrium,

$$\sum F_v = T_2 - w_2 - T_1' = 0,$$

$$T_2 = w_2 + T_1'. \quad \text{(1st law)}$$

The reaction to T_2 is the downward force T_2' in part (d), exerted on the ceiling by the cord.

$$T_2 = T_2'. \quad \text{(3rd law)}$$

As a numerical example, let the body weigh 20 lb and the cord weigh 1 lb. Then

$$T_1 = w_1 = 20 \text{ lb},$$

$$T_1' = T_1 = 20 \text{ lb},$$

$$T_2 = w_2 + T_1' = 1 \text{ lb} + 20 \text{ lb} = 21 \text{ lb},$$

$$T_2' = T_2 = 21 \text{ lb}.$$

If the weight of the cord were so small as to be negligible, then in effect no forces would act on it except at its ends. The forces T_2 and T_2' would then each equal 20 lb and, as explained earlier, the cord could be considered to transmit a 20-lb force from one end to the other without change. We could then consider the upward pull of the cord on the block as an "action" and the downward pull on the ceiling as its "reaction." The tension in the cord would then be 20 lb.

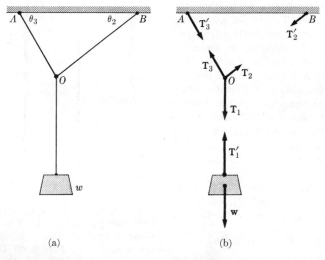

(a)   (b)

Fig. 2–6. (a) A block hanging in equilibrium. (b) Forces acting on the block, on the knot, and on the ceiling.

EXAMPLE 2. In Fig. 2–6(a), a block of weight w hangs from a cord which is knotted at O to two other cords fastened to the ceiling. We wish to find the tensions in these three cords. The weights of the cords are negligible.

In order to use the conditions of equilibrium to compute an unknown force, we must consider some body which is in equilibrium and on which the desired force acts. The hanging block is one such body and, as shown in the preceding example, the tension in the vertical cord supporting the block is equal to the weight of the block. The inclined cords do not exert forces on the block, but they do act on the knot at O. Hence we consider the *knot* as a small body in equilibrium whose own weight is negligible.

The free-body diagrams for the block and the knot are shown in Fig. 2–6(b), where $\mathbf{T}_1$, $\mathbf{T}_2$, and $\mathbf{T}_3$ represent the forces exerted *on the knot* by the three cords and $\mathbf{T}_1'$, $\mathbf{T}_2'$, and $\mathbf{T}_3'$ are the reactions to these forces.

Consider first the hanging block. Since it is in equilibrium,

$$T_1' = w. \qquad \text{(1st law)}$$

Since $\mathbf{T}_1$ and $\mathbf{T}_1'$ form an action-reaction pair,

$$T_1' = T_1. \qquad \text{(3rd law)}$$

Hence

$$T_1 = w.$$

To find the forces $\mathbf{T}_2$ and $\mathbf{T}_3$, we resolve these forces (see Fig. 2–7) into rectangular components. Then, from Newton's *first* law,

$$\sum F_x = T_2 \cos \theta_2 - T_3 \cos \theta_3 = 0,$$

$$\sum F_y = T_2 \sin \theta_2 + T_3 \sin \theta_3 - T_1 = 0.$$

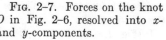

FIG. 2–7. Forces on the knot O in Fig. 2–6, resolved into x- and y-components.

As a numerical example, let $w = 50$ lb, $\theta_2 = 30°$, $\theta = 60°$. Then $T_1 = 50$ lb, and from the two preceding equations,

$$T_2 = 25 \text{ lb},$$

$$T_3 = 43.3 \text{ lb}.$$

Finally, we know from Newton's *third* law that the inclined cords exert on the ceiling the forces $\mathbf{T}_2'$ and $\mathbf{T}_3'$, equal and opposite to $\mathbf{T}_2$ and $\mathbf{T}_3$ respectively.

EXAMPLE 3. Figure 2–8(a) shows a strut AB, pivoted at end A, attached to a wall by a cable, and carrying a load w at end B. The weights of the strut and of the cable are negligible. Suppose the weight w, and the angles θ_1 and θ_2 are known.

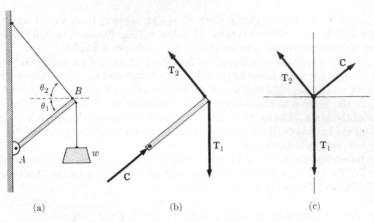

(a)   (b)   (c)

FIGURE 2–8

Figure 2–8(b) shows the forces acting on the strut. T_1 is the force exerted by the vertical cable, T_2 is the force exerted by the inclined cable, and C is the force exerted by the pivot. Force T_1 is known both in magnitude and in direction; force T_2 is known in direction only, and neither the magnitude nor the direction of C is known. However, the forces T_1 and T_2 must intersect at the outer end of the strut, and since the strut is in equilibrium under three forces, the line of action of force C must also pass through the outer end of the strut. In other words, the direction of force C is along the line of the strut.

Hence the resultant of T_1 and T_2 is also along this line and the strut, in effect, is acted on by forces at its ends, directed toward each other along the line of the strut. The effect of these forces is to compress the strut, and it is said to be in *compression*.

If the forces acting on a strut are *not* all applied at its ends, the direction of the resultant force at the ends is *not* along the line of the strut. This is illustrated in the next example.

In Fig. 2–8(c), the force C has been transferred along its line of action to the point of intersection of the three forces. The force diagram is exactly like that of Fig. 2–7, and the problem is solved in the same way.

EXAMPLE 4. In Fig. 2–9 a ladder, which is in equilibrium, leans against a vertical frictionless wall. The forces on the ladder are (1) its weight w, (2) the force F_1 exerted on the ladder by the vertical wall and which is perpendicular to the wall if there is no friction, and (3) the force F_2 exerted by the ground on the base of the ladder. The force w is known in magnitude and in direction, the force F_1 is known in direction only, and the force F_2 is unknown in both magnitude and direction. As in the preceding example, the ladder is in equilibrium under three forces, which must be concurrent. Since the lines of action of F_1 and w are known, their point of intersection (point O) can be located. The line of action of F_2 must then pass through this point also. Note that neither the direction of F_1 nor that of F_2 lies along the line of the ladder. In part (b) the forces have been transferred

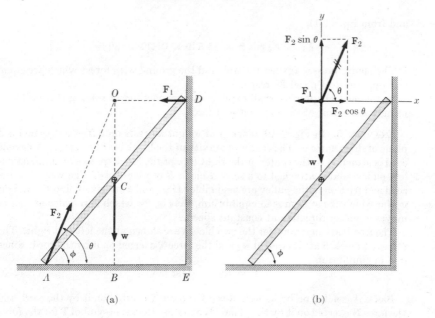

(a)　　　　　　　　　　　　　　　　(b)

FIG. 2–9. Forces on a ladder leaning against a vertical frictionless wall.

to the point of intersection of their lines of action, and

$$\sum F_x = F_2 \cos \theta - F_1 = 0, \tag{2-1}$$

$$\sum F_y = F_2 \sin \theta - w = 0. \tag{2-2}$$

As a numerical example, suppose the ladder weighs 80 lb, is 20 ft long, has its center of gravity at its center, and makes an angle $\phi = 53°$ with the ground. We wish to find the angle θ, and the forces $\mathbf{F}_1$ and $\mathbf{F}_2$. To calculate θ, we first find the lengths of AB and BO. From the right triangle ABC, we have

$$AB = AC \cos \phi = 10 \text{ ft} \times 0.60 = 6.0 \text{ ft,}$$

and from the right triangle AED,

$$DE = AD \sin \phi = 20 \text{ ft} \times 0.80 = 16 \text{ ft.}$$

Then, from the right triangle AOB, since $OB = DE$, we have

$$\tan \theta = \frac{OB}{AB} = \frac{16 \text{ ft}}{6.0 \text{ ft}} = 2.67,$$

$$\theta = 69.5°, \qquad \sin \theta = 0.937, \qquad \cos \theta = 0.350.$$

$$F_2 = \frac{w}{\sin \theta} = \frac{80 \text{ lb}}{0.937} = 85.5 \text{ lb,}$$

and from Eq. (2–1),

$$F_1 = F_2 \cos \theta = 85.5 \text{ lb} \times 0.350 = 30 \text{ lb.}$$

The ladder presses against the wall and the ground with forces which are equal and opposite to $\mathbf{F}_1$ and $\mathbf{F}_2$ respectively.

In the next chapter we shall explain another method of solving this problem, using the concept of the moment of a force.

EXAMPLE 5. In Fig. 2–10, block A of weight w_1 rests on a frictionless inclined plane of slope angle θ. The center of gravity of the block is at its center. A flexible cord is attached to the center of the right face of the block, passes over a frictionless pulley, and is attached to a second block B of weight w_2. The weight of the cord and friction in the pulley are negligible. If w_1 and θ are given, find the weight w_2 for which the system is in equilibrium, that is, for which it remains at rest or moves in either direction at constant speed.

The free-body diagrams for the two blocks are shown at the left and right. The forces on block B are its weight $\mathbf{w}_2$ and the force $\mathbf{T}$ exerted on it by the cord. Since it is in equilibrium,

$$T = w_2. \quad \text{(1st law)} \tag{2–3}$$

Block A is acted on by its weight $\mathbf{w}_1$, the force $\mathbf{T}$ exerted on it by the cord, and the force $\mathbf{N}$ exerted on it by the plane. We can use the same symbol $\mathbf{T}$ for the force exerted on each block by the cord, because, as explained in Section 2–4, these forces are equivalent to an action-reaction pair and have the same magnitude. The force $\mathbf{N}$, if there is no friction, is perpendicular or *normal* to the surface of the plane. Since the lines of action of $\mathbf{w}_1$ and $\mathbf{T}$ intersect at the center of gravity of the block, the line of action of $\mathbf{N}$ passes through this point also. It is simplest to choose x- and y-axes parallel and perpendicular to the surface of the plane, because then only the weight $\mathbf{w}_1$ needs to be resolved into components. The conditions of equilibrium give

$$\left. \begin{aligned} \sum F_x &= T - w_1 \sin \theta = 0, \\ \sum F_y &= N - w_1 \cos \theta = 0. \end{aligned} \right\} \quad \text{(1st law)} \qquad \begin{aligned} &(2–4) \\ &(2–5) \end{aligned}$$

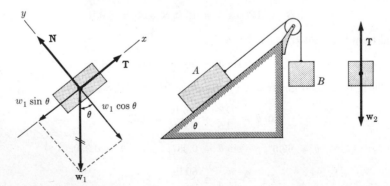

FIG. 2–10. Forces on a block in equilibrium on a frictionless inclined plane.

Thus if $w_1 = 100$ lb and $\theta = 30°$, we have from Eqs. (2–3) and (2–4),

$$w_2 = T = w_1 \sin \theta = 100 \text{ lb} \times 0.500 = 50 \text{ lb,}$$

and from Eq. (2–5),

$$N = w_1 \cos \theta = 100 \text{ lb} \times 0.866 = 86.6 \text{ lb.}$$

Note carefully that *in the absence of friction* the same weight w_2 of 50 lb is required whether the system remains at rest or moves with constant speed in *either* direction. This is not the case when friction is present.

2–6 Friction. Whenever the surface of one body slides over that of another, each body exerts a frictional force on the other, parallel to the surfaces. The force *on* each body is opposite to the direction of its motion relative to the other. Thus when a block slides from left to right along the surface of a table, a frictional force to the left acts on the block and an equal force toward the right acts on the table. Frictional forces may also act when there is no relative motion. A horizontal force on a heavy packing case resting on the floor may not be enough to set the case in motion, the applied force being balanced by an equal frictional force exerted on the case by the floor.

The origin of these frictional forces is not fully understood, and the study of them is an important field of research. When one unlubricated metal slides over another, there appears to be an actual momentary welding of the metals together at the "high spots" where they make contact. The observed friction force is the force required to break these tiny welds. The mechanism of the friction force between two blocks of wood, or between two bricks, must be quite different.

Friction forces also act on a body moving through a fluid (liquid or gas). The fluid is said to exhibit *viscosity*. The motion of one body rolling on another is opposed by a force called *rolling friction* and which results from the deformation of the two bodies where they make contact.

In this chapter we shall consider only so-called "dry friction," the force observed when the surface of one unlubricated solid slides over that of another.

In Fig. 2–11(a) a block is at rest on a horizontal surface, in equilibrium under the action of its weight **w** and the upward force **P** exerted on it by the surface.

Suppose now that a cord is attached to the block as in Fig. 2–11(b) and the tension **T** in the cord is gradually increased. Provided the tension is not too great, the block remains at rest. The force **P** exerted on the block by the surface is inclined toward the left as shown, since the three forces **P**, **w**, and **T** must be concurrent. The component of **P** parallel to the surface is called the *force of static friction*, $\mathbf{f}_s$. The other component,

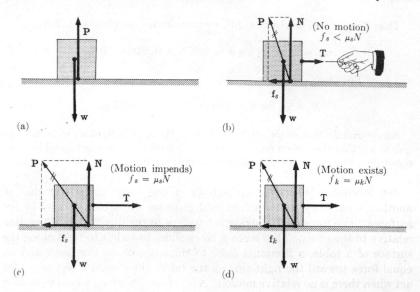

FIG. 2–11. The friction force f is less than or equal to $\mu_s N$ when there is no relative motion, and is equal to $\mu_k N$ when motion exists.

N, is the *normal* force exerted on the block by the surface. From the conditions of equilibrium, the force of static friction $\mathbf{f}_s$ equals the force $\mathbf{T}$, and the normal force **N** equals the weight **w**.

As the force **T** is increased further, a limiting value is reached at which the block breaks away from the surface and starts to move. In other words, there is a certain maximum value which the force of static friction $\mathbf{f}_s$ can have. Figure 2–11(c) is the force diagram when **T** is just below its limiting value and motion impends. If the force **T** exceeds this limiting value the block is no longer in equilibrium.

For a given pair of surfaces, the maximum value of f_s is nearly proportional to the normal force N. The actual force of static friction can therefore have any value between zero (when there is no applied force parallel to the surface) and a maximum value proportional to N or equal to $\mu_s N$. The factor μ_s is called the *coefficient of static friction*. Thus,

$$f_s \leq \mu_s N. \qquad (2\text{–}6)$$

The equality sign holds only when the applied force **T**, parallel to the surface, has such a magnitude that motion is about to start [Fig. 2–11(c)]. When T is less than this, [Fig. 2–11(b)], the inequality sign holds and the magnitude of the friction force must be computed from the conditions of equilibrium.

As soon as sliding begins, it is found that the friction force decreases. This new friction force, for a given pair of surfaces, is also nearly proportional to the normal force. The proportionality factor, μ_k, is called the *coefficient of sliding friction* or *kinetic* friction. Thus, when the block is in motion, the force of sliding or kinetic friction is given by

$$f_k = \mu_k N. \tag{2–7}$$

This is illustrated in Fig. 2–11(d).

The coefficients of static and sliding friction depend primarily on the nature of both of the surfaces in contact, being relatively large if the surfaces are rough and small if they are smooth. Typical numerical values are given in Table 2–1. The coefficient of sliding friction varies somewhat

TABLE 2–1

COEFFICIENTS OF FRICTION

Materials	Static, μ_s	Kinetic, μ_k
Steel on steel	0.74	0.57
Aluminum on steel	0.61	0.47
Copper on steel	0.53	0.36
Brass on steel	0.51	0.44
Zinc on cast iron	0.85	0.21
Copper on cast iron	1.05	0.29
Glass on glass	0.94	0.4
Copper on glass	0.68	0.53
Teflon on teflon	0.04	0.04
Teflon on steel	0.04	0.04

with the relative velocity, but for simplicity we shall assume it to be independent of velocity. It is also nearly independent of the contact area. However, since two real surfaces actually touch each other only at a relatively small number of high spots, the true contact area is very different from the over-all area. Equations (2–6) and (2–7) are useful empirical relations, but do not represent fundamental physical laws like Newton's laws.

EXAMPLE 1. In Fig. 2–11, suppose that the block weighs 20 lb, that the tension T can be increased to 8 lb before the block starts to slide, and that a force of 4 lb will keep the block moving at constant speed once it has been set in motion. Find the coefficients of static and kinetic friction.

From Fig. 2–11(c) and the data above, we have

$$\left.\begin{array}{l} \sum F_y = N - w = N - 20 \text{ lb} = 0, \\ \sum F_x = T - f_s = 8 \text{ lb} - f_s = 0, \end{array}\right\} \quad \text{(1st law)}$$

$$f_s = \mu_s N \text{ (motion impends)}.$$

Hence

$$\mu_s = \frac{f_s}{N} = \frac{8 \text{ lb}}{20 \text{ lb}} = 0.40.$$

From Fig. 2–11(d), we have

$$\left.\begin{array}{l} \sum F_y = N - w = N - 20 \text{ lb} = 0, \\ \sum F_x = T - f_k = 4 \text{ lb} - f_k = 0, \end{array}\right\} \quad \text{(1st law)}$$

$$f_k = \mu_k N \text{ (motion exists)}.$$

Hence

$$\mu_k = \frac{f_k}{N} = \frac{4 \text{ lb}}{20 \text{ lb}} = 0.20.$$

EXAMPLE 2. What is the friction force if the block in Fig. 2–11(b) is at rest on the surface and a horizontal force of 5 lb is exerted on it?

We have

$$\sum F_x = T - f_s = 5 \text{ lb} - f_s = 0, \quad \text{(1st law)}$$

$$f_s = 5 \text{ lb}.$$

Note that in this case

$$f_s < \mu_s N.$$

EXAMPLE 3. What force $\mathbf{T}$, at an angle of 30° above the horizontal, is required to drag a 20-lb block to the right at constant speed as in Fig. 2–12, if the coefficient of kinetic friction between block and surface is 0.20?

The forces on the block are shown in the diagram. From the first condition of equilibrium,

$$\sum F_x = T \cos 30° - 0.2N = 0,$$

$$\sum F_y = T \sin 30° + N - 20 \text{ lb} = 0.$$

Simultaneous solution gives

$$T = 4.15 \text{ lb},$$

$$N = 17.9 \text{ lb}.$$

Notice that in this example the normal force $\mathbf{N}$ is not equal to the weight of the block, but is less than the weight by the vertical component of the force $\mathbf{T}$.

EXAMPLE 4. In Fig. 2–13, a block has been placed on an inclined plane and the slope angle θ of the plane has been adjusted until the block slides down the plane at constant speed, once it has been set in motion. Find the angle θ.

The forces on the block are its weight **w** and the normal and frictional components of the force exerted by the plane. Since motion exists, the friction force $f_k = \mu_k N$. Take axes perpendicular and parallel to the surface of the plane. Then

$$\left.\begin{aligned} \sum F_x &= \mu_k N - w \sin \theta = 0, \\ \sum F_y &= N - w \cos \theta = 0. \end{aligned}\right\} \quad \text{(1st law)}$$

Hence

$$\mu_k N = w \sin \theta,$$
$$N = w \cos \theta.$$

Dividing the former by the latter, we get

$$\mu_k = \tan \theta.$$

It follows that a block, regardless of its weight, slides down an inclined plane with constant speed if the tangent of the slope angle of the plane equals the coefficient of kinetic friction. Measurement of this angle then provides a simple experimental method of determining the coefficient of kinetic friction.

It is left as a problem for the reader to show that if a block is placed on an inclined plane and the slope angle of the plane is slowly increased, the block breaks away from the plane and starts to slide when the tangent of the slope angle becomes equal to the coefficient of static friction, μ_s.

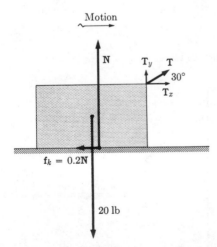

FIG. 2–12. Forces on a block being dragged to the right on a level surface at constant speed.

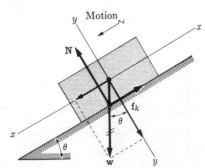

FIG. 2–13. Forces on a block sliding down an inclined plane (with friction) at constant speed.

PROBLEMS

2-1. A block rests on a horizontal surface. (a) What two forces act on it? (b) By what bodies are each of the forces exerted? (c) What are the reactions to these forces? (d) On what body is each reaction exerted, and by what body is each exerted?

2-2. A block is given a push along a table top, and slides off the edge of the table. (a) What force or forces are exerted on it while it is falling from the table to the floor? (b) What is the reaction to each force, that is, on what body and by what body is the reaction exerted? Neglect air resistance.

2-3. Two 10-lb weights are suspended at opposite ends of a rope which passes over a light frictionless pulley. The pulley is attached to a chain which goes to the ceiling. (a) What is the tension in the rope? (b) What is the tension in the chain?

2-4. In Fig. 2-6, let the weight of the hanging block be 50 lb. Find the tensions T_2 and T_3, (a) if $\theta_2 = \theta_3 = 60°$, (b) if $\theta_2 = \theta_3 = 10°$, (c) if $\theta_2 = 60°$, $\theta_3 = 0$, and (d) if $AB = 10$ ft, $AO = 6$ ft, $OB = 8$ ft.

2-5. Find the tension in each cord in Fig. 2-14 if the weight of the suspended body is 200 lb.

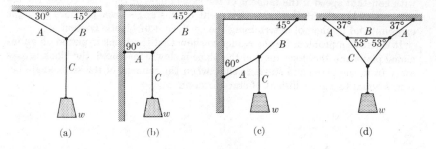

(a)   (b)   (c)   (d)

FIGURE 2-14

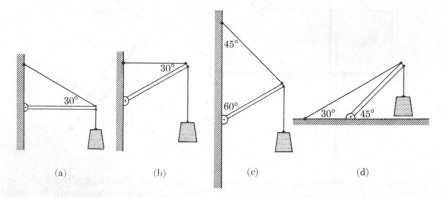

(a)   (b)   (c)   (d)

FIGURE 2-15

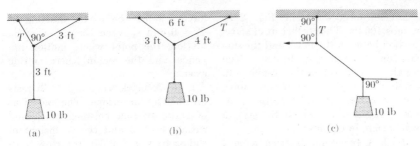

FIGURE 2–16

2–6. Find the tension T in the cable, and the magnitude and direction of the force C exerted on the strut by the pivot in the arrangements in Fig. 2–15. Let the weight of the suspended object in each case be 1000 lb. Neglect the weight of the strut.

2–7. (a) In which of the arrangements in Fig. 2–16 can the tension T be computed, if the only quantities known are those explicitly given? (b) For each case in which insufficient information is given, state one additional quantity, a knowledge of which would permit solution.

2–8. A horizontal boom 8 ft long is hinged to a vertical wall at one end, and a 500-lb body hangs from its outer end. The boom is supported by a guy wire from its outer end to a point on the wall directly above the boom. (a) If the tension in this wire is not to exceed 1000 lb, what is the minimum height above the boom at which it may be fastened to the wall? (b) By how many pounds would the tension be increased if the wire were fastened 1 ft below this point, the boom remaining horizontal? Neglect the weight of the boom.

2–9. One end of a rope 50 ft long is attached to an automobile. The other end is fastened to a tree. A man exerts a force of 100 lb at the mid-point of the rope, pulling it 2 ft to the side. What is the force exerted on the automobile?

2–10. Find the largest weight w which can be supported by the structure in Fig. 2–17 if the maximum tension the upper rope can withstand is 1000 lb and the maximum compression the strut can withstand is 2000 lb. The vertical rope is strong enough to carry any load required. Neglect the weight of the strut.

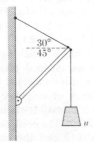

FIGURE 2–17

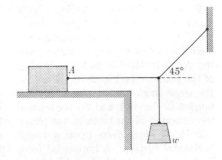

FIGURE 2–18

2–11. (a) Block A in Fig. 2–18 weighs 100 lb. The coefficient of static friction between the block and the surface on which it rests is 0.30. The weight w is 20 lb and the system is in equilibrium. Find the friction force exerted on block A. (b) Find the maximum weight w for which the system will remain in equilibrium.

2–12. A block hangs from a cord 10 ft long. A second cord is tied to the midpoint of the first, and a horizontal pull equal to half the weight of the block is exerted on it, the second cord being always kept horizontal. (a) How far will the block be pulled to one side? (b) How far will it be lifted?

2–13. A flexible chain of weight w hangs between two hooks at the same height, as shown in Fig. 2–19. At each end the chain makes an angle θ with the horizontal. (a) What is the magnitude and direction of the force $\mathbf{F}$ exerted by the chain on the hook at the left? (b) What is the tension $\mathbf{T}$ in the chain at its lowest point?

FIGURE 2–19

2–14. A 30-lb block is pulled at constant speed up a frictionless inclined plane by a weight of 10 lb hanging from a cord attached to the block and passing over a frictionless pulley at the top of the plane. (See Fig. 2–10.) Find (a) the slope angle of the plane, (b) the tension in the cord, and (c) the normal force exerted on the block by the plane.

2–15. A block rests upon a rough horizontal surface. A horizontal force $\mathbf{T}$ is applied to the block and is slowly increased from zero. Draw a graph with T along the x-axis and the friction force f along the y-axis, starting at $T = 0$ and showing the region of no motion, the point where motion impends, and the region where motion exists.

2–16. A block weighing 20 lb rests on a horizontal surface. The coefficient of static friction between block and surface is 0.40 and the coefficient of sliding friction is 0.20. (a) How large is the friction force exerted on the block? (b) How great will the friction force be if a horizontal force of 5 lb is exerted on the block? (c) What is the minimum force which will start the block in motion? (d) What is the minimum force which will keep the block in motion once it has been started? (e) If the horizontal force is 10 lb, how great is the friction force?

2–17. A block is pulled to the right at constant velocity by a 10-lb force acting 30° above the horizontal. The coefficient of sliding friction between block and surface is 0.5. What is the weight of the block? Assume all of the forces on the block to act at its center.

2–18. A block weighing 14 lb is placed on an inclined plane and connected to a 10-lb block by a cord passing over a small frictionless pulley, as in Fig. 2–10. The coefficient of sliding friction between the block and the plane is 1/7. For what two values of θ will the system move with constant velocity? Assume that all the forces on the 14-lb block act at its center. [Hint: $\cos \theta = \sqrt{1 - \sin^2 \theta}$.]

2–19. A block weighing 100 lb is placed on an inclined plane of slope angle 30° and is connected to a second hanging block of weight w by a cord passing over a small frictionless pulley, as in Fig. 2–10. The coefficient of static friction is 0.40 and the coefficient of sliding friction is 0.30. (a) Find the weight w for which the 100-lb block moves up the plane at constant speed.

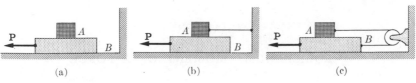

FIGURE 2-20

(b) Find the weight w for which it moves down the plane at constant speed. (c) For what range of values of w will the block remain at rest?

2-20. What force P at an angle ϕ above the horizontal is needed to drag a box of weight w at constant speed along a level floor if the coefficient of sliding friction between box and floor is μ?

2-21. A safe weighing 600 lb is to be lowered at constant speed down skids 8 ft long, from a truck 4 ft high. If the coefficient of sliding friction between safe and skids is 0.30, (a) will the safe need to be pulled down or held back? (b) How great a force parallel to the plane is needed?

2-22. If a force of 86 lb parallel to the surface of a 20° inclined plane will push a 120-lb block up the plane at constant speed, (a) what force parallel to the plane will push it down at constant speed? (b) What is the coefficient of sliding friction?

2-23. Block A in Fig. 2-20 weighs 4 lb and block B weighs 8 lb. The coefficient of sliding friction between all surfaces is 0.25. Find the force P

necessary to drag block B to the left at constant speed (a) if A rests on B and moves with it, (b) if A is held at rest, and (c) if A and B are connected by a light flexible cord passing around a fixed frictionless pulley.

2-24. Block A, of weight w, slides down an inclined plane S of slope angle 37° at constant velocity while the plank B, also of weight w, rests on top of A. The plank is attached by a cord to the top of the plane (Fig. 2-21). (a) Draw a diagram of all the forces acting on block A. (b) If the coefficient of kinetic friction is the same between the surfaces A and B and between S and A, determine its value.

2-25. Two blocks, A and B, are placed as in Fig. 2-22 and connected by ropes to block C. Both A and B weigh 20 lb and the coefficient of sliding friction between each block and the surface is 0.5. Block C descends with constant velocity. (a) Draw two separate force diagrams showing the forces acting on A and B. (b) Find the tension in the rope connecting blocks A and B. (c) What is the weight of block C?

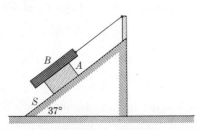

FIGURE 2-21

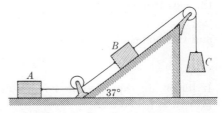

FIGURE 2-22

CHAPTER 3

EQUILIBRIUM. MOMENT OF A FORCE

3–1 Moment of a force. The effect produced on a body by a force of given magnitude and direction depends on the position of the *line of action* of the force. Thus in Fig. 3–1 the force F_1 would produce a counter-clockwise rotation (together with a translation toward the right), while F_2 would produce a clockwise rotation.

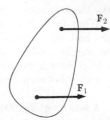

The line of action of a force can be specified by giving the perpendicular distance from some reference point to the line of action. In many instances, we shall be studying the motion of a body which is free to rotate about some axis, and which is acted on by a number of coplanar forces all lying in a plane perpendicular to the axis. It is then most convenient to select as the reference point the point at which

FIGURE 3–1

the axis intersects the plane of the forces. The perpendicular distance from this point to the line of action of a force is called the *force arm* or the *moment arm* of the force about the axis. The product of the magnitude of a force and its force arm is called the *moment* of the force about the axis, or the *torque.*

Thus Fig. 3–2 is a top view of a flat object, pivoted about an axis perpendicular to the plane of the diagram and passing through point O. The body is acted on by the forces F_1 and F_2, lying in the plane of the diagram. The moment arm of F_1 is the perpendicular distance OA, of length l_1, and the moment arm of F_2 is the perpendicular distance OB of length l_2.

The effect of the force F_1 is to produce counterclockwise rotation about the axis, while that of F_2 is to produce clockwise rotation. To distinguish between these directions of rotation, we shall adopt the convention that counterclockwise moments are positive, and that clockwise moments are negative. Hence the moment Γ_1 (Greek gamma) of the force F_1 about the axis through O is

$$\Gamma_1 = +F_1 l_1,$$

and the moment Γ_2 of F_2 is

$$\Gamma_2 = -F_2 l_2.$$

If forces are expressed in pounds and lengths in feet, torques are expressed in pound·feet.

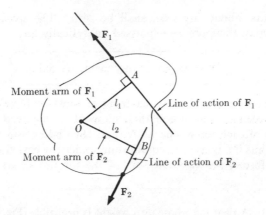

FIG. 3–2. The moment of a force about an axis is the product of the force and its moment arm.

3–2 The second condition of equilibrium. We saw in Section 2–2 that when a body is acted on by any number of coplanar forces, the forces can always be reduced to two, as in Fig. 2–2. If the body is in equilibrium, these forces must (a) be equal in magnitude and opposite in direction, and (b) must have the same line of action.

Requirement (a) is satisfied by the *first condition of equilibrium*,

$$\Sigma F_x = 0, \qquad \Sigma F_y = 0.$$

Requirement (b), which is the second condition of equilibrium, can be simply expressed in terms of the moments of the forces. Figure 3–3 again shows a flat object acted on by two forces $\mathbf{F}_1$ and $\mathbf{F}_2$. If the object is in equilibrium, the magnitudes of $\mathbf{F}_1$ and $\mathbf{F}_2$ are equal and both forces have the same line of action. Hence they have the same moment arm OA, of length l, about an axis perpendicular to the plane of the body and passing through any arbitrary point O. Their moments about the axis are therefore equal in magnitude and opposite in sign, and the algebraic sum of their moments is zero. The necessary and sufficient condition, therefore, that two equal and opposite forces have the same line of action is that the algebraic sum of

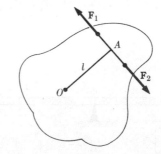

FIG. 3–3. When two forces are in equilibrium, their resultant moment about any axis is zero.

their moments, about any axis, shall be zero. The *second condition of equilibrium* may therefore be expressed analytically as

$$\sum \Gamma = 0 \text{ (about any arbitrary axis)}.$$

It is not necessary to first reduce a set of coplanar forces to two forces in order to calculate the sum of their moments. One need only calculate the moment of each force separately, and then add these moments algebraically. Thus if a body is in equilibrium under the action of any number of coplanar forces, the algebraic sum of the torques about any arbitrary axis is zero.

EXAMPLE 1. A rigid rod whose own weight is negligible (Fig. 3–4) is pivoted at point O and carries a body of weight w_1 at end A. Find the weight w_2 of a second body which must be attached at end B if the rod is to be in equilibrium, and find the force exerted on the rod by the pivot at O.

Figure 3–4(b) is the free-body diagram of the rod. The forces T_1 and T_2 are equal respectively to w_1 and w_2. The conditions of equilibrium, taking moments about an axis through O, perpendicular to the diagram, give

$$\sum F_y = P - T_1 - T_2 = 0, \quad \text{(1st condition)}$$

$$\Gamma_O = T_1 l_1 - T_2 l_2 = 0. \quad \text{(2nd condition)}$$

Let $l_1 = 3$ ft, $l_2 = 4$ ft, $w_1 = 4$ lb. Then, from the equations above,

$$P = 7 \text{ lb}, \qquad T_2 = w_2 = 3 \text{ lb}.$$

To illustrate that the resultant moment about *any* axis is zero, let us compute moments about an axis through point A.

$$\sum \Gamma_A = P l_1 - T_2 (l_1 + l_2) = 7 \text{ lb} \times 3 \text{ ft} - 4 \text{ lb} \times 7 \text{ ft} = 0.$$

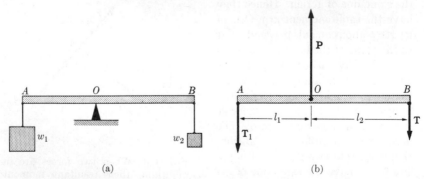

FIG. 3–4. A rod in equilibrium under three parallel forces.

The point about which moments are computed need not lie on the rod. To verify this, let the reader calculate the resultant moment about a point 1 ft to the left of A and 1 ft above it.

EXAMPLE 2. Figure 3–5 illustrates a problem that has already been solved in Example 5 at the end of Section 2–5. A ladder 20 ft long, of weight $w = 80$ lb, with its center of gravity at its center, in equilibrium, leans against a vertical frictionless wall and makes an angle of 53° with the horizontal. We wish to find the magnitudes and directions of the forces F_1 and F_2.

If the wall is frictionless, F_1 is horizontal. The direction of F_2 is unknown (except in special cases, its direction does *not* lie along the ladder). Instead of considering its magnitude and direction as unknowns, it is simpler to resolve the force F_2 into x- and y-components and solve for these. The magnitude and direction of F_2 may then be computed. The first condition of equilibrium therefore provides the equations

$$\left. \begin{array}{l} \sum F_x = F_2 \cos \theta - F_1 = 0, \\ \sum F_y = F_2 \sin \theta - 80 \text{ lb} = 0. \end{array} \right\} \quad \text{(1st condition)}$$

In writing the second condition, moments may be computed about an axis through any point. The resulting equation is simplest if one selects a point through which two or more forces pass, since these forces then do not appear in

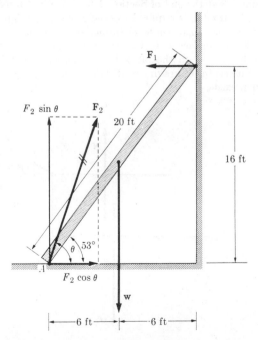

FIG. 3–5. Forces on a ladder in equilibrium, leaning against a frictionless wall.

the equation. Let us therefore take moments about an axis through point A.

$$\sum \Gamma_A = F_1 \times 16 \text{ ft} - 80 \text{ lb} \times 6 \text{ ft} = 0. \qquad \text{(2nd condition)}$$

From the second equation, $F_2 \sin \theta = 80$ lb, and from the third,

$$F_1 = \frac{480 \text{ lb} \cdot \text{ft}}{16 \text{ ft}} = 30 \text{ lb}.$$

Then from the first equation,

$$F_2 \cos \theta = 30 \text{ lb}.$$

Hence

$$F_2 = \sqrt{(80 \text{ lb})^2 + (30 \text{ lb})^2} = 85.5 \text{ lb},$$

$$\theta = \tan^{-1} \frac{80 \text{ lb}}{30 \text{ lb}} = 69.5°.$$

This method is simpler than that used in Section 2–5, since it is unnecessary to locate the point of intersection of the concurrent forces, $\mathbf{F}_1$, $\mathbf{F}_2$, and $\mathbf{w}$.

EXAMPLE 3. Figure 3–6 illustrates a problem that has already been solved, in part, in Example 3 at the end of Section 2–6. (a) What force $\mathbf{T}$, at an angle of 30° above the horizontal, is required to drag a block of weight $w = 20$ lb to the right at constant speed along a level surface if the coefficient of sliding friction between block and surface is 0.20? (b) Determine the line of action of the normal force $\mathbf{N}$ exerted on the block by the surface. The block is 1 ft high, 2 ft long, and its center of gravity is at its center.

Since motion exists,

$$f_k = \mu_k N.$$

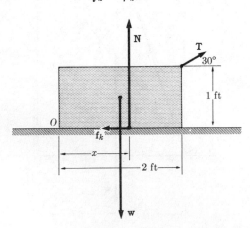

FIGURE 3–6

From the first condition of equilibrium,

$$\Sigma F_x = T\cos 30° - f_k = 0,$$
$$\Sigma F_y = T\sin 30° + N - 20\text{ lb} = 0.$$

(1st condition)

Let x represent the distance from point O to the line of action of $\mathbf{N}$, and take moments about an axis through O. Then, from the second condition of equilibrium,

$$\Sigma \Gamma_O = T\sin 30° \times 2\text{ ft} - T\cos 30° \times 1\text{ ft} + N \times x - 20\text{ lb} \times 1\text{ ft} = 0.$$

(2nd condition)

From the first two equations, we get

$$T = 4.15\text{ lb}, \qquad N = 17.9\text{ lb},$$

and from the third equation,

$$x = 1.08\text{ ft}.$$

The line of action of $\mathbf{N}$ therefore lies 0.08 ft to the right of the center of gravity.

3–3 Resultant of parallel forces. The direction of the resultant of a set of parallel forces is the same as that of the forces, and its magnitude equals the sum of their magnitudes. The line of action of the resultant can be found from the requirement that the moment of the resultant, about any axis, shall equal the sum of the moments of the given forces.

Consider the parallel forces $\mathbf{F}_1$ and $\mathbf{F}_2$ in Fig. 3–7. Point O is any arbitrary point and the x-axis has been taken at right angles to the directions of the forces. The forces have no x-components, so the magnitude of the resultant is

$$R = \Sigma F_y = F_1 + F_2.$$

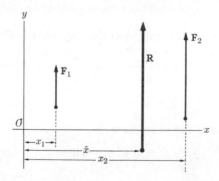

Fig. 3–7. Vector $\mathbf{R}$ represents the resultant of the parallel forces $\mathbf{F}_1$ and $\mathbf{F}_2$, in magnitude, direction, and line of action.

If x_1 and x_2 are the perpendicular distances from O to the lines of action of the forces, their resultant moment about an axis through O is

$$\Sigma\Gamma_O = x_1F_1 + x_2F_2.$$

Let $\bar{x}$ represent the distance from O to the line of action of the resultant. The moment of the resultant about O is then

$$R\bar{x} = (F_1 + F_2)\bar{x},$$

and since this equals the resultant moment, we have

$$(F_1 + F_2)\bar{x} = F_1x_1 + F_2x_2.$$

Therefore

$$\bar{x} = \frac{F_1x_1 + F_2x_2}{F_1 + F_2},$$

and the magnitude, direction, and line of action of the resultant are determined.

The resultant of any number of parallel forces is found in the same way. The magnitude of the resultant is

$$R = \Sigma F,$$

and, if the forces are parallel to the y-axis, the x-coordinate of its line of action is

$$\bar{x} = \frac{\Sigma Fx}{\Sigma F} = \frac{\Sigma Fx}{R}.$$

EXAMPLE. When a body is in equilibrium under the action of three forces, the resultant of any two is equal and opposite to the third and has the same line of action. Show that these conditions are satisfied by the three parallel forces in Fig. 3–4(b).

It was shown in Example 1 at the end of Section 3–2 that if $l_1 = 3$ ft, $l_2 = 4$ ft, and $T_1 = 4$ lb, then $T_2 = 3$ lb and $P = 7$ lb.

Let us first find the resultant of T_1 and T_2. Take the x-axis along the rod with origin at point A. The magnitude of the resultant is

$$R = \Sigma F = -4\text{ lb} - 3\text{ lb} = -7\text{ lb}.$$

The coordinate of its line of action is

$$\bar{x} = \frac{\Sigma Fx}{\Sigma F} = \frac{4\text{ lb} \times 0 - 3\text{ lb} \times 7\text{ ft}}{-7\text{ lb}} = 3\text{ ft}.$$

Hence the resultant of T_1 and T_2 is equal and opposite to P and has the same line of action.

The resultant of $\mathbf{P}$ and $\mathbf{T}_2$ has a magnitude

$$R = \Sigma F = 7\,\mathrm{lb} - 3\,\mathrm{lb} = 4\,\mathrm{lb}.$$

The coordinate of its line of action is

$$\bar{x} = \frac{\Sigma Fx}{\Sigma F} = \frac{7\,\mathrm{lb} \times 3\,\mathrm{ft} - 3\,\mathrm{lb} \times 7\,\mathrm{ft}}{4\,\mathrm{lb}} = 0,$$

so the resultant of $\mathbf{P}$ and $\mathbf{T}_2$ is equal and opposite to $\mathbf{T}_1$ and has the same line of action.

3–4 Center of gravity. Every particle of matter in a body is attracted by the earth, and the single force which we call the *weight* of the body is the resultant of all these forces of attraction. The direction of the force on each particle is toward the center of the earth, but the distance to the earth's center is so great that for all practical purposes the forces can be considered parallel to one another. Hence the weight of a body is the resultant of a large number of parallel forces.

Figure 3–8(a) shows a flat object of arbitrary shape in the xy-plane, the y-axis being vertical. Let the body be subdivided into a large number of small particles of weights $\mathbf{w}_1$, $\mathbf{w}_2$, etc., and let the coordinates of these particles be x_1 and y_1, x_2 and y_2, etc. The total weight W of the object is

$$W = w_1 + w_2 + \cdots = \Sigma w. \tag{3–1}$$

The x-coordinate of the line of action of $\mathbf{W}$ is

$$\bar{x} = \frac{w_1 x_1 + w_2 x_2 + \cdots}{w_1 + w_2 + \cdots} = \frac{\Sigma wx}{\Sigma w} = \frac{\Sigma wx}{W}. \tag{3–2}$$

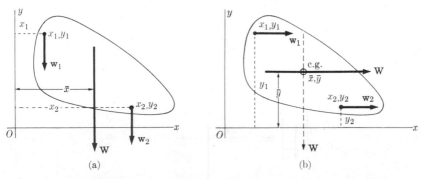

(a)   (b)

FIG. 3–8. The body's weight $\mathbf{W}$ is the resultant of a large number of parallel forces. The line of action of $\mathbf{W}$ always passes through the center of gravity.

Now let the object and the reference axes be rotated 90° clockwise or, which amounts to the same thing, let us consider the gravitational forces to be rotated 90° counterclockwise as in Fig. 3–8(b). The total weight W is unaltered and the y-coordinate of its line of action is

$$\bar{y} = \frac{w_1 y_1 + w_2 y_2 + \cdots}{w_1 + w_2 + \cdots} = \frac{\sum wy}{\sum w} = \frac{\sum wy}{W}. \qquad (3\text{–}3)$$

The point of intersection of the lines of action of **W** in the two parts of Fig. 3–8 has the coordinates $\bar{x}$ and $\bar{y}$ and is called the *center of gravity* of the object. By considering some arbitrary orientation of the object, one can show that the line of action of **W** *always* passes through the center of gravity.

If the centers of gravity of each of a number of bodies have been determined, the coordinates of the center of gravity of the combination can be computed from Eqs. (3–1) and (3–2), letting w_1, w_2, etc., be the weights of the bodies and x_1 and y_1, and y_2, etc., be the coordinates of the center of gravity of each.

Symmetry considerations are often useful in finding the position of the center of gravity. Thus the center of gravity of a homogeneous sphere, cube, circular disk, or rectangular plate is at its center. That of a cylinder or right circular cone is on the axis of symmetry, and so on.

EXAMPLE. Locate the center of gravity of the machine part in Fig. 3–9, consisting of a disk 2 inches in diameter and one inch long, and a rod 1 inch in diameter and 6 inches long, constructed of a homogeneous material.

By symmetry, the center of gravity lies on the axis and the center of gravity of each part is midway between its ends. The volume of the disk is π in^3 and that of the rod is $3\pi/2$ in^3. Since the weights of the two parts are proportional to their volumes,

$$\frac{w \text{ (disk)}}{w \text{ (rod)}} = \frac{w_1}{w_2} = \frac{\pi}{3\pi/2} = \frac{2}{3}.$$

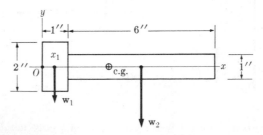

FIGURE 3–9

Take the origin O at the left face of the disk, on the axis. Then $x_1 = 0.5$ inch, $x_2 = 4.0$ inches, and

$$\bar{x} = \frac{w_1 \times 0.5 \text{ in.} + \frac{3}{2}w_1 \times 4.0 \text{ in.}}{w_1 + \frac{3}{2}w_1} = 2.6 \text{ in.}$$

The center of gravity is on the axis, 2.6 inches to the right of O.

―――――――――――――

The center of gravity of a flat object can be located experimentally as shown in Fig. 3–10. In part (a) the body is suspended from some arbitrary point A. When allowed to come to equilibrium, the center of gravity must lie on a vertical line through A. When the object is suspended from a second point B, as in part (b), the center of gravity lies on a vertical line through B and hence lies at the point of intersection of this line and the first. If the object is now suspended from a third point C, as in part (c), a vertical line through C will be found to pass through the point of intersection of the first two lines.

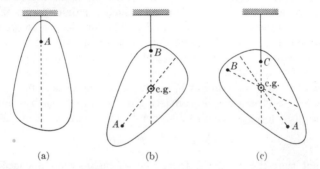

Fig. 3–10. Locating the center of gravity of a flat object.

The center of gravity of a body has another important property. A force **F** whose line of action lies at one side or the other of the center of gravity, as in Fig. 3–11(a), will change both the translational and rotational motion of the body on which it acts. However, if the line of action passes through the center of gravity, as in part (b), only the translational motion is affected and the body remains in rotational equilibrium. Thus when a body is tossed in the air with a whirling motion it continues to rotate at a constant rate, since the line of action of its weight passes through the center of gravity.

It may also be pointed out that when one object rests on or slides over another, the normal and frictional forces are sets of parallel forces distributed over the area in contact. The single vectors which have been used

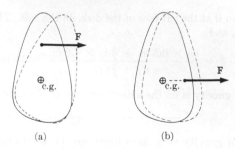

(a)   (b)

FIG. 3–11. A body is in rotational but not translational equilibrium when acted on by a force whose line of action passes through the center of gravity, as in (b).

to represent these forces are therefore actually the resultants of sets of parallel forces.

3–5 Couples. It often happens that the forces on a body reduce to two forces of equal magnitude and opposite direction, having lines of action which are parallel but do not coincide. Such a pair of forces is called a *couple*. A common example is afforded by the forces on a compass needle in the earth's magnetic field. The north and south poles of the needle are acted on by equal forces, one toward the north and the other toward the south as shown in Fig. 3–12. Except when the needle points in the N-S direction, the two forces do not have the same line of action.

Figure 3–13 shows a couple consisting of two forces, each of magnitude F, separated by a perpendicular distance l. The resultant R of the forces is

$$R = F - F = 0.$$

The fact that the resultant force is zero means that a couple has no effect in producing translation as a whole of the body on which it acts. The only effect of a couple is to produce rotation.

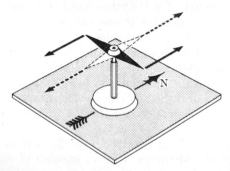

FIG. 3–12. Forces on the poles of a compass needle.

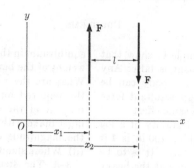

FIG. 3–13. Two equal and opposite forces having different lines of action are called a couple. The moment of the couple is the same about all points, and is equal to lF.

The resultant torque of the couple in Fig. 3–13, about an arbitrary point O, is

$$\Gamma_O = x_1 F - x_2 F$$
$$= x_1 F - (x_1 + l)F$$
$$= -lF.$$

Since the distances x_1 and x_2 do not appear in the result, we conclude that the torque of the couple is the same about *all* points in the plane of the forces forming the couple and is equal to the product of the magnitude of either force and the perpendicular distance between their lines of action.

A body acted on by a couple can be kept in equilibrium only by another couple of the same moment and in the opposite direction. As an example, the ladder in Fig. 3–5 can be considered as acted on by two couples, one formed by the forces $F_2 \sin \theta$ and w, the other by the forces $F_2 \cos \theta$ and F_1. The moment of the first is

$$\Gamma_1 = 6 \text{ ft} \times 80 \text{ lb} = 480 \text{ lb·ft.}$$

The moment of the second is

$$\Gamma_2 = 16 \text{ ft} \times 30 \text{ lb} = 480 \text{ lb·ft.}$$

The first moment is clockwise and the second is counterclockwise.

PROBLEMS

3–1. Give an example to show that the following statement is false: Any two forces acting on a body can be combined into a single resultant force that would have the same effect.

3–2. The center of gravity of a log 10 ft long and weighing 100 lb is 4 ft from one end of the log. It is to be carried by two men, one at the heavy end. Where should the other man hold the log if each is to carry half the load?

3–3. A rod AB which is 3 ft long and whose own weight can be neglected rests on a knife-edge 1 ft from end A. A 10-lb weight hangs from end B. (a) What weight must be hung from A to maintain equilibrium? (b) What is then the force exerted by the knife-edge?

3–4. The rod in Fig. 3–14 is pivoted about an axis through O. (a) Find the moment of each force, and the resultant torque, about the axis. (b) Find the magnitude and direction of the force which must be exerted at the right end, perpendicular to the rod, to maintain equilibrium.

3–5. A single force is to be applied to the bar in Fig. 3–15 to maintain it in equilibrium in the position shown. The weight of the bar can be neglected. (a) What are the x- and y-components of the required force? (b) What is the tangent of the angle which the force must make with the bar? (c) What is the magnitude of the required force? (d) Where should the force be applied?

3–6. The strut in Fig. 3–16 weighs 40 lb and its center of gravity is at its center. Find (a) the tension in the cable, and (b) the horizontal and vertical components of the force exerted on the strut at the wall.

3–7. The boom in Fig. 3–17 is uniform and weighs 500 lb. Find the tension in the guy wire, and the horizontal and vertical components of the force exerted on the boom at its lower end.

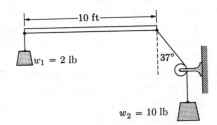

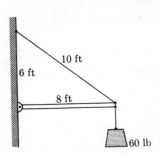

FIGURE 3–15

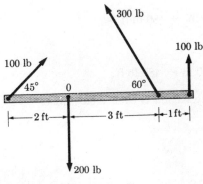

FIGURE 3–14

FIGURE 3–16

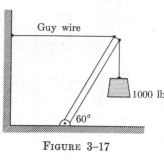

FIGURE 3–17

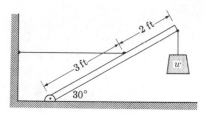

FIGURE 3–19

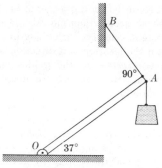

FIGURE 3–18

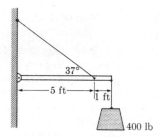

FIGURE 3–20

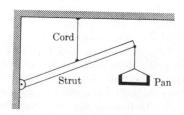

FIGURE 3–21

3–8. The uniform boom OA in Fig. 3–18 is 20 ft long and supports a weight of 3600 lb at end A. (a) If the weight of the boom is negligible, find the tension in the cable AB and the magnitude and direction of the force exerted on the pin at O. (b) If the boom weighs 2800 lb, find the tension in the cable and the magnitude and direction of the force on the pin at O.

3–9. If the weight of the strut in Fig. 3–19 is neglected, (a) what weight w is necessary to produce a tension of 200 lb in the horizontal cable? (b) What will then be the magnitude and direction of the force exerted on the strut at its lower end?

3–10. Find the tension in the cable and the force exerted on the strut by the wall in Fig. 3–20. Neglect the weight of the strut.

3–11. In Fig. 3–21 the vertical cord is attached to the midpoint of the strut, which is weightless. The cord will break if the tension in it exceeds 500 lb. Weights of 100 lb each are placed one by one in the pan. What is the maximum number of such weights that can be safely put into the pan without the cord's breaking?

3–12. End A of the bar AB in Fig. 3–22 rests on a frictionless horizontal surface, while end B is hinged. A hori-

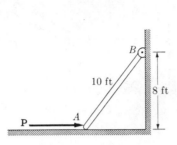

FIGURE 3–22

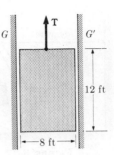

FIGURE 3–23

zontal force **P** of magnitude 12 lb is exerted on end A. Neglect the weight of the bar. What are the horizontal and vertical components of the force exerted by the bar on the hinge at B?

3–13. A ladder 13 ft long leans against a vertical frictionless wall with its lower end 5 ft from the wall. The ladder weighs 80 lb and its center of gravity is at its center. Find the magnitude and direction of the force exerted on the lower end of the ladder.

3–14. A uniform ladder 20 ft long weighing 80 lb, leans against a vertical frictionless wall with its lower end 12 ft from the wall. Compute the magnitude and direction of the resultant force exerted on the lower end of the ladder.

3–15. A uniform ladder 35 ft long rests against a frictionless vertical wall with its lower end 21 ft from the wall. The ladder weighs 80 lb. The coefficient of static friction between the foot of the ladder and the ground is 0.4. A man weighing 150 lb starts up the ladder. How far up the ladder can he climb before the ladder starts to slip?

3–16. A freight elevator weighing 2000 lb and having dimensions of 8 × 8 × 12 ft hangs from a cable with a small clearance between vertical frictionless guides, G and G', as shown in Fig. 3–23. A load of 1200 lb is placed in the elevator with its center of gravity

2 ft to the left of the center of the floor. The elevator is then moved upward at constant velocity. (a) Show in a diagram the location and direction of the forces exerted by the guides on the elevator. (b) Compute the magnitude of these forces.

3–17. A roller 20 inches in diameter weighs 72 lb. What horizontal force is necessary to pull the roller over a brick 2 inches high when (a) the force is applied at the center, (b) at the top?

3–18. Find the tension in cord A in Fig. 3–24. The boom is uniform and weighs 400 lb.

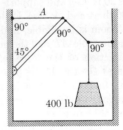

FIGURE 3–24

3–19. A door 7 ft high and 3 ft wide is hung from hinges 6 ft apart and 6 inches from the top and bottom of the door. The door weighs 60 lb, its center of gravity is at its center, and each hinge carries half the weight of the door. Find the horizontal component of the force exerted on the door at each hinge.

3–20. A gate 8 ft long and 4 ft high weighs 80 lb. Its center of gravity is at its center, and it is hinged at A and B. To relieve the strain on the top hinge a wire CD is connected as shown in Fig. 3–25. The tension in CD is increased until the horizontal force at hinge A is zero. (a) What is the tension in the wire CD? (b) What is the magnitude of the horizontal component of force at hinge B? (c) What is the combined vertical force exerted by hinges A and B?

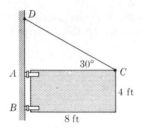

FIGURE 3–25

3–21. A garage door is mounted on an overhead rail as in Fig. 3–26. The wheels at A and B have rusted so that they do not roll, but slide along the track. The coefficient of sliding friction is 0.5. The distance between the wheels is 4 ft, and each is 1 ft in from the vertical sides of the door. The door is symmetrical and weighs 160 lb. It is pushed to the left at constant velocity

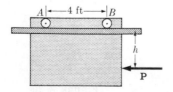

FIGURE 3–26

by a horizontal force $\mathbf{P}$. (a) If the distance h is 3 ft, what is the vertical component of the force exerted on each wheel by the track? (b) Find the maximum value h can have without causing one wheel to leave the track.

3–22. A rectangular block 1 ft wide and 2 ft high is dragged to the right along a level surface at constant speed by a horizontal force $\mathbf{P}$, as shown in Fig. 3–27. The coefficient of sliding friction is 0.40, the block weighs 50 lb, and its center of gravity is at its center. (a) Find the force $\mathbf{P}$ required. (b) Find the line of action of the nor-

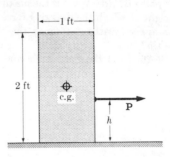

FIGURE 3–27

mal force $\mathbf{N}$ exerted on the block by the surface if the height h is 6 inches. (c) Find the value of h at which the block just starts to tip.

3–23. A table 8 ft long and 3 ft high, weighing 100 lb, has its center of gravity 6 inches below the center of the table top. The table is pushed at constant speed along a horizontal surface by a horizontal force applied at one end of the table top. The coefficient of sliding friction is 0.40. Compute the upward force and the friction force at each table leg.

3–24. A bench is 6 ft long, 2 ft high, and weighs 50 lb. Its center of gravity is midway between its ends. (a) What force applied at the upper right corner and 30° above the horizontal will drag the bench at constant speed along a horizontal surface? (b) What is the upward force at each end of the bench? The coefficient of sliding friction is 0.20.

3–25. The chair in Fig. 3–28 is to be dragged to the right at constant speed along a horizontal surface, the coefficient of sliding friction being 0.30. The chair weighs 50 lb. (a) What horizontal force is needed? (b) What is the upward force at each leg if the force dragging the chair is applied at point A? (c) What is the upward force at each leg if the force is applied at point B? (d) What is the maximum height at which the dragging force can be applied without causing the chair to tip?

3–26. Find the magnitude and line of action of the resultant of the four forces in Fig. 3–29.

3–27. Weights of 3, 6, 9, and 12 lb are fastened to the corners of a light wire frame 2 ft square. Find the position of the center of gravity of the weights.

3–28. Find the position of the center of gravity of the T-shaped plate in Fig. 3–30.

3–29. A machine part, shown in cross section in Fig. 3–31, consists of two homogeneous, solid, coaxial cylinders. Where is its center of gravity?

3–30. Find the position of the center of gravity of the L-shaped plate in Fig. 3–32.

3–31. Find the position of the center of gravity of the U-shaped plate in Fig. 3–33.

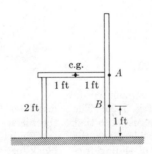

FIGURE 3–28

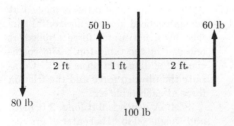

FIGURE 3–29

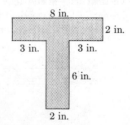

FIGURE 3–30

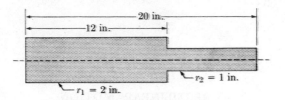

FIGURE 3-31

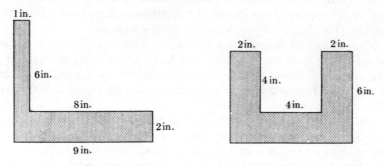

FIGURE 3-32

FIGURE 3-33

CHAPTER 4

RECTILINEAR MOTION

4–1 Motion. The preceding chapters have been concerned with forces, and we are now ready to discuss the mathematical methods of describing motion. This branch of mechanics is called *kinematics*.

Motion may be defined as a continuous change of position. In most actual motions, different points in a body move along different paths. The complete motion is known if we know how each point in the body moves, so to begin with we consider only a moving point, or a very small body called a *particle*.

The position of a particle is conveniently specified by its projections onto the three axes of a rectangular coordinate system. As the particle moves along any path in space, its projections move in straight lines along the three axes. The actual motion can be reconstructed from the motions of these three projections, so we shall begin by discussing the motion of a single particle along a straight line, or *rectilinear motion*.

4–2 Average velocity. Consider a particle moving along the x-axis, as in Fig. 4–1(a). The curve in Fig. 4–1(b) is a graph of its coordinate x plotted as a function of time t. At a time t_1 the particle is at point P in Fig. 4–1(a), where its coordinate is x_1, and at a later time t_2 it is at point Q, whose coordinate is x_2. The corresponding points on the coordinate-time graph in part (b) are lettered p and q.

The *displacement* of a particle as it moves from one point of its path to another is defined as the vector $\Delta \mathbf{x}$ drawn from the first point to the second. Thus in Fig. 4–1(a) the vector PQ, of magnitude $x_2 - x_1 = \Delta x$, is the displacement. The *average velocity* of the particle is defined as the ratio of the displacement to the time interval $t_2 - t_1 = \Delta t$. We shall represent average velocity by the symbol $\bar{\mathbf{v}}$ (the bar signifying an average value).

$$\bar{\mathbf{v}} = \frac{\Delta \mathbf{x}}{\Delta t}.$$

Average velocity is a vector, since the ratio of a vector to a scalar is itself a vector. Its direction is the same as that of the displacement vector. The magnitude of the average velocity is

$$\bar{v} = \frac{x_2 - x_1}{t_2 - t_1} = \frac{\Delta x}{\Delta t}. \tag{4–1}$$

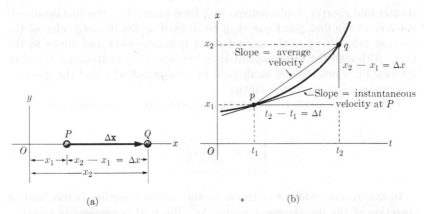

FIG. 4-1. (a) Particle moving on the x-axis. (b) Coordinate-time graph of the motion. The average velocity between t_1 and t_2 equals the slope of the chord pq. The instantaneous velocity at p equals the slope of the tangent at p.

In Fig. 4-1(b), the average velocity is represented by the slope of the chord pq (due allowance being made for the scales to which x and t are plotted), since the slope is the ratio of the "rise," $x_2 - x_1$ or Δx, to the "run," $t_2 - t_1$ or Δt.

Equation (4-1) can be cleared of fractions and written

$$x_2 - x_1 = \bar{v}\,(t_2 - t_1). \qquad (4\text{-}2)$$

Since our time-measuring device can be started at any instant, we can let $t_1 = 0$ and let t_2 be any arbitrary time t. Then if x_0 is the coordinate when $t = 0$ (x_0 is called the *initial position*), and x is the coordinate at time t, Eq. (4-2) becomes

$$x - x_0 = \bar{v}t. \qquad (4\text{-}3)$$

If the particle is at the origin when $t = 0$, then $x_0 = 0$ and Eq. (4-3) simplifies further to

$$x = \bar{v}t. \qquad (4\text{-}4)$$

4-3 Instantaneous velocity. The velocity of a particle at some one instant of time, or at some one point of its path, is called its *instantaneous velocity*. This concept requires careful definition.

Suppose we wish to find the instantaneous velocity of the particle in Fig. 4-1 at the point P. The average velocity between points P and Q is associated with the entire displacement Δx, and with the entire time interval Δt. Imagine the second point Q to be taken closer and closer to the first point P, and let the average velocity be computed over these shorter and shorter displacements and time intervals. The instantaneous velocity at the first point can then be defined as the *limiting value* of the average velocity when the second point is taken closer and closer to the first. Although the displacement then becomes extremely small, the time interval by which it must be divided becomes small also and the quotient is not necessarily a small quantity.

Then if **v** represents the instantaneous velocity, its magnitude is

$$v = \lim_{\Delta t \to 0} \frac{\Delta x}{\Delta t} \cdot \qquad (4\text{-}5)$$

Instantaneous velocity is also a vector, whose direction is the limiting direction of the displacement vector $\Delta \mathbf{x}$. Since Δt is necessarily positive, it follows that v has the same algebraic sign as Δx. Hence a positive velocity indicates motion toward the right along the x-axis, if we use the usual convention of signs.

As point Q approaches point P in Fig. 4–1(a), point q approaches point p in Fig. 4–1(b). In the limit, the slope of the chord pq equals the slope of the *tangent* to the curve at point p, due allowance being made for the scales to which x and t are plotted. *The instantaneous velocity at any point of a coordinate-time graph therefore equals the slope of the tangent to the graph at that point.* If the tangent slopes upward to the right, its slope is positive, the velocity is positive, and the motion is toward the right. If the tangent slopes downward to the right, the velocity is negative. At a point where the tangent is horizontal, its slope is zero and the velocity is zero.

If we express distance in feet and time in seconds, velocity is expressed in *feet per second* (ft/sec). Other common units of velocity are meters per second (m/sec), centimeters per second (cm/sec), miles per hour (mi/hr), and knots (1 knot = 1 nautical mile per hour).

EXAMPLE. The coordinate of a body moving along the x-axis is given by

$$x = 10 \frac{\text{cm}}{\text{sec}^2} t^2.$$

Compute the average velocity $\bar{v}$ over the time interval from (a) 2 sec to 2.1 sec, (b) from 2 sec to 2 sec + Δt. (c) Compute the instantaneous velocity v at $t = 2$ sec.

(a) At $t_1 = 2$ sec,

$$x_1 = 10 \frac{\text{cm}}{\text{sec}^2} (2 \text{ sec})^2 = 40 \text{ cm}.$$

At $t_2 = 2.1$ sec,

$$x_2 = 10 \frac{cm}{sec^2} (2.1 \text{ sec})^2 = 44.1 \text{ cm}.$$

Hence

$$\bar{v} = \frac{x_2 - x_1}{t_2 - t_1} = \frac{44.1 \text{ cm} - 40 \text{ cm}}{2.1 \text{ sec} - 2 \text{ sec}}$$

$$= 41 \frac{cm}{sec}.$$

(b) At $t_1 = 2$ sec, $x_1 = 40$ cm. At $t_2 = 2 \text{ sec} + \Delta t$,

$$x_2 = 10 \frac{cm}{sec^2} (2 \text{ sec} + \Delta t)^2$$

$$= 10 \frac{cm}{sec^2} (4 \text{ sec}^2 + 4 \text{ sec } \Delta t + \Delta t^2)$$

$$= 40 \text{ cm} + 40 \frac{cm}{sec} \Delta t + 10 \frac{cm}{sec^2} \Delta t^2.$$

Hence

$$\bar{v} = \frac{\Delta x}{\Delta t} = \frac{\Delta t[(40 \text{ cm/sec}) + (10 \text{ cm/sec})^2 \Delta t]}{\Delta t}$$

$$= 40 \frac{cm}{sec} + 10 \frac{cm}{sec^2} \Delta t.$$

(c) The instantaneous velocity is

$$v = \lim_{\Delta t \to 0} \frac{\Delta x}{\Delta t} = \lim_{\Delta t \to 0} \left(40 \frac{cm}{sec} + 10 \frac{cm}{sec^2} \Delta t \right)$$

$$= 40 \frac{cm}{sec}.$$

———————————

The term *speed* has two different meanings. It is sometimes used to mean the *magnitude* of the instantaneous velocity. In this sense, two automobiles traveling at 50 mi/hr, one north and the other south, are both said to have a speed of 50 mi/hr. In another sense, the *average speed* of a body means the total length of path covered, divided by the elapsed time. Thus if an automobile travels a total distance of 90 miles in 3 hours, its average speed is said to be 30 mi/hr even if the trip starts and ends at the same point. The average *velocity*, in the latter case, would be zero, since the displacement is zero.

4–4 Average and instantaneous acceleration. Except in certain special cases, the velocity of a moving body changes continuously as the motion proceeds. When this is the case the body is said to move with *accelerated motion*, or to have an *acceleration*.

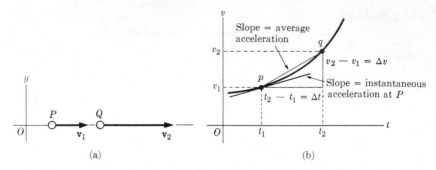

FIG. 4-2. (a) Particle moving on the x-axis. (b) Velocity-time graph of the motion. The average acceleration between t_1 and t_2 equals the slope of the chord pq. The instantaneous acceleration at p equals the slope of the tangent at p.

Figure 4-2(a) shows a particle moving along the x-axis. The vector $\mathbf{v}_1$ represents its instantaneous velocity at point P, and the vector $\mathbf{v}_2$ represents its instantaneous velocity at point Q. Figure 4-2(b) is a graph of the instantaneous velocity v plotted as a function of time, points p and q corresponding to P and Q in part (a).

The *average acceleration* of the particle as it moves from P to Q is defined as the ratio of the change in velocity to the elapsed time.

$$\bar{\mathbf{a}} = \frac{\mathbf{v}_2 - \mathbf{v}_1}{t_2 - t_1} = \frac{\Delta \mathbf{v}}{\Delta t}, \tag{4-6}$$

where t_1 and t_2 are the times corresponding to the velocities $\mathbf{v}_1$ and $\mathbf{v}_2$. Since $\mathbf{v}_1$ and $\mathbf{v}_2$ are vectors, the quantity $\mathbf{v}_2 - \mathbf{v}_1$ is a *vector difference* and must be found by the methods explained in Section 1-7. However, since in rectilinear motion both vectors lie in the same straight line, the magnitude of the vector difference in this special case equals the difference between the magnitudes of the vectors. The more general case, in which $\mathbf{v}_1$ and $\mathbf{v}_2$ are not in the same direction, will be considered in Chapter 6.

In Fig. 4-2(b), the magnitude of the average acceleration is represented by the slope of the chord pq.

The *instantaneous acceleration* of a body, that is, its acceleration at some one instant of time or at some one point of its path, is defined in the same way as instantaneous velocity. Let the second point Q in Fig. 4-2(a) be taken closer and closer to the first point P, and let the average acceleration be computed over shorter and shorter intervals of time. The instantaneous acceleration at the first point is defined as the limiting value of the average acceleration when the second point is taken closer and closer to the first. Then if **a** represents the instantaneous acceleration, its magnitude is

$$a = \lim_{\Delta t \to 0} \frac{\Delta v}{\Delta t}. \tag{4–7}$$

The direction of the instantaneous acceleration is the limiting direction of the vector change in velocity, $\Delta \mathbf{v}$.

Instantaneous acceleration plays an important part in the laws of mechanics. Average acceleration is less frequently used. Hence from now on when the term "acceleration" is used we shall understand it to mean instantaneous acceleration.

The definition of acceleration just given applies to motion along any path, straight or curved. When a particle moves in a curved path the *direction* of its velocity changes and this change in direction also gives rise to an acceleration, as will be explained in Chapter 6.

As point Q approaches point P in Fig. 4–2(a), point q approaches point p in Fig. 4–2(b) and the slope of the chord pq approaches the slope of the tangent to the velocity-time graph at point p. *The instantaneous acceleration at any point of the graph therefore equals the slope of the tangent to the graph at that point.*

If we express velocity in feet per second and time in seconds, acceleration is expressed in feet per second, per second (ft/sec/sec). This is usually written as ft/sec², and is read "feet per second squared." Other common units of acceleration are meters per second squared (m/sec²) and centimeters per second squared (cm/sec²).

When the absolute value of the magnitude of the velocity of a body is decreasing (in other words, when the body is slowing down), the body is said to be *decelerated* or to have a *deceleration*.

EXAMPLE. Suppose the velocity of the particle in Fig. 4–2 is given by the equation

$$v = m + nt^2,$$

where $m = 10$ cm/sec and $n = 2$ cm/sec³. (a) Find the change in velocity of the particle in the time interval between $t_1 = 2$ sec and $t_2 = 2$ sec $+ \Delta t$.

At time $t_1 = 2$ sec,

$$v_1 = 10 \frac{\text{cm}}{\text{sec}} + 2 \frac{\text{cm}}{\text{sec}^3} \times (2 \text{ sec})^2$$

$$= 18 \frac{\text{cm}}{\text{sec}}.$$

At time $t_2 = 2 \text{ sec} + \Delta t$,

$$
\begin{aligned}
v_2 &= 10\frac{\text{cm}}{\text{sec}} + 2\frac{\text{cm}}{\text{sec}^3}(2 \text{ sec} + \Delta t)^2 \\
&= 10\frac{\text{cm}}{\text{sec}} + 2\frac{\text{cm}}{\text{sec}^3}(4 \text{ sec}^2 + 4 \text{ sec } \Delta t + \Delta t^2) \\
&= 18\frac{\text{cm}}{\text{sec}} + \Delta t\left(8\frac{\text{cm}}{\text{sec}^2} + 2\frac{\text{cm}}{\text{sec}^3}\Delta t\right).
\end{aligned}
$$

The change in velocity is therefore

$$
v_2 - v_1 = \Delta t\left(8\frac{\text{cm}}{\text{sec}^2} + 2\frac{\text{cm}}{\text{sec}^3}\Delta t\right).
$$

(b) Find the average acceleration in this time interval.

$$
\begin{aligned}
\bar{a} &= \frac{v_2 - v_1}{t_2 - t_1} = \frac{\Delta t[(8 \text{ cm/sec}^2) + (2 \text{ cm/sec}^3)\,\Delta t]}{\Delta t} \\
&= 8\frac{\text{cm}}{\text{sec}^2} + 2\frac{\text{cm}}{\text{sec}^3}\Delta t.
\end{aligned}
$$

(c) Find the instantaneous acceleration at $t = 2$ sec.

$$
\begin{aligned}
a &= \lim_{\Delta t \to 0}\frac{\Delta v}{\Delta t} = \lim_{\Delta t \to 0}\left(8\frac{\text{cm}}{\text{sec}^2} + 2\frac{\text{cm}}{\text{sec}^3}\Delta t\right) \\
&= 8\frac{\text{cm}}{\text{sec}^2}.
\end{aligned}
$$

4–5 Rectilinear motion with constant acceleration. The simplest kind of accelerated motion is rectilinear motion in which the acceleration is constant, that is, in which the velocity changes at the same rate throughout the motion. The velocity-time graph is then a straight line as in Fig. 4–3, the velocity increasing by equal amounts in equal intervals of time. The slope of a cord between any two points on the line is the same as the slope of a tangent at any point. The instantaneous and average accelerations are therefore equal and, since the slope of a straight line is constant, the acceleration is constant. Its magnitude is

$$
a = \frac{v_2 - v_1}{t_2 - t_1}.
$$

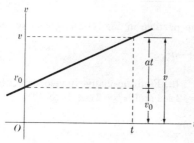

FIG. 4–3. Velocity-time graph for rectilinear motion with constant acceleration.

Now let $t_1 = 0$ and let t_2 be any arbitrary time t. Let v_0 represent the velocity when $t = 0$ (v_0 is called the *initial* velocity), and let

v be the velocity at time t. Then the preceding equation becomes

$$a = \frac{v - v_0}{t - 0},$$

or

$$\boxed{v = v_0 + at.} \tag{4–8}$$

This equation can be interpreted as follows. The acceleration a is the constant rate of change of velocity, or the change per unit time. The term at is the product of the change in velocity per unit time, a, and the duration of the time interval, t. Therefore it equals the total change in velocity. The velocity v at the time t then equals the velocity v_0 at the time $t = 0$, plus the change in velocity at. Graphically, the ordinate v at time t, in Fig. 4–3, can be considered as the sum of two segments: one of length v_0, equal to the initial velocity, the other of length at equal to the change in velocity in time t.

To find the displacement of a particle moving with constant acceleration, we make use of the fact that when the acceleration is constant and the velocity-time graph is a straight line, as in Fig. 4–3, the average velocity in any time interval equals one-half the sum of the velocities at the beginning and the end of the interval. Hence the average velocity between zero and t is

$$\bar{v} = \frac{v_0 + v}{2}. \tag{4–9}$$

This is *not* true, in general, when the acceleration is not constant and the velocity-time graph is curved as in Fig. 4–2.

We have shown that for a particle which is at the origin when $t = 0$, the coordinate x at any time t is

$$x = \bar{v}t, \tag{4–10}$$

where $\bar{v}$ is the average velocity. Hence from the two preceding equations,

$$\boxed{x = \frac{v_0 + v}{2} \times t.} \tag{4–11}$$

Two more very useful equations can be obtained from Eqs. (4–8) and (4–11), first by eliminating v and then by eliminating t. When we substitute in Eq. (4–11) the expression for v in Eq. (4–8), we get

$$x = \frac{v_0 + v_0 + at}{2} \times t,$$

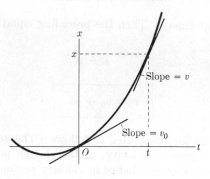

FIGURE 4-4

or

$$x = v_0 t + \tfrac{1}{2}at^2. \tag{4-12}$$

When Eq. (4–8) is solved for t and the result substituted in Eq. (4–11), we have

$$x = \frac{v_0 + v}{2} \times \frac{v - v_0}{a}$$

$$= \frac{v^2 - v_0^2}{2a}$$

or, finally,

$$v^2 = v_0^2 + 2ax. \tag{4-13}$$

Equations (4–8), (4–11), (4–12), and (4–13) are the *equations of motion with constant acceleration,* for the special case where the particle is at the origin when $t = 0$.

The curve in Fig. 4–4 is the coordinate-time graph for motion with constant acceleration. That is, it is a graph of Eq. (4–12). The curve is a *parabola*. The slope of the tangent at $t = 0$ equals the initial velocity v_0, and the slope of the tangent at time t equals the velocity v at that time. It is evident that the slope continually increases, and measurements would show that the *rate* of increase is constant, that is, that the acceleration is constant.

A special case of motion with constant acceleration is that in which the acceleration is zero. The *velocity* is then constant and the equations of motion become simply

$$v = \text{constant},$$

$$x = vt.$$

4–6 Freely falling bodies. The most common example of motion with (nearly) constant acceleration is that of a body falling toward the earth. In the absence of air resistance it is found that all bodies, regardless of their size or weight, fall with the same acceleration at the same point on the earth's surface, and if the distance covered is not too great the acceleration remains constant throughout the fall. The effect of air resistance and the decrease in acceleration with altitude will be neglected. This idealized motion is spoken of as "free fall," although the term includes rising as well as falling.

The acceleration of a freely falling body is called the acceleration due to gravity, or the acceleration of gravity. Its magnitude is denoted by the letter g. At or near the earth's surface its magnitude is approximately 32 ft/sec^2, 9.8 m/sec^2, or 980 cm/sec^2. More precise values, and small variations with latitude and elevation, will be considered later.

Note. The quantity "g" is sometimes referred to simply as "gravity," or as "the force of gravity," both of which are incorrect. "Gravity" is a phenomenon, and the "force of gravity" means the force with which the earth attracts a body, otherwise known as the weight of the body. The letter "g" represents the *acceleration* caused by the force resulting from the phenomenon of gravity.

Example 1. A body is released from rest and falls freely. Compute its position and velocity after 1, 2, 3, and 4 seconds. Take the origin O at the elevation of the starting point, the y-axis vertical, and the upward direction as positive.

The initial coordinate y_0 and the initial velocity v_0 are both zero. The acceleration is downward, in the negative y-direction, so $a = -g = -32 \text{ ft/sec}^2$.

From Eqs. (4–12) and (4–8),

$$y = v_0 t + \tfrac{1}{2}at^2 = 0 - \tfrac{1}{2}gt^2 = -16 \frac{\text{ft}}{\text{sec}^2} \times t^2,$$

$$v = v_0 + at = 0 - gt = -32 \frac{\text{ft}}{\text{sec}^2} \times t.$$

When $t = 1$ sec,

$$y = -16 \frac{\text{ft}}{\text{sec}^2} \times 1 \text{ sec}^2 = -16 \text{ ft},$$

$$v = -32 \frac{\text{ft}}{\text{sec}^2} \times 1 \text{ sec} = -32 \frac{\text{ft}}{\text{sec}}.$$

The body is therefore 16 ft below the origin (y is negative) and has a downward velocity (v is negative) of magnitude 32 ft/sec.

The position and velocity at 2, 3, and 4 sec are found in the same way. The results are illustrated in Fig. 4–5.

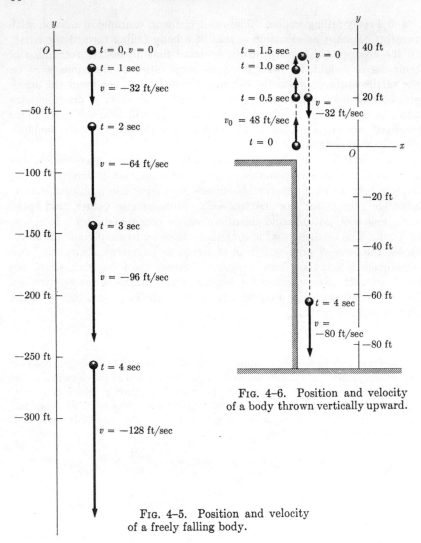

$t = 0, v = 0$

$t = 1$ sec

$v = -32$ ft/sec

-50 ft

$t = 2$ sec

$v = -64$ ft/sec

-100 ft

-150 ft

$t = 3$ sec

$v = -96$ ft/sec

-200 ft

-250 ft

$t = 4$ sec

-300 ft

$v = -128$ ft/sec

$t = 1.5$ sec $v = 0$ 40 ft
$t = 1.0$ sec

$t = 0.5$ sec $v =$ 20 ft
                     -32 ft/sec
$v_0 = 48$ ft/sec

$t = 0$

O

-20 ft

-40 ft

-60 ft
$t = 4$ sec

$v =$
-80 ft/sec -80 ft

FIG. 4–6. Position and velocity of a body thrown vertically upward.

FIG. 4–5. Position and velocity of a freely falling body.

EXAMPLE 2. A ball is thrown (nearly) vertically upward from the cornice of a tall building, leaving the thrower's hand with a speed of 48 ft/sec and just missing the cornice on the way down. (See Fig. 4–6. The dotted line does not represent the actual path of the body.) Find (a) the position and velocity of the ball, 1 sec and 4 sec after leaving the thrower's hand; (b) the velocity when the ball is 20 ft above its starting point; (c) the maximum height reached and the time at which it is reached. Take the origin at the elevation at which the ball leaves the thrower's hand, the y-axis vertical and positive upward.

The initial position y_0 is zero. The initial velocity v_0 is $+48$ ft/sec, and the acceleration is -32 ft/sec^2.

The velocity at any time is

$$v = v_0 + at = 48\,\frac{\text{ft}}{\text{sec}} - 32\,\frac{\text{ft}}{\text{sec}^2} \times t. \qquad (4\text{–}14)$$

The coordinate at any time is

$$y = v_0 t + \tfrac{1}{2}at^2 = 48\,\frac{\text{ft}}{\text{sec}} \times t - 16\,\frac{\text{ft}}{\text{sec}^2} \times t^2.$$

The velocity at any coordinate is

$$v^2 = v_0^2 + 2ay = \left(48\,\frac{\text{ft}}{\text{sec}}\right)^2 - 64\,\frac{\text{ft}}{\text{sec}^2} \times y. \qquad (4\text{–}15)$$

(a) When $t = 1$ sec,

$$y = +32 \text{ ft}, \qquad v = +16\,\frac{\text{ft}}{\text{sec}}.$$

The ball is 32 ft above the origin (y is positive) and it has an upward velocity (v is positive) of 16 ft/sec.

When $t = 4$ sec,

$$y = -64 \text{ ft}, \qquad v = -80\,\frac{\text{ft}}{\text{sec}}.$$

The ball has passed its highest point and is 64 ft *below* the origin (y is negative). It has a *downward* velocity (v is negative) of magnitude 80 ft/sec. Note that it is not necessary to find the highest point reached, or the time at which it was reached. The equations of motion give the position and velocity at *any* time, whether the ball is on the way up or the way down.

(b) When the ball is 20 ft above the origin,

$$y = +20 \text{ ft}$$

and

$$v^2 = 1024\,\frac{\text{ft}^2}{\text{sec}^2}, \qquad v = \pm 32\,\frac{\text{ft}}{\text{sec}}.$$

The ball passes this point twice, once on the way up and again on the way down. The velocity on the way up is $+32$ ft/sec, and on the way down it is -32 ft/sec.

(c) At the highest point, $v = 0$. Hence

$$y = +36 \text{ ft}.$$

The time can now be found either from Eq. (4–14), setting $v = 0$, or from Eq. (4–15), setting $y = 36$ ft. From either equation, we get

$$t = 1.5 \text{ sec}.$$

Figure 4–7 is a "multiflash" photograph of a freely falling golf ball. This photograph was taken with the aid of the ultra-high-speed stroboscopic light source developed by Dr. Harold E. Edgerton of the Massachusetts Institute of Technology. By means of this source a series of intense flashes of light can be produced. The interval between successive flashes is controllable at will, and the duration of each flash is so short (a few millionths of a second) that there is no blur in the image of even a rapidly moving body. The camera shutter is left open during the entire motion, and as each flash occurs the position of the ball at that instant is recorded on the photographic film.

The equally spaced light flashes subdivide the motion into equal time intervals Δt. Since the time intervals are all equal, the velocity of the ball between any two flashes is directly proportional to the separation of its corresponding images in the photograph. If the velocity were constant, the images would be equally spaced. The increasing separation of the images during the fall shows that the velocity is continually increasing or the motion is accelerated. By comparing two successive displacements of the ball, the *change* in velocity in the corresponding time interval can be found. Careful measurements, preferably on an enlarged print, show that this change in velocity is the same in each time interval. In other words, the motion is one of *constant* acceleration.

FIG. 4–7.   Multiflash photograph (retouched) of freely falling golf ball.

4–7 Velocity components.   Relative velocity.   Velocity is a vector quantity involving both magnitude and direction. A velocity may therefore be resolved into components, or a number of velocity components combined into a resultant. As an example of the former process, suppose that a ship is steaming 30° E of N at 20 mi/hr in still water. Its velocity may be represented by the arrow in Fig. 4–8, and one finds by the usual method that its velocity component toward the east is 10 mi/hr, while toward the north it is 17.3 mi/hr.

Velocity, like position, can only be specified relative to some reference frame or set of axes; the axes themselves may or may not be in motion. Ordinarily, velocities are specified relative to axes fixed with respect to the earth and considered to be "at rest," although of course they partake of the motion of the earth through space. In what follows, the expression "the velocity of a body" is understood to mean its velocity relative to the earth.

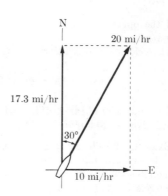

FIG. 4–8. Resolution of a velocity vector into components.

The velocity of one body relative to another when the second is in motion (relative to the earth) *is the vector difference between the velocities of the bodies* (relative to the earth). Specifically, if the bodies are designated by A and B, and their velocities (relative to the earth) by $\mathbf{v}_A$ and $\mathbf{v}_B$, the velocity of A relative to B is

$$\mathbf{v}_{AB} = \mathbf{v}_A - \mathbf{v}_B \tag{4–16}$$

and the velocity of B relative to A is

$$\mathbf{v}_{BA} = \mathbf{v}_B - \mathbf{v}_A.$$

Equation (4–16) may be written

$$\mathbf{v}_A = \mathbf{v}_B + \mathbf{v}_{AB}. \tag{4–17}$$

That is, the velocity of body A (relative to the earth) is the vector sum of the velocity of B (relative to the earth) and the velocity of A relative to B. In general, then, when one body is in motion relative to a second, *the velocity of the first is the vector sum of the velocity of the second and the velocity of the first relative to the second.*

EXAMPLE 1. Automobile A, traveling at 30 mi/hr on a straight level road, is ahead of automobile B traveling in the same direction at 20 mi/hr. What is the velocity of A relative to B and the velocity of B relative to A?

Since both vectors are in the same straight line, the magnitude of their vector difference equals their arithmetic difference. The velocity of A relative to B is

$$v_{AB} = v_A - v_B = 30\,\frac{\text{mi}}{\text{hr}} - 20\,\frac{\text{mi}}{\text{hr}} = +10\,\frac{\text{mi}}{\text{hr}},$$

and the operator of car B sees car A pulling away from him at the rate of 10 mi/hr.

The velocity of B relative to A is

$$v_{BA} = v_B - v_A = 20\,\frac{\text{mi}}{\text{hr}} - 30\,\frac{\text{mi}}{\text{hr}} = -10\,\frac{\text{mi}}{\text{hr}},$$

and the operator of car A (if he looks back) sees car B dropping behind him (v_{BA} is negative) at 10 mi/hr.

EXAMPLE 2. The compass of an airplane indicates that it is headed due north, and its airspeed indicator shows that it is moving through the air at 120 mi/hr. If there is a wind of 50 mi/hr blowing from west to east, what is the velocity of the plane relative to the earth?

The velocity of the air is 50 mi/hr, due east. The velocity of the plane *relative to the air* is 120 mi/hr, due north. The velocity of the plane is the vector sum of these velocities, and from the construction in Fig. 4–9 it is 130 mi/hr, 22.5° E of N. The two velocities of 120 mi/hr and 50 mi/hr can be considered the components of the actual velocity of the plane.

EXAMPLE 3. In what direction should the pilot of the plane set his course in order to travel due north? What will then be his velocity relative to the earth?

The course set by the pilot is the direction in which the plane would actually travel in still air. It is thus in the direction of the velocity of the plane relative to the air. The resultant velocity must be due north. These velocities are related as in Fig. 4–10, from which we find the angle θ to be 24.5° W of N, and the resultant velocity to be 109 mi/hr, due north.

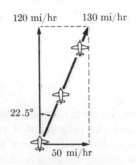

FIGURE 4–9

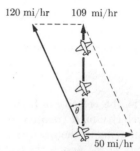

FIGURE 4–10

PROBLEMS

4-1. Suppose that a runner on a straight track covers a distance of 1 mile in exactly 4 minutes. What was his average velocity in (a) mi/hr, (b) ft/sec, (c) cm/sec?

4-2. A body moves along a straight line, its distance from the origin at any instant being given by the equation $x = 8t - 3t^2$, where x is in centimeters and t is in seconds. Find the average velocity of the body in the interval from $t = 0$ to $t = 1$ sec, and in the interval from $t = 0$ to $t = 4$ sec.

4-3. Refer to the example at the end of Section 4-3, in which the motion of a body along the x-axis was described by the equation $x = (10 \text{ cm/sec}^2)t^2$. Compute the instantaneous velocity of the body at time $t = 3$ sec. Let Δt first equal 0.1 sec, then 0.01 sec, and finally 0.001 sec. What limiting value do the results seem to be approaching?

4-4. An automobile is provided with a speedometer calibrated to read ft/sec rather than mi/hr. The following series of speedometer readings was obtained during a start.

Time (sec) 0 2 4 6 8 10 12 14 16
Velocity
  (ft/sec) 0 0 2 5 10 15 20 22 22

(a) Compute the average acceleration during each 2-sec interval. Is the acceleration constant? Is it constant during any part of the time? (b) Make a velocity-time graph of the data above, using scales of 1 in. = 2 sec horizontally, and 1 in. = 5 ft/sec vertically. Draw a smooth curve through the plotted points. What distance is represented by 1 sq in.? What is the displacement in the first 8 sec? What is the acceleration when $t = 8$ sec? When $t = 13$ sec? When $t = 15$ sec?

4-5. The graph in Fig. 4-11 shows the velocity of a body plotted as a function of time.

(a) What is the instantaneous acceleration at $t = 3$ sec?

(b) What is the instantaneous acceleration at $t = 7$ sec?

(c) What is the instantaneous acceleration at $t = 11$ sec?

(d) How far does the body go in the first 5 sec?

(e) How far does the body go in the first 9 sec?

(f) How far does the body go in the first 13 sec?

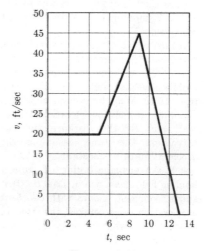

FIGURE 4-11

4-6. Each of the following changes in velocity takes place in a 10-sec interval. What is the magnitude, the algebraic sign, and the direction of the average acceleration in each interval?

(a) At the beginning of the interval a body is moving toward the right along the x-axis at 5 ft/sec, and at the end of the interval it is moving toward the right at 20 ft/sec.

(b) At the beginning it is moving toward the right at 20 ft/sec, and at the end it is moving toward the right at 5 ft/sec.

(c) At the beginning it is moving toward the left at 5 ft/sec, and at the end it is moving toward the left at 20 ft/sec.

(d) At the beginning it is moving toward the left at 20 ft/sec, and at the end it is moving toward the left at 5 ft/sec.

(e) At the beginning it is moving toward the right at 20 ft/sec, and at the end it is moving toward the left at 20 ft/sec.

(f) At the beginning it is moving toward the left at 20 ft/sec, and at the end it is moving toward the right at 20 ft/sec.

(g) In which of the above instances is the body decelerated?

4–7. The makers of a certain automobile advertise that it will accelerate from 15 to 50 mi/hr in high in 13 sec. Compute (a) the acceleration in ft/sec², and (b) the distance the car travels in this time, assuming the acceleration to be constant.

4–8. An airplane taking off from a landing field has a run of 1200 ft. If it starts from rest, moves with constant acceleration, and makes the run in 30 sec, with what velocity in ft/sec did it take off?

4–9. An automobile starts from rest and acquires a velocity of 40 mi/hr in 15 sec. (a) Compute the acceleration in miles per hour per second, and in feet per second per second, assuming it to be constant. (b) If the automobile continues to gain velocity at the same rate, how many more seconds are needed for it to acquire a velocity of 60 mi/hr? (c) Find the distances covered by the automobile in parts (a) and (b).

4–10. A body moving with constant acceleration covers the distance between two points 180 ft apart in 6 sec. Its velocity as it passes the second point is 45 ft/sec. (a) What is its acceleration? (b) What is its velocity at the first point?

4–11. A ball is released from rest and rolls down an inclined plane, requiring 4 sec to cover a distance of 100 cm. (a) What was its acceleration in cm/sec²? (b) How many centimeters would it have fallen vertically in the same time?

4–12. The "reaction time" of the average automobile driver is about 0.7 sec. (The reaction time is the interval between the perception of a signal to stop and the application of the brakes.) If an automobile can decelerate at 16 ft/sec², compute the total distance covered in coming to a stop after a signal is observed: (a) from an initial velocity of 30 mi/hr, (b) from an initial velocity of 60 mi/hr.

4–13. At the instant the traffic lights turn green, an automobile that has been waiting at an intersection starts ahead with a constant acceleration of 6 ft/sec². At the same instant a truck, traveling with a constant velocity of 30 ft/sec, overtakes and passes the automobile. (a) How far beyond its starting point will the automobile overtake the truck? (b) How fast will it be traveling?

4–14. The engineer of a passenger train traveling at 100 ft/sec sights a freight train whose caboose is 600 ft ahead on the same track. The freight train is traveling in the same direction as the passenger train with a velocity of 30 ft/sec. The engineer of the passenger train immediately applies the brakes, causing a constant deceleration of 4 ft/sec², while the freight train continues with constant speed. (a)

Will there be a collision? (b) If so, where will it take place?

4–15. A sled starts from rest at the top of a hill and slides down with a constant acceleration. The sled is 140 ft from the top of the hill 2 sec after passing a point which is 92 ft from the top. Four sec after passing the 92-ft point it is 198 ft from the top, and 6 sec after passing the point it is 266 ft from the top.

(a) What is the average velocity of the sled during each of the 2-sec intervals after passing the 92-ft point?

(b) What is the acceleration of the sled?

(c) What was the velocity of the sled when it passed the 92-ft point?

(d) How long did it take to go from the top to the 92-ft point?

(e) How far did the sled go during the first sec after passing the 92-ft point?

(f) How long does it take the sled to go from the 92-ft point to the midpoint between the 92-ft and the 140-ft mark?

(g) What is the velocity of the sled as it passes the midpoint in part (f)?

4–16. A subway train starts from rest at a station and accelerates at a rate of 4 ft/sec^2 for 10 sec. It then runs at constant speed for 30 sec, and decelerates at 8 ft/sec^2 until it stops at the next station. Find the *total* distance covered.

4–17. A body starts from rest, moves in a straight line with constant acceleration, and covers a distance of 64 ft in 4 sec. (a) What was the final velocity? (b) How long a time was required to cover half the total distance? (c) What was the distance covered in one-half the total time? (d) What was the velocity when half the total distance had been covered? (e) What was the velocity after one-half the total time?

4–18. The speed of an automobile going north is reduced from 45 to 30 mi/hr in a distance of 264 ft. Find (a) the magnitude and direction of the acceleration, assuming it to be constant, (b) the elapsed time, (c) the distance in which the car can be brought to rest from 30 mi/hr, assuming the acceleration of part (a).

4–19. An automobile and a truck start from rest at the same instant, with the automobile initially at some distance behind the truck. The truck has a constant acceleration of 4 ft/sec^2 and the automobile an acceleration of 6 ft/sec^2. The automobile overtakes the truck after the truck has moved 150 ft. (a) How long does it take the auto to overtake the truck? (b) How far was the auto behind the truck initially? (c) What is the velocity of each when they are abreast?

4–20. (a) With what velocity must a ball be thrown vertically upward in order to rise to a height of 50 ft? (b) How long will it be in the air?

4–21. A ball is thrown vertically downward from the top of a building, leaving the thrower's hand with a velocity of 30 ft/sec.

(a) What will be its velocity after falling for 2 sec?

(b) How far will it fall in 2 sec?

(c) What will be its velocity after falling 30 ft?

(d) If it moved a distance of 3 ft while in the thrower's hand, find its acceleration while in his hand.

(e) If the ball was released at a point 120 ft above the ground, in how many seconds will it strike the ground?

(f) What will be its velocity when it strikes?

4–22. A balloon, rising vertically with a velocity of 16 ft/sec, releases a sandbag at an instant when the balloon is 64 ft above the ground. (a) Compute the position and velocity of the sandbag at the following times after its release: $\frac{1}{4}$ sec, $\frac{1}{2}$ sec, 1 sec, 2 sec. (b) How many seconds after its release will the bag strike the ground? (c) With what velocity will it strike?

4–23. A stone is dropped from the top of a tall cliff, and 1 sec later a second stone is thrown vertically down with a velocity of 60 ft/sec. How far below the top of the cliff will the second stone overtake the first?

4–24. A ball dropped from the cornice of a building takes 0.25 sec to pass a window 9 ft high. How far is the top of the window below the cornice?

4–25. A ball is thrown nearly vertically upward from a point near the cornice of a tall building. It just misses the cornice on the way down, and passes a point 160 ft below its starting point 5 sec after it leaves the thrower's hand. (a) What was the initial velocity of the ball? (b) How high did it rise above its starting point? (c) What was the magnitude of its velocity as it passed a point 64 ft below the starting point?

4–26. A juggler performs in a room whose ceiling is 9 ft above the level of his hands. He throws a ball vertically upward so that it just reaches the ceiling. (a) With what initial velocity does he throw the ball? (b) What time is required for the ball to reach the ceiling?

He throws a second ball upward with the same initial velocity, at the instant that the first ball is at the ceiling. (c) How long after the second ball is thrown do the two balls pass each other?

(d) When the balls pass each other, how far are they above the juggler's hands?

4–27. An object is thrown vertically upward. It has a speed of 32 ft/sec when it has reached one-half its maximum height. (a) How high does it rise? (b) What is its velocity and acceleration 1 sec after it is thrown? (c) 3 sec after? (d) What is the average velocity during the first half-sec?

4–28. A student determined to test the law of gravity for himself walks off a skyscraper 900 ft high, stopwatch in hand, and starts his free fall (zero initial velocity). Five seconds later, Superman arrives at the scene and dives off the roof to save the student. (a) What must Superman's initial velocity be in order that he catch the student just before the ground is reached? (b) What must be the height of the skyscraper so that even Superman can't save him? (Assume that Superman's acceleration is that of any freely falling body.)

4–29. A ball is thrown vertically upward from the ground and a student gazing out of the window sees it moving upward past him at 16 ft/sec. The window is 32 ft above the ground. (a) How high does the ball go above the ground? (b) How long does it take to go from a height of 32 ft to its highest point? (c) Find its velocity and acceleration $\frac{1}{2}$ sec after it left the ground, and 2 sec after it left the ground.

4–30. A ball is thrown vertically upward from the ground with a velocity of 80 ft/sec. (a) How long will it take to rise to its highest point? (b) How high does the ball rise? (c) How long after projection will the ball have a velocity of 16 ft/sec upward? (d) of 16 ft/sec downward? (e) When is the displacement of the ball zero? (f) When is the magnitude of the ball's velocity equal to half its velocity of projection? (g) When is the magnitude of the ball's displacement equal to half the greatest height to which it rises? (h) What is the magnitude and direction of the acceleration while the ball is moving upward? while moving downward? when at the highest point?

4–31. A ball rolling on an inclined plane moves with a constant acceleration. One ball is released from rest at the top of an inclined plane 18-m long and reaches the bottom 3 sec later. At the same instant that the first ball is released, a second ball is projected upward along the plane from its bottom with a certain initial velocity. The second ball is to travel part way up the plane, stop, and return to the bottom so that it arrives simultaneously with the first ball. (a) Find the acceleration. (b) What must be the initial velocity of the second ball? (c) How far up the plane will it travel?

4–32. Two piers A and B are located on a river, one mile apart. Two men must make round trips from pier A to pier B and return. One man is to row a boat at a velocity of 4 mi/hr relative to the water, and the other man is to walk on the shore at a velocity of 4 mi/hr. The velocity of the river is 2 mi/hr in the direction from A to B. How long does it take each man to make the round trip?

4–33. A passenger on a ship traveling due east with a speed of 18 knots observes that the stream of smoke from the ship's funnels makes an angle of 20° with the ship's wake. The wind is blowing from south to north. Assume that the smoke acquires a velocity (with respect to the earth) equal to the velocity of the wind, as soon as it leaves the funnels. Find the velocity of the wind.

4–34. An airplane pilot wishes to fly due north. A wind of 60 mi/hr is blowing toward the west. If the flying speed of the plane (its speed in still air) is 180

mi/hr, in what direction should the pilot set his course? What is the speed of the plane over the ground? Illustrate with a vector diagram.

4–35. An airplane pilot sets a compass course due west and maintains an air speed of 120 mi/hr. After flying for one-half hour he finds himself over a town which is 75 mi west and 20 mi south of his starting point. (a) Find the wind velocity, in magnitude and direction. (b) If the wind velocity were 60 mi/hr due south, in what direction should the pilot set his course in order to travel due west? Take the same air speed of 120 mi/hr.

4–36. When a train has a speed of 10 mi/hr eastward, raindrops which are falling vertically with respect to the earth make traces on the windows of the train, which are inclined 30° to the vertical. (a) What is the horizontal component of a drop's velocity with respect to the earth? with respect to the train? (b) What is the velocity of the raindrop with respect to the earth? with respect to the train?

4–37. A river flows due north with a velocity of 3 mi/hr. A man rows a boat across the river, his velocity relative to the water being 4 mi/hr due east. (a) What is his velocity relative to the earth? (b) If the river is 1 mile wide, how far north of his starting point will he reach the opposite bank? (c) How long a time is required to cross the river?

4–38. (a) In what direction should the rowboat in Problem 4–37 be headed in order to reach a point on the opposite bank directly east from the start? (b) What will be the velocity of the boat relative to the earth? (c) How long a time is required to cross the river?

CHAPTER 5

NEWTON'S SECOND LAW. GRAVITATION

5-1 Introduction. In the preceding chapters we have discussed separately the concepts of force and acceleration. We have made use, in problems in equilibrium, of Newton's first law, which states that when the resultant force on a body is zero, the acceleration of the body is also zero. The next logical step is to ask how a body behaves when the resultant force on it is *not* zero. The answer to this question is contained in Newton's second law, which states that when the resultant force is not zero the body moves with accelerated motion, and that the acceleration, with a given force, depends on a property of the body known as its *mass*.

This part of mechanics, which includes both the study of motion and the forces that bring about the motion, is called *dynamics*. In its broadest sense, dynamics includes nearly the whole of mechanics. Statics treats of special cases in which the acceleration is zero, and kinematics deals with motion only.

5-2 Newton's second law. Mass. We know from experience that an object at rest will never start to move of itself; a push or pull must be exerted on it by some other body. It is also a familiar fact that a force is required to slow down or to stop a body which is already in motion, and that a sidewise force must be exerted on a moving body to deviate

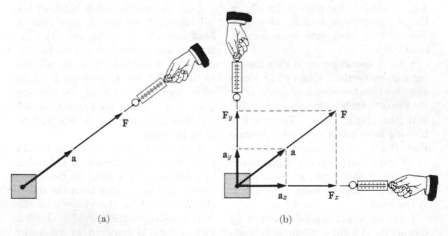

(a) (b)

Fig. 5-1. (a) The acceleration **a** is in the same direction as the resultant force **F**. (b) Each component of a force can be considered to produce its own component of acceleration.

it from a straight line. All the processes above (i.e., speeding up, slowing down, or changing direction) involve a change in either the magnitude or the direction of the velocity of the body. In other words, in every case the body is accelerated, and an external force must act on it to produce this acceleration.

Let us consider the following experiments. As shown in Fig. 5–1(a), which is a top view, an arbitrary body is placed on a level frictionless surface and a horizontal force **F** is exerted on it. We shall assume that the body is not rotating and that the line of action of the force passes through the center of gravity of the body. The body acquires no rotational motion and only its translational motion is affected. For concreteness, suppose that the force is measured by a spring balance calibrated in pounds, as described in Section 1–2. With a stopwatch and scale we determine the resulting acceleration a. Let a large number of similar pairs of measurements of force and acceleration be made, first on the same body, using forces that differ in magnitude and direction, and then using different bodies. The results of these experiments show the following:

(a) In every case, the *direction* of the acceleration is the same as that of the force. This is true whether the body is initially at rest or is moving in any direction and with any speed.

(b) For a given body, the ratio of the magnitude of the force to that of the acceleration is always the same, or is a constant.

$$\frac{F}{a} = \text{constant (for a given body).}$$

The ratio is, in general, different for different bodies.

This constant ratio of force to acceleration can be considered a property of the body called its *mass m*, where

$$m = \frac{F}{a},$$

or

$$F = ma. \tag{5–1}$$

Mass is a scalar quantity.

The mass of a body therefore represents *the force per unit of acceleration*. Since experiment shows that the ratio of force to acceleration is always the same, for a given body, it suffices to make one pair of measurements of force and acceleration to determine the mass. For example, if the acceleration of a certain body is found to be 5 ft/sec² when the force is 20 lb, the mass of the body is

$$m = \frac{F}{a} = \frac{20 \text{ lb}}{5 \text{ ft/sec}^2} = 4 \frac{\text{lb}}{\text{ft/sec}^2}.$$

When a large force is needed to speed up a body, slow it down, or deviate it sidewise if it is moving, the mass of the body is large. In everyday language, we would say that the body has a large *inertia*. If only a small force is needed per unit of acceleration, the mass is small and the inertia is small. The mass of a body can therefore be considered to represent in a quantitative way that property of matter which is described qualitatively by the word *inertia*.

The equation

$$\mathbf{F} = m\mathbf{a}$$

is a *vector* equation. That is, the vector $\mathbf{F}$ has the same magnitude and direction as a vector which is m times as great as the vector $\mathbf{a}$. If two vectors are equal their rectangular components are equal also and the vector equation above (for forces and accelerations in the xy-plane) is equivalent to the pair of scalar equations

$$F_x = ma_x, \qquad F_y = ma_y. \tag{5-2}$$

For example, suppose that instead of applying the force $\mathbf{F}$ directly, as in Fig. 5–1(a), we apply instead the force components $\mathbf{F}_x$ and $\mathbf{F}_y$ as in Fig. 5–1(b). We find that the acceleration $\mathbf{a}$ has the same magnitude and direction as in part (a), and that the components a_x and a_y are those given by Eq. (5–2). This means that each component of the force can be considered to produce its own component of acceleration.

It follows that if any number of forces act on a body simultaneously, the forces may be resolved into x- and y-components, the algebraic sums $\sum F_x$ and $\sum F_y$ may be computed, and the components of acceleration are given by

$$\boxed{\sum F_x = ma_x, \qquad \sum F_y = ma_y.} \tag{5-3}$$

This pair of equations is equivalent to the single vector equation

$$\boxed{\sum \mathbf{F} = m\mathbf{a},} \tag{5-4}$$

where $\sum \mathbf{F}$ is the vector sum or *resultant* of *all* the *external* forces acting *on* the body.

Equation (5–4) is the mathematical statement of Newton's *second law of motion*. Newton phrased the law as follows: *"The change of motion is proportional to the motive force impressed; and is made in the direction of the straight line in which that force is impressed."* If for "change of motion" we read "rate of change of velocity," or acceleration, the second law states that *the acceleration is proportional to the resultant force and is in the same direction as this force.*

We can see from Eq. (5–4) the physical conditions that must be fulfilled for motion with *constant* acceleration; namely, if **a** is constant, then the resultant force $\sum \mathbf{F}$ must be constant also. In other words, motion with constant acceleration is motion under the action of a constant force. If the force varies, the acceleration varies in direct proportion, since the mass m is constant.

It is also evident from Eq. (5–4) that if the resultant force on a body is zero, the acceleration of the body is zero and its velocity is constant. Hence, if the body is in motion, it continues to move with no change in the magnitude or direction of its velocity; if at rest, it remains at rest (its velocity is then constant and equal to zero). But these are evidently the conditions to which Newton's *first* law applies, and we see that the first law is merely a special case of the second when the resultant force and the acceleration are both zero. There are thus only two independent laws of Newton, the second and the third.

5–3 Systems of units. The mass of a body is the ratio of the resultant force on the body to its acceleration. Consider first the *British engineering system* of units, in which forces are expressed in pounds and accelerations in ft/sec². In this system, the mass of a body is expressed in lb/(ft/sec²). It is often convenient to introduce a single term for the combination of units in which a physical quantity is expressed, and the unit above, 1 lb/(ft/sec²), is called one *slug*. (This term arose from the concept of mass as inertia or sluggishness.) Thus

$$\sum F \text{ (lb)} = m \text{ (slugs)} \times a \text{ (ft/sec}^2).$$

For example, if the acceleration of a body is 5 ft/sec² when the resultant force on it is 20 lb, its mass is

$$m = \frac{\sum F}{a} = \frac{20 \text{ lb}}{5 \text{ ft/sec}^2} = 4 \frac{\text{lb}}{\text{ft/sec}^2} = 4 \text{ slugs.}$$

The numerical value of the mass of a given body depends on the units in which force and acceleration are expressed. By selecting as a unit of force, that force which acts on any arbitrary body when it has unit acceleration, the mass of that body automatically becomes equal to one unit of mass.

In setting up the *meter-kilogram-second* (mks) system of units, the mass of the *standard kilogram* is chosen to be the unit of mass. The unit of force in this system is then that force which gives a standard kilogram an acceleration of 1 m/sec². This force is called *one newton*, and is

TABLE 5–1

SYSTEMS OF UNITS

System of units	Force	Mass	Acceleration
Engineering	pound (lb)	slug	ft/sec²
mks	newton (n)	kilogram (kgm)	m/sec²
cgs	dyne	gram (gm)	cm/sec²

approximately equal to one-quarter of a pound of force (more precisely, 1 newton = 0.22481 lb).

Thus, in the mks system,

$$F \text{ (newtons)} = m \text{ (kgm)} \times a \text{ (m/sec}^2).$$

The mass unit in the *centimeter-gram-second* (cgs) system is *one gram*, equal to 1/1000 kilogram. The force unit in this system is the force which gives a body of mass 1 gm an acceleration of 1 cm/sec², and is called *one dyne*. In the cgs system, then,

$$\sum F \text{ (dynes)} = m \text{ (gm)} \times a \text{ (cm/sec}^2).$$

Since 1 kgm = 10^3 gm and 1 m/sec² = 10^2 cm/sec², it follows that 1 newton = 10^5 dynes.

The units of force, mass, and acceleration in the three systems are summarized in Table 5–1.

It is unnecessary for the National Bureau of Standards to maintain a physical object embodying the engineering mass unit, the slug, or the engineering unit of length, the foot, since both of these are defined in terms of the standard kilogram and the standard meter. One foot, by definition, is exactly 0.3048 meter. One standard pound, by definition, is a body of mass 0.45359237 kgm. The pound of force is the force which gives a standard pound an acceleration equal to the standard acceleration of gravity, 32.1740 ft/sec². Finally, the slug is the mass of a body whose acceleration is 1 ft/sec² when the force on it is one pound.

5–4 Mass and weight. The *weight* of a body means the gravitational force exerted on it by the earth. When a body is released and allowed to fall freely, the only force acting on it is its weight **w**, and its acceleration is that of any freely falling body, the acceleration of gravity **g**. Its mass is then

$$m = \frac{\sum F}{a} = \frac{w}{g}.$$

Since the weight of a body is a force, it must be expressed in units of force. Thus in the engineering system weight is expressed in *pounds;* in the mks system, in *newtons;* and in the cgs system, in *dynes.* The preceding equation gives the relation between the mass and weight of a body in any consistent system of units. In the engineering system a body is usually described by stating its weight w in pounds, and computing its mass m in slugs, if this is desired. Thus the mass of a man whose weight is 160 lb at a point where $g = 32.0$ ft/sec^2 is

$$m = \frac{w}{g} = \frac{160 \text{ lb}}{32.0 \text{ ft/sec}^2} = 5.00 \text{ slugs}.$$

His weight at a second point where $g = 32.2$ ft/sec^2 is

$$w = mg = 5.00 \text{ slugs} \times 32.2 \frac{\text{ft}}{\text{sec}^2} = 161 \text{ lb}.$$

Thus, unlike his mass, which is a constant, his weight varies from one point to another on the earth's surface.

If the mass of a body is 1 slug, its weight at a point where $g = 32.0$ ft/sec^2 is

$$w = mg = 1 \text{ slug} \times 32.0 \frac{\text{ft}}{\text{sec}^2} = 32.0 \text{ lb}.$$

In the mks and cgs systems, a body is usually described by stating its mass m in kilograms or grams, and computing its weight w if this is desired. Thus, at a point where $g = 9.80$ m/sec^2, the weight of a body whose mass is 10 kgm is

$$w = mg = 10 \text{ kgm} \times 9.80 \frac{\text{m}}{\text{sec}^2} = 98.0 \text{ newtons}.$$

Since 10 kgm $= 10^4$ gm, and 9.80 m/sec$^2 = 980$ cm/sec^2, the weight of the same body in cgs units is

$$w = mg = 10^4 \text{ gm} \times 980 \frac{\text{cm}}{\text{sec}^2} = 9.80 \times 10^6 \text{ dynes}.$$

The mass of a body whose weight at a point where $g = 9.80$ m/sec^2 is 1 newton, is

$$m = \frac{w}{g} = \frac{1 \text{ n}}{9.80 \text{ m/sec}^2} = 0.102 \text{ kgm},$$

and the mass of a body whose weight at the same point is 1 dyne, is

$$m = \frac{w}{g} = \frac{1 \text{ dyne}}{980 \text{ cm/sec}^2} = 1.02 \times 10^{-3} \text{ gm},$$

or about a milligram.

There are also two other systems of units in which, as in the engineering system, the unit of force rather than of mass is arbitrarily defined. These systems take as their units of force the weight of the standard kilogram and the weight of a gram. The former force is called "one kilogram of force" and the latter "one gram of force." One "kilogram of force" is about 2.2 lb of force or about 9.8 newtons; one "gram of force" is about 0.0022 lb or 980 dynes. The "gram of force" is commonly used as a force unit in elementary physics texts, where the reader has probably met it. The "kilogram force" is used as a force unit in engineering work in those countries which use the metric system exclusively. We shall use neither of these units in this book, and "gram" and "kilogram" will refer to mass only.

5–5 Newton's law of universal gravitation.   Throughout our study of mechanics we have been continually encountering forces due to gravitational attraction between the earth and bodies on its surface, forces which are called the weights of the bodies. We now wish to study this phenomenon of gravitation in somewhat more detail.

The law of universal gravitation was discovered by Sir Isaac Newton, and was first announced by him in the year 1686. It may be stated:

Every particle of matter in the universe attracts every other particle with a force which is directly proportional to the product of the masses of the particles and inversely proportional to the square of the distance between them.

$$F \propto \frac{mm'}{r^2}.$$

The proportion above may be converted to an equation on multiplication by a constant G, which is called the *gravitational constant*.

$$F = G\,\frac{mm'}{r^2}. \tag{5–5}$$

There seems to be some evidence that Newton was led to deduce this law from speculations concerning the fall of an apple to the earth. However, his first published calculations to justify its correctness had to do with the motion of the moon around the earth.

The numerical value of the constant G depends on the units in which force, mass, and distance are expressed. Its magnitude can be found experimentally by measuring the force of gravitational attraction between two bodies of known masses m and m', at a known separation. For bodies of moderate size the force is extremely small, but it can be measured with an instrument which was invented by the Rev. John Michell, although it was first used for this purpose by Sir Henry Cavendish in 1798. The same type of instrument was also used by Coulomb for studying forces of electrical and magnetic attraction and repulsion.

The Cavendish balance consists of two small spheres of mass m (Fig. 5–2), usually of gold or platinum, mounted at opposite ends of a light horizontal rod which is supported at its center by a fine vertical fiber such as a quartz thread. A small mirror fastened to the fiber reflects a beam of light onto a scale. To use the balance, two large spheres of mass m', usually of lead, are brought up to the positions shown. The forces of gravitational attraction between the large and small spheres result in a couple which twists the fiber and mirror through a small angle, thereby moving the light beam along the scale.

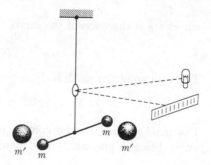

FIG. 5–2. Principle of the Cavendish balance.

By using an extremely fine fiber, the deflection of the light beam may be made sufficiently large so that the gravitational forces can be measured quite accurately. The gravitational constant, measured in this way, is found to be

$$G = 6.670 \times 10^{-8} \text{ dyne} \cdot \text{cm}^2/\text{gm}^2$$
$$= 6.670 \times 10^{-11} \text{ newton} \cdot \text{m}^2/\text{kgm}^2.$$

EXAMPLE: Compute the force of gravitational attraction between the large and small spheres of a Cavendish balance, if $m = 1$ gm, $m' = 500$ gm, $r = 5$ cm. (Two spheres attract each other as if the mass of each were concentrated at its center.)

$$F = \frac{(6.67 \times 10^{-8} \text{ dyne} \cdot \text{cm}^2/\text{gm}^2) \times (1 \text{ gm}) \times (500 \text{ gm})}{(5 \text{ cm})^2} = 1.33 \times 10^{-6} \text{ dyne},$$

or about one-millionth of a dyne!

5–6 The mass of the earth. Since the constant G in Eq. (5–5) can be found from measurements in the laboratory, the mass of the earth may be computed. From measurements on freely falling bodies, we know that the earth attracts a one-gram mass at its surface with a force of (about) 980 dynes. The distance between the centers of the masses is the radius of the earth, 6380 km or 6.38×10^8 cm. Therefore,

$$980 \text{ dynes} = \frac{(6.67 \times 10^{-8} \text{ dyne} \cdot \text{cm}^2/\text{gm}^2) \times (1 \text{ gm}) \times m_E}{(6.38 \times 10^8 \text{ cm})^2},$$

where m_E is the mass of the earth. Hence

$$m_E = 5.98 \times 10^{27} \text{ gm.}$$

The volume of the earth is

$$V = \tfrac{4}{3}\pi R^3 = 1.09 \times 10^{27} \text{ cm}^3.$$

The mass divided by the volume is known as the *density*, the value for water being 1 gm/cm³. The average density of the earth is therefore

$$\frac{m_E}{V} = \frac{5.98 \times 10^{27} \text{ gm}}{1.09 \times 10^{27} \text{ cm}^3} = 5.5 \frac{\text{gm}}{\text{cm}^3}.$$

This is considerably larger than the average density of the material near the earth's surface, so that the interior of the earth must be of much higher density.

5–7 Variations in "g." The acceleration of gravity, g, is the acceleration imparted to a body by its own weight. Its weight, however, can be written

$$w = G\frac{mm_E}{R^2},$$

where m is the mass of the body, m_E is the mass of the earth, and R is the distance to the earth's center. Then, since $w = mg$,

$$mg = G\frac{mm_E}{R^2},$$

$$g = \frac{Gm_E}{R^2}. \tag{5–6}$$

Since G and m_E are constants, the acceleration of gravity decreases with increasing distance from the center of the earth, and it is only approximately correct to state that a body falls toward the earth with constant acceleration. Actually, the acceleration continually increases as the body approaches the earth, air resistance being neglected. For most purposes, however, this variation is negligible. The acceleration of gravity varies somewhat from point to point on the earth's surface, partly because of variations in the distance to the earth's center and partly because of local deposits of ore, oil, or other substances whose density is greater or less than the average density of the earth. The greatest variation, however, arises from the rotation of the earth, and will be discussed in Chapter 6.

TABLE 5–2

VARIATIONS OF g WITH LATITUDE AND ELEVATION

Station	North latitude	Elevation, m	g, cm/sec^2	g, ft/sec^2
Canal Zone	9°	0	978.243	32.0944
Jamaica	18°	0	978.591	32.1059
Bermuda	32°	0	979.806	32.1548
Denver	40°	1638	979.609	32.1393
Cambridge	42°	0	980.398	32.1652
Standard station			980.665	32.1740
Greenland	70°	0	982.534	32.2353

From a survey of variations in the value of g, conclusions can be drawn as to the presence of deposits of ore or oil beneath the earth's surface. Hence the precise measurement of g is one of the methods of geophysical prospecting. Some representative values of g are given in Table 5–2.

5–8 Applications of Newton's second law. We now give a number of examples of the application of Newton's second law to specific problems. In all these examples, and in the problems at the end of the chapter, it will be assumed that the acceleration of gravity is 32.0 ft/sec^2 or 9.8 m/sec^2, unless otherwise specified.

EXAMPLE 1. What is the resultant force on a body weighing 48 lb when its acceleration is 6 ft/sec^2?

We must first find the mass of the body. From the relation $m = w/g$,

$$m = \frac{48 \text{ lb}}{32 \text{ ft/sec}^2} = 1.5 \frac{\text{lb}}{\text{ft/sec}^2} = 1.5 \text{ slugs}.$$

Hence

$$\sum F = ma = 1.5 \text{ slugs} \times 6 \frac{\text{ft}}{\text{sec}^2} = 9 \text{ lb}.$$

EXAMPLE 2. What is the resultant force on a body of mass 48 kgm when its acceleration is 6 m/sec^3?

The mass of the body is given, and hence

$$\sum F = ma = 48 \text{ kgm} \times 6 \frac{\text{m}}{\text{sec}^2} = 28.8 \text{ newtons}.$$

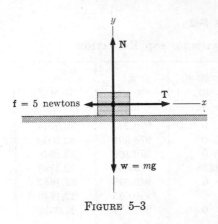

$f = 5$ newtons

$w = mg$

FIGURE 5-3

EXAMPLE 3. A block whose mass is 10 kgm rests on a horizontal surface. What constant horizontal force **T** is required to give it a velocity of 4 m/sec in 2 sec, starting from rest, if the friction force between the block and the surface is constant and is equal to 5 newtons? Assume that all forces act at the center of the block. (See Fig. 5–3.)

The mass of the block is given. Its y-acceleration is zero. Its x-acceleration can be found from the data on the velocity acquired in a given time. Since the forces are constant, the x-acceleration is constant and from the equations of motion with constant acceleration,

$$a_x = \frac{v - v_0}{t} = \frac{4 \text{ m/sec} - 0}{2 \text{ sec}} = 2 \frac{\text{m}}{\text{sec}^2}.$$

Hence from Newton's second law in component form,

$$\sum F_y = ma_y, \qquad N - w = 0,$$

$$N = w = mg = 10 \text{ kgm} \times 9.80 \frac{\text{m}}{\text{sec}^2} = 98 \text{ newtons},$$

$$\sum F_x = ma_x, \qquad T - 5\text{n} = 10 \text{ kgm} \times 2 \frac{\text{m}}{\text{sec}^2},$$

$$T = 25 \text{ newtons}.$$

EXAMPLE 4. An elevator and its load weigh a total of 1600 lb. Find the tension **T** in the supporting cable when the elevator, originally moving downward at 20 ft/sec, is brought to rest with constant acceleration in a distance of 50 ft. (See Fig. 5–4.)

The mass of the elevator is

$$m = \frac{w}{g} = \frac{1600 \text{ lb}}{32 \text{ ft/sec}^2} = 50 \text{ slugs}.$$

From the equations of motion with constant acceleration,

$$v^2 = v_0^2 + 2ay, \qquad a = \frac{v^2 - v_0^2}{2y}.$$

The initial velocity v_0 is -20 ft/sec; the velocity v is zero. If we take the origin at the point where the deceleration begins, then $y = -50$ ft. Hence

$$a = \frac{0 - (-20 \text{ ft/sec})^2}{-2 \times 50 \text{ ft}} = 4 \frac{\text{ft}}{\text{sec}^2}.$$

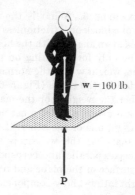

w = 160 lb

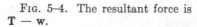

FIG. 5–4. The resultant force is **T — w**.

FIG. 5–5. The resultant force is **P — w**.

The acceleration is therefore positive (upward).

From the free-body diagram (Fig. 5–4) the resultant force is

$$\sum F = T - w = T - 1600 \text{ lb}.$$

Hence

$$\sum F = ma,$$

$$T - 1600 \text{ lb} = 50 \text{ slugs} \times 4 \frac{\text{ft}}{\text{sec}^2} = 200 \text{ lb},$$

$$T = 1800 \text{ lb}.$$

EXAMPLE 5. With what force will the feet of a passenger press downward on the elevator floor when the elevator has the acceleration above, if the passenger weighs 160 lb?

This example illustrates a problem that is frequently encountered, in which it is necessary to find a desired force by first computing the force that is the *reaction* to the one desired, and then using Newton's third law. That is, we first calculate the force with which the elevator floor pushes upward on the passenger; the force desired is the reaction to this.

Figure 5–5 shows the forces acting on the passenger. The resultant force is $P - w$, and since the mass of the passenger is 5 slugs and his acceleration is the same as that of the elevator,

$$\sum F = ma,$$

$$P - 160 \text{ lb} = 5 \text{ slugs} \times 4 \frac{\text{ft}}{\text{sec}^2} = 20 \text{ lb},$$

$$P = 180 \text{ lb}.$$

The passenger exerts an equal and opposite force downward on the elevator floor.

EXAMPLE 6.   What is the acceleration of a block on a frictionless plane inclined at an angle θ with the horizontal?

The only forces acting on the block
are its weight **w** and the normal force **N**
exerted by the plane (Fig. 5–6). Since
neither the weight nor the mass of the
block is given, a letter must be used to
represent one or the other. Let us call
the mass m; the weight is then mg.
Take axes parallel and perpendicular to
the surface of the plane and resolve the
weight into x- and y-components. Then

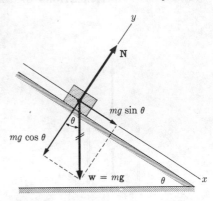

$$\sum F_y = N - mg \cos \theta,$$

$$\sum F_x = mg \sin \theta.$$

FIG. 5–6. A block on a frictionless
inclined plane.

But we know that $a_y = 0$, so from the equation $\sum F_y = ma_y$ we find that $N = mg \cos \theta$. From the equation $\sum F_x = ma_x$, we have

$$mg \sin \theta = ma_x,$$

$$a_x = g \sin \theta.$$

The mass does not appear in the final result, which means that any block, regardless of its mass, will slide on a frictionless inclined plane with an acceleration
down the plane of $g \sin \theta$. (Note that the *velocity* is not necessarily down the
plane.)

EXAMPLE 7.   Refer to Fig. 2–4 (Chapter 2). Let the mass of the block be 4
kgm and that of the rope be 0.5 kgm. If the force F_1 is 9 newtons, what are the
forces F'_1, F_2, and F'_2? The surface on which the block moves is level and frictionless.

We know from Newton's third law that $F_1 = F'_1$ and that $F_2 = F'_2$. Hence
$F'_2 = 9$ newtons. The force F_2 could be computed by applying Newton's second
law to the block, if its acceleration were known, or the force F'_2 could be computed
by applying this law to the rope if its acceleration were known. The acceleration
is not given, but it can be found by considering the block and rope together as a
single system. The vertical forces on this system need not be considered. Since
there is no friction, the resultant *external* force acting *on* the system is the force
F_1. (The forces F_2 and F'_2 are *internal* forces when we consider block and rope
as a single system, and the force F'_1 does not act on the system, but *on the man*.)
Then, from Newton's second law,

$$\sum F = ma,$$

$$9 \text{ n} = (4 \text{ kgm} + 0.5 \text{ kgm}) \times a,$$

$$a = 2 \frac{\text{m}}{\text{sec}^2}.$$

We can now apply Newton's second law to the block.

$$\sum F = ma,$$
$$F_2 = 4 \text{ kgm} \times 2 \frac{\text{m}}{\text{sec}^2} = 8 \text{ newtons}.$$

Considering the rope alone, the resultant force on it is

$$\sum F = F_1 - F_2' = 9 \text{ n} - F_2',$$

and from the second law,

$$9 \text{ n} - F_2' = 0.5 \text{ kgm} \times 2 \frac{\text{m}}{\text{sec}^2} = 1 \text{ n},$$
$$F_2' = 8 \text{ newtons}.$$

In agreement with Newton's third law, which was tacitly used when the forces F_2 and F_2' were omitted in considering the system as a whole, we find that F_2 and F_2' are equal in magnitude. Notice, however, that the forces F_1 and F_2 are *not* equal and opposite (the rope is not in equilibrium) and that these forces are *not* an action-reaction pair.

EXAMPLE 8. In Fig. 5–7, a block of weight $w_1 = 16$ lb moves on a level frictionless surface, connected by a light flexible cord passing over a small frictionless pulley to a second hanging block of weight $w_2 = 8$ lb. What is the acceleration of the system, and what is the tension in the cord connecting the two blocks?

The diagram shows the forces acting on each block. The forces exerted on the blocks by the cord can be considered an action-reaction pair, so we have used the same symbol **T** for each. For the block on the surface,

$$\sum F_x = T = 0.5 \text{ slug} \times a,$$
$$\sum F_y = N - w_1 = N - 16 \text{ lb} = 0.$$

For the hanging block,

$$\sum F_y = w_2 - T = 8 \text{ lb} - T$$
$$= 0.25 \text{ slug} \times a.$$

Since a is the same for both blocks, on solving the first and third equations simultaneously, we obtain

$$a = 10.7 \frac{\text{ft}}{\text{sec}^2}, \qquad T = 5.3 \text{ lb}.$$

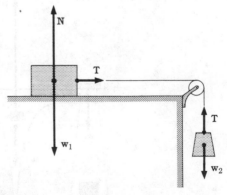

FIGURE 5–7

Note carefully that although the earth pulls on the hanging block with a force of 8 lb, the force exerted on the 16-lb block is only 5.3 lb. It is the connecting cord which pulls on the 16-lb block, and the tension in this cord must be less than 8 lb or the hanging block would not accelerate downward,

5–9 The equal-arm analytical balance. As with many other physical quantities, the mass of a body can be measured in several different ways. One is to use the relation by which the quantity is defined, which in this case is the ratio of the force on the body to its acceleration. A measured force is applied to the body, its acceleration is measured, and the unknown mass is obtained by dividing the force by the acceleration. This method, however, is both cumbersome and inexact because of the difficulty of making precise measurements on an accelerating body.

The second method consists of finding by trial some other body whose mass is (a) equal to that of the given body, and (b) already known. Consider first a method of determining when two masses are equal. It will be recalled that at the same point on the earth's surface all bodies fall freely with the same acceleration g. Since the weight w of a body equals the product of its mass m and the acceleration g, it follows that if, at the same point, the weights of two bodies are equal, their masses are equal also. The *equal-arm balance* is an instrument by means of which one can determine very precisely when the weights of two bodies are equal, and hence when their masses are equal.

The essential feature of the balance, shown schematically in Fig. 5–8, is a light, rigid beam on which are firmly mounted three equally spaced agate knife-edges, parallel to one another and perpendicular to the length of the beam. The central knife-edge at O rests on a polished plane agate plate supported from the floor of the balance case. The scale pans are

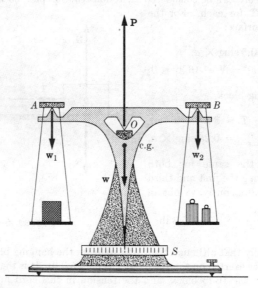

FIG. 5–8. The equal-arm analytical balance.

hung from two similar plates at A and B. A pointer fastened to the beam swings in front of the scale S. The knife-edges and plates act as practically frictionless pivots. Since the scale pans can swing freely about their supporting knife-edges, the centers of gravity of the pans and of any bodies placed on them will always be directly below the knife-edges. The weight of the beam is w, and its center of gravity is directly below the central knife-edge when the beam is horizontal. The weights of the scale pans are equal.

In using the balance, the body whose mass m_1 is desired is placed in the left scale pan, and a combination of known masses m_2 is placed in the right pan. If the combined weights of bodies and scale pans, w_1 and w_2, are exactly equal, the beam remains in stable equilibrium in a horizontal position as in Fig. 5-8, under the action of the four parallel forces w_1, w_2, w, and the upward force P exerted at the central knife-edge. Then the weight of the unknown body equals that of the bodies in the right scale pan, and hence their masses m_1 and m_2 are equal also.

There remains the question as to how a set of bodies of known mass (usually referred to as a set of "weights") is obtained in the first place. This is also done with the equal-arm balance. Let us start with a standard kilogram and make two bodies (a) whose masses are *equal*, as determined by the balance, and (b) which when combined will just balance the standard kilogram. Each of these then has a mass of one-half kilogram, or 500 grams. Other submultiples, or multiples, of the standard can be prepared by a similar procedure.

PROBLEMS

(For problem work, use the approximate values of $g = 32$ ft/sec^2 = 9.80 m/sec^2 = 980 cm/sec^2. A force diagram should be constructed for each problem.)

5-1. (a) What resultant force is required to give an automobile weighing 1600 lb an acceleration of 8 ft/sec^2? (b) What resultant force is required to give a block whose mass is 1600 gm an acceleration of 8 cm/sec^2? (c) What resultant force is required to give a block of mass 1600 kgm an acceleration of 8 m/sec^2?

5-2. The Springfield rifle bullet weighs 150 grains (7000 grains = 1 lb), its muzzle velocity is 2700 ft/sec, and the length of the rifle barrel is 30 in. Compute the resultant force accelerating the bullet, assuming it to be constant.

5-3. A body of mass 15 kgm rests on a frictionless horizontal plane and is acted on by a horizontal force of 30 newtons. (a) What acceleration is produced? (b) How far will the body travel in 10 sec? (c) What will be its velocity at the end of 10 sec?

5-4. A body of mass 50 gm is at rest at the origin, $x = 0$, on a horizontal frictionless surface. At time $t = 0$ a force of 10 dynes is applied to the body parallel to the x-axis, and 5 sec later this force is removed. (a) What are the position and velocity of the body at $t = 5$ sec? (b) If the same force (10 dynes) is again applied at $t = 15$ sec, what are the position and velocity of the body at $t = 20$ sec?

5-5. If action and reaction are always equal in magnitude and opposite in direction, why don't they always cancel one another and leave no net force for accelerating a body?

5-6. The mass of a certain object is 10 gm. (a) What would its mass be if taken to the planet Mars? (b) Is the expression $F = ma$ valid on Mars? (c) Newton's second law is sometimes written in the form $F = wa/g$ instead of $F = ma$. Would this expression be valid on Mars? (d) If a Martian scientist hangs a standard pound body on a spring balance calibrated correctly on the earth, would the spring balance read 1 lb? Explain.

5-7. A constant horizontal force of 10 lb acts on a body on a smooth horizontal plane. The body starts from rest and is observed to move 250 ft in 5 sec. (a) What is the mass of the body? (b) If the force ceases to act at the end of 5 sec, how far will the body move in the next 5 sec?

5-8. A .22 rifle bullet, traveling at 36,000 cm/sec, strikes a block of soft wood, which it penetrates to a depth of 10 cm. The mass of the bullet is 1.8 gm. Assume a constant retarding force. (a) How long a time was required for the bullet to stop? (b) What was the decelerating force, in dynes? in lb?

5-9. An electron (mass = 9×10^{-28} gm) leaves the cathode of a radio tube with zero initial velocity and travels in a straight line to the anode, which is 1 cm away. It reaches the anode with a velocity of 6×10^8 cm/sec. If the accelerating force was constant, compute (a) the accelerating force, in dynes, (b) the time to reach the anode, (c) the acceleration. The gravitational force on the electron may be neglected.

5-10. A 5-kgm block is supported by a cord and pulled upward with an acceleration of 2 m/sec^2. (a) What is the tension in the cord? (b) After the block has been set in motion the tension in the cord is reduced to 49 newtons. What sort of motion will the block perform? (c) If the cord is now slackened completely, the block is observed to move up 2 meters farther before coming to rest. With what velocity was it traveling?

5–11. A body of mass 10 kgm is moving with a constant velocity of 5 m/sec on a horizontal surface. The coefficient of sliding friction between body and surface is 0.20. (a) What horizontal force is required to maintain the motion? (b) If the force is removed, how soon will the body come to rest?

5–12. A hockey puck leaves a player's stick with a velocity of 30 ft/sec and slides 120 ft before coming to rest. Find the coefficient of friction between the puck and the ice.

5–13. A 16-lb block rests on a horizontal surface. The coefficient of sliding friction between block and surface is 0.25, and the coefficient of static friction is 0.30. (a) What is the resultant force on the block when an external horizontal force of 8 lb is exerted on it? (b) If the 8-lb force acts for 4 sec and is then removed, find the total distance moved by the block before coming to rest.

5–14. An elevator weighing 3200 lb rises with an acceleration of 4 ft/sec^2. What is the tension in the supporting cable?

5–15. An 8-lb block is accelerated upward by a cord whose breaking strength is 20 lb. Find the maximum acceleration which can be given the block without breaking the cord.

5–16. A block weighing 10 lb is held up by a string which can be moved up or down. What conclusions can you draw regarding magnitude and direction of the acceleration and velocity of the upper end of the string when the tension in the string is (a) 5 lb, (b) 10 lb, (c) 15 lb?

5–17. A body hangs from a spring balance supported from the roof of an elevator. (a) If the elevator has an upward acceleration of 4 ft/sec^2 and the balance reads 45 lb, what is the true weight of the body? (b) Under what circumstances will the balance read 35 lb? (c) What will the balance read if the elevator cable breaks?

5–18. A transport plane is to takeoff from a level landing field with two gliders in tow, one behind the other. Each glider weighs 2400 lb, and the friction force or drag on each may be assumed constant and equal to 400 lb. The tension in the towrope between the transport plane and the first glider is not to exceed 2000 lb. (a) If a velocity of 100 ft/sec is required for the take-off, how long a runway is needed? (b) What is the tension in the towrope between the two gliders while the planes are accelerating for the take-off?

5–19. If the coefficient of friction between tires and road is 0.5, what is the shortest distance in which an automobile can be stopped when traveling at 60 mi/hr?

5–20. An 80-lb packing case is on the floor of a truck. The coefficient of static friction between the case and the truck floor is 0.30, and the coefficient of sliding friction is 0.20. Find the magnitude and direction of the friction force acting on the case (a) when the truck is accelerating at 6 ft/sec^2, (b) when it is decelerating at 10 ft/sec^2.

5–21. A block of mass 2.5 slugs rests on a horizontal surface. The coefficient of static friction between the block and the surface is 0.30, and the coefficient of sliding friction is 0.25. The block is acted upon by a variable horizontal force P. This force is initially zero and increases with time at the constant rate of 2 lb/sec. (a) When will the block start to move? (b) What is its acceleration 8 sec after it starts to move?

5–22. A 200-gm body starts from rest and slides down a smooth inclined plane. If it travels 120 cm during the third second, what is the angle of inclination of the plane?

5–23. A balloon is descending with a constant acceleration a, less than the acceleration of gravity g. The weight of the balloon, with its basket and contents, is w. What weight, W, of ballast should be released so that the balloon will begin to be accelerated upward with constant acceleration a? Neglect air resistance.

5–24. A ˙64-lb block is pushed up a 37° inclined plane by a horizontal force of 100 lb. The coefficient of sliding friction is 0.25. Find (a) the acceleration, (b) the velocity of the block after it has moved a distance of 20 ft along the plane, (c) the normal force exerted by the plane. Assume that all forces act at the center of the block.

5–25. A block rests on an inclined plane which makes an angle θ with the horizontal. The coefficient of sliding friction is 0.50, and the coefficient of static friction is 0.75. (a) As the angle θ is increased, find the minimum angle at which the block starts to slip. (b) At this angle, find the acceleration once the block has begun to move. (c) How long a time is required for the block to slip 20 ft along the inclined plane?

5–26. (a) What constant horizontal force is required to drag a 16-lb block along a horizontal surface with an acceleration of 4 ft/sec^2 if the coefficient of sliding friction between block and surface is 0.5? (b) What weight, hanging from a cord attached to the 16-lb block and passing over a small frictionless pulley, will produce this acceleration?

5–27. A block weighing 8 lb resting on a horizontal surface is connected by a cord passing over a light frictionless pulley to a hanging block weighing 8 lb. The coefficient of friction between the block and the horizontal surface is 0.5. Find (a) the tension in the cord, and (b) the acceleration of each block.

5–28. A block having a mass of 2 kgm is projected up a long 30° incline with an initial velocity of 22 m/sec. The coefficient of friction between the block and the plane is 0.3. (a) Find the friction force acting on the block as it moves up the plane. (b) How long does the block move up the plane? (c) How far does the block move up the plane? (d) How long does it take the block to slide down from its position in part (c) to its starting point? (e) With what velocity does it arrive at this point? (f) If the mass of the block had been 5 kgm instead of 2 kgm, would the answers in the preceding parts be changed?

5–29. A 30-lb block on a level frictionless surface is attached by a cord passing over a small frictionless pulley to a hanging block originally at rest 4 ft above the floor. The hanging block strikes the floor in 2 sec. (a) Find the weight of the hanging block. (b) Find the tension in the string while both blocks were in motion.

5–30. Two blocks, each having mass 20 kgm, rest on frictionless surfaces as

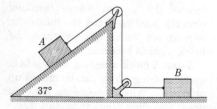

FIGURE 5–9

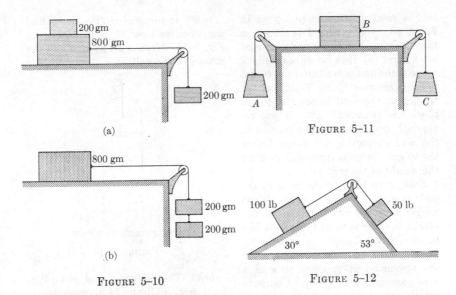

(a)

FIGURE 5–11

(b)

FIGURE 5–10

FIGURE 5–12

shown in Fig. 5–9. Assuming the pulleys to be light and frictionless, compute: (a) the time required for block A to move 1 m down the plane, starting from rest, (b) the tension in the cord connecting the blocks.

5–31. A block of mass 200 gm rests on the top of a block of mass 800 gm. The combination is dragged along a level surface at constant velocity by a hanging block of mass 200 gm as in Fig. 5–10(a). (a) The first 200-gm block is removed from the 800-gm block and attached to the hanging block, as in Fig. 5–10(b). What is now the acceleration of the system? (b) What is the tension in the cord attached to the 800-gm block in part (b) of the figure?

5–32. Block A in Fig. 5–11 weighs 3 lb and block B weighs 30 lb. The coefficient of friction between B and the horizontal surface is 0.1. (a) What is the weight of block C if the acceleration of B is 6 ft/sec^2 toward the right? (b) What is the tension in each cord

when B has the acceleration stated above?

5–33. Two blocks connected by a cord passing over a small frictionless pulley rest on frictionless planes as shown in Fig. 5–12. (a) Which way will the system move? (b) What is the acceleration of the blocks? (c) What is the tension in the cord?

5–34. Two 100-gm blocks hang at the ends of a light flexible cord passing

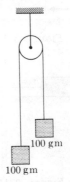

100 gm

100 gm

FIGURE 5–13

over a small frictionless pulley as in Fig. 5–13. A 40-gm block is placed on the block on the right, and removed after 2 sec. (a) How far will each block move in the first second after the 40-gm block is removed? (b) What was the tension in the cord before the 40-gm block was removed? after it was removed? (c) What was the tension in the cord supporting the pulley before the 40-gm block was removed? Neglect the weight of the pulley.

5–35. Two 10-lb blocks hang at the ends of a cord as in Fig. 5–13. What weight must be added to one of the blocks to cause it to move down a distance of 4 ft in 2 sec?

5–36. An 8-kgm and a 16-kgm block are suspended at opposite ends of a cord passing over a pulley. Compute (a) the acceleration of the system, (b) the tension in the cord connecting the blocks, and (c) the tension in the cord supporting the pulley. The weight of the pulley may be neglected.

5–37. A force of 10 lb is exerted horizontally against a 60-lb block, which in turn pushes a 40-lb block as in Fig. 5–14. If the blocks are on a frictionless surface, what force does one block exert on the other?

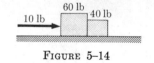

FIGURE 5–14

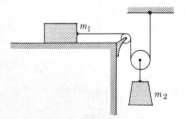

FIGURE 5–15

5–38. In terms of m_1, m_2, and g, find the accelerations of both blocks in Fig. 5–15. Neglect all friction and the masses of the pulleys.

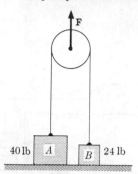

FIGURE 5–16

5–39. The bodies A and B in Fig. 5–16 weigh 40 lb and 24 lb respectively. They are initially at rest on the floor and are connected by a weightless string passing over a weightless and frictionless pulley. An upward force F is applied to the pulley. Find the accelerations a_1 of body A and a_2 of body B when F is (a) 24 lb, (b) 40 lb, (c) 72 lb, (d) 90 lb, (e) 120 lb.

5–40. The two blocks in Fig. 5–17 are connected by a heavy uniform rope which weighs 8 lb. An upward force of 48 lb is applied as shown. (a) What is the acceleration of the system? (b) What is the tension at the top of the 8-lb rope? (c) What is the tension at the midpoint of the rope?

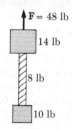

FIGURE 5–17

5-41. Two blocks, weighing 8 and 16 lb respectively, are connected by a string and slide down a 30° inclined plane, as in Fig. 5-18. The coefficient of sliding friction between the 8-lb block and the plane is 0.25, and between the 16-lb block and the plane it is 0.50. (a) Calculate the acceleration of each block. (b) Calculate the tension in the string.

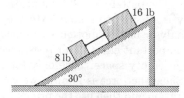

FIGURE 5-18

5-42. Two bodies weighing 10 lb and 6 lb respectively hang 4 ft above the floor from the ends of a cord 12 ft long passing over a frictionless pulley. Both bodies start from rest. Find the maximum height reached by the 6-lb body.

5-43. A man who weighs 160 lb stands on a platform which weighs 80 lb. He pulls a rope which is fastened to the platform and runs over a pulley on the ceiling. With what force does he have to pull in order to give himself and the platform an upward acceleration of 2 ft/sec^2?

5-44. What acceleration must the cart in Fig. 5-19 have in order that the

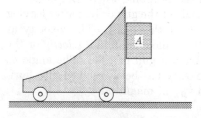

FIGURE 5-19

block A will not fall? The coefficient of friction between the block and the cart is μ.

5-45. In an experiment using the Cavendish balance to measure the gravitational constant G, it is found that a sphere of mass 800 gm attracts another sphere of mass 4 gm with a force of 13×10^{-6} dyne when the distance between the centers of the spheres is 4 cm. The acceleration of gravity at the earth's surface is 980 cm/sec^2, and the radius of the earth is 6400 km. Compute the mass of the earth from these data.

5-46. Two spheres, each of mass 6400 gm, are fixed at points A and B (Fig. 5-20). (a) Find the magnitude and direction of the initial acceleration of a sphere of mass 10 gm if released from rest at point P and acted on only by forces of gravitational attraction of the spheres at A and B.

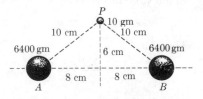

FIGURE 5-20

5-47. The mass of the moon is one eighty-first, and its radius one-fourth, that of the earth. What is the acceleration of gravity on the surface of the moon?

5-48. In round numbers, the distance from the earth to the moon is 250,000 mi, the distance from the earth to the sun is 93 million miles, the mass of the earth is 6×10^{27} gm, and the mass of the sun is 2×10^{33} gm. Approximately, what is the ratio of the gravitational pull of the sun on the moon to that of the earth on the moon?

CHAPTER 6

MOTION IN A PLANE

6–1 Motion of a projectile. Thus far we have considered only motion along a straight line, or *rectilinear motion*. In this chapter we shall discuss two common types of motion along a curved path, namely, the motion of a projectile and of a particle moving in a circle.

The term "projectile" is applied to a baseball or golf ball, a bomb released from an airplane, or a rifle bullet. The path followed by a projectile is called its *trajectory*. The trajectory is affected to a large extent by air resistance, which makes an exact analysis of the motion extremely complex. We shall, however, neglect the important effect of air resistance and assume that the motion takes place in empty space. The only force on the projectile is then its weight mg. Since the force is known, we can use Newton's second law to find the acceleration and then use the principles of kinematics to determine the velocity and position.

Newton's second law, in rectangular component form, is

$$\sum F_x = ma_x, \qquad \sum F_y = ma_y.$$

In our present problem, if the x-axis is horizontal and the y-axis vertical,

$$\sum F_x = 0, \qquad \sum F_y = -mg.$$

Therefore

$$a_x = \frac{\sum F_x}{m} = 0, \qquad a_y = \frac{\sum F_y}{m} = \frac{-mg}{m} = -g.$$

That is, the horizontal component of acceleration is zero, and the vertical component is downward and equal to that of a freely falling body. Since zero acceleration means constant velocity, the motion can be described as a combination of *horizontal motion with constant velocity* and *vertical motion with constant acceleration*.

Consider next the velocity of the projectile. In Fig. 6–1, x- and y-axes have been constructed with the origin at the point where the projectile begins its flight, i.e., just outside the muzzle of the gun or just after leaving the thrower's hand. We shall set $t = 0$ at this point. The velocity at the origin is represented by the vector $\mathbf{v}_0$, called the *initial velocity* or the *muzzle velocity* if the projectile is shot from a gun or rifle. The angle θ_0 is the *angle of departure*. The initial velocity has been resolved into horizontal and vertical components $\mathbf{v}_{0x}$ and $\mathbf{v}_{0y}$, of magnitudes

$$v_{0x} = v_0 \cos \theta, \qquad v_{0y} = v_0 \sin \theta.$$

98

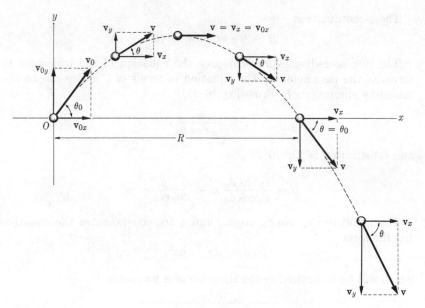

Fig. 6–1. Trajectory of a body projected with an initial velocity $\mathbf{v_0}$ at an angle of departure θ_0. The distance R is the *horizontal range*.

Since the horizontal acceleration a_x is zero, the horizontal component of velocity v_x remains constant throughout the motion, and at any later time t we have

$$v_x = v_{0x} = v_0 \cos \theta_0.$$

The vertical velocity v_y at any time, since the vertical acceleration $a_y = -g$, is

$$v_y = v_{0y} - gt = v_0 \sin \theta_0 - gt.$$

The magnitude of the resultant velocity v at any instant is

$$v = \sqrt{v_x^2 + v_y^2},$$

and the angle θ it makes with the horizontal can be found from

$$\tan \theta = \frac{v_y}{v_x}.$$

The velocity vector $\mathbf{v}$, at every point, is tangent to the trajectory. The x-coordinate at any time, since the x-velocity is constant, is

$$x = (v_0 \cos \theta_0)t. \qquad (6\text{–}1)$$

The y-coordinate is

$$y = (v_0 \sin \theta_0)t - \tfrac{1}{2}gt^2. \tag{6-2}$$

The two preceding expressions give the equation of the trajectory in terms of the parameter t. The equation in terms of x and y can be obtained by eliminating t. From Eq. (6-1),

$$t = \frac{x}{v_0 \cos \theta_0},$$

and substitution in Eq. (6-2) gives

$$y = \frac{v_0 \sin \theta_0}{v_0 \cos \theta_0}\, x - \frac{g}{2v_0 \cos \theta_0}\, x^2.$$

The quantities v_0, $\sin \theta_0$, $\cos \theta_0$, and g are constants, so the equation has the form

$$y = ax - bx^2,$$

which will be recognized as the equation of a *parabola*.

———————

EXAMPLE 1. A ball is projected horizontally with a velocity v_0 of 8 ft/sec. Find its position and velocity after $\tfrac{1}{4}$ sec (see Fig. 6-2).

In this case, the departure angle is zero. The initial vertical velocity component is therefore zero. The horizontal velocity component equals the initial velocity and is constant.

The x- and y-coordinates, when $t = \tfrac{1}{4}$ sec, are

$$x = v_x t = 8\,\frac{\text{ft}}{\text{sec}} \times \frac{1}{4}\,\text{sec} = 2\,\text{ft},$$

$$y = -\frac{1}{2}gt^2 = -\frac{1}{2} \times 32\,\frac{\text{ft}}{\text{sec}^2} \times \left(\frac{1}{4}\,\text{sec}\right)^2 = -1\,\text{ft}.$$

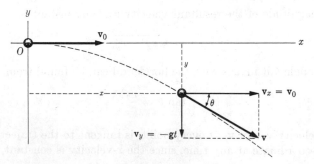

FIGURE 6-2

The components of velocity are

$$v_x = v_0 = 8\ \frac{\text{ft}}{\text{sec}},$$

$$v_y = -gt = -32\ \frac{\text{ft}}{\text{sec}^2} \times \frac{1}{4}\ \text{sec} = -8\ \frac{\text{ft}}{\text{sec}}.$$

The resultant velocity is

$$v = \sqrt{v_x^2 + v_y^2} = \sqrt{(8\ \text{ft/sec})^2 + (-8\ \text{ft/sec})^2} = 8\sqrt{2}\ \frac{\text{ft}}{\text{sec}}.$$

The angle θ is

$$\theta = \tan^{-1} \frac{v_y}{v_x} = \tan^{-1} \frac{-8\ \text{ft/sec}}{8\ \text{ft/sec}} = -45°.$$

That is, the velocity is 45° *below* the horizontal.

EXAMPLE 2. In Fig. 6–2, let $v_0 = 160$ ft/sec, $\theta_0 = 53°$. Then

$$v_0 \cos \theta_0 = 160\ \frac{\text{ft}}{\text{sec}} \times 0.60 = 96\ \frac{\text{ft}}{\text{sec}},$$

$$v_0 \sin \theta_0 = 160\ \frac{\text{ft}}{\text{sec}} \times 0.80 = 128\ \frac{\text{ft}}{\text{sec}}.$$

(a) Find the position of the projectile, and the magnitude and direction of its velocity, when $t = 2.0$ sec. We have

$$x = 96\ \frac{\text{ft}}{\text{sec}} \times 2.0\ \text{sec} = 192\ \text{ft},$$

$$y = 128\ \frac{\text{ft}}{\text{sec}} \times 2.0\ \text{sec} - \frac{1}{2} \times 32\ \frac{\text{ft}}{\text{sec}^2} \times (2.0\ \text{sec})^2 = 192\ \text{ft},$$

$$v_x = 96\ \frac{\text{ft}}{\text{sec}},$$

$$v_y = 128\ \frac{\text{ft}}{\text{sec}} - 32\ \frac{\text{ft}}{\text{sec}^2} \times 2.0\ \text{sec} = 64\ \frac{\text{ft}}{\text{sec}},$$

$$\theta = \tan^{-1} \frac{64\ \text{ft/sec}}{96\ \text{ft/sec}} = \tan^{-1} 0.667 = 33.5°.$$

(b) Find the time at which the projectile reaches the highest point of its flight, and find the elevation of this point.

At the highest point, the vertical velocity v_y is zero. If t_1 is the time at which this point is reached,

$$v_y = 0 = 128\ \frac{\text{ft}}{\text{sec}} - 32\ \frac{\text{ft}}{\text{sec}^2} \times t_1, \qquad t_1 = 4\ \text{sec}.$$

The elevation of the point is then

$$y = 128 \frac{ft}{sec} \times 4 \, sec - \frac{1}{2} \times 32 \frac{ft}{sec^2} \times (4 \, sec)^2 = 256 \, ft.$$

(c) Find the *horizontal range R*, that is, the horizontal distance from the starting point to the point at which the projectile returns to its original elevation and at which, therefore, $y = 0$. Let t_2 be the time at which this point is reached. Then

$$y = 0 = 128 \frac{ft}{sec} \times t_2 - \frac{1}{2} \times 32 \frac{ft}{sec^2} \times t_2^2.$$

This quadratic equation has two roots,

$$t_2 = 0 \quad and \quad t_2 = 8 \, sec,$$

corresponding to the two points at which $y = 0$. Evidently the time desired is the second root, $t_2 = 8$ sec, which is just twice the time to reach the highest point. The time of descent therefore equals the time of rise.

The horizontal range is

$$R = v_x t_2 = 96 \frac{ft}{sec} \times 8 \, sec = 768 \, ft.$$

The vertical velocity at this point is

$$v_y = 96 \frac{ft}{sec} - 32 \frac{ft}{sec^2} \times 8 \, sec = - 96 \frac{ft}{sec}.$$

That is, the vertical velocity has the same magnitude as the initial vertical velocity, but the opposite direction. Since v_x is constant, the angle below the horizontal at this point equals the angle of departure.

(d) If unimpeded, the projectile continues to travel beyond its horizontal range. It is left as an exercise to compute the position and velocity at a time 10 sec after the start, corresponding to the last position shown in Fig. 6–2. The results are:

$$x = 960 \, ft, \quad y = -320 \, ft, \quad v_x = 96 \frac{ft}{sec}, \quad v_y = -192 \frac{ft}{sec}.$$

For a given initial velocity, there is one particular angle of departure for which the horizontal range is a maximum. To find this angle, write the general algebraic expression for R (see the example above) as

$$R = v_x t_2 = v_0 \cos \theta_0 \times \frac{2v_0 \sin \theta_0}{g}$$

$$= \frac{2v_0^2 \sin \theta_0 \cos \theta_0}{g} = \frac{v_0^2 \sin 2\theta_0}{g}.$$

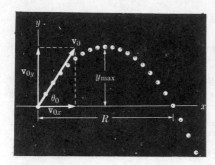

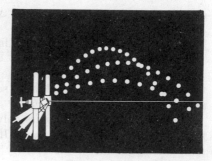

FIG. 6–3. Trajectory of a body pro-   FIG. 6–4. An angle of elevation of 45°
jected at an angle with the horizontal. gives the maximum horizontal range.

The quantities v_0 and g are constants, so the maximum range results
when $\sin 2\theta_0$ is a maximum. This occurs when $2\theta_0 = 90°$, or when
$\theta_0 = 45°$.

Figure 6–3 is a multiflash photograph of the trajectory of a ball, to
which have been added x- and y-axes and the initial velocity vector.
The horizontal distances between consecutive positions are all equal,
showing that the horizontal velocity component is constant. The vertical
distances first decrease and then increase, showing that the vertical motion
is accelerated.

Figure 6–4 is a composite photograph of three trajectories with departure angles of 30°, 45°, and 60°. Note that the horizontal range is the
same for the angles of 30° and 60°, and is less than that for the angle of 45°.

6–2 Circular motion. Let us consider next a small body (a particle)
revolving in a circle of radius R. Points
P and Q in Fig. 6–5 represent two
successive positions of the particle. Its
displacement as it moves from P to Q
is the vector $\Delta \mathbf{s}$. The *average velocity* $\bar{\mathbf{v}}$ is
defined, just as in the case of rectilinear
motion, as the vector $\Delta \mathbf{s}$ divided by the
elapsed time Δt.

$$\bar{\mathbf{v}} = \frac{\Delta \mathbf{s}}{\Delta t}. \qquad (6\text{–}3)$$

The direction of $\bar{\mathbf{v}}$ is the same as that
of $\Delta \mathbf{s}$.

The *instantaneous velocity* $\mathbf{v}$, at the
point P, is defined as the limit of the
average velocity when Q is taken closer

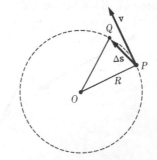

FIG. 6–5. The instantaneous
velocity $\mathbf{v}$, at point P, is tangent
to the circle. It is defined as the
limiting ratio of $\Delta \mathbf{s}$ to Δt when
Q approaches P.

and closer to P and when Δs and Δt approach zero.

$$\mathbf{v} = \lim_{\Delta t \to 0} \frac{\Delta \mathbf{s}}{\Delta t}. \qquad (6\text{--}4)$$

As point Q approaches point P, the direction of the vector $\Delta \mathbf{s}$ approaches that of the *tangent* to the circle at P, so that *the direction of the instantaneous velocity vector is tangent to the circle.*

At this point we shall discuss only the special case in which the *magnitude* of the velocity is constant. If T is the time of a complete revolution, the magnitude of the velocity is equal to the circumference of the circle, $2\pi R$, divided by T.

$$v = \frac{2\pi R}{T}. \qquad (6\text{--}5)$$

Although the magnitude of the velocity is constant, its *direction* is not. In Fig. 6–6(a), the vectors $\mathbf{v}_1$ and $\mathbf{v}_2$ represent the instantaneous velocities at P and Q. The vectors have the same length, but different directions. Again, just as in rectilinear motion, we define the *average acceleration* $\bar{\mathbf{a}}$ as the *vector change in velocity* between P and Q, divided by the elapsed time. The vector change in velocity means the *vector difference* $\mathbf{v}_2 - \mathbf{v}_1$, which we write as $\Delta \mathbf{v}$.

$$\bar{\mathbf{a}} = \frac{(\mathbf{v}_2 - \mathbf{v}_1)}{\Delta t} = \frac{\Delta \mathbf{v}}{\Delta t}. \qquad (6\text{--}6)$$

Referring to Section 1–9, recall that the vector difference $\mathbf{v}_2 - \mathbf{v}_1$ can be considered as the vector *sum* of $\mathbf{v}_2$ and $-\mathbf{v}_1$, where $-\mathbf{v}_1$ is a vector of the same length as $\mathbf{v}_1$ but in the opposite direction. Since $\bar{\mathbf{a}}$ is an *average* acceleration over the time interval while the particle moves from P to Q, we construct the vector diagram for obtaining $\Delta \mathbf{v}$ at the midpoint of this interval. This has been done in Fig. 6–6(b), where the vector $\mathbf{v}_2$ has been

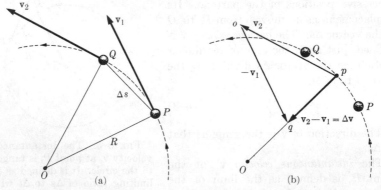

Fig. 6–6. Vector $\Delta \mathbf{v}$ is the vector change in velocity between points P and Q.

transferred to point p, midway between P and Q, and the vector difference $\Delta\mathbf{v}$ has been found by the triangle method. We see that the vector difference $\Delta\mathbf{v}$ points toward the center of the circle, and hence the average acceleration, $\Delta\mathbf{v}/\Delta t$, points in this direction also.

The magnitude of $\Delta\mathbf{v}$ can be expressed as follows. The triangles OPQ and opq in Fig. 6-6(a) and (b) are similar, since both are isosceles triangles and their long sides are mutually perpendicular. Hence if v represents the *magnitude* of either $\mathbf{v}_1$ or $\mathbf{v}_2$, we have

$$\frac{\Delta v}{v} = \frac{\Delta s}{R},$$

or

$$\Delta v = \frac{v}{R}\,\Delta s.$$

The average acceleration $\bar{a}$ is therefore

$$\bar{a} = \frac{\Delta v}{\Delta t} = \frac{v}{R}\frac{\Delta s}{\Delta t}. \tag{6-7}$$

The *instantaneous acceleration* $\mathbf{a}$ at the point P is defined in magnitude and direction as the limit of the average acceleration when Q approaches P and $\Delta\mathbf{v}$ and Δt approach zero. As this occurs, the vector $\Delta\mathbf{v}$ in Fig. 6-6(b) becomes shorter (always pointing toward the center, however), while Δt becomes smaller also. In the limit, the *direction* of the acceleration is still toward the center and its magnitude is

$$a = \lim_{\Delta t \to 0} \frac{v}{R}\frac{\Delta s}{\Delta t} = \frac{v}{R}\lim_{\Delta t \to 0}\frac{\Delta s}{\Delta t}.$$

But

$$\lim_{\Delta t \to 0}\frac{\Delta s}{\Delta t} = v,$$

so

$$\boxed{a = \frac{v^2}{R}.} \tag{6-8}$$

The magnitude of the instantaneous acceleration is therefore equal to the square of the velocity divided by the radius, and its direction is toward the center of the circle. Because of this it is called a *central*, a *centripetal*, or a *radial* acceleration. (The term "centripetal" means "seeking a center.") The units of radial acceleration are the same as those of an acceleration resulting from a change in the *magnitude* of a velocity. Thus in the engineering system the units or v^2/R are

$$\frac{(\text{ft/sec})^2}{\text{ft}} = \frac{\text{ft}}{\text{sec}^2}.$$

A centrifuge is a device for whirling an object with a high velocity. The consequent large radial acceleration is equivalent to increasing the value of g, and such processes as sedimentation, which would otherwise take place only slowly, can be greatly accelerated in this way. Very high speed centrifuges, called ultracentrifuges, have been operated at velocities as high as 180,000 rev/min, and small experimental units have been driven as fast as 1,300,000 rev/min.

Figure 6–7 shows the directions of the velocity and acceleration vectors at a number of points for a particle revolving in a circle with a velocity of constant magnitude.

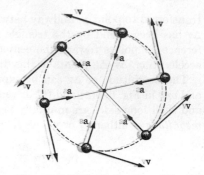

FIG. 6–7. Velocity and acceleration vectors of a particle in uniform circular motion.

EXAMPLE. The moon revolves about the earth in a circle (very nearly) of radius $R = 239{,}000$ mi or 12.6×10^8 ft, and requires 27.3 days or 23.4×10^5 sec to make a complete revolution. (a) What is the acceleration of the moon toward the earth?

The velocity of the moon is

$$v = \frac{2\pi R}{T} = \frac{2\pi \times 12.6 \times 10^8 \text{ ft}}{23.4 \times 10^5 \text{ sec}} = 3360 \frac{\text{ft}}{\text{sec}}.$$

Its radial acceleration is therefore

$$a = \frac{v^2}{R} = \frac{(3360 \text{ ft/sec})^2}{12.6 \times 10^8 \text{ ft}} = 0.00896 \frac{\text{ft}}{\text{sec}^2}.$$

(b) If the gravitational force exerted on a body by the earth is inversely proportional to the square of the distance from the earth's center, the acceleration produced by this force should vary in the same way. Therefore, if the acceleration of the moon is caused by the gravitational attraction of the earth, the ratio of the moon's acceleration to that of a falling body at the earth's surface should equal the ratio of the square of the earth's radius (3950 mi or 2.09×10^6 ft) to the square of the radius of the moon's orbit. Is this true?

The ratio of the two accelerations is

$$\frac{8.96 \times 10^{-3} \text{ ft/sec}^2}{32.2 \text{ ft/sec}^2} = 2.78 \times 10^{-4}.$$

The ratio of the squares of the distances is

$$\frac{(2.09 \times 10^6 \text{ ft})^2}{(12.6 \times 10^8 \text{ ft})^2} = 2.75 \times 10^{-4}$$

The agreement is very close, although not exact because we have used average values.

It was the calculation above which Newton made to first justify his hypothesis that gravitation was truly *universal* and that the earth's pull extended out indefinitely into space. The numerical values available in Newton's time were not highly precise. While he did not obtain as close an agreement as that above, he states that he found his results to "answer pretty nearly," and he concluded that his hypothesis was verified.

6–3 Centripetal force. Having obtained an expression for the acceleration of a particle revolving in a circle, we can now use Newton's second law to find the resultant force on the particle. Since the magnitude of the acceleration equals v^2/R, and its direction is toward the center, the magnitude of the resultant force on a particle of mass m is

$$\Sigma F = m \frac{v^2}{R}. \tag{6–9}$$

The direction of the resultant force is toward the center also, and it is called a *centripetal force*. (It is unfortunate that it has become common practice to characterize the force by the adjective "centripetal," since this seems to imply that there is some difference in nature between centripetal forces and other forces. This is not the case. Centripetal forces, like other forces, are pushes and pulls exerted by sticks and strings, or arise from the action of gravitational or other causes. The term "centripetal" refers to the *effect* of the force, that is, to the fact that it results in a change in the *direction* of the velocity of the body on which it acts, rather than a change in the *magnitude* of this velocity.)

Anyone who has ever tied an object to a cord and whirled it in a circle will realize the necessity of exerting this inward, centripetal force. If the cord breaks, the direction of the velocity ceases to change (unless other forces are acting) and the object flies off along a tangent to the circle.

EXAMPLE 1. A small body of mass 200 gm revolves in a circle on a horizontal frictionless surface, attached by a cord 20 cm long to a pin set in the surface. If the body makes two complete revolutions per second, find the force **P** exerted on it by the cord. (See Fig. 6–8.)

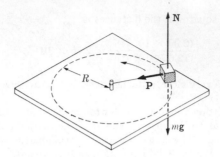

FIGURE 6–8

The circumference of the circle is $2\pi \times 20$ cm $= 40\pi$ cm, so the velocity is 80π cm/sec. The magnitude of the centripetal acceleration is

$$a = \frac{v^2}{R} = \frac{(80\pi \text{ cm/sec})^2}{20 \text{ cm}} = 3150 \frac{\text{cm}}{\text{sec}^2}.$$

Since the body has no vertical acceleration, the forces $\mathbf{N}$ and $m\mathbf{g}$ are equal and opposite and the force $\mathbf{P}$ is the resultant force. Therefore

$$\sum F = P = ma = 200 \text{ gm} \times 3150 \frac{\text{cm}}{\text{sec}^2} = 6.3 \times 10^5 \text{ dynes.}$$

EXAMPLE 2. The centripetal force retaining the moon in its orbit is the gravitational attraction exerted on it by the earth. Show that if the gravitational constant G, the radius of the moon's orbit R, and its time of revolution T are known, the mass of the earth can be computed.

Let m_E and m_M be the masses of earth and moon respectively. Then

$$\sum F = m \frac{v^2}{R},$$

$$G \frac{m_E m_M}{R^2} = m_M \frac{(2\pi R/T)^2}{R},$$

and hence

$$m_E = \frac{4\pi^2 R^3}{GT^2}.$$

EXAMPLE 3. Figure 6–9 is a view of the earth looking down on the north pole and showing a (greatly enlarged) view of a body of mass m at the equator, hanging from a spring balance. The forces on the hanging body are the force of gravitational attraction $\mathbf{F}$ and the upward pull $\mathbf{w}$ of the spring balance. Since the body is carried along by the earth's rotation, it is not in equilibrium but has a radial acceleration a_R toward the earth's center. The force $\mathbf{F}$ must therefore be slightly larger than the force $\mathbf{w}$ in order to provide the necessary centripetal force. That is, the balance reading $\mathbf{w}$ is somewhat less than the true force of gravitational attraction.

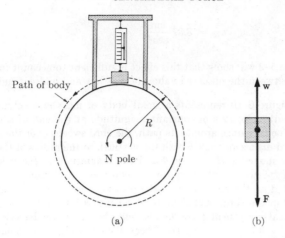

FIG. 6–9. The apparent weight is less than the force of gravitational attraction.

From Newton's law of gravitation,

$$F = G\,\frac{m m_E}{R^2},$$

where m_E is the mass of the earth.

From Newton's second law,

$$F - w = m a_R.$$

Replacing F by $G(m m_E/R^2)$ and w by mg, where g is the acceleration of gravity at the equator, we get, after canceling m,

$$g \text{ (equator)} = \frac{G m_E}{R^2} - a_R.$$

At the poles, where v and a_R are zero,

$$g \text{ (poles)} = \frac{G m_E}{R^2}.$$

This is the expression we previously derived for g in Eq. (5–6), where the rotation of the earth was neglected. We can now see that the effect of the rotation is to reduce the value of g at the equator, relative to that at the poles, by an amount equal to a_R, where for the equator

$$a_R = \frac{v^2}{R} = \frac{(2\pi R/T)^2}{R} = \frac{4\pi^2 R}{T^2}.$$

Approximate numerical values are

$$R = 6.4 \times 10^8 \text{ cm},$$
$$T = 8.64 \times 10^4 \text{ sec}.$$

Hence

$$a_R = 3.37 \frac{cm}{sec^2}.$$

Reference to Table 5–2 will show that this effect is sufficient to account for most of the difference between the observed values of g at low and high latitudes.

EXAMPLE 4. Figure 6–10 represents a small body of mass m revolving in a horizontal circle with velocity v of constant magnitude at the end of a cord of length L. As the body swings around its path, the cord sweeps over the surface of a cone. The cord makes an angle θ with the vertical, so the radius of the circle in which the body moves is $R = L \sin \theta$ and the magnitude of the velocity v equals $2\pi L \sin \theta/T$, where T is the time for one complete revolution.

The forces exerted on the body when in the position shown are its weight mg and the tension $\mathbf{P}$ in the cord. Let $\mathbf{P}$ be resolved into a horizontal component $P \sin \theta$ and a vertical component $P \cos \theta$. The body has no vertical acceleration, so the forces $P \cos \theta$ and mg are equal, and the resultant inward, radial, or centripetal force is the component $P \sin \theta$.

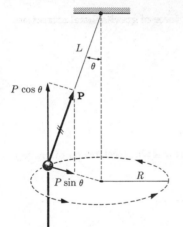

Then

$$P \sin \theta = m \frac{v^2}{R}, \qquad P \cos \theta = mg.$$

When the first of these equations is divided by the second, we get

$$\tan \theta = \frac{v^2}{Rg}. \qquad (6\text{–}10)$$

Making use of the relations $R = L \sin \theta$ and $v = 2\pi L \sin \theta/T$, we can also write

$$\cos \theta = \frac{gT^2}{4\pi^2 L}, \qquad (6\text{–}11)$$

FIG. 6–10. The conical pendulum.

or

$$T = 2\pi \sqrt{L \cos \theta/g}. \qquad (6\text{–}12)$$

Equation (6–12) indicates how the angle θ depends on the time of revolution T and the length L of the cord. For a given length L, $\cos \theta$ *decreases* as the time is made shorter, and the angle θ *increases*. The angle never becomes 90°, however, since this requires that $T = 0$.

Equation (6–12) is similar in form to the expression for the time of swing of a simple pendulum, which will be derived in Chapter 11. Because of this similarity, the present device is called a *conical pendulum*.

Some readers may wish to add to the forces shown in Fig. 6–10 an outward, "centrifugal," force, to "keep the body out there," or to "keep it in equilibrium." ("Centrifugal" means "fleeing a center.") Let us examine this point of view. In the first place, to look for a force to "*keep* the body out there" is an example of faulty observation, because the body doesn't stay there. A moment later it will be at a different position on its circular path. At the instant shown it is moving toward the reader, and unless a resultant force acts on it, it will, according to Newton's first law, continue to move in this direction. If an outward force *were* acting on it, equal and opposite to the inward component of the force **P**, there would be no resultant inward force to deviate it sidewise from its present direction of motion.

Those who wish to add a force to "keep the body in equilibrium" forget that the term equilibrium refers to a state of rest, or of motion *in a straight line* with constant speed. Here, the body is not moving in a straight line, but in a circle. It is not in equilibrium, but has an acceleration toward the center of the circle and must be acted on by a resultant or *un*balanced force to produce this acceleration.

EXAMPLE 5. Figure 6–11(a) represents an automobile or a railway car rounding a curve of radius R on a level road or track. The forces acting on it are its weight mg, the normal force **N**, and the centripetal force **T**. The force **T** must be provided by friction, in the case of an automobile, or by a force exerted by the rails against the flanges on the wheels of a railway car.

In order not to have to rely on friction, or to reduce wear on the rails and flanges, the road or the track may be banked as shown in Fig. 6–11(b). The normal force **N** then has a vertical component $N \cos \theta$, and a horizontal component $N \sin \theta$ toward the center, which provides the centripetal force. The banking angle θ can be computed as follows. If v is the velocity and R the radius, then

$$N \sin \theta = \frac{mv^2}{R}.$$

Since there is no vertical acceleration,

$$N \cos \theta = mg.$$

Dividing the first equation by the second, we get

$$\tan \theta = \frac{v^2}{Rg}.$$

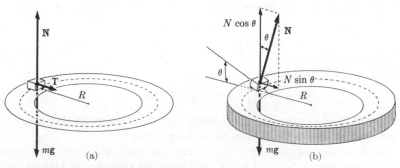

FIG. 6–11. (a) Forces on a vehicle rounding a curve on a level track. (b) Forces when the track is banked.

The tangent of the angle of banking is proportional to the square of the velocity and inversely proportional to the radius. For a given radius no one angle is correct for all velocities. Hence in the design of highways and railroads, curves are banked for the average velocity of the traffic over them.

The same considerations apply to the correct banking angle of a plane when it makes a turn in level flight.

Note that the banking angle is given by the same expression as that for the angle with the vertical made by the cord of a conical pendulum. In fact, the force diagrams in Fig. 6–10 and Fig. 6–11 are identical.

6–4 Motion in a vertical circle. Figure 6–12 represents a small body attached to a cord of length R and whirling in a vertical circle about a fixed point O to which the other end of the cord is attached. The motion, while circular, is not uniform, since the body accelerates on the way down and decelerates on the way up.

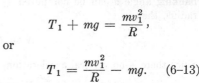

FIG. 6–12. Forces on a body moving in a vertical circle.

Let $\mathbf{v}_1$ represent the velocity of the body as it passes the highest point. The forces acting on it at this point are its weight $m\mathbf{g}$ and the tension $\mathbf{T}_1$ in the cord, both acting downward. The resultant force is $\mathbf{T}_1 + m\mathbf{g}$, and therefore at this point

$$T_1 + mg = \frac{mv_1^2}{R},$$

or

$$T_1 = \frac{mv_1^2}{R} - mg. \quad (6\text{–}13)$$

Since by definition the centripetal force is the resultant inward force on a body in circular motion, the centripetal force in this instance is provided partly by the body's weight and partly by the tension in the cord.

Similarly, at the lowest point of the circle

$$T_2 - mg = \frac{mv_2^2}{R},$$

or

$$T_2 = \frac{mv_2^2}{R} + mg, \quad (6\text{–}14)$$

where T_2 and v_2 represent the tension and the velocity at this point, and the upward direction has been taken as positive.

With motion of this sort, it is a familiar fact that there is a certain critical velocity below which the cord becomes slack at the highest point.

FIGURE 6–13(a)

FIGURE 6–13(b)

FIGURE 6–13(c)

FIGURE 6–13(d)

To find this velocity, set $T_1 = 0$ in Eq. (6–13).

$$0 = \frac{mv_1^2}{R} - mg,$$

$$v_1 = \sqrt{gR}. \tag{6–15}$$

The multiflash photographs of Fig. 6–13 illustrate another case of motion in a vertical circle: a small ball "looping-the-loop" on the inside of a vertical circular track. The inward normal force exerted on the ball by the track takes the place of the tension **T** in Fig. 6–12.

In Fig. 6–13(a) the ball is released from such an elevation that its velocity at the top of the track is greater than the critical velocity, $\sqrt{gR}$. In Fig. 6–13(b) the ball starts from a lower elevation and reaches the top of the circle with a velocity such that its own weight is larger than the requisite centripetal force. In other words, the track would have to pull outward to maintain the circular motion. Since this is impossible, the ball leaves the track and moves for a short distance in a parabola. This parabola soon intersects the circle, however, and the remainder of the trip is completed successfully.

In Fig. 6–13(c) the start is made from a still lower elevation, the ball leaves the track sooner, and the parabolic path is clearly evident. In Fig. 6–13(d), while the ball eventually returns to the track, the collision is so nearly at right angles that it bounces a few times and finally rolls off.

6–5 Tangential acceleration. We now take up the more general case of circular motion in which the magnitude of the velocity is not constant. Figure 6–14(a) shows a particle revolving in a circle. In moving from

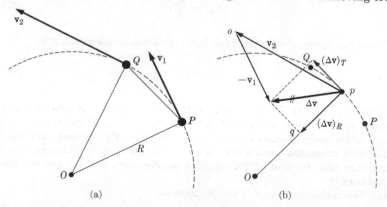

FIG. 6–14. (a) Body moving in nonuniform circular motion. (b) The vector $\Delta\mathbf{v}$ is the change in velocity between points P and Q. It has a tangential component $(\Delta\mathbf{v})_T$ and a radial component $(\Delta\mathbf{v})_R$.

P to Q, its velocity changes from $\mathbf{v}_1$ to $\mathbf{v}_2$, where $\mathbf{v}_2$ has a greater magnitude than $\mathbf{v}_1$ as well as a different direction. In part (b), the vector $\mathbf{v}_2$ has been transferred to point p, midway between P and Q, and the vector change in velocity, $\Delta\mathbf{v}$, has been found as in Fig. 6–6. The ratio $\Delta\mathbf{v}/\Delta t$ is the *average acceleration* between P and Q. Its direction is the same as that of $\Delta\mathbf{v}$, and it does not point toward the center of the circle.

The vector $\Delta\mathbf{v}$ can be resolved into a radial component $(\Delta\mathbf{v})_R$ and a tangential component $(\Delta\mathbf{v})_T$. The ratio $(\Delta\mathbf{v})_R/\Delta t$ is the radial component of the average acceleration, $\bar{a}_R$, and the ratio $(\Delta\mathbf{v})_T/\Delta t$ is its tangential component, $\bar{a}_T$.

$$\bar{a}_R = \frac{(\Delta\mathbf{v})_R}{\Delta t}, \qquad \bar{a}_T = \frac{(\Delta\mathbf{v})_T}{\Delta t}.$$

The radial and tangential components of the *instantaneous* acceleration are the limits of these ratios as Δt approaches zero or as point Q is taken closer and closer to point P. As Q approaches P, the magnitude of the component $(\Delta\mathbf{v})_T$ becomes more and more nearly equal to the difference between the magnitudes of $\mathbf{v}_1$ and $\mathbf{v}_2$, and the ratio $(\Delta\mathbf{v})_T/\Delta t$ approaches a_T.

$$a_T = \lim_{\Delta t \to 0} \frac{(\Delta\mathbf{v})_T}{\Delta t}. \tag{6–16}$$

Also, as Q approaches P, the figure opq approaches an isosceles triangle, similar to OPQ. Hence the ratio $(\Delta\mathbf{v})_R/\Delta t$ approaches the same limit as for motion with constant velocity and the magnitude of the instantaneous radial acceleration is

$$a_R = \frac{v^2}{R}. \tag{6–17}$$

The magnitude of the resultant instantaneous acceleration a is

$$a = \sqrt{a_T^2 + a_R^2}. \tag{6–18}$$

EXAMPLE. In Fig. 6–15, a small body of mass $m = 0.10$ kgm swings in a vertical circle at the end of a cord of length $R = 1.0$ m. If its velocity v is 2.0 m/sec when the cord makes an angle $\theta = 30°$ with the vertical, find (a) the radial and tangential components of its acceleration at this instant, (b) the magnitude and direction of its resultant acceleration, and (c) the tension $\mathbf{P}$ in the cord.

(a) The radial component of acceleration is

$$a_R = \frac{v^2}{R} = \frac{(2.0 \text{ m/sec})^2}{1.0 \text{ m}} = 4 \frac{\text{m}}{\text{sec}^2}.$$

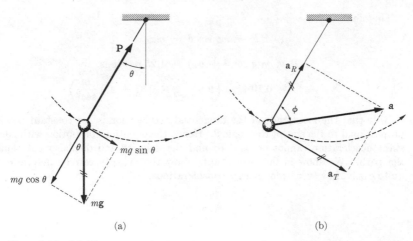

(a)   (b)

FIG. 6–15. (a) Forces on a body swinging in a vertical circle. (b) The radial and tangential components of acceleration are combined to obtain the resultant acceleration **a**.

The tangential component of acceleration can be found from Newton's second law. Let us take axes in the radial and tangential directions. Then

$$\sum F_T = ma_T, \qquad \sum F_R = ma_R,$$

where $\sum F_T$ and $\sum F_R$ are the resultant tangential and radial forces. We see from the force diagram that

$$\sum F_T = mg \sin \theta,$$

so

$$mg \sin \theta = ma_T,$$

$$a_T = g \sin \theta = 9.8 \frac{m}{\sec^2} \times 0.50 = 4.9 \frac{m}{\sec^2}.$$

(b) The resultant acceleration a [see Fig. 6–15(b)] is

$$a = \sqrt{(4.9)^2 + (4.0)^2} \frac{m}{\sec^2} = 6.3 \frac{m}{\sec^2}.$$

The angle ϕ is

$$\phi = \tan^{-1} \frac{a_T}{a_R} = \tan^{-1} \frac{4.9}{4.0} = 50.5°.$$

(c) The resultant radial force is

$$\sum F_R = P - mg \cos \theta.$$

Therefore

$$P - mg \cos \theta = ma_R,$$

$$P = m(g \cos \theta + a_R) = 1.25 \text{ newtons}$$

$$= 0.10 \text{ kgm} \left(9.8 \frac{\text{m}}{\text{sec}^2} \times 0.87 + 4.0 \frac{\text{m}}{\text{sec}^2} \right).$$

Note that the magnitude of the tangential acceleration is not constant but is proportional to the sine of the angle θ. Hence the equations of motion with constant acceleration cannot be used to find the velocity and displacement along the path. We show in the next chapter how the velocity can be determined quite easily, however, from energy considerations.

Problems

(In all the problems in projectile motion, let $g = 32.0$ ft/sec^2 or 980 cm/sec^2, and neglect air resistance.)

6–1. A ball rolls off the edge of a horizontal tabletop 4 ft high and strikes the floor at a distance of 5 ft horizontally from the edge of the table. What was the velocity of the ball at the instant of leaving the table?

6–2. A block slides off a horizontal tabletop 4 ft high with a velocity of 12 ft/sec. Find (a) the horizontal distance from the table at which the block strikes the floor, and (b) the horizontal and vertical components of its velocity when it reaches the floor.

6–3. A level-flight bomber, flying at 300 ft/sec, releases a bomb at an elevation of 6400 ft. (a) How long before the bomb strikes the earth? (b) How far does it travel horizontally? (c) Find the horizontal and vertical components of its velocity when it strikes.

6–4. A block passes a point 10 ft from the edge of a table with a velocity of 12 ft/sec. It slides off the edge of the table, which is 4 ft high, and strikes the floor 4 ft from the edge of the table. What was the coefficient of sliding friction between block and table?

6–5. A golf ball is driven horizontally from an elevated tee with a velocity of 80 ft/sec. It strikes the fairway 2.5 sec later. (a) How far has it fallen vertically? (b) How far has it traveled horizontally? (c) Find the horizontal and vertical components of its velocity, and the magnitude and direction of its resultant velocity, just before it strikes.

6–6. A .22 rifle bullet is fired in a horizontal direction with a muzzle velocity of 900 ft/sec. In the absence of air resistance, how far will it have dropped in traveling a horizontal distance of (a) 50 yd? (b) 100 yd? (c) 150 yd? (d) How far will it drop in one second?

6–7. A bomb is released from an airplane flying horizontally at an elevation of 1600 ft, with a velocity of 200 mi/hr. (a) How far does the bomb travel horizontally before striking the earth? (b) What will be the magnitude and direction of its velocity just before striking? (c) How long is it in the air?

6–8. A level-flight bombing plane, flying at an altitude of 1024 ft with a velocity of 240 ft/sec, is overtaking a motor torpedo boat traveling at 80 ft/sec in the same direction as the plane. At what distance astern of the boat should a bomb be released in order to hit the boat?

6–9. A bomber is making a horizontal bombing run on a destroyer from an altitude of 25,600 ft. The magnitude of the velocity of the bomber is 300 mi/hr. (a) How much time is available for the destroyer to change its course after the bombs are released? (b) If the bomber is to be shot down before its bombs can reach the ship, what is the maximum angle that the line of sight from ship to bomber can make with the horizontal? Draw a diagram, showing distances approximately to scale.

6–10. A ball is projected with an initial upward velocity component of 80 ft/sec and a horizontal velocity component of 100 ft/sec. (a) Find the position and velocity of the ball after 2 sec; 3 sec; 6 sec. (b) How long a time is required to reach the highest point of the trajectory? (c) How high is this point? (d) How long a time is required for the ball to return to its original level? (e) How far has it traveled horizontally during this time? Show your results in a neat sketch, large enough to show all features clearly.

6–11. A batted baseball leaves the bat at an angle of 30° above the horizontal, and is caught by an outfielder 400 ft from the plate. (a) What was the initial velocity of the ball? (b) How high did it rise? (c) How long was it in the air?

6–12. A golf ball is driven with a velocity of 200 ft/sec at an angle of 37° above the horizontal. It strikes a green at a horizontal distance of 800 ft from the tee. (a) What was the elevation of the green above the tee? (b) What was the velocity of the ball when it struck the green?

6–13. If a baseball player can throw a ball a maximum distance of 200 ft over the ground, what is the maximum vertical height to which he can throw it? Assume the ball to have the same initial speed in each case.

6–14. A player kicks a football at an angle of 37° with the horizontal and with an initial velocity of 48 ft/sec. A second player standing at a distance of 100 ft from the first in the direction of the kick starts running to meet the ball at the instant it is kicked. How fast must he run in order to catch the ball before it hits the ground?

6–15. A baseball leaves the bat at a height of 4 ft above the ground, traveling at an angle of 45° with the horizontal, and with a velocity such that the horizontal range would be 400 ft. At a distance of 360 ft from home plate is a fence 30 ft high. Will the ball be a home run?

6–16. A ball A is projected from O with an initial velocity $v_0 = 700$ cm/sec in a direction 37° above the horizontal. A ball B 300 cm from O on a line 37°

above the horizontal is released from rest at the instant A starts. (a) How far will B have fallen when it is hit by A? (b) In what direction is A moving when it hits B? (See Fig. 6–16.)

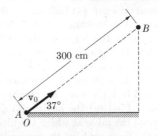

FIGURE 6–16

6–17. A projectile shot at an angle of 60° above the horizontal strikes a building 80 ft away at a point 48 ft above the point of projection. (a) Find the velocity of projection. (b) Find the magnitude and direction of the velocity of the projectile when it strikes the building.

6–18. (a) What must be the velocity of a projectile fired vertically upward to reach an altitude of 20,000 ft? (b) What velocity is required to reach the same height if the gun makes an angle of 45° with the vertical? (c) Compute the time required to reach the highest point in both trajectories. (d) How many feet would a plane traveling at 300 mi/hr move in this time?

6–19. The angle of elevation of an anti-aircraft gun is 70° and the muzzle velocity is 2700 ft/sec. For what time after firing should the fuse be set if the shell is to explode at an altitude of 5000 ft?

6–20. A projectile has an initial velocity of 80 ft/sec at an angle of 53° above the horizontal. Calculate (a) the horizontal distance from the starting point three seconds after it is fired, (b) the vertical distance above the starting point at the same time, and (c) the horizontal and vertical components of its velocity at this time.

6–21. A trench mortar fires a projectile at an angle of 53° above the horizontal with a muzzle velocity of 200 ft/sec. A tank is advancing directly toward the mortar on level ground at a speed of 10 ft/sec. What should be the distance from mortar to tank at the instant the mortar is fired in order to score a hit?

6–22. The projectile of a trench mortar has a muzzle velocity of 300 ft/sec. (a) Find the two angles of elevation to hit a target at the same level as the mortar and 300 yd distant. (b) Compute the maximum height of each trajectory, and (c) the time of flight of each. Make a neat sketch of the trajectories, approximately to scale.

6–23. A gun fires a projectile with a muzzle velocity of 1200 ft/sec. It is desired to hit a target 1000 yd distant horizontally from the gun, and at an elevation of 980 ft above it. What is the minimum angle of elevation of the gun?

6–24. A bomber, diving at an angle of 53° with the vertical, releases a bomb at an altitude of 2400 ft. The bomb is observed to strike the ground 5 sec after its release. (a) What was the velocity of the bomber, in ft/sec? (b) How far did the bomb travel hori-

zontally during its flight? (c) What were the horizontal and vertical components of its velocity just before striking?

6–25. A 15-lb stone is dropped from a cliff in a high wind. The wind exerts a steady horizontal 10-lb force on the stone as it falls. Is the path of the stone a straight line, a parabola, or some more complicated path? Explain.

6–26. A ball is thrown, as shown in Fig. 6–17, with an initial velocity v_0 at an angle of 37° above the horizontal, from a point 192 ft from the edge of a vertical cliff 160 ft high. The ball just misses the edge of the cliff. (a) Find the initial velocity v_0. (b) Find the distance x beyond the foot of the cliff where the ball strikes the ground.

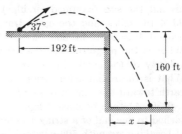

FIGURE 6–17

6–27. A man is riding on a flatcar traveling with a constant velocity of 30 ft/sec (Fig. 6–18). He wishes to throw a ball through a stationary hoop

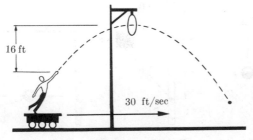

FIGURE 6–18

16 ft above the height of his hands in such a manner that the ball will move horizontally as it passes through the hoop. He throws the ball with a velocity of 40 ft/sec with respect to himself. (a) What must be the vertical component of the initial velocity of the ball? (b) How many seconds after he releases the ball will it pass through the hoop? (c) At what horizontal distance in front of the hoop must he release the ball?

6–28. At time $t = 0$ a body is moving east at 10 cm/sec. At time $t = 2$ sec it is moving 25° north of east at 14 cm/sec. Find graphically the magnitude and direction of its change in velocity and the magnitude and direction of its average acceleration.

6–29. The radius of the earth's orbit around the sun (assumed circular) is 93×10^6 miles, and the earth travels around this orbit in 365 days. (a) What is the magnitude of the orbital velocity of the earth, in mi/hr? (b) What is the radial acceleration of the earth toward the sun, in ft/sec^2?

6–30. A stone of mass 1 kgm is attached to one end of a string 1 m long, of breaking strength 500 newtons, and is whirled in a horizontal circle on a frictionless tabletop. The other end of the string is kept fixed. Find the maximum velocity the stone can attain without breaking the string.

6–31. A phonograph turntable rotates at a constant rate of 78 rev/min. It is found that a small object placed on a record will remain at rest relative to the record if its distance from the center is less than 3 in., but will slip if the distance is any greater. What is the coefficient of static friction between the object and the record?

6–32. (a) At how many revolutions per second must the apparatus of Fig. 6–19 rotate about a vertical axis in order that the cord shall make an angle of 45° with the vertical? (b) What is then the tension in the cord? (Given: $L = 20$ cm, $a = 10$ cm, $m = 200$ gm.)

6–33. The 8-lb block in Fig. 6–20 is attached to a vertical rod by means of two strings. When the system rotates about the axis of the rod the strings are extended as shown in the diagram. (a) How many revolutions per minute must the system make in order that the tension in the upper cord shall be 15 lb? (b) What is then the tension in the lower cord?

6–34. A curve of 600 ft radius on a level road is banked at the correct angle

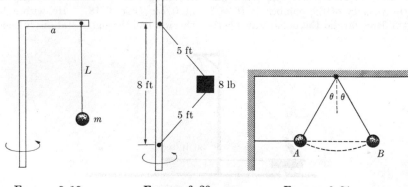

FIGURE 6–19   FIGURE 6–20   FIGURE 6–21

for a velocity of 30 mi/hr. If an automobile rounds this curve at 60 mi/hr, what is the minimum coefficient of friction between tires and road so that the automobile will not skid? Assume all forces to act at the center of gravity.

6–35. A 2400-lb automobile rounds a level curve of radius 400 ft, on an unbanked road, with a velocity of 40 mi/hr. (a) What is the minimum coefficient of friction between tires and road in order that the automobile shall not skid? (b) At what angle should the roadbed be banked for this velocity?

6–36. An aircraft in level flight is said to make a standard turn when it makes a complete circular turn in two minutes. (a) What is the banking angle in a standard turn if the velocity of the plane is 400 ft/sec? (b) What is the radius of the circle in which it turns?

6–37. The radius of the circular track in Fig. 6–13 is 40 cm and the mass of the ball is 100 gm. (a) Find the critical velocity at the highest point of the track. (b) If the actual velocity at this point is twice the critical velocity, find the force exerted by the ball against the track.

6–38. The pilot of a dive bomber who has been diving at a velocity of 400 mi/hr pulls out of the dive by changing his course to a circle in a vertical plane. (a) What is the minimum radius of the circle in order that the acceleration at the lowest point shall not exceed "$7g$"? (b) How much does a 180-lb pilot apparently weigh at the lowest point of the pull-out?

6–39. A bicycle and rider, weighing together 160 lb, loop-the-loop in a circular track of radius 8 ft. The velocity at the lowest point is $32\sqrt{2}$ ft/sec. (a) Find the radial acceleration at the highest point. Assume that the bicycle "coasts" without friction. (b) Show in a diagram all the forces acting on the bicycle and rider at the highest point, and compute the force with which the track pushes against the bicycle. (c) With what force does the bicycle press against the track? (d) What is the minimum velocity the bicycle can have at the highest point without leaving the track?

6–40. A cord is tied to a pail of water and the pail is swung in a vertical circle of radius 4 ft. What must be the minimum velocity of the pail at the highest point of the circle if no water is to spill from the pail?

6–41. A ball is held at rest in position A in Fig. 6–21 by two light cords. The horizontal cord is cut, and the ball swings to position B. What is the ratio of the tension in the cord, in position B, to that in position A?

6–42. What would be the length of a day if the rate of rotation of the earth were such that $g = 0$ at the equator?

6–43. Suppose one wishes to establish a space platform or satellite moving in a circle in the earth's equatorial plane and at such a height above the earth's surface that it remains always above the same point. Find the height of the space platform.

6–44. The weight of a man as determined by a spring balance at the equator is 180 lb. By how many ounces does this differ from the true force of gravitational attraction at the same point?

6–45. It is desired to launch a satellite 400 miles above the earth in a circular orbit. If suitable rockets are used to reach this elevation, what horizontal orbital velocity must be imparted to the satellite? The radius of the earth is 3950 miles.

CHAPTER 7

WORK AND ENERGY

7–1 Work. In everyday life, the word *work* is applied to any form of activity that requires the exertion of muscular or mental effort. In physics, however, the term is used in a very restricted sense. Figure 7–1 represents a body moving in a horizontal direction which we shall take as the x-axis.

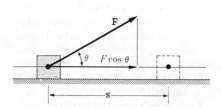

FIG. 7–1. The work done by the force **F** in a displacement **s** is $(F \cos \theta) \cdot s$.

A constant force **F**, at an angle θ with the direction of motion, is exerted on the body by some outside agent. The work W of this force (or the work done by the force) when its point of application undergoes a displacement **s**, is defined as the product of the magnitudes of the displacement and of the component of the force in the direction of the displacement.

The magnitude of the component of **F** in the direction of **s** is $F \cos \theta$. Then

$$W = F \cos \theta \cdot s. \qquad (7\text{–}1)$$

Work is a *scalar* quantity, equal to the product of the *magnitudes* of $F \cos \theta$ and **s**.

Work is done only when a force is exerted on a body while the body at the same time moves in such a way that the force has a component along the line of motion of its point of application. If the component of the force is in the *same direction* as the displacement, the work W is *positive*. If it is *opposite* to the displacement, the work is *negative*. If the force is at *right angles* to the displacement, it has no component in the direction of the displacement and the work is *zero*.

Thus when a body is lifted, the work of the lifting force is positive; when a spring is stretched, the work of the stretching force is positive; when a gas is compressed in a cylinder, again the work of the compressing force is positive. On the other hand, the work of the gravitational force on a body being lifted is negative, since the (downward) gravitational force is opposite to the (upward) displacement. When a body slides on a fixed surface, the work of the frictional force exerted *on the body* is negative since this force is always opposite to the displacement of the body. No work is done by the frictional force acting *on the fixed surface* because there is no motion of this surface. Also, although it would be considered "hard work" to hold a heavy object stationary at arm's length, no work would be done in the technical sense because there is no motion. Even if one were to walk along a level floor while carrying the object, no work would be done since the (vertical) supporting force has no component in the direction of the (horizontal) motion. Similarly, the work of the normal force exerted on a body by a surface on which it moves is zero, as is the work of the centripetal force on a body moving in a circle.

In the engineering system, the unit of force is the pound and the unit of distance is the foot. The unit of work in this system is therefore *one foot-pound* (ft·lb). (The order of terms is interchanged to distinguish this unit from the unit of torque, the pound-foot.) *One foot-pound* may be defined as *the work done when a constant force of one pound is exerted on a body which moves a distance of one foot in the same direction as the force.*

In the mks system, where forces are expressed in newtons and distances in meters, the unit of work is the *newton-meter* (n·m). The reader can supply the definition of a newton-meter from the definition above of a foot-pound. In the cgs system the unit of work is the *dyne-centimeter* (dyne·cm). One dyne-centimeter is called *one erg;* one newton-meter is called *one joule.* There is no corresponding single term for one foot-pound.

Since 1 meter = 100 cm and 1 newton = 10^5 dynes, it follows that 1 newton-meter = 10^7 dynes-centimeters, or

$$1 \text{ joule} = 10^7 \text{ ergs.}$$

Also, from the relations between the newton and pound, and the meter and foot,

$$1 \text{ joule} = 0.7376 \text{ foot-pound,}$$

$$1 \text{ foot-pound} = 1.356 \text{ joules.}$$

Figure 7–2 shows *all* the forces on the body of Fig. 7–1. (The inclined force is now represented by **P**.) The earth exerts a downward force **w** = m**g**; the surface exerts an upward force **N** and a friction force **f**. What is the work of each force when the box moves a distance s along the surface toward the right?

The component of **P** in the direction of motion is $P \cos \theta$. The work of the force **P** is therefore

$$W_P = (P \cos \theta) \cdot s.$$

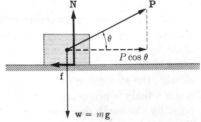

FIG. 7–2. An object on a rough horizontal surface moving to the right under the action of a force **P** inclined at an angle θ.

The forces **w** and **N** are both at right angles to the displacement. Hence

$$W_w = 0, \qquad W_N = 0.$$

The friction force **f** is opposite to the displacement, so the work of the friction force is

$$W_f = -fs.$$

Since work is a scalar quantity, the total work W of all forces on the body is the algebraic (not the vector) sum of the individual works.

$$W = W_P + W_w + W_N + W_f$$
$$= (P \cos \theta) \cdot s + 0 + 0 - f \cdot s$$
$$= (P \cos \theta - f)s.$$

But $(P \cos \theta - f)$ is the *resultant* force on the body. Hence *the total work of all forces is equal to the work of the resultant force.*

Suppose that $w = 100$ lb, $P = 50$ lb, $f = 15$ lb, $\theta = 37°$, and $s = 20$ ft. Then

$$W_P = (P \cos \theta) \cdot s = 50 \times 0.8 \times 20 = 800 \text{ ft·lb,}$$

$$W_f = -fs = -15 \times 20 = -300 \text{ ft·lb,}$$

$$W = W_P + W_w + W_N + W_f$$
$$= 800 \text{ ft·lb} + 0 + 0 - 300 \text{ ft·lb}$$
$$= 500 \text{ ft·lb.}$$

As a check, the total work may be expressed as

$$W = (P \cos \theta - f) \cdot s$$
$$= (40 \text{ lb} - 15 \text{ lb}) \times 20 \text{ ft}$$
$$= 500 \text{ ft·lb.}$$

7–2 Work done by a varying force. In the preceding section we defined the work of a *constant* force. In many important cases, however, work is done by a force which varies in magnitude or direction during the displacement of the body on which it acts. Thus when a spring is stretched slowly, the stretching force increases steadily as the spring elongates, and when a body is projected vertically upward, the gravitational force exerted on it by the earth decreases inversely with the square of its distance from the earth's center.

The work of a varying force can always be found graphically as follows. In Fig. 7–3(a), the curved line is a graph of the component $F \cos \theta$, for a force which varies in some arbitrary way (in magnitude and direction)

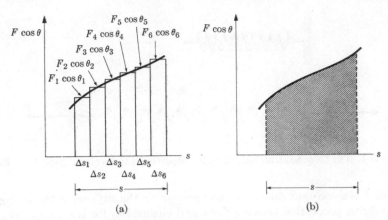

FIG. 7-3. The work of a variable force equals the shaded area in part (b).

with the distance s. Let the distance be subdivided into short segments Δs_1, Δs_2, etc., and approximate the varying force component by one that remains constant at the value $F_1 \cos \theta_1$ over the distance Δs_1, then increases to the constant value $F_2 \cos \theta_2$ over the distance Δs_2, etc., as indicated by the zigzag line. The work that would be done by the constant force $F_1 \cos \theta_1$ in the displacement Δs_1 would be $F_1 \cos \theta_1 \cdot \Delta s_1$; the work done in the displacement Δs_2 would be $F_2 \cos \theta_2 \cdot \Delta s_2$, etc. The work total W would be

$$W = F_1 \cos \theta_1 \cdot \Delta s_1 + F_2 \cos \theta_2 \cdot \Delta s_2 + \cdots.$$

But the products $F_1 \cos \theta_1 \cdot \Delta s_1$, $F_2 \cos \theta_2 \cdot \Delta s_2$, etc., are the *areas* of the various vertical strips, and the total work is evidently equal to the total area of these strips. As the subdivisions are made smaller and smaller, the total area of these strips becomes more and more nearly equal to the shaded area between the smooth curve ánd the horizontal axis, bounded by vertical lines at the ends of the displacement s as in Fig. 7-3(b).

Hence if a graph is constructed of the component $F \cos \theta$ of any variable force, the work of the force can be determined by computing (or measuring) the area between the curve and the displacement axis.

As an illustration of this method, let us compute the work done when a spring is stretched. To keep a spring stretched at an elongation x above its no-load length, a force $\mathbf{F}$ must be exerted at one end and a force equal in magnitude but opposite in direction at the other end, as shown in Fig. 7-4. If the elongation is not too great,

$$F = kx, \tag{7-2}$$

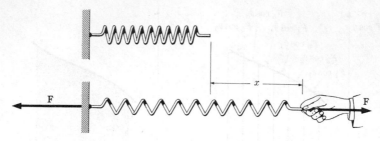

FIG. 7-4. The force to stretch a spring is proportional to its elongation; $F = kx$.

where k is a constant called the *force constant* or the *stiffness* of the spring. This direct proportion between force and elongation, for elongations that are not too great, was discovered by Robert Hooke in 1678 and is known as *Hooke's law*. It will be discussed more fully in a later chapter.

Suppose that forces equal in magnitude and opposite in direction are exerted on the ends of a spring, and that the forces are gradually increased from zero. Let one end of the spring be kept fixed. The work of the force at the fixed end will be zero, but work will be done by the varying force **F** at the moving end. This force is in the same direction as the displacement. In Fig. 7-5, the force F is plotted vertically and the displacement x of the moving end (or the elongation of the spring) is plotted horizontally. The work of the force F when the elongation increases from zero to x is equal to the shaded triangular area. The area of a triangle equals one-half the product of base and altitude. The base of the triangle is x, its altitude is kx, and its area is

$$\text{Area} = \tfrac{1}{2} \cdot x \cdot kx = \tfrac{1}{2}kx^2. \tag{7-3}$$

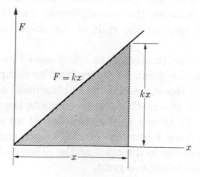

FIG. 7-5. The work done in stretching a spring is equal to the area of the shaded triangle.

The work is therefore equal to one-half the product of the force constant k and the *square* of the elongation x. When the elongation is doubled, the work increases by a factor of 4.

The reader should convince himself that the work done in changing the elongation of a spring from x_1 to x_2 is

$$W = \tfrac{1}{2}kx_2^2 - \tfrac{1}{2}kx_1^2.$$

7–3 Work and kinetic energy. Consider again the body illustrated in Fig. 7–2. The resultant force F on the body is $P\cos\theta - f$, and from Newton's second law,

$$F = ma.$$

Suppose the speed of the body increases from v_1 to v_2 while the body undergoes a displacement s. Then

$$v_2^2 = v_1^2 + 2as,$$

$$a = \frac{v_2^2 - v_1^2}{2s}.$$

Hence

$$F = m\,\frac{v_2^2 - v_1^2}{2s},$$

and

$$Fs = \tfrac{1}{2}mv_2^2 - \tfrac{1}{2}mv_1^2. \tag{7–4}$$

The product Fs is the work W of the resultant force F. The quantity $\tfrac{1}{2}mv^2$, one-half the product of the mass of the body and the square of its speed, is called its *kinetic energy*, E_k.

$$\boxed{E_k = \tfrac{1}{2}mv^2.} \tag{7–5}$$

The first term on the right side of Eq. (7–4) is the final kinetic energy of the body, E_{k2}, and the second term is the initial kinetic energy, E_{k1}. The difference between these terms is the *change* in kinetic energy, and we have the important result that *the work of the resultant external force on a body is equal to the change in kinetic energy of the body.* As we have shown, the work of the resultant force is equal to the algebraic sum of the works of the individual forces.

$$\boxed{W = E_{k2} - E_{k1} = \Delta E_k.} \tag{7–6}$$

Kinetic energy, like work, is a scalar quantity. The kinetic energy of a moving body depends only on its speed, or the *magnitude* of its velocity, and not on the direction in which it is moving. The *change* in kinetic energy depends only on the work $W = Fs$ and not on the individual values of F and s. That is, the force F could have been large and the displacement s small, or the reverse might have been true. If the mass m and the speeds v_1 and v_2 are known, the *work* of the resultant force can be found without any knowledge of the force F and the displacement s.

If the work W is *positive*, the final kinetic energy is greater than the initial kinetic energy and the kinetic energy *increases*. If the work is *negative*, the kinetic energy *decreases*. In the special case in which the work is *zero*, the kinetic energy remains *constant*.

Although Eq. (7–4) was derived for the special case of a *constant* resultant force, it is true even when the force varies in any arbitrary way. The work of *any* resultant force on a rigid body equals the change in kinetic energy of the body.

In computing the kinetic energy of a body, consistent units must be used for m and v. In the cgs system, m must be expressed in grams and v in cm/sec. In the mks system, m must be in kilograms and v in m/sec. In the engineering system, m must be in slugs and v in ft/sec. The corresponding units of kinetic energy are $1 \text{ gm·cm}^2/\text{sec}^2$, $1 \text{ kgm·m}^2/\text{sec}^2$, and $1 \text{ slug·ft}^2/\text{sec}^2$. However, the unit of kinetic energy in any system is equal to the unit of work in that system, and kinetic energy is customarily expressed in ergs, joules, or foot·pounds. That is,

$$1 \text{ gm} \frac{\text{cm}^2}{\text{sec}^2} = 1 \frac{\text{dyne}}{\text{cm/sec}^2} \frac{\text{cm}^2}{\text{sec}^2} = 1 \text{ dyne·cm} = 1 \text{ erg.}$$

In the same way,

$$1 \text{ kgm} \frac{\text{m}^2}{\text{sec}^2} = 1 \text{ joule,} \qquad 1 \text{ slug} \frac{\text{ft}^2}{\text{sec}^2} = 1 \text{ ft·lb.}$$

EXAMPLE. Refer again to the body in Fig. 7–2 and the numerical values given at the end of Section 7–1. The total work of the external forces was shown to be 500 ft·lb. Hence the kinetic energy of the body increases by 500 ft·lb. To verify this, suppose the initial speed v_1 is 4 ft/sec. The initial kinetic energy is

$$E_{k1} = \frac{1}{2} m v_1^2 = \frac{1}{2} \frac{100}{32} \text{ slugs} \times 16 \frac{\text{ft}^2}{\text{sec}^2} = 25 \text{ ft·lb.}$$

To find the final kinetic energy we must first find the acceleration.

$$a = \frac{F}{m} = \frac{40 \text{ lb} - 15 \text{ lb}}{(100/32) \text{ slugs}} = 8 \frac{\text{ft}}{\text{sec}^2} .$$

Then

$$v_2^2 = v_1^2 + 2as = 16\,\frac{\text{ft}^2}{\text{sec}^2} + 2 \times 8\,\frac{\text{ft}}{\text{sec}^2} \times 20\text{ ft} = 336\,\frac{\text{ft}^2}{\text{sec}^2}.$$

and

$$E_{k2} = \frac{1}{2}\,\frac{100}{32}\text{ slugs} \times 336\,\frac{\text{ft}^2}{\text{sec}^2} = 525\text{ ft·lb}.$$

The increase in kinetic energy is therefore 500 ft·lb.

7–4 Gravitational potential energy. Suppose a body of mass m (and of weight $\mathbf{w} = m\mathbf{g}$) moves vertically as in Fig. 7–6 from a point where its center of gravity is at a height y_1 above an arbitrarily chosen plane (the *reference level*) to a point at a height y_2. The downward gravitational force on the body is its weight $m\mathbf{g}$. Let $\mathbf{P}$ represent the resultant of all other forces acting on the body, and let W' be the work of these forces. The direction of the gravitational force $m\mathbf{g}$ is opposite to the upward displacement, and the work of this force is

$$W_{\text{grav}} = -mg(y_2 - y_1) = -(mgy_2 - mgy_1).$$

(The reader should convince himself that the work of the gravitational force is given by $-mg(y_2 - y_1)$ whether the body moves up or down.)

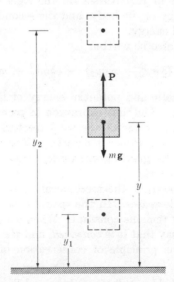

FIG. 7–6. Lifting an object in a gravitational field.

Since the total work equals the change in kinetic energy,

$$W' + W_{\text{grav}} = \Delta E_k,$$

$$W' - (mgy_2 - mgy_1) = (\tfrac{1}{2}mv_2^2 - \tfrac{1}{2}mv_1^2).$$

The quantities $\tfrac{1}{2}mv_2^2$ and $\tfrac{1}{2}mv_1^2$ depend only on the final and initial *speeds;* the quantities mgy_2 and mgy_1 depend only on the final and initial *elevations.* Let us therefore rearrange this equation, transferring the quantities mgy_2 and mgy_1 from the "work" side of the equation to the "energy" side.

$$W' = (\tfrac{1}{2}mv_2^2 - \tfrac{1}{2}mv_1^2) + (mgy_2 - mgy_1). \qquad (7\text{–}7)$$

The left side of Eq. (7–7) contains only the work of the force **P**. The terms on the right depend only on the final and initial states of the body (its speed and elevation) and not specifically on the way in which it moved. The quantity mgy, the product of the weight mg of the body and the height y of its center of gravity above the reference level, is called its *gravitational potential energy, E_p.*

$$E_p \ (\text{gravitational}) = mgy. \qquad (7\text{–}8)$$

The first expression in parentheses on the right of Eq. (7–7) is the change in kinetic energy of the body, and the second is the change in its gravitational potential energy.

Equation (7–7) can also be written

$$W' = (\tfrac{1}{2}mv_2^2 + mgy_2) - (\tfrac{1}{2}mv_1^2 + mgy_1). \qquad (7\text{–}9)$$

The sum of the kinetic and potential energy of the body is called its *total mechanical energy.* The first expression in parentheses on the right of Eq. (7–9) is the final value of the total mechanical energy, and the second is the initial value. Hence, *the work of all forces acting on the body,* **with the exception of the gravitational force,** *equals the change in the total mechanical energy of the body.*

If the work W' is positive, the mechanical energy increases. If W' is negative, the energy decreases. In the special case in which W' is zero, the mechanical energy remains constant. When a quantity remains constant in a process we say that it is *conserved,* and the preceding statement is a special case of the principle of conservation of mechanical energy.

EXAMPLE 1. A man holds a ball of weight $w = \tfrac{1}{4}$ lb at rest in his hand. He then throws the ball vertically upward. In this process, his hand moves up

2 ft and the ball leaves his hand with an upward velocity of 48 ft/sec. Discuss the motion of the ball from the work-energy standpoint.

First consider the throwing process. Take the reference level at the initial position of the ball. Then $E_{k1} = 0$, $E_{p1} = 0$. Take point 2 at the point where the ball leaves the thrower's hand. Then

$$E_{p2} = mgy_2 = \tfrac{1}{4} \text{ lb} \times 2 \text{ ft} = 0.5 \text{ ft·lb},$$

$$E_{k2} = \tfrac{1}{2}mv_2^2 = \tfrac{1}{2} \times (\tfrac{1}{4}/32) \text{ slug} \times (48 \text{ ft/sec})^2 = 9 \text{ ft·lb}.$$

Let P represent the upward force exerted on the ball by the man in the throwing process. The work W' is then the work of this force, and is equal to the sum of the changes in kinetic and potential energy of the ball.

The kinetic energy of the ball increases by 9 ft·lb and its potential energy by 0.5 ft·lb. The work W' of the upward force P is therefore 9.5 ft·lb.

If the force P is constant, the work of this force is given by

$$W' = P(y_2 - y_1),$$

and the force P is then

$$P = \frac{W'}{y_2 - y_1} = \frac{9.5 \text{ ft·lb}}{2 \text{ ft}} = 4.75 \text{ lb}.$$

However, the *work* of the force P is 9.5 ft·lb whether or not the force is constant.

Now consider the flight of the ball after it leaves the thrower's hand. In the absence of air resistance, the only force on the ball is then its weight mg. Hence the total mechanical energy of the ball remains constant. The calculations will be simplified if we take a new reference level at the point where the ball leaves the thrower's hand. Calling this point 1, we have

$$E_{k1} = 9 \text{ ft·lb}, \qquad E_{p1} = 0,$$

$$E_k + E_p = 9 \text{ ft·lb},$$

and the total mechanical energy at any point of the path equals 9 ft·lb.

Suppose we wish to find the speed of the ball at a height of 20 ft above the reference level. Its potential energy at this elevation is 5 ft·lb. ·(Why?) Its kinetic energy is therefore 4 ft·lb. To find its speed, we have

$$\tfrac{1}{2}mv^2 = E_k, \qquad v = \pm\sqrt{2E_k/m} = \pm\, 32 \, \frac{\text{ft}}{\text{sec}}.$$

The significance of the $\pm$ sign is that the ball passes this point *twice*, once on the way up and again on the way down. Its *potential* energy at this point is the same whether it is moving up or down. Hence its kinetic energy is the same and its *speed* is the same. The algebraic sign of the speed is $+$ when the ball is moving up and $-$ when it is moving down.

Next, let us find the height of the highest point reached. At this point, $v = 0$ and $E_k = 0$. Therefore $E_p = 9$ ft·lb, and the ball rises to a height of 36 ft above the point where it leaves the thrower's hand.

Finally, suppose we were asked to find the speed at a point 40 ft above the reference level. The potential energy at this point would be 10 ft·lb. But the total energy is only 9 ft·lb, so the ball never reaches a height of 40 ft.

Now suppose that a body starts at an elevation y_1 but moves an extremely small distance Δy_1 vertically upward, then is given a very small horizontal displacement, then a small vertical displacement Δy_2, then a small horizontal displacement, and so on until it has been transferred along a zigzag path to any point at a height y_2 above the reference level. The gravitational force $m\mathbf{g}$ does no work in the small horizontal steps since it is at right angles to these steps, and the total work of this force is the sum of the works in the vertical displacements only. Therefore

$$W_{\text{grav}} = -mg(\Delta y_1 + \Delta y_2 + \cdots).$$

But

$$\Delta y_1 + \Delta y_2 + \cdots = y_2 - y_1,$$

so

$$W_{\text{grav}} = -mg(y_2 - y_1).$$

By making the zigzag steps as small as we please, we may cause the body to move from any point at a height y_1 above the reference level to any other point at a height y_2 along a path which is any desired approximation to a smooth curve. Hence the work of the gravitational force will always be $-mg(y_2 - y_1)$ regardless of the nature of the path between the two points. Then if W' represents the work done by all other forces, we have again

$$W' - mg(y_2 - y_1) = \tfrac{1}{2}mv_2^2 - \tfrac{1}{2}mv_1^2,$$

or

$$W' = (\tfrac{1}{2}mv_2^2 - \tfrac{1}{2}mv_1^2) + (mgy_2 - mgy_1).$$

Hence when the body moves along *any path whatever*, the work of all forces except the gravitational force is equal to the sum of the changes in kinetic and potential energy. In the special case in which $W' = 0$, there is no change in this sum, and the total mechanical energy remains constant.

EXAMPLE 2. A body slides down a curved track which is one quadrant of a circle of radius R, as in Fig. 7–7. If it starts from rest and there is no friction, find its speed at the bottom of the track.

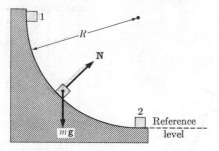

FIG. 7–7. An object sliding down a frictionless curved track.

The equations of motion with constant acceleration cannot be used, since the acceleration decreases during the motion. (The slope angle of the track becomes smaller and smaller as the body descends.) However, if there is no friction, the only force on the body in addition to its weight is the normal force **N** exerted on it by the track. The normal force does no work, so $W' = 0$ and mechanical energy is conserved. Take point 1 at the starting point and point 2 at the bottom of the track. Take the reference level at point 2. Then $y_1 = R$, $y_2 = 0$, and

$$E_{k2} + E_{p2} = E_{k1} + E_{p1},$$

$$\tfrac{1}{2}mv_2^2 + 0 = 0 + mgR,$$

$$v_2 = \pm\sqrt{2gR}.$$

The speed is therefore the same as if the body had fallen *vertically* through a height R. (What is now the significance of the $\pm$ sign?)

As a numerical example, let $R = 1$ m. Then

$$v = \pm\sqrt{2 \times 9.8(\text{m/sec}^2) \times 1\,\text{m}} = \pm 4.43\,\frac{\text{m}}{\text{sec}}.$$

EXAMPLE 3. Suppose a body of mass 0.5 kgm slides down a track of radius $R = 1$ m, like that in Fig. 7–7, but its speed at the bottom is only 3 m/sec. How much work was done by the frictional force acting on the body?

In this case, $W' = W_f$, and

$$W_f = (\tfrac{1}{2}mv_2^2 - \tfrac{1}{2}mv_1^2) + (mgy_2 - mgy_1)$$

$$= \left(\frac{1}{2} \times 0.5\,\text{kgm} \times 9\,\frac{\text{m}^2}{\text{sec}^2} - 0\right) + \left(0 - 0.5\,\text{kgm} \times 9.8\,\frac{\text{m}}{\text{sec}^2} \times 1\,\text{m}\right)$$

$$= 2.25\,\text{j} - 4.9\,\text{j} = -2.65\,\text{j}.$$

The frictional work was therefore -2.65 j, and the total mechanical energy *decreased* by 2.65 joules. The mechanical energy of a body is *not* conserved when friction forces act on it.

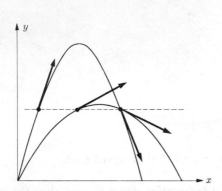

Fig. 7–8. For the same initial velocity, the speed is the same at all points at the same elevation.

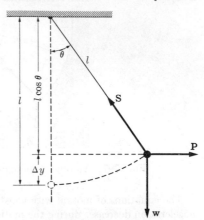

Fig. 7–9. $\Delta y = l(1 - \cos \theta)$.

EXAMPLE 4. In the absence of air resistance, the only force on a projectile is its weight, and the mechanical energy of the projectile remains constant. Figure 7–8 shows two trajectories of a projectile with the same initial velocity (and hence the same total energy) but with different angles of departure. At all points at the same elevation the potential energy is the same; hence the kinetic energy is the same and the speed is the same.

EXAMPLE 5. A small object of weight w hangs from a string of length l, as shown in Fig. 7–9. A *variable* horizontal force **P**, which starts at zero and gradually increases, is used to pull the object very slowly until the string makes an angle θ with the vertical. Calculate the work of the force **P**.

The sum of the works W' of all the forces other than the gravitational force must equal the change of kinetic energy plus the change of gravitational potential energy. Hence

$$W' = W_P + W_S = \Delta E_k + \Delta E_p.$$

Since **S** is perpendicular to the path of its point of application, $W_S = 0$; and since the body was pulled very slowly at all times, the change of kinetic energy is also zero. Hence

$$W_P = \Delta E_p = w \, \Delta y,$$

where Δy is the distance that the object has been raised. From Fig. 7–9, Δy is seen to be $l(1 - \cos \theta)$. Therefore

$$W_P = wl(1 - \cos \theta).$$

7–5 Elastic potential energy. Figure 7–10 shows a body of mass m on a level surface. One end of a spring is attached to the body, the other end being fixed. Take the origin of coordinates at the position of the body

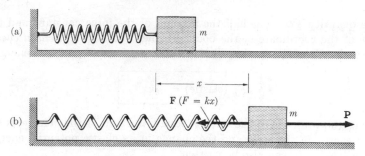

FIG. 7–10. Work done in stretching a spring.

when the spring is unstretched. Then at a position where the coordinate of the body is x, the spring exerts on the body an elastic force $\mathbf{F}$ of magnitude kx (see Section 7–2).

Let $\mathbf{P}$ represent the resultant of all other forces acting on the body, and let W' be the work of these forces when the body moves from a coordinate x_1 to a coordinate x_2. We showed in Section 7–2 that when the elongation of a spring is changed from x_1 to x_2, the work of the stretching force exerted *on* the spring is $\frac{1}{2}k(x_2^2 - x_1^2)$. In the present case, we wish to find the work W_{el} of the *reaction* to this force, that is, the force exerted *by* the spring on the body in Fig. 7–10. This will be given by $-\frac{1}{2}k(x_2^2 - x_1^2)$, since the force exerted *by* the spring is equal in magnitude but opposite in direction to that exerted *on* the spring.

$$W_{el} = -\tfrac{1}{2}k(x_2^2 - x_1^2) = -(\tfrac{1}{2}kx_2^2 - \tfrac{1}{2}kx_1^2).$$

It is easy to show by the same method as in the preceding section that if the body in Fig. 7–10 is moved along *any path whatever* in such a way that the elongation of the spring changes from x_1 to x_2, the work of the elastic force is given by the same expression, $-(\tfrac{1}{2}kx_2^2 - \tfrac{1}{2}kx_1^2)$.

Setting the total work equal to the change in kinetic energy of the body, we have

$$W' + W_{el} = \Delta E_k,$$

$$W' - (\tfrac{1}{2}kx_2^2 - \tfrac{1}{2}kx_1^2) = (\tfrac{1}{2}mv_2^2 - \tfrac{1}{2}mv_1^2).$$

The quantities $\frac{1}{2}kx_2^2$ and $\frac{1}{2}kx_1^2$ depend only on the initial and final positions of the body and not specifically on the way in which it moved. Let us therefore transfer them from the "work" side of the equation to the "energy" side. Then

$$W' = (\tfrac{1}{2}mv_2^2 - \tfrac{1}{2}mv_1^2) + (\tfrac{1}{2}kx_2^2 - \tfrac{1}{2}kx_1^2). \qquad (7\text{–}10)$$

The quantity $\frac{1}{2}kx^2$, one-half the product of the force constant and the square of the coordinate of the body, is called the *elastic potential energy* of the body, E_p. (The symbol E_p is used for any form of potential energy.)

$$E_p \text{ (elastic)} = \tfrac{1}{2}kx^2. \qquad (7\text{--}11)$$

Hence the work W' of the force $\mathbf{P}$ equals the sum of the change in the kinetic energy of the body and the change in its elastic potential energy. Equation (7–10) can also be written

$$W' = (\tfrac{1}{2}mv_2^2 + \tfrac{1}{2}kx_2^2) - (\tfrac{1}{2}mv_1^2 + \tfrac{1}{2}kx_1^2). \qquad (7\text{--}12)$$

The sum of the kinetic and potential energies of the body is its total mechanical energy and *the work of all forces acting on the body,* **with the exception of the elastic force,** *equals the change in the total mechanical energy of the body.*

If the work W' is positive, the mechanical energy increases. If W' is negative, it decreases. In the special case in which W' is zero, the mechanical energy remains constant or is *conserved.*

EXAMPLE 1. Let the force constant k of the spring in Fig. 7–10 be 24 newtons/meter, and let the mass of the body be 4 kgm. The body is initially at rest, and the spring is initially unstretched. Suppose that a constant force $\mathbf{P}$ of 10 newtons is exerted on the body, and that there is no friction. What will be the speed of the body when it has moved 0.50 meters?

The equations of motion with constant acceleration cannot be used, since the resultant force on the body varies as the spring is stretched. However, the speed can be found from energy considerations.

$$W' = \Delta E_k + \Delta E_p,$$

$$10 \text{ n} \times 0.5 \text{ m} = (\tfrac{1}{2} \times 4 \text{ kgm} \times v_2^2 - 0) + \left(\frac{1}{2} \times 24 \, \frac{\text{n}}{\text{m}} \times 0.25 \text{ m}^2 - 0\right),$$

$$v_2 = 1 \, \frac{\text{m}}{\text{sec}}.$$

EXAMPLE 2. Suppose the force $\mathbf{P}$ ceases to act when the body has moved 0.50 m. How much farther will the body move before coming to rest?

The elastic force is now the only force, and mechanical energy is conserved. The kinetic energy is $\frac{1}{2}mv^2 = 2$ joules, and the potential energy is $\frac{1}{2}kx^2 = 3$ joules. The total energy is therefore 5 joules (equal to the work of the force $\mathbf{P}$). When the body comes to rest, its kinetic energy is zero and its potential energy is therefore 5 joules. Hence

$$\tfrac{1}{2}kx_{\text{max}}^2 = 5 \text{ j}, \qquad x_{\text{max}} = 0.707 \text{ m}.$$

7–6 Conservative and dissipative forces. When an object is moved from any position above a zero reference level to any other position, the work of the gravitational force is found to be independent of the path and equal to the difference between the final and the initial values of a function called the gravitational potential energy. If the gravitational force alone acts on the object, the total mechanical energy (the sum of the kinetic and gravitational potential energies) is constant or conserved, and therefore the gravitational force is called a *conservative force*. Thus, if the object is ascending, the work of the gravitational force is accomplished at the expense of the kinetic energy. If, however, the object is descending, the work of the gravitational force serves to increase the kinetic energy, or, in other words, this work is *completely recovered*. Complete recoverability is an important aspect of the work of a conservative force.

When an object attached to a spring is moved from one value of the spring extension to any other value, the work of the elastic force is also independent of the path and equal to the difference between the final and initial values of a function called the elastic potential energy. If the elastic force alone acts on the object, the sum of the kinetic and elastic potential energies is conserved, and therefore the elastic force is also a conservative force. If the object moves so as to increase the extension of the spring, the work of the elastic force is accomplished at the expense of the kinetic energy. If, however, the extension is decreasing, the work of the elastic force serves to increase the kinetic energy so that this work is completely recovered also.

To summarize, the work of a conservative force has the following properties:

(1) It is independent of the path.

(2) It is equal to the difference between the final and initial values of an energy function.

(3) It is completely recoverable.

Contrast a conservative force with a friction force exerted on a moving object by a fixed surface. The work of the friction force *depends* on the path; the longer the path, the greater the work. There is *no* function the difference in two values of which equals the work of the friction force. When we slide an object on a rough fixed surface back to its original position, the friction force reverses, and instead of recovering the work done in the first displacement we must again do work on the return trip. In other words, frictional work is *not* completely recoverable. When the friction force acts alone, the total mechanical energy is *not* conserved. The friction force is therefore called a *nonconservative* or a *dissipative* force. The mechanical energy of a body is conserved only when no dissipative forces act on it.

We find that when friction forces act on a moving body, *heat* is always developed. The more general principle of conservation of energy includes this heat as another form of energy, along with kinetic and potential energy, and when it is included the *total* energy of any system remains constant. We shall study this general conservation principle more fully in a later chapter.

EXAMPLE. Example 3 in Section 7–4 illustrates the motion of a body acted on by a dissipative, friction force. The initial mechanical energy of the body is its initial potential energy of 4.9 j. Its final mechanical energy is its final kinetic energy of 2.25 j. The frictional work W_f is −2.65 j. A quantity of heat equivalent to 2.65 j is developed as the body slides down the track. The sum of this heat and the final mechanical energy equals the initial mechanical energy, and the total energy of the system is conserved.

7–7 Internal work and internal potential energy. Thus far in this chapter we have considered only the work of the *external* forces on a *single* body. The work of these forces is called *external work*, W^e. When two (or more) bodies exert forces on each other and we wish to consider them as a single system, the forces between the bodies become *internal* forces. The work of these forces is called *internal work*, W^i.

Suppose that both external and internal forces act on the bodies of a system. The total work W of all forces, external and internal, is the sum of the works W^e and W^i and is equal to the change in the total kinetic energy of the system.

$$W = W^e + W^i = \Delta E_k.$$

EXAMPLE 1. A man stands at rest on frictionless roller skates on a level surface, facing a brick wall. He sets himself in motion (backward) by pushing against the wall. Discuss the problem from the work-energy standpoint.

The *external* forces on the man are his weight, the upward force exerted by the surface, and the horizontal force exerted by the wall. (The latter is the reaction to the force with which the man pushes against the wall.) No work is done by the first two forces because they are at right angles to the motion. No work is done by the third force because there is no motion of its point of application. The external work is therefore zero and the internal work (of the man's muscular forces) equals the change in his kinetic energy.

If any of the *external* forces on the bodies of a system are conservative (gravitational or elastic), the work of these forces can be transferred to the energy side of the work-energy equation and called the change in *external potential energy*. In many instances, the *internal* forces depend only on the distances between pairs of bodies. The internal work then depends only on the initial and final distances between the bodies, and not on the particular way in which they moved. The work of these internal forces can then also be transferred to the energy side of the work-energy equation and called the change in *internal potential energy of the system.* Internal potential energy is a property of the system as a whole and cannot be assigned to any specific body.

Let W' represent the works of all external and internal forces that have *not* been transferred to the energy side of the work-energy equation and called changes in external and internal potential energy. Let E_p^e and E_p^i represent the external and internal potential energies. The work-energy equation then takes the form

$$W' = \Delta E_k + \Delta E_p^e + \Delta E_p^i, \qquad (7\text{–}13)$$

where the total mechanical energy now includes the kinetic energy of the system and both its external and internal potential energy. If the work W' is zero, the total mechanical energy is conserved.

EXAMPLE 2. Consider a system consisting of two bodies in "outer space," very far from all other matter. No external forces act on the system, no external work is done when the bodies move, and the system has no external potential energy. A gravitational force of attraction acts between the bodies, which depends only on the distance between them. We can therefore say that the system has an internal potential energy. Suppose the bodies start from rest and accelerate toward each other. The total kinetic energy of the system increases and its internal potential energy decreases. The sum of its kinetic energy and internal potential energy remains constant.

Energy considerations *alone* do not suffice to tell us how much kinetic energy is gained by each body separately. This can be determined, however, from *momentum* considerations, as will be explained in the next chapter.

EXAMPLE 3. In Section 7–5 we computed the elastic potential energy of a body acted on by a force exerted by a spring. This force was an *external* force acting on the body, and the elastic potential energy $\frac{1}{2}kx^2$ should properly be called the *external* elastic potential energy *of the body.*

Let us now consider the spring itself. The spring is a *system,* composed of an enormous number of molecules which exert internal forces on one another. When the spring is stretched, the distances between its molecules change. The intermolecular forces depend only on the distances between pairs of molecules, so that a stretched spring has an internal elastic potential energy. To calculate this, suppose the spring is slowly stretched from its no-load length by equal and opposite forces applied at its ends, as described in Section 7–2. The work of these forces was shown to equal $\frac{1}{2}kx^2$, where x is the elongation of the spring above its no-load length. Let us retain this work on the left side of the work-energy equation so that it becomes the work W' in Eq. (7–13). There is no change in the kinetic energy of the spring and no change in its external potential energy. If we call the internal potential energy zero when $x = 0$, the *change* in internal potential energy in the stretching process equals the final potential energy E_p^i. Then

$$W' = \Delta E_p^i = E_p^i,$$

$$E_p^i = \tfrac{1}{2}kx^2.$$

Hence the *internal elastic potential energy of a stretched spring* is equal to $\tfrac{1}{2}kx^2$. Note that the internal potential energy can be calculated without any detailed information regarding the intermolecular forces.

EXAMPLE 4. A block of mass m, initially at rest, is dropped from a height h onto a spring whose force constant is k. Find the maximum distance y that the spring will be compressed. See Fig. 7–11.

This is a process for which the principle of the conservation of mechanical energy holds. At the moment of release, the kinetic energy is zero. At the moment when maximum compression occurs, there is also no kinetic energy. Hence, the loss of gravitational potential energy of the block equals the gain of elastic potential energy of the spring. As shown in Fig. 7–11, the total fall of the block is $h + y$, whence

$$mg(h + y) = \tfrac{1}{2}ky^2,$$

or

$$y^2 - \frac{2mg}{k}y - \frac{2mgh}{k} = 0.$$

Therefore

$$y = \frac{1}{2}\left[\frac{2mg}{k} \pm \sqrt{(2mg/k)^2 + (8mgh/k)}\right].$$

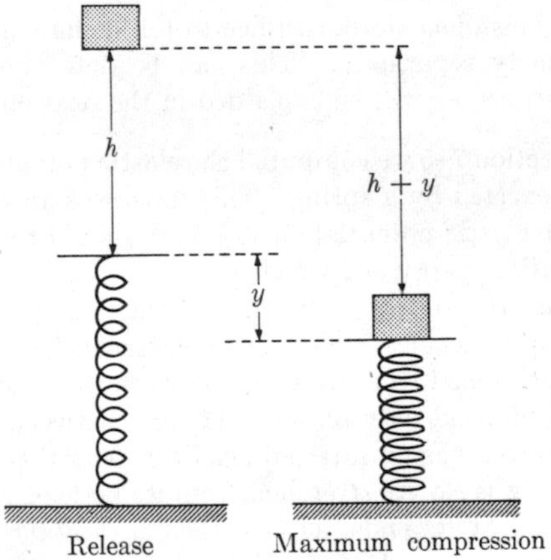

FIG. 7–11. The total fall of the block is $h + y$.

7–8 Power. The time element is not involved in the definition of work. The same amount of work is done in raising a given weight through a given height whether the work is done in one second, or one hour, or one year. In many instances, however, it is necessary to consider the *rate* at which work is done as well as the total amount of work accomplished. The rate at which work is done by a working agent is called the *power* developed by that agent.

If a quantity of work W is done in a time interval t, the average power $\overline{P}$ is defined as

$$\text{Average power} = \frac{\text{work done}}{\text{time interval}}, \qquad \overline{P} = \frac{W}{t}.$$

If the rate of doing work is not uniform, the power at any instant is the ratio of the work done to the time interval, when both are extremely small.

$$\boxed{\text{Instantaneous power } P = \frac{\Delta W}{\Delta t}.} \qquad (7\text{–}14)$$

In the engineering system, where work is expressed in foot·pounds and time in seconds, the unit of power is 1 foot·pound per second. Since this unit is inconveniently small, a larger unit called the *horsepower* (hp) is in common use. 1 hp = 550 ft·lb/sec = 33,000 ft·lb/min. That is, a 1-hp motor running at full load is doing 33,000 ft·lb of work every minute it runs.

The mks unit of power is 1 joule per second, which is called one *watt*. This is also an inconveniently small unit, and power is more commonly expressed in *kilowatts* (1 kw = 1000 watts = 1000 joules/sec) or *megawatts* (1 megawatt = 1000 kw = 1,000,000 watts).

The cgs power unit is 1 erg per second. No single term is assigned to this unit.

A common misconception is that there is something inherently *electrical* about a watt or a kilowatt. This is not the case. It is true that electrical power is usually expressed in watts or kilowatts, but the power consumption of an incandescent lamp could equally well be expressed in horsepower, or an automobile engine rated in kilowatts.

From the relations between the newton, pound, meter, and foot, it is easy to show that 1 hp = 746 watts = 0.746 kw, or about $\frac{3}{4}$ of a kilowatt. This is a useful figure to remember.

Having defined two units of power, the horsepower and the kilowatt, we may use these in turn to define two new units of work, the *horsepower·hour* and the *kilowatt·hour* (kwh).

One horsepower·hour is the work done in one hour by an agent working at the constant rate of one horsepower.

Since such an agent does 33,000 ft·lb of work each minute, the work done in one hour is $60 \times 33{,}000 = 1{,}980{,}000$ ft·lb.

$$1 \text{ horsepower·hour} = 1.98 \times 10^6 \text{ foot·pounds.}$$

One kilowatt·hour is the work done in one hour by an agent working at the constant rate of one kilowatt.

Since such an agent does 1000 joules of work each second, the work done in one hour is $3600 \times 1000 = 3{,}600{,}000$ joules.

$$1 \text{ kilowatt·hour} = 3.6 \times 10^6 \text{ joules.}$$

Note carefully that the horsepower·hour and the kilowatt·hour are units of *work*, not power.

One aspect of work or energy which may be pointed out here is that although it is an abstract physical quantity, it nevertheless has a monetary value. A pound of force or a foot per second of velocity are not things which are bought and sold as such, but a foot·pound or a kilowatt·hour of energy are quantities offered for sale at a definite market rate. In the form of electrical energy, a kilowatt·hour can be purchased at a price varying from a few tenths of a cent to a few cents, depending on the locality and the quantity purchased. In the form of heat, 778 ft·lb (one Btu) costs about a thousandth of a cent.

7–9 Power and velocity. Suppose a constant force **F** is exerted on a body while the body undergoes a displacement **x** in the direction of the force. The work done is
$$W = Fx,$$
and the average power developed is
$$\overline{P} = \frac{W}{t} = F\,\frac{x}{t}. \tag{7–15}$$

But x/t is the average velocity, $\bar{v}$. Hence
$$\overline{P} = F\bar{v}.$$

If the time interval is made extremely short, Eq. (7–15) reduces to
$$P = F\,\frac{\Delta x}{\Delta t}$$

or

$$P = Fv, \qquad (7\text{--}16)$$

where P and v are instantaneous values.

EXAMPLE. A locomotive traveling at 50 ft/sec exerts a draw-bar pull of 20,000 lb. What horsepower does it develop?

$$P = Fv = 20,000 \times 50 = 1,000,000 \, \frac{\text{ft·lb}}{\text{sec}} = \frac{1,000,000}{550} = 1820 \text{ hp.}$$

7-10 Simple machines. A machine is a force-multiplying device. Its purpose is not to convert one form of energy into another, but merely to exert a force on an object which is different from (usually larger than) the force which is applied on the machine from the outside. Simple machines

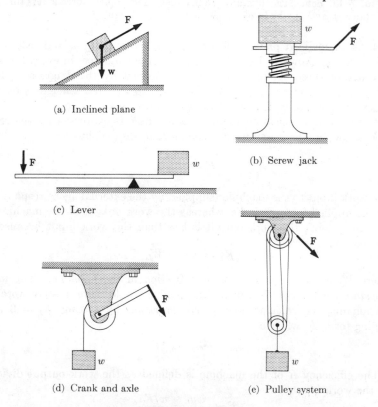

(a) Inclined plane

(b) Screw jack

(c) Lever

(d) Crank and axle

(e) Pulley system

FIG. 7-12. Simple machines.

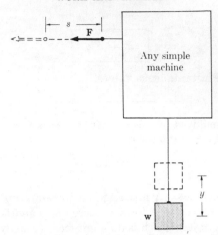

$$F$$

FIG. 7–13. Schematic diagram of a machine. The applied force **F** acts through a distance s, and the body of weight **w** is lifted a height y.

such as an inclined plane, a screw jack, a lever, a crank and axle, or a pully system, shown in Fig. 7–12, play an important role in everyday life. Any one of these machines may be symbolized by the diagram of Fig. 7–13, where a body of weight **w** is imagined to be lifted a height y by the application of a force **F** acting through a distance s.

The force multiplication factor of a machine is expressed by the ratio w/F, known as the *actual mechanical advantage* R_A. Thus

$$R_A = \frac{w}{F}.$$

The work input to the machine (supplied by the external agent responsible for the applied force F) is Fs, whereas the work output of the machine is wy. In general, the work output is less than the work input because of friction. Hence

$$Fs = wy + W_f,$$

where W_f is the work done against friction in the machine. The *ideal mechanical advantage* R_I which the machine would have if there were no friction may be calculated from this equation by setting $W_f = 0$ and solving for w/F, whence

$$R_I = \frac{s}{y}.$$

The efficiency E of the machine is defined as the work output divided by the work input, or

$$E = \frac{wy}{Fs} = \frac{w/F}{s/y},$$

or

$$E = \frac{R_A}{R_I}.$$ (7–17)

The ideal mechanical advantage of a machine, i.e., the ratio of s to y, may usually be calculated from simple geometrical considerations. If, therefore, w and F are measured, the efficiency of the machine may be computed from Eq. (7–17).

7–11 Mass and energy. While the mass of a body can ordinarily be considered constant, there is ample experimental evidence that it is actually a function of the velocity of the body, increasing with increasing velocity according to the relation

$$m = \frac{m_0}{\sqrt{1 - v^2/c^2}},$$

where m_0 is the "rest mass" of the body, c is the velocity of light, and v the velocity of the body.

This equation was predicted by Lorentz and Einstein on theoretical grounds based on relativity considerations, and it has been directly verified by experiments on rapidly moving electrons and ions. The increase in mass is not appreciable until the velocity approaches that of light, and therefore it ordinarily escapes detection.

When one calculates the work done in setting a body in motion and takes into account the variation of mass with velocity, the expression for the work, which is equal to the kinetic energy E_k, is

$$E_k = mc^2 - m_0c^2 = (m - m_0)c^2.$$ (7–18)

That is, the kinetic energy equals the increase in mass over the rest mass, multiplied by the square of the velocity of light. This is the famous Einstein relation between mass and energy. The kinetic energy is in ergs if m is in grams and c is in cm/sec.

When the velocity is small compared with the velocity of light, the expression above reduces to the familiar form $\frac{1}{2}mv^2$. Let us write it

$$E_k = m_0c^2(1 - \beta^2)^{-1/2} - m_0c^2,$$

where, for brevity, we define a new variable β by the relation

$$\beta = \frac{v}{c}.$$

Now expand $(1 - \beta^2)^{-1/2}$ by the binomial theorem.

$$(1 - \beta^2)^{-1/2} = 1 + \tfrac{1}{2}\beta^2 + \text{terms in } \beta^4, \beta^6, \text{ etc.}$$

Since by hypothesis β is a small quantity, higher powers than the second can be neglected. Then

$$E_k = m_0 c^2(1 + \tfrac{1}{2}\beta^2) - m_0 c^2 = m_0 c^2 \times \tfrac{1}{2}\beta^2 = \tfrac{1}{2}m_0 v^2,$$

and at small velocities the kinetic energy equals one-half the product of the rest mass and the square of the velocity.

We shall illustrate the general form of the kinetic energy equation by an example taken from the field of nuclear physics. When the nucleus of a lithium atom is struck by a rapidly moving proton (the nucleus of a hydrogen atom), a momentary union of the two nuclei takes place, after which the compound nucleus breaks up into two alpha particles. (Alpha particles are the nuclei of helium atoms.) The alpha particles recoil in almost opposite directions and move initially with very high velocities. Their combined kinetic energy is much greater than the kinetic energy of the original proton. The source of this kinetic energy is the so-called "binding energy" of the nuclear particles, which is a form of internal potential energy. That is, the internal potential energy of the assemblage of protons and neutrons that makes up the unstable composite nucleus is larger than the potential energy when the same number of particles are combined in the form of two helium nuclei. A crude analogy is that of two masses forced apart by a compressed spring, but tied together by a cord. If the cord is cut, the internal potential energy of the spring is transformed into kinetic energy of the recoiling masses.

The rest mass of a proton is 1.6715×10^{-24} gm. The rest mass of a lithium nucleus is 11.6399×10^{-24} gm, and that of an alpha particle is 6.6404×10^{-24} gm. Although the proton is moving when it collides with the lithium nucleus, its velocity is not great and we may assume its mass equal to its rest mass. Hence the mass of the original system is

$$(1.6715 + 11.6399) \times 10^{-24} \text{ gm} = 13.3114 \times 10^{-24} \text{ gm}.$$

The rest mass of the two alpha particles is

$$2 \times 6.6404 \times 10^{-24} \text{ gm} = 13.2808 \times 10^{-24} \text{ gm}.$$

The alpha particles must therefore be traveling with such velocity that their (combined) masses are increased from 13.2808×10^{-24} gm to 13.3114×10^{-24} gm. Then from Eq. (7–18) their (combined) kinetic energy is

$$E_k = (13.3114 - 13.2808) \times 10^{-24} \, \text{gm} \times \left(3 \times 10^{10} \, \frac{\text{cm}}{\text{sec}}\right)^2$$

$$= 2.75 \times 10^{-5} \, \text{erg}.$$

Let us compare this with the energy released in a typical chemical reaction. When 2 moles of hydrogen combine with 1 mole of oxygen to form 2 moles of water in the reaction

$$2H_2 + O_2 = 2H_2O,$$

116,000 calories are released. This energy is shared among the H_2O molecules, of which there are $2 \times 6.02 \times 10^{23} = 12 \times 10^{23}$ molecules. (One mole of any substance contains 6.02×10^{23} molecules.) Since 1 calorie $= 4.2$ joules $= 4.2 \times 10^7$ ergs, 1.16×10^5 cal $= 4.87 \times 10^{12}$ ergs, and the energy per molecule is

$$\frac{4.87 \times 10^{12} \, \text{ergs}}{12 \times 10^{23} \, \text{molecules}} = 4 \times 10^{-12} \, \text{erg/molecule}.$$

The energy released in the nuclear reaction is therefore about 10 million times as great as that released in the chemical reaction.

The computation of the energy released in the nuclear reaction is verified by observing the distance the alpha particles travel in air at atmospheric pressure before being brought to rest by collisions with other molecules. This distance is found to be 8.31 cm. (One way of making such measurements is with the help of a cloud chamber, illustrated in Fig. 49–5.) A series of independent experiments is then performed in which the range of alpha particles of known energy is measured. These experiments show that in order to travel 8.31 cm, an alpha particle must have an initial kinetic energy of 1.38×10^{-5} erg. The energy of the two alphas together is therefore

$$2 \times 1.38 \times 10^{-5} \, \text{erg} = 2.76 \times 10^{-5} \, \text{erg}.$$

This is in excellent agreement with the energy computed from the excess mass.

PROBLEMS

7–1. The locomotive of a freight train exerts a constant force of 6 tons on the train while drawing it at 50 mi/hr on a level track. How many foot·pounds of work are done in a distance of 1 mi?

7–2. An 80-lb block is pushed a distance of 20 ft along a level floor at constant speed by a force at an angle of 30° below the horizontal. The coefficient of friction between block and floor is 0.25. How many foot·pounds of work are done?

7–3. A horse is towing a canal boat, the towrope making an angle of 10° with the towpath. If the tension in the rope is 100 lb, how many foot·pounds of work are done while moving 100 ft along the towpath?

7–4. A block is pushed 4 ft along a fixed horizontal surface by a horizontal force of 10 lb. The opposing force of friction is 2 lb. (a) How much work is done by the 10-lb force? (b) What is the work of the friction force?

7–5. (a) Compute the kinetic energy of an 1800-lb automobile traveling at 30 mi/hr. (b) How many times as great is the kinetic energy if the velocity is doubled?

7–6. Compute the kinetic energy, in ergs and in joules, of a 2-gm rifle bullet traveling at 500 m/sec.

7–7. An electron strikes the screen of a cathode-ray tube with a velocity of 10^9 cm/sec. Compute its kinetic energy in ergs. The mass of an electron is 9×10^{-28} gm.

7–8. What is the potential energy of a 1600-lb elevator at the top of the Empire State building, 1248 ft above street level? Assume the potential energy at street level to be zero.

7–9. What is the increase in potential energy of a 1-kgm body when lifted from the floor to a table 1 meter high?

7–10. A meter stick whose mass is 300 gm is pivoted at one end as in Fig. 7–14 and displaced through an angle of 60°. What is the increase in its potential energy?

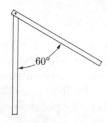

FIGURE 7–14

7–11. The force in pounds required to stretch a certain spring a distance of x ft beyond its unstretched length is given by $F = 10x$. (a) What force will stretch the spring 6 in? 1 ft? 2 ft? (b) How much work is required to stretch the spring 6 in? 1 ft? 2 ft?

7–12. The scale of a certain spring balance reads from zero to 400 lb and is 8 in. long. (a) What is the potential energy of the spring when it is stretched 8 in? 4 in? (b) When a 50-lb weight hangs from the spring?

7–13. A body moves a distance of 10 ft under the action of a force which has the constant value of 5.5 lb for the first 6 ft and then decreases to a value of 2 lb as shown by the graph in Fig. 7–15. (a) How much work is done in the first 6 ft of the motion? (b) How much work is done in the last 4 ft?

7–14. A block weighing 16 lb is pushed 20 ft along a horizontal frictionless surface by a horizontal force of 8 lb. The block starts from rest. (a) How much work is done? What becomes of this work? (b) Check

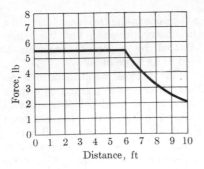

FIGURE 7-15

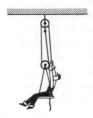

FIGURE 7-16

your answer by computing the acceleration of the block, its final velocity, and its kinetic energy.

7-15. In the preceding problem, suppose the block had an initial velocity of 10 ft/sec, other quantities remaining the same. (a) How much work is done? (b) Check by computing the final velocity and the increase in kinetic energy.

7-16. A 16-lb block is lifted vertically at a constant velocity of 10 ft/sec through a height of 20 ft. (a) How great a force is required? (b) How much work is done? What becomes of this work?

7-17. A 25-lb block is pushed 100 ft up the sloping surface of a plane inclined at an angle of 37° to the horizontal by a constant force F of 32.5 lb acting parallel to the plane. The coefficient of friction between the block and plane is 0.25. (a) What is the work of the force F? (b) Compute the increase in kinetic energy of the block. (c) Compute the increase in potential energy of the block. (d) Compute the work done against friction. What becomes of this work? (e) What can you say about the sum of (b), (c), and (d)?

7-18. A man weighing 150 lb sits on a platform suspended from a movable pulley and raises himself by a rope passing over a fixed pulley (Fig. 7-16). Assuming no friction losses, find (a) the force he must exert, (b) the increase in his energy when he raises himself 2 ft. Answer part (b) by calculating his increase in potential energy, and also by computing the product of the force on the rope and the length of rope passing through his hands.

7-19. A barrel weighing 250 lb is suspended by a rope 30 ft long. (a) What horizontal force is necessary to hold the barrel sideways 5 ft from the vertical? (b) How much work is done in moving it to this position?

7-20. The system in Fig. 7-17 is released from rest with the 24-lb block 8 ft above the floor. Use the principle of conservation of energy to find the

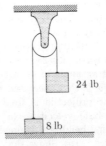

24 lb

8 lb

FIGURE 7-17

velocity with which the block strikes the floor. Neglect friction and inertia of the pulley.

7–21. The spring of a spring gun has a force constant of 3 lb per inch. It is compressed 2 inches and a ball weighing 0.02 lb is placed in the barrel against the compressed spring. (a) Compute the maximum velocity with which the ball leaves the gun when released. (b) Determine the maximum velocity if a resisting force of 2.25 lb acts on the ball.

7–22. A block weighing 2 lb is forced against a horizontal spring of negligible mass, compressing the spring an amount $x_1 = 6$ inches. When released, the block moves on a horizontal table top a distance $x_2 = 2$ ft before coming to rest. The spring constant k is 8 lb/ft (Fig. 7–18). What is the coefficient of friction, μ, between the block and the table?

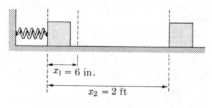

FIGURE 7–18

7–23. A 2-kgm block is dropped from a height of 40 cm onto a spring whose force constant k is 1960 newtons/meter. Find the maximum distance the spring will be compressed.

7–24. A 16-lb projectile is fired from a gun with a muzzle velocity of 800 ft/sec at an angle of departure of 45°. The angle is then increased to 90° and a similar projectile is fired with the same muzzle velocity. (a) Find the maximum heights attained by the projectiles. (b) Show that the total energy at the top of the trajectory is the same in the two cases. (c) Using the energy principle, find the height attained by a similar projectile if fired at an angle of 30°.

7–25. A block weighing 2 lb is released from rest at point A on a track which is one quadrant of a circle of radius 4 ft (Fig. 7–19). It slides down the track and reaches point B with a velocity of 12 ft/sec. From point B it slides on a level surface a distance of 9 ft to point C, where it comes to rest. (a) What was the coefficient of sliding friction on the horizontal surface? (b) How much work was done against friction as the body slid down the circular arc from A to B?

FIGURE 7–19

7–26. A small sphere of mass m is fastened to a weightless string of length 2 ft to form a pendulum. The pendulum is swinging so as to make a maximum angle of 60° with the vertical. (a) What is the velocity of the sphere when it passes through the vertical position? (b) What is the instantaneous acceleration when the pendulum is at its maximum deflection?

7–27. A ball is tied to a cord and set in rotation in a vertical circle. Prove that the tension in the cord at the lowest point exceeds that at the highest point by six times the weight of the ball.

7–28. A small body of mass m slides without friction around the loop-the-loop apparatus shown in Fig. 7–20. It starts from rest at point A at a height $3R$ above the bottom of the loop.

When it reaches point B at the end of a horizontal diameter of the loop, compute (a) its radial acceleration, (b) its tangential acceleration, and (c) its resultant acceleration. Show these accelerations in a diagram, approximately to scale.

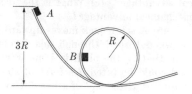

FIGURE 7–20

7–29. A meter stick, pivoted about a horizontal axis through its center, has a body of mass 2 kgm attached to one end and a body of mass 1 kgm attached to the other. The mass of the meter stick can be neglected. The system is released from rest with the stick horizontal. What is the velocity of each body as the stick swings through a vertical position?

7–30. A variable force $\mathbf{P}$ is maintained tangent to a frictionless cylindrical surface of radius a, as shown in Fig. 7–21. By slowly varying this force, a block of weight w is moved and the spring to which it is attached is stretched from position 1 to position 2. Calculate the work of the force $\mathbf{P}$.

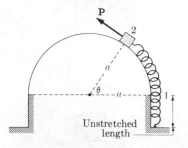

FIGURE 7–21

7–31. What average horsepower is developed by a 180-lb man when climbing in 10 sec a flight of stairs which rises 20 ft vertically? Express this power in watts and kilowatts.

7–32. The hammer of a pile driver weighs 1000 lb and must be lifted a vertical distance of 6 ft in 3 sec. What horsepower engine is required?

7–33. A ski tow is to be operated on a 37° slope 800 ft long. The rope is to move at 8 mi/hr and power must be provided for 80 riders at one time, each weighing, on an average, 150 lb. Estimate the horsepower required to operate the tow.

7–34. (a) If energy costs 5 cents per kwh, how much is one horsepower·hour worth? (b) How many ft·lb can be purchased for one cent?

7–35. Compute the monetary value of the kinetic energy of the projectile of a 14-in. naval gun, at the rate of 2 cents per kwh. The projectile weighs 1400 lb and its muzzle velocity is 2800 ft/sec.

7–36. At 5 cents per kwh, what does it cost to operate a 10-hp motor for 8 hr?

7–37. The engine of an automobile develops 20 hp when the automobile is traveling at 30 mi/hr. (a) What is the resisting force in pounds? (b) If the resisting force is proportional to the velocity, what horsepower will drive the car at 15 mi/hr? At 60 mi/hr?

7–38. The engine of a motorboat delivers 40 hp to the propeller while the boat is making 20 mi/hr. What would be the tension in the towline if the boat were being towed at the same speed?

7–39. A man whose mass is 70 kgm walks up to the third floor of a building. This is a vertical height of 12 meters above the street level. (a) How many joules of work has he done? (b) By how much has he increased his potential energy? (c) If he climbs the stairs in 20 sec, what was his rate of working in horsepower?

7–40. A pump is required to lift 200 gallons of water per minute from a well 20 ft deep and eject it with a speed of 30 ft/sec. (a) How much work is done per minute in lifting the water? (b) How much in giving it kinetic energy? (c) What horsepower engine is needed?

7–41. A 4800-lb elevator starts from rest and is pulled upward with a constant acceleration of 10 ft/sec^2. (a) Find the tension in the supporting cable. (b) What is the velocity of the elevator after it has risen 45 ft? (c) Find the kinetic energy of the elevator 3 sec after it starts. (d) How much is its potential energy increased in the first 3 sec? (e) What horsepower is required when the elevator is traveling 22 ft/sec?

7–42. An automobile weighing 2000 lb has a speed of 100 ft/sec on a horizontal road when the engine is developing 50 hp. What is its speed, with the same horsepower, if the road rises 1 ft in 20 ft? Assume all friction forces to be constant.

7–43. A string is attached to the upper side of a 350-gm block of wood placed on an inclined plane. When the string is parallel to the plane, a tension of 260,000 dynes in the string will pull the block up the plane at a constant speed. When the tension in the string is 150,000 dynes, the block moves down the plane with constant speed. (a) What is the force of friction between the block and the plane? (b) What is the actual mechanical advantage of the inclined plane? (c) What is the ideal mechanical advantage of the inclined plane? (d) What is the efficiency of the inclined plane?

7–44. An 800-lb weight is to be raised with uniform speed by means of a screw jack. The lever arm of the screw jack is 18 inches long and there are 4 threads to the inch. (a) Find the least force required if the efficiency is 20%. (b) What is the actual mechanical advantage? (c) What is the ideal mechanical advantage?

7–45. A screw jack moves upward $\frac{1}{4}$ in. when turned through one revolution; that is, the pitch is $\frac{1}{4}$ in. What load could be lifted if a force of 20 lb is applied at the end of a bar 2 ft long if friction is neglected?

7–46. A force of 6 lb is required to raise a weight of 30 lb by means of a pulley system. If the weight is raised 1 ft while the applied force acts through a distance of 8 ft, find (a) the ideal mechanical advantage, (b) the actual mechanical advantage, and (c) the efficiency.

7–47. Prove that the ideal mechanical advantage of the inclined plane shown in Fig. 7–12(a) is equal to the length of the plane divided by its height.

7–48. Prove that the ideal mechanical advantage of the lever shown in Fig. 7–12(c) is the distance from the

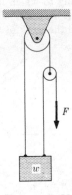

FIGURE 7–22

fulcrum to the point of application of F divided by the distance from the fulcrum to the point of application of the load.

7–49. Prove that the ideal mechanical advantage of the crank and axle shown in Fig. 7–12(d) is equal to the length of the crank divided by the radius of the wheel.

7–50. Calculate the ideal mechanical advantage of the device shown in Fig. 7–22.

7–51. An atomic bomb containing 20 kgm of plutonium explodes. The rest mass of the products of the explosion is less than the original rest mass by one ten-thousandth of the original rest mass. (a) How much energy is released in the explosion? (b) If the explosion takes place in one microsecond, what is the average power developed by the bomb? (c) How much water could the released energy lift to a height of one mile?

CHAPTER 8

IMPULSE AND MOMENTUM

8-1 Impulse and momentum. In the preceding chapter it was shown how the concepts of work and energy are developed from Newton's laws of motion. We shall next see how two similar concepts, those of *impulse* and *momentum*, also arise from Newton's laws. The most common use of these concepts is in connection with problems in impact. For the present, we shall consider only problems in which all velocities and all forces are parallel to a fixed direction.

Figure 8-1 represents two bodies that approach one another on a smooth horizontal surface, collide, and then recede from one another. Quantities relating to the first body are unprimed, those relating to the second are primed. The subscript 0 refers to values before the collision, and symbols without subscripts refer to values after the collision.

Since the plane is horizontal and frictionless, the only forces of interest are those which either body exerts on the other during the time the two are in contact. These forces are designated by $\mathbf{F}$ and $\mathbf{F}'$ in Fig. 8-1(b). From Newton's third law, $\mathbf{F}$ and $\mathbf{F}'$ are equal in magnitude and oppositely directed. That is, $F = -F'$. The forces $\mathbf{F}$ and $\mathbf{F}'$ will both vary during the collision. Of course, both are zero before contact. Both are small at the first instant of contact, then both increase to a maximum, and both decrease and become zero when the bodies separate. A force that varies with the time in this manner is called an *impulsive force*, and is plotted on a force-time diagram in Fig. 8-2(a) where the impulsive force is seen to start at time t_0, rise to a large maximum, and end at time t. Suppose the total time interval $t - t_0$ is subdivided into any number of parts Δt_1, $\Delta t_2, \ldots$, and rectangles are drawn as in Fig. 8-2(b) whose jagged outline approximates the smooth curve. Clearly, the larger the number of subdivisions the more closely will the smooth curve be approximated and the more closely will the sum of the areas of the rectangles approach the area under the smooth curve.

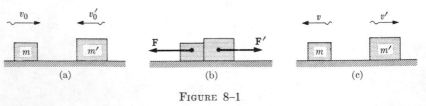

(a) (b) (c)

FIGURE 8-1

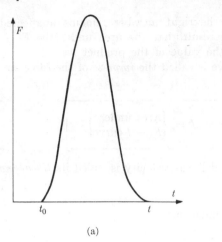

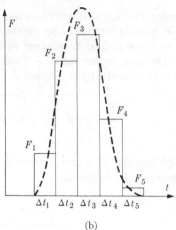

(a)   (b)

FIGURE 8–2

Let us therefore replace the continuously varying impulsive force by a force which remains constant at the value F_1 during the time interval Δt_1, then jumps instantaneously to the value F_2, maintaining this value for a time Δt_2, and so on. If the velocity of the body of mass m is originally v_0, and changes to the value v_1 at the end of the first time interval, we have, from Newton's second law,

$$F_1 = m \frac{v_1 - v_0}{\Delta t_1}$$

or

$$F_1 \Delta t_1 = mv_1 - mv_0;$$

and similarly for the other time intervals,

$$F_2 \Delta t_2 = mv_2 - mv_1,$$

$$F_3 \Delta t_3 = mv_3 - mv_2,$$

$$F_4 \Delta t_4 = mv_4 - mv_3,$$

$$F_5 \Delta t_5 = mv - mv_4,$$

where v is the velocity at the end of the last time interval. Adding these equations, we note that all terms in the right member cancel except mv_0 and mv. Hence

$$\sum F \, \Delta t = mv - mv_0. \tag{8–1}$$

If we now imagine the total time interval $t - t_0$ subdivided into a larger number of steps, the left member of Eq. (8–1) becomes the area under the smooth curve, while the right member remains unaffected. We have, therefore, the *rigorous* result that the area under the $F - t$ curve is equal to the *change* in the value of the product mv.

The area under the $F - t$ curve is called the *impulse* of the force, and is represented by the symbol J.

$$\text{Impulse of a force} = J = \begin{Bmatrix} \text{Area under} \\ F - t \text{ curve} \end{Bmatrix}.$$

The product of a body's mass and linear velocity is called its *linear momentum*. In magnitude,

$$\text{Linear momentum} = mv.$$

The result of the calculation of the previous paragraph may therefore be written

$$J = mv - mv_0. \qquad (8\text{--}2)$$

Equation (8–2) may be stated verbally as follows: *The change in linear momentum of a body equals the impulse of the force exerted on it.*

If in a special case the force is constant, the area is merely $F(t - t_0)$ and

$$\text{Impulse of a constant force} = J = F(t - t_0).$$

The unit of impulse is 1 pound·second in the engineering system, 1 newton·second in the mks system, and 1 dyne·second in the cgs system. The units of momentum in the three systems are 1 slug·ft/sec, 1 kgm·m/sec, and 1 gm·cm/sec. The unit of impulse in any system is equivalent to the corresponding unit of linear momentum, as is easily seen, for example, by recalling from Newton's second law that

$$F = m \times a,$$

$$1 \text{ lb} = 1 \text{ slug} \times 1 \frac{\text{ft}}{\text{sec}^2}.$$

Hence

$$1 \text{ lb·sec} = 1 \frac{\text{slug·ft}}{\text{sec}}.$$

EXAMPLE. A baseball weighing 5.5 ounces and traveling horizontally with a velocity of 80 ft/sec is struck by a bat. Its velocity after leaving the bat is 100 ft/sec, in the direction opposite to its original motion. What was the impulse of the blow?

If the force exerted on the ball were known as a function of time, the impulse could be computed by the method shown in Fig. 8–2. This information is not given, but we can find the impulse from the impulse-momentum theorem. The mass of the ball is 10.7×10^{-3} slug. Hence

$$\text{Impulse} = \text{change in momentum}$$
$$= mv - mv_0 = m(v - v_0)$$
$$= 10.7 \times 10^{-3} \text{ slug} \times \left[\left(-100 \frac{\text{ft}}{\text{sec}} \right) - \left(80 \frac{\text{ft}}{\text{sec}} \right) \right]$$
$$= -1.93 \text{ lb·sec.}$$

(The positive direction is that of the original velocity.) The *force* of the blow cannot be found from the given data. Any force whose impulse is -1.93 lb·sec will produce the same change in momentum. For instance, if the bat and ball were in contact for 0.001 sec, and if the force were constant during this time, its value would be

$$F = \frac{-1.93 \text{ lb·sec}}{10^{-3} \text{ sec}} = -1930 \text{ lb.}$$

It is the *impulse* of a blow, rather than the *force* of a blow, which is significant as far as changes in momentum are concerned.

8–2 Conservation of linear momentum. Let us return to a consideration of the colliding bodies in Fig. 8–1. If J' is the impulse of the force F' acting on the right-hand body, then from Eq. (8–2),

$$J' = m'v' - m'v_0'. \tag{8–3}$$

But since at every instant $F' = -F$, it follows that

$$J' = -J.$$

Hence from Eqs. (8–2) and (8–3), we have

$$mv - mv_0 = -(m'v' - m'v_0'),$$

and finally, after rearranging terms,

$$\boxed{mv_0 + m'v_0' = mv + m'v'.} \tag{8–4}$$

The left side of Eq. (8–4) is the total linear momentum of the system before the collision, the right side is the total momentum after the collision. We have therefore derived the extremely important result that *the total linear momentum of the colliding bodies is unaltered by the collision.* This fact is called the *principle of conservation of linear momentum.* It is one of the most important principles in mechanics.

Note that detailed knowledge of how the forces F and F' vary is unnecessary. The impulses of the forces are necessarily equal in magnitude and opposite in direction and hence they produce equal and opposite changes in momentum. The net change in momentum is therefore zero.

The momentum of a body is a vector quantity, in the same direction as its velocity **v**. If forces and velocities are not all parallel to a given direction but lie in a plane which we shall take as the xy-plane, the preceding calculations can be carried out twice, first for velocities and forces in the x-direction and second for velocities and forces in the y-direction. We then obtain two equations like Eq. (8–4), one for the x-components of momentum and the other for the y-components. That is, both the x-component and y-component of momentum are conserved. It follows that *the linear momentum of the system is conserved in both magnitude and direction.*

A more general statement of the principle of conservation of linear momentum, which does not restrict it to a collision between *two* bodies, is as follows:

The total linear momentum of a system can only be changed by **external** *forces acting on the system.* The internal forces, being equal and opposite and acting for equal times, produce equal and opposite changes in momentum which cancel one another. Hence, *the total linear momentum of an isolated system is constant in magnitude and direction.*

EXAMPLE 1. The Springfield rifle weighs 9.69 lb and fires a bullet weighing 150 grains (1 lb = 7000 grains) at a muzzle velocity of 2700 ft/sec. Compute the recoil velocity of the rifle if freely suspended.

The linear momentum of rifle and bullet before firing is zero. Hence, after firing, the forward momentum of the bullet is numerically equal to the backward momentum of the rifle. The mass of the rifle is 9.69/32 slugs and that of the bullet is 150/(7000 × 32) slugs. Then

$$\frac{150}{7000 \times 32} \text{ slugs} \times 2700 \frac{\text{ft}}{\text{sec}} = \frac{9.69}{32} \text{ slugs} \times v,$$

$$v = 5.9 \frac{\text{ft}}{\text{sec}}.$$

(The forward momentum of the burnt gases, which is quite appreciable, has been neglected.)

It is important to note that the kinetic energies of the bullet and rifle are *not* equal. The explanation is evident when one considers that a body acquires kinetic energy when work is done on it, the work being the product of the force and the distance moved. While the gases are propelling the bullet forward and the rifle backward, although the force on each is the same, the distance moved by the bullet is relatively large (the length of the barrel) while the distance moved by the slowly recoiling rifle is much less. Hence the work done on the bullet is much greater than the work done on the rifle, and its kinetic energy is correspondingly greater. Momentum, however, being equal to the product of force and *time*, is the same for both bullet and rifle.

Referring to the example of the Springfield, we find

$$E_{k(\text{bullet})} = \frac{1}{2} mv^2 = \frac{1}{2}\left(\frac{150}{7000 \times 32} \text{ slugs}\right)\left(2700 \frac{\text{ft}}{\text{sec}}\right)^2 = 2440 \text{ ft·lb.}$$

$$E_{k(\text{rifle})} = \frac{1}{2} MV^2 = \frac{1}{2}\left(\frac{9.69}{32} \text{ slugs}\right)\left(5.9 \frac{\text{ft}}{\text{sec}}\right)^2 = 5.25 \text{ ft·lb.}$$

EXAMPLE 2. Consider a system consisting of two bodies in "outer space" of mass m and m', very far from all other matter. Suppose the bodies start from rest at a distance r_1 apart and accelerate toward each other until they are at a distance r_2 apart. At this moment, what are the velocities v and v' of the two bodies?

The total initial linear momentum of the system is zero. Since no external force acts on the system, the final momentum must also be zero. Thus

$$mv - m'v' = 0,$$

or

$$v' = \frac{m}{m'} v.$$

An internal force, the gravitational force of attraction, acts between the two bodies, where

$$F = G \frac{mm'}{r^2}.$$

Since this force depends only on the distance between the two bodies, it is possible to ascribe to the system an internal potential energy E_p^i which can be shown to be equal to

$$E_p^i = -G \frac{mm'}{r}.$$

As the bodies approach each other, the total kinetic energy of the system increases and its internal potential energy decreases. The sum of its kinetic energy and internal potential energy remains constant. Hence

$$0 + 0 - G \frac{mm'}{r_1} = \frac{1}{2} mv^2 + \frac{1}{2} m'v'^2 - G \frac{mm'}{r_2},$$

or

$$\frac{1}{2} mv^2 + \frac{1}{2} m'v'^2 = Gmm'\left(\frac{1}{r_2} - \frac{1}{r_1}\right).$$

Substituting for v' its value mv/m', we get

$$\frac{1}{2}\, mv^2 + \frac{1}{2}\, m'\, \frac{m^2 v^2}{m'^2} = Gmm'\left(\frac{1}{r_2} - \frac{1}{r_1}\right)$$

or

$$\frac{1}{2}\, mv^2 \left(1 + \frac{m}{m'}\right) = Gmm'\left(\frac{1}{r_2} - \frac{1}{r_1}\right).$$

Therefore

$$v = m'\sqrt{[2G/(m + m')](1/r_2 - 1/r_1)},$$

and

$$v' = m\sqrt{[2G/(m + m')](1/r_2 - 1/r_1)}.$$

8–3 Elastic and inelastic collisions. Although linear momentum is always conserved in a collision, the same is not true of the kinetic energy. If the kinetic energy *does* remain constant, the collision is called *completely elastic*. If the colliding bodies stick together and move as a unit after the collision, it is called *completely inelastic*. These represent the two extremes, and all intermediate cases are possible.

The only completely elastic collisions known are those between atomic and subatomic particles, and even these may not be completely elastic if the energies of the colliding particles are sufficiently great. However, collisions between many objects, such as a pair of billiard balls, are very nearly completely elastic.

If a collision between two bodies is completely elastic, the equations

$$(\tfrac{1}{2}mv_0^2 + \tfrac{1}{2}m'v_0'^2) = (\tfrac{1}{2}mv^2 + \tfrac{1}{2}m'v'^2) \quad \text{(Conservation of energy)}$$

and

$$(mv_0 + m'v_0') = (mv + m'v') \quad \text{(Conservation of linear momentum)}$$

must both be satisfied. (The primes and subscripts have the same significance as in Fig. 8–1.) These may be written

$$m(v_0^2 - v^2) = m'(v'^2 - v_0'^2),$$

$$m(v_0 - v) = m'(v' - v_0').$$

When the first is divided by the second, we obtain

$$v_0 + v = v' + v_0'$$

or finally,

$$v_0 - v_0' = -(v - v').$$

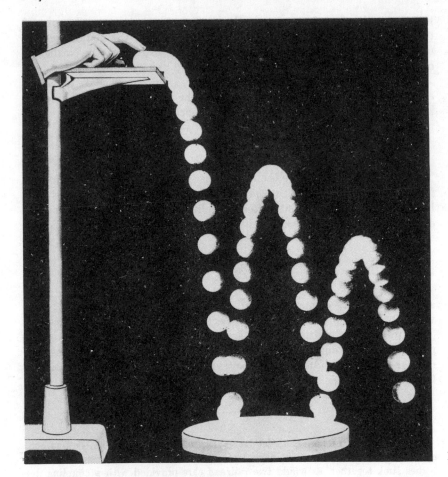

FIGURE 8–3

But $v_0 - v_0'$ is the relative velocity before the collision and $v - v'$ is the relative velocity after the collision. Hence, in a perfectly elastic collision the relative velocity is reversed in direction but unaltered in magnitude.

The degree to which a pair of colliding bodies approach complete elasticity is expressed by their *coefficient of restitution, e*, which is defined as the negative ratio of the relative velocity after collision to the relative velocity before collision.

$$e = - \frac{v - v'}{v_0 - v_0'}. \tag{8–5}$$

From what has just been shown, the coefficient of restitution is unity if the colliding bodies are perfectly elastic, and is zero if the bodies are perfectly inelastic. These are the two extremes and, in general, the coefficient of restitution has some value between zero and unity.

When a ball is dropped onto and rebounds from a fixed plate it has, in effect, collided with the earth. The mass of the earth is so large its velocity is practically unaltered by the collision. Hence in this special case,

$$e = -\frac{v}{v_0}.$$

The relative velocity before the collision is simply the velocity acquired in falling from a height h_0 or $\sqrt{2gh_0}$. If, after colliding, the ball rises to a height h, the relative velocity after the collision is $-\sqrt{2gh}$ (the downward direction is considered positive). Hence the coefficient of restitution is

$$e = -\frac{-\sqrt{2gh}}{\sqrt{2gh_0}} = \sqrt{\frac{h}{h_0}},$$

and a simple way of measuring it is to measure these two heights. The value obtained represents a joint property of the ball and the surface.

Figure 8–3 is a multiflash photograph of a golf ball dropping onto and rebounding from an iron plate. The heights h_0 and h can be measured from the photograph, and the velocities before and after colliding can be found from the spacing of the images before and after impact.

EXAMPLE 1. In Fig. 8–1, let $m = 1$ kgm, $m' = 2$ kgm, $v_0 = 5$ m/sec, $v_0' = 2$ m/sec. Suppose that, instead of separating after the collision, the two bodies stick together, as would two railroad cars provided with a coupling device, so that $v = v'$. We wish to compute this final velocity. From the principle of conservation of linear momentum,

$$mv_0 + m'v_0' = (m + m')v,$$

$$v = \frac{mv_0 + m'v_0'}{m + m'} = \frac{1 \text{ kgm} \times 5 \text{ m/sec} + 2 \text{ kgm} \times 2 \text{ m/sec}}{1 \text{ kgm} + 2 \text{ kgm}} = 3 \frac{\text{m}}{\text{sec}}.$$

The system therefore moves to the right after the collision with a velocity of 3 m/sec. This is an example of a completely inelastic collision. The original kinetic energy was

$$E_{k_0} = \frac{1}{2} \times 1 \text{ kgm} \times 25 \frac{\text{m}^2}{\text{sec}^2} + \frac{1}{2} \times 2 \text{ kgm} \times 4 \frac{\text{m}^2}{\text{sec}^2} = 16.5 \text{ joules.}$$

The final kinetic energy was

$$E_k = \frac{1}{2} \times 3 \text{ kgm} \times 9 \frac{\text{m}^2}{\text{sec}^2} = 13.5 \text{ joules.}$$

Therefore, although the momentum did not change in the collision, the kinetic energy decreased from 16.5 to 13.5 joules. The difference, 3 joules, was converted to heat.

EXAMPLE 2. Suppose the collision in the preceding example had been completely elastic. What would then have been the velocities v and v' after the collision?

From the principle of the conservation of linear momentum,

$$1 \text{ kgm} \times 5 \frac{\text{m}}{\text{sec}} + 2 \text{ kgm} \times 2 \frac{\text{m}}{\text{sec}} = 1 \text{ kgm} \times v + 2 \text{ kgm} \times v'.$$

Since the collision is completely elastic, the coefficient of restitution is 1, or

$$-\frac{v - v'}{(5 \text{ m/sec}) - (2 \text{ m/sec})} = 1.$$

Hence

$$v + 2v' = 9 \frac{\text{m}}{\text{sec}}, \qquad -v + v' = 3 \frac{\text{m}}{\text{sec}}.$$

Solving simultaneously, we obtain

$$v = 1 \frac{\text{m}}{\text{sec}}, \qquad v' = 4 \frac{\text{m}}{\text{sec}}.$$

EXAMPLE 3. The *ballistic pendulum* is a device for measuring the velocity of a bullet. The bullet is allowed to make a completely inelastic collision with a body of much greater mass. The momentum of the system immediately after the collision equals the original momentum of the bullet, but since the velocity is very much smaller it can be determined more easily. Although the ballistic pendulum has now been superseded by other devices, it is still an important laboratory experiment for illustrating the concepts of momentum and energy.

In Fig. 8–4, the pendulum, consisting perhaps of a large wooden block of mass M, hangs vertically by two cords. A bullet of mass m, traveling with a velocity v, strikes the pendulum and remains embedded in it. If the collision time is very small compared with the time of swing of the pendulum, the supporting cords remain practically vertical during this time. Hence no external horizontal forces act on the system during the collision, and the horizontal momentum is conserved. Then if V represents the velocity of bullet and block immediately after the collision,

$$mv = (m + m')V.$$

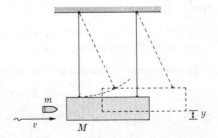

FIG. 8–4. The ballistic pendulum.

The kinetic energy of the system, immediately after the collision, is

$$E_k = \tfrac{1}{2}(m + m')V^2.$$

The pendulum now swings to the right and upward until its kinetic energy is converted to gravitational potential energy. (Small frictional effects can be neglected.) Hence

$$\tfrac{1}{2}(m + m')V^2 = (m + m')gy,$$

and

$$v = \frac{m + m'}{m}\sqrt{2gy}.$$

By measuring m, m', and y, the original velocity v of the bullet can be computed.

It is important to remember that kinetic energy is not conserved *in the collision*. The ratio of the kinetic energy of bullet and pendulum, after the collision, to the original kinetic energy of the bullet, is

$$\frac{\tfrac{1}{2}(m + m')V^2}{\tfrac{1}{2}mv^2} = \frac{m}{m + m'}.$$

Thus if $m' = 1000$ gm and $m = 1$ gm, only about one-tenth of one percent of the original energy remains as kinetic energy; 99.9% is converted to heat.

8–4 Newton's second law. Newton himself did not state his second law in the form in which we have used it. A free translation (Newton's "Principia" was written in Latin) is as follows:

> *Change of motion is proportional to the applied force, and takes place in the direction of the force.... Quantity of motion is proportional to mass and velocity conjointly.*

From Newton's definition of "motion," or "quantity of motion," it is evident that he used this term for the concept we now call linear momentum. It is also clear from his writings that the term "change" meant "rate of change" and that the "applied force" referred to the resultant force. Hence in current terminology Newton's statement is:

> *Rate of change of linear momentum is proportional to the resultant force and is in the direction of this force.*

In mathematical language this becomes

$$\frac{\Delta(m\mathbf{v})}{\Delta t} \propto \mathbf{F},$$

or

$$\mathbf{F} = k\,\frac{\Delta(m\mathbf{v})}{\Delta t}. \tag{8–6}$$

If the mass m is constant, this reduces to

$$\mathbf{F} = km\,\frac{\Delta \mathbf{v}}{\Delta t} = km\mathbf{a},$$

which is the form we have used, with k made equal to unity by proper choice of units.

We have pointed out in Section 7–11 that while the mass of a body can ordinarily be considered constant, it increases with increasing velocity according to the relation

$$m = \frac{m_0}{\sqrt{1 - (v^2/c^2)}},$$

where m_0 is the "rest mass" of the body, c is the velocity of light, and v the velocity of the body. However, if the mass cannot be considered constant, we cannot set $\mathbf{F} = m\mathbf{a}$, and the original form of Newton's law must be used.

It is a striking example of Newton's genius that, although he could scarcely have foreseen the theory of relativity, he appreciated the fact that momentum is an entity more fundamental than mass.

8–5 The rocket. A rocket motor is merely a combustion chamber in which liquid or solid fuel is burned and which has an opening to direct the gaseous products of combustion in the desired direction. An ascending rocket can be compared to a machine gun pointed vertically downward and firing a steady stream of blank cartridges. The gases expelled from the rocket acquire a downward momentum and the rocket, like a recoiling machine gun, acquires an equal upward momentum.

Let us consider the flight of a rocket directed vertically upward from the earth's surface. Figure 8–5(a) shows the rocket at an instant when the mass of rocket and unburned fuel is m, the upward velocity is v, and the momentum is mv. In a short time interval Δt, a mass Δm of gas is ejected from the rocket. Let v represent the downward velocity of this gas *relative to the rocket*. The velocity v' of the gas relative to the earth is then

$$v' = v - v_r,$$

and its momentum is

$$\Delta m \cdot v' = \Delta m(v - v_r).$$

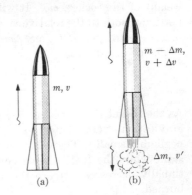

FIGURE 8–5

At the end of the time interval, the mass of rocket and unburned fuel has decreased to $m - \Delta m$, and its velocity has increased to $v + \Delta v$. Its momentum is therefore

$$(m - \Delta m)(v + \Delta v).$$

Figure 8–5(b) represents rocket and ejected gas at this time.

We now make use of Eq. (8–6), with $k = 1$, writing it as

$$F \, \Delta t = \Delta(mv).$$

That is, the product of the resultant external force F on a system, and the time interval Δt during which it acts, is equal to the change in momentum of the system. If air resistance is neglected, the external force F on the rocket is its weight, $-mg$. (We take the upward direction as positive.) The change in momentum, in time Δt, is the difference between the momentum of the system at the end and at the beginning of the time interval. Hence

$$-mg \, \Delta t = [(m - \Delta m)(v + \Delta v) + \Delta m(v - v_r)] - mv.$$

Now expand the right side of this equation and neglect the term $\Delta m \, \Delta v$ (the product of two small quantities). After canceling and rearranging terms, we get

$$m \frac{\Delta v}{\Delta t} = v_r \frac{\Delta m}{\Delta t} - mg.$$

The ratio $\Delta v / \Delta t$ is the acceleration of the rocket, so the left side of this equation (mass times acceleration) equals the resultant force on the rocket. The first term on the right equals the upward thrust on the rocket, and the resultant force equals the difference between this thrust and the weight of the rocket, mg. It will be seen that the upward thrust is proportional both to the relative velocity v_r of the ejected gas and to the mass of gas ejected per unit time, $\Delta m / \Delta t$.

The acceleration is

$$\frac{\Delta v}{\Delta t} = \frac{v_r}{m} \frac{\Delta m}{\Delta t} - g.$$

As the rocket rises, the value of g decreases according to Newton's law of gravitation. (In "outer space," far from all other bodies, g becomes negligibly small.) The values of v_r and $\Delta m / \Delta t$ remain approximately constant while the fuel is being consumed, but the remaining mass m continually decreases. Hence the acceleration *increases* until all the fuel is burned.

EXAMPLE. In the first second of its flight, a rocket ejects 1/60 of its mass with a relative velocity of 6800 ft·sec. What is the acceleration of the rocket? We have: $\Delta m = m/60$, $\Delta t = 1$ sec.

$$\frac{\Delta v}{\Delta t} = 6800 \frac{\text{ft}}{\text{sec}} \times \frac{1}{60} \times \frac{1}{1 \text{ sec}} - 32 \frac{\text{ft}}{\text{sec}^2}$$

$$= 113 \frac{\text{ft}}{\text{sec}^2} - 32 \frac{\text{ft}}{\text{sec}^2} = 81 \frac{\text{ft}}{\text{sec}^2}.$$

Since the acceleration continually increases, the equations of motion with *constant* acceleration cannot be used to find the final velocity. The methods of calculus lead to the following expression for the velocity v after the fuel is exhausted, assuming that v_r and g are constant:

$$v = 2.3 \, v_r \log \frac{m_0}{m} - gt,$$

where m_0 is the initial mass of rocket and fuel, m is the mass of the rocket alone, and t is the time required to burn all the fuel.

EXAMPLE. Suppose the ratio of initial mass to final mass for the rocket above is 4 and that the fuel is consumed in a time $t = 60$ sec. The velocity at the end of this time is then

$$v = 2.3 \times 6800 \frac{\text{ft}}{\text{sec}} \times \log 4 - 32 \frac{\text{ft}}{\text{sec}^2} \times 60 \text{ sec}$$

$$- 9420 \frac{\text{ft}}{\text{sec}} - 1920 \frac{\text{ft}}{\text{sec}} = 7500 \frac{\text{ft}}{\text{sec}}.$$

At the start of the flight, when the velocity of the rocket is zero, the ejected gases are moving downward, relative to the earth, with a velocity equal to the relative velocity v_r. When the velocity of the rocket has increased to v_r, the ejected gases have a velocity zero relative to the earth. When the rocket velocity becomes greater than v_r, the velocity of the ejected gases is in the same direction as that of the rocket. Thus the velocity acquired by the rocket can be greater (and is often much greater) than the relative velocity v_r. In the example above, where the final velocity of the rocket was 7500 ft/sec and the relative velocity was 6800 ft/sec, the last portion of the ejected fuel had an upward velocity of (7500–6800) ft/sec = 700 ft/sec.

Problems

8-1. (a) What is the momentum of a 10-ton truck whose velocity is 30 mi/hr? At what velocity will a 5-ton truck have (b) the same momentum, (c) the same kinetic energy?

8-2. A baseball weighs $5\frac{1}{2}$ oz. (a) If the velocity of a pitched ball is 80 ft/sec, and after being batted it is 120 ft/sec in the opposite direction, find the change in momentum of the ball and the impulse of the blow. (b) If the ball remains in contact with the bat for 0.002 sec, find the average force of the blow.

8-3. A bullet having a mass of 0.05 kgm, moving with a velocity of 400 m/sec, penetrates a distance of 0.1 m in a wooden block firmly attached to the earth. Assume the decelerating force constant. Compute (a) the deceleration of the bullet, (b) the decelerating force, (c) the time of deceleration, (d) the impulse of the collision. Compare the answer to part (d) with the initial momentum of the bullet.

8-4. An empty freight car weighing 10 tons rolls at 3 ft/sec along a level track and collides with a loaded car weighing 20 tons, standing at rest with brakes released. If the two cars couple together, find (a) their velocity after the collision, and (b) the decrease in kinetic energy as a result of the collision.

8-5. With what velocity should the loaded car in Problem 8-4 be rolling toward the empty one in order that both shall be brought to rest by the collision?

8-6. A bullet weighing 0.02 lb is fired with a muzzle velocity of 2700 ft/sec from a rifle weighing 7.5 lb. (a) Compute the recoil velocity of the rifle, assuming it free to recoil. (b) Find the ratio of the kinetic energy of the bullet to that of the rifle.

8-7. A 75-mm gun fires a projectile weighing 16 lb with a muzzle velocity of 1900 ft/sec. By how many mi/hr is the velocity of a plane mounting such a gun decreased when a projectile is fired directly ahead? The plane weighs 32,000 lb.

8-8. The projectile of a 16-in. seacoast gun weighs 2400 lb, travels a distance of 38 ft in the bore of the gun, and has a muzzle velocity of 2250 ft/sec. The gun weighs 300,000 lb. (a) Compute the initial recoil velocity of the gun, assuming it free to recoil. (b) Find the ratio of the kinetic energy of the projectile to that of the recoiling gun.

8-9. A 4000-lb automobile going eastward on Chestnut Street at 40 mi/hr collides with a truck weighing 4 tons which is going southward across Chestnut Street at 15 mi/hr. If they become coupled on collision, what is the magnitude and direction of their velocity immediately after colliding?

8-10. A body of mass 600 gm is initially at rest. It is struck by a second body of mass 400 gm initially moving with a velocity of 125 cm/sec toward the right along the x-axis. After the collision the 400-gm body has a velocity of 100 cm/sec at an angle of 37° above the x-axis in the first quadrant. Both bodies move on a horizontal frictionless plane. (a) What is the magnitude and direction of the velocity of the 600-gm body after the collision? (b) What is the loss of kinetic energy during the collision?

8-11. (a) Prove that when a moving body makes a perfectly inelastic collision with a second of equal mass, initially at rest, one-half of the original kinetic energy is "lost." (b) Prove that when a very heavy particle makes a perfectly elastic collision with a very light stationary particle the light one goes off with twice the velocity of the heavy one.

8-12. On a frictionless table, a 3-kgm block moving 4 m/sec to the right collides with an 8-kgm block moving 1.5 m/sec to the left. (a) If the two blocks stick together, what is the final velocity? (b) If the two blocks make a completely elastic head-on collision, what are their final velocities? (c) How much mechanical energy is converted into heat in the collision of part (a)?

8-13. Two blocks of mass 300 gm and 200 gm are moving toward each other along a horizontal frictionless surface with velocities of 50 cm/sec and 100 cm/sec, respectively. (a) If the blocks collide and stick together, find their final velocity. (b) Find the loss of kinetic energy during the collision. (c) Find the final velocity of each block if the collision is completely elastic.

8-14. A 10-gm blocks slides at a velocity of 20 cm/sec on a smooth level surface and makes a head-on collision with a 30-gm block moving in the opposite direction with a velocity of 10 cm/sec. If the collision is perfectly elastic, find the velocity of each block after the collision.

8-15. A block of mass 200 gm, sliding with a velocity of 12 cm/sec on a smooth level surface, makes a perfectly elastic head-on collision with a block of mass m gm, initially at rest. After the collision the velocity of the 200-gm block is 4 cm/sec in the same direction as its initial velocity. Find (a) the mass m, and (b) its velocity after the collision.

8-16. A rifle bullet of mass 10 gm strikes and embeds itself in a block of mass 990 gm which rests on a horizontal frictionless surface and is attached to a coil spring as shown in Fig. 8-6. The impact compresses the spring 10 cm. Calibration of the spring shows that a force of 100,000 dynes is required to compress the spring 1 cm. (a) Find the maximum potential energy of the spring. (b) Find the velocity of the block just after the impact. (c) What was the initial velocity of the bullet?

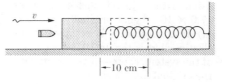

FIGURE 8-6

8-17. A projectile is fired at an angle of departure of 60° and with a muzzle velocity of 1200 ft/sec. At the highest point of its trajectory the projectile explodes into two fragments of equal mass, one of which falls vertically. How far from the point of firing does the other fragment strike if the terrain is level?

8-18. A railroad handcar is moving along straight frictionless tracks. In each of the following cases the car initially has a total weight (car and contents) of 500 lb and is traveling with a velocity of 10 ft/sec. Find the final velocity of the car in each of the three cases. (a) A 50-lb weight is thrown sideways out of the car with a velocity of 8 ft/sec relative to the car. (b) A 50-lb weight is thrown backwards out of the car with a velocity of 10 ft/sec relative to the car. (c) A 50-lb weight is thrown into the car with a velocity of 12 ft/sec relative to the ground and opposite in direction to the velocity of the car.

8–19. An open-topped freight car weighing 10 tons is coasting without friction along a level track. It is raining very hard, with the rain falling vertically down. The car is originally empty and moving with a velocity of 2 ft/sec. What is the velocity of the car after it has traveled long enough to collect one ton of rain water?

8–20. A neutron of mass 1.67×10^{-24} gm, moving with a velocity of 2×10^6 cm/sec, makes a head-on collision with a boron nucleus of mass 17.0×10^{-24} gm, originally at rest. (a) If the collision is completely inelastic, what is the final kinetic energy of the system, expressed as a fraction of the original kinetic energy? (b) If the collision is perfectly elastic, what fraction of its original kinetic energy does the neutron transfer to the boron nucleus?

8–21. A nucleus, originally at rest, decays radioactively by emitting an electron of momentum 9.22×10^{-16} gm·cm/sec, and at right angles to the direction of the electron a neutrino with momentum 5.33×10^{-16} gm·cm/sec. (a) In what direction does the residual nucleus recoil? (b) What is its momentum? (c) If the mass of the residual nucleus is 3.90×10^{-22} gm, what is its kinetic energy?

8–22. A ball is dropped from rest onto a fixed horizontal surface and rebounds to a height which is 64% of the original height. (a) What is the coefficient of restitution? (b) With what vertical velocity must the ball strike the surface to rebound to a height of 25 ft?

8–23. A golf ball is dropped on a hard surface from a height of 1 m and rebounds to a height of 64 cm. (a) What is the height of the second bounce? of the nth bounce? After (about) how many bounces is the height reduced to 1 cm? (b) What is the time of the first bounce, i.e., between the first and second contacts with the surface? What is the time of the nth bounce? (c) What is the coefficient of restitution?

8–24. A 1-lb rubber ball bounces down a flight of stairs, each time rising to the height y of the step above, as shown in Fig. 8–7. (a) Find the coefficient of restitution. (b) If the height of each step, y, is 1 ft, what is the maximum kinetic energy of the ball?

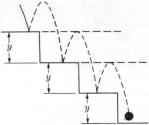

FIGURE 8–7

8–25. A freight elevator is rising with a constant velocity of 5 ft/sec. A stationary observer drops a ball from a point which is 21 ft above the platform at the instant the ball is released. The coefficient of restitution between ball and platform is 0.50. How far above (or below) its starting point does the ball rise on its first bounce?

8–26. A ball is thrown against a vertical wall, striking it at a point 4 ft above the floor with a horizontal velocity of 20 ft/sec. After rebounding from the wall, the ball strikes the floor at a point 8 ft from the wall. (a) What was the coefficient of restitution? (b) If the ball weighed 0.5 lb, how much kinetic energy was "lost" in the impact with the wall?

8–27. When a bullet of mass 10 gm strikes a ballistic pendulum of mass 2 kgm, the center of gravity of the pendulum is observed to rise a vertical distance of 10 cm. The bullet remains embedded in the pendulum. Calculate the velocity of the bullet.

8–28. A bullet weighing 0.01 lb is shot through a 2-lb wooden block suspended on a string 5 ft long. The center of gravity of the block is observed to rise a distance of 0.0192 ft. Find the speed of the bullet as it emerges from the block if the initial speed is 1000 ft/sec.

8–29. A bullet of mass 2 gm, traveling in a horizontal direction with a velocity of 500 m/sec, is fired into a wooden block of mass 1 kgm, initially at rest on a level surface. The bullet passes through the block and emerges with its velocity reduced to 100 m/sec. The block slides a distance of 20 cm along the surface from its initial position. (a) What was the coefficient of sliding friction between block and surface? (b) What was the decrease in kinetic energy of the bullet? (c) What was the kinetic energy of the block at the instant after the bullet passed through it?

8–30. A rifle bullet weighing 0.02 lb is fired with a velocity of 2500 ft/sec into a ballistic pendulum. The pendulum weighs 10 lb and is suspended from a cord 3 ft long. Compute (a) the vertical height through which the pendulum rises, (b) the initial kinetic energy of the bullet, (c) the kinetic energy of bullet and pendulum after the bullet is embedded in the pendulum.

8–31. A 5-gm bullet is fired horizontally into a 3-kgm wooden block resting on a horizontal surface. The coefficient of sliding friction between block and surface is 0.20. The bullet remains embedded in the block, which is observed to slide 25 cm along the surface. What was the velocity of the bullet?

8–32. A bullet of mass 2 gm, traveling at 500 m/sec, is fired into a ballistic pendulum of mass 1 kgm suspended from a cord 1 m long. The bullet penetrates the pendulum and emerges with a velocity of 100 m/sec. Through what vertical height will the pendulum rise?

8–33. A 160-lb man standing on ice throws a 6-oz ball horizontally with a speed of 80 ft/sec. (a) With what speed and in what direction will the man begin to move? (b) If the man throws 4 such balls every 3 sec, what is the average force acting on him?

8–34. Find the average recoil force on a machine gun firing 120 shots per minute. The weight of each bullet is 0.025 lb, and the muzzle velocity is 2700 ft/sec. [*Hint:* average force equals average rate of change of momentum.]

8–35. A rifleman, who together with his rifle weighs 160 lb, stands on roller skates and fires 10 shots horizontally from an automatic rifle. Each bullet weighs 0.0257 lb (180 grains) and has a muzzle velocity of 2500 ft/sec. (a) If the rifleman moves back without friction, what is his velocity at the end of the ten shots? (b) If the shots were fired in 10 sec, what was the average force exerted on him? (c) Compare his kinetic energy with that of the 10 bullets.

8–36. A rocket burns 50 gm of fuel per second, ejecting it as a gas with a velocity of 500,000 cm/sec. (a) What force does this gas exert on the rocket? Give the result in dynes and newtons. (b) Would the rocket operate in free space? (c) If it would operate in free space, how would you steer it? Could you brake it?

CHAPTER 9

ROTATION

9–1 Introduction. The most general type of motion which a body can undergo is a combination of *translation* and *rotation*. Thus far we have considered only the special case of translational motion, along a straight line or along a curve. We next discuss motion of rotation about a fixed axis, that is, motion of rotation without translation. We shall see that many of the equations describing rotation about a fixed axis are exactly analogous to those encountered in rectilinear motion. If the axis is *not* fixed, the problem becomes much more complicated, and we shall not attempt to give a complete discussion of the general case of translation plus rotation.

9–2 Angular velocity. Figure 9–1 represents a rigid body of arbitrary shape rotating about a fixed axis through point O and perpendicular to the plane of the diagram. Line OP is a line fixed with respect to the body and rotating with it. The position of the entire body is evidently completely specified by the angle θ which the line OP makes with some reference line fixed in space, such as Ox. The motion of the body is therefore analogous to the rectilinear motion of a particle, whose position is completely specified by a single coordinate such as x or y. The equations of motion are greatly simplified if the angle θ is expressed in *radians*.

One radian is the angle subtended at the center of a circle by an arc of length equal to the radius of the circle [Fig. 9–2(a)]. Since the radius is contained 2π times ($2\pi = 6.28\ldots$) in the circumference, there are 2π or $6.28\ldots$ radians in

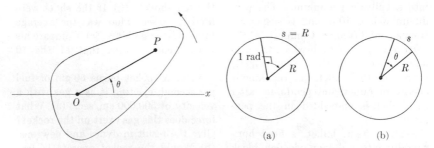

FIG. 9–1. Body rotating about a fixed axis through point O.

FIG. 9–2. An angle θ in radians is defined as the ratio of the arc s to the radius R.

174

one complete revolution or 360°. Hence

$$1 \text{ radian} = \frac{360}{2\pi} = 57.3 \dots \text{degrees}$$

$$
\begin{aligned}
360° &= 2\pi \text{ radians} = 6.28 \dots \text{radians} \\
180° &= \pi \quad\quad\text{``} \quad= 3.14 \dots \quad\text{``} \\
90° &= \pi/2 \quad\text{``} \quad= 1.57 \dots \quad\text{``} \\
60° &= \pi/3 \quad\text{``} \quad= 1.05 \dots \quad\text{``}
\end{aligned}
$$

and so on.

In general [Fig. 9–2(b)], if θ represents any arbitrary angle subtended by an arc of length s on the circumference of a circle of radius R, then θ (in radians) is equal to the length of the arc s divided by the radius R.

$$\theta = \frac{s}{R}, \qquad s = R\theta. \tag{9-1}$$

An angle in radians, being defined as the ratio of a length to a length, is a pure number.

In Fig. 9–3, a reference line OP in a rotating body makes an angle θ_1 with the reference line Ox, at a time t_1. At a later time t_2 the angle has increased to θ_2. The *average angular velocity* of the body, $\bar{\omega}$, in the time interval between t_1 and t_2, is defined as the ratio of the *angular displacement* $\theta_2 - \theta_1$, or $\Delta\theta$, to the elapsed time $t_2 - t_1$ or Δt.

$$\bar{\omega} = \frac{\theta_2 - \theta_1}{t_2 - t_1} = \frac{\Delta\theta}{\Delta t}.$$

The *instantaneous angular velocity* ω is defined as the limit approached by this ratio as Δt approaches zero.

$$\omega = \lim_{\Delta t \to 0} \frac{\Delta\theta}{\Delta t}. \tag{9-2}$$

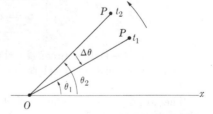

Since the body is rigid, *all* lines in it rotate through the same angle in the same time, and the angular velocity is characteristic of the body as a whole. If the angle θ is in radians, the angular velocity is in *radians per*

Fig. 9–3. Angular displacement $\Delta\theta$ of a rotating body.

second. Other units, such as the revolution per minute, are in common use.

9–3 Angular acceleration.

When the angular velocity of a body changes, it is said to have an angular acceleration. If ω_1 and ω_2 are the instantaneous angular velocities at times t_1 and t_2, the *average angular acceleration* $\bar{\alpha}$ is defined as

$$\bar{\alpha} = \frac{\omega_2 - \omega_1}{t_2 - t_1} = \frac{\Delta\omega}{\Delta t},$$

and the *instantaneous angular acceleration* α is defined as the limit of this ratio when Δt approaches zero:

$$\alpha = \lim_{\Delta t \to 0} \frac{\Delta\omega}{\Delta t}. \tag{9–3}$$

Angular acceleration is expressed in rad/sec^2. Angular velocity and angular acceleration are exactly analogous to linear velocity and acceleration.

9–4 Rotation with constant angular acceleration. When the angular velocity of a body changes by equal amounts in equal intervals of time, the angular acceleration is constant. Under these circumstances the average and instantaneous angular accelerations are equal, whatever the duration of the time interval. One may therefore write

$$\alpha = \frac{\omega - \omega_0}{t - t_0}$$

or

$$\omega = \omega_0 + \alpha(t - t_0),$$

where α is the constant instantaneous angular acceleration.

If $t_0 = 0$,

$$\omega = \omega_0 + \alpha t. \tag{9–4}$$

Equation (9–4) has precisely the same form as Eq. (4–8) for linear motion with constant acceleration and may be interpreted in the same way.

The angular displacement of a rotating body, or the angle turned through by the body, corresponds to the linear displacement of a body moving along a straight line. The expression for the angular displacement can be found with the help of the average angular velocity. If the angular acceleration is constant, the angular velocity increases at a uniform rate and its average value during any time interval equals half the sum of its values at the beginning and end of the interval. That is,

$$\bar{\omega} = \frac{\omega_0 + \omega}{2}.$$

If $\theta_0 = 0$ when $t_0 = 0$, $\theta = \bar{\omega}t$ and hence

$$\theta = \frac{\omega_0 + \omega}{2} \cdot t. \tag{9-5}$$

Equations (9-4) and (9-5) are the fundamental equations applicable to rotation with constant angular acceleration. By combining them we may obtain two more very useful equations. Thus, substituting for ω in Eq. (9-5) the value of ω given by Eq. (9-4), we have

$$\theta = \frac{\omega_0 + \omega_0 + \alpha t}{2} \cdot t$$

or

$$\theta = \omega_0 t + \tfrac{1}{2}\alpha t^2. \tag{9-6}$$

Also, substituting for t in Eq. (9-5) the value of t given by Eq. (9-4), we have

$$\theta = \frac{\omega_0 + \omega}{2} \cdot \frac{\omega - \omega_0}{\alpha} = \frac{\omega^2 - \omega_0^2}{2\alpha},$$

or finally

$$\omega^2 = \omega_0^2 + 2\alpha\theta. \tag{9-7}$$

The following table will serve to emphasize the similarity between the equations for motion with constant linear acceleration and those for motion with constant angular acceleration.

Motion with constant linear acceleration	Motion with constant angular acceleration
$a = $ constant	$\alpha = $ constant
$v = v_0 + at$	$\omega = \omega_0 + \alpha t$
$x = v_0 t + \tfrac{1}{2}at^2$	$\theta = \omega_0 t + \tfrac{1}{2}\alpha t^2$
$x = \dfrac{v_0 + v}{2} t$	$\theta = \dfrac{\omega_0 + \omega}{2} t$
$v^2 = v_0^2 + 2ax$	$\omega^2 = \omega_0^2 + 2\alpha\theta$

EXAMPLE. The angular velocity of a body is 4 rad/sec at time $t = 0$, and its angular acceleration is constant and equal to 2 rad/sec². A line OP in the body is horizontal at time $t = 0$. (a) What angle does this line make with the horizontal at time $t = 3$ sec? (b) What is the angular velocity at this time?

(a) $$\theta = \omega_0 t + \frac{1}{2}\alpha t^2 = 4 \frac{rad}{sec} \times 3 \text{ sec} + \frac{1}{2} \times 2 \frac{rad}{sec^2} \times (3 \text{ sec})^2$$

$$= 21 \text{ radians} = 3.34 \text{ revolutions.}$$

(b) $$\omega = \omega_0 + \alpha t = 4 \frac{rad}{sec} + 2 \frac{rad}{sec} \times 3 \text{ sec} = 10 \frac{rad}{sec}.$$

Alternatively, from Eq. (9–7),

$$\omega^2 = \omega_0^2 + 2\alpha\theta$$

$$= \left(4 \frac{rad}{sec}\right)^2 + 2 \times 2 \frac{rad}{sec^2} \times 21 \text{ rad} = 100 \frac{rad^2}{sec^2},$$

$$\omega = 10 \frac{rad}{sec}.$$

9–5 Relation between angular and linear velocity and acceleration. In Section 6–5 we discussed the linear velocity and acceleration of a *particle* revolving in a circle. When a *rigid body* rotates about a fixed axis, every point in the body moves in a circle whose center is on the axis and which lies in a plane perpendicular to the axis. There are some useful and simple relations between the angular velocity and acceleration of the rotating body and the linear velocity and acceleration of points within it.

Let r be the distance from the axis to some point P in the body, so that the point moves in a circle of radius r, as in Fig. 9–4. When the radius makes an angle θ with the reference axis, the distance s to the point P, measured along the circular path, is

$$\boxed{s = r\theta.} \qquad (9\text{–}8)$$

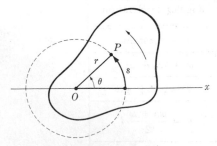

When the angle is very small, say $\Delta\theta$, the length of the arc Δs is also small and the time interval Δt for the body to rotate through the angle $\Delta\theta$ is also small. We have

FIG. 9–4. The distance s moved through by point P equals $r\theta$.

$$\Delta s = r\,\Delta\theta, \qquad \frac{\Delta s}{\Delta t} = r\,\frac{\Delta\theta}{\Delta t}$$

and, in the limit, as $\Delta t \to 0$,

$$v = r\omega. \tag{9–9}$$

If the angular velocity about the given axis should change *in magnitude only* (the axis remaining fixed) by $\Delta\omega$, the linear velocity in a direction tangent to a circle of radius r will change by Δv, where

$$\Delta v = r\,\Delta\omega.$$

If these changes take place in a short time interval Δt, then

$$\frac{\Delta v}{\Delta t} = r\,\frac{\Delta\omega}{\Delta t}$$

and, in the limit, as $\Delta t \to 0$,

$$a_T = r\alpha, \tag{9–10}$$

where a_T is the tangential component of the linear acceleration of a point a distance r for the axis.

The *radial* component of acceleration v^2/r of the point P can also be expressed in terms of the angular velocity.

$$a_R = \frac{v^2}{r} = \omega^2 r. \tag{9–11}$$

The tangential and radial components of acceleration of any arbitrary point P in a rotating body are shown in Fig. 9–5.

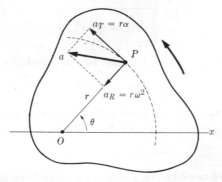

Fig. 9–5. Nonuniform rotation about a fixed axis through point O. The tangential component of acceleration of point P equals $r\alpha$; the radial component equals $r\omega^2$.

9–6 Kinetic energy of rotation. Moment of inertia. We have shown that the magnitude of the velocity of a particle in a rigid body rotating about a fixed axis is

$$v = r\omega,$$

where r is the distance of the particle from the axis and ω is the angular velocity of the body. The kinetic energy of a particle of mass m is therefore

$$\tfrac{1}{2}mv^2 = \tfrac{1}{2}mr^2\omega^2.$$

The total kinetic energy of the body is the sum of the kinetic energy of all particles in the body.

$$E_k = \sum \tfrac{1}{2}mr^2\omega^2.$$

Since ω is the same for all particles in a rigid body,

$$E_k = \tfrac{1}{2}[\sum mr^2]\omega^2.$$

To obtain the sum $\sum mr^2$ the body is subdivided (in imagination) into a large number of particles, the mass of each particle is multiplied by the square of its distance from the axis, and these products are summed over all particles. The result is called the *moment of inertia* of the body, about the axis of rotation, and is represented by I.

$$I = \sum mr^2. \tag{9–12}$$

Moment of inertia is expressed in *slug·feet*^{2}, *kilogram·meters*^{2}, or *gram· centimeters*^{2}.

The rotational kinetic energy can now be written as

$$E_k = \tfrac{1}{2}I\omega^2, \tag{9–13}$$

in which form it is exactly analogous to the translational kinetic energy,

$$E_k = \tfrac{1}{2}mv^2.$$

That is, for rotation about a fixed axis, moment of inertia I is analogous to mass m (or inertia), and angular velocity ω is analogous to linear velocity v.

EXAMPLE. Three small bodies, which can be considered as particles, are connected by light rigid rods as in Fig. 9–6. What is the moment of inertia of the system (a) about an axis through point A, perpendicular to the plane of the diagram, and (b) about an axis coinciding with the rod BC?

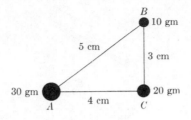

FIGURE 9–6

(a) The particle at point A lies on the axis. Its distance *from* the axis is zero and it contributes nothing to the moment of inertia. Therefore

$$I = \sum mr^2 = 10 \text{ gm} \times (5 \text{ cm})^2 + 20 \text{ gm} \times (4 \text{ cm})^2$$

$$= 570 \text{ gm·cm}^2.$$

(b) The particles at B and C both lie on the axis. The moment of inertia is

$$I = \sum mr^2 = 30 \text{ gm} \times (4 \text{ cm})^2 = 480 \text{ gm·cm}^2.$$

This illustrates the important fact that the moment of inertia of a body, unlike its mass, is not a unique property of the body but depends on the axis about which it is computed.

(c) If the body rotates about an axis through A and perpendicular to the plane of the diagram, with an angular velocity $\omega = 4$ rad/sec, what is the rotational kinetic energy?

$$E_k = \tfrac{1}{2}I\omega^2 = \tfrac{1}{2} \times 570 \text{ gm·cm}^2 \times \left(4 \frac{\text{rad}}{\text{sec}}\right)^2$$

$$= 4560 \text{ ergs.}$$

For a body which is not composed of discrete point masses but is a continuous distribution of matter, the summation expressed in the definition of moment of inertia, $I = \sum mr^2$, must be evaluated by the methods of calculus. The moments of inertia of a few simple but important bodies are listed in Fig. 9–7 for convenience.

Whatever the shape of a body, it is always possible to find a radial distance from any given axis at which the mass of the body could be concentrated without altering the moment of inertia of the body about that axis. This distance is called the *radius of gyration* of the body about the given axis, and is represented by k.

If the mass m of the body actually were concentrated at this distance, the moment of inertia would be that of a particle of mass m at a distance

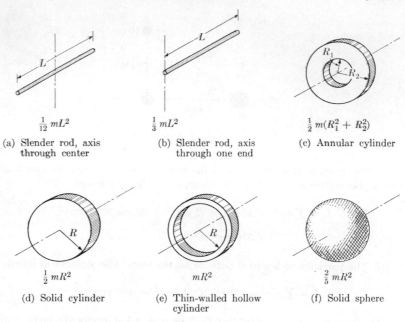

$\frac{1}{12} mL^2$

(a) Slender rod, axis
through center

$\frac{1}{3} mL^2$

(b) Slender rod, axis
through one end

$\frac{1}{2} m(R_1^2 + R_2^2)$

(c) Annular cylinder

$\frac{1}{2} mR^2$

(d) Solid cylinder

mR^2

(e) Thin-walled hollow
cylinder

$\frac{2}{5} mR^2$

(f) Solid sphere

Fig. 9-7. Moments of inertia.

k from an axis, or mk^2. Since this equals the actual moment of inertia, I, then

$$mk^2 = I,$$

$$\boxed{k = \sqrt{I/m}.}$$ (9-14)

Equation (9-14) may be considered the definition of radius of gyration.

EXAMPLE. What is the radius of gyration of a slender rod of mass m and length L about an axis perpendicular to its length and passing through the center?

The moment of inertia about an axis through the center is $I_0 = \frac{1}{12}mL^2$. Hence

$$k_0 = \sqrt{(mL^2/12)/m} = L/(2\sqrt{3}) = 0.289L.$$

The radius of gyration, like the moment of inertia, depends on the location of the axis.

Note carefully that, in general, the mass of a body can*not* be considered as concentrated at its center of gravity for the purpose of computing its moment of inertia. For example, when a rod is pivoted about its center, the distance from the axis to the center of gravity is zero, although the radius of gyration is $L/2\sqrt{3}$.

9–7 Work and power in rotational motion. Suppose a force **F** acts as shown in Fig. 9–8 at the rim of a pivoted wheel of radius R while the wheel rotates through a small angle $\Delta\theta$. If this angle is small enough, the force may be regarded as constant during the correspondingly small time interval. By definition, the work of the force **F** is

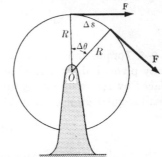

$$\Delta W = F \, \Delta s.$$

But $\Delta s = R \, \Delta \theta$, so that

$$\Delta W = FR \, \Delta \theta.$$

But FR is the torque, Γ, due to the force **F**, so we have finally

$$\boxed{\Delta W = \Gamma \, \Delta \theta.} \qquad (9\text{--}15)$$

FIGURE 9–8

If the torque is constant while the angle changes by a finite amount from θ_1 to θ_2,

$$W = \Gamma(\theta_2 - \theta_1).$$

That is, the work done by a constant torque equals the product of the torque and the angular displacement.

If Γ is expressed in pound·feet, the work is in foot·pounds. If Γ is in meters·newton, the work is in joules; and if Γ is in centimeters·dyne, the work is in ergs.

When both sides of Eq. (9–15) are divided by the small time interval Δt, we obtain

$$\Delta W / \Delta t = \Gamma \, \Delta \theta / \Delta t .$$

But $\Delta W / \Delta t$ is the rate of doing work or the power, and $\Delta \theta / \Delta t$ is the angular velocity. Hence

$$\boxed{P = \Gamma \omega.} \qquad (9\text{--}16)$$

That is, the instantaneous power developed by an agent exerting a torque equals the product of the torque and the instantaneous angular velocity. This is the analog of $P = Fv$ for linear motion.

EXAMPLE. The drive shaft of an automobile rotates at 3600 rpm and transmits 80 hp from the engine to the rear wheels. Compute the torque developed by the engine.

$$\omega = 3600 \times \frac{2\pi}{60} = 120\pi \ \frac{\text{rad}}{\text{sec}},$$

$$80 \text{ hp} = 44,000 \ \frac{\text{ft·lb}}{\text{sec}},$$

$$\Gamma = \frac{P}{\omega} = \frac{44,000 \text{ ft·lb/sec}}{120\pi \text{ rad/sec}} = 117 \text{ lb·ft}.$$

9–8 Torque and angular acceleration. If a number of forces act on a body pivoted about a fixed axis, the torque Γ in Eq. (9–15) must be replaced by the resultant torque $\sum\Gamma$, so in general the work ΔW done in a small angular displacement $\Delta\theta$ is

$$\Delta W = (\textstyle\sum\Gamma) \cdot \Delta\theta.$$

If the resultant torque remains constant during a finite angular displacement θ, then the work W is given by

$$W = (\textstyle\sum\Gamma) \cdot \theta.$$

Experiment shows that *a constant resultant torque causes a constant angular acceleration,* just as a constant resultant force produces a constant linear acceleration. When, therefore, a constant resultant torque acts on a body, the body undergoes a constant angular acceleration α, and its angular velocity changes from its original value ω_0 to its final value ω, according to the equation developed earlier in this chapter,

$$\omega^2 = \omega_0^2 + 2\alpha\theta. \tag{9–17}$$

The kinetic energy of rotation changes from $\frac{1}{2}I\omega_0^2$ to $\frac{1}{2}I\omega^2$, and this change is equal to the work done. Thus.

$$W = (\textstyle\sum\Gamma) \cdot \theta = \tfrac{1}{2}I\omega^2 - \tfrac{1}{2}I\omega_0^2,$$

or

$$\textstyle\sum\Gamma = I \ \frac{\omega^2 - \omega_0^2}{2\theta}.$$

Since, from Eq. (9–17), $(\omega^2 - \omega_0^2)/2\theta = \alpha$, we write finally

$$\boxed{\textstyle\sum\Gamma = I\alpha.} \tag{9–18}$$

This is the rotational analog of Newton's second law, $\sum F = ma$, for rotation of a rigid body about a fixed axis.

EXAMPLE. A rope is wrapped around the surface of a flywheel 2 ft in radius, and a 10-lb weight hangs from the rope (Fig. 9–9). The wheel is free to rotate about a horizontal axis through its center. Compute its angular acceleration and the tension in the rope if the moment of inertia of the wheel is 1.5 slug·ft².

Isolate the flywheel, as in Fig. 9–9(b). Taking moments about the axis,

$$\sum \Gamma = I\alpha,$$

$$2 \text{ ft} \times T = 1.5 \text{ slug·ft}^2 \times \alpha.$$

Isolating the 10-lb weight, as in Fig. 9–9(c),

$$\sum F = ma,$$

$$10 \text{ lb} - T = \frac{10}{32} \text{ slugs } a.$$

Also, since the linear acceleration of the weight equals the tangential acceleration of the surface of the flywheel,

$$a = R\alpha = 2 \text{ ft} \times \alpha.$$

Simultaneous solution of these equations gives

$$a = 14.5 \frac{\text{ft}}{\text{sec}^2}, \qquad \alpha = 7.27 \frac{\text{rad}}{\text{sec}^2}, \qquad T = 5.45 \text{ lb}.$$

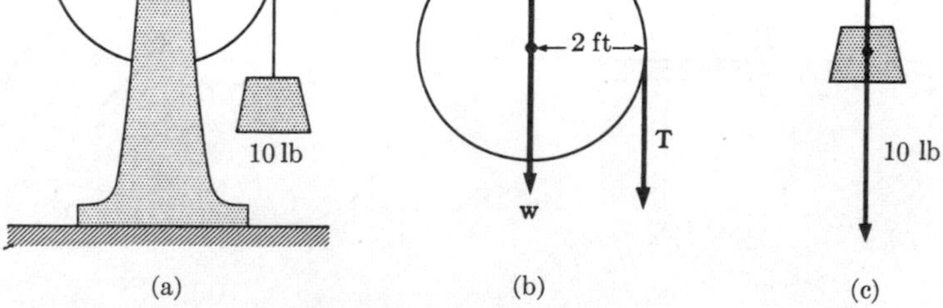

FIGURE 9–9

9–9 Angular momentum and angular impulse. Figure 9–10(a) represents a small body of mass m moving in the plane of the diagram with a speed v and a momentum mv. We define its *angular momentum* about an axis through O perpendicular to the plane of the diagram, as the product of its linear momentum and the perpendicular distance from the axis to its line of motion. That is,

Angular momentum of a particle $= mvr$.

It will be seen that angular momentum is defined in the same way as the moment of a force, and it is often referred to as *moment of momentum*.

Figure 9–10(b) represents a body of finite size rotating in the plane of the diagram about an axis through O. The velocity v of a small element of the body is related to the angular velocity of the body by $v = \omega r$. The angular momentum of the element is therefore $mvr = \omega mr^2$, and the total angular momentum of the body is $\sum \omega mr^2 = \omega \sum mr^2$. But $\sum mr^2$ is the moment of inertia of the body about its axis of rotation. Hence the angular momentum can be written as $I\omega$. In this form it is completely analogous to linear momentum mv. Thus, denoting angular momentum by the symbol L,

$$L = I\omega. \qquad (9\text{–}19)$$

Figure 9–11(a) represents two disks with moments of inertia I and I', respectively, rotating with angular velocities ω_0 and ω_0'. Suppose at moment t_0 the two disks engage and, after a very short interval of time, say $t - t_0$, the disks have the same final angular velocity ω, as in Fig. 9–11(b). (Subscript zero means before engaging, and the absence of a subscript, after.) During the very short time interval necessary to cause these changes in angular velocity, the larger disk exerts a torque Γ on the smaller, and the smaller exerts a torque Γ' on the larger. From Newton's third law Γ and Γ' are at all times equal in magnitude and oppositely directed. That is, $\Gamma = -\Gamma'$. Both Γ and Γ' vary during the

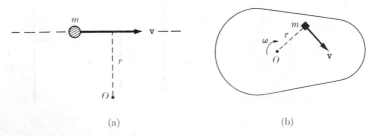

(a)   (b)

Fig. 9–10. Angular momentum.

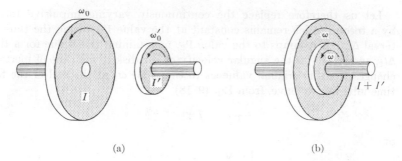

(a)   (b)

FIG. 9–11. An impulsive torque acts when two rotating disks engage.

contact. Both are zero before contact, both are small at the first instant
of contact, then both increase to a maximum, and both decrease and
become zero when the disks attain their final angular velocity.

A torque that varies with the time in this manner is called an *impulsive torque* and is plotted on a torque-time diagram in Fig. 9–12(a) and
is seen to have the same characteristics as those of the impulsive force
shown in Fig. 8–2(a). Suppose the total time interval $t - t_0$ is subdivided
into any number of parts Δt_1, Δt_2, . . . , and rectangles are drawn as in
Fig. 9–12(b) whose jagged outline approximates the smooth curve. As
before, the larger the number of subdivisions, the more closely will the
smooth curve be approximated and the more closely will the sum of the
areas of the rectangles approach the area under the smooth curve.

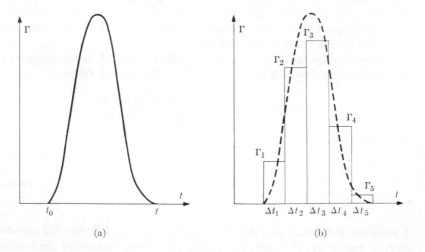

(a)   (b)

FIGURE 9–12

Let us therefore replace the continuously varying impulsive torque by a torque which remains constant at the value Γ_1 during the time interval Δt_1, then jumps to the value Γ_2, maintaining this value for a time Δt_2, and so on. If the angular velocity of the disk of moment of inertia I changes from its original value ω_0 to the value ω_1 at the end of the first time interval, we have, from Eq. (9–18)

$$\Gamma_1 = I \frac{\omega_1 - \omega_0}{\Delta t_1}$$

or

$$\Gamma_1 \, \Delta t_1 = I\omega_1 - I\omega_0,$$

and similarly for all the other intervals

$$\Gamma_2 \, \Delta t_2 = I\omega_2 - I\omega_1,$$

$$\Gamma_3 \, \Delta t_3 = I\omega_3 - I\omega_2,$$

$$\Gamma_4 \, \Delta t_4 = I\omega_4 - I\omega_3,$$

$$\Gamma_5 \, \Delta t_5 = I\omega_5 - I\omega_4,$$

where ω is the angular velocity at the end of the last time interval. Adding these equations, we get

$$\sum \Gamma \, \Delta t = I\omega - I\omega_0.$$

If we now imagine the total time interval subdivided into a larger and larger number of steps, the left member becomes the area under the smooth curve, while the right member remains unaffected. We have therefore the *rigorous* result that the area under the $\Gamma - t$ curve is equal to the *change* in the value of the product $I\omega$.

The area under the $\Gamma - t$ curve is called the *impulse* of the torque (or the *angular impulse*) and is represented by the symbol J_θ, thus

$$\text{Angular impulse } J_\theta = \begin{Bmatrix} \text{Area under} \\ \Gamma - t \text{ curve} \end{Bmatrix}.$$

We have, therefore,

$$\boxed{\begin{aligned} J_\theta &= I\omega - I\omega_0, \\ J'_\theta &= I'\omega - I'\omega'_0. \end{aligned}} \qquad (9\text{–}20)$$

Equations (9–20) may therefore be stated verbally as follows: *The angular impulse acting on either body is equal to the change in angular momentum of that body about the same axis.*

9–10 Conservation of angular momentum. Since the torque Γ acting on the smaller disk of Fig. 9–11 is at all times equal in magnitude and opposite in direction to the torque Γ' acting on the larger disk, we have

$$J_\theta = -J'_\theta$$

and therefore, from Eqs. (9–20),

$$I\omega - I\omega_0 = -(I'\omega - I'\omega'_0)$$

or

$$\boxed{I\omega_0 + I'\omega'_0 = (I + I')\omega.} \tag{9–21}$$

The left side of Eq. (9–21) is the total angular momentum of the system (consisting of both disks) before engaging, and the right side is the total angular momentum after engaging. We have therefore derived the important result that the total angular momentum of the whole system is unaltered. When both disks are regarded as one system, then the torques Γ and Γ' are *internal* torques and during the engaging process no external torque acts. We therefore have the result that *if the resultant external torque on a system is zero, the angular momentum of the system remains constant;* and hence any interaction between the parts of a system cannot alter its total angular momentum. This is the *principle of conservation of angular momentum,* and it ranks with the principles of conservation of linear momentum and conservation of energy as one of the most fundamental of physical laws.

A circus acrobat, a diver, or a skater performing a pirouette on the toe of one skate, all take advantage of the principle. Suppose an acrobat has just left a swing as in Fig. 9–13, with arms and legs extended and with a small clockwise angular momentum. When he pulls his arms and legs in, his moment of inertia I becomes much smaller. Since his angular momentum $I\omega$ remains constant and I decreases, his angular velocity ω increases.

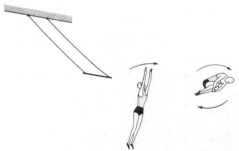

FIG. 9–13. Conservation of angular momentum.

EXAMPLE 1. A 10-lb disk with a radius of gyration of 9 inches and rotating with an angular velocity of 120 rpm engages with another disk of weight 15 lb, radius of gyration 12 inches, originally rotating in the same direction as the first with an angular velocity of 40 rpm. What is the final angular velocity of both disks?

$$I = \frac{w}{g} k^2 = \frac{10}{32} \text{ slugs} \left(\frac{9}{12} \text{ ft}\right)^2 = 0.176 \text{ slug·ft}^2,$$

$$I' = \frac{w'}{g} k'^2 = \frac{15}{32} \text{ slugs} (1 \text{ ft})^2 = 0.468 \text{ slug·ft}^2,$$

$$\omega_0 = \frac{120 \times 2\pi}{60} = 4\pi \frac{\text{rad}}{\text{sec}},$$

$$\omega_0' = \frac{40 \times 2\pi}{60} = \frac{4}{3} \pi \frac{\text{rad}}{\text{sec}}.$$

Since $I\omega_0 + I'\omega_0' = (I + I')\omega$,

$$\omega = \frac{0.176 \text{ slug·ft}^2 \times 4\pi \text{ rad/sec} + 0.468 \text{ slug·ft}^2 \times \frac{4}{3}\pi \text{ rad/sec}}{(0.176 + 0.468) \text{ slug·ft}^2}$$

$$= 2.19\pi \frac{\text{rad}}{\text{sec}} = 65.7 \text{ rpm}.$$

EXAMPLE 2. A man stands at the center of a turntable, holding his arms extended horizontally with a 10-lb weight in each hand. He is set rotating about a vertical axis with an angular velocity of one revolution in 2 sec. Find his new angular velocity if he drops his hands to his sides. The moment of inertia of the man may be assumed constant and equal to 4 slugs·ft². The original distance of the weights from the axis is 3 ft, and their final distance is 6 inches.

If friction in the turntable is neglected, no external torques act about a vertical axis and the angular momentum about this axis is constant. That is,

$$I\omega = (I\omega)_0 = I_0\omega_0,$$

where I and ω are the final moment of inertia and angular velocity, and I_0 and ω_0 are the initial values of these quantities.

$$I = I_{\text{man}} + I_{\text{weights}},$$

$$I = 4 + 2 \left(\frac{10}{32}\right) \left(\frac{1}{2}\right) = 4.16 \text{ slugs·ft}^2,$$

$$I_0 = 4 + 2 \left(\frac{10}{32}\right) (3)^2 = 9.63 \text{ slugs·ft}^2,$$

$$\omega_0 = \pi \frac{\text{rad}}{\text{sec}},$$

$$\omega = \omega_0 \frac{I_0}{I} = 2.31\pi \frac{\text{rad}}{\text{sec}}.$$

That is, the angular velocity is more than doubled.

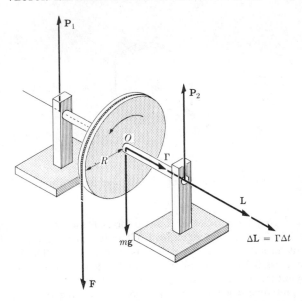

FIG. 9–14. Vector $\Delta\mathbf{L}$ is the change in angular momentum produced in time Δt by the moment $\mathbf{\Gamma}$ of the force $\mathbf{F}$. Vectors $\Delta\mathbf{L}$ and $\mathbf{\Gamma}$ are in the same direction.

9–11 Vector representation of angular quantities. It is an important point that a quantity associated with an axis, such as angular velocity, angular acceleration, etc., can be represented by a vector along the axis. Thus, torque $\mathbf{\Gamma}$ and angular momentum $\mathbf{L}$ are vector quantities. In Fig. 9–14, a disk is mounted on a shaft through its center, the shaft being supported by fixed bearings. If the disk is rotating as indicated, its angular momentum vector $\mathbf{L}$ points toward the right, along the axis.

Suppose a cord is wrapped around the rim of the disk and a force $\mathbf{F}$ is exerted on the cord. The resultant torque on the disk is $\Gamma = FR$, and the torque vector $\mathbf{\Gamma}$ also points along the axis. In a time Δt, the torque produces a vector change $\Delta\mathbf{L}$ in the angular momentum, equal to $\mathbf{\Gamma}\,\Delta t$ and having the same direction as $\mathbf{\Gamma}$. When this change is added vectorially to the original angular momentum $\mathbf{L}$, the resultant is a vector of length $\mathbf{L} + \Delta\mathbf{L}$, in the same direction as $\mathbf{L}$. In other words, the *magnitude* of the angular momentum is increased, its *direction* remaining the same. An increase in the magnitude of the angular momentum simply means that the body rotates more rapidly.

The lengthy argument above appears at first to be nothing more than a difficult way of solving an easy problem in rotation about a fixed axis. However, the vector nature of torque and angular momentum are essential to an understanding of the gyroscope, to be discussed in the next section.

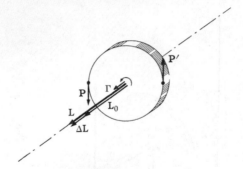

FIG. 9–15. Vector $\Delta \mathbf{L}$ is the change in angular momentum produced by the couple $\mathbf{P}$ - $\mathbf{P}'$.

EXAMPLE. A couple consisting of the two forces $\mathbf{P}$ and $\mathbf{P}'$, each of magnitude 4 lb, is applied for 3 sec to a disk of radius 1.5 ft and moment of inertia 20 slugs·ft², pivoted about an axis through its center as in Fig. 9–15. The initial angular velocity of the disk is 5 rad/sec. Show in a vector diagram the torque, the initial angular momentum, and the final angular momentum.

From the preceding discussion, the vectors representing the torque $\boldsymbol{\Gamma}$ due to the couple, and the initial angular momentum $\mathbf{L}_0$, are directed as in Fig. 9–15. The magnitude of the initial angular momentum is

$$L_0 = I\omega_0 = 20 \times 5 = 100 \,\frac{\text{slugs·ft}^2}{\text{sec}}.$$

The angular impulse, which was defined as the area under the torque-time curve, is in this problem merely the product of the constant torque Γ and the time interval Δt. Since this must equal the change in angular momentum, we have

$$\Gamma \,\Delta t = I\omega - I\omega_0 = \Delta(I\omega) = \Delta L.$$

But $\Gamma = 4 \,\text{lb} \times 3 \,\text{ft} = 12 \,\text{lb·ft}$, and $\Delta t = 3$ sec. Hence

$$\Delta L = 12 \times 3 \,\frac{\text{lb·ft}}{\text{sec}} = 36 \,\frac{\text{slugs·ft}^2}{\text{sec}}.$$

This increase has been represented by the vector $\Delta \mathbf{L}$ in Fig. 9–15. The final angular momentum, $\mathbf{L}$, is the vector sum of $\mathbf{L}_0$ and $\Delta \mathbf{L}$. Since both are in the same direction, the vector sum is simply the arithmetic sum. That is

$$L = L_0 + \Delta L = 136 \,\frac{\text{slugs·ft}^2}{\text{sec}}.$$

9–12 The top and the gyroscope. A symmetrical object rotating about an axis, one point of which is fixed, is called a *top*. If the fixed point is at the center of gravity, the object is called a *gyroscope*. The axis of rotation

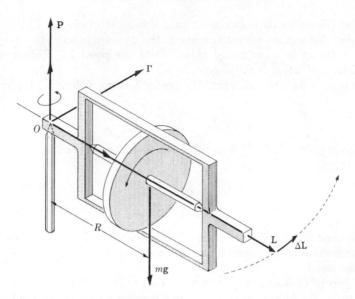

FIG. 9–16. Vector $\Delta \mathbf{L}$ is the change in angular momentum produced in time Δt by the moment $\boldsymbol{\Gamma}$ of the force $m\mathbf{g}$. Vectors $\Delta \mathbf{L}$ and $\boldsymbol{\Gamma}$ are in the same direction.

of a top or gyroscope can itself rotate about the fixed point. When this is the case, the angular momentum vector no longer lies on the axis. However, if the angular velocity *of* the axis is small compared with the angular velocity *about* the axis, the component of angular momentum arising from the former effect is small and we shall neglect it.

Figure 9–16 illustrates the usual mounting of a toy gyroscope, more properly called a top, since the fixed point O is not at the center of gravity. Vector $\mathbf{L}$ is the angular momentum. The upward force $\mathbf{P}$ at the pivot has no moment about this point, and the resultant moment is that due to the weight $m\mathbf{g}$ and given by

$$\Gamma = mgR.$$

Its direction is perpendicular to the axis of rotation as shown. In a time Δt this torque produces a change $\Delta \mathbf{L}$ in the angular momentum, having the same direction as $\boldsymbol{\Gamma}$ and given by

$$\Delta \mathbf{L} = \boldsymbol{\Gamma} \, \Delta t.$$

The angular momentum $\mathbf{L} + \Delta \mathbf{L}$, after a time Δt, is the vector sum of $\mathbf{L}$ and $\Delta \mathbf{L}$. Since $\Delta \mathbf{L}$ is perpendicular to $\mathbf{L}$ and is very small, the new angular momentum vector has the same *magnitude* as the old but a different *direction*. The tip of the angular momentum vector moves as shown, and as time goes on it swings around a horizontal circle. But since the angular momentum vector lies along the gyroscope axis, the axis turns also, rotating in a horizontal plane about the point P. This motion of the axis of rotation is called *precession*.

The angle $\Delta\phi$, through which the vector **L** turns in time Δt, is given by

$$\Delta\phi = \frac{\Delta L}{L} = \frac{\Gamma \, \Delta t}{L}.$$

The *angular velocity of precession* Ω is $\Delta\phi/\Delta t$, and therefore

$$\boxed{\Omega = \frac{\Gamma}{L}.} \qquad (9\text{--}22)$$

The angular velocity of precession is therefore inversely proportional to the angular momentum. If this is large, the precessional angular velocity will be small.

A gyroscope does not necessarily retain a fixed direction in space. We can make the gyroscope turn in any direction we please by applying the appropriate torque.

Why doesn't the gyroscope in Fig. 9–16 fall? The answer is that the upward force **P** exerted on it by the pivot is just equal to its weight mg, so that the resultant vertical *force* is zero and the vertical acceleration of the center of gravity is zero. In other words, the vertical component of its linear momentum remains zero, since there is no resultant vertical force. The two forces **P** and mg constitute a *couple* of moment $\Gamma = mgR$, so the resultant moment is *not* zero and the angular momentum changes. If the gyroscope were not rotating, it would have no angular momentum **L** to start with. Its angular momentum after a time Δt would be that acquired from the couple acting on it and would be in the same direction as the moment of this couple. In other words, the gyroscope would rotate about an axis through O in the direction of the vector Γ. But if the gyroscope is originally rotating, the change in its angular momentum produced by the couple adds vectorially to the large angular momentum it already has, and since Δ**L** is horizontal and perpendicular to **L**, the result is a motion of precession with both the angular momentum vector and the axis remaining horizontal.

To understand why the vertical force **P** should equal mg, we must look further into the way in which the precessional motion in Fig. 9–16 originated. If the frame of the gyroscope is initially held at rest, say by supporting the projecting portion of the frame opposite O with one's finger, the upward forces exerted by the finger and by the pivot are each equal to $mg/2$. If the finger is suddenly removed, the upward force at O, at the first instant, is still $mg/2$. The resultant vertical *force* is not zero, and the center of gravity has an initial downward acceleration. At the same time, precessional motion begins, although with a smaller angular velocity than that in the final steady state. The result of this motion is to cause the end of the frame at O to press down on the pivot with a greater force, so that the upward force at O increases and eventually becomes greater than mg. When this happens, the center of gravity starts to accelerate upward. The process repeats itself and the motion consists of a precession together with an up-and-down oscillation of the axis called *nutation*.

To start the gyroscope off with pure precession, it is necessary to give the outer end of the axis a push in the direction in which it would normally precess. This causes the end of the frame at O to bear down on the pivot so that the upward force at O increases. When this force equals mg, the

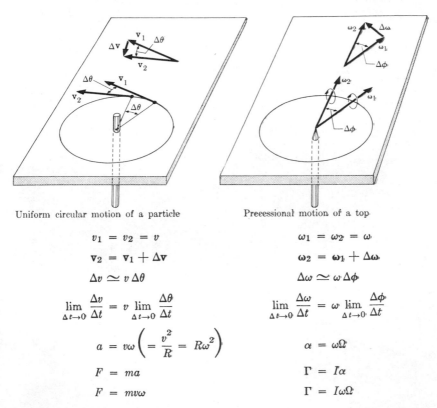

Uniform circular motion of a particle   Precessional motion of a top

$$v_1 = v_2 = v \qquad\qquad \omega_1 = \omega_2 = \omega$$

$$\mathbf{v}_2 = \mathbf{v}_1 + \Delta\mathbf{v} \qquad\qquad \omega_2 = \omega_1 + \Delta\omega$$

$$\Delta v \simeq v\,\Delta\theta \qquad\qquad \Delta\omega \simeq \omega\,\Delta\phi$$

$$\lim_{\Delta t \to 0}\frac{\Delta v}{\Delta t} = v \lim_{\Delta t \to 0}\frac{\Delta\theta}{\Delta t} \qquad\qquad \lim_{\Delta t \to 0}\frac{\Delta\omega}{\Delta t} = \omega \lim_{\Delta t \to 0}\frac{\Delta\phi}{\Delta t}$$

$$a = v\omega \left(= \frac{v^2}{R} = R\omega^2\right) \qquad\qquad \alpha = \omega\Omega$$

$$F = ma \qquad\qquad \Gamma = I\alpha$$

$$F = mv\omega \qquad\qquad \Gamma = I\omega\Omega$$

Fig. 9–17. Analogy between uniform circular motion of a particle and precessional motion of a top.

vertical forces are in equilibrium, the outer end can be released, and the precession continues as in Fig. 9–16.

From a purely kinematic point of view, precessional motion of a top is the rotational analog of uniform circular motion of a particle, as pointed out by Benfield in 1958. The analogy is illustrated in Fig. 9–17, where the diagram and calculation for uniform circular motion are shown on the left and the corresponding diagram and calculation for precessional motion of a top are displayed on the right.

PROBLEMS

9–1. (a) What angle in radians is subtended by an arc 6 ft in length, on the circumference of a circle whose radius is 4 ft? (b) What angle in radians is subtended by an arc of length 78.54 cm on the circumference of a circle of diameter 100 cm? What is this angle in degrees? (c) The angle between two radii of a circle is 0.60 radian. What length of arc is intercepted on the circumference of a circle of radius 200 cm? of radius 200 ft?

9–2. Compute the angular velocity, in rad/sec, of the crankshaft of an automobile engine rotating at 4800 rev/min.

9–3. (a) A cylinder 6 inches in diameter rotates in a lathe at 750 rev/min. What is the tangential velocity of the surface of the cylinder? (b) The proper tangential velocity for machining cast iron is about 2 ft/sec. At how many rev/min should a piece of stock 2 inches in diameter be rotated in a lathe?

9–4. An electric motor running at 1800 rev/min has on its shaft three pulleys, of diameters 2, 4, and 6 in. respectively. Find the linear velocity of the surface of each pulley in ft/sec. The pulleys may be connected by a belt to a similar set on a countershaft, the 2 in. to the 6 in., the 4 in. to the 4 in., and the 6 in. to the 2 in. Find the three possible angular velocities of the countershaft in rev/min.

9–5. A wheel 2.4 ft in diameter starts from rest and accelerates uniformly to an angular velocity of 100 rad/sec in 20 sec. Find the angular acceleration and the angle turned through.

9–6. The angular velocity of a flywheel decreases uniformly from 1000 rev/min to 400 rev/min in 5 sec. Find the angular acceleration and the number of revolutions made by the wheel in the 5-sec interval. How many more seconds are required for the wheel to come to rest?

9–7. A flywheel requires 3 sec to rotate through 234 radians. Its angular velocity at the end of this time is 108 rad/sec. Find its constant angular acceleration.

9–8. A flywheel whose angular acceleration is constant and equal to 2 rad/sec^2, rotates through an angle of 100 radians in 5 sec. How long had it been in motion at the beginning of the 5-sec interval if it started from rest?

9–9. (a) Distinguish clearly between tangential and radial acceleration. (b) A flywheel rotates with constant angular velocity. Does a point on its rim have a tangential acceleration? a radial acceleration? (c) A flywheel is rotating with constant angular acceleration. Does a point on its rim have a tangential acceleration? a radial acceleration? Are these accelerations constant in magnitude?

9–10. A wheel 30 inches in diameter is rotating about a fixed axis with an initial angular velocity of 2 rev/sec. The acceleration is 3 rev/sec^2. (a) Compute the angular velocity after 6 sec. (b) Through what angle has the wheel turned in this time interval? (c) What is the tangential velocity of a point on the rim of the wheel at $t = 6$ sec? (d) What is the resultant acceleration of a point on the rim of the wheel at $t = 6$ sec?

9–11. A wheel having a diameter of 1 ft starts from rest and accelerates uniformly to an angular velocity of 900 rev/min in 5 sec. (a) Find the position at the end of 1 sec of a point originally at the top of the wheel. (b) Compute and show in a diagram the magnitude and direction of the acceleration at the end of 1 sec.

9–12. A flywheel of radius 30 cm starts from rest and accelerates with a constant angular acceleration of 0.50 rad/sec². Compute the tangential acceleration, the radial acceleration, and the resultant acceleration, of a point on its rim (a) at the start, (b) after it has turned through 120°, (c) after it has turned through 240°.

9–13. A wheel starts from rest and accelerates uniformly to an angular velocity of 900 rmp in 20 sec. At the end of 1 sec, (a) find the angle through which the wheel has rotated, and (b) compute and show in a diagram the magnitude and direction of the tangential and radial components of acceleration of a point 6 in. from the axis.

9–14. A wheel rotates with a constant angular velocity of 10 rad/sec. (a) Compute the radial acceleration of a point 2 ft from the axis, from the relation $a_R = \omega^2 R$. (b) Find the tangential velocity of the point, and compute its radial acceleration from the relation $a_R = v^2/R$.

9–15. Find the required angular velocity of an ultracentrifuge, in rpm, in order that the radial acceleration of a point 1 cm from the axis shall equal 300,000 g (i.e., 300,000 times the acceleration of gravity).

9–16. (a) Prove that when a body starts from rest and rotates about a fixed axis with constant angular acceleration, the radial acceleration of a point in the body is directly proportional to its angular displacement. (b) Through what angle will the body have turned when the resultant acceleration makes an angle of 60° with the radial acceleration?

9–17. Find the moment of inertia of a rod 4 cm in diameter and 2 m long, of mass 8 kgm, (a) about an axis perpen-

dicular to the rod and passing through its center, (b) about an axis perpendicular to the rod and passing through one end, (c) about a longitudinal axis through the center of the rod.

9–18. The inner radius of a hollow cylinder is 3 inches, the outer radius is 4 inches, and the length is 6 inches. What is the radius of gyration of the cylinder about its axis?

9–19. The four bodies shown in Fig. 9–18 have equal masses m. Body A is a solid cylinder of radius R. Body B is a hollow thin cylinder of radius R. Body C is a solid square with length of side $= 2R$. Body D is the same size as C, but hollow (i.e., made up of four thin sticks). The bodies have axes of rotation perpendicular to the page and through the center of gravity of each body. (a) Which body has the smallest moment of inertia? (b) Which body has the largest moment of inertia?

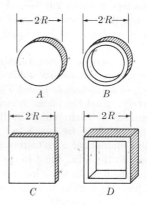

FIGURE 9–18

9–20. Small blocks, each of mass m, are clamped at the ends and at the center of a light rigid rod of length L. Compute the moment of inertia and the radius of gyration of the system about an axis perpendicular to the rod and passing through a point one-quarter of the length from one end. Neglect the moment of inertia of the rod.

9–21. The radius of the earth is 4000 mi and its mass is 4×10^{21} slugs (approximately). Find (a) its moment of inertia about an axis through its center, and (b) its radius of gyration in miles. Assume the density to be uniform.

9–22. A flywheel consists of a solid disk 1 ft in diameter and 1 inch thick, and two projecting hubs 4 inches in diameter and 3 inches long. If the material of which it is constructed weighs 480 lb/ft^3, find (a) its moment of inertia, and (b) its radius of gyration about the axis of rotation.

9–23. A grinding wheel 6 inches in diameter, weighing 4 lb, is rotating at 3600 rpm. (a) What is its kinetic energy? (b) How far would it have to fall to acquire the same kinetic energy?

9–24. A disk of mass m and radius R is pivoted about a horizontal axis through its center, and a small body of mass m is attached to the rim of the disk. If the disk is released from rest with the small body at the end of a horizontal radius, find the angular velocity when the small body is at the bottom.

9–25. The flywheel of a gasoline engine is required to give up 380 ft·lb of kinetic energy while its angular velocity decreases from 600 rpm to 540 rpm. What moment of inertia is required?

9–26. The flywheel of a punch press has a moment of inertia of 15 slug·ft^2 and it runs at 300 rev/min. The flywheel supplies all the energy needed in a quick punching operation. (a) Find the speed in rev/min to which the flywheel will be reduced by a sudden punching operation requiring 4500 ft·lb of work. (b) What must be the con-

stant power supply to the flywheel in horsepower to bring it back to its initial speed in 5 sec?

9–27. A magazine article described a passenger bus in Zurich, Switzerland, which derived its motive power from the energy stored in a large flywheel. The wheel was brought up to speed periodically, when the bus stopped at a station, by an electric motor which could then be attached to the electric power lines. The flywheel was a solid cylinder of mass 1000 kgm, diameter 180 cm, and its top speed was 3000 rev/min. (a) At this speed, what is the kinetic energy of the flywheel? (b) If the average power required to operate the bus is 25 hp, how long can it operate between stops?

9–28. A grindstone in the form of a solid cylinder has a radius of 2 ft and weighs 96 lb. (a) What torque will bring it from rest to an angular velocity of 300 rev/min in 10 sec? (b) What is its kinetic energy when rotating at 300 rev/min?

9–29. The flywheel of a motor weighs 640 lb and has a radius of gyration of 4 ft. The motor develops a constant torque of 1280 lb·ft, and the flywheel starts from rest. (a) What is the angular acceleration of the flywheel? (b) What will be its angular velocity after making 4 revolutions? (c) How much work is done by the motor during the first 4 revolutions?

9–30. The flywheel of a stationary engine has a moment of inertia of 20 slugs·ft^2. (a) What constant torque is required to bring it up to an angular velocity of 900 rpm in 10 sec, starting from rest? (b) What is its final kinetic energy?

9–31. A grindstone 3 ft in diameter, weighing 96 lb, is rotating at 900 rpm. A tool is pressed normally against the rim with a force of 45 lb, and the grindstone comes to rest in 10 sec. Find the coefficient of friction between the tool and the grindstone. Neglect friction in the bearings.

9–32. A constant torque of 20 newtons·meter is exerted on a pivoted wheel for 10 sec, during which time the angular velocity of the wheel increases from zero to 100 rpm. The external torque is then removed and the wheel is brought to rest by friction in its bearings in 100 sec. Compute (a) the moment of inertia of the wheel, (b) the friction torque, (c) the total number of revolutions made by the wheel.

9–33. A cord is wrapped around the rim of a flywheel 2 ft in radius, and a steady pull of 10 lb is exerted on the cord as in Fig. 9–19(a). The wheel is mounted in frictionless bearings on a horizontal shaft through its center. The moment of inertia of the wheel is 2 slugs·ft². (a) Compute the angular acceleration of the wheel. (b) Show that the work done in unwinding 20 ft of cord equals the gain in kinetic energy of the wheel. (c) If a 10-lb weight hangs from the cord as in Fig. 9–19(b), compute the angular acceleration of the wheel. Why is this not the same as in part (a)?

9–34. A solid cylinder of mass 15 kgm, 30 cm in diameter, is pivoted about a horizontal axis through its center, and a rope wrapped around the surface of the cylinder carries at its end a block of mass 8 kgm. (a) How far does the block descend in 5 sec, starting from rest? (b) What is the tension in the rope? (c) What is the force exerted on the cylinder by its bearings?

9–35. A bucket of water weighing 64 lb is suspended by a rope wrapped around a windlass in the form of a solid cylinder 1 ft in diameter, also weighing 64 lb. The bucket is released from rest at the top of a well and falls 64 ft to the water. (a) What is the tension in the rope while the bucket is falling? (b) With what velocity does the bucket strike the water? (c) What was the time of fall? Neglect the weight of the rope.

9–36. A 16-lb block rests on a horizontal frictionless surface. A cord attached to the block passes over a pulley, whose diameter is 6 inches, to a hanging block which also weighs 16 lb. The system is released from rest, and the blocks are observed to move 16 ft in 2 sec. (a) What was the moment of inertia of the pulley? (b) What was the tension in each part of the cord?

9–37. Figure 9–20 represents an Atwood's machine. Find the linear accelerations of blocks A and B, the angular acceleration of the wheel C,

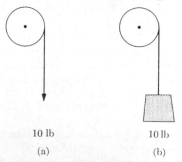

10 lb

(a)

10 lb

(b)

FIGURE 9–19

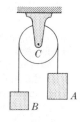

A

B

C

FIGURE 9–20

and the tension in each side of the cord (a) If the surface of the wheel is frictionless, (b) if there is no slipping between the cord and the surface of the wheel. Let the weights of blocks A and B be 8 lb and 4 lb respectively, the moment of inertia of the wheel about its axis be 0.125 slug·ft^2, and the radius of the wheel be 0.5 ft.

9–38. A flywheel 3 ft in diameter is pivoted on a horizontal axis. A rope is wrapped around the outside of the flywheel and a steady pull of 10 lb is exerted on the rope. It is found that 24 ft of rope are unwound in 4 sec. (a) What was the angular acceleration of the flywheel? (b) What was its final angular velocity? (c) What was its final kinetic energy? (d) What is its moment of inertia?

9–39. A light rigid rod 100 cm long has a small block of mass 50 gm attached at one end. The other end is pivoted, and the rod rotates in a vertical circle. At a certain instant the rod makes an angle of 53° with the vertical, and the tangential speed of the block is 400 cm/sec. (a) What are the horizontal and vertical components of the velocity of the block? (b) What is the moment of inertia of the system? (c) What is the radial acceleration of the block? (d) What is the tangential acceleration of the block? (e) What is the tension or compression in the rod?

9–40. (a) Compute the torque developed by an airplane engine whose output is 2000 hp at an angular velocity of 2400 rev/min. (b) If a drum 18 inches in diameter were attached to the motor shaft, and the power output of the motor were used to raise a weight hanging from a rope wrapped around the shaft, how large a weight could be lifted? (c) With what velocity would it rise?

9–41. A block of mass m = 5 kgm slides down a surface inclined 37° to the horizontal as shown in Fig. 9–21. The coefficient of sliding friction is 0.25. A string attached to the block is wrapped around a flywheel on a fixed axis at O. The flywheel has a mass M = 20 kgm, an outer radius R = 0.2 m, and a radius of gyration with respect to the axis k_0 = 0.1 m. (a) What is the acceleration of the block down the plane? (b) What is the tension in the string?

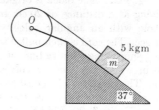

FIGURE 9–21

9–42. A man sits on a piano stool holding a pair of dumbbells at a distance of 3 ft from the axis of rotation of the stool. He is given an angular velocity of 2 rad/sec, after which he pulls the dumbbells in until they are but 1 ft distant from the axis. The moment of inertia of the man about the axis of rotation is 3 slugs·ft^2 and may be considered constant. The dumbbells weigh 16 lb each and may be considered point masses. Neglect friction. (a) What is the initial angular momentum of the system? (b) What is the angular velocity of the system after the dumbbells are pulled in toward the axis? (c) Compute the kinetic energy of the system before and after the dumbbells are pulled in. Account for the difference, if any.

9–43. A block of mass 50 gm is attached to a cord passing through a hole in a horizontal frictionless surface

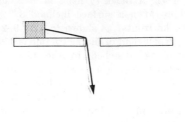

FIGURE 9–22

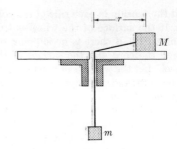

FIGURE 9–23

as in Fig. 9–22. The block is originally revolving at a distance of 20 cm from the hole with an angular velocity of 3 rad/sec. The cord is then pulled from below, shortening the radius of the circle in which the block revolves to 10 cm. The block may be considered a point mass. (a) What is the new angular velocity? (b) Find the change in kinetic energy of the block.

9–44. A small block weighing 8 lb is attached to a cord passing through a hole in a horizontal frictionless surface. The block is originally revolving in a circle of radius 2 ft about the hole with a tangential velocity of 12 ft/sec. The cord is then pulled slowly from below, shortening the radius of the circle in which the block revolves. The breaking strength of the cord is 144 lb. What will be the radius of the circle when the cord breaks?

9–45. A block of mass M rests on a turntable which is rotating at constant angular velocity ω. A smooth cord runs from the block through a hole in the center of the table down to a hanging block of mass m. The coefficient of friction between the first block and the turntable is μ. (See Fig. 9–23.) Find the largest and smallest values of the radius r for which the first block will remain at rest relative to the turntable.

9–46. A uniform rod of mass 30 gm and 20 cm long rotates in a horizontal plane about a fixed vertical axis through its center. Two small bodies, each of mass 20 gm, are mounted so that they can slide along the rod. They are initially held by catches at positions 5 cm on each side of the center of the rod, and the system is rotating at 15 rev/min. Without otherwise changing the system, the catches are released and the masses slide outward along the rod and fly off at the ends. (a) What is the angular velocity of the system at the instant when the small masses reach the ends of the rod? (b) What is the angular velocity of the rod after the small masses leave it?

9–47. A turntable rotates about a fixed vertical axis, making one revolution in 10 sec. The moment of inertia of the turntable about this axis is 720 slugs·ft². A man weighing 160 lb, initially standing at the center of the turntable, runs out along a radius. What is the angular velocity of the turntable when the man is 6 ft from the center?

9–48. Disks A and B are mounted on a shaft SS and may be connected or disconnected by a clutch C, as in Fig. 9–24. The moment of inertia of disk A is one-half that of disk B. With the

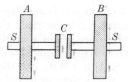

FIGURE 9–24

clutch disconnected, A is brought up to an angular velocity ω_0. The accelerating torque is then removed from A and it is coupled to disk B by the clutch. Bearing friction may be neglected. It is found that 3000 ft·lb of heat are developed in the clutch when the connection is made. What was the original kinetic energy of disk A?

9–49. A man weighing 160 lb stands at the rim of a turntable of radius 10 ft and moment of inertia 2500 slugs·ft^2, mounted on a vertical frictionless shaft at its center. The whole system is initially at rest. The man now walks along the outer edge of the turntable with a velocity of 2 ft/sec, relative to the earth. (a) With what angular velocity and in what direction does the turntable rotate? (b) Through what angle will it have rotated when the man reaches his initial position on the turntable? (c) Through what angle will it have rotated when he reaches his initial position relative to the earth?

9–50. A man weighing 160 lb runs around the edge of a horizontal turntable mounted on a vertical frictionless axis through its center. The velocity of the man, relative to the earth, is 4 ft/sec. The turntable is rotating in the opposite direction with an angular velocity of 0.2 rad/sec. The radius of the turntable is 8 ft and its moment of inertia about the axis of rotation is 320 slugs·ft^2. Find the final angular velocity of the system if the man comes to rest, relative to the turntable.

9–51. Two flywheels, A and B, are mounted on shafts which can be connected or disengaged by a friction clutch C. (Fig. 9–24.) The moment of inertia of wheel A is 4 slugs·ft^2. With the clutch disengaged, wheel A is brought up to an angular velocity of 600 rpm. Wheel B is initially at rest. The clutch is now engaged, accelerating B and decelerating A until both wheels have the same angular velocity. The final angular velocity of the system is 400 rpm. (a) What was the moment of inertia of wheel B? (b) How much energy was lost in the process? Neglect all bearing friction.

9–52. The stabilizing gyroscope of a ship weighs 50 tons, its radius of gyration is 5 ft, and it rotates about a vertical axis with an angular velocity of 900 rev/min. (a) How long a time is required to bring it up to speed, starting from rest, with a constant power input of 100 hp? (b) Find the torque needed to cause the axis to precess in a vertical fore-and-aft plane at the rate of 1 degree/sec.

9–53. The mass of the rotor of a toy gyroscope is 150 gm and its moment of inertia about its axis is 1500 gm·cm^2. The mass of the frame is 30 gm. The gyroscope is supported on a single pivot as in Fig. 9–25, with its center of gravity distant 4 cm horizontally from the pivot, and is precessing in a horizontal plane at the rate of one revolution in 6 sec. (a) Find the upward

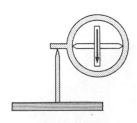

FIGURE 9–25

force exerted by the pivot. (b) Find the angular velocity with which the rotor is spinning about its axis, expressed in rev/min. (c) Copy the diagram, and show by vectors the angular momentum of the rotor and the torque acting on it.

9–54. The moment of inertia of the front wheel of a bicycle is 0.25 slug·ft², its radius is 15 inches, and the forward speed of the bicycle is 20 ft/sec. With what angular velocity must the front wheel be turned about a vertical axis to counteract the capsizing torque due to a weight of 120 lb, one inch horizontally to the right or left of the line of contact of wheels and ground? (Bicycle riders: compare with experience and see if your answer seems reasonable.)

CHAPTER 10

ELASTICITY

10-1 Stress. The preceding chapter dealt with the motion of a "rigid" body, a convenient mathematical abstraction since every real substance yields to some extent under the influence of applied forces. Ultimately, the change in shape or volume of a body when outside forces act on it is determined by the forces between its molecules. Although molecular theory is at present not sufficiently advanced to enable one to calculate the elastic properties of, say, a block of copper starting from the properties of a copper atom, the study of the solid state is an active subject in many research laboratories and our knowledge of it is steadily increasing. In this chapter we shall, however, confine ourselves to quantities that are directly measurable, and not attempt any molecular explanation of the observed behavior.

Figure 10-1(a) shows a bar of uniform cross-sectional area A subjected to equal and opposite pulls **F** at its ends. The bar is said to be in *tension*. Consider a section through the bar at right angles to its length, as indicated by the dotted line. Since every portion of the bar is in equilibrium, that portion at the right of the section must be pulling on the portion at the left with a force **F**, and vice versa. If the section is not too near the ends of the bar, these pulls are uniformly distributed over the cross-sectional area A, as indicated by the short arrows in Fig. 10-1(b). We define the *stress S* at the section as the ratio of the force F to the area A.

$$\text{Stress} = \frac{F}{A}. \tag{10-1}$$

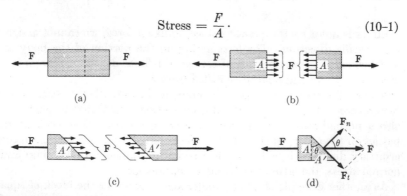

Fig. 10-1. (a) A bar in tension. (b) The stress at a perpendicular section equals F/A. (c) and (d) The stress at an inclined section can be resolved into a *normal* stress, F_n/A', and a *tangential* or *shearing* stress, F_t/A'.

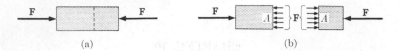

FIG. 10–2. A bar in compression.

The stress is called a *tensile* stress, meaning that each portion *pulls* on the other, and it is also a *normal* stress because the distributed force is perpendicular to the area. Stress is expressed in newtons/m^2, dynes/cm^2, and lb/ft^2. (The lb/in^2 is also commonly used, but it is not a unit of the engineering system.)

Consider next a section through the bar in some arbitrary direction, as in Fig. 10–1(c). The resultant force exerted on the portion at either side of this section, by the portion at the other, is equal and opposite to the force F at the end of the section. Now, however, the force is distributed over a larger area A' and is not at right angles to the area. If we represent the resultant of the distributed forces by a single vector of magnitude F, as in Fig. 10–1(d), this vector can be resolved into a component F_n normal to the area A', and a component F_t tangent to the area. The *normal* stress is defined, as before, as the ratio of the component F_n to the area A'. The ratio of the component F_t to the area A' is called the *tangential* stress or, more commonly, the *shearing* stress at the section.

$$\left.\begin{aligned} \text{Normal stress} &= \frac{F_n}{A'} \\[2mm] \text{Tangential (shearing) stress} &= \frac{F_t}{A'} \end{aligned}\right\} \qquad (10\text{–}2)$$

Stress is not a vector quantity since, unlike a force, we cannot assign to it a specific direction. The *force* acting on the portion of the body on a specified side of a section has, of course, a definite direction. Stress is one of a class of physical quantities called *tensors*.

A bar subjected to pushes at its ends, as in Fig. 10–2, is said to be in *compression*. The stress on the dotted section, illustrated in part (b), is also a normal stress but is now a *compressive* stress, since each portion pushes on the other. It should be evident that if we take a section in some arbitrary direction it will be subject to both a tangential (shearing) and a normal stress, the latter now being a compression.

As another example of a body under stress, consider the block of square cross section in Fig. 10–3(a), acted on by two equal and opposite couples produced by the pairs of forces $\mathbf{F}_x$ and $\mathbf{F}_y$ distributed over its surfaces. The block is in equilibrium, and any portion of it is in equilibrium also.

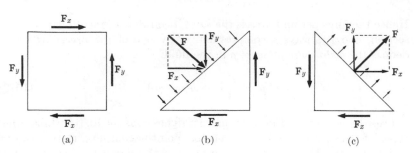

(a)   (b)   (c)

FIG. 10–3. (a) A body in shear. The stress on one diagonal, part (b), is a pure compression; that on the other, part (c), is a pure tension.

Thus the distributed forces over the diagonal face in part (b) must have a resultant $\mathbf{F}$ whose components are equal to $\mathbf{F}_x$ and $\mathbf{F}_y$. The stress at this section is therefore a pure compression, although the stresses at the right face and the bottom are both shearing stresses. Similarly, we see from Fig. 10–3(c) that the other diagonal is in pure tension.

Consider next a fluid under pressure. The term "fluid" means a substance that can flow, hence the term applies to both liquids and gases. If there is a shearing stress at any point in a fluid, the fluid slips sidewise as long as the stress is maintained. Hence in a fluid at rest, the shearing stress is everywhere zero. (Shearing stresses in moving fluids are discussed in Chapter 14.) Figure 10–4 represents a fluid in a cylinder provided with a piston, on which is exerted a downward force. The triangle is a side view of a wedge-shaped portion of the fluid. If for the moment we neglect the weight of the fluid, the only forces on this portion are those exerted by the rest of the fluid, and since these forces can have no shearing (or tangential) component, they must be normal to the surfaces of the wedge. Let $\mathbf{F}_x$, $\mathbf{F}_y$, and $\mathbf{F}$ represent the forces against the three faces. Since the fluid is in equilibrium, it follows that

$$F \sin \theta = F_x, \quad F \cos \theta = F_y.$$

Also,

$$A \sin \theta = A_x, \quad A \cos \theta = A_y.$$

Dividing the upper equations by the lower, we find

$$\frac{F}{A} = \frac{F_x}{A_x} = \frac{F_y}{A_y}.$$

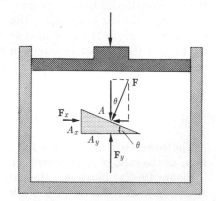

FIG. 10–4. A fluid under hydrostatic pressure. The force on a surface in any direction is normal to the surface.

Hence the force per unit area is the *same*, regardless of the direction of the section, and is always a compression. Any one of the preceding ratios defines the *hydrostatic pressure p* in the fluid.

$$p = \frac{F}{A}, \qquad F = pA. \qquad (10\text{-}3)$$

Pressure is expressed in newtons/m^2, dynes/cm^2, or lb/ft^2. Like other types of stress, pressure is not a vector quantity and no direction can be assigned to it. The *force* against any area within (or bounding) a fluid at rest and under pressure is normal to the area, regardless of the orientation of the area. This is what is meant by the common statement that "the pressure in a fluid is the same in all directions."

The stress within a solid can also be a hydrostatic pressure, provided the stress at all points of the surface of the solid is of this nature. That is, the force per unit area must be the same at *all* points of the surface, and the force must be normal to the surface and directed inward. This is not the case in Fig. 10–2, where forces are applied at the ends of the bar only, but it is automatically the case if a solid is immersed in a fluid under pressure.

10–2 Strain. The term *strain* refers to the relative change in dimensions or shape of a body which is subjected to stress. Associated with each type of stress described in the preceding section is a corresponding type of strain.

Figure 10–5 shows a bar whose natural length is l_0 and which elongates to a length l when equal and opposite pulls are exerted at its ends. The elongation, of course, does not occur at the ends only; every element of the bar stretches in the same proportion as does the bar as a whole. The *tensile strain* in the bar is defined as the ratio of the increase in length to the original length.

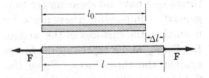

Tensile strain $= \dfrac{l - l_0}{l_0} = \dfrac{\Delta l}{l_0}.$

$(10\text{-}4)$

Fig. 10–5. The longitudinal strain is defined as $\Delta l / l_0$.

The *compressive strain* of a bar in compression is defined in the same way, as the ratio of the decrease in length to the original length.

Figure 10–6(a) illustrates the nature of the deformation when shearing stresses act on the faces of a block, as in Fig. 10–3. The dotted outline *abcd* represents the unstressed block, and the full lines *a'b'c'd'* represent the block under stress. In part (a), the centers of the stressed and unstressed block coincide. In part (b), the edges *ad* and *a'd'* coincide. The

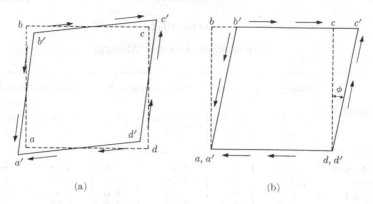

FIG. 10–6. Change in shape of a block in shear. The shearing strain is defined as $\tan \phi \approx \phi$.

lengths of the faces under shear remain very nearly constant, while all dimensions parallel to the diagonal ac increase in length, and those parallel to the diagonal bd decrease in length. Note that this is to be expected in view of the nature of the corresponding internal stresses (see Fig. 10–3). This type of strain is called a *shearing strain*, and is defined as the tangent of the angle ϕ. Since ϕ is always small, $\tan \phi$ is very nearly equal to ϕ (in radians).

$$\text{Shearing strain} = \tan \phi \approx \phi \text{ (radians)}. \tag{10–5}$$

Like other types of strain, shearing strain is a pure number.

The strain produced by a hydrostatic pressure, called a *volume strain*, is defined as the ratio of the change in volume, ΔV, to the original volume V_0. It also is a pure number.

$$\text{Volume strain} = \frac{\Delta V}{V_0}. \tag{10–6}$$

10–3 Elastic modulus. The ratio of a stress to the corresponding strain is called an elastic modulus and, provided the elastic limit is not exceeded, this ratio is found experimentally to be constant, characteristic of a given material. In other words, the stress is directly proportional to the strain, or is a linear function of the strain (within the elastic limit). This linear relationship between stress and strain is called *Hooke's law*.

Let us first consider longitudinal (i.e., tensile or compressive) stresses and strains. Experiment shows that with a given material, a given longitudinal stress produces a strain of the same magnitude whether the stress is a compression or a tension. Hence the ratio of tensile stress to tensile strain, for a given material, equals the ratio of compressive stress to com-

TABLE 10–1

APPROXIMATE ELASTIC MODULI

Material	Young's modulus, Y		Shear modulus, S		Bulk modulus, B	
	10^{12} dynes cm^2	10^6 lb in^2	10^{12} dynes cm^2	10^6 lb in^2	10^{12} dynes cm^2	10^6 lb in^2
Aluminum	0.70	10	0.24	3.4	0.70	10
Brass	0.91	13	0.36	5.1	0.61	8.5
Copper	1.1	16	0.42	6.0	1.4	20
Glass	0.55	7.8	0.23	3.3	0.37	5.2
Iron	0.91	13	0.70	10	1.0	14
Lead	0.16	2.3	0.056	0.8	0.077	1.1
Nickel	2.1	30	0.77	11	2.6	34
Steel	2.0	29	0.84	12	1.6	23
Tungsten	3.6	51	1.5	21	2.0	29

pressive strain. This ratio is called the *stretch modulus* or *Young's modulus* of the material and will be denoted by Y.

$$Y = \frac{\text{tensile stress}}{\text{tensile strain}} = \frac{\text{compressive stress}}{\text{compressive strain}}$$

or

$$Y = \frac{F_n/A}{\Delta l/l_0}. \qquad (10\text{--}7)$$

Since a strain is a pure number, the units of Young's modulus are the same as those of stress, namely, force per unit area. Tabulated values are usually in lb/in^2 or dynes/cm^2. Some typical values are listed in Table 10–1.

The ratio of a shearing stress to the corresponding shearing strain is called the *shear modulus* of a material and will be represented by S. It is also called the *modulus of rigidity* or the *torsion modulus*.

$$S = \frac{\text{shearing stress}}{\text{shearing strain}} = \frac{F_t/A}{\phi}. \qquad (10\text{--}8)$$

(Refer to Fig. 10–6 for the meaning of ϕ.) The shear modulus of a material is also expressed as force per unit area. For most materials it is one-half to one-third as great as Young's modulus.

The modulus relating an increase in hydrostatic pressure to the corresponding fractional decrease in volume is called the *bulk modulus*, and we shall represent it by B.

$$B = - \frac{p}{\Delta V / V_0}. \qquad (10\text{--}9)$$

The minus sign is included in the definition of B since an increase of pressure always causes a decrease in volume. That is, if p is positive, ΔV is negative. By including a minus sign in its definition, the bulk modulus itself is a positive quantity.

The reciprocal of the bulk modulus is called the *compressibility*, k. Tables of physical constants often list the compressibility rather than the bulk modulus. From its definition,

$$k = \frac{1}{B} = - \frac{1}{p} \frac{\Delta V}{V_0}. \qquad (10\text{--}10)$$

The ratio $\Delta V / V_0$ is the fractional change in volume. Hence the compressibility of a substance may be defined as its fractional change in volume per unit increase in pressure.

The units of a bulk modulus, from Eq. (10–9), are the same as those of pressure, and the units of compressibility, from Eq. (10–10), are those of a reciprocal pressure. In tabulating compressibilities, the pressure is often expressed in atmospheres (1 atmosphere = 14.7 lb/in^2). The corresponding units of compressibility are therefore "reciprocal atmospheres," or atm^{-1}. For example, the statement that the compressibility of water (see Table 10–2) is 50×10^{-6} atm^{-1}, or 50×10^{-6} per atmosphere, means that the volume decreases by 50 one-millionths of the original volume for each atmosphere increase in pressure.

Table 10–3 shows the relation between the various types of stress, strain, and elastic moduli.

When a metal rod is subjected to an increasing tensile stress, the strain is found to change as in Fig. 10–7. The first part of the curve, from O to

TABLE 10–2

COMPRESSIBILITY OF LIQUIDS

Liquid	Compressibility, atm^{-1} ($\times 10^{-6}$)
Carbon disulphide	66
Ethyl alcohol	112
Glycerine	22
Mercury	3.8
Water	50

TABLE 10–3

STRESSES AND STRAINS

Type of stress	Stress	Strain	Elastic modulus	Name of modulus
Tension	$\dfrac{F_n}{A}$	$\dfrac{\Delta l}{l_0}$	$Y = \dfrac{F_n/A}{\Delta l/l_0}$	Young's modulus
Compression	$\dfrac{F_n}{A}$	$\dfrac{\Delta l}{l_0}$	$Y = \dfrac{F_n/A}{\Delta l/l_0}$	
Shear	$\dfrac{F_t}{A}$	$\tan \phi \approx \phi$	$S = \dfrac{F_t/A}{\phi}$	Shear modulus
Hydrostatic pressure	$p\left(= \dfrac{F_n}{A} \right)$	$\dfrac{\Delta V}{V_0}$	$B = - \dfrac{p}{\Delta V/V_0}$	Bulk modulus

A, is a straight line. That is, in this region there is a linear relationship between stress and strain and the material obeys Hooke's law. If the stress is not carried beyond that corresponding to point A, the specimen returns to its original length when the stress is removed. In other words, the portion of the curve from O to A is the region of perfect elasticity.

If the stress is increased to a value corresponding to point B and then removed, the specimen does not return to its original length but retains a *permanent strain* or a *set*. Point A is called the *elastic limit* or the *proportional limit* of the material. Finally, when the stress is increased sufficiently, the specimen breaks at point C.

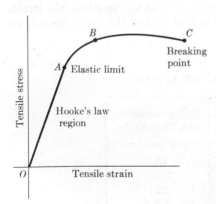

FIG. 10–7. Stress-strain diagram for a metal in tension.

EXAMPLE 1. In an experiment to measure Young's modulus, a load of 1000 lb hanging from a steel wire 8 ft long, of cross section 0.025 in², was found to stretch the wire 0.12 inch above its no-load length. What were the stress, the strain, and the value of

Young's modulus for the steel of which the wire was composed?

$$\text{Stress} = \frac{F_n}{A} = \frac{1000}{0.025} = 40,000 \ \frac{\text{lb}}{\text{in}^2}.$$

$$\text{Strain} = \frac{\Delta l}{l_0} = \frac{0.010}{8} = 0.00125.$$

$$Y = \frac{\text{stress}}{\text{strain}} = \frac{40,000}{0.00125} = 32 \times 10^6 \ \frac{\text{lb}}{\text{in}^2}.$$

EXAMPLE 2. Suppose the object in Fig. 10–6 is a brass plate 2 ft square and $\frac{1}{4}$ inch thick. How large a force F must be exerted on each of its edges if the displacement cc' in Fig. 10–6(b) is 0.01 inch? The shear modulus of brass is 5×10^6 lb/in^2.

The shearing stress on each edge is

$$\text{Shearing stress} = \frac{F_t}{A} = \frac{F}{24 \times \frac{1}{4}} = \frac{F}{6} \ \frac{\text{lb}}{\text{in}^2}.$$

The shearing strain is

$$\text{Shearing strain} = \tan \phi = \frac{0.01}{24} = 4.17 \times 10^{-4}.$$

$$\text{Shear modulus } S = \frac{\text{stress}}{\text{strain}},$$

$$5 \times 10^6 = \frac{F/6}{4.17 \times 10^{-4}},$$

$$F = 12,500 \text{ lb}.$$

EXAMPLE 3. The volume of oil contained in a certain hydraulic press is 5 ft^3. Find the decrease in volume of the oil when subjected to a pressure of 2000 lb/in^2. The compressibility of the oil is 20×10^{-6} per atm.

The volume decreases by 20 parts per million for a pressure increase of one atm. Since 2000 lb/in^2 = 136 atm, the volume decrease is $136 \times 20 = 2720$ parts per million. Since the original volume is 5 ft^3, the actual decrease is

$$\frac{2720}{1,000,000} \times 5 \text{ ft}^3 = 0.0136 \text{ ft}^3 = 23.5 \text{ in}^3.$$

Or, from Eq. (10–10),

$$\Delta V = -kV_0 p = -20 \times 10^{-6} \text{ atm}^{-1} \times 5 \text{ ft}^3 \times 136 \text{ atm}$$

$$= -0.0136 \text{ ft}^3.$$

10–4 The force constant. The various elastic moduli are quantities which describe the elastic properties of a particular *material* and do not directly indicate how much a given rod, cable, or spring constructed of the material will distort under load. If Eq. (10–7) is solved, for F, one obtains

$$F = \frac{YA}{l_0}\, \Delta l$$

or, if YA/l_0 is replaced by a single constant k, and the elongation Δl is represented by x,

$$F = kx. \qquad (10\text{–}11)$$

In other words, the elongation of a body in tension above its no-load length is directly proportional to the stretching force. Hooke's law was originally stated in this form, rather than in terms of stress and strain.

When a helical wire spring is stretched, the stress in the wire is practically a pure shear. The elongation of the spring as a whole is directly proportional to the stretching force. That is, an equation of the form $F = kx$ still applies, the constant k depending on the shear modulus of the wire, its radius, the radius of the coils, and the number of coils.

The constant k, or the ratio of the force to the elongation, is called the *force constant* or the *stiffness* of the spring, and is expressed in pounds per foot, newtons per meter, or dynes per centimeter. It is equal numerically to the force required to produce unit elongation.

PROBLEMS

10-1. A steel wire 10 ft long and 0.1 square inch in cross section is found to stretch 0.01 ft under a tension of 2500 lb. What is Young's modulus for this steel?

10-2. The elastic limit of a steel elevator cable is 40,000 lb/in². Find the maximum upward acceleration which can be given a 2-ton elevator when supported by a cable whose cross section is $\frac{1}{2}$ in² if the stress is not to exceed $\frac{1}{4}$ of the elastic limit.

10-3. A copper wire 12 ft long and 0.036 inch in diameter was given the test below. A load of 4.5 lb was originally hung from the wire to keep it taut. The position of the lower end of the wire was read on a scale.

Added load (lb)	Scale reading (in.)
0	3.02
2	3.04
4	3.06
6	3.08
8	3.10
10	3.12
12	3.14
14	3.65

(a) Make a graph of these values, plotting the increase in length horizontally and the added load vertically. (b) Calculate the value of Young's modulus. (c) What was the stress at the elastic limit?

10-4. A steel wire has the following properties:

Length $= 10$ ft
Cross section $= 0.01$ in²
Young's modulus $= 30,000,000$ lb/in²
Shear modulus $= 10,000,000$ lb/in²
Elastic limit $= 60,000$ lb/in²
Breaking stress $= 120,000$ lb/in²

The wire is fastened at its upper end and hangs vertically. (a) How great a load can be supported without exceeding the elastic limit? (b) How much will the wire stretch under this load? (c) What is the maximum load that can be supported?

10-5. (a) What is the maximum load that can be supported by an aluminum wire 0.05 inch in diameter without exceeding the elastic limit of 14,000 lb/in²? (b) If the wire was originally 20 ft long, how much will it elongate under this load?

10-6. A 10-lb weight hangs on a vertical steel wire 2 ft long and 0.001 in² in cross section. Hanging from the bottom of this weight is a similar steel wire which supports a 5-lb weight. Compute (a) the longitudinal strain, and (b) the elongation of each wire.

10-7. A 32-lb weight, fastened to the end of a steel wire of unstretched length 2 ft, is whirled in a vertical circle with an angular velocity at the bottom of the circle of 2 rps. The cross section of the wire is 0.01 in². Calculate the elongation of the wire when the weight is at the lowest point of its path.

10-8. A copper wire 320 inches long and a steel wire 160 inches long, each of cross section 0.1 in², are fastened end-to-end and stretched with a tension of 100 lb. (a) What is the change in length of each wire? (b) What is the elastic potential energy of the system?

10-9. A copper rod of length 3 ft and cross-sectional area 0.5 in² is fastened end-to-end to a steel rod of length L and cross-sectional area 0.2 in². The compound rod is subjected to equal and opposite pulls of magnitude 6000 lb at its ends. (a) Find the length L of the steel rod if the elongations of the two rods are equal. (b) What is the stress in each rod? (c) What is the strain in each rod?

10–10. A rod 105 cm long, whose weight is negligible, is supported at its ends by wires A and B of equal length. The cross section of A is 1 mm^2, that of B is 2 mm^2. Young's modulus for wire A is 30×10^6 lb/in^2 and for B it is 20×10^6 lb/in^2. At what point along the bar should a weight w be suspended in order to produce (a) equal stresses in A and B, (b) equal strains in A and B? (Fig. 10–8.)

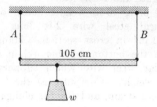

FIGURE 10–8

10–11. A bar of length L, cross-sectional area A, Young's modulus Y, is subjected to a tension F. Represent the stress in the bar by S and the strain by P. Derive the expression for the elastic potential energy, per unit volume, of the bar in terms of S and P.

10–12. The compressibility of sodium is to be measured by observing the displacement of the piston in Fig. 10–4 when a force is applied. The sodium is immersed in an oil which fills the cylinder below the piston. Assume that the piston and walls of the cylinder are perfectly rigid, that there is no friction, and no oil leak. Compute the compressibility of the sodium in terms of the applied force F, the piston displacement x, the piston area A, the initial volume of the oil V_0, the initial volume of the sodium v_0, and the compressibility of the oil k_0.

10–13. Two strips of metal are riveted together at their ends by four rivets, each of diameter 0.25 inch. What is the maximum tension that can be exerted by the riveted strip if the shearing stress on the rivets is not to exceed 10,000 lb/in^2? Assume each rivet to carry one-quarter of the load.

10–14. Find the weight per cubic foot of ocean water at a depth where the pressure is 4700 lb/ft^2. The weight at the surface is 64 lb/ft^3.

10–15. Compute the compressibility of steel, in reciprocal atmospheres, and compare with that of water. Which material is the more readily compressed?

10–16. A steel post 6 inches in diameter and 10 ft long is placed vertically and is required to support a load of 20,000 lb. (a) What is the stress in the post? (b) What is the strain in the post? (c) What is the change in length of the post?

10–17. A bar of cross section A is subjected to equal and opposite tensile forces $\mathbf{F}$ at its ends. Consider a plane through the bar making an angle θ with a plane at right angles to the bar (Fig. 10–9). (a) What is the tensile (normal) stress at this plane, in terms of F, A, and θ? (b) What is the shearing (tangential) stress at the plane, in terms of F, A, and θ? (c) For what value of θ is the tensile stress a maximum? (d) For what value of θ is the shearing stress a maximum?

10–18. Suppose the block in Fig. 10–3 is rectangular instead of square,

FIGURE 10–9

but is in equilibrium under the action of shearing stresses on those outside faces perpendicular to the plane of the diagram. (Note that then $F_x \neq F_y$.) (a) Show that the shearing stress is the same on all outside faces perpendicular to the plane of the diagram. (b) Show that on all sections perpendicular to the plane of the diagram and making an angle of 45° with an end face, the stress is still a pure tension or compression.

CHAPTER 11

HARMONIC MOTION

11-1 Introduction. The motion of a body when acted upon by a constant force was considered in detail in Chapters 4 and 5. The motion is one of constant acceleration, and it was found useful to derive expressions for the position and velocity of the body at any time, and for its velocity in any position. In the present chapter we are to study the motion of a body when the resultant force on it is not constant, but varies during the motion. Naturally, there are an infinite number of ways in which a force may vary and hence no general expressions can be given for the motion of a body when acted on by a variable force, except that the acceleration at each instant must equal the force at that instant divided by the mass of the body. There is, however, one particular mode of variation which is met with in practice so frequently that it is worth while to develop formulas for this special case. The force referred to is an elastic restoring force, brought into play whenever a body is distorted from its normal shape. When released, the body will be found to vibrate about its equilibrium position.

Examples of this sort of motion are the up-and-down motion which ensues when a weight hanging from a spring is pulled down and released; the vibrations of the strings or air columns of musical instruments; the vibration of a bridge or building under impact loads; and the oscillation of the balance wheel of a watch or of a clock pendulum. Furthermore, many reciprocating motions such as those of the crosshead in a steam engine or the piston of an automobile engine, while not exactly of this type, do approximate it quite closely.

It turns out that the equations of motion involve sines or cosines, and the term *harmonic* is applied to expressions containing these functions. This type of vibratory motion is therefore called *harmonic motion*.

11-2 Elastic restoring forces. It has been shown in Chapter 10 that when a body is caused to change its shape, the distorting force is proportional to the amount of the change, provided the elastic limit is not exceeded. The change may be in the nature of an increase in length, as of a rubber band or a coil spring; or a decrease in length; or a bending as of a flat spring; or a twisting of a rod about its axis; or of many other forms. The term "force" is to be interpreted liberally as the force, or torque, or pressure, or whatever may be producing the distortion. If we restrict the discussion to the case of a push or a pull, where the distortion

218

is simply the displacement of the point of application of the force, the force and displacement are related by Hooke's law,

$$F = kx,$$

where k is a proportionality constant called the *force constant* and x is the displacement from the equilibrium position.

In this equation, F stands for the magnitude of the force which must be exerted *on* an elastic body to produce the displacement x. The force with which the elastic body pulls back on an object to which it is attached is called the *restoring force* and is equal to $-kx$.

11–3 Definitions. To fix our ideas, suppose that a flat strip of steel such as a hacksaw blade is clamped vertically in a vise and a small body is attached to its upper end, as in Fig. 11–1. We shall assume that the strip is sufficiently long and the displacement sufficiently small so that the motion is essentially along a straight line. The mass of the strip itself is negligible.

Let the top of the strip be pulled to the right a distance A, as in Fig. 11–1, and released. The attached body is then acted on by a restoring force exerted by the steel strip and directed toward the equilibrium position O. It therefore accelerates in the direction of this force, and moves in toward the center with increasing speed. The *rate* of increase (i.e., the acceleration) is not constant, however, since the accelerating force becomes smaller as the body approaches the center.

When the body reaches the center, the restoring force has decreased to zero, but because of the velocity which has been acquired, the body "overshoots" the equilibrium position and continues to move toward the left. As soon as the equilibrium position is passed, the restoring force again comes into play, directed now toward the right. The body therefore decelerates, and at a rate which increases with increasing distance from O.

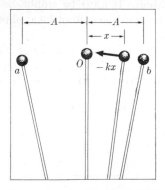

FIG. 11–1. Motion under an elastic restoring force.

It will therefore be brought to rest at some point to the left of O, and repeat its motion in the opposite direction.

Both experiment and theory show that the motion will be confined to a range $\pm A$ on either side of the equilibrium position, each to-and-fro movement taking place in the same length of time. If there were no loss of energy by friction, the motion would continue indefinitely once it had been started. This type of motion, under the influence of an elastic restoring force and in the absence of all friction, is called *simple harmonic motion*, often abbreviated *SHM*.

Any sort of motion which repeats itself in equal intervals of time is called *periodic*, and if the motion is back and forth over the same path, it is also called *oscillatory*.

A *complete vibration* or *oscillation* means one round trip, say from a to b and back to a, or from O to b to O to a and back to O.

The *periodic time*, or simply the *period* of the motion, represented by T, is the time required for one complete vibration.

The *frequency*, f, is the number of complete vibrations per unit time. Evidently the frequency is the reciprocal of the period, or

$$ T = \frac{1}{f}. $$

The *coordinate*, x, at any instant, is the distance away from the equilibrium position or center of the path at that instant.

The *amplitude*, A, is the maximum coordinate. The total range of the motion is therefore $2A$.

11–4 Equations of simple harmonic motion. We now wish to find expressions for the coordinate, velocity, and acceleration of a body moving with simple harmonic motion, just as we found those for a body moving with constant acceleration. It must be emphasized that the equations of motion with *constant* acceleration cannot be applied, since the acceleration is continually changing.

Figure 11–2 represents the vibrating body of Fig. 11–1 at some instant when its coordinate is x. The resultant force on it is simply the elastic restoring force, $-kx$, and from Newton's second law,

$$ F = -kx = ma, $$

or

$$ a = -\frac{k}{m}\,x, \qquad (11\text{–}1) $$

where m is the mass of the body.

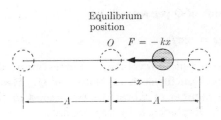

FIGURE 11-2

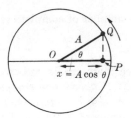

FIG. 11-3. Coordinate of a body in simple harmonic motion.

Since k and m are both constants, the ratio k/m is constant. Hence the acceleration is directly proportional to the displacement and, because of the minus sign, is in the opposite direction to the displacement. That is, when the body is at the right of its equilibrium position, its acceleration is toward the left, and vice versa. Another way of stating this is that the acceleration is always directed toward the center of the path. With the help of calculus, the equation above can be solved at once to find the desired expressions for displacement and velocity. However, we shall make use of a simple geometrical method of deducing these equations.

Consider a type of motion determined as follows. Let Q, Fig. 11-3, be a point revolving in a circle of radius A with a constant angular velocity of ω rad/sec. Let P be a point on the horizontal diameter of the circle, directly below Q. Point P is called the projection of Q onto the diameter. Point Q is referred to as the *reference point*, and the circle in which it moves as the *reference circle*.

As the reference point revolves, the point P moves back and forth along a horizontal line, keeping always directly below (or above) Q. We shall show that the motion of P is the same as that of a body moving under the influence of an elastic restoring force in the absence of friction.

The displacement of P at any time t is the distance OP or x, and if θ represents the angle which OQ makes with the horizontal diameter,

$$x = A \cos \theta.$$

The angle θ is called the *phase angle*, or simply the *phase* of the motion.
If point Q is at the extreme right end of the diameter at time $t = 0$, the angle θ may be written

$$\theta = \omega t.$$

Hence

$$x = A \cos \omega t.$$

Now ω, the angular velocity of Q in radians per second, is related to f, the number of complete revolutions of Q per second, by

$$\omega = 2\pi f,$$

since there are 2π radians in one complete revolution. Furthermore, the point P makes one complete vibration for each revolution of Q. Hence f may also be interpreted as the number of vibrations per second or the frequency of vibration of point P. Replacing ω by $2\pi f$, we have

$$x = A \cos 2\pi ft. \qquad (11\text{-}2)$$

Eq. (11-2) gives the displacement of point P at any time t after the start of the motion, and thus corresponds to

$$x = v_0 t + \tfrac{1}{2} a t^2$$

for a body moving with constant acceleration. Note carefully that x, in Eq. (11-2), represents the *distance from the center of the path*, not the distance from the starting point.

The instantaneous velocity of P may be found with the aid of Fig. 11-4. The reference point Q moves with a tangential velocity

$$v_T = \omega A = 2\pi f A.$$

Since point P is always directly below or above the reference point, the velocity of P at each instant must equal the X-component of the velocity of Q. That is, from Fig. 11-4,

$$v = v_T \sin \theta = -2\pi f A \sin \theta$$

or

$$v = -2\pi f A \sin 2\pi ft. \qquad (11\text{-}3)$$

The minus sign is introduced since the direction of the velocity is toward the left. When Q is below the horizontal diameter, the velocity of P will be toward the right, but since $\sin \theta$ is negative at such points, the minus sign is still needed. Eq. (11-3) gives the velocity of point P at any time, and corresponds to

$$v = v_0 + at$$

for motion with constant acceleration.

Since $\sin \theta = \sqrt{1 - \cos^2 \theta}$ and $\cos \theta = x/A$, Eq. (11-3) may be written

$$v = \pm 2\pi f A \sqrt{1 - (x^2/A^2)},$$

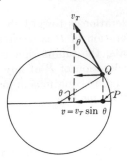

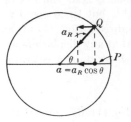

FIG. 11–4. Velocity in simple harmonic motion.

FIG. 11–5. Acceleration in simple harmonic motion.

or

$$v = \pm 2\pi f \sqrt{A^2 - x^2}. \qquad (11\text{--}4)$$

The symbol $\pm$ is required, since at any given displacement x the point may be moving either toward the right or left. Eq. (11–4) gives the velocity of P at any *displacement*. It thus corresponds to

$$v^2 = v_0^2 + 2ax$$

for constant acceleration.

Finally, the acceleration of point P may be found, making use again of the fact that, since P is always directly below or above Q, its acceleration must equal the X-component of the acceleration of Q. Point Q, since it moves in a circular path with a constant angular velocity ω, has at each instant an acceleration toward the center given by

$$a_R = \omega^2 A = 4\pi^2 f^2 A.$$

From Fig. 11–5, the X-component of this acceleration is

$$a = a_R \cos \theta,$$

or

$$a = -4\pi^2 f^2 A \cos 2\pi f t, \qquad (11\text{--}5)$$

and since $A \cos 2\pi f t = x$,

$$a = -4\pi^2 f^2 x. \qquad (11\text{--}6)$$

The minus sign is introduced since the acceleration is toward the left. When Q is at the left of the center, the acceleration of P is toward the right, but since $\cos \theta$ is negative at such points, the minus sign is still required. Eqs. (11–5) and (11–6) give the acceleration of P at any time and at any displacement. There are no corresponding equations in motion with constant acceleration except the extremely simple one

$$a = \text{constant}.$$

Eq. (11–6) states that the acceleration of point P, moving in the manner described, is proportional to the displacement x and is in the direction opposite to x. But this is just the condition which must be fulfilled by a body moving under the influence of an elastic restoring force (Eq. 11–1). Hence it may be concluded that Eqs. (11–2) through (11–6) describe the motion of a body when acted on by such a force, and are the equations which we set out to find.

In order that the motion of point P may coincide in all respects with that of a given vibrating body, the radius A of the reference circle must equal the amplitude A of the actual vibration, and the frequency of revolution of Q must be the same as the frequency of the actual vibration. The proper value of the latter may be found by combining Eq. (11–1),

$$a = - \frac{k}{m} x,$$

which gives the acceleration of the vibrating body at any displacement, and Eq. (11–6)

$$a = -4\pi^2 f^2 x,$$

TABLE 11–1

Motion with constant linear acceleration	Simple harmonic motion (in terms of k/m)	Simple harmonic motion (using $2\pi f = \sqrt{k/m}$)
$a = \text{constant}$	$a = -(k/m)x$ $a = -(k/m)A \cos \sqrt{k/m}\, t$	$a = -4\pi^2 f^2 x$ $a = -4\pi^2 f^2 A \cos 2\pi f t$
$v^2 = v_0^2 + 2ax$ $v = v_0 + at$	$v = \pm\sqrt{k/m}\, \sqrt{A^2 - x^2}$ $v = -\sqrt{k/m}\, A \sin \sqrt{k/m}\, t$	$v = \pm 2\pi f \sqrt{A^2 - x^2}$ $v = -2\pi f A \sin 2\pi f t$
$x = v_0 t + \frac{1}{2}at^2$	$x = A \cos \sqrt{k/m}\, t$	$x = A \cos 2\pi f t$

which gives the acceleration of point P at any displacement. Since these accelerations must be the same,

$$k/m = 4\pi^2 f^2,$$

and therefore

$$f = \frac{1}{2\pi}\sqrt{\frac{k}{m}}. \qquad (11\text{–}7)$$

Eq. (11–7) may be used to find the vibration frequency of a body of given mass when vibrating under the influence of an elastic restoring force of given force constant.

Since the period is the reciprocal of the frequency, Eq. (11–7) may also be written

$$T = 2\pi\sqrt{m/k}. \qquad (11\text{–}8)$$

In using Eqs. (11–7) or (11–8), m must be expressed in slugs, kilograms, or grams, and k in lb/ft, newtons/meter, or dynes/cm. The frequency f will then be in vibrations per second, and the period T in seconds per vibration.

A somewhat unexpected conclusion to be drawn from these equations is that the period does not depend on the amplitude, but on the mass and force constant alone.

The equations for simple harmonic motion may be conveniently summarized by comparing them with similar equations for motion with constant linear acceleration, as shown in the first two columns of Table 11–1.

It is helpful in visualizing harmonic motion to represent the coordinate, velocity, and acceleration of the vibrating body graphically. Graphs of these quantities against time are given in Fig. 11–6, which may be considered as a graph of Eqs. (11–2), (11–3), and (11–5). Notice that the velocity is a maximum when the coordinate is zero, that is, at the center; while the velocity is zero when the coordinate is a maximum. The acceleration, on the other

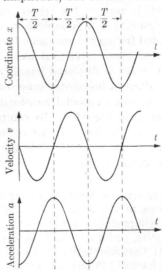

Fig. 11–6. Graphs of coordinate, velocity, and acceleration of a body moving with simple harmonic motion

FIG. 11–7. Multiflash photograph of the motion of a ball suspended from a spring.

hand, is zero at the center and a maximum at the ends of the path.

Figure 11–7 is a multiflash photograph of the motion of a mass suspended from a coil spring and set into vertical vibration. The camera was rotated about a vertical axis while the photographs were taken so that each image is displaced laterally from the preceding image. In effect this introduces a horizontal time scale into the motion, and the body traces out its own sinusoidal coordinate-time graph corresponding to the upper diagram in Fig. 11–6. By comparing the *vertical* separation of successive images, it is seen that the velocity is greatest at the center of the path and zero at the ends, while the acceleration is greatest at the ends and zero at the center.

EXAMPLE. A flat steel strip is mounted as in Fig. 11–1. By attaching a spring balance to the end of the strip and pulling it sidewise, it is found that a force of 1 lb will produce a deflection of 6 inches. A 4-lb body is attached to the end of the strip, pulled aside a distance of 8 inches, and released.

(a) Compute the force constant of the spring.

A force of 1 lb produces a displacement of 6 inches or $\frac{1}{2}$ ft. Hence

$$k = \frac{F}{x} = \frac{1}{\frac{1}{2}} = 2 \frac{\text{lb}}{\text{ft}} \, .$$

(b) Compute the period of vibration.

$$T = 2\pi\sqrt{m/k} = 2\pi\sqrt{(4/32)/2} = \frac{\pi}{2} \text{ sec.}$$

(c) Compute the maximum velocity attained by the vibrating body.

The maximum velocity occurs at the center, where the coordinate is zero. Since

$$v = \pm 2\pi f\sqrt{A^2 - x^2},$$

then when $x = 0$,

$$v = v_{max} = \pm 2\pi f A.$$

Also,

$$f = \frac{1}{T} = \frac{2}{\pi} \frac{\text{vib}}{\text{sec}},$$

$$A = 8 \text{ in.} = \tfrac{2}{3} \text{ ft.}$$

$$\therefore \ v_{max} = \pm 2\pi \times \frac{2}{\pi} \times \frac{2}{3} = \pm \frac{8}{3} \frac{\text{ft}}{\text{sec}}.$$

(d) Compute the maximum acceleration.

The maximum acceleration occurs at the ends of the path where $x = \pm A$. Therefore

$$a_{max} = \mp 4\pi^2 f^2 A = \mp 4\pi^2 \times \left(\frac{2}{\pi}\right)^2 \times \frac{2}{3} = \mp \frac{32}{3} \frac{\text{ft}}{\text{sec}^2}.$$

(e) Compute the velocity and acceleration when the body has moved halfway in toward the center from its initial position.

At this point,

$$x = \frac{A}{2} = \frac{1}{3} \text{ ft,}$$

$$v = -2\pi \times \frac{2}{\pi} \sqrt{(2/3)^2 - (1/3)^2} = -\frac{4}{\sqrt{3}} \frac{\text{ft}}{\text{sec}},$$

$$a = -4\pi^2 \times \left(\frac{2}{\pi}\right)^2 \times \frac{1}{3} = -\frac{16}{3} \frac{\text{ft}}{\text{sec}^2}.$$

(f) How long a time is required for the body to move halfway in to the center from its initial position?

Note that the motion is neither one of constant velocity nor of constant acceleration. The simplest method of handling a problem involving the time required to move from one point to another in harmonic motion is to make use of the reference circle. While the body moves halfway in, the reference point revolves through an angle of 60° (Fig. 11–8). Since the reference point moves with constant angular velocity and makes one complete revolution in $\pi/2$ sec (in this particular example), the time to rotate through 60° is $1/6 \times \pi/2 = \pi/12$ sec.

The time may also be computed directly from the equation

$$x = A \cos 2\pi ft,$$

$$A/2 = A \cos (2\pi \times 2/\pi \times t),$$

$$\cos 4t = \tfrac{1}{2},$$

$$4t = \cos^{-1} \tfrac{1}{2} = \pi/3,$$

$$\therefore \ t = \pi/12 \text{ sec.}$$

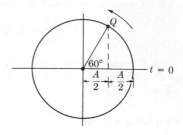

FIGURE 11–8

11–5 The simple pendulum. A simple pendulum consists of a body of small dimensions suspended by an inextensible weightless string. When pulled to one side of its equilibrium position and released, the pendulum bob vibrates about this position with motion which is both periodic and oscillatory. We wish to discover if the motion is simple harmonic.

The necessary condition for simple harmonic motion is that the restoring force F shall be directly proportional to the coordinate x and oppositely directed. The path of the bob, of course, is not a straight line, but the arc of a circle of radius L, where L is the length of the supporting cord. The coordinate refers to distances measured along this arc. (See Fig. 11–9.) Hence if $F = -kx$, the motion will be simple harmonic, or since $x = L\theta$, the requirement may be written $F = -kL\theta$.

Figure 11–9 shows the forces on the bob at an instant when its coordinate is x. Choose axes tangent to the circle and along the radius, and resolve the weight into components. The restoring force F is

$$F = -mg \sin \theta. \quad (11\text{–}9)$$

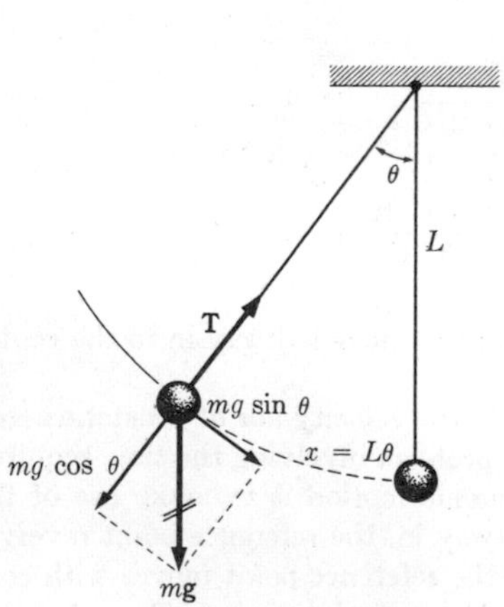

The restoring force is therefore *not* proportional to θ but to $\sin \theta$, so the motion is *not* simple harmonic. However, *if the angle θ is small,* $\sin \theta$ is very nearly equal to θ and Eq. (11–9) becomes

$$F = -mg\theta = -mg \frac{x}{L},$$

or

$$F = - \frac{mg}{L} x.$$

FIG. 11–9. The simple pendulum.

The restoring force is then proportional to the coordinate *for small dis-*

placements, and the constant mg/L represents the force constant k. The period of a simple pendulum when its amplitude is small is therefore

$$T = 2\pi\sqrt{m/k} = 2\pi\sqrt{m/(mg/L)}\,,$$

or

$$T = 2\pi\sqrt{L/g}\,. \tag{11–10}$$

What constitutes a "small" amplitude? It can be shown that the general equation for the time of swing, when the maximum angular displacement is α, is

$$T = 2\pi\sqrt{L/g}\left(1 + \frac{1^2}{2^2}\sin^2\frac{\alpha}{2} + \frac{1^2 \cdot 3^2}{2^2 \cdot 4^2}\sin^4\frac{\alpha}{2} + \cdots\right).$$

The time may be computed to any desired degree of precision by taking enough terms in the infinite series. When $\alpha = 15°$ (on either side of the central position), the true period differs from that given by the approximate Eq. (11–10) by less than one-half of one percent.

The utility of the pendulum as a timekeeper is based on the fact that the period is practically independent of the amplitude. Thus, as a clock runs down and the amplitude of the swings becomes slightly smaller, the clock will still keep very nearly correct time.

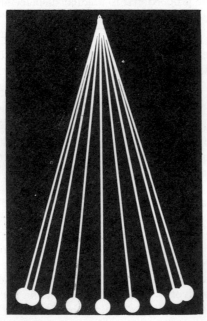

Fig. 11–10. Multiflash photograph of a single swing of a simple pendulum.

The simple pendulum is also a precise and convenient method of measuring the acceleration of gravity g without actually resorting to free fall, since L and T may readily be measured. More complicated pendulums find considerable application in the field of geophysics. Local deposits of ore or oil, if their density differs from that of their surroundings, affect the local value of g, and precise measurements of this quantity over an area which is being prospected often furnish valuable information regarding the nature of underlying deposits.

Figure 11–10 is a multiflash photograph of a single swing of a simple pendulum. The motion is evidently of the simple harmonic type with maximum speed at the center and maximum acceleration at the ends of the swing.

11–6 Angular harmonic motion. Angular harmonic motion results when a body which is pivoted about an axis experiences a restoring torque proportional to the angular displacement from its equilibrium position. This type of vibration is very similar to linear harmonic motion, and the corresponding equations may be written down immediately from the analogies between linear and angular quantities. The oscillatory motion of the balance wheel of a watch is an example of angular harmonic motion.

A restoring torque proportional to angular displacement is expressed by

$$\Gamma = -k'\theta. \tag{11-11}$$

The moment of inertia of the pivoted body corresponds to the mass of a body in linear motion. Hence the period formula for angular harmonic motion is

$$T = 2\pi\sqrt{I/k'}, \tag{11-12}$$

where k' is the constant in Eq. (11–11).

The equations for angular displacement, angular velocity, and angular acceleration can be obtained by comparison with the corresponding equations in Section 11–4.

11–7 The physical pendulum. A so-called "physical" pendulum is any real pendulum, as contrasted with a simple pendulum in which all the mass is assumed to be concentrated at a point. Let Fig. 11–11 represent a body of irregular shape pivoted about a horizontal frictionless axis and displaced from the vertical by an angle θ. The distance from the pivot to the center of gravity is l, the moment of inertia of the pendulum about an axis through the pivot is I, and the mass of the pendulum is m. The restoring torque in the position shown in the figure is

$$\Gamma = -mgl \sin \theta.$$

If θ is small we may replace sin θ
by θ, and

$$\Gamma = -mgl\theta.$$

Hence the pendulum is acted on,
in effect, by an elastic restoring
torque with $k' = mgl$. The period
of vibration is therefore

$$T = 2\pi\sqrt{I/k'} = 2\pi\sqrt{I/mgl}$$

$$(11\text{–}13)$$

(for small amplitudes).

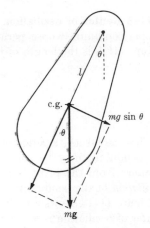

FIG. 11–11. The physical pendulum.

EXAMPLE 1. Let the body in Fig. 11–11 be a meter stick pivoted at one end.
Then if L stands for the length of 1 meter,

$$I = \tfrac{1}{3}mL^2, \qquad l = \frac{L}{2}, \qquad g = 9.8\,\frac{m}{sec^2},$$

$$T = 2\pi\sqrt{\tfrac{1}{3}mL^2/(mgL/2)} = 2\pi\sqrt{(2/3)(L/g)}$$

$$= 2\pi\sqrt{(2/3)(1/9.8)} = 1.65\ sec.$$

EXAMPLE 2. Equation (11–13) may be solved for the moment of inertia I,
giving

$$I = \frac{T^2 mgl}{4\pi^2}. \qquad\qquad (11\text{–}14)$$

The quantities on the right of the equation are all directly measurable. Hence
the moment of inertia of a body of any complex shape may be found by suspending
the body as a physical pendulum and measuring its period of vibration. The
location of the center of gravity can be found by balancing. Since T, m, g, and l
are known, I can be computed. For example,
Fig. 11–12 illustrates a connecting rod pivoted about a horizontal knife-edge. The connecting rod weighs 4 lb, and its center of
gravity has been found by balancing to be 8
inches below the knife-edge. When set into
oscillation, it is found to make 100 complete
vibrations in 120 sec, so that $T = 120/100 =$
1.2 sec. Therefore

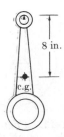

$$I = \frac{(1.2)^2 \times 4 \times \tfrac{2}{3}}{4\pi} = 0.097\ slug\cdot ft^2.$$

FIGURE 11–12

11–8 Center of oscillation. It is always possible to find an *equivalent* simple pendulum whose period is equal to that of a given physical pendulum. If L is the length of the equivalent simple pendulum,

$$T = 2\pi\sqrt{L/g} = 2\pi\sqrt{I/mgl},$$

or

$$L = \frac{I}{ml}. \qquad (11\text{--}15)$$

Thus, as far as its period of vibration is concerned, the mass of a physical pendulum may be considered to be concentrated at a point whose distance from the pivot is $L = I/ml$. This point is called the *center of oscillation* of the pendulum.

Figure 11–13 shows a body pivoted about an axis through P and whose center of oscillation is at point C. The center of oscillation and the point of support have the following interesting property, namely, if the pendulum is pivoted about a new axis through point C its period is unchanged and point P becomes the new center of oscillation. The point of support and the center of oscillation are said to be *conjugate* to each other.

The center of oscillation has another important property. Figure 11–14 shows a baseball bat pivoted at O. If a ball strikes the bat at its center of oscillation, no impulsive force is exerted on the pivot and hence no "sting" is felt if the bat is held at that point. Because of this property, the center of oscillation is called the *center of percussion*.

Figure 11–15 is a series of multiflash photographs illustrating the motion of a body suspended by a cord when the body is struck a horizontal blow. The *center of gravity* is marked by a black band. In (a), the body is struck at its center of percussion relative to a pivot at the upper end of the cord,

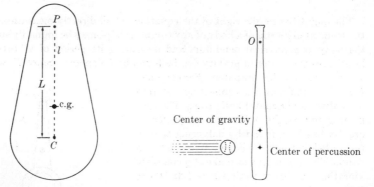

Fig. 11–13.   Center of oscillation. The length L equals that of the equivalent simple pendulum.

Fig. 11–14. The center of percussion coincides with the center of oscillation.

used it starts to swerve according about this point. In (d) the bow is struck

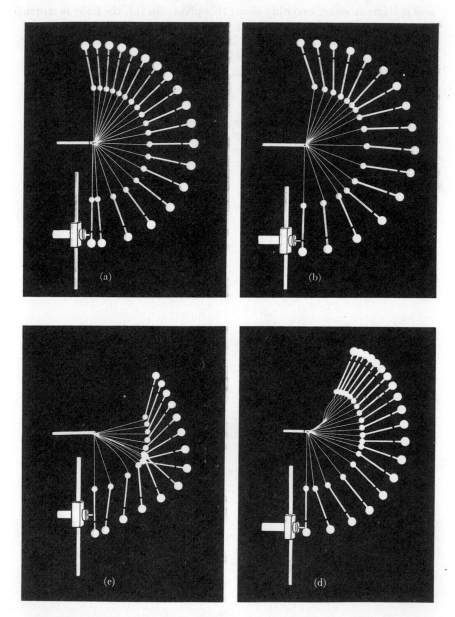

FIG. 11–15. The center of gravity is marked by a black band. A blow is struck (a) at the center of percussion, (b) at the center of gravity, (c) above, and (d) below the center of percussion.

and it starts to swing smoothly about this pivot. In (b), the body is struck at its center of gravity. Note that it does not start to rotate about the pivot, but that its initial motion is one of pure translation. That is, the center of percussion does not coincide with the center of gravity. In (c), the body is struck above, and in (d) below its center of percussion.

Problems

11-1. A body is vibrating with simple harmonic motion of amplitude 15 cm and frequency 4 vib/sec. Compute (a) the maximum values of the acceleration and velocity, (b) the acceleration and velocity when the co-ordinate is 9 cm, (c) the time required to move from the equilibrium position to a point 12 cm distant from it.

11-2. A body of mass 10 gm moves with simple harmonic motion of amplitude 24 cm and period 4 sec. The coordinate is $+24$ cm when $t = 0$. Compute (a) the position of the body when $t = 0.5$ sec, (b) the magnitude and direction of the force acting on the body when $t = 0.5$ sec, (c) the minimum time required for the body to move from its initial position to the point where $x = -12$ cm, (d) the velocity of the body when $x = -12$ cm.

11-3. The motion of the piston of an automobile engine is approximately simple harmonic. (a) If the stroke of an engine (twice the amplitude) is 4 inches and the angular velocity is 3600 rev/min, compute the acceleration of the piston at the end of its stroke. (b) If the piston weighs 1 lb, what resultant force must be exerted on it at this point? (c) What is the velocity of the piston, in mi/hr, at the midpoint of its stroke?

11-4. A 4-lb weight hung from a spring is found to stretch the spring 8 inches. (a) What is the force constant of the spring? (b) What would be the period of vibration of the 4-lb weight, if suspended from this spring? (c) What would be the period of an 8-lb weight hanging from the same spring?

11-5. The scale of a spring balance reading from zero to 32 lb is 6 inches long. A body suspended from the balance is observed to oscillate vertically at 1.5 vib/sec. What is the weight of the body?

11-6. A body of mass 100 gm hangs from a long spiral spring. When pulled down 10 cm below its equilibrium position and released, it vibrates with a period of 2 sec. (a) What is its velocity as it passes through the equilibrium position? (b) What is its acceleration when it is 5 cm above the equilibrium position? (c) When it is moving upward, how long a time is required for it to move from a point 5 cm below its equilibrium position to a point 5 cm above it? (d) How much will the spring shorten if the body is removed?

11-7. A body whose mass is 4.9 kgm hangs from a spring and oscillates with a period of 0.5 sec. How much will the spring shorten when the body is removed?

11-8. Four passengers whose combined weight is 600 lb are observed to compress the springs of an automobile by 2 inches when they enter the automobile. If the total load supported by the springs is 1800 lb, find the period of vibration of the loaded automobile.

11-9. A body of mass m is vibrating with simple harmonic motion of amplitude A. (a) At any moment, when the coordinate is x and the velocity is v, what is the total energy? (b) What is the total energy when $x = A$? (c) Derive the equation

$$v = \sqrt{k/m} \cdot \sqrt{A^2 - x^2}.$$

11-10. A block suspended from a spring vibrates with simple harmonic motion. At an instant when the displacement of the block is equal to one-half the amplitude, what fraction of the total energy of the system is kinetic and what fraction is potential?

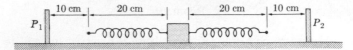

FIGURE 11–16

11–11. Two springs, each of unstretched length 20 cm but having different force constants k_1 and k_2, are attached to opposite ends of a block of mass m on a level frictionless surface. The outer ends of the springs are now attached to the two pins P_1 and P_2, 10 cm from the original positions of the springs. Let $k_1 = 1000$ dynes/cm, $k_2 = 3000$ dynes/cm, $m = 100$ gm. (See Fig. 11–16.) (a) Find the length of each spring when the block is in its new equilibrium position, after the springs have been attached to the pins. (b) Show that the effective force constant of the combination is 4000 dynes/cm. (c) Find the period of vibration of the block if it is slightly displaced from its new equilibrium position and released.

11–12. A body weighing 8 lb is attached to a coil spring and oscillates vertically in simple harmonic motion. The amplitude is 2 ft, and at the highest point of the motion the spring has its natural unstretched length. Calculate the elastic potential energy of the spring, the kinetic energy of the body, its gravitational potential energy relative to the lowest point of the motion, and the sum of these three energies, when the body is (a) at its lowest point, (b) at its equilibrium position, and (c) at its highest point.

11–13. A load of 320 lb suspended from a wire whose unstretched length l_0 is 10 ft, is found to stretch the wire by 0.12 inch. The cross-sectional area of the wire, which can be assumed constant, is 0.016 in². (a) If the load is

pulled down a small additional distance and released, find the frequency at which it will vibrate. (b) Compute Young's modulus for the wire.

11–14. (a) With what additional force must a vertical spring carrying an 8-lb body in equilibrium be stretched so that, when released, it will perform 48 complete oscillations in 32 seconds with an amplitude of 3 inches? (b) What force is exerted by the spring on the body when it is at the lowest point, the middle, and the highest point of the path? (c) What is the kinetic energy of the system when the body is 1 inch below the middle of the path? its potential energy?

11–15. A simple pendulum 8 ft long swings with an amplitude of 1 ft. (a) Compute the velocity of the pendulum at its lowest point. (b) Compute its acceleration at the ends of its path.

11–16. Find the length of a simple pendulum whose period is exactly 1 sec at a point where $g = 32.2$ ft/sec².

11–17. A pendulum clock which keeps correct time at a point where $g = 980.0$ cm/sec² is found to lose 10 sec per day at a higher altitude. Find the value of g at the new location.

11–18. A simple pendulum with a supporting steel wire of cross-sectional area 0.01 cm² is observed to have a period of 2 sec when a 10-kgm lead bob is used. The lead bob is replaced by an aluminum bob of the same dimensions having a mass of 2 kgm, and the period is remeasured. (a) What was the length of the pendulum with the lead bob? (b) By what fraction is the period changed when the aluminum bob is used? Is it an increase or decrease?

11-19. The balance wheel of a watch vibrates with an angular amplitude of π radians and with a period of 0.5 sec. (a) Find its maximum angular velocity. (b) Find its angular velocity when its displacement is one-half its amplitude. (c) Find its angular acceleration when its displacement is 45°.

11-20. A monkey wrench is pivoted at one end and allowed to swing as a physical pendulum. The period is 0.9 sec and the pivot is 6 inches from the center of gravity. (a) What is the radius of gyration of the wrench about an axis through the pivot? (b) If the wrench was initially displaced 0.1 radian from its equilibrium position, what is the angular velocity of the wrench as it passes through the equilibrium position?

11-21. A meter stick is pivoted at one end. At what distance below the pivot should it be struck in order that it start swinging smoothly about the pivot?

CHAPTER 12

HYDROSTATICS

12–1 Introduction. The term "hydrostatics" is applied to the study of fluids at rest, and "hydrodynamics" to fluids in motion. The special branch of hydrodynamics relating to the flow of gases and of air in particular is called "aerodynamics."

A fluid is a substance which can flow. Hence the term includes both liquids and gases. Liquids and gases differ markedly in their compressibilities; a gas is easily compressed, while a liquid is practically incompressible. The small volume changes of a liquid under pressure can usually be neglected in this part of the subject.

The density of a homogeneous material is defined as its mass per unit volume. Densities are therefore expressed in grams per cubic centimeter, kilograms per cubic meter, or slugs per cubic foot. We shall represent density by the greek letter ρ (rho).

$$\rho = \frac{m}{V}, \qquad m = \rho V. \tag{12-1}$$

For example, the weight of 1 cubic foot of water is 62.5 lb; its density is $62.5/32.2 = 1.94$ slugs per cubic foot.

TABLE 12–1

DENSITIES

Material	Density, gm/cm^3	Material	Density, gm/cm^3
Aluminum	2.7	Silver	10.5
Brass	8.6	Steel	7.8
Copper	8.9	Mercury	13.6
Gold	19.3	Ethyl alcohol	0.81
Ice	0.92	Benzene	0.90
Iron	7.8	Glycerin	1.26
Lead	11.3	Water	1.00
Platinum	21.4		

The *specific gravity* of a material is the ratio of its density to that of water and is therefore a pure number. "Specific gravity" is an exceedingly poor term, since it has nothing to do with gravity. "Relative density" would describe the concept more precisely.

12–2 Pressure in a fluid. When the concept of hydrostatic pressure was introduced in Section 10–1, the weight of the fluid was neglected and the pressure was assumed the same at all points. It is a familiar fact, however, that atmospheric pressure decreases with increasing altitude and that the pressure in a lake or in the ocean decreases with increasing distance from the bottom. We therefore generalize the definition of pressure and define the pressure *at any point* as the ratio of the normal force ΔF exerted on a small area ΔA including the point, to the area ΔA.

$$p = \frac{\Delta F}{\Delta A}, \qquad \Delta F = p \, \Delta A. \tag{12–2}$$

If the pressure is the same at all points of a finite plane surface of area A, these equations reduce to Eqs. (10–3),

$$p = \frac{F}{A}, \qquad F = pA.$$

Let us find the general relation between the pressure p at any point in a fluid and the elevation of the point, y. If the fluid is in equilibrium, every volume element is in equilibrium. Consider an element in the form of a thin slab, shown in Fig. 12–1, whose thickness is Δy and whose faces have an area A. If ρ is the density of the fluid, the mass of the element is $\rho A \, \Delta y$ and its weight Δw is $\rho g A \, \Delta y$. The force exerted on the element by the surrounding fluid is everywhere normal to its surface. By symmetry, the resultant horizontal force on its rim is zero. The upward force on

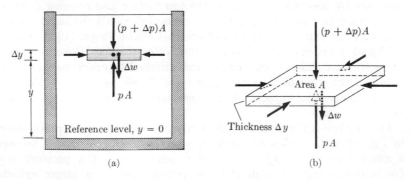

Fig. 12–1. Forces on an element of fluid in equilibrium.

its lower face is pA, and the downward force on its upper face is $(p + \Delta p)A$. Since it is in equilibrium,

$$\Sigma F_y = 0,$$

$$pA - (p + \Delta p)A - \rho g A \, \Delta y = 0,$$

or

$$\boxed{\Delta p = -\rho g \, \Delta y.} \tag{12-3}$$

Since ρ and g are both positive quantities, it follows that a positive Δy (an increase of elevation) is accompanied by a negative Δp (decrease of pressure). If p_1 and p_2 are the pressures at elevations y_1 and y_2 above some reference level, then

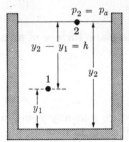

$$p_2 - p_1 = -\rho g(y_2 - y_1).$$

Let us apply this equation to a liquid in an open vessel, such as that shown in Fig. 12-2. Take point 1 at any level and let p represent the pressure at this point. Take point 2 at the top where the pressure is atmospheric pressure, p_a. Then

$$p_a - p = -\rho g(y_2 - y_1),$$

$$p = p_a + \rho g h. \tag{12-4}$$

FIGURE 12-2

Notice that the shape of the containing vessel does not affect the pressure, and that the pressure is the same at all points at the same depth. It also follows from Eq. (12-4) that if the pressure p_a is increased in any way, say by inserting a piston on the top surface and pressing down on it, the pressure p at any depth must increase by exactly the same amount. This fact was stated by the French scientist Blaise Pascal (1623-1662) in 1653 and is called "Pascal's law." It is often stated: "Pressure applied to an enclosed fluid is transmitted undiminished to every portion of the fluid and the walls of the containing vessel." We can see now that it is not an independent principle but a necessary consequence of the laws of mechanics.

Pascal's law is illustrated by the operation of a hydraulic press, shown in Fig. 12-3. A piston of small cross-sectional area a is used to exert a small force f directly on a liquid such as oil. The pressure $p = f/a$ is transmitted through the connecting pipe to a larger cylinder equipped with a larger piston of area A. Since the pressure is the same in both cylinders,

$$p = \frac{f}{a} = \frac{F}{A}$$

and

$$F = \frac{A}{a} \times f.$$

It follows that the hydraulic press is a force-multiplying device with an ideal mechanical advantage equal to the ratio of the areas of the two pistons. Barber chairs, dentist chairs, car lifts, and hydraulic brakes are all devices that make use of the principle of the hydraulic press.

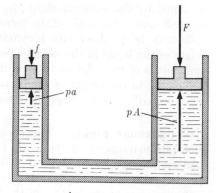

Fig. 12–3. Principle of the hydraulic press.

12–3 The hydrostatic paradox. If a number of vessels of different shapes are interconnected as in Fig. 12–4(a), it will be found that a liquid poured into them will stand at the same level in each. Before the principles of hydrostatics were completely understood, this seemed a very puzzling phenomenon and was called the "hydrostatic paradox." It would appear at first sight, for example, that vessel C should develop a greater pressure at its base than should B, and hence that liquid would be forced from C into B.

Equation (12–4), however, states that the pressure depends only on the depth below the liquid surface and not at all on the shape of the containing vessel. Since the depth of the liquid is the same in each vessel, the pressure at the base of each is the same and hence the system is in equilibrium.

A more detailed explanation may be helpful in understanding the situation. Consider vessel C in Fig. 12–4(b). The forces exerted against

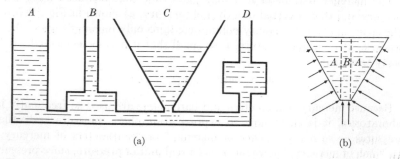

(a)   (b)

Fig. 12–4. (a) The hydrostatic paradox. The top of the liquid stands at the same level in each vessel. (b) Forces on the liquid in vessel C.

the liquid by the walls are shown by arrows, the force being everywhere perpendicular to the walls of the vessel. The inclined forces at the sloping walls may be resolved into horizontal and vertical components. The weight of the liquid in the sections lettered A is supported by the vertical components of these forces. Hence the pressure at the base of the vessel is due only to the weight of the liquid in the cylindrical column B. Any vessel, regardless of its shape, may be treated the same way.

12–4 Pressure gauges.   The simplest type of pressure gauge is the open-tube manometer, illustrated in Fig. 12–5(a). It consists of a U-shaped tube containing a liquid, one end of the tube being at the pressure p which it is desired to measure, while the other end is open to the atmosphere.

The pressure at the bottom of the left column is

$$p + \rho g y_1,$$

while that at the bottom of the right column is

$$p_a + \rho g y_2,$$

where ρ is the density of the manometric liquid. Since these pressures both refer to the same point, it follows that

$$p + \rho g y_1 = p_a + \rho g y_2,$$

and

$$p - p_a = \rho g (y_2 - y_1) = \rho g h.$$

The pressure p is called the *absolute pressure*, whereas the difference $p - p_a$ between this and the atmospheric pressure is called the *gauge pressure*. It is seen that the gauge pressure is proportional to the difference in height of the liquid columns.

The mercury barometer is a long glass tube that has been filled with mercury and then inverted in a dish of mercury, as shown in Fig. 12–5(b). The space above the mercury column contains only mercury vapor whose pressure, at room temperature, is so small that it may be neglected. It is easily seen that

$$p_a = \rho g (y_2 - y_1) = \rho g h.$$

Because mercury manometers and barometers are used so frequently in laboratories, it is customary to express atmospheric pressure and other pressures as so many "inches of mercury" or "centimeters of mercury." An "inch of mercury," however, is *not* a real unit of pressure, since pressure is the ratio of force to area.

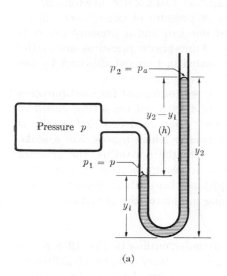
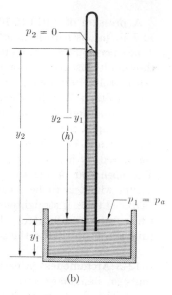

FIG. 12–5. (a) The open-tube manometer. (b) The barometer.

EXAMPLE. Compute the atmospheric pressure on a day when the height of the barometer is 76.0 cm.

The height of the mercury column depends on ρ and g as well as on the atmospheric pressure. Hence both the density of mercury and the local acceleration of gravity must be known. The density varies with the temperature, and g with the latitude and elevation above sea level. All accurate barometers are provided with a thermometer and with a table or chart from which corrections for temperature and elevation can be found. If we assume $g = 980$ cm/sec^2 and $\rho = 13.6$ gm/cm^3,

$$p_a = \rho g h = 13.6 \, \frac{\text{gm}}{\text{cm}^3} \times 980 \, \frac{\text{cm}}{\text{sec}^2} \times 76 \, \text{cm}$$

$$= 1{,}013{,}000 \, \frac{\text{dynes}}{\text{cm}^2}.$$

(About a million dynes per square centimeter.) In British engineering units,

$$76 \, \text{cm} = 30 \, \text{in.} = 2.5 \, \text{ft},$$

$$\rho g = 850 \, \frac{\text{lb}}{\text{ft}^3},$$

$$p_a = 2120 \, \frac{\text{lb}}{\text{ft}^2} = 14.7 \, \frac{\text{lb}}{\text{in}^2}.$$

A pressure of 1.013×10^6 dynes/cm^2 = 1.013×10^5 newtons/m^2 = 14.7 lb/in^2, is called *one atmosphere*. A pressure of exactly one million dynes per square centimeter is called one *bar*, and a pressure one one-thousandth as great is one *millibar*. Atmospheric pressures are of the order of 1000 millibars, and are now stated in terms of this unit by the United States Weather Bureau.

The Bourdon-type pressure gauge is more convenient for most purposes than a liquid manometer. It consists of a flattened brass tube closed at one end and bent into a circular form. The closed end of the tube is connected by a gear and pinion to a pointer which moves over a scale. The open end of the tube is connected to the apparatus, the pressure within which is to be measured. When pressure is exerted within the flattened tube, it straightens slightly just as a bent rubber hose straightens when water is admitted. The resulting motion of the closed end of the tube is transmitted to the pointer.

12–5 Archimedes' principle. The irregular outline in Fig. 12–6 represents an imaginary surface bounding an arbitrary portion of a fluid at rest. The short arrows represent the forces exerted by the surrounding fluid against small elements of the boundary surface of equal area ΔA. The force ΔF against each element is normal to that element and equal to $p \, \Delta A$, where p depends only on the vertical depth below the free surface and not on the shape or orientation of the boundary surface.

Since the entire fluid is at rest, the x-component of the resultant of these surface forces is zero. The y-component of the resultant, F_y, must equal the weight of the fluid inside the arbitrary surface, $m\mathbf{g}$, and its line of action must pass through the center of gravity of this fluid.

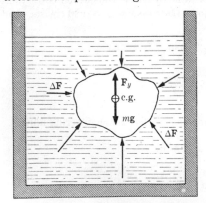

FIG. 12–6. Archimedes' principle. The buoyant force F_y equals the weight of the displaced fluid.

Now suppose the fluid inside the surface to be removed and replaced by a solid body having exactly the same shape. The pressure at every point will be exactly the same as before, so the force exerted on the body by the surrounding fluid will be unaltered. That is, *the fluid exerts on the body an upward force F_y, which is equal to the weight $m\mathbf{g}$ of the fluid originally occupying the boundary surface and whose line of action passes through the original center of gravity.*

The submerged body, in general, will *not* be in equilibrium. Its weight may be greater or less than F_y, and if it is not homogeneous, its center of gravity may not lie on the line of $\mathbf{F}_y$. Therefore, in general, it will be acted on by a resultant force through its own center of gravity and by a couple, and will rise or fall and also rotate.

The fact that a body immersed in a fluid should be "buoyed up" with a force equal to the weight of the displaced fluid was deduced by Archimedes (287–212 B.C.) from reasoning along the same lines as above. It is called *Archimedes' principle* and is, of course, a consequence of Newton's laws and the properties of a fluid. The position of the line of action of the upward force, usually omitted from a statement of the principle, is equal in importance to the magnitude of the force.

The weight of a dirigible floating in air, or of a submarine floating at some depth below the surface of the water, is just equal to the weight of a volume of air, or water, that is equal to the volume of the dirigible or submarine. That is, the average density of the dirigible equals that of air, and the average density of the submarine equals the density of water.

A body whose average density is less than that of a liquid can float *partially* submerged at the free upper surface of the liquid. However, we not only want a ship to float, but to float upright in stable equilibrium without capsizing. This requires that normally the line of action of the buoyant force should pass through the center of gravity of the ship and also, when the ship heels, the couple set up by its weight and the buoyant force should be in such a direction as to right it.

Figure 12–7 represents a section of the hull of a yacht, when on an even keel and when heeled over. In (a), the weight of the yacht $\mathbf{w}$ and the buoyant force $\mathbf{B}$ are equal and opposite, and the lines of action of both pass through the center of gravity of the yacht (c.g.). In (b), the center of gravity of the displaced water has shifted to point b and the line of

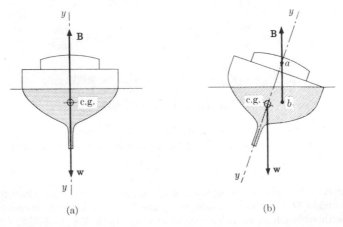

FIG. 12–7. Forces on the hull of a yacht.

action of the buoyant force **B** passes through this point. The line of action of **w** still passes through the center of gravity of the yacht. (Actually, a simple diagram like Fig. 12–7 would apply only if the shape of the hull were the same at all cross sections.) The weight **w** and the buoyant force **B** give rise to a couple in such a direction as to right the yacht. If the line of action of **B** should intersect yy at a point below the center of gravity, the yacht would be unstable and would capsize.

When making "weighings" with a sensitive analytical balance, correction must be made for the buoyant force of the air if the density of the body being "weighed" is very different from that of the standard "weights," which are usually of brass. For example, suppose a block of wood of density 0.4 gm/cm^3 is balanced on an equal-arm balance by brass "weights" of 20 gm, density 8.0 gm/cm^3. The apparent weight of each body is the difference between its true weight and the buoyant force of the air. If ρ_w, ρ_b, and ρ_a are the densities of the wood, brass, and air, and V_w and V_b are the volumes of the wood and brass, the apparent weights, which are equal, are

$$\rho_w V_w g - \rho_a V_w g = \rho_b V_b g - \rho_a V_b g.$$

The true mass of the wood is $\rho_w V_w$, and the true mass of the standard is $\rho_b V_b$. Hence,

$$\text{True mass} = \rho_w V_w = \rho_b V_b + \rho_a(V_w - V_b)$$
$$= \text{mass of standard} + \rho_a(V_w - V_b).$$

In the specific example cited

$$V_w = \frac{20}{0.4} = 50 \text{ cm}^3 \text{ (very nearly)},$$

$$V_b = \frac{20}{8} = 2.5 \text{ cm}^3, \qquad \rho_a = 0.0013 \frac{\text{gm}}{\text{cm}^3}.$$

Hence

$$\rho_a(V_w - V_b) = 0.0013 \times 47.5 = 0.062 \text{ gm}.$$

$$\text{True mass} = 20.062 \text{ gm}.$$

If measurements are being made to one one-thousandth of a gram, it is obvious that the correction of 62 thousandths is of the greatest importance.

EXAMPLE. A tank containing water is placed on a spring scale, which registers a total weight **W**. A stone of weight **w** is hung from a string and lowered into the water without touching the sides or bottom of the tank [Fig. 12–8(a)]. What will be the reading on the spring scale?

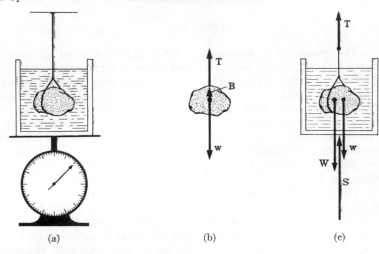

(a)   (b)   (c)

FIGURE 12–8

First, for the stone alone, the forces are as shown in Fig. 12–8(b), where **B** is the buoyant force and **T** is the tension in the string. Since $\sum F_y = 0$,

$$T + B = w.$$

Next, for the tank with the water and stone in it, the forces are as shown in Fig. 12–8(c), where **S** is the force exerted by the spring scale on the isolated system and, by Newton's third law, is equal in magnitude and opposite in direction to the force exerted on the scale. The condition for equilibrium yields the equation

$$T + S = w + W.$$

Subtracting the first equation from the second, we get

$$S = W + B.$$

That is, the reading of the spring scale has been increased by an amount equal to the buoyant force.

PROBLEMS

12–1. The piston of a hydraulic automobile lift is 12 inches in diameter. What pressure, in lb/in², is required to lift a car weighing 2400 lb?

12–2. The expansion tank of a household hot-water heating system is open to the atmosphere and is 30 ft above a pressure gauge attached to the furnace. What is the gauge pressure at the furnace, in lb/in²?

12–3. The submarine Squalus sank at a depth of 240 ft. Compute the absolute pressure at this depth, in lb/in² and lb/ft². The specific gravity of sea water is 1.025.

12–4. A piece of gold-aluminum alloy weighs 10 lb. When suspended from a spring balance and submerged in water, the balance reads 8 lb. What is the weight of gold in the alloy if the specific gravity of gold is 19.3 and the specific gravity of aluminum is 2.5?

12–5. What is the area of the smallest block of ice 1 ft thick that will just support a man weighing 180 lb? The specific gravity of the ice is 0.917, and it is floating in fresh water.

12–6. A cubical block of wood 10 cm on a side floats at the interface between oil and water as in Fig. 12–9, with its lower surface 2 cm below the interface. The density of the oil is 0.6 gm/cm³. (a) What is the mass of the block? (b) What is the gauge pressure at the lower face of the block?

12–7. The densities of air, helium, and hydrogen (at standard conditions) are, respectively, 0.00129 gm/cm³, 0.000178 gm/cm³, and 0.0000899 gm/cm³. What is the volume in cubic feet displaced by a hydrogen-filled dirigible which has a total "lift" of 10 tons? What would be the "lift" if helium were used instead of hydrogen?

12–8. A piece of wood is 2 ft long, 1 ft wide, and 2 inches thick. Its specific gravity is 0.6. What volume of lead must be fastened underneath to sink the wood in calm water so that its top is just even with the water level?

12–9. A cubical block of wood 10 cm on a side and of density 0.5 gm/cm³ floats in a jar of water. Oil of density 0.8 gm/cm³ is poured on the water until the top of the oil layer is 4 cm below the top of the block. (a) How deep is the oil layer? (b) What is the gauge pressure at the lower face of the block?

12–10. A cubical block of steel (density = 7.8 gm/cm³) floats on mercury (density = 13.6 gm/cm³). (a) What fraction of the block is above the mercury surface? (b) If water is poured on the mercury surface, how deep must the water layer be so that the water surface just rises to the top of the steel block?

12–11. Block A in Fig. 12–10 hangs by a cord from spring balance D and is submerged in a liquid C contained in beaker B. The weight of the beaker is 2 lb, the weight of the liquid is 3 lb. Balance D reads 5 lb and balance E reads 15 lb. The volume of block A is 0.1 ft³. (a) What is the weight per unit volume of the liquid? (b) What will each balance read if block A is pulled up out of the liquid?

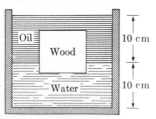

FIGURE 12–9

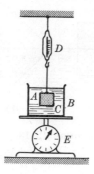

FIGURE 12–10

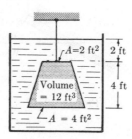

FIGURE 12–11

12–12. A hollow sphere of inner radius 9 cm and outer radius 10 cm floats half submerged in a liquid of specific gravity 0.8. (a) Calculate the density of the material of which the sphere is made. (b) What would be the density of a liquid in which the hollow sphere would just float completely submerged?

12–13. Two spherical bodies having the same diameter are released simultaneously from the same height. If the mass of one is ten times that of the other and if the air resistance on each is the *same*, show that the heavier body will arrive at the ground first.

12–14. When a life preserver having a volume of 0.75 ft³ is immersed in sea water (specific gravity 1.1) it will just support a 160-lb man (specific gravity 1.2) with 2/10 of his volume above water. What is the weight per unit volume of the material composing the life preserver?

12–15. An object in the shape of a truncated cone weighs 1000 lb in vacuum and is suspended by a rope in an open tank of liquid density 2 slugs/ft³, as in Fig. 12–11. (a) Find the total downward force exerted by the liquid on the top of the object, of area 2 ft². (b) Find the total upward force exerted

by the liquid on the bottom of the object, of area 4 ft². (c) Find the tension in the cord supporting the object.

12–16. A hollow cylindrical can 20 cm in diameter floats in water with 10 cm of its height above the water line when a 10-kgm iron block hangs from its bottom. If the block is now placed inside the can, how much of the cylinder's height will be above the water line? The density of iron is 7.8 gm/cm³.

12–17. A block of balsa wood placed in one scale pan of an equal-arm balance is found to be exactly balanced by a 100-gm brass "weight" in the other scale pan. Find the true mass of the balsa wood, if its specific gravity is 0.15.

12–18. A 3200-lb cylindrical can buoy floats vertically in salt water (specific gravity = 1.03). The diameter of the buoy is 3 ft. Calculate (a) the additional distance the buoy will sink when a 150-lb man stands on top, (b) the period of the resulting vertical simple harmonic motion when the man dives off.

12–19. A uniform rod AB, 12 ft long, weighing 24 lb, is supported at end B by a flexible cord and weighted at end A with a 12-lb lead weight. The rod

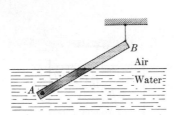

FIGURE 12-12

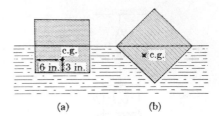

FIGURE 12-13

floats as shown in Fig. 12-12 with one-half its length submerged. The buoyant force on the lead weight can be neglected. (a) Show in a diagram all the forces acting on the rod. (b) Find the tension in the cord. (c) Find the total volume of the rod.

12-20. A cubical block of wood 1 ft on a side is weighted so that its center of gravity is at the point shown in Fig. 12-13(a), and it floats in water with one-half its volume submerged. Compute the righting moment when the block is "heeled" at an angle of 45° as in Fig. 12-13(b).

12-21. A hydrometer consists of a spherical bulb and a cylindrical stem of cross section 0.4 cm². The total volume of bulb and stem is 13.2 cm³. When immersed in water the hydrometer floats with 8 cm of the stem above the

water surface. In alcohol, 1 cm of the stem is above the surface. Find the density of the alcohol.

12-22. A 12-lb uniform rod 6 ft long, whose specific gravity is 0.50, is hinged at one end 3 ft below a water surface as in Fig. 12-14. (a) What weight w must be attached to the other end of the rod so that 5 ft of the rod are submerged? (b) Find the magnitude and direction of the force exerted by the hinge on the rod.

12-23. The following is quoted from a letter. How would you reply?

"It is the practice of carpenters hereabouts, when laying out and leveling up the foundations of relatively long buildings, to use a garden hose filled with water, into the ends of the hose being thrust glass tubes 10–12 inches long.

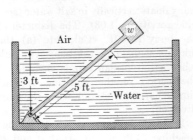

FIGURE 12-14

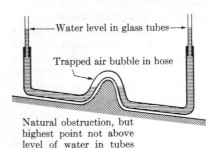

FIGURE 12-15

"The theory is that the water, seeking a common level, will be of the same height in both the tubes and thus effect a level. Now the question rises as to what happens if a bubble of air is left in the hose. Our greybeards contend the air will not affect the reading from one end to the other. Others say that it will cause important inaccuracies.

"Can you give a relatively simple answer to this question, together with an explanation? I include a rough sketch (Fig. 12–15) of the situation that caused the dispute."

CHAPTER 13

SURFACE TENSION

13–1 Surface tension. A liquid flowing slowly from the tip of a medicine dropper emerges, not as a continuous stream, but as a succession of drops. A sewing needle, if placed carefully on a water surface, makes a small depression in the surface and rests there without sinking, even though its density may be as much as ten times that of water. When a clean glass tube of small bore is dipped into water, the water rises in the tube, but if the tube is dipped in mercury, the mercury is depressed. All these phenomena, and many others of a similar nature, are associated with the existence of a boundary surface between a liquid and some other substance.

All surface phenomena indicate that the surface of a liquid can be considered to be in a state of stress such that if one considers any line lying in or bounding the surface, the material on either side of the line exerts a pull on the material on the other side. This pull lies in the plane of the surface and is perpendicular to the line. The effect can be demonstrated with the simple apparatus shown in Fig. 13–1. A wire ring a few inches in diameter has attached to it a loop of thread, as shown. When the ring and thread are dipped in a soap solution and removed, a thin film of liquid is formed in which the thread "floats" freely, as shown in part (a). If the film inside the loop of thread is punctured, the thread springs out into a circular shape as in part (b), as if the surfaces of the liquid were pulling radially outward on it, as shown by the arrows. Presumably, the same forces were acting before the film was punctured, but since there was film on *both* sides of the thread the net force exerted by the film on every portion of the thread was zero.

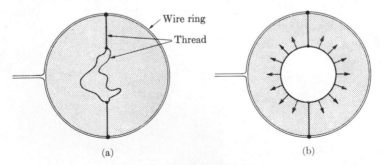

Fig. 13–1. A wire ring with a flexible loop of thread, dipped in a soap solution, (a) before and (b) after puncturing the surface films inside the loop.

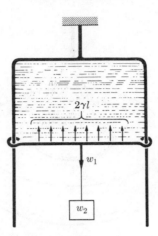

Fig. 13–2. The horizontal slide wire is in equilibrium under the action of the upward surface force $2\gamma l$ and the downward pull $w_1 + w_2$.

Another simple apparatus for demonstrating surface effects is shown in Fig. 13–2. A piece of wire is bent into the shape of a U and a second piece of wire is used as a slider. When the apparatus is dipped in a soap solution and removed, the slider (if its weight w_1 is not too great) is quickly pulled up to the top of the U. It may be held in equilibrium by adding a second weight w_2. Surprisingly, the same total force $F = w_1 + w_2$ will hold the slider at rest in *any* position, regardless of the area of the liquid film, provided the film remains at constant temperature. This is very different from the elastic behavior of a sheet of rubber, for which the force would be greater as the sheet was stretched.

Although a soap film like that in Fig. 13–2 is very thin, its thickness is still enormous compared with the size of a molecule. Hence it can be considered as made up chiefly of bulk liquid, bounded by two surface layers a few molecules thick. When the crossbar in Fig. 13–2 is pulled down and the area of the film is increased, molecules formerly in the main body of the liquid move into the surface layers. That is, these layers are not "stretched" as a rubber sheet would be, but more surface is created by molecules moving from the bulk liquid.

Let l be the length of the wire slider. Since the film has two surfaces, the total length along which the surface force acts is $2l$. The *surface tension* in the film, γ, is defined as *the ratio of the surface force to the length* (perpendicular to the force) *along which the force acts*. Hence in this case,

$$\gamma = F/2l. \tag{13–1}$$

Surface tension is expressed in dynes/cm in the cgs system.

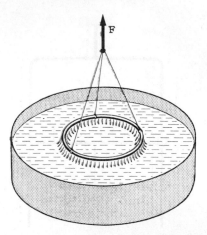

FIG. 13-3. Lifting a circular wire of length l out of a liquid requires an additional force **F** to balance the surface forces $2\gamma l$. This method is commonly used to measure surface tension.

Another less spectacular way of showing a surface force is embodied in the actual apparatus, shown in Fig. 13-3, that is often used to measure surface tension. A circular wire whose circumference is of length l is lifted out from the body of a liquid. The additional force F needed to balance the surface forces $2\gamma l$ due to the two surface films on each side is measured either by the stretch of a delicate spring or by the twist of a torsion wire. The surface tension is then given by

$$\gamma = \frac{F}{2l}.$$

Other methods of measuring surface tension will be apparent in what is to follow. Some typical values are shown in Table 13-1.

The surface tension of a liquid surface in contact with its own vapor or with air is found to depend only on the nature of the liquid and on the temperature. The values for water in Table 13-1 are typical of the general result that surface tension decreases as the temperature increases. Measurements of the surface tension of an extremely thin layer of oil on the surface of water indicate that, in this case, the surface tension depends on the area of the oil film as well as on the temperature.

Another useful viewpoint regarding surface effects is the following. Suppose the wire in Fig. 13-2 is moved down a distance y by applying a downward force $F = w_1 + w_2$. The force F will remain constant provided the temperature of the surface film is kept constant during the motion. The work done is Fy, and the total surface area of the film is

TABLE 13–1

EXPERIMENTAL VALUES OF SURFACE TENSION

Liquid in contact with air	t, °C	Surface tension, dynes/cm
Benzene	20	28.9
Carbon tetrachloride	20	26.8
Ethyl alcohol	20	22.3
Glycerine	20	63.1
Mercury	20	465
Olive oil	20	32.0
Soap solution	20	25.0
Water	0	75.6
Water	20	72.8
Water	60	66.2
Water	100	58.9
Oxygen	−193	15.7
Neon	−247	5.15
Helium	−269	0.12

increased by $2ly$. The *work done per unit area*, in increasing the area, is therefore

$$\frac{\text{Work}}{\text{Increase in area}} = \frac{Fy}{2ly} = \frac{F}{2l}. \tag{13–2}$$

But, from Eq. (13–1), this is equal to the surface tension γ as previously defined, and hence this quantity can be considered either as the *force per unit length* at right angles to the force, or as the *work done per unit area* to increase the area. Using the second definition, the cgs units of γ would be ergs/cm², which are equivalent to dynes/cm, since 1 erg = 1 dyne·cm.

13–2 Pressure difference across a surface film. A soap bubble consists of two spherical surface films very close together, with liquid between. If we isolate one-half of the bubble and apply the principles of statics to the equilibrium of this half-bubble, we obtain a simple relation between the surface tension and the difference in pressure of the air inside and that outside the bubble. Consider first a small element ΔA of a surface, shown in Fig. 13–4. Suppose the air pressure on the left of this element is p and that on the right is p_a. The force normal to the element is therefore $(p - p_a)\,\Delta A$. The component of this force in the x-direction is

$$(p - p_a)\,\Delta A \cos\theta.$$

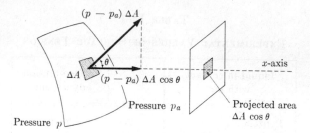

FIG. 13–4. The force in the x-direction is the difference of pressure multiplied by the *projected* area in the x-direction.

But $\Delta A \cos \theta$ is the area projected on a plane perpendicular to the x-axis. The force in the x-direction is therefore the difference of pressure multiplied by the projected area in the x-direction.

Now consider the half-bubble shown in Fig. 13–5. The other half exerts a force to the left equal to twice the surface tension times the perimeter or

$$F \text{ (to the left) } = 2\gamma \times 2\pi R.$$

The force to the right is equal to the pressure difference $p - p_a$ multiplied by the area obtained by projecting the half-bubble on a plane perpendicular to the direction in question. Since this projected area is πR^2,

$$F \text{ (to the right) } = (p - p_a)\pi R^2.$$

Since the half-bubble is in **equilibrium**,

$$(p - p_a)\pi R^2 = 4\pi R\gamma,$$

or

$$\boxed{p - p_a = \frac{4\gamma}{R}. \quad \text{(Soap bubble)}} \qquad (13\text{–}3)$$

It follows from this result that if the surface tension remains constant (this means constant temperature), the pressure difference is larger the smaller the value of R. If two bubbles, therefore, are blown at opposite ends of a pipe, the smaller of the two will force air into the larger. In other words, the smaller one will get still smaller, and the larger will increase.

It may easily be verified that in the case of a liquid drop which has only one surface film, the difference between the pressure of the liquid

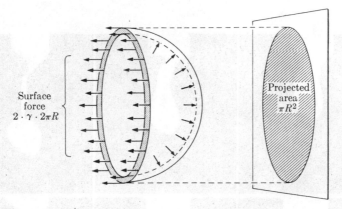

Fig. 13–5. Equilibrium of half of a soap bubble. The force exerted by the other half is $2 \cdot \gamma \cdot 2\pi R$, and the net force exerted by the air inside and outside the bubble is the pressure difference times the projected area, or $(p - p_a)\pi R^2$.

and that of the outside air is given by

$$p - p_a = \frac{2\gamma}{R}. \qquad \text{(Liquid drop)} \qquad (13\text{–}4)$$

EXAMPLE. Calculate the excess pressure inside a drop of mercury whose temperature is 20°C and whose radius is 4 mm.

$$p - p_a = \frac{2\gamma}{R} = \frac{2 \times 465 \text{ dynes/cm}}{0.4 \text{ cm}} = 2325 \frac{\text{dynes}}{\text{cm}^2}.$$

13–3 Minimal surfaces. Any surface under tension tends to contract until it occupies the minimum area consistent with the boundaries of the surface and with the difference of pressure on opposite sides of the surface. A small volume of heavy engine oil injected into the center of a mixture of alcohol and water whose density is the same as that of the oil will therefore contract until it has the smallest surface area consistent with its volume. The shape of such a surface is spherical.

A more interesting situation is depicted in Fig. 13–6, which shows a series of high-speed photographs of successive stages in the formation of a drop of milk at the end of a vertical tube. The photographs were taken by Dr. Edgerton of M.I.T. It will be seen that the process, if examined in detail, is exceedingly complex. An interesting feature is the small drop that follows the larger one. Both drops execute a few oscillations after their formation (4, 5, and 6) and eventually assume a spherical shape (7),

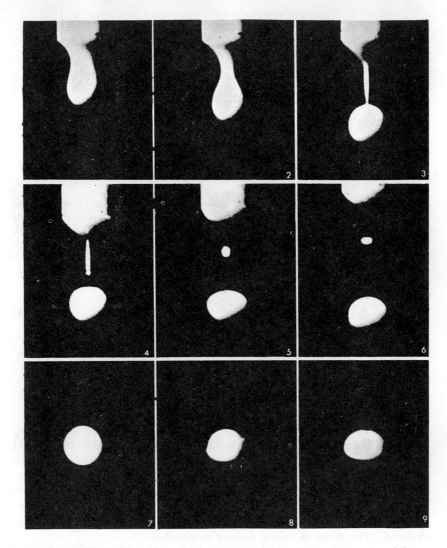

FIG. 13–6. Successive stages in the formation of a drop. (Reproduced from *Flash*, courtesy of Ralph S. Hale & Co.)

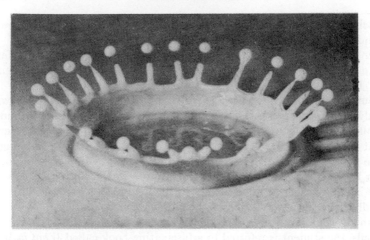

FIGURE 13–7

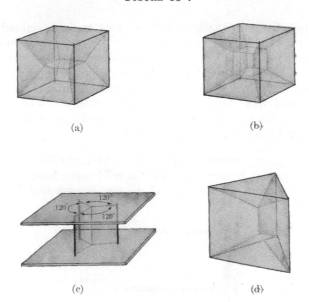

FIG. 13–8. Solution of mathematical problems involving minimal surfaces by means of surface films. (a) Cubical wire framework dipped once. (b) Cubical wire framework dipped twice to entrap an air bubble in the center. (c) Two plastic plates connected by three wires form three plane surface films at angles of 120° to each other. (d) A wire framework in the form of a prism shows that at most three surface films can intersect in a line and at most four edges can intersect at a point.

which would be retained but for the effects of air resistance, as shown in 8 and 9. The drop in 9 has fallen 14 ft.

A beautiful photograph of the splash made by a drop of milk falling on a hard surface is reproduced in Fig. 13–7. It also was taken by Dr. Edgerton.

Surface films may be used to solve problems in mathematics whose analytic solution presents great difficulties. If it is required to find the minimal surface (surface of minimum area) bounded by a wire framework bent into an arbitrary shape, the problem may be solved by dipping the wire framework into a soap solution and waiting a few seconds for the film to contract. The results for two frames in the form of a cube and one in the form of a prism are shown in Fig. 13–8. These results could hardly have been guessed, and their prediction by purely mathematical methods would have been attended by considerable difficulty. For further details, the student is referred to a fascinating book called *What is Mathematics?* by Courant and Robbins.

13–4 Capillarity. In the preceding sections we have limited the discussion of surface phenomena to suface films lying in the boundary between a liquid and a gas. There are other boundaries, however, in which surface films exist. One is the boundary between a solid wall and a liquid, and another is the boundary between a solid and a vapor. The three boundaries and their accompanying films are shown schematically in Fig. 13–9. The films are only a few molecules thick. Associated with each film is an appropriate surface tension. Thus

$$\gamma_{SL} = \text{surface tension of the solid-liquid film,}$$
$$\gamma_{SV} = \text{surface tension of the solid-vapor film,}$$
$$\gamma_{LV} = \text{surface tension of the liquid-vapor film.}$$

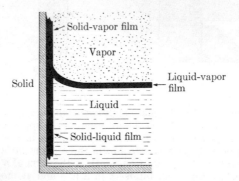

Fig. 13–9. Surface films exist at the solid-vapor boundary and at the solid-liquid boundary as well as at the liquid-vapor boundary.

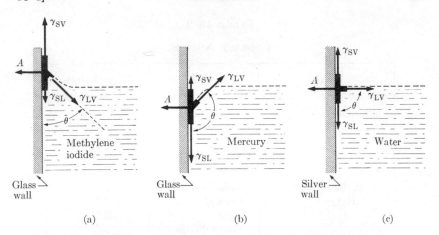

Fig. 13–10. The surface of a liquid near a solid wall is curved if the solid-vapor surface tension γ_{SV} differs from the solid-liquid surface tension γ_{SL}.

The symbol γ without any subscripts, defined and used in the preceding sections, now appears as γ_{LV}.

The curvature of the surface of liquid near a solid wall depends upon the difference between γ_{SV} and γ_{SL}. Consider a portion of a glass wall in contact with methylene iodide, as shown in Fig. 13–10(a). At the wall the three films meet. If we isolate a small portion of all three films at their junction and imagine the films to extend unit distance in a direction perpendicular to the diagram, the isolated portion will be in equilibrium under the action of four forces, three of which are the surface tensions of the three films. The fourth force A is an attraction between the isolated portion and the wall, and is called the *adhesive force*. Applying the conditions for equilibrium, we get

$$\sum F_x = \gamma_{LV} \sin \theta - A = 0,$$

$$\sum F_y = \gamma_{SV} - \gamma_{SL} - \gamma_{LV} \cos \theta = 0,$$

from which

$$A = \gamma_{LV} \sin \theta, \tag{13–5}$$

$$\gamma_{SV} - \gamma_{SL} = \gamma_{LV} \cos \theta. \tag{13–6}$$

The first equation enables us to calculate the adhesive force from measurements of γ_{LV} and the angle θ, known as the *contact angle*. The second equation shows that the contact angle, which is a measure of the curvature of the liquid-vapor surface adjacent to the wall, depends on the difference between γ_{SV} and γ_{SL}. Thus, in Fig. 13–10(a), γ_{SV} is greater than γ_{SL},

TABLE 13-2

CONTACT ANGLES

Liquid	Wall	Contact angle
α-Bromonaphthalene ($C_{10}H_7Br$)	Soda-lime glass Lead glass Pyrex Fused quartz	5° 6°45′ 20°30′ 21°
Methylene iodide (CH_2I_2)	Soda-lime glass Lead glass Pyrex Fused quartz	29° 30° 29° 33°
Water	Paraffin	107°
Mercury	Soda-lime glass	140°

$\cos \theta$ is positive, and θ lies between $0°$ and $90°$. The liquid is said to *wet* the glass.

In Fig. 13-10(b) a glass wall is in contact with mercury. The contact angle θ is about 140°, $\cos \theta$ is negative, and hence γ_{SV} is less than γ_{SL}. When θ lies between 90° and 180°, as it does here, we say that the liquid does *not* wet the glass.

In Fig. 13-10(c) a situation closely approximated by silver in contact with water is shown. In this case, γ_{SV} is very nearly equal to γ_{SL}, $\cos \theta$ is zero, and θ is 90°.

There are a number of liquids whose contact angles are zero when the liquids are in contact with soda-lime glass, lead glass, pyrex, and fused quartz. Such is the case for water, alcohol, ether, carbon tetrachloride, xylene, glycerine, and acetic acid. Some liquids, however, such as the first two listed in Table 13-2, have contact angles that depend upon the nature of the wall with which they are in contact.

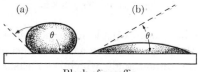

(a)   (b)

Block of paraffin

FIG. 13-11. Effect of decreasing contact angle by a wetting agent.

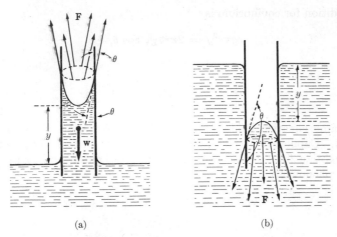

(a)   (b)

FIG. 13–12. Surface tension forces on a liquid in a capillary tube. The liquid rises if $\theta < 90°$ and is depressed if $\theta > 90°$.

Impurities and adulterants present in or added to a liquid may alter the contact angle considerably. In recent years a number of chemicals have been developed which are very potent as *wetting agents* or *detergents*. These compounds change the contact angle from a large value, greater than 90°, to a value much smaller than 90°. Conversely, waterproofing agents applied to a cloth cause the contact angle of water in contact with the cloth to be larger than 90°. The effect of a detergent on a drop of water resting on a block of paraffin is shown in Fig. 13–11.

The most familiar surface effect is the elevation of a liquid in an open tube of small cross section. The term "capillarity," used to describe effects of this sort, originates from the description of such tubes as "capillary" or "hairlike." In the case of a liquid that wets the tube, the contact angle is less than 90° and the liquid rises until an equilibrium height y is reached, as shown in Fig. 13–12(a). If the tube radius is r, the liquid makes contact with the tube along a line of length $2\pi r$. When we isolate the cylinder of liquid of height y and radius r along with its liquid-vapor film, the total upward force is

$$F = 2\pi r \gamma_{LV} \cos \theta.$$

The downward force is the weight of the cylinder w, which is equal to the weight density ρg times the volume $\pi r^2 y$, or

$$w = \rho g \pi r^2 y.$$

The condition for equilibrium is

$$\rho g \pi r^2 y = 2\pi r \gamma_{LV} \cos \theta,$$

or

$$\boxed{y = \frac{2\gamma_{LV} \cos \theta}{\rho g r}.}$$

The same equation holds for the capillary depression, shown in Fig. 13–12(b). Capillarity accounts for the rise of ink in blotting paper, the rise of lighting fluid in the wick of a cigarette lighter, and many other common phenomena.

13–1. Compare the tension of a soap bubble with that of a rubber balloon in the following respects: (a) Has each a surface tension? (b) Does the surface tension depend on area? (c) Is Hooke's law applicable?

13–2. Water can rise to a height y in a certain capillary. Suppose that this tube is immersed in water so that only a length $y/2$ is above the surface. Will you have a fountain or not? Explain.

13–3. A capillary tube is dipped in water with its lower end 10 cm below the water surface. Water rises in the tube to a height of 4 cm above that of the surrounding liquid, and the angle of contact is zero. What gauge pressure is required to blow a hemispherical bubble at the lower end of the tube?

13–4. A glass tube of inside diameter 1 mm is dipped vertically into a container of mercury, with its lower end 1 cm below the mercury surface. (a) What must be the gauge pressure of air in the tube to blow a hemispherical bubble at its lower end? (b) To what height will mercury rise in the tube if the air pressure in the tube is 3×10^4 dynes/cm^2 below atmospheric? The angle of contact between mercury and glass is 140°.

13–5. On a day when the atmospheric pressure is 950 millibars, (a) what would be the height of the mercury column in a barometric tube of inside diameter 2 mm? (b) What would be the height in the absence of any surface tension effects? (c) What is the minimum diameter a barometric tube may have in order that the correc-

tion for capillary depression shall be less than 0.01 cm of mercury?

13–6. (a) Derive the expression for the height of capillary rise in the space between two parallel plates dipping in a liquid. (b) Two glass plates, parallel to each other and separated by 0.5 mm, are dipped in water. To what height will the water rise between them? Assume zero angle of contact.

13–7. A tube of circular cross section and outer radius 0.14 cm is closed at one end. This end is weighted and the tube floats vertically in water, heavy end down. The total mass of the tube and weights is 0.20 gm. If the angle of contact is zero, how far below the water surface is the bottom of the tube?

13–8. Find the gauge pressure, in dynes/cm^2, in a soap bubble 5 cm in diameter. The surface tension is 25 dynes/cm.

13–9. Two large glass plates are clamped together along one edge and separated by spacers a few millimeters thick along the opposite edge to form a wedge-shaped air film. These plates are then placed vertically in a dish of colored liquid. Show that the edge of the liquid forms an equilateral hyperbola.

13–10. A soap bubble may be drawn out into a cylinder by touching to it a ring of the same diameter as the tube from which the bubble is blown, and then "stretching" the bubble between the tube and the ring. By isolating half of the cylindrical surface, show that the gauge pressure within the bubble is given by γ_{LV}/R, where R is the radius of the cylindrical surface.

CHAPTER 14

HYDRODYNAMICS AND VISCOSITY

14–1 Streamline flow. Hydrodynamics is the study of fluids in motion. It is one of the most complex branches of mechanics, as will be realized by considering such common examples of fluid flow as a river in flood or a swirling cloud of cigarette smoke. While it must be true that $F = ma$ at each instant for each drop of water or each smoke particle, imagine attempting to write their equations of motion! However, the problem is not as hopeless as it seems at first sight.

When the proper conditions are fulfilled, the flow of a fluid is of a relatively simple type called *streamline* or *laminar* flow. Figure 14–1 represents a portion of a pipe in which a fluid is flowing from left to right. If the flow is of the streamline type, every particle passing a point such as a follows exactly the same path as the preceding particles which passed the same point. These paths are called *lines of flow* or *streamlines*, and three of them are shown in the figure. If the cross section of the pipe varies from point to point, the velocity of any one particle will vary along its line of flow, but at any fixed point in the pipe the velocity of the particle which happens to be at that point is always the same. The particle which is now at a in the figure will be a moment later at point b, traveling in a different direction with a different speed, and a moment later yet it will be at c, having again changed its velocity. However, if we fix our attention on the point of space marked b, then each successive particle as it passes through b will be traveling in exactly the same direction and with the same speed as is the particle which is at that point now.

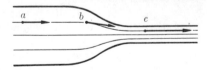

Fig. 14–1. Streamline or laminar flow.

Any real fluid, because of its viscosity, will have a higher velocity at the center of the pipe than at the outside. For the present we shall assume the fluid to be nonviscous and the velocity to be the same at all points of a transverse cross section.

The flow of a fluid is of the streamline type provided the velocity is not too great and the obstructions, constrictions, or bends in the pipe are not such as to cause the lines of flow to change their direction too abruptly. If these conditions are not fulfilled, the flow is of a much more complicated type called *turbulent*.

14–2 Bernoulli's equation. The fundamental equation of hydrodynamics is Bernoulli's equation, which is a relation between the pressure, velocity, and elevation at points along a line of flow. Figure 14–2 represents a portion of a pipeline in which an incompressible, nonviscous fluid is flowing with streamline flow. The portion of the pipe shown in the figure has a uniform cross section A_1 at the left, followed by a region of diminishing cross section, and then a length of uniform but smaller cross section A_2. Focusing our attention on a portion of the fluid represented by both cross shading and horizontal shading (hereafter called the "system"), let us consider the motion of this system from the position shown in (a) to that in (b).

At all points in the wide part of the pipe, the pressure is p_1 and the velocity v_1. At all points in the narrow part, the pressure is p_2 and the velocity v_2. Since the left end of the system advances a distance l_1 parallel to an external force $p_1 A_1$, it follows that the

$$\text{Work done } on \text{ the system} = p_1 A_1 l_1.$$

The right end advances a distance l_2 while an external force $p_2 A_2$ in the opposite direction is acting. Therefore

$$\text{Work done } by \text{ the system} = p_2 A_2 l_2.$$

To move the system from position (a) to position (b), a net amount of work must be done by some agent (a pump, in this case) equal to

$$\text{Net work done on the system} = p_1 A_1 l_1 - p_2 A_2 l_2.$$

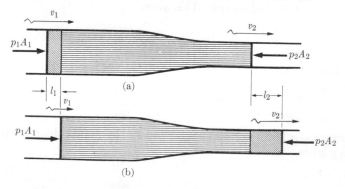

FIGURE 14–2

But A_1l_1 and A_2l_2 are the volumes of the two cross-shaded regions, which must be equal, since the fluid is incompressible. If m is the mass of either cross-shaded region, and ρ is the density of the fluid, then

$$A_1l_1 = A_2l_2 = \frac{m}{\rho},$$

and, finally,

$$\text{Net work} = (p_1 - p_2)\frac{m}{\rho}.$$

Since the kinetic energy of the horizontally shaded portion undergoes no change whatever in the transition from (a) to (b), it follows that the total change of kinetic energy of the system is the change in the cross-shaded portions only, or

$$\text{Net change of kinetic energy} = \tfrac{1}{2}mv_2^2 - \tfrac{1}{2}mv_1^2.$$

In Fig. 14–2, where the pipe is horizontal, there is no change in gravitational potential energy. In general, the cross-shaded portion in (b) will be at a different elevation from that of the cross-shaded portion in (a), and the

$$\text{Net change of gravitational potential energy} = mgy_2 - mgy_1,$$

where y_2 and y_1 are the respective elevations of the cross-shaded portions above some arbitrary reference level.

Strictly speaking, there is always some resistance to the flow of a fluid through a pipe. If the pipe is smooth, large in diameter, and short in length, and if the fluid has a small viscosity and flows slowly, the frictional resistance may be small enough to neglect. For the present let us assume these conditions to be satisfied. We may then equate the net work done on the system to the sum of the increases in its kinetic energy and its gravitational potential energy. This gives

$$(p_1 - p_2)\frac{m}{\rho} = (\tfrac{1}{2}mv_2^2 - \tfrac{1}{2}mv_1^2) + (mgy_2 - mgy_1). \quad (14\text{–}1)$$

Dividing by mg and rearranging terms, we obtain

$$\frac{p_1}{\rho g} + \frac{v_1^2}{2g} + y_1 = \frac{p_2}{\rho g} + \frac{v_2^2}{2g} + y_2, \quad (14\text{–}2)$$

and since the subscripts 1 and 2 refer to *any* two points along the pipeline, we may write

$$\boxed{\frac{p}{\rho g} + \frac{v^2}{2g} + y = \text{constant.}} \quad (14\text{–}3)$$

Either Eq. (14–2) or Eq. (14–3) may be considered the special form of *Bernoulli's equation* applicable to streamline flow without resistance.

Note carefully: p is the *absolute* (not gauge) pressure and must be expressed in pounds per square foot, newtons per square meter, or dynes per square centimeter. The density ρ must be expressed in slugs per cubic foot, kilograms per cubic meter, or grams per cubic centimeter. When this is done, every term in Bernoulli's equation has the dimension of length and is called a *head*. The term $p/\rho g$ is called the *pressure head*, $v^2/2g$ the *velocity head*, and y the *elevation head*.

14–3 The equation of continuity. Figure 14–3 represents a pipe in which a fluid is flowing from left to right. Let A_1 be the cross-sectional area at point 1, v_1 the velocity. In time t, those particles of the fluid originally at point 1 will advance a distance v_1t and a volume of fluid equal to A_1v_1t will cross the area A_1. The volume of fluid crossing per unit time is therefore equal to A_1v_1. Similarly, the volume of fluid crossing the area A_2 per unit time is A_2v_2. If the fluid is incompressible, the rates of flow across the two sections must be equal and

$$A_1v_1 = A_2v_2$$

or

$$\boxed{Av = \text{constant,}} \qquad (14\text{–}4)$$

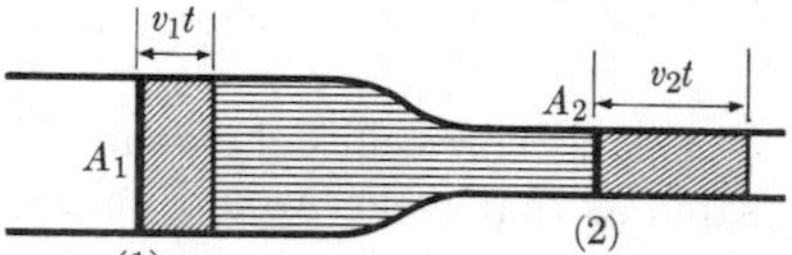

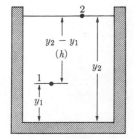

Fig. 14–3. Discharge rate of a pipe.

where A and v are the area and velocity at any point. This is the *equation of continuity* for the steady flow of an incompressible fluid. A consequence of this relation is that the velocity increases if the cross section decreases and vice versa.

14–4 Applications of Bernoulli's equation. (1) The equations of hydrostatics are special cases of Bernoulli's equation, when the velocity is everywhere zero. For example, the variation of pressure with depth in an incompressible liquid may be found by applying Bernoulli's equation to points 1 and 2 in Fig. 14–4. We have

$$p_2 = p_a \text{ (atmospheric)},$$

$$v_1 = v_2 = 0.$$

Let elevations be measured, as usual,

FIGURE 14–4

from the bottom. Then

$$\frac{p_1}{\rho g} + y_1 = \frac{p_a}{\rho g} + y_2,$$

or

$$p_1 = p_a + \rho g(y_2 - y_1) = p_a + \rho gh, \qquad (14\text{--}5)$$

which is the same as Eq. (12–4).

(2) *Torricelli's theorem.* Figure 14–5 represents a liquid flowing from an orifice in a tank at a depth h below the surface of the liquid in the tank. Take point 1 at the orifice and point 2 at the surface. The pressure at each point is the atmospheric pressure p_a, since both are open to the atmosphere. Take the reference level at the bottom of the tank. If the orifice is small, the level of liquid in the tank will fall only slowly. Hence v_2 is small and we shall assume it zero. Then

$$\frac{p_a}{\rho g} + \frac{v_1^2}{2g} + y_1 = \frac{p_a}{\rho g} + 0 + y_2,$$

or

$$v_1^2 = 2g(y_2 - y_1) = 2gh. \qquad (14\text{--}6)$$

This is Torricelli's theorem. Note that the velocity of discharge is the same as that which would be acquired by a body falling freely from rest through a height h.

If A is the area of the opening, the volume of fluid flowing out of the tank per unit time is

$$Av = A\sqrt{2gh}. \qquad (14\text{--}7)$$

Because of the converging of the streamlines as they approach the orifice, the cross section of the stream continues to diminish for a short distance outside the tank. It is the area of smallest cross section, known as the *vena contracta*, which should be used in Eq. (14–7). For a sharp-edged circular opening, the area of the *vena contracta* is about 65% as great as the area of the orifice.

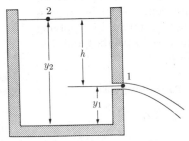

FIG. 14–5. Velocity of efflux $= \sqrt{2gh}$.

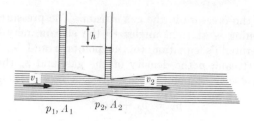

FIG. 14–6. The Venturi meter.

(3) *The Venturi meter.* The Venturi meter, illustrated in Fig. 14–6, consists of a constriction or throat inserted in a pipeline, and having properly designed tapers at inlet and outlet to avoid turbulence and assure streamline flow. Bernoulli's equation, applied to the wide and to the constricted portions of the pipe, becomes

$$p_1 + \tfrac{1}{2}\rho v_1^2 = p_2 + \tfrac{1}{2}\rho v_2^2$$

(the "y" terms drop out if the pipe is level).

Since v_2 is greater than v_1, it follows that p_2 is less than p_1. That is, the pressure in the throat is smaller than in the main pipeline. The pressure difference may be measured by attaching vertical side tubes as shown in the diagram. If h is the difference in height of the liquid in the tubes, then

$$p_1 - p_2 = \rho g h.$$

The reduced pressure at a constriction finds a number of technical applications. Gasoline vapor is drawn into the intake manifold of an internal combustion engine by the low pressure produced in a Venturi throat to which the carburetor is connected. The aspirator pump is a Venturi throat through which water is forced. Air is drawn into the low-pressure water rushing through the constricted portion. The injection pump used on a steam locomotive to draw water from the tender makes use of the same principle.

(4) *The pitot tube.* A pitot tube is shown in Fig. 14–7 as it would be used to measure the velocity of a gas flowing in a tube or pipe. An open tube manometer is connected as shown to the tube in which the gas is flowing. The pressure at the left arm of the manometer, whose opening is parallel to the direction of

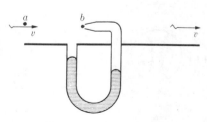

FIG. 14–7. The pitot tube.

flow, is equal to the pressure in the gas stream. The pressure in the right arm, whose opening is at right angles to the stream, may be computed by applying Bernoulli's equation to the points a and b. Let v be the velocity of the stream, ρ the density of the gas, and p_a the pressure at point a. The velocity at point b, of course, is zero. Then

$$p_b = p_a + \tfrac{1}{2}\rho v^2.$$

Since p_b is greater than p_a, the liquid in the manometer becomes displaced as shown. If ρ_0 is the density of the liquid in the manometer and h the difference in height of the liquid in its arms, then

$$p_b = p_a + \rho_0 g h.$$

When this is combined with the preceding equation, we get

$$\rho_0 g h = \tfrac{1}{2}\rho v^2,$$

from which v may be expressed in terms of measurable quantities.

(5) *The curved flight of a spinning ball.* Figure 14–8(a) represents a top view of a ball spinning about a vertical axis. Because of friction between the ball and the surrounding air, a thin layer of air is dragged around by the spinning ball.

Figure 14–8(b) represents a stationary ball in a blast of air moving from right to left. The motion of the air stream around and past the ball is the same as though the ball were moving through still air from left to right. If the ball is moving from left to right and spinning at the same time, the actual velocity of the air at any point is the resultant of the velocities at the same point in (a) and (b). At the top of the diagram the two velocities are in opposite directions, while the reverse is true at the bottom of the diagram. The top is a region of low velocity and high pressure, while the bottom is a region of high velocity and low pressure. There is therefore an excess pressure forcing the ball down in the diagram, so that if moving from left to right and spinning at the same time, it deviates from a straight line as shown in the top view in Fig. 14–8(c).

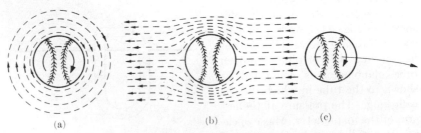

(a)   (b)   (c)

FIG. 14–8. Curved flight of a spinning ball.

(6) *Lift on an aircraft wing.* Figure 14–9 is a photograph of stream-line flow around a section in the shape of an aircraft wing or an airfoil, at three different angles of attack. The apparatus consists of two parallel glass plates spaced about 1 mm apart. The wing section, whose thickness equals the separation of the plates, is inserted between them and alternate streams of clear water and ink flow by gravity between the plates and past the section. The photographs have been turned through 90° to give the effect of horizontal air flow past an aircraft wing. Because the fluid is water flowing relatively slowly, the nature of the flow pattern is not identical with that of air moving at high speed past an actual wing.

Consider the first photograph, which corresponds to a plane in level flight. It will be seen that there is relatively little disturbance of the flow below the wing, but because of the shape of the airfoil there is a marked crowding together of the streamlines above it, much as if they were being forced through the throat of a Venturi. Hence the region above the wing is one of increased velocity and reduced pressure, while below the wing the pressure is nearly atmospheric. It is this pressure differential between upper and lower wing surfaces which gives rise to the lift on the wing. The wing is not simply forced up by air blowing against its lower surface.

There is a mistaken impression that the flow around an aircraft wing results in an upward "pull" on the upper surface of the wing. Of course this cannot happen. The air presses against all portions of the wing surface, but the reduction below atmospheric pressure, at the upper surface, usually exceeds the increase above atmospheric pressure at the lower surface.

The second and third photographs show how, as the angle of attack is increased, the streamlines above the wing have to change direction sharply to follow the contour of the wing surface and join smoothly with the streamline flow below the wing. While the slowly moving water in

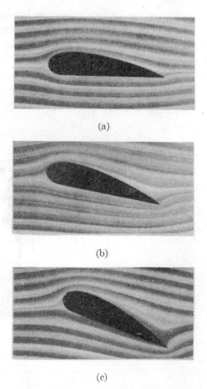

(a)

(b)

(c)

Fig. 14–9. Lines of flow around an airfoil.

Fig. 14–9 does retain its streamline form even at the large angle of attack in the third photograph, it is much more difficult for the air moving rapidly past an aircraft wing to do so. As a consequence, if the angle of attack is too great, the streamline flow in the region above and behind the wing breaks down and a complicated system of whirls and eddies known as *turbulence* is set up. Bernoulli's equation no longer applies, the pressure above the wing rises, and the lift on the wing decreases and the plane stalls.

14–5 Viscosity. Viscosity may be thought of as the internal friction of a fluid. Because of viscosity, a force must be exerted to cause one layer of a fluid to slide past another, or to cause one surface to slide past another if there is a layer of fluid between the surfaces. Both liquids and gases exhibit viscosity, although liquids are much more viscous than gases. In developing the fundamental equations of viscous flow, it will be seen that the problem is very similar to that of the shearing stress and strain in a solid.

Figure 14–10 illustrates one type of apparatus for measuring the viscosity of a liquid. A cylinder is pivoted on nearly frictionless bearings so as to rotate concentrically within a cylindrical vessel. The liquid whose viscosity is to be measured is poured into the annular space between the cylinders. A torque can be applied to the inner cylinder by the weight-pulley system. When the weight is released, the inner cylinder accelerates momentarily but very quickly comes up to a constant angular velocity and continues to

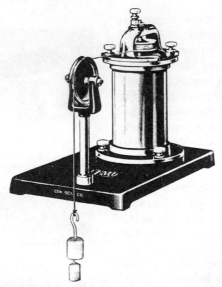

Fig. 14–10. One type of viscosimeter. (Courtesy of Central Scientific Co.)

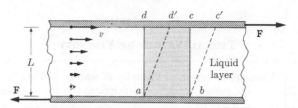

FIG. 14–11. Laminar flow of a viscous liquid.

rotate at that velocity as long as the torque acts. It is obvious that this velocity will be smaller with a liquid such as glycerin in the annular space than it will be if the liquid is water or kerosene. From a knowledge of the torque, the dimensions of the apparatus, and the angular velocity, the viscosity of the liquid may be computed.

To reduce the problem to its essential terms, imagine that the cylinders are of nearly the same size so that the liquid layer between them is thin. A short arc of this layer will then be approximately a straight line. Figure 14–11 shows a portion of the liquid layer between the moving inner wall and the stationary outer wall. The liquid in contact with the moving surface is found to have the same velocity as that surface; the liquid adjacent to the stationary inner wall is at rest. The velocities of intermediate layers of the liquid increase uniformly from one wall to the other as shown by the arrows.

Flow of this type is called *laminar*. (A lamina is a thin sheet.) The layers of liquid slide over one another much as do the leaves of a book when it is placed flat on a table and a horizontal force applied to the top cover. As a consequence of this motion, a portion of the liquid which at some instant has the shape *abcd*, will a moment later take the shape *abc'd'*, and will become more and more distorted as the motion continues. In other words, the liquid is in a state of continually increasing shearing strain.

In order to maintain the motion, it is necessary that a force be continually exerted to the right on the upper, moving plate, and hence indirectly on the upper liquid surface. This force tends to drag the liquid and the lower plate as well to the right. Therefore an equal force must be exerted toward the left on the lower plate to hold it stationary. These forces are lettered **F** in Fig. 14–11. If A is the area of the liquid over which these forces are applied, the ratio F/A is the shearing stress exerted on the liquid.

When a shearing stress is applied to a solid, the effect of the stress is to produce a certain displacement of the solid such as dd'. The shearing strain is defined as the ratio of this displacement to the transverse dimension L, and within the elastic limit the shearing stress is proportional to

TABLE 14–1

TYPICAL VALUES OF VISCOSITY

t, °C	Viscosity of castor oil, poise	Viscosity of water, centipoise	Viscosity of air, μpoise
0	53	1.792 10^{-2}	171 10^{-6}
20	9.86	1.005	181
40	2.31	0.656	190
60	0.80	0.469	200
80	0.30	0.357	209
100	0.17	0.284	218

the shearing strain. With a fluid, on the other hand, the shearing strain increases without limit so long as the stress is applied, and the stress is found by experiment to be proportional, not to the shearing strain, but to its *rate of change*. The strain in Fig. 14–11 at the instant when the volume of fluid has the shape $abc'd'$ is dd'/ad, or dd'/L. Since L is constant, the rate of change of strain equals $1/L$ times the rate of change of dd'. But the rate of change of dd' is simply the velocity of point d', or the velocity v of the moving wall. Since shearing stress is proportional to rate of change of shearing strain,

$$\frac{F}{A} \propto \frac{v}{L}, \quad \text{or} \quad \frac{F}{A} = \eta \frac{v}{L},$$

or

$$F = \eta \frac{Av}{L}. \tag{14–8}$$

The proportionality constant, represented by the Greek letter η (eta), is called the *coefficient of viscosity*, or simply the *viscosity*. It is small for liquids which flow readily, like kerosene, and larger for liquids like molasses or glycerin.

From Eq. (14–8), the unit of viscosity is that of force times distance divided by area times velocity or, in the cgs system, 1 dyne·sec/cm². A viscosity of 1 dyne·sec/cm² is called a *poise*. Small viscosities are usually expressed in centipoises (1 cp = 10^{-2} poise) or micropoises (1 μp = 10^{-6} poise). Some typical values of viscosity are given in Table 14–1.

The coefficient of viscosity is markedly dependent on temperature, increasing for gases and decreasing for liquids as the temperature is increased.

A common technical method of measuring viscosity makes use of a small container in the bottom of which is an orifice of specified dimensions. A specified volume of liquid is poured into the container and the time required for the liquid to run out through the orifice is measured. The viscosity is then computed by an empirical formula.

Viscosities of lubricating oils are commonly expressed on an arbitrary scale established by the Society of Automotive Engineers. An oil whose SAE number is 10 has a viscosity at 130°F between about 160 and 220 centipoise; the viscosity of SAE 20 is between 230 and 300 centipoise, and that of SAE 30 is between 360 and 430 centipoise.

14–6 Laminar and turbulent flow. In the derivation of Bernoulli's equation and of the equation of continuity, the effect of viscosity was neglected. As a result, the velocities of all particles of fluid at one section of a pipe were equal, and the fluid advanced as a unit along the pipe. In Fig. 14–12(a) the velocity vectors of a number of fluid particles, momentarily at any section of a pipe, are shown when the fluid has no viscosity. The surface determined by the heads of these vectors is a plane, and the fluid flow is said to be characterized by a *plane velocity profile*.

When the fluid is viscous and the velocity is not too great, the flow will be *laminar* and the velocity profile has the shape shown in Fig. 14–12(b). The velocity is a maximum on the axis of the pipe and decreases to zero at the wall. There is therefore a stagnant film of fluid, called the *boundary layer*, at the wall. The laminar motion of the fluid is like that of a number of telescoping tubes sliding relative to one another, with the central tube advancing most rapidly and the outer tube remaining at rest.

When the velocity exceeds a certain critical value, the nature of the flow becomes much more complicated. Random, irregular, local circular currents, called *vortices*, develop throughout the fluid, with a large increase in the resistance to flow. At each point of a cross section, however, the fluid has a forward component of velocity, and the velocity profile of these components has the shape shown in Fig. 14–12(c). Flow of this sort is called *turbulent*.

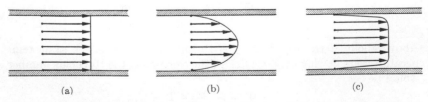

(a) (b) (c)

Fig. 14–12. (a) Plane velocity profile. (b) Laminar flow. (c) Turbulent flow.

14–7 Reynolds number. Experiment indicates that there is a combination of four factors which determines whether the flow of viscous fluid through a pipe is laminar or turbulent. This combination is known as the *Reynolds number*, N_R, and is defined as

$$N_R = \frac{\rho v D}{\eta}, \qquad (14\text{–}9)$$

where ρ is the density of the fluid, v the average velocity, η the viscosity, and D the diameter of the pipe. (The actual velocity is not the same over the entire cross section of the pipe, and the average velocity is defined as the uniform velocity which would result in the same discharge rate.)

The Reynolds number is a pure number and therefore its numerical value is the same in any consistent set of units. For example, for water at 20°C flowing in a pipe of diameter 1 cm with an average velocity of 10 cm/sec, the Reynolds number is

$$N_R = \frac{\rho v D}{\eta} = \frac{1 \text{ gm/cm}^3 \times 10 \text{ cm/sec} \times 1 \text{ cm}}{0.01 \text{ dyne·sec/cm}^2},$$

and since 1 dyne $= 1$ gm·cm/sec^2,

$$N_R = 1000 \, \frac{\text{gm}}{\text{cm}^3} \times \frac{\text{cm}}{\text{sec}} \times \text{cm} \times \frac{\text{sec}^2 \cdot \text{cm}^2}{\text{gm·cm·sec}} = 1000.$$

Had the four quantities been expressed originally in the engineering system of units, the same value of 1000 would have been obtained.

All experiments show that when the Reynolds number lies between 0 and 2000, the flow of viscous fluid is laminar, whereas above about 3000 the flow is turbulent. Between 2000 and 3000 there is a transition region in which the flow is unstable and may change from one type to the other. Thus for water at 20°C flowing in a pipe 1 cm in diameter, the flow is laminar when

$$\frac{\rho v D}{\eta} \lesssim 2000,$$

or when

$$v \lesssim \frac{2000 \times 0.01}{1 \times 1} \, \frac{\text{cm}}{\text{sec}} \lesssim 20 \, \frac{\text{cm}}{\text{sec}}.$$

Above about 30 cm/sec the flow is turbulent. If air at the same temperature were flowing at 30 cm/sec in the same pipe, the Reynolds number would be

$$N_R = \frac{0.0013 \times 30 \times 1}{181 \times 10^{-6}} = 216.$$

Since this is much less than 3000, the flow would be laminar and would not become turbulent unless the velocity were as great as 420 cm/sec.

14–8 Flow of a viscous fluid through a pipe. Let us write Bernoulli's equation in the form

$$\frac{p_1 - p_2}{\rho g} = (y_2 - y_1) + \frac{1}{2g} (v_2^2 - v_1^2).$$

This relation was obtained by setting the work done on a moving fluid equal to the change in kinetic energy plus the change in gravitational potential energy. When the effect of viscosity cannot be ignored, some work must also be done against friction, and the pressure difference needed to maintain the flow is greater than that given by the preceding equation. For the special case of a fluid flowing in a pipe of uniform cross section, of length L and diameter D, the velocities v_2 and v_1 are equal. In the absence of friction, the pressure difference between two points would arise only from the difference in elevations of the points. The effect of friction, however, is to introduce an additional pressure head, or *friction head*, given by

$$\frac{\Delta p}{\rho g} = f \frac{L}{D} \frac{v^2}{2g},$$

where v is the average velocity and f, called the *friction factor*, is a function of the Reynolds number N_R. The *total* pressure head between points 1

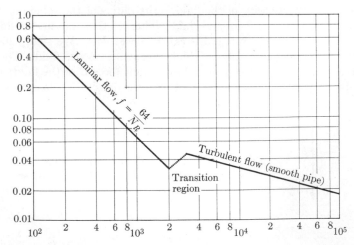

FIG. 14–13. The friction factor f plotted as a function of the Reynolds number.

and 2 is thus

$$\frac{p_1 - p_2}{\rho g} = (y_2 - y_1) + f \frac{L}{D} \frac{v^2}{2g}. \tag{14-10}$$

When the flow is laminar ($N_R \lesssim 2000$), the friction factor is given by the simple equation

$$f = \frac{64}{N_R}. \quad \text{(Laminar flow)}$$

When the flow is turbulent ($N_R > 3000$), the friction factor varies as a fractional power of the Reynolds number. Both situations are depicted in the logarithmic graph of Fig. 14–13. (Strictly speaking, the friction factor for turbulent flow is a different function of the Reynolds number for pipes of different degrees of roughness. The curve in Fig. 14–13 applies only to smooth pipes.)

14–9 Stokes' law. When a viscous fluid flows past a sphere with laminar flow, or when a sphere moves through a viscous fluid at rest, a resisting force is exerted on the sphere. (A force, of course, is experienced by a body of any shape, but only for a sphere is the expression for the force readily calculable.) Analysis which is beyond the scope of this book shows that the resisting force R is given by

$$R = 6\pi \eta r v, \tag{14-11}$$

where η is the viscosity of the fluid, r the radius of the sphere, and v the relative velocity of sphere and fluid. This relation was first deduced by Sir George Stokes in 1845 and is called *Stokes' law*. We shall consider it briefly in relation to a sphere falling through a viscous fluid. The forces on the sphere are its weight mg, the buoyant force B of the fluid, and the resisting force R (see Fig. 14–14). If ρ is the density of the sphere and ρ_0 the density of the fluid,

$$mg = \tfrac{4}{3}\pi r^3 \rho g, \qquad B = \tfrac{4}{3}\pi r^3 \rho_0 g.$$

Since the net downward force on the sphere is equal to the product of its mass times its acceleration,

$$mg - B - R = ma,$$

$$a = g - \frac{B + R}{m}.$$

FIGURE 14–14

If the sphere is released from rest ($v = 0$), the viscous force R at the start is zero. The initial acceleration a_0 is therefore

$$a_0 = g - \frac{B}{m} = g\frac{\rho - \rho_0}{\rho}.$$

As a result of this acceleration, the sphere acquires a downward velocity and therefore experiences a retarding force given by Stokes' law. As the velocity increases, the retarding force also increases in direct proportion, and eventually a velocity is reached such that the downward force and the retarding force are equal. The sphere then ceases to accelerate and moves with a constant velocity called its *terminal velocity*. This velocity can be found by setting the downward force mg equal to the upward force $B + R$. Thus,

$$\tfrac{4}{3}\pi r^3 \rho g = \tfrac{4}{3}\pi r^3 \rho_0 g + 6\pi\eta r v,$$

or

$$v = \frac{2}{9}\frac{r^2 g}{\eta}(\rho - \rho_0). \qquad (14\text{--}12)$$

The relation above holds provided the velocity is not so great that turbulence sets in. When this occurs, the retarding force is much greater than that given by Stokes' law.

EXAMPLE. Find the terminal velocity of a steel ball 2 mm in radius, falling in a tank of glycerin.

$$\rho_{\text{steel}} = \text{(about)} \ 8 \ \frac{\text{gm}}{\text{cm}^3},$$

$$\rho_{\text{glycerin}} = \text{(about)} \ 1.3 \ \frac{\text{gm}}{\text{cm}^3},$$

$$\eta_{\text{glycerin}} = \text{(about)} \ 8.3 \ \text{poise}.$$

$$v = \frac{2}{9}\frac{(0.2)^2 \times 980}{8.3}(8 - 1.3) = 7 \ \frac{\text{cm}}{\text{sec}}.$$

This velocity is attained in a very short distance from the start of the motion. The experiment above is used as one method of measuring viscosity.

PROBLEMS

(In Problems 1–24, neglect friction.)

14–1. A circular hole 1 inch in diameter is cut in the side of a large standpipe, 20 ft below the water level in the standpipe. Find (a) the velocity of efflux, and (b) the volume discharged per unit time. Neglect the contraction of the streamlines after emerging from the hole.

14–2. Water stands at a depth H in a large open tank whose side walls are vertical (Fig. 14–15). A hole is made in one of the walls at a depth h below the water surface. (a) At what distance R from the foot of the wall does the emerging stream of water strike the floor? (b) At what height above the bottom of the tank could a second hole be cut so that the stream emerging from it would have the same range?

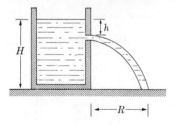

FIGURE 14–15

14–3. Water in an enclosed tank is subjected to a gauge pressure of 4 lb/in² applied by compressed air introduced into the top of the tank. There is a small hole in the side of the tank 16 ft below the level of the water. Calculate the velocity with which water escapes from this hole.

14–4. What gauge pressure is required in the city mains in order that a stream from a fire hose connected to the mains may reach a vertical height of 60 ft?

14–5. A tank of large area is filled with water to a depth of one foot. A hole of 1 in² cross section in the bottom allows water to drain out in a continuous stream. (a) What is the rate at which water flows out of the tank, in ft³/sec? (b) At what distance below the bottom of the tank is the cross-sectional area of the stream equal to one-half the area of the hole?

14–6. A sealed tank containing sea water to a height of 5 ft also contains air above the water at a gauge pressure of 580 lb/ft². Water flows out from a hole at the bottom. The cross-sectional area of the hole is 1.6 in². (a) Calculate the efflux velocity of the water. (b) Calculate the reaction force on the tank exerted by the water in the emergent stream. (Force equals rate of change of momentum.)

14–7. A pipeline 6 inches in diameter, flowing full of water, has a constriction of diameter 3 in. If the velocity in the 6-inch portion is 4 ft/sec, find (a) the velocity in the constriction, and (b) the discharge rate in ft³/sec.

14–8. A horizontal pipe of 6 in² cross section tapers to a cross section of 2 in². If sea water of density 2 slugs/ft³ is flowing with a velocity of 180 ft/min in the large pipe where a pressure gauge reads 10.5 lb/in², what is the gauge pressure in the adjoining part of the small pipe? The barometer reads 30 inches of mercury.

14–9. Sea water (weighing 64 lb/ft³) stands to a height of 4 ft in a tank. The tank contains compressed air at a gauge pressure of 1 lb/in². The horizontal outlet pipe has cross-sectional areas of 2.88 in² and 1.44 in² at the

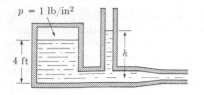

$p = 1 \text{ lb/in}^2$

4 ft

h

FIGURE 14–16

larger and smaller sections (Fig. 14–16). (a) What is the discharge rate from the outlet? (b) To what height h does water stand in the open end pipe? (c) If now the tank is punctured at the top of the gauge pressure drops to zero, what will be the height h?

14–10. The section of pipe shown in Fig. 14–17 has a cross section of 0.04 ft^2 at the wider portions and 0.01 ft^2 at the constriction. One cubic foot of water is discharged from the pipe in 5 sec. (a) Find the velocities at the wide and the narrow portions. (b) Find the pressure difference between these portions. (c) Find the difference in height between the mercury columns in the U-tube.

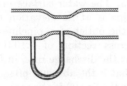

FIGURE 14–17

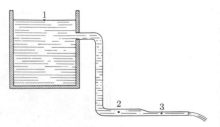

FIGURE 14–18

14–11. Water flows steadily from a reservoir shown in Fig. 14–18. The elevation of point 1 is 40 ft; of points 2 and 3 it is 4 ft. The cross section at point 2 is 0.5 ft^2 and at point 3 it is 0.25 ft^2. The area of the reservoir is very large compared with the cross sections of the pipe. (a) Compute the gauge pressure at point 2. (b) Compute the discharge rate in ft^3/sec.

14–12. Sea water of density 2 slugs/ft^3 flows steadily in a pipeline of constant cross section leading out of an elevated tank. At a point 4.5 ft below the water level in the tank the gauge pressure in the flowing stream is 1 lb/in^2. (a) What is the velocity of the water at this point? (b) If the pipe rises to a point 9 ft above the level of the water in the tank, what are the velocity and the pressure at the latter point?

14–13. Water flows from a reservoir to a turbine 330 ft below. The efficiency of the turbine is 80% and it receives 100 ft^3 of water per minute. Compute the horsepower output of the turbine.

14–14. Sea water weighing 64 lb/ft^3 flows through a horizontal pipe of cross-sectional area 1.44 in^2. At one section the cross-sectional area is 0.72 in^2. The pressure difference between the two sections is 0.048 lb/in^2. How many cubic feet of water will flow out of the pipe in one minute?

14–15. The water level in a tank on the top of a building is 100 ft above the ground. The tank supplies water, through pipes of 0.02 ft^2 cross-sectional area, to the various apartments. Each faucet through which the water emerges has an orifice of 0.01 ft^2 effective area. (a) How long will it take to fill a 1-ft^3 pail in an apartment 75 ft above the ground? (b) What is the gauge pressure in a water pipe (not in the faucet) on the ground level when the faucet is closed? (c) What is the gauge pressure in a pipe on the ground level when the faucet is open?

14–16. Water in an enclosed tank stands at a level of 16 ft above a short efflux pipe at the base (Fig. 14–19). (a) What pressure (gauge) of compressed air above the tank will result in a velocity of efflux from the pipe of 40 ft/sec? (b) A manometer tube is attached to the efflux pipe close to the tank. To what height will water rise in this tube?

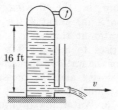

16 ft

v

FIGURE 14–19

14–17. At a certain point in a horizontal pipeline the gauge pressure is 6.24 lb/in². At another point the gauge pressure is 4.37 lb/in². If the areas of the pipe at these two points are 3 in² and 1.5 in² respectively, compute the number of cubic feet of water which flow across any cross section of the pipe per minute.

14–18. Water flowing in a horizontal pipe discharges at the rate of 0.12 ft³/sec. At a point in the pipe where the cross section is 0.01 ft², the absolute pressure is 18 lb/in². What must be the cross section of a constriction in the pipe such that the pressure there is reduced to 15 lb/in²?

14–19. The pressure difference between the main pipeline and the throat of a Venturi meter is 15 lb/in². The areas of the pipe and the constriction are 1 ft² and 0.5 ft². How many cubic

feet per second are flowing through the pipe? The liquid in the pipe is water.

14–20. Assume that air is streaming horizontally past an aircraft wing such that the velocity is 100 ft/sec over the top surface and 80 ft/sec past the bottom surface. If the wing weighs 600 lb and has an area of 40 ft², what is the net force on the wing? The density of air is 0.0013 gm/cm³.

14–21. Modern airplane design calls for a "lift" of about 20 lb/ft² of wing area. Assume that air flows past the wing of an aircraft with streamline flow. If the velocity of flow past the lower wing surface is 300 ft/sec, what is the required velocity over the upper surface to give a "lift" of 20 lb/ft²? The density of air is 0.0013 gm/cm³.

14–22. At a certain point in a pipeline the velocity is 2 ft/sec and the gauge pressure is 35 lb/in². Find the gauge pressure at a second point in the line 50 ft lower than the first, if the cross section at the second point is one-half that at the first. The liquid in the pipe is water.

14–23. The water surface in a large standpipe is at an elevation of 64 ft above the outlet of a pipeline of uniform cross section of 0.10 ft². (a) What is the discharge rate, in ft³/sec? (b) What is the absolute pressure at a point in the line 20 ft above the outlet?

14–24. Two very large open tanks, A and F (Fig. 14–20), both contain the

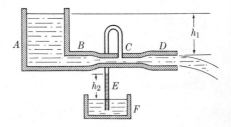

A B C D h_1

h_2 E F

FIGURE 14–20

same liquid. A horizontal pipe BCD having a constriction at C leads out of the bottom of tank A, and a vertical pipe E opens into the constriction at C and dips into the liquid in tank F. Assume streamline flow and no viscosity. If the cross section at C is one-half that at D, and if D is at a distance h_1 below the level of the liquid in A, to what height h_2 will liquid rise in pipe E? Express your answer in terms of h_1. Neglect changes in atmospheric pressure with elevation.

14–25. Water at 20°C flows with a speed of 50 cm/sec through a pipe of diameter 3 mm. (a) What is the Reynolds number? (b) What is the nature of the flow? (c) What is the friction factor? (d) What would be the "friction head" if the pipe were 100 cm long?

14–26. Oil having a viscosity of 300 centipoise and a density of 0.90 gm/cm^3 is to be pumped from one large open tank to another through 1 km of smooth steel pipe 15 cm in diameter. The line discharges into the air at a point 30 m above the level of the oil in the supply tank. (a) What gauge pressure, in atmospheres, must the pump exert in order to maintain a flow of 50 liters/sec? (b) What is the power consumed by the pump?

14–27. Water at 20°C is pumped through a horizontal smooth pipe 15 cm in diameter and discharges into the air. If the pump maintains an absolute pressure of 1.02 atm at a point 300 m from the discharge end of the pipe, (a) what is the velocity of flow? (b) What is the nature of the flow? (c) What is the discharge rate in liters/sec?

14–28. (a) With what terminal velocity will an air bubble 1 mm in diameter rise in a liquid of viscosity 150 cp and density 0.90 gm/cm^3? (b) What is the terminal velocity of the same bubble in water?

14–29. (a) With what velocity is a steel ball 1 mm in radius falling in a tank of glycerin at an instant when its acceleration is one-half that of a freely falling body? (b) What is the terminal velocity of the ball? The densities of steel and of glycerin are 8.5 gm/cm^3 and 1.32 gm/cm^3 respectively.

CHAPTER 15

TEMPERATURE—EXPANSION

15–1 Concept of temperature. To describe the equilibrium states of mechanical systems, as well as to study and predict the motions of rigid bodies and fluids, only three fundamental indefinables were needed: length, mass, and time. Every other physical quantity of importance in mechanics could be expressed in terms of these three indefinables. We come now, however, to a series of phenomena, called *thermal effects* or *heat phenomena*, which involve aspects that are essentially nonmechanical and which require for their description a fourth fundamental indefinable, the *temperature*.

Consider a cake of ice with a volume of about 1 cubic foot at atmospheric pressure. It is in mechanical equilibrium because the vector sum of the forces acting on it is zero. Suppose, in the neighborhood of the ice, there is a small spherical rubber balloon inflated with air. It is also in mechanical equilibrium because the difference between the inside and outside pressure is twice the surface tension divided by the radius. Even though the ice and the air balloon are separately in mechanical equilibrium, it will be found that both systems undergo changes when they are placed together: the volume of the ice decreases (because some of it melts) and both the pressure and volume of the air in the balloon change. After a while these changes cease. The final state of the two systems is called "thermal equilibrium."

The tendency of systems originally in mechanical equilibrium to change their states when placed in contact cannot be explained in terms of length, mass, and time alone. The results of many experiments on systems which change their mechanical states when placed together and finally reach thermal equilibrium lead us to infer that all ordinary objects have a new physical property that determines whether they will be in thermal equilibrium when placed in contact with other objects. This property is called *temperature. The temperatures associated with two objects are said to be equal only when the two objects are in thermal equilibrium.* The temperature of all objects in thermal equilibrium may be represented by a number. The establishment of a temperature scale is merely the adoption of a set of rules for assigning different numbers to different temperatures. Once this is done the necessary and sufficient condition for thermal equilibrium between two systems is that they have the same temperature. Also, when the temperatures are different, we may be sure that the systems are not in thermal equilibrium.

286

Human beings are endowed with a temperature sense which enables them to tell at least roughly whether two objects will be in thermal equilibrium when placed together. We have learned to describe our sensations when touching other objects by using adjectives such as "cold," "warm," "hot," etc. These words mean roughly the same thing to most people, just as the words "low pitch" and "high pitch" or "red" and "blue" mean about the same thing when used to describe our sensations on hearing sounds or seeing colors. When two objects have been left together for some time and are then touched, their "hotness" or "coldness" feel about the same and the two objects are described as having the same temperature. Temperature is therefore the property of a body that determines our sensation of hotness or coldness when we touch the body.

Our temperature sense is much too unreliable to serve as a means of measurement. An object with at least one easily measurable property that changes appreciably while the object is coming to thermal equilibrium is preferable as a temperature measuring device, or *thermometer*. With the aid of an arbitrarily chosen thermometer it is possible to formulate a set of rules for representing temperatures with numbers, that is, for setting up a *temperature scale*.

15–2 Thermometers. Of all the properties of systems that have been studied with an eye toward possible use in the measurement of temperature, *the pressure of a gas* whose volume is maintained constant has been found to excel in *sensitivity*, *accuracy* of measurement, and *reproducibility*. The constant-volume gas thermometer is illustrated schematically in Fig. 15–1. The materials, construction, and dimensions differ in various laboratories throughout the world and depend on the nature of the gas and the temperature range to be covered.

The gas, usually hydrogen or helium, is contained in bulb C, and the pressure exerted by it can be measured by the open-tube mercury ma-

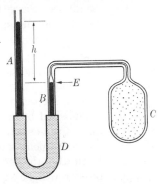

Fig. 15–1. Constant-volume gas thermometer.

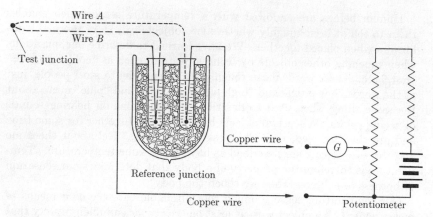

Fig. 15–2. Thermocouple of wires A and B with a reference junction consisting of two junctions with copper, connected to a potentiometer.

nometer. As the temperature of the gas is increased, it expands, forcing the mercury down in tube B and up in tube A. Tubes A and B are connected by the flexible rubber tube D, and by raising A, the mercury level in B may be brought back to the reference mark E. The gas is thus kept at constant volume.

Gas thermometers are absolute instruments and are used mainly in bureaus of standards and in some university research laboratories. They are usually large, bulky, and slow in coming to thermal equilibrium.

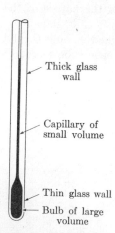

Fig. 15–3. Construction of liquid-in-glass-thermometer.

In most research and engineering laboratories, secondary thermometers that are small and fast must be used. The most commonly used is the *thermocouple*, which consists of a junction of two different metals or alloys. Since the junction is small and has a small mass, it can follow temperature changes rapidly and come to equilibrium quickly. The junction forms part of an electric circuit, as shown in Fig. 15–2. When it is in contact with an object or immersed in a fluid, the temperature measurement is accomplished by measuring a quantity called an emf (ee-em-eff, electromotive force) with an instrument known as a potentiometer. Both the thermocouple and the potentiometer will be studied in later sections of this book.

The best known but least accurate thermometer is a liquid such as mercury or alcohol contained in a bulb which communicates with a very narrow tube or capillary, as shown in Fig. 15–3. The height of the liquid in the capillary is an indication of the temperature. The main fault of the liquid-in-glass thermometer is that its reading changes over the years because of aging of the glass.

In each of the three thermometers mentioned above there is one physical quantity called a *thermometric property* whose change is used to indicate a change of temperature. In the case of a gas at constant volume it is the pressure p; with the thermocouple it is the emf $\mathcal{E}$; and with the liquid-in-glass thermometer it is the height h of the liquid in the capillary.

15–3 The measurement of temperature. Let X stand for any thermometric property such as p, $\mathcal{E}$, or h. Let us define the temperature T common to the thermometer and to all systems in thermal equilibrium with it as a linear function of X. That is,

$$T = aX,$$

where a is an arbitrary constant. It follows that two temperatures on this "linear X scale" are to each other as the ratio of the corresponding X's, or

$$\frac{T_1}{T_2} = \frac{X_1}{X_2}. \tag{15–1}$$

Note that the linear function of X was an *arbitrary choice*. A different algebraic function, or even a logarithmic function, could have been chosen, and the resulting temperature scale would be equally legitimate.

To determine the temperature T of any system, the thermometer must first be brought to thermal equilibrium with *an arbitrarily chosen standard system in an easily reproducible state*. The temperature of the standard system in the chosen state is called a *fixed point*. Before 1954 there were two fixed points: (1) the temperature of pure ice in equilibrium with air-saturated water at one atmosphere pressure (the ice point), and (2) the equilibrium temperature of pure water and pure steam at one atmosphere pressure (the steam point). The temperature interval between these two fixed points was chosen to be 100 degrees.

The use of two fixed points was found unsatisfactory, partly because of the difficulty of achieving equilibrium between pure ice and air-saturated water. When ice melts, it surrounds itself with pure water and thus prevents intimate contact of ice and air-saturated water. Also, the steam point is extremely sensitive to a change in pressure. The temperature scale in use since 1954 is based on one fixed point only. This is the temperature at which ice, liquid water, and water vapor coexist in equilibrium, a state known as the *triple point* of water. To obtain the best agreement between the old and new scales, the temperature of the triple point is assigned the value 273.16 degrees kelvin, abbreviated 273.16°K. (The reason for the use of Kelvin's name will be made clear later.) Thus, designating the triple point of water by the subscript 3, we have from Eq. (15–1),

$$\frac{T}{T_3} = \frac{X}{X_3},$$

with

$$T_3 = 273.16°K.$$

Hence,

$$T = 273.16° \frac{X}{X_3}. \tag{15-2}$$

The temperature of the triple point of water is the *standard fixed point* of thermometry. To achieve the triple point, water of the highest purity is distilled into a vessel shown schematically in Fig. 15–4. When all air has been removed, the vessel is sealed off. With the aid of a freezing mixture in the inner well, a layer of ice is formed around the well, as shown in Fig. 15–4(a). When the freezing mixture is replaced by a thermometer bulb, a thin layer of ice is melted nearby, as shown in Fig. 15–4(b). So long as the solid, liquid, and vapor phases coexist in equilibrium, the

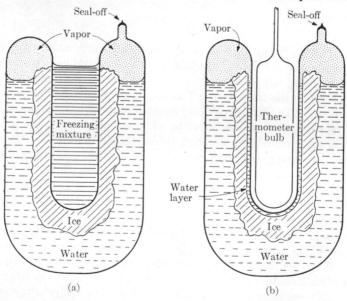

FIG. 15–4. Triple-point cell, (a) with freezing mixture in the central well to freeze a layer of ice; (b) with a thermometer in the well, which melts a thin layer of ice nearby.

system is at the triple point. The actual shape of the apparatus used by the U.S. National Bureau of Standards is shown in Fig. 15–5.

To determine an unknown temperature T using a thermometer with a thermometric property X, two measurements of X have to be made: one at the unknown temperature and the other at the triple point of water. The temperature is then found from Eq. (15–2).

If a series of tests is carried out in which the temperature of a given system is measured with a number of different thermometers, each making use of a different thermometric property, the thermometers will be found to give slightly different results. Even different varieties of the same kind of thermometer yield different results. The smallest variation, however, is found among different gas thermometers. For this reason, and also because of its accuracy and reproducibility, the gas thermometer has been chosen as a world standard. The principles of its operation are as follows. Suppose that an amount of gas is introduced into the bulb of a constant-volume gas thermometer so that the

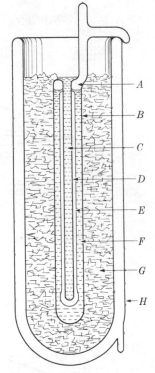

Fig. 15–5. Diagram of the NBS triple-point cell (B, D) in use in an ice bath (G) within a Dewar flask (H). A, water vapor; C, thermometer well; E, ice mantle; F, liquid water.

pressure p_3, when the bulb is surrounded by water at its triple point, is equal to 1000 mm Hg. Keeping the volume constant, measure the pressure p when the bulb is at some unknown temperature, such as that of steam condensing at atmospheric pressure, and calculate the quantity

$$273.16° \frac{p}{1000}.$$

Now remove some of the gas so that the pressure p_3 has a smaller value, say 500 mm Hg. Measure the new pressure p when the bulb is at the temperature of condensing steam, and calculate the quantity

$$273.16° \frac{p}{500}.$$

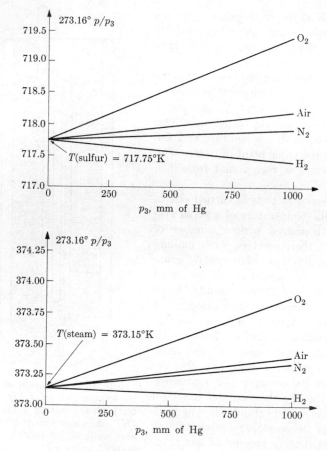

FIG. 15–6. Readings of a constant-volume gas thermometer for the temperature of condensing steam and for that of condensing sulfur, when different gases are used at various values of p_3.

The value of this quantity will be found to be slighly different from that obtained with $p_3 = 1000$ mm Hg.

Continue reducing the amount of gas in the bulb and calculate the quantity $273.16° \, p/p_3$ at each value of p_3. Construct a graph of this quantity against the pressure p_3 and extrapolate the resulting curve to the axis where $p_3 = 0$.

The results of a series of measurements of this sort are plotted in Fig. 15–6, for the temperatures of condensing steam and of condensing sulfur. The graphs show that although the readings of a constant-volume gas thermometer depend both on the kind of gas used and on the pressure p_3, *all gases indicate the same temperature as p_3 is lowered and approaches zero.* We therefore define the gas temperature T by the equation

$$T = [273.16°\text{K}] \lim_{p_3 \to 0} \left(\frac{p}{p_3}\right)_{\text{const. vol.}} \tag{15–3}$$

It should be emphasized that this equation, or the set of rules for measuring temperature which it embodies, does not rest on the assumption that "the pressure of a gas at constant volume is directly proportional to the temperature." Such a statement, before a temperature scale is set up, is meaningless.

Although the temperature scale of Eq. (15–3) is independent of the properties of any one particular gas, it still depends on the properties of gases in general. To measure a low temperature, a gas must be used at that low temperature. The lowest temperature that can be measured with a gas thermometer is about 1°K, provided low-pressure helium is used. *The temperature $T = 0$ remains as yet undefined.*

The kelvin temperature scale, which is independent of the properties of any particular substance, will be described in Chapter 20. It can be shown that in the temperature region in which a gas thermometer can be used, the gas scale and the kelvin scale are identical. In anticipation of this result, we write °K after a gas temperature. It will also be shown in Chapter 20 how the absolute zero of temperature is defined on the kelvin scale. Until then, the term "absolute zero" will have no meaning. The statement made so often that all molecular activity ceases at the temperature $T = 0$ is entirely erroneous. When it is necessary in statistical mechanics to correlate temperature with molecular activity, it is found that classical statistical mechanics must be modified with the aid of quantum mechanics. When this modification is carried out, the molecules of a substance at absolute zero have a *finite* amount of kinetic energy known as the *zero-point* energy.

15–4 The celsius, rankine, and fahrenheit scales. The celsius temperature scale (formerly called the centigrade scale in the United States and Great Britain) employs a degree of the same magnitude as that of the kelvin scale, but its zero point is shifted so that *the celsius temperature of the triple point of water is 0.01 degree celsius,* abbreviated 0.01°C. Thus, if t denotes the celsius temperature,

$$t = T - 273.15°\text{K}. \tag{15–4}$$

The celsius temperature t_S at which steam condenses at 1 atm pressure is

$$t_S = T_S - 273.15°K,$$

and reading T_S from Fig. 15–6,

$$t_S = 373.15° - 273.15°$$

or

$$t_S = 100.00°C.$$

There are two other scales in common use in engineering and in everyday life in the United States and in Great Britain. The *rankine* temperature T_R (written °R) is proportional to the kelvin temperature according to the relation

$$\boxed{T_R = \tfrac{9}{5}T.} \tag{15-5}$$

A degree of the same size is used in the *fahrenheit* scale t_F (written °F), but with the zero point shifted according to the relation

$$\boxed{t_F = T_R - 459.67°R.} \tag{15-6}$$

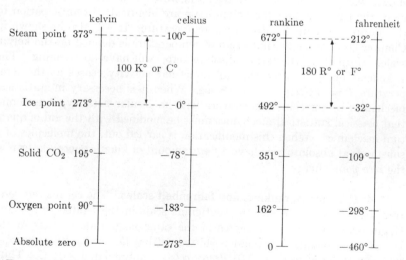

FIG. 15–7. Relation between kelvin ($T = 273.16°K \times \lim_{p_3 \to 0} (p/p_3)$ for any gas at constant volume), celsius ($t = T - 273.15°K$), rankine ($T_R = \tfrac{9}{5}T$), and fahrenheit ($t_F = T_R - 459.67°R$) temperature scales. Temperatures have been rounded off to the nearest degree.

TABLE 15–1

TEMPERATURES OF FIXED POINTS

Basic fixed points	T, °K	t, °C	T_R, °R	t_F, °F
Standard: Triple point of water	273.16	0.01	491.688	32.018
Boiling point of oxygen	90.18	−182.97	162.32	−297.35
Equil. of ice and air-saturated water (ice point)	273.15	0.00	491.67	32.00
Boiling point of water (steam point)	373.15	100.00	671.67	212.00
Boiling point of sulfur	717.75	444.60	1291.95	832.28
Melting point of antimony	903.65	630.50	1626.57	1166.90
Melting point of silver	1233.95	960.80	2221.11	1761.44
Melting point of gold	1336.15	1063.00	2405.07	1945.40

Substituting Eqs. (15–4) and (15–5) into Eq. (15–6), we get

$$t_F = \tfrac{9}{5}t + 32°F, \qquad (15\text{–}7)$$

from which it follows that the fahrenheit temperature of the ice point ($t = 0°C$) is 32°F and of the steam point ($t = 100°C$) is 212°F. The 100 celsius or kelvin degrees between the ice point and the steam point correspond to 180 fahrenheit or rankine degrees, as shown in Fig. 15–7 when the four scales are compared.

The accurate measurement of a boiling point or melting point with the aid of a gas thermometer requires months of painstaking laboratory work and mathematical computation. Fortunately, this has been done for a large number of substances which are obtainable with high purity. Some of these results are shown in Table 15–1. With the aid of these basic fixed points other thermometers may be calibrated. The calibration of the liquid-in-glass thermometer is accomplished by immersing it first in a mixture of ice and water and later in a steam bath and marking the liquid level in both cases. Subdividing the space between these two marks into 100 equal divisions provides a rough celsius scale, and the subdivision into 180 equal divisions, a rough fahrenheit scale.

The calibration of thermocouples and other important types of thermometers will be explained in later portions of the book.

Suppose the temperature of a beaker of water is raised from 20°C to 30°C, through a temperature interval of 10 celsius degrees. It is desirable to distinguish between such a temperature interval and the actual temperature of 10 degrees above the celsius zero. Hence we shall use the phrase "10 degrees celsius," or "10°C," when referring to an *actual temperature*, and "10 celsius degrees," or "10 C°" to mean a temperature *interval*. Thus there is an interval of 10 celsius degrees between 20 degrees celsius and 30 degrees celsius.

15–5 Linear expansion. With a few exceptions, the dimensions of all substances increase as the temperature of the substance is increased. If a given specimen is in the form of a rod or cable, one is usually interested in its change of *length* with changes in temperature. Figure 15–8 represents a rod whose length is L_0 at some reference temperature t_0, and whose length is L at some higher temperature t. The difference $L - L_0 = \Delta L$ is the amount the rod has expanded on heating. It is found experimentally that the increase in length, ΔL, is proportional to the original length L_0, and very nearly proportional to the increase in temperature, $t - t_0$ or Δt. That is,

$$\Delta L \propto L_0 \, \Delta t, \qquad \text{or} \qquad \Delta L = \alpha L_0 \, \Delta t, \qquad (15\text{–}8)$$

where α is a proportionality constant, different for different materials, and is called the *coefficient of linear expansion*.

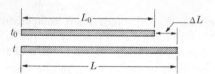

Fig. 15–8. Linear expansion.

Equation (15–8) may be solved for α and written

$$\alpha = \frac{\Delta L}{L_0} \frac{1}{\Delta t}. \qquad (15\text{–}9)$$

The coefficient of linear expansion of a substance may therefore be described as the fractional change in length per degree rise in temperature. Another useful relation is obtained by replacing ΔL by $L - L_0$ and solving for L.

$$L = L_0(1 + \alpha \, \Delta t) \qquad (15\text{–}10)$$

Since L_0, L, and ΔL are all expressed in the same unit, the units of α are "reciprocal degrees" (celsius or fahrenheit). Thus the coefficient of

Table 15-2

Coefficients of Linear Expansion

Substance	α (C°)$^{-1}$
Aluminum	24×10^{-6}
Brass	20×10^{-6}
Copper	14×10^{-6}
Glass	$4\text{-}9 \times 10^{-6}$
Steel	12×10^{-6}
Invar	0.9×10^{-6}
Quartz (fused)	0.4×10^{-6}
Zinc	26×10^{-6}

linear expansion of copper is written

$$\alpha = 14 \times 10^{-6} \text{ per celsius degree}$$

or

$$\alpha = 14 \times 10^{-6} \text{ (C°)}^{-1}.$$

This means that a copper rod one centimeter long at 0°C, increases in length by 0.000014 cm when heated to 1°C. A rod one foot long at 0°C increases by 0.000014 ft, and so on.

Since the fahrenheit degree is only $\frac{5}{9}$ as large as the celsius degree, coefficients of expansion per fahrenheit degree are $\frac{5}{9}$ as large as their values on the celsius scale.

Example. An iron steam pipe is 200 ft long at 0°C. What will be its increase in length when heated to 100°C? $\alpha = 10 \times 10^{-6}$ per celsius degree.

$L_0 = 200$ ft, $\alpha = 10 \times 10^{-6}$ per C°, $t = 100$°C, $t_0 = 0$°C.

Increase in length $= \Delta L = \alpha L_0 \Delta t$
$$= (10 \times 10^{-6})(200)(100)$$
$$= 0.20 \text{ ft.}$$

The coefficient of expansion of a substance in the form of a rod is measured by making two fine lines on the rod near its ends, and measuring the displacement of each line with a measuring microscope while the temperature of the rod is changed by a measured amount.

The *bimetallic* element is a device which has come into wide use in recent years, both as a thermometer and as a part of many thermostatic controls.

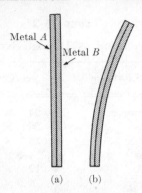

Metal A

Metal B

(a)   (b)

FIG. 15–9 The bimetallic element.

It consists of two thin flat strips of different metals, welded or riveted to-gether as in Fig. 15–9(a). If metal A has a larger coefficient of expansion than metal B, the compound strip, if originally straight, bends into a curve when heated as shown in Fig. 15–9(b). The transverse motion of the end of the strip is very much larger than the increase in length of either metal.

When used as a thermostat, one end of the strip is fixed and the motion of the other end is made to open or close an electrical control circuit. The common oven thermometer consists of a bimetallic strip coiled in a helix. With changes in temperature the helix winds or unwinds, and this motion is transmitted to a pivoted pointer which moves over a calibrated scale. Because of lost motion and friction, such thermometers are not precision instruments.

15–6 Surface and volume expansion. When a plate or sheet of material is heated, both the length and breadth of the plate increase. Consider a rectangular plate whose length and breadth at temperature t_0 are L_0 and b_0 respectively. When heated to a temperature t, these dimensions become

$$L = L_0(1 + \alpha \, \Delta t),$$

and

$$b = b_0(1 + \alpha \, \Delta t).$$

The original area of the plate was

$$A_0 = L_0 b_0,$$

and the area after heating is

$$A = Lb = L_0 b_0 (1 + \alpha \, \Delta t)\,(1 + \alpha \, \Delta t).$$
$$= A_0[1 + 2\alpha \, \Delta t + (\alpha \, \Delta t)^2].$$

TABLE 15–3

COEFFICIENTS OF CUBICAL EXPANSION

Substance	$\beta \ (C°)^{-1}$
Alcohol, ethyl	0.745×10^{-3}
Carbon disulphide	1.140×10^{-3}
Glycerin	0.485×10^{-3}
Mercury	0.182×10^{-3}
Petroleum	0.899×10^{-3}

But since α is a small quantity, α^2 will be extremely small and the term $(\alpha \, \Delta t)^2$ may be neglected. Hence

$$A = A_0(1 + 2\alpha \, \Delta t).$$

If we now define a *surface* coefficient of expansion γ so that

$$A = A_0(1 + \gamma \, \Delta t), \qquad (15\text{–}11)$$

it follows that

$$\boxed{\gamma = 2\alpha,}$$

and the coefficient of surface expansion is twice the coefficient of linear expansion. Although derived for the special case of a rectangular plate, the result holds for a plate of any shape whatever.

If the plate contains a hole, the area *of the hole* expands at the same rate as does the surrounding material. This remains true even if the hole becomes so large that the "plate" is reduced to nothing but a rim around the hole. Thus the area of the "hole" enclosed by a steel wagon tire expands at the same rate as would a disk of this size, if constructed of the same kind of steel as is the rim.

By considering a solid block of material in the form of a rectangular parallelepiped whose dimensions at t_0 are L_0, b_0, and c_0, it is easy to show by the same type of reasoning that

$$V = V_0(1 + 3\alpha \, \Delta t) = V_0(1 + \beta \, \Delta t), \qquad (15\text{–}12)$$

where V is the volume at the temperature t, V_0 is the volume at t_0, and

$$\boxed{\beta = 3\alpha}$$

is the *volume* coefficient or *cubical* coefficient of expansion. This equation holds regardless of the shape of the body.

It is also true that the volume enclosed by a solid, such as the volume of a tank, a flask, or a thermometer bulb, expands at the same rate as would a solid body of the same material as that of which the walls are composed.

Equation (15–12) may also be used to compute the expansion of a liquid. The linear and surface coefficients of expansion of a liquid are of little significance.

EXAMPLE. The volume of the bulb of a mercury thermometer at 0°C is V_0, and the cross section of the capillary is A_0. The linear coefficient of expansion of the glass is α_G per C°, and the cubical coefficient of expansion of mercury is β_M per C°. If the mercury just fills the bulb at 0°C, what is the length of the mercury column in the capillary at a temperature of t°C?

The volume of the bulb at a temperature t is

$$V = V_0(1 + \beta_G t),$$

where $\beta_G = 3\alpha_G$ is the cubical coefficient of expansion of the glass.

The volume of the mercury at a temperature t is

$$V_M = V_0(1 + \beta_M t).$$

The volume of mercury that has been expelled from the bulb is the difference between these, or

$$V_0(1 + \beta_M t) - V_0(1 + \beta_G t) = V_0 t(\beta_M - \beta_G).$$

This volume is also equal to the length l of the mercury column multiplied by the cross section A of the capillary, where

$$A = A_0(1 + 2\alpha_G t).$$

Table 15–2 shows that the linear coefficient of expansion of glass is of the order of 5×10^{-6} per C°. Hence even if t is as great as 300°C, the term $2\alpha_G t$ is only 0.003. It may therefore be neglected in comparison with unity, which is equivalent to considering the cross section of the capillary constant. Then

$$lA_0 = V_0 t(\beta_M - \beta_G)$$

and

$$l = \frac{V_0}{A_0} (\beta_M - \beta_G)t.$$

The length of the mercury column is therefore proportional to the temperature and to the difference between the cubical coefficients of expansion of mercury and the glass of which the thermometer is constructed.

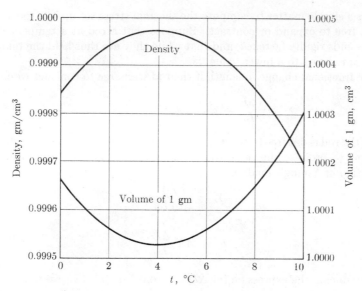

FIG. 15–10. Density of water, and volume of 1 gm, in the temperature range from 0°C to 10°C.

Water, in the temperature range from 0°C to 4°C, *decreases* in volume with increasing temperature, contrary to the behavior of most substances. That is, between 0°C and 4°C, the coefficient of expansion of water is *negative*. Above 4°C, water expands when heated. Since the volume of a given mass of water is smaller at 4°C than at any other temperature, the density of water is a maximum at 4°C. This behavior of water is the reason why lakes and ponds freeze first at their upper surface. Figure 15–10 illustrates the anomalous expansion of water in the temperature range from 0°C to 10°C.

15–7 Thermal stresses. If the ends of a rod are rigidly fixed so as to prevent expansion or contraction and the temperature of the rod is changed, tensile or compressive stresses, called *thermal stresses*, will be set up in the rod. These stresses may become very large, sufficiently so to stress the rod beyond its elastic limit or even beyond its breaking strength. Hence in the design of any structure which is subject to changes in temperature, some provision must, in general, be made for expansion. In a long steam pipe this is accomplished by the insertion of expansion joints or a section of pipe in the form of a U. In bridges, one end may be rigidly fastened to its abutment while the other rests on rollers.

It is a simple matter to compute the thermal stress set up in a rod which is not free to expand or contract. Suppose that a rod at a temperature t has its ends rigidly fastened, and that while they are thus held the temperature is reduced to a lower value, t_0.

The fractional change in length if the rod were free to contract would be

$$\frac{\Delta L}{L_0} = \alpha(t - t_0) = \alpha \, \Delta t. \qquad (15\text{--}13)$$

Since the rod is not free to contract, the tension must increase by a sufficient amount to produce the same fractional change in length. But from the definition of Young's modulus,

$$Y = \frac{F/A}{\Delta L/L_0},$$

and hence

$$F = AY \frac{\Delta L}{L_0}.$$

Introducing the expression for $\Delta L/L_0$ from Eq. (15–13), we have

$$F = AY\alpha \, \Delta t, \qquad (15\text{--}14)$$

which gives the tension F in the rod. The *stress* in the rod is

$$\frac{F}{A} = Y\alpha \, \Delta t. \qquad (15\text{--}15)$$

PROBLEMS

15–1. (a) Prove that

$$t_F = \tfrac{9}{5}t + 32°F.$$

(b) Prove that the celsius and fahrenheit scales have the same reading at —40°.

15–2. The pendulum shaft of a clock is of aluminum. What is the fractional change in length of the shaft when it is cooled from 75°F to 45°F?

15–3. The length of Technology Bridge is about 2000 ft. Find the difference between its length on a winter day when the temperature is —20°F, and a summer day when the temperature is 100°F. Use the coefficient of expansion of steel.

15–4. A surveyor's 100-ft steel tape is correct at a temperature of 65°F. The distance between two points, as measured by this tape on a day when the temperature is 95°F, is 86.57 ft. What is the true distance between the points?

15–5. One steel meter bar is correct at 0°C, and another at 25°C. What is the difference between their lengths at 20°C?

15–6. To ensure a tight fit, the aluminum rivets used in airplane construction are made slightly larger than the rivet holes and cooled by "dry ice" (solid CO_2) before being driven. If the diameter of a hole is 0.2500 inch, what should be the diameter of a rivet at 20°C if its diameter is to equal that of the hole when the rivet is cooled to —78°C, the temperature of dry ice?

15–7. A glass flask whose volume is exactly 1000 cm³ at 0°C is filled level full of mercury at this temperature. When flask and mercury are heated to 100°C, 15.2 cm³ of mercury overflow. If the cubical coefficient of expansion of mercury is 0.000182 per celsius degree, compute the linear coefficient of expansion of the glass.

15–8. Steel rails 120 ft long are laid with their ends in contact on a day when the temperature is 110°F. What length gap will there be between rails on a day when the temperature is —20°F?

15–9. A steel wire which is 10 ft long at 20°C is found to increase in length by ¾ inch when heated to 520°C. Compute its coefficient of linear expansion. (b) Find the stress in the wire if it is stretched taut at 520° and cooled to 20° without being allowed to contract.

15–10. A wire 60 cm long is bent into a circular ring, having a gap of 1.0 cm. The temperature of the wire is increased uniformly by 100°C. At the new temperature the gap is found to be 1.002 cm. What is the linear temperature coefficient of expansion of the wire? Assume no stresses within the wire before or after heating.

15–11. A steel ring of 3.000 inches inside diameter at 20°C is to be heated and slipped over a brass shaft measuring 3.002 inches in diameter at 20°C. (a) To what temperature should the ring be heated? (b) If the ring and shaft together are cooled by some means such as liquid air, at what temperature will the ring just slip off the shaft?

15–12. At a temperature of 20°C, the volume of a certain glass flask, up to a reference mark on the stem of the flask, is exactly 100 cm³. The flask is filled to this point with a liquid whose cubical coefficient of expansion is 120×10^{-5} per C°, with both flask and liquid at 20°C. The linear coefficient of expansion of the glass is 8×10^{-6} per C°. The cross section of the stem is 1 mm² and can be considered constant. How far will the liquid rise or fall in the stem when the temperature is raised to 40°C?

15–13. A slender steel rod oscillates as a physical pendulum about a horizontal axis through one end. If the rod is 8 ft long at 30°C, compute the fractional change in its period when the temperature is decreased to 0°C.

15–14. A steel rod 1.5 cm^2 in cross section is 70 cm long at 20°C. If it is heated to 520°C and cooled to 20°C without being allowed to contract, compute the stress in the rod.

15–15. The cross section of a steel rod is 1.5 in^2. What is the least force that will prevent it from contracting while cooling from 520°C to 20°C?

15–16. What hydrostatic pressure is necessary to prevent a copper block from expanding when its temperature is increased from 20°C to 30°C?

15–17. A steel bomb is filled with water at 10°C. If the whole is heated to 75°C and no water is allowed to escape, compute the increase in pressure in the bomb. Assume the bomb to be sufficiently strong so that it is not stretched by the increased pressure. The average coefficient of volume expansion of water in this temperature range is 0.39×10^{-3} (C°)$^{-1}$.

15–18. Steel railroad rails 60 ft long are laid on a winter day when the temperature is 20°F. (a) How much space must be left between rails if they are to just touch on a summer day when the temperature is 110°F? (b) If the rails were originally laid in contact, what would be the stress in them on a summer day when the temperature is 110°F?

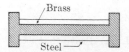

FIGURE 15–11

15–19. A heavy brass bar has projections at its ends, as in Fig. 15–11. Two fine steel wires fastened between the projections are just taut (zero tension) when the whole system is at 0°C. What is the tensile stress in the steel wires when the temperature of the system is raised to 300°C? Make any simplifying assumptions you think are justified, but state what they are.

15–20. A liquid is enclosed in a metal cylinder provided with a piston of the same metal. The system is originally at atmospheric pressure and at a temperature of 80°C. The piston is forced down until the pressure on the liquid is increased by 100 atm, and it is then clamped in this position. Find the new temperature at which the pressure of the liquid is again 1 atmosphere. Assume that the cylinder is sufficiently strong so that its volume is not altered by changes in pressure, but only by changes in temperature. Compressibility of liquid $(k) = 50 \times 10^{-6}$ atm^{-1}. Cubical coefficient of expansion of liquid $(\beta) = 5.3 \times 10^{-4}$ (C°)$^{-1}$. Linear coefficient of expansion of metal $(\alpha) = 10 \times 10^{-6}$ (C°)$^{-1}$.

15–21. A steel rod of length 40 cm and a copper rod of length 36 cm, both of the same diameter, are placed end to end between two rigid supports, with no initial stress in the rods. The temperature of the rods is now raised 50°C. What is the stress in each rod?

CHAPTER 16

QUANTITY OF HEAT

16-1 Heat, a form of energy. Heat was formerly thought to be an invisible weightless fluid called *caloric*, which was produced when a substance burned and which could be transmitted by conduction from one body to another. The abandonment of the caloric theory was a part of the general development of physics during the 18th and 19th centuries. The two men who were probably chiefly responsible for the views we hold today were Count Rumford (1753–1814) (a native of Woburn, Mass.) and Sir James Prescott Joule.

Rumford was engaged in supervising the boring of cannon for the government of Bavaria. To prevent overheating, the bore of the cannon was kept filled with water, and as this boiled away during the boring process the supply had to be continually replenished. It was admitted that caloric had to be supplied to water in order to boil it, and the continual production of caloric was explained by the hypothesis that when matter was more finely subdivided (as in the process of boring) its capacity for retaining caloric grew smaller and the caloric thus released was what caused the water to boil.

Rumford noted, however, that the cooling water continued to boil away even when his boring tools became so dull that they were no longer cutting. That is, even a dull boring tool was apparently an inexhaustible supply of caloric *as long as mechanical work was being done to rotate the tool.*

Now one of the features which justifies our acceptance of many abstract ideas in physics is that they obey a "conservation principle." Here was a process in which *two* quantities failed to be conserved. Mechanical energy was not conserved since work was continually being expended, and caloric was not conserved since it was continually being created. Although Rumford did not express his ideas in just this way, he saw the opportunity to eliminate two cases of nonconservation and at the same time to extend the principle of conservation of energy as it was then understood. He asserted that what had formerly been thought a separate entity, namely caloric, was in reality merely energy in another form. The process was not the continual disappearance of one thing and the appearance of another, but merely the transformation of energy from one form to another. As we would say today, mechanical energy was continually being transformed into heat, the process being one example of conservation of energy.

Rumford made some measurements of the quantities of work done and of cooling water boiled away, but his experiments were not of great precision. When Joule, in the period from 1843 to 1878, showed that whenever a given quantity of mechanical energy was converted to heat the *same* quantity of heat was always developed, the equivalence of heat and work as two forms of energy was definitely established.

There are, of course, processes for whose explanation the caloric theory is entirely satisfactory. When heat flows from one body to another by conduction, or when substances at different temperatures are mixed in a calorimeter, heat *is* conserved, and for such processes the caloric theory would serve perfectly well.

16–2 Quantity of heat. Heat, like mechanical energy, is an intangible thing and a unit of heat is not something that can be preserved in a standards laboratory. The quantity of heat transferred in a process is measured by some change which accompanies the process, and a unit of heat is defined as the heat necessary to produce some standard, agreed-on change. Three such units are in common use, the calorie (cal), the kilogram·calorie (kcal), and the British thermal unit (Btu).

One calorie is the quantity of heat which must be supplied to one gram of water to raise its temperature through one celsius degree.

One kilogram·calorie is the quantity of heat which must be supplied to one kilogram of water to raise its temperature through one celsius degree.

One Btu is the quantity of heat which must be supplied to one pound of water to raise its temperature through one fahrenheit degree.*

Evidently, 1 kilogram·calorie = 1000 calories.

Since 454 gm = 1 lb, and since $1 \text{ F}° = \frac{5}{9} \text{ C}°$, the Btu may be defined as the quantity of heat which must be supplied to 454 gm (0.454 kgm) of water to raise its temperature through $\frac{5}{9} \text{ C}°$, which is $454 \times \frac{5}{9} = 252$ cal or 0.252 kcal. Hence

$$1 \text{ Btu} = 252 \text{ cal} = 0.252 \text{ kcal}.$$

The heat units here defined vary somewhat with the location of the degree, i.e., whether it is from 0° to 1°, 47° to 48°, etc. It is generally agreed to use the temperature interval from 14.5°C to 15.5°C (the "15° calorie"), and in English units to use the temperature interval from 63°F to 64°F. For most purposes this variation is small enough to be neglected.

It is essential that the distinction between "quantity of heat" and "temperature" shall be clearly understood. The terms are commonly mis-

---

* In this part of the subject we shall depart from the engineering system of units which we used throughout mechanics, and adopt as a mass unit the *mass of the standard pound*. This unit is also called one pound, and is equal to a mass of 454 grams, or (about) $\frac{1}{32}$ slug. Also, for simplicity, we shall confine metric units chiefly to the cgs system.

used in everyday life. Suppose that two pans, one containing a small and the other a large amount of water, are placed over identical gas burners and heated for the same length of time. It is obvious that at the end of this time the temperature of the small amount of water will have risen higher than that of the large amount. In this instance, equal quantities of heat have been supplied to each pan of water, but the increases in temperature are not equal.

On the other hand, suppose the two pans are both initially at a temperature of 60°F and that both are to be heated to 212°F. It is evident that more heat must be supplied to the pan containing the larger amount of water. The temperature change is the same for both but the quantities of heat supplied are very different.

We shall represent a quantity of heat by the letter Q.

16-3 Internal energy. The temperature of a body may be increased by placing it in contact with a second body at a higher temperature, or by doing mechanical work on the body. For example, the air in a bicycle pump becomes hotter when the piston is pushed down, although it could also be heated by placing it in a furnace.

If one were given a sample of hot air, it would be impossible to tell by any tests whether it had been heated by compression or by heat flow from a hotter body. This raises the question as to whether one is justified in speaking of the "heat in a body," since the present state of the body may have been brought about either by adding heat to it or by doing work on it. We shall show later that the proper term to use is "internal energy," and that the expression "heat energy of a body" is meaningless.

From the atomic point of view, the internal energy of a body is the sum total of the kinetic and potential energies of its molecules, apart from any kinetic or potential energy of the body as a whole. Not enough is known at present about the molecular structure of matter to be able to express internal energies wholly in terms of a molecular model. To a first approximation, the internal energy of a gas at low pressure may be identified with the aggregate kinetic energy of its molecules.

Even though the details of the molecular picture of matter are not fully understood, we do have definite evidence that molecular energies and velocities, whether in a solid, liquid, or gas, increase with increasing temperature. Such statements as "the heat in a body is the energy of motion of its molecules" should, however, be avoided.

16-4 The mechanical equivalent of heat. Energy in mechanical form is usually expressed in ergs, joules, or foot-pounds; energy in the form of heat is expressed in calories or Btu. The relative magnitudes of the "heat units" and the "mechanical units" can be found by an experiment in which a measured quantity of mechanical energy is completely converted into a measured quantity of heat. The first accurate experiments were performed by Joule, using an apparatus in which falling weights rotated a set of paddles in a container of water. The energy transformed was computed in mechanical units from a knowledge of the weights and their height of fall, and in heat units from a measurement of the mass of water and its rise in temperature. In more recent methods, which are also more precise, electrical energy is converted to heat in a resistance wire immersed in water. The best results to date give:

$$778 \text{ ft·lb} = 1 \text{ Btu,}$$
$$4.186 \text{ joules} = 1 \text{ cal,}$$
$$4186 \text{ joules} = 1 \text{ kcal.}$$

That is, 778 ft·lb of mechanical energy, when converted to heat, will raise the temperature of 1 lb of water through 1 F°, etc.

These relations are often expressed by the statement that *the mechanical equivalent of heat* is 4.186 joules/cal, or 778 ft·lb/Btu. The phraseology is a carry-over from the early days when the equivalence of mechanical energy and heat was being established.

The precise value of the mechanical equivalent of heat depends on the particular temperature interval used in the definition of the calorie or Btu. To avoid this confusion, an international commission has agreed to *define* 1 kcal as *exactly* 1/860 kilowatt·hour. Then by definition, 1 cal = 4.18605 joules and 1 Btu = 778.26 ft·lb. It follows that 1 Btu = 251.996 cal.

16–5 Heat capacity. Specific heat. Materials differ from one another in the quantity of heat required to produce a given elevation of temperature in a given mass. Suppose that a quantity of heat Q is supplied to a given body, resulting in a temperature rise Δt. The ratio of the heat supplied to the corresponding temperature rise is called the *heat capacity* of the body.

$$\text{Heat capacity} = \frac{Q}{\Delta t}. \qquad (16\text{--}1)$$

Heat capacities are ordinarily expressed in calories per celsius degree, or Btu per fahrenheit degree. If we set $\Delta t = 1$ degree in Eq. (16–1), it will be seen that the heat capacity of a body is numerically equal to the quantity of heat which must be supplied to it to increase its temperature by one degree.

To obtain a figure that is characteristic of the material of which a body is composed, the *specific heat capacity*, abbreviated *specific heat*, of a

TABLE 16–1

SPECIFIC HEAT CAPACITIES

Substance	Specific heat, cal/gm·C°	Temperature interval
Aluminum	0.217	17–100°C
Brass	0.094	15–100
Copper	0.093	15–100
Glass	0.199	20–100
Ice	0.55	−10–0
Iron	0.113	18–100
Lead	0.031	20–100
Mercury	0.033	0–100
Silver	0.056	15–100

material is defined as the *heat capacity per unit mass* of a body composed of the material. We shall represent specific heat capacity by the letter c.

$$c = \frac{\text{heat capacity}}{\text{mass}} = \frac{Q}{m\,\Delta t}. \qquad (16\text{–}2)$$

Specific heat capacity is expressed in calories per gram·celsius degree, or Btu per pound·fahrenheit degree.

The specific heat capacity of a material is numerically equal to the quantity of heat which must be supplied to *unit mass* of the material to increase its temperature through 1 degree. The specific heat capacities of a few common materials are listed in Table 16–1. The units are cal/gm·C° or Btu/lb·F°.

It follows from Eq. (16–2) that the heat which must be supplied to a body of mass m, whose specific heat capacity is c, to increase its temperature through an interval Δt, is

$$Q = mc\,\Delta t = mc(t_2 - t_1). \qquad (16\text{–}3)$$

Strictly speaking, Eq. (16–2) defines the *mean* specific heat capacity over the temperature range Δt. It is found that the quantity of heat required to raise the temperature of a material through a small interval varies with the location of the interval in the temperature scale. At ordinary temperatures, and over temperature intervals which are not too great, however, specific heats may be considered constant. At extremely low temperatures, approaching absolute zero, all specific heats decrease and approach zero.

It should be pointed out that the significance of the word "capacity" in "heat capacity" is not the same as when one speaks of the "capacity" of a bucket. The bucket can hold just so much water and no more, while heat can be added to a body indefinitely with, of course, a corresponding rise in temperature.

For some purposes, particularly in dealing with gases, it is more convenient to express specific heat capacities on the basis of one gram·molecular weight rather than one gram. It was first noted in 1819 by Dulong and Petit that the specific heat capacities of the metals, expressed in this way, were all very nearly equal to 6 cal/gm·molecular wt·C°. This fact is known as the *Dulong and Petit law*. Since the number of molecules is the same in one gram·molecular weight of all substances, this means that the heat capacity of a metallic object depends only on the *number* of molecules it contains, not on the mass of each molecule.

16–6 Calorimetry. The term calorimetry relates to the measurement of quantities of heat. Two types of calorimeter, the *water calorimeter* and the *continuous-flow calorimeter*, will be described.

The water calorimeter in its simple form consists of a thin-walled metal can A (Fig. 16–1) whose capacity is about two liters, and whose outer surface is nickel plated. The can contains a measured quantity of water, and is provided with a cover through which passes thermometer B. Heat losses are further reduced by surrounding the can with the heat-insulating jacket C. If the thermometer is read before and after an unknown quantity of heat Q is introduced into the calorimeter, Q may be found from the measured rise in temperature.

The water calorimeter may be used to measure specific heat as follows: a sample of the material whose specific heat is desired is heated in a furnace or steam bath to a known temperature, say t_s. Let the mass of the sample be m_s and its specific heat c_s.

The water in the calorimeter is thoroughly stirred and its temperature is measured. The sample is then quickly transferred to the calorimeter, the water is again thoroughly stirred, and the new temperature of the water is recorded. Let t_1 and t_2

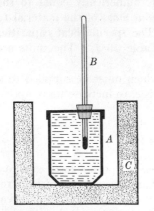

FIG. 16–1. The water calorimeter.

be the initial and final temperatures of the water, m_w the mass of the water, m_c the mass of the calorimeter can, and c_c its specific heat.

If no heat is lost from the calorimeter during the experiment, the heat given up by the sample in cooling from t_s to t_2 must equal the heat gained by the water and the calorimeter can. Hence

$$m_s c_s (t_s - t_2) = m_w \times 1(t_2 - t_1) + m_c c_c (t_2 - t_1)$$

$$= (m_w + m_c c_c)(t_2 - t_1)$$

and c_s may be found, since the other factors are known.

The effect of the heat capacity of the calorimeter, $m_c c_c$, is evidently equivalent to increasing the mass of the water by an amount $m_c c_c$ and using a calorimeter of zero heat capacity. The product $m_c c_c$ is called the *water equivalent* of the calorimeter.

Actually the calorimeter will gain (or lose) heat from its surroundings during an experiment unless special precautions are taken. One way of minimizing the heat transfer is to start with the calorimeter somewhat cooler than its surroundings and finish with its temperature the same amount higher than the surroundings. Then the heat gained during the first part of the experiment offsets the heat lost in the latter part. Another method (the so-called "adiabatic jacket") is to heat the jacket by an electric heating coil so that its temperature rises at the same rate as does that of the calorimeter. If both temperatures are always equal there will be no gain or loss of heat.

It should be noted that this method of measuring specific heat gives only the *average* specific heat over the temperature range from t_s to t_2.

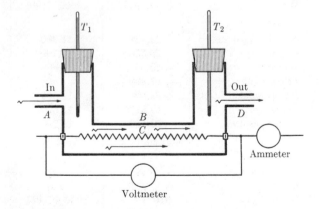

Fig. 16–2. The continuous-flow calorimeter.

Much more elaborate apparatus is required to measure the true specific heat at any desired temperature.

The continuous-flow calorimeter, as used to measure the mechanical equivalent of heat, is illustrated in Fig. 16–2. A continuous stream of water enters the apparatus at A, flows through the tube B around the resistance wire C, and leaves at D. Thermometers T_1 and T_2 read the temperatures t_1 and t_2 at inlet and outlet, and the electrical power expended is measured by the ammeter and voltmeter.

To use the calorimeter, the water is started flowing and the heating current is turned on. Thermometers T_1 and T_2 are read at intervals of, say, one minute, and their temperatures recorded. After sufficient time has elapsed, both thermometer readings become constant. Of course the temperature t_2 at the outlet is higher than the temperature t_1 at the inlet. When this steady state has been reached the apparatus itself is absorbing no heat, since its temperature remains constant. Heat is therefore being

TABLE 16–2

HEATS OF COMBUSTION

Substance	Btu/lb	cal/gm
Solids:		
Charcoal	14,600	8100
Coal	11,000–14,000	6100–7800
Coke	14,300	7950
Paraffin	19,800	11,000
Pitch	15,100	8400
Wood	8300–9200	4600–5100
Liquids:		
Aviation gasoline	20,420	11,300
Diesel fuel oil	19,350	10,700
Domestic fuel oil	19,450	10,800
Ethyl alcohol	14,000	7800
Jet-propulsion fuels	~19,000	~10,500
Kerosene	19,810	11,000
Motor gasoline	20,120	11,200
Gases:	(Btu/ft³)	(kcal/m³)
Acetylene	1448	12,870
Coal gas	488	4320
Hydrogen	275	2445
Natural gas	910–1970	8040–17,400
Propane	2330	20,600

carried away by the flowing water at exactly the same rate as it is developed by the heating coil.

If then the mass of water passing through the calorimeter in a certain time is found, usually by catching the water in a beaker placed below the outlet, the quantity of heat developed can be computed from the rise in temperature of this mass of water. The energy input in the same time can be found from the ammeter and voltmeter readings.

16–7 Heat of combustion. The heat of combustion of a substance is the quantity of heat liberated per unit mass, or per unit volume, when the substance is completely burned. Heats of combustion of solid and liquid fuels are usually expressed in Btu/lb or in cal/gm. The heat of combustion of gases is commonly expressed in Btu/ft^3. Some values are given in Table 16–2.

Heats of combustion of solid and liquid fuels are measured with a *bomb calorimeter.* A measured mass of the fuel is inserted in a strong steel bomb which is filled with oxygen under pressure to ensure complete combustion. The bomb is placed in a water calorimeter and the fuel ignited by sending a momentary electric current through a fine heater wire. From the measured temperature rise, the mass of water, and the water equivalent of calorimeter and bomb, the heat of combustion can be computed.

The heat of combustion of gaseous fuels is usually measured with a type of continuous flow calorimeter, illustrated in Fig. 16–3.

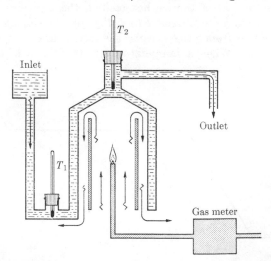

Fig. 16–3. Continuous-flow calorimeter used to measure the heat of combustion of gaseous fuel.

16–8 Change of phase. The term *phase* as used here relates to the fact that matter exists either as a solid, liquid, or gas. Thus the chemical substance H_2O exists in the *solid phase* as ice, in the *liquid phase* as water, and in the *gaseous phase* as steam. Provided they do not decompose at high temperatures, all substances can exist in any of the three phases under the proper conditions of temperature and pressure. Transitions from one phase to another are accompanied by the absorption or liberation of heat and usually by a change in volume.

As an illustration, suppose that ice is taken from a refrigerator where its temperature was, say, $-25°C$. Let the ice be crushed quickly, placed in a container, and a thermometer inserted in the mass. Imagine the container to be surrounded by a heating coil which supplies heat to the ice at a uniform rate, and suppose that no other heat reaches the ice. The temperature of the ice would be observed to increase steadily as shown by the portion of the graph (Fig. 16–4) from *a* to *b*, or until the temperature has risen to $0°C$. As soon as this temperature is reached, some liquid water will be observed in the container. In other words, the ice begins to melt. The melting process is a *change of phase*, from the solid phase to the liquid phase. The thermometer, however, will show no *increase in temperature*, and even though heat is being supplied at the same rate as before, the temperature will remain at $0°C$ until all the ice is melted (point *c*, Fig. 16–4). (The ice and water mixture must be kept thoroughly stirred, otherwise the temperature of that part of the water closest to the heater will rise above $0°C$.)

As soon as the last of the ice has melted, the temperature begins to rise again at a uniform rate (from *c* to *d*, Fig. 16–4) although this rate will be slower than that from *a* to *b* because the specific heat of water is greater than that of ice. When a temperature of $100°C$ is reached (point *d*),

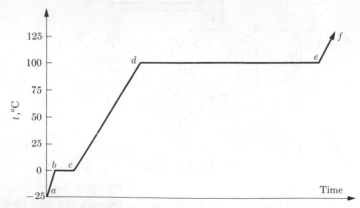

Fɪɢ. 16–4. The temperature remains constant during each change of phase.

bubbles of steam (gaseous water or water vapor) start to escape from the liquid surface, or the water begins to boil. The temperature remains constant at 100°C until all the water has boiled away. Another change of phase has therefore taken place, from the liquid phase to the gaseous phase.

If all the water vapor had been trapped and not allowed to diffuse away (a very large container would be needed), the heating process could be continued as from *e* to *f*. The gas would now be called "superheated steam."

Although water was chosen as an example in the process just described, the same type of curve as in Fig. 16–4 is obtained for many other substances. Some, of course, decompose before reaching a melting or boiling point, and others, such as glass or pitch, do not change state at a definite temperature but become gradually softer as their temperature is raised. Crystalline substances, such as ice, or a metal, melt at a definite temperature. Glass and pitch are actually supercooled liquids of very high viscosity.

The temperature at which a crystalline solid melts when heat is supplied to it at atmospheric pressure is called its *normal melting point*, and the temperature at which a liquid boils when heat is supplied to it at atmospheric pressure is called its *normal boiling point*. The quantity of heat per unit mass that must be supplied to a material at its melting point to convert it completely to a liquid at the same temperature, is called the *heat of fusion* of the material. The quantity of heat per unit mass that must be supplied to a material at its boiling point to convert it completely to a gas at the same temperature, is called the *heat of vaporization* of the material. Heats of fusion and vaporization are expressed in calories per gram, or Btu per pound. Thus the heat of fusion of ice is about 80 cal/gm or 144 Btu/lb. The heat of vaporization of water (at 100°C) is 539 cal/gm or 970 Btu/lb. Some heats of fusion and vaporization are listed in Table 16–3.

When heat is removed from a gas, its temperature falls and at the same temperature at which it boiled, it returns to the liquid phase, or *condenses*. In so doing it gives up to its surroundings the same quantity of heat which was required to vaporize it. The heat so given up, per unit mass, is called the *heat of condensation* and is equal to the heat of vaporization. Similarly, a liquid returns to the solid phase, or freezes, when cooled to the temperature at which it melted, and gives up heat called *heat of solidification* exactly equal to the heat of fusion. Thus the melting point and the freezing point are at the same temperature, and the boiling point and condensation point are at the same temperature.

Whether a substance, at its melting point, is freezing or melting depends on whether heat is being supplied or removed. That is, if heat is supplied to a beaker containing both ice and water at 0°C, some of the ice will

TABLE 16–3

HEATS OF FUSION AND VAPORIZATION

Substance	Normal melting point		Heat of fusion, cal/gm	Normal boiling point		Heat of vaporization, cal/gm
	°K	°C		°K	°C	
Helium	3.5	−269.65	1.25	4.216	−268.93	5
Hydrogen	13.84	−259.31	14	20.26	−252.89	108
Nitrogen	63.18	−209.97	6.09	77.34	−195.81	48
Oxygen	54.36	−218.79	3.30	90.18	−182.97	51
Ethyl alcohol	159	−114	24.9	351	78	204
Mercury	234	− 39	2.82	630	357	65
Water	273.15	0.00	79.7	373.15	100.00	539
Sulphur	392	119	9.1	717.75	444.60	78
Lead	600.5	327.3	5.86	2023	1750	208
Antimony	903.65	630.50	39.4	1713	1440	
Silver	1233.95	960.80	21.1	2466	2193	558
Gold	1336.15	1063.00	15.4	2933	2660	377

melt; if heat is removed, some of the water will freeze; the temperature in either case remains at 0°C so long as both ice and water are present. If heat is *neither supplied nor removed*, no change at all takes place and the relative amounts of ice and water, and the temperature, all remain constant.

This furnishes, then, another point of view which may be taken regarding the melting point. That is, the melting (or freezing) point of a substance is *that temperature at which both the liquid and solid phases can exist together*. At any higher temperature, the substance can only be a liquid; at any lower temperature, it can only be a solid.

The general term *heat of transformation* is applied both to heats of fusion and heats of vaporization, and both are designated by the letter L. Since L represents the heat absorbed or liberated in the change of phase of unit mass, the heat Q absorbed or liberated in the change of phase of a mass m is

$$Q = mL. \qquad (16\text{–}4)$$

The household steam-heating system makes use of a boiling-condensing process to transfer heat from the furnace to the radiators. Each pound of water which is turned to steam in the furnace absorbs 970 Btu (the heat of vaporization of water) from the furnace, and gives up 970 Btu when it condenses in the radiators. (This figure is correct if the steam pressure is one atmosphere. It will be slightly smaller at higher pressures.) Thus the steam-heating system does not need to circulate as much water as a hot-water heating system. If water leaves a hot-water furnace at 140°F and returns at 100°F, dropping 40 F°, about 24 lb of water must circulate to carry the same heat as is carried in the form of heat of vaporization by one pound of steam.

Under the proper conditions of temperature and pressure, a substance can change directly from the solid to the gaseous phase without passing through the liquid phase. The transfer from solid to vapor is called *sublimation*, and the solid is said to *sublime*. "Dry ice" (solid carbon dioxide) sublimes at atmospheric pressure. Liquid carbon dioxide cannot exist at a pressure lower than about 73 lb/in^2.

Heat is absorbed in the process of sublimation, and liberated in the reverse process. The quantity of heat per unit mass is called the *heat of sublimation.*

16–9 Measurement of heats of fusion and vaporization.

The method of mixtures is used to measure heats of fusion and of vaporization. For example, the heat of fusion of ice may be found by dropping a weighed sample of ice at 0°C into a calorimeter containing a measured amount of water, and observing the temperature of the water before and after the addition of the ice. Let a mass m_i of ice at 0°C be dropped in a calorimeter containing a mass m_w of water, lowering the temperature of the water from t_1 to t_2. We shall assume that all the ice melts, and neglect the heat capacity of the calorimeter. Then if L represents the heat of fusion of the ice, the ice absorbs a quantity of heat m_iL on melting (this converts it to water at 0°C) and a further quantity of heat m_it_2 on warming up to the final temperature t_2. The water in the calorimeter gives up a quantity of heat $m_w(t_1 - t_2)$. Hence,

$$m_w(t_1 - t_2) = m_i(L + t_2),$$

so that L can be found if the other quantities are known.

The heat of condensation (= heat of vaporization) of steam can be measured in a similar way, by allowing steam from a boiler to condense within a calorimeter. The condensation usually takes place in a coiled tube immersed in the calorimeter, so that the amount of steam condensing may be found by weighing the coil before and after the experiment. We have:

Heat given up by condensing steam = m_sL.

$\begin{cases} \text{Heat given up by condensed steam} \\ \quad \text{(water at 100°C) cooling to } t_2 \end{cases}$ = $m_s(100 - t_2)$.

Heat absorbed by calorimeter = $m_w(t_2 - t_1)$.

The heat of vaporization may be found by equating heat loss to heat gain.

16–10 Effect of dissolved substances on freezing and boiling points.
The freezing point of a liquid is lowered when some other substance is
dissolved in the liquid. A common example is the use of an "antifreeze"
to lower the freezing point of the water in the cooling system of an automobile engine.

The freezing point of a saturated solution of common salt in water is
about −20°C. To understand why a mixture of ice and salt may be used
as a freezing mixture, let us make use of the definition of the freezing
point as the only temperature at which the liquid and solid phases can
exist in equilibrium. When a concentrated salt solution is cooled, it freezes
at −20°C, and crystals of ice (pure H_2O) separate from the solution. In
other words, ice crystals and a salt solution can exist in equilibrium only
at −20°C, just as ice crystals and pure water can exist together only at
0°C.

When ice at 0°C is mixed with a salt solution at 20°C, some of the
ice melts, abstracting its heat of fusion from the solution until the temperature falls to 0°C. But ice and salt solution cannot remain in equilibrium
at 0°C, so that the ice continues to melt. Heat is now supplied both by
the ice and the solution, and both cool down until the equilibrium temperature of −20°C is reached. If no heat is supplied from outside, the mixture remains unchanged at this temperature. If the mixture is brought
into contact with a warmer body, say an ice-cream mixture at 20°C,
heat flows from the ice-cream mixture to the cold salt solution, melting
more of the ice but producing no rise in temperature as long as any ice
remains. The flow of heat from the ice-cream mixture lowers its temperature to its freezing point (which will be below 0°C, since it is itself a
solution). Further loss of heat to the ice-salt mixture causes the ice
cream to freeze.

The boiling point of a liquid is also affected by dissolved substances,
but may be either increased or decreased. Thus the boiling point of a
water-alcohol solution is *lower* than that of pure water, while the boiling
point of a water-salt solution is *higher* than that of pure water.

Both boiling and freezing points are affected by the external pressure,
a matter which will be taken up in Chapter 19.

PROBLEMS

16-1. How many cubic feet of a coal gas must be burned to raise the temperature of 40 gallons of water from 50°F to 150°F, assuming 25% stack loss? (There are 7.5 gallons in a cubic foot.)

16-2. A certain Diesel engine consumes 20 lb of fuel oil per hour. The heat of combustion of the oil is 20,000 Btu/lb. If the over-all efficiency of the engine is 30%, (a) how many Btu/hr are converted into mechanical work? (b) How many Btu are wasted? (c) What horsepower does the engine develop?

16-3. An automobile weighing 2000 lb is traveling at 10 ft/sec. How many Btu are developed in the brakes when it is brought to rest?

16-4. (a) What quantity of heat, in Btu, is required to raise the temperature of the water in a 40-gallon hot-water tank from 60°F to 140°F? (There are 7.5 gallons in a cubic foot.) (b) If the water is heated by the combustion of gas, how many cubic feet of gas must be burned if stack losses amount to 20%? (c) If the water is heated by an electric heater, how many kwh are required? The efficiency of the electric heater may be assumed 100%.

16-5. (a) A certain house burns. 10 tons of coal in a heating season. If stack losses are 15%, how many Btu were actually used to heat the house? (b) In some localities large tanks of water are heated by solar radiation during the summer and the stored energy is used for heating during the winter. Find the required dimensions of the storage tank, assuming it to be a cube, to store a quantity of energy equal to that computed in part (a). Assume that the water is heated to 120°F in the summer and cooled to 80°F in the winter.

16-6. An automobile engine whose output is 40 hp uses 4.5 gallons of gasoline per hour. The heat of combustion of gasoline is 3×10^7 calories per gallon. What is the efficiency of the engine?

16-7. The electric power input to a certain electric motor is 0.50 kw, and the mechanical power output is 0.54 hp. (a) What is the efficiency of the motor? (b) How many Btu are developed in the motor in one hour of operation?

16-8. 400 gm of water are contained in a copper vessel of mass 200 gm. The water is heated by a friction device which dissipates mechanical energy, and it is observed that the temperature of the system rises at the rate of 3 C° per minute. Neglect heat losses to the surroundings. What power in watts is dissipated in the water?

16-9. How long could a 2000 hp motor be operated on the heat energy liberated by one cubic mile of ocean water when the temperature of the water is lowered by 1 C° if all this heat were converted to mechanical energy? Why do we not utilize this tremendous reservoir of energy?

16-10. An aluminum can of mass 500 gm contains 117.5 gm of water at a temperature of 20°C. A 200-gm block of iron at 75°C is dropped into the can. Find the final temperature, assuming no heat loss to the surroundings.

16-11. A casting weighing 100 lb is taken from an annealing furnace where its temperature was 900°F and plunged into a tank containing 800 lb of oil at a temperature of 80°F. The final temperature is 100°F, and the specific heat of the oil is 0.5 Btu/lb·F°. What was the specific heat of the casting? Neglect the heat capacity of the tank itself and any heat losses.

16–12. Compute from Table 16–1 the heat capacities of one gram-molecular weight of Al, Cu, Pb, Hg, and Ag, and compare with the values predicted by the Dulong and Petit law.

16–13. Compare the heat capacities of equal *volumes* of water, copper, and lead.

16–14. A lead bullet, traveling at 350 m/sec, strikes a target and is brought to rest. What would be the rise in temperature of the bullet if none of the heat developed were lost to the surroundings?

16–15. A copper calorimeter whose mass is 300 gm contains 500 gm of water at a temperature of 15°C. A 560-gm block of copper, at a temperature of 100°C, is dropped into the calorimeter and the temperature is observed to increase to 22.5°C. Neglect heat losses to the surroundings. (a) Find the specific heat of copper. (b) What is the water equivalent of the calorimeter?

16–16. A 50-gm sample of a material, at a temperature of 100°C, is dropped into a calorimeter containing 200 gm of water initially at 20°C. The calorimeter is of copper and its mass is 100 gm. The final temperature of the calorimeter is 22°C. Compute the specific heat of the sample.

16–17. How much heat is required to convert 1 gm of ice at −10°C to steam at 100°C?

16–18. A beaker whose heat capacity is negligible contains 500 gm of water at a temperature of 80°C. How many grams of ice at a temperature of −20°C must be dropped in the water so that the final temperature of the system will be 50°C?

16–19. Ice cubes at 0°C are dropped into a jug of salt water at 0°C. It is observed that the temperature of the mixture drops below 0°C. What happens to the heat that is released by the salt water when its temperature decreases?

16–20. An open vessel contains 500 gm of ice at −20°C. The heat capacity of the container can be neglected. Heat is supplied to the vessel at the constant rate of 1000 cal/min for 100 min. Plot a curve showing the elapsed time as abscissa and the temperature as ordinate.

16–21. A copper calorimeter of mass 100 gm contains 150 gm of water and 8 gm of ice in thermal equilibrium at atmospheric pressure. 100 gm of lead at a temperature of 200°C are dropped into the calorimeter. Find the final temperature if no heat is lost to the surroundings.

16–22. 500 gm of ice at −16°C are dropped into a calorimeter containing 1000 gm of water at 20°C. The calorimeter can is of copper and has a mass of 278 gm. Compute the final temperature of the system, assuming no heat losses.

16–23. A tube leads from a flask in which water is boiling under atmospheric pressure to a calorimeter. The mass of the calorimeter is 150 gm, its heat capacity is 15 cal/C° and it contains originally 340 gm of water at 15°C. Steam is allowed to condense in the calorimeter until its temperature increases to 71°C, after which the total mass of calorimeter and contents is found to be 525 gm. Compute the heat of condensation of steam from these data.

16–24. An aluminum canteen whose mass is 500 gm contains 750 gm of water and 100 gm of ice. The canteen is dropped from an aircraft to the ground. After landing, the temperature of the canteen is found to be 25°C. Assuming that no energy is given to the ground in the impact, what was the velocity of the canteen just before it landed?

16–25. A calorimeter contains 500 gm of water and 300 gm of ice, all at a temperature of 0°C. A block of metal of mass 1000 gm is taken from a furnace where its temperature was 240°C and is dropped quickly into the calorimeter. As a result, all the ice is just melted. What would the final temperature of the system have been if the mass of the block had been twice as great? Neglect heat loss from the calorimeter, and the heat capacity of the calorimeter.

16–26. An ice cube whose mass is 50 gm is taken from a refrigerator where its temperature was −10°C and is dropped into a glass of water at 0°C. If no heat is gained or lost from outside, how much water will freeze onto the cube?

16–27. A copper calorimeter can, having a heat capacity of 30 cal/deg, contains 50 gm of ice. The system is initially at 0°C. 12 gm of steam at 100°C and 1 atm pressure are run into the calorimeter. What is the final temperature of the calorimeter and its contents?

16–28. A vessel whose walls are thermally insulated contains 2100 gm of water and 200 gm of ice, all at a temperature of 0°C. The outlet of a tube leading from a boiler, in which water is boiling at atmospheric pressure, is inserted in the water. How many grams of steam must condense to raise the temperature of the system to 20°C? Neglect the heat capacity of the container.

16–29. A 2-kgm iron block is taken from a furnace where its temperature was 650°C and placed on a large block of ice at 0°C. Assuming that all the heat given up by the iron is used to melt the ice, how much ice is melted?

16–30. In a household hot-water heating system, water is delivered to the radiators at 140°F and leaves at 100°F. The system is to be replaced by a steam system in which steam at atmospheric pressure condenses in the radiators, the condensed steam leaving the radiators at 180°F. How many pounds of steam will supply the same heat as was supplied by 1 lb of hot water in the first installation?

16–31. A piece of ice falls from rest into a lake at 0°C, and one-half of one percent of the ice melts. Compute the minimum height from which the ice falls.

16–32. What must be the initial velocity of a lead bullet at a temperature of 25°C, so that the heat developed when it is brought to rest shall be just sufficient to melt it?

16–33. Inspect the following datasheet, which was prepared for an experiment to measure the heat of vaporization of water:

Mass of empty beaker	50 grams
Mass of filled beaker	150 grams
Mass of water	_____
Initial temperature of water	25°C
Final temperature of water	45°C
Change in temperature of water	_____
Mass of water, beaker, and condensed steam	154 grams
Mass of condensed steam	_____

CALCULATED HEAT OF VAPORIZATION OF WATER _____

Describe the experiment performed,

then fill in the blank spaces and use the data to calculate the heat of vaporization of water. What would you say about the experimental error?

16–34. A "solar house" has storage facilities for 4 million Btu. Compare the space requirements for this storage on the assumption (a) that the heat is stored in water heated from a minimum temperature of 80°F to a maximum at 120°F, and (b) that the heat is stored in Glauber salt $(Na_2SO_4 \cdot 10 H_2O)$ heated in the same temperature range.

Properties of Glauber salt:

Specific heat (solid)	0.46 Btu/lb·F°
Specific heat (liquid)	0.68 Btu/lb·F°
Specific gravity	1.6
Melting point	90°F
Heat of fusion	104 Btu/lb

CHAPTER 17

TRANSFER OF HEAT

17–1 Conduction. If one end of a metal rod is placed in a flame while the other is held in the hand, that part of the rod one is holding will be felt to become hotter and hotter, although it was not itself in direct contact with the flame. Heat is said to reach the cooler end of the rod by *conduction* along or through the material of the rod. The molecules at the hot end of the rod increase the violence of their vibration as the temperature of the hot end increases. Then, as they collide with their more slowly moving neighbors farther out on the rod, some of their energy of motion is shared with these neighbors and they in turn pass it along to those still farther out from the flame. Hence energy of thermal motion is passed along from one molecule to the next, while each individual molecule remains at its original position.

It is well known that metals are good conductors of electricity and also good conductors of heat. The ability of a metal to conduct an electric current is due to the fact that there are within it so-called "free" electrons, that is, electrons that have become detached from their parent molecules. The free electrons also play a part in the conduction of heat, and the reason metals are such good heat conductors is that the free electrons, as well as the molecules, share in the process of handing on thermal energy from the hotter to the cooler portions of the metal.

Conduction of heat can take place in a body only when different parts of the body are at different temperatures, and the direction of heat flow is always from points of higher to points of lower temperature. The phenomenon of heat flow is sometimes made the basis for the definition of temperature equality or inequality. That is, if heat flows from one body to another when the two are in contact, the temperature of the first, by definition, is higher than that of the second. If there is no heat flow, the temperatures are equal.

Figure 17–1 represents a slab of material of cross section A and thickness L. Let the whole of the left face of the slab be kept at a temperature t_2, and the whole of the right face at a lower temperature t_1. The direction of the heat current is then from left to right through the slab.

After the faces of the slab have been kept at the temperatures t_1 and t_2 for a sufficient length of time, the temperature at points within the slab is found to decrease uniformly with distance from the hot to the cold face. At each point, however, the temperature remains constant with time. The slab is said to be in a "steady state." (Nonsteady state

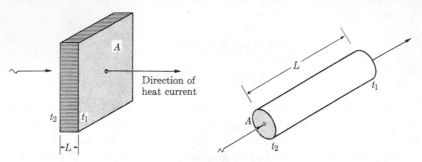

FIG. 17–1.   Conduction of heat   FIG. 17–2. Conduction of heat along
through a slab.   a rod.

problems in heat conduction involve mathematical methods beyond the
scope of this book.)

It is found by experiment that the rate of flow of heat through the slab
in the steady state is proportional to the area A, proportional to the
temperature difference $(t_2 - t_1)$, and inversely proportional to the thickness L. Let H represent the quantity of heat flowing through the slab
per unit time. Then

$$H \propto \frac{A(t_2 - t_1)}{L}.$$

This proportion may be converted to an equation on multiplication
by a constant K whose numerical value depends on the material of the
slab. The quantity K is called the *coefficient of thermal conductivity* or
simply the thermal conductivity of the material.

$$H = \frac{KA(t_2 - t_1)}{L}. \qquad (17–1)$$

Equation (17–1) may also be used to compute the rate of heat flow
along a rod whose side walls are thermally insulated (see Fig. 17–2, where
the letters have the same meaning as in Fig. 17–1).

In some circumstances, either because of nonsteady conditions or
because of the geometry of the conductor, the temperature in a body
through which heat is flowing does not decrease uniformly along the
direction of heat flow as it did in the slab of Fig. 17–1. We can then
consider a thin slab of thickness Δx between whose faces the temperature
difference is Δt, and Eq. (17–1) becomes

$$H = -KA \frac{\Delta t}{\Delta x}. \qquad (17–2)$$

TABLE 17–1

THERMAL CONDUCTIVITY

Substance	$K,$ cal/sec·cm·C°
Metals:	
Aluminum	0.49
Brass	0.26
Copper	0.92
Lead	0.083
Mercury	0.020
Silver	0.97
Steel	0.12
Various solids:*	
Firebrick	0.0025
Insulating brick	0.00035
Red brick	0.0015
Concrete	0.002
Cork	0.0001
Felt	0.0001
Glass	0.002
Ice	0.004
Rock wool	0.0001
Wood	0.0003–0.0001
Gases:	
Air	0.000057
Argon	0.000039
Helium	0.00034
Hydrogen	0.00033
Oxygen	0.000056

* Representative values

The minus sign is introduced because if the temperature increases from left to right, the direction of the heat current is from right to left. Equation (17–2) is the general equation of heat conduction. The ratio $\Delta t/\Delta x$ is called the *temperature gradient*. Equation (17–1) evidently relates to a special case in which the temperature gradient is constant and equal to $(t_2 - t_1)/L$.

The cgs unit of rate of heat flow, or heat current, is one calorie per second, and a temperature difference is expressed in celsius degrees. The unit of thermal conductivity is found from the equation

$$K = \frac{H\,\Delta x}{A\,\Delta t} = \frac{(\text{cal/sec})\cdot\text{cm}}{\text{cm}^2\cdot\text{C}^\circ} \, ,$$

or K is expressed in cal/sec·cm·C°. A material for which K is large is therefore a good heat conductor, while if K is small, the material is a poor conductor or a good insulator. There is no such thing as a "perfect heat conductor" ($K = \infty$) or a "perfect heat insulator" ($K = 0$). However, it will be seen from Table 17–1, which lists some representative values of thermal conductivity, that the metals as a group have much greater thermal conductivities than the nonmetals.

17–2 Convection. The term *convection* is applied to the transfer of heat from one place to another by the actual motion of hot material. The hot-air furnace and the hot-water heating system are examples. If the heated material is forced to move by a blower or pump, the process is called *forced convection;* if the material flows due to differences in density, the process is called *natural* or *free* convection. To understand the latter, consider a U-tube as illustrated in Fig. 17–3.

In (a), the water is at the same temperature in both arms of the U and hence stands at the same level in each. In (b), the right side of the U has been heated. The water in this side expands and therefore, being of smaller density, a longer column is needed to balance the pressure produced by the cold water in the left column. The stopcock may now be opened and water will flow from the top of the warmer column into the colder column. This increases the pressure at the bottom of the U produced by the cold column, and decreases the pressure at this point due

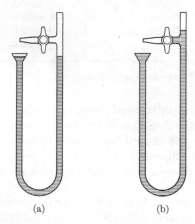

(a)   (b)

Fig. 17–3. Natural convection is brought about by differences in density.

to the hot column. Hence at the bottom of the U, water is forced from the cold to the hot side. If heat is continually applied to the hot side and removed from the cold side, the circulation continues of itself. The net result is a continual transfer of heat from the hot to the cold side of the column. In the common household hot-water heating system, the "cold" side corresponds to the radiators and the "hot" side to the furnace.

The anomalous expansion of water which was mentioned in Chapter 15 has an important effect on the way in which lakes and ponds freeze in winter. Consider a pond at a temperature of, say, 20°C throughout, and suppose the air temperature at its surface falls to −10°C. The water at the surface becomes cooled to, say, 19°C. It therefore contracts, becomes more dense than the warmer water below it, and sinks in this less dense water, its place being taken by water at 20°C. The sinking of the cooled water causes a mixing process, which continues until all the water has been cooled to 4°C. Now, however, when the surface water cools to 3°C, it expands, is less dense than the water below it, and hence floats on the surface. Convection and mixing then cease, and the remainder of the water can only lose heat by *conduction*. Since water is an extremely poor heat conductor, cooling takes place very slowly after 4°C is reached, with the result that the pond freezes first at its surface. Then, since the density of ice is even smaller than that of water at 0°C, the ice floats on the water below it, and further freezing can only result from heat flow upward by conduction.

The mathematical theory of heat convection is quite involved. There is no simple equation for convection as in the case of conduction. This arises from the fact that the heat lost or gained by a surface at one temperature in contact with a fluid at another temperature depends on many circumstances, such as

1. Whether the surface is flat or curved.

2. Whether the surface is horizontal or vertical.

3. Whether the fluid in contact with the surface is a gas or a liquid.

4. The density, viscosity, specific heat, and thermal conductivity of the fluid.

5. Whether the velocity of the fluid is small enough to give rise to laminar flow or large enough to cause turbulent flow.

6. Whether evaporation, condensation, or formation of scale takes place.

The procedure adopted in practical calculations is first to define a *convection coefficient h* by means of the equation

$$H = hA \, \Delta t, \qquad\qquad (17\text{--}3)$$

TABLE 17–2

COEFFICIENTS OF NATURAL CONVECTION IN AIR AT ATMOSPHERIC PRESSURE

Equipment	Convection coefficient h, cal/sec·cm²·deg
Horizontal plate, facing upward	$0.595 \times 10^{-4} \, (\Delta t)^{1/4}$
Horizontal plate, facing downward	$0.314 \times 10^{-4} \, (\Delta t)^{1/4}$
Vertical plate	$0.424 \times 10^{-4} \, (\Delta t)^{1/4}$
Horizontal or vertical pipe $\left(\dfrac{\text{diameter}}{D}\right)$	$1.00 \times 10^{-4} \left(\dfrac{\Delta t}{D}\right)^{1/4}$

where H is the heat convection current (the heat gained or lost by convection by a surface per unit of time), A is the area of the surface, and Δt is the temperature difference between the surface and the main body of fluid. The next step is the determination of numerical values of h that are appropriate to a given piece of equipment. Such a determination is accomplished partly by reasoning known as *dimensional analysis* and partly by an elaborate series of experiments. An enormous amount of research in this field has been done in recent years so that, by now, there are in existence fairly complete tables and graphs from which the physicist or engineer may obtain the convection coefficient appropriate to certain standard types of apparatus.

A case of common occurrence is that of natural convection from a wall or a pipe at a constant temperature, surrounded by air at atmospheric pressure and differing in temperature by an amount Δt. The convection coefficients applicable in this situation are given in Table 17–2. As an example of a problem involving natural convection to and from a vertical wall, consider the following.

EXAMPLE. The air in a room is at a temperature of 25°C, and the outside air is at −15°C. How much heat is transferred per unit area of a glass windowpane of thermal conductivity 2.5×10^{-3} cgs unit and of thickness 2 mm?

To assume that the inner surface of the glass is at 25°C and the outer surface is at −15°C is entirely erroneous, as anyone can verify by touching the inner surface of a glass windowpane on a cold day. One must expect a much smaller temperature difference across the windowpane, so that in the steady state, the rates of transfer of heat (1) by convection in the room, (2) by conduction through the glass, and (3) by convection in the outside air, are all equal.

As a first approximation in the solution of this problem, let us assume that the window is at a uniform temperature t. If $t = 5°C$, then the temperature difference between the inside air and the glass is the same as that between the glass and the outside air, or 20 deg. Hence the convection coefficient in both cases is

$$h = 0.424 \times 10^{-4} (20)^{1/4} \frac{\text{cal}}{\text{sec·cm}^2\text{·deg}}$$

$$= 0.895 \times 10^{-4} \frac{\text{cal}}{\text{sec·cm}^2\text{·deg}},$$

and, from Eq. (17–4), the heat transferred per unit area is

$$\frac{H}{A} = 0.895 \times 10^{-4} \times 20 = 17.9 \times 10^{-4} \frac{\text{cal}}{\text{sec·cm}^2}.$$

The glass, however, is not at a uniform temperature; there must be a temperature difference Δt across the glass sufficient to provide heat conduction at the rate of 17.9×10^{-4} cal/sec·cm^2. Using the conduction equation, Eq. (17–1),

$$\Delta t = \frac{L}{K} \times \frac{H}{A} = \frac{0.2}{2.5 \times 10^{-3}} \times 17.9 \times 10^{-4} \text{ deg} = 0.14 \text{ deg.}$$

With sufficient accuracy we may therefore say that the inner surface is at 5.07°C and the outer surface is at 4.93°C.

17–3 Radiation. When one's hand is placed in direct contact with the surface of a hot-water or steam radiator, heat reaches the hand by *conduction* through the radiator walls. If the hand is held above the radiator but not in contact with it, heat reaches the hand by way of the upward-moving *convection* currents of warm air. If the hand is held at one side of the radiator it still becomes warm, even though conduction through the air is negligible and the hand is not in the path of the convection currents. Energy now reaches the hand by *radiation*.

The term radiation refers to the continual emission of energy from the surface of all bodies. This energy is called *radiant energy* and is in the form of electromagnetic waves. These waves travel with the velocity of light and are transmitted through a vacuum as well as through air. (Better, in fact, since they are absorbed by air to some extent.) When they fall on a body which is not transparent to them, such as the surface of one's hand or the walls of the room, they are absorbed and their energy converted to heat.

The radiant energy emitted by a surface, per unit time and per unit area, depends on the nature of the surface and on its temperature. At low temperatures the rate of radiation is small and the radiant energy is chiefly of relatively long wavelength. As the temperature is increased,

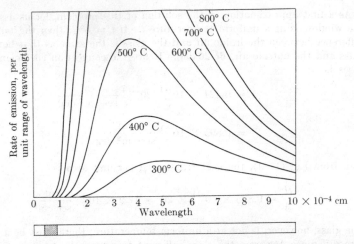

FIG. 17-4. Rate of emission of radiant energy by a blackbody, per unit of wavelength, as a function of wavelength. Shaded area indicates visible spectrum.

the rate of radiation increases very rapidly, in proportion to the 4th power of the absolute temperature. For example, a copper block at a temperature of 100°C (373°K) radiates about 300,000 ergs/sec or 0.03 watt from each square centimeter of its surface. At a temperature of 500°C (773°K) it radiates about 0.54 watt from each square centimeter, and at 1000°C (1273°K) it radiates about 4 watts per square centimeter. This rate is 130 times as great as that at a temperature of 100°C.

At each of these temperatures the radiant energy emitted is a mixture of waves of different wavelengths. At a temperature of 300°C the most intense of these waves has a wavelength of about 5×10^{-4} cm; for wavelengths either greater or less than this value the intensity decreases as shown by the curve in Fig. 17-4. The corresponding distribution of energy at higher temperatures is also shown in the figure. The area between each curve and the horizontal axis represents the total rate of radiation at that temperature. It is evident that this rate increases rapidly with increasing temperature, and also that the wavelength of the most intense wave shifts toward the left, or toward shorter wavelengths with increasing temperature.

At a temperature of 300°C, practically all the radiant energy emitted by a body is carried by waves longer than those corresponding to red light. Such waves are called *infrared*, meaning "beyond the red." At a temperature of 800°C a body emits enough visible radiant energy to be self-luminous and appears "red hot." By far the larger part of the energy emitted, however, is still carried by infrared waves. At 3000°C, which is about the temperature of an incandescent lamp filament, the radiant energy contains enough of the shorter wavelengths so that the body appears nearly "white hot."

17-4 Stefan's law. Experimental measurements of the rate of emission of radiant energy from the surface of a body were made by John Tyndall (1820–1893) and on the basis of these Josef Stefan (1835–1893), in 1879, concluded that the rate of emission could be expressed by the relation

$$R = e\sigma T^4, \qquad (17\text{--}4)$$

which is *Stefan's law*. R is the rate of emission of radiant energy per unit area and is expressed in ergs per second per square centimeter, in the cgs system, and in watts per square meter in the mks system. The constant σ has a numerical value of 5.672×10^{-5} in cgs units and 5.672×10^{-8} in mks units. T is the Kelvin temperature of the surface and e is a quantity, sometimes called the *emissivity* or *relative emittance*, which depends on the nature of the surface. Numerical values of e are given in Table 17–3 where it may be seen that e lies between 0 and 1, being small for polished metals and almost 1 for black, rough materials.

TABLE 17–3

EMISSIVITIES OR RELATIVE EMITTANCES OF VARIOUS SURFACES

Material	Temperature range, °C	Emissivity or relative emittance
Polished metals:		
Aluminum	250–600	0.039–0.057
Brass	250–400	0.033–0.037
Copper	100	0.018
Iron	150–1000	0.05–0.37
Filaments:		
Molybdenum	750–2600	0.096–0.29
Platinum	30–1200	0.036–0.19
Tantalum	1300–3000	0.19–0.31
Tungsten	30–3300	0.032–0.35
Other materials:		
Asbestos	40–350	0.93–0.95
Lampblack	20–350	0.95
Rubber	25	0.86

It may be wondered why it is, if the surfaces of all bodies are continually emitting radiant energy, that all bodies do not eventually radiate
away all their internal energy and cool down to a temperature of absolute
zero [where $R = 0$ by Eq. (17–4)]. The answer is that they would do
so if energy were not supplied to them in some way. In the case of a
Sunbowl heater element ·or the filament of an electric lamp, energy is
supplied electrically to make up for the energy radiated. As soon as this
energy supply is cut off, these bodies do, in fact, cool down very quickly
to room temperature. The reason that they do not cool further is that
their surroundings (the walls, and other objects in the room) are also
radiating, and some of this radiant energy is intercepted, absorbed, and
converted into internal energy. The same thing is true of all other objects in the room—each is both emitting and absorbing radiant energy
simultaneously. If any object is hotter than its surroundings, its rate of
emission will exceed its rate of absorption. There will thus be a net loss
of energy and the body will cool down ·unless heated by some other
method. If a body is at a lower temperature than its surroundings, its
rate of absorption will be larger than its rate of emission and its temperature will rise. When the body is at the same temperature as its surroundings the two rates become equal, there is no net gain or loss of energy,
and no change in temperature.

If a small body of emissivity e at a temperature T is completely surrounded by walls at the same temperature, the rate of *absorption* of
radiant energy per unit area by the body is the same as the rate of
emission, or

$$R = e\sigma T^4.$$

Hence for such a body at a temperature T_1, surrounded by walls at a
temperature T_2, the *net* rate of loss (or gain) of energy per unit area
by radiation is

$$R_{\text{net}} = e\sigma T_1^4 - e\sigma T_2^4 = e\sigma(T_1^4 - T_2^4). \qquad (17\text{–}5)$$

17–5 The ideal radiator. Imagine that the walls of the enclosure in
Fig. 17–5 are kept at the temperature T_2 and a number of different bodies
having different emissivities are suspended one after another within the
enclosure. Regardless of their temperature when they were inserted, it
will be found that eventually each comes to the same temperature as
that of the walls, T_2, even if the enclosure is evacuated. If the bodies
are small compared with the size of the enclosure, radiant energy from
the walls strikes the surface of each body at the same rate. Of this
energy, a part is reflected and the remainder absorbed. In the absence
of any other process, the energy absorbed will raise the temperature of
the absorbing body, but since the temperature is observed *not* to change,

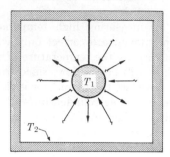

FIG. 17-5. In thermal equilibrium, the rate of emission of radiant energy equals the rate of absorption. Hence a good absorber is a good emitter.

each body must *emit* radiant energy at the same rate as it *absorbs* it. Hence a good absorber is a good emitter, and a poor absorber is a poor emitter. But since each body must either absorb or reflect the radiant energy reaching it, a poor absorber must also be a good reflector. Hence a *good reflector is a poor emitter*.

This is the reason for silvering the walls of vacuum ("Thermos") bottles. A vacuum bottle is constructed with double glass walls, the space between the walls being evacuated so that heat flow by conduction and convection is practically eliminated. To reduce the radiant emission to as low a value as possible, the walls are covered with a coating of silver which is highly reflecting and hence is a very poor emitter.

Since a good absorber is a good emitter, the *best* emitter will be that surface which is the best absorber. But no surface can absorb more than all the radiant energy which strikes it. Any surface which does absorb all the incident energy will be the best emitting surface possible. Such a surface would reflect no radiant energy, and hence would appear black in color (provided its temperature is not so high that it is self-luminous). It is called an *ideally black surface*, and a body having such a surface is called an ideal blackbody, an ideal radiator, or simply a *blackbody*.

No actual surface is ideally black, the closest approach being lampblack, which reflects only about 1%. Blackbody conditions can be closely realized, however, by a small opening in the walls of a closed container. Radiant energy entering the opening is in part absorbed by the interior walls. Of the part reflected, only a very little escapes through the opening, the remainder being eventually absorbed by the walls. Hence the *opening* behaves like an ideal absorber.

Conversely, the radiant energy emitted by the walls or by any body within the enclosure, and escaping through the opening, will, if the walls are of uniform temperature, be of the same nature as that emitted by an ideal radiator. This fact is of importance when using an optical pyrometer, a device for measuring high temperatures optically. The readings of such an instrument are correct only when it is sighted on a blackbody. If used to measure the temperature of a red-hot ingot of iron in the open, its readings will be too low, since iron is a poorer emitter than a blackbody. If, however, the pyrometer is sighted on the iron while still in the furnace, where it is surrounded by walls at the same temperature, "blackbody conditions" are fulfilled and the reading will be correct. The failure of the iron to emit as effectively as a blackbody is just compensated by the radiant energy which it reflects.

The emissivity e of an ideally black surface is equal to unity. For all real surfaces, it is a fraction, less than one.

Problems

17-1. A slab of a thermal insulator is 100 cm^2 in cross section and 2 cm thick. Its thermal conductivity is 2×10^{-4} cal/sec·cm·C°. If the temperature difference between opposite faces is 100 C°, how many calories flow through the slab in one day?

17-2. One end of a copper bar 18 cm long and 4 cm^2 in cross section is in a steam bath and the other end is in a mixture of melting ice and water. Heat loss across the curved surface can be neglected. (a) What is the heat current in the bar? (b) What is the temperature at a point 4 cm from the cooler end?

17-3. A long rod, insulated to prevent heat losses, has one end immersed in boiling water (at atmospheric pressure) and the other end in a water-ice mixture. The rod consists of 100 cm of copper (one end in steam) and a length, L_2, of steel (one end in ice). Both rods are of cross-sectional area 5 cm^2. The temperature of the copper-iron junction is 60°C, after a steady state has been set up. (a) How many calories per second flow from the steam bath to the ice-water mixture? (b) How long is L_2?

17-4. A rod is initially at a uniform temperature of 0°C throughout. One end is kept at 0°C and the other is brought into contact with a steam bath at 100°C. The surface of the rod is insulated so that heat can flow only lengthwise along the rod. The cross-sectional area of the rod is 2 cm^2, its length is 100 cm, its thermal conductivity is 0.8 cgs units, its density is 10 gm/cm^3, and its specific heat capacity is 0.10 cal/gm·C°. Consider a short cylindrical element of the rod 1 cm in length. (a) If the temperature gradient at one end of this element is 200 C°/cm, how many calories flow across this end per second? (b) If the average temperature of the element is increasing at the rate of 5 C°/sec, what is the temperature gradient at the other end of the element?

17-5. Rods of copper, brass, and steel are welded together to form a Y-shaped figure. The cross-sectional area of each rod is 2 cm^2. The end of the copper rod is maintained at 100°C and the ends of the brass and steel rods at 0°C. Assume there is no heat loss from the surfaces of the rods. The lengths of the rods are: copper,

46 cm; brass, 13 cm; steel, 12 cm. (a) What is the temperature of the junction point? (b) What is the heat current in the copper rod?

17–6. A compound bar 2 meters long is constructed of a solid steel core 1 cm in diameter surrounded by a copper casing whose outside diameter is 2 cm. The outer surface of the bar is thermally insulated and one end is maintained at 100°C, the other at 0°C. (a) Find the total heat current in the bar. (b) What fraction is carried by each material?

17–7. One experimental method of measuring the thermal conductivity of an insulating material is to construct a box of the material and measure the power input to an electric heater, inside the box, which maintains the interior at a measured temperature above that of the outside surface. Suppose that in such an apparatus a power input of 120 watts is required to keep the interior of the box 70 C° above the outside temperature. The total area of the box is 25,000 cm² and the wall thickness is 4 cm. Find the thermal conductivity of the material.

17–8. A container of wall area 5000 cm² and thickness 2 cm is filled with water in which there is a stirrer. The outer surface of the walls is kept at a constant temperature of 0°C. The thermal conductivity of the walls is 0.000478 cgs units, and the effect of edges and corners can be neglected. The power required to run the stirrer at an angular velocity of 1800 rpm is found to be 100 watts. What will be the final steady-state temperature of the water in the container? Assume that the stirrer keeps the entire mass of water at a uniform temperature.

17–9. A boiler with a steel bottom 1.5 cm thick rests on a hot stove. The area of the bottom of the boiler is 1500 cm². The water inside the boiler is at 100°C, and 750 gm are evaporated every 5 minutes. Find the temperature of the lower surface of the boiler, which is in contact with the stove.

17–10. An icebox, having wall area of 2 m² and thickness 5 cm, is constructed of insulating material having a thermal conductivity of 10^{-4} cal/sec·cm·C°. The outside temperature is 20°C, and the inside of the box is to be maintained at 5°C by ice. The melted ice leaves the box at a temperature of 15°C. If ice costs one cent per kgm, what will it cost to run the icebox for one hour?

17–11. An electric transformer is in a cylindrical tank 60 cm in diameter and 1 m high, with flat top and bottom. If the tank transfers heat to the air only by natural convection, and the electrical losses are to be dissipated at the rate of 1 kwh, how many degrees will the tank surface rise above room temperature?

17–12. A flat wall is maintained at a constant temperature of 100°C, and the air on both sides is at atmospheric pressure and at 20°C. How much heat is lost by natural convection from 1 sq meter of wall (both sides) in one hour if (a) the wall is vertical, (b) the wall is horizontal?

17–13. A vertical steam pipe of outside diameter 7.5 cm and height 4 meters has its outer surface at the constant temperature of 95°C. The surrounding air is at atmospheric pressure and at 20°C. How much heat is delivered to the air by natural convection in one hour?

17–14. The operating temperature of a tungsten filament in an incandescent lamp is 2450°K and its emissivity is 0.30. Find the surface area of the filament of a 25-watt lamp.

17–15. A blackened solid copper

sphere of radius 2 cm is placed in an evacuated enclosure whose walls are kept at 100°C. At what rate must energy be supplied to the sphere to keep its temperature constant at 127°C?

17–16. A cylindrical metal can 10 cm high and 5 cm in diameter contains liquid helium at 4°K, at which temperature its heat of vaporization is 5 cal/gm. Completely surrounding the helium can are walls maintained at the temperature of liquid nitrogen, 80°K, the intervening space being evacuated. How much helium is lost per hour? Assume the emissivity to be 0.2.

17–17. A solid cylindrical copper rod 10 cm long has one end maintained at a temperature of 20.00°K. The other end is blackened and exposed to thermal radiation from a body at 300°K, no energy being lost or gained elsewhere. When equilibrium is reached, what is the temperature of the blackened end? [*Hint:* Since copper is a very good conductor of heat at low temperature $(K = 4 \text{ cal/sec·cm·C°})$, the temperature of the blackened end is only slightly greater than 20°K.]

17–18. An uninsulated steam pipe of diameter 8 cm and absorptivity 0.8 passes vertically through a room in which the air and all solid surfaces are at the average temperature of 27°C. If the surface temperature of the steam pipe is 97°C, compare the rate of heat loss per meter of pipe by radiation with that by natural convection.

CHAPTER 18

THE FIRST LAW OF THERMODYNAMICS

18–1 External work. We have seen that when the temperature of a body is raised, many different effects may take place: gases expand, solids and liquids usually expand but in rare instances they may contract, thermocouples develop an electromotive force, wires undergo a change of resistance, and many other phenomena occur. In such processes there is usually a flow of heat, and also the application of a force which undergoes a displacement, thereby bringing about the performance of work. The study of these phenomena and the energy changes involved in the flow of heat and performance of work constitute a subject known as *thermodynamics*.

Thermodynamics is an intensely practical subject. It concerns itself with a clearly defined *system* (a gas contained in a cylinder, a pound of steam moving through a nozzle, etc.) that is caused to interact directly with its surroundings and, by such interaction, to perform some useful function.

If an external force is exerted on a system by its surroundings, and the point of application of the force is displaced, we say that *external work* is done by the force. Thus when the gas in the cylinder of an automobile engine is compressed, external work is done by the force exerted on it by the moving piston.

Forces acting between parts of the same system are internal forces, and the work of these forces is called *internal work*. Thus any work done by the forces between the molecules or electrons of a system is internal work. *Internal work has no place in thermodynamics.*

18–2 Work in changing the volume. Let us consider a system consisting of a fluid contained in a cylinder equipped with a movable piston. Suppose the cylinder has a cross-sectional area A and that the pressure at the piston face is p. The piston therefore exerts an inward force pA on the system. If the piston moves out a small distance Δx, the magnitude of the work ΔW of the force it exerts on the system is

$$\Delta W = pA \, \Delta x.$$

According to the sign conventions used in mechanics, the work would be negative because the (inward) force on the system is opposite to the (outward) displacement of the piston. In thermodynamics it is conven-

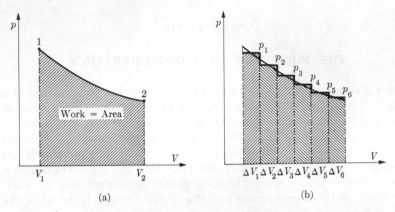

FIG. 18–1. The work done when a substance changes its volume and pressure is the area under the curve on a p-V diagram.

tional to consider work as *positive* when force and displacement are in *opposite* directions. Thus when a system expands against a piston, as in the present example, the work is positive. When a system is compressed, the work is negative.

But $A \, \Delta x = \Delta V$, where ΔV is the change of volume. Therefore

$$\Delta W = p \, \Delta V. \tag{18–1}$$

If the pressure remains constant while the volume changes a finite amount, say from V_1 to V_2, then the work W is

$$W = p(V_2 - V_1) \quad \text{(constant pressure only)}. \tag{18–2}$$

If, on the other hand, the pressure decreases as the volume increases, then we may imagine that the whole series of changes consists of a small volume change ΔV_1 while the pressure is p_1, then another small volume change ΔV_2 while the pressure is p_2, and so on. The work will then be

$$W = p_1 \, \Delta V_1 + p_2 \, \Delta V_2 + \cdots.$$

Suppose that the pressure is plotted along the y-axis and the volume along the x-axis. The changes of pressure and volume will then be indicated by a smooth curve such as that shown in Fig. 18–1(a). If the total volume change $V_2 - V_1$ is divided into a number of small steps ΔV_1, ΔV_2, etc., as shown in Fig. 18–1(b), then the smooth curve may be approximated with any desired degree of accuracy by a jagged curve

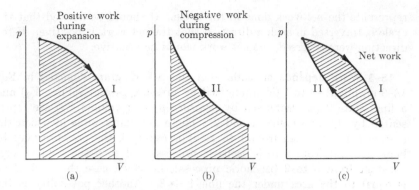

FIG. 18–2. The net work done in a cyclic process equals the area enclosed by the curve representing the process.

where the pressure is p_1 only during the volume change ΔV_1, and is p_2 only during ΔV_2, and so on. The total work, $p_1 \Delta V_1 + p_2 \Delta V_2 + \cdots$, is thus seen to be the sum of the areas of all the rectangles which make up the total area under the jagged curve. If now the number of steps is increased indefinitely, the area under such a jagged curve approaches the area under the smooth curve, and we have the result that

$$W = \begin{Bmatrix} \text{Area under a curve} \\ \text{on a } p\text{-}V \text{ diagram} \end{Bmatrix}. \qquad (18\text{–}3)$$

Notice that this method of finding the work of a varying pressure is the same as that for finding the work of a varying force, as explained in Section 7–6.

According to the conventions of thermodynamics, the work is positive when a system expands. Thus if a system expands from 1 to 2 in Fig. 18–1(a), the area is regarded as positive. A compression from 2 to 1 would give rise to a negative area.

In Fig. 18–2(a) the pressure and volume changes of a system during expansion are indicated by curve I. The work is indicated by the shaded area under curve I. Similarly, for a compression, the work is represented by the shaded area under curve II in Fig. 18–2(b). In conformity with the sign convention for work, the area under I is positive, and that under II is negative. In Fig. 18–2(c), curves I and II are drawn together so that they constitute a series of processes whereby the system is brought back to its initial state. Such a series of processes, represented by a closed figure, is called a *cycle*. The area within the closed figure is obviously the difference between the areas under curves I and II and therefore represents the *net* work done in the cycle. It should be noticed that the cycle is traversed in such a direction that the net work is positive. If the direction were reversed, the net work would be negative.

18–3 Work depends on path. On the p-V diagram depicted in Fig. 18–3 an initial state 1 (characterized by pressure p_1 and volume V_1) and a final state 2 (characterized by pressure p_2 and volume V_2) are represented by the two points 1 and 2. There are many ways in which the system may be taken from 1 to 2. For example, the pressure may be kept constant from 1 to 3 (isobaric process) and then the volume kept constant from 3 to 2 (isochoric process), in which case the work done is equal to the area under the line $1 \rightarrow 3$. Another possibility is the path $1 \rightarrow 4 \rightarrow 2$, in which case the work is the area under the line $4 \rightarrow 2$. The jagged line and the continuous curve from 1 to 2 represent other possibilities, in each of which the work done is different. We can see, therefore, that *the work depends not only on the initial and final states but also on the intermediate states, i.e., on the path.*

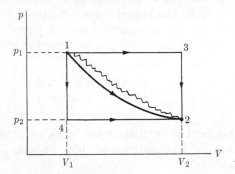

FIG. 18–3. Work depends on the path.

18–4 Work and heat. We have seen how a system may be caused to go from state 1 to state 2 by any number of processes, all of which involve the performance of work. There are other means, however, of changing the state of a system. Consider, for example, the four situations depicted in Fig. 18–4. In (a) the system is a composite one consisting of some water and a paddle wheel, which is caused to rotate and churn the water by means of a falling weight. In (b) both the water and an electric resistance wire embedded in the water constitute the system. An electric current in the resistor is maintained by a generator turned by means of a falling weight. In both cases the state of the system is caused to change and, since the agency for changing the state of the system is a falling weight, *both processes involve the performance of work.*

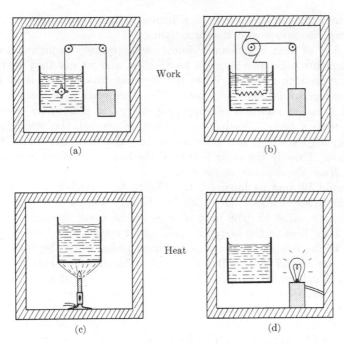

Work

Heat

FIG. 18–4. Distinction between work and heat.

In (c) and (d), however, the situation is quite different. The system in both cases is some water in a heat-conducting container. In (c) the system is in contact with the burning gases from a Bunsen burner, i.e., with another body at a higher temperature, whereas in (d) the system is near but not in contact with an electric lamp whose temperature is much higher than that of the water. In both cases the state of the system is caused to change, but in neither case can the agency for the change be described by mechanical means. *In these cases there is a flow of heat.*

It is important to observe that the decision as to whether a particular change of state involves the performance of work or the transfer of heat requires first an unequivocal answer to the questions "What is the system?" and "What are the surroundings?" For example, in Fig. 18–4(b), if the resistor is regarded as the system and the water as the surroundings, then there is a transfer of heat from the resistor by virtue of the temperature difference between the resistor and the water. Also, if a small part of the water is regarded as the system, the rest of the water being the surroundings, then again there is a transfer of heat. Regarding, however, the composite system composed of both the water and the resistor, the surroundings do not contain any object whose temperature differs from that of the system, and hence no heat is transferred between *this composite system* and its surroundings.

The flow of heat is a *nonmechanical energy transfer* brought about by a temperature difference between two bodies, and we say that heat flows from one place to another. When the flow has ceased, there is no longer any occasion to use the word heat. The performance of work and the flow of heat are methods of supplying energy to a body or extracting energy from a body. We have seen that, in general, the work depends on the path by which the system was brought from the initial to the final state. Exactly the same is true of the heat transferred to or from a body. *Heat also depends on the path.*

It would be just as incorrect to refer to the "heat in a body" as it would be to speak about the "work in a body." For suppose we assigned an arbitrary value to "the heat in a body" in some standard reference state. The "heat in the body" in some other state would then equal the "heat" in the reference state plus the heat added when the body is carried to the second state. But the heat added depends entirely on the path by which we go from one state to the other, and since there are an infinite number of paths which might be followed, there are an infinite number of values which might equally well be assigned to the "heat in the body" in the second state. Since it is not possible to assign any one value to the "heat in the body" we conclude that this concept is meaningless, or at any rate useless.

18–5 The first law of thermodynamics. Suppose a system is caused to change from state 1 to state 2 along a definite path and that the heat absorbed Q and the work W are measured. Expressing both Q and W either in thermal units or in mechanical units we may then calculate the difference $Q - W$. If now we do the same thing over again for many different paths (between the same states 1 and 2), the important result is obtained that $Q - W$ *is the same for all paths connecting* 1 *and* 2. But Q is the energy that has been added to a system by the transfer of heat and W is equal to the energy that has been extracted from the system by the performance of work. The difference $Q - W$, therefore, must represent the internal energy change of the system. It follows that *the internal energy change of a system is independent of the path*, and is therefore equal to the energy of the system in state 2 minus the energy in state 1, or $U_2 - U_1$.

$$U_2 - U_1 = Q - W.$$

If some arbitrary value is assigned to the internal energy in some standard reference state, its value in any other state is uniquely defined, since $Q - W$ is the same for all processes connecting the states.

The simple algebraic statement of these facts in the form

$$Q = U_2 - U_1 + W \tag{18-4}$$

is known as *the first law of thermodynamics*. In applying the law in this form it must be remembered that (1) all quantities must be expressed in the same units, (2) Q is positive when heat goes into the system, (3) W is positive when the force *on* the system is opposite the displacement.

18–6 Adiabatic process. A process that takes place in such a manner that no heat enters or leaves a system is called an *adiabatic process*. This may be accomplished either by surrounding the system with a thick layer of heat insulating material (such as cork, asbestos, firebrick, or any light, porous powder) or by performing the process quickly. The flow of heat is a fairly slow process, so that any process performed quickly enough will be practically adiabatic. Applying the first law to an adiabatic process, we get

$$U_2 - U_1 = -W \quad \text{(Adiabatic process)}.$$

Thus the change in the internal energy of a system, in an adiabatic process, is equal in absolute magnitude to the work. If the work W is negative, as when a system is compressed, then $-W$ is positive, U_2 is greater than U_1, and the internal energy of the system increases. If W is positive, as when a system expands, the internal energy of the system decreases. An increase of internal energy is usually accompanied by a rise in temperature and a decrease in internal energy by a temperature drop.

The compression of the mixture of gasoline vapor and air that takes place during the compression stroke of a gasoline engine is an example of an approximately adiabatic process involving a temperature rise. The expansion of the combustion products during the power stroke of the engine is an approximately adiabatic process involving a temperature decrease. Adiabatic processes, therefore, play a very important role in mechanical engineering.

18–7 Isochoric process. If a substance undergoes a process in which the volume remains unchanged, the process is called *isochoric*. The rise of pressure and temperature produced by a flow of heat into a substance contained in a nonexpanding chamber is an example of an isochoric process. If the volume does not change, no work is done and, therefore, from the first law,

$$Q = U_2 - U_1 \quad \text{(Isochoric process)},$$

or all the heat that has been added has served to increase the internal energy. The very sudden increase of temperature and pressure accompanying the explosion of gasoline vapor and air in a gasoline engine may be treated mathematically as though it were an isochoric addition of heat.

18–8 Isobaric process. A process taking place at constant pressure is called an *isobaric process*. When water enters the boiler of a steam engine and is heated to its boiling point, vaporized, and then the steam is superheated, all these processes take place isobarically. Such processes play an important role in mechanical engineering and also in chemistry.

Consider the change of phase of a mass m of liquid to vapor at constant pressure and temperature. If V_L is the volume of liquid and V_V the volume of vapor, the work done in expanding from V_L to V_V at constant pressure p is

$$W = p(V_V - V_L).$$

The heat absorbed by each unit of mass is the heat of vaporization L. Hence

$$Q = mL.$$

From the first law,

$$mL = (U_V - U_L) + p(V_V - V_L). \tag{18–5}$$

EXAMPLE. One gram of water (1 cm^3) becomes 1671 cm^3 of steam when boiled at a pressure of 1 atm. The heat of vaporization at this pressure is 539 cal/gm. Compute the external work and the increase in internal energy.

$$\begin{aligned}
\text{External work} &= p(V_V - V_L) \\
&= 1.013 \times 10^6 \text{ dynes/cm}^2 \,(1671 - 1) \text{ cm}^3 \\
&= 1.695 \times 10^9 \text{ ergs} \\
&= 169.5 \text{ joules} \\
&= 41 \text{ calories.}
\end{aligned}$$

From Eq. (18–5)

$$U_V - U_L = mL - W = 539 - 41 = 498 \text{ calories.}$$

Hence the external work, or the external part of the heat of vaporization, equals 41 calories, and the increase in internal energy, or the internal part of the heat of vaporization, is 498 calories.

18–9 Free expansion. Imagine a vessel with rigid walls and covered with asbestos. Suppose the vessel is divided into two parts by a thin partition, and that one part contains a gas while the other is evacuated. If the partition is suddenly broken, the gas rushes into a vacuum, undergoing what is known as a *free expansion*. Since the walls of the container are rigid, no external work is done, and since the vessel is heat-insulated, the process is adiabatic. Thus, $Q = 0$ and $W = 0$. Hence, from the first law,

$$U_1 = U_2 \quad \text{(Free expansion)},$$

or the initial and final internal energies are equal.

The magnitude of the temperature change (if any) that takes place as a result of a free expansion is of some theoretical interest and, as a result, many attempts have been made to perform an experiment of this sort. The experimental difficulties, however, are enormous and no one has really succeeded so far. From a practical point of view a free expansion is of no importance whatever.

18–10 Throttling process. A throttling process is one in which a fluid, originally at a constant high pressure, seeps through a porous wall or a narrow opening (needle valve or throttling valve) into a region of constant lower pressure, without a transfer of heat taking place. The experiment is sometimes called the porous plug experiment. Figure 18–5(a) will help to make the process clear. A fluid is discharged from a pump at a high pressure, then passes through a throttling valve into a pipe which leads directly to the intake or low-pressure side of the pump. Every successive element of fluid undergoes the throttling process in a continuous stream.

Consider any element of fluid enclosed between the piston and throttling valve of Fig. 18–5(b). Suppose this piston to move toward the right and another piston on the other side of the valve to move to the right also at such rates that the pressure on the left remains at a constant high value and that on the right at a constant lower value. After all the fluid

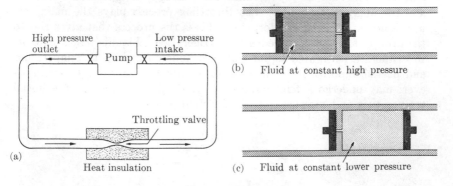

(a)

High pressure outlet Pump Low pressure intake

Throttling valve

Heat insulation

(b) Fluid at constant high pressure

(c) Fluid at constant lower pressure

FIG. 18–5. Throttling process.

has been forced through the valve, the final state is that of Fig. 18–5(c).

The net work done in this process is the difference between the work done in forcing the right-hand piston out and the work done in forcing the left-hand piston in. Let

$p_1 =$ high pressure (on the left),
$V_1 =$ volume of fluid at the high pressure,
$p_2 =$ lower pressure (on the right),
$V_2 =$ volume of fluid at the low pressure.

Since the low-pressure fluid changes in volume from zero to V_2 at the constant pressure p_2, the work is

$$p_2(V_2 - 0),$$

and since the high-pressure fluid changes in volume from V_1 to zero at the constant high pressure p_1, the work is

$$p_1(0 - V_1).$$

The net work W is therefore

$$W = p_2 V_2 - p_1 V_1.$$

Since the process is adiabatic, $Q = 0$, and hence from the first law,

$$0 = U_2 - U_1 + (p_2 V_2 - p_1 V_1)$$

or

$$U_1 + p_1 V_1 = U_2 + p_2 V_2.$$

This result is of great importance in steam engineering and in refrigeration. The sum $U + pV$, called the *enthalpy*, is tabulated for steam and for many refrigerants. The throttling process plays the main role in the action of a refrigerator, since this is the process that gives rise to the drop in temperature needed for refrigeration. Liquids that are about to evaporate (saturated liquids) always undergo a drop in temperature and partial vaporization as a result of a throttling process. Gases, however, may undergo a temperature rise or drop depending on the initial temperature and pressure and on the final pressure.

Problems

18–1. A pound of water whose volume is 0.0190 ft^3 is converted into steam of volume 1.50 ft^3 at the constant pressure of 309 lb/in^2. How many foot·pounds of work are done?

18–2. A gas contained in a cylinder surrounded by a thick layer of felt is quickly compressed, the temperature rising several degrees. (a) Has there been a transfer of heat? (b) Has work been done?

18–3. A combustion experiment is performed by burning a mixture of fuel and oxygen in a constant-volume "bomb" surrounded by a water bath. During the experiment the temperature of the water is observed to rise. Regarding the mixture of fuel and oxygen as the system, (a) Has heat been transferred? (b) Has work been done? (c) What is the sign of ΔU?

18–4. A liquid is irregularly stirred in a well-insulated container and thereby undergoes a rise in temperature. Regarding the liquid as the system, (a) Has heat been transferred? (b) Has work been done? (c) What is the sign of ΔU?

18–5. A resistor, immersed in running water, carries an electric current. Consider the resistor as the system under consideration. (a) Is there a flow of heat into the resistor? (b) Is there a flow of heat into the water? (c) Is work done? (d) Assuming the state of the resistor to remain unchanged, apply the first law to this process.

18–6. In a certain process, 500 cal of heat are supplied to a system, and at the same time 100 joules of work are done. What is the increase in its internal energy?

18–7. 200 Btu are supplied to a system in a certain process, and at the same time the system expands against a constant external pressure of 100 lb/in^2. The internal energy of the system is the same at the beginning and end of the process. Find the increase in volume of the system.

18–8. A substance undergoes a series of processes which bring it back to its initial state. In this cycle, heat Q_2 is absorbed by the substance and heat Q_1 is rejected. What is the net amount of work done?

18–9. An inventor claims to have developed an engine which takes in 100,000 Btu from its fuel supply, rejects 25,000 Btu in the exhaust, and delivers 25 kwh of mechanical work. Do you advise investing money to put this engine on the market?

18–10. A vessel with rigid walls and covered with asbestos is divided into two parts by an insulating partition. One part contains a gas at temperature T and pressure P. The other part contains a gas at temperature T' and pressure P'. The partition is removed. What conclusion may be drawn by applying the first law of thermodynamics?

18–11. A mixture of hydrogen and oxygen is enclosed in a rigid insulating container and exploded by a spark. The temperature and pressure both increase considerably. Neglecting the small amount of energy provided by the spark itself, what conclusion may be drawn by applying the first law of thermodynamics?

18–12. When water is boiled under a pressure of 2 atm, the heat of vaporization is 946 Btu/lb and the boiling point is 250°F. One lb of steam occupies a volume of 14 ft^3, and 1 lb of water a volume of 0.017 ft^3. (a) Compute the external work, in ft·lb and in

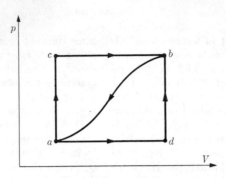

FIGURE 18–6

Btu, when 1 lb of steam is formed at this temperature. (b) Compute the increase in internal energy, in Btu.

18–13. When a system is taken from state a to state b, in Fig. 18–6, along the path acb, 80 Btu of heat flow into the system, and 30 Btu of work are done. (a) How much heat flows into the system along path adb if the work is 10 Btu? (b) When the system is returned from b to a along the curved path, the work is 20 Btu. Does the system absorb or liberate heat and how much? (c) If $U_a = 0$ and $U_d = 40$ Btu, find the heat absorbed in the processes ad and db.

18–14. A steel cylinder of cross-sectional area 0.1 ft^2 contains 0.4 ft^3 of glycerin. The cylinder is equipped with a tightly fitting piston which supports a load of 6000 lb. The temperature of the system is increased from 60°F to 160°F. Neglect the expansion of the steel cylinder. Find (a) the increase in volume of the glycerin, (b) the mechanical work of the 6000-lb force. (c) the amount of heat added to the glycerin (specific heat of glycerin = 0.58 Btu/lb·F°), (d) the change in internal energy of the glycerin.

CHAPTER 19

THERMAL PROPERTIES OF SOLIDS, LIQUIDS, AND GASES

19–1 The ideal gas law. We know that the atoms of a gas are much more widely separated than are those of a liquid or solid; hence the forces between atoms are of less consequence and the behavior of a gas is governed by simpler laws than those applying to liquids and solids.

Robert Boyle, in 1660, reported on one of the first quantitative experiments relating to gaseous behavior. He found that if the temperature of a fixed mass of gas was held constant while its volume was varied over wide limits, the pressure exerted by the gas varied also, and in such a way that the product of pressure and volume remained approximately constant. This relation is known as *Boyle's law*. If p stands for the *absolute* pressure and V for the volume of any constant mass of gas, then Boyle's law may be written

$$pV = \text{constant} \begin{Bmatrix} \text{constant temperature} \\ \text{constant mass} \end{Bmatrix}. \tag{19–1}$$

Many measurements of the pressure and volume of gases carried out since Boyle's time have shown that, at a temperature near that at which the gas condenses into a liquid, the product pV varies considerably. Only at temperatures far above the condensation point is Boyle's law obeyed. In the case of oxygen, nitrogen, air, hydrogen, and helium, Boyle's law is obeyed quite well in the neighborhood of room temperature and atmospheric pressure.

In describing the behavior of gases, it is very useful to use the *gram-mole* as a unit of mass. *A gram-mole of gas is M grams where M is the molecular weight.* Thus, a mole of hydrogen, H_2, is 2 gm, a mole of oxygen, O_2, is 32 gm, etc. Suppose the pressure p, volume V, and the number of moles n of a gas are measured at constant temperature and the product pv (v is the volume per mole, V/n, or *molar volume*) is calculated. The remarkable property of gases that makes them so valuable in thermometry is displayed in Fig. 19–1 where the product pv is plotted against p for four different gases, all at the temperature of boiling sulfur in the top graph, all at the temperature of boiling water in the one beneath, all at the triple point of water in the next lower graph, and all at the temperature of solid CO_2 in the lowest. In each case it is seen that, as the pressure approaches zero, *the product pv approaches the same value for all gases at the same temperature.*

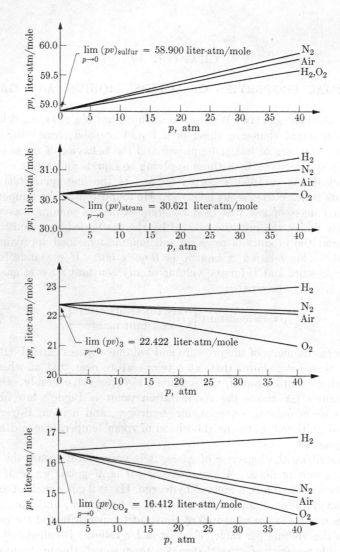

FIG. 19–1. The fundamental property of gases is that $\lim_{p \to 0} (pv)_T$ is independent of the nature of the gas and depends only on T.

According to the rules developed in Chapter 15, the kelvin temperature divided by T_3 ($T_3 = 273.16°K$) is obtained by taking the limiting value, as the pressure approaches zero, of the ratio p/p_3, *no matter what gas is chosen.* We have, therefore, two fundamental properties that hold *for all gases in the limit of low pressures,* thus:

$$pv = \text{constant} \quad \text{(constant temperature)}, \quad (19\text{--}2)$$

$$\frac{p}{p_3} = \frac{T}{T_3} \quad \text{(constant volume).} \quad (19\text{--}3)$$

In Fig. 19–2, the relation between p and v at small values of p (Boyle's law) is plotted for two different temperatures: an arbitrary temperature T and the triple point temperature T_3.

At temperature T,

$$pv = k,$$

where k is a constant.

At temperature T_3,

$$(pv)_3 = k_3,$$

where k_3 is another constant.

Dividing the first equation by the second, we get that

$$\frac{pv}{(pv)_3} = \frac{k}{k_3} = \text{constant}, \quad (19\text{--}4)$$

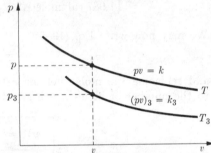

FIG. 19–2. The relation between p and v at small pressures and at two different temperatures.

which must hold for *any two points,* one on the upper curve and the other on the lower. If we apply this result to the two points shown in Fig. 19–2 *on the same constant volume line,* Eq. (19–4) reduces to

$$\frac{p}{p_3} = \frac{k}{k_3} \quad \text{(constant } v\text{).}$$

But p/p_3 is none other than the ratio T/T_3 as given in Eq. (19–3). It follows therefore that

$$\frac{k}{k_3} = \frac{T}{T_3},$$

and after substitution back into Eq. (19–4),

$$\frac{pv}{(pv)_3} = \frac{T}{T_3}.$$

Therefore, for all gases in the limit of low pressures,

$$pv = \left[\frac{(pv)_3}{273.16°} \right] \cdot T. \tag{19-5}$$

The expression in brackets is called the *universal gas constant* and is denoted by R. The best value obtained so far for the limiting value of $(pv)_3$ is 22.4216 liters·atm/mole, or 2271.87 joules/mole. Hence

$$R = \frac{22.4216 \text{ liters·atm/mole}}{273.16°K} = \frac{2271.87 \text{ joules/mole}}{273.16°K},$$

$$R = \begin{cases} 0.08208 \text{ liter·atm/mole·K°,} \\ 8.317 \times 10^7 \text{ ergs/mole·K°,} \\ 8.317 \text{ joules/mole·K°,} \\ 1.987 \text{ cal/mole·K°.} \end{cases}$$

We may now write Eq. (19–5)

$$pv = RT,$$

and replacing the molar volume v by the ratio of the total volume V to the number of moles n, we get finally

$$\boxed{pV = nRT.} \tag{19-6}$$

Equation (19–6) expresses the behavior of real gases only at *low* pressures where the forces of attraction among the molecules are very weak. If there were no forces whatever among the molecules, the equation would hold exactly. It is found useful to define an *ideal gas* as one that would obey Eq. (19–6) at *all* pressures, and hence this equation is called the *ideal gas law*.

19–2 Properties of an ideal gas. The relation between the pressure and molar volume of an ideal gas at constant temperature is shown by the curves of Fig. 19–2. The curves are equilateral hyperbolas, asymptotic to the p- and v-axes. Each curve corresponds to a different temperature. That is, while $pv = $ a constant at any one temperature, the constant is larger the higher the temperature.

Each of the curves in Fig. 19–2 can be considered to represent a *process* through which the gas is carried, for example, a process in which the gas is compressed from a large to a small volume in a bicycle pump. We shall show later that to keep the temperature constant in such a compression it would be necessary to remove heat from the gas, and therefore the process would have to be carried out slowly in order to keep the temperature the same throughout the gas. Such a slow compression carries the gas through a series of states, each of which is very nearly an equilibrium state, and it is called a *quasi-static*, or a "nearly static" process. Unless stated otherwise, we shall assume in what follows that all processes are to be carried out in this way, so that at each stage of the process the gas is, for all practical purposes, in an equilibrium state.

Any process in which the temperature remains constant is called *isothermal*, and the curves in Fig. 19–2 are the isothermal curves or, more briefly, the *isotherms* of an ideal gas.

The first accurate statement of the law connecting the volume changes of a gas with changes in its temperature was published by Joseph Louis Gay-Lussac in 1802. Earlier work on the subject had been carried on by many other investigators, among them Jacques A. C. Charles, whose name is often associated with Gay-Lussac's in connection with the relation between volume and temperature of a gas at constant pressure. The proportionality between volume v and kelvin temperature T follows from the ideal gas law, Eq. (19–6). Thus

$$v = \text{constant } T \qquad (\text{constant } p) \qquad (19\text{–}7)$$

is the mathematical statement of Gay-Lussac's law. A graph of this law (not to scale) is shown in Fig. 19–3 for three different pressures. If an actual gas behaved like an ideal gas at very low temperatures, the straight lines shown in Fig. 19–3 would remain straight and pass through the origin. The absolute zero of temperature could then be defined as the temperature at which the volume of a gas held at constant pressure shrinks to zero! The stubborn fact remains, however, that at some low temperature, a gas maintained at constant pressure becomes a liquid, and Gay-Lussac's law breaks down.

Any process in which the pressure remains constant is called *isobaric*, and the lines in Fig. 19–3 are the isobaric lines or, more briefly, the *isobars* of an ideal gas.

The number of moles n in a sample of gas equals the mass m of the gas divided by its molecular weight. If the latter is represented by M, then $n = m/M$. Hence we may write,

$$pV = m \frac{R}{M} T.$$

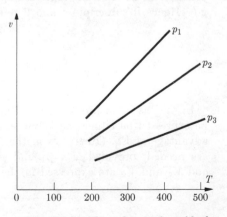

FIG. 19–3. The volume of an ideal gas is proportional to the kelvin temperature at constant pressure (Gay-Lussac's law).

TABLE 19–1

Gas	Density, gm/cm³ at 1 atm, 0°C
Air	1.2929×10^{-3}
Argon	1.7832×10^{-3}
Carbon dioxide	1.9769×10^{-3}
Helium	0.1785×10^{-3}
Hydrogen	0.0899×10^{-3}
Nitrogen	1.2506×10^{-3}
Oxygen	1.4290×10^{-3}

Dividing both sides by V and remembering that the definition of the density ρ is m/V, we get

$$\rho = \frac{Mp}{RT}. \tag{19-8}$$

The density of a gas is seen to depend on its pressure and temperature as well as on its molecular weight. Hence in tabulating gas densities the pressure and temperature must be specified. The densities of a few common gases are listed in Table 19–1.

In numerical calculation on gases which may be assumed to be ideal, it is often necessary to compute a final value of p, V, T, or n in terms of given values. For this purpose we note that the quantity pV/nT has the constant value R at all stages of any process through which the gas may go. Hence if subscripts 1 and 2 refer to any two states,

$$\boxed{\frac{p_1 V_1}{n_1 T_1} = \frac{p_2 V_2}{n_2 T_2}.} \tag{19-9}$$

In this, as in all forms of the ideal gas equation, the temperature *must* be expressed on either the kelvin scale or on the rankine scale. A great advantage of Eq. (19–9) lies in the fact that no special units of p and V are needed, provided *both* p_1 and p_2 are expressed in the same units, and V_1 and V_2 are expressed in the same units.

EXAMPLE 1. How many kilograms of O_2 are contained in a tank whose volume is 2 ft³ when the gauge pressure is 2000 lb/in² and the temperature is 27°C?

Assume the ideal gas laws to hold. The molecular weight of oxygen is 32 gm/mole.

$$2 \text{ ft}^3 = 2 \times 28.3 = 56.6 \text{ liters.}$$

$$p_{\text{abs}} = 2015 \frac{\text{lb}}{\text{in}^2} = \frac{2015}{14.7} = 137 \text{ atm.}$$

$$T = t + 273 = 300°\text{K.}$$

Hence, from Eq. (19–6),

$$n = \frac{pV}{RT} = \frac{137 \text{ atm} \times 56.6 \text{ liters}}{0.082 \text{ liter·atm/mole·K°} \times 300°\text{K}} = 315 \text{ moles.}$$

$$m = 315 \times 32 = 10,100 \text{ gm} = 10.1 \text{ kgm.}$$

EXAMPLE 2. What volume would be occupied by this gas if it were allowed to expand to atmospheric pressure at a temperature of 50°C?

Since we are dealing with a fixed mass of gas, we may write

$$\frac{p_1 V_1}{T_1} = \frac{p_2 V_2}{T_2},$$

$$V_2 = V_1 \frac{p_1}{p_2} \frac{T_2}{T_1} = 2 \times \frac{137}{1} \times \frac{323}{300} = 295 \text{ ft}^3.$$

19–3 Molecular theory of matter. The fact that matter is compressible suggests that all substances have a granular or spongy structure with spaces into which the granules can penetrate when the external pressure is increased. The ease with which liquids can flow and gases can diffuse points more to a collection of tiny particles than to a spongelike structure. Thousands of physical and chemical facts support the contention that matter in all phases is composed of tiny particles called *molecules*. The molecules of any one substance are identical. They have the same structure, the same mass, and the same mechanical and electrical properties. Many of the large-scale properties of matter which have been discussed heretofore, such as elasticity, surface tension, condensation, vaporization, etc., can be comprehended with deeper understanding of their significance in terms of the molecular theory. For this purpose we may conceive of a molecule as a rigid sphere, like a small billiard ball, capable of moving, of colliding with other molecules or with a wall, and of exerting attractive or repulsive forces on neighboring molecules. In other parts of physics and chemistry it is important to consider the structure of the molecule, but this is not necessary at this point.

One of the outstanding characteristics of a molecule is the force that exists between it and a neighbor. There is, of course, a force of gravitational attraction between every pair of molecules, but it turns out that

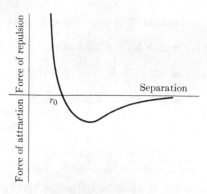

FIG. 19–4. The force between two molecules changes from an attraction, when the separation is large, to a repulsion when the separation is small.

this is negligible in comparison with the forces we are now considering. The forces that hold the molecules of a liquid (or solid) together are, in part at least, of electrical origin and do not follow a simple inverse square law. When the separation of the molecules is large, as in a gas, the force is extremely small and is an attraction. The attractive force increases as a gas is compressed and its molecules brought closer together. But since tremendous pressures are needed to compress a liquid, i.e., to force its molecules closer together than their normal spacing in the liquid state, we conclude that at separations only slightly less than the dimensions of a molecule the force is one of repulsion and is relatively large. The force must then vary with separation in somewhat the fashion shown in Fig. 19–4. At large separations the force is one of attraction but is extremely small. As the molecules are brought closer together the force of attraction becomes larger, passes through a maximum, and then decreases to zero at a separation r_0. When the distance between the molecules is less than r_0, the force is one of repulsion.

A single pair of molecules could remain in equilibrium at a center-to-center spacing equal to r_0 in Fig. 19–4. If they were separated slightly, the force between them would be attractive and they would be drawn together. If they were forced closer together than the distance r_0, the force would be one of repulsion and they would spring apart. If they were either pulled apart or pushed together, and then released, they would oscillate about their equilibrium separation r_0.

If the only property of a molecule were the force of attraction between it and its neighbors, all matter would eventually coalesce into the liquid or solid phase. The existence of gases points to another property which enables molecules to stay apart. This is accomplished by molecular motion. The more vigorous the motion the less chance there is for con-

TABLE 19-2

Phase	Attractive forces among molecules	Molecular kinetic energy	Temperature
Solid	Strong	Small	Low
Liquid	Moderate	Moderate	Medium
Gas	Weak	Large	High

densation into the liquid or solid phase. In solids the molecules execute vibratory motion about more or less fixed centers. This vibratory motion is relatively weak, and the centers remain fixed at regularly spaced positions which comprise a *space lattice*. This gives rise to the extraordinary regularity and symmetry of crystals. In liquids the molecules execute vibratory motion of greater energy about centers which are free to move but which remain at approximately the same distance from one another. The molecules of gases have the greatest kinetic energy. The motion is linear until collision takes place either with another molecule or with a wall. The average distance between molecules of a gas is so great that only small attractive forces exist.

A common substance like water exists in the solid phase at low temperatures. When the temperature is raised beyond a definite value, the liquid phase results, and when the temperature of the liquid is raised further, the water exists in the gaseous phase. That is, from a large-scale or *macroscopic* point of view, the transition from solid to liquid to gas is in the direction of increasing temperature. From a *molecular* point of view this transition is in the direction of increasing molecular kinetic energy. Evidently, *there must be some connection between temperature and molecular kinetic energy.*

The preceding paragraphs may be conveniently summarized by means of Table 19-2.

19-4 Kinetic theory of an ideal gas. If the molecules of a gas are, on the average, far enough apart, the forces of attraction are exceedingly weak. We define an ideal gas as one whose molecules exert no forces on one another, except when they collide. Collisions are assumed to be completely elastic, so that the total kinetic energy of two molecules before collision is the same as that after collision. Suppose that the gas is in a container in the shape of a parallelepiped, and that the total number of molecules is enormously large. The gas is homogeneous; that is, the number of molecules in any small volume element is the same regardless of the position of the element. Moreover, the rectilinear motions of the molecule are completely chaotic, so that, at any moment, there are as many molecules moving one way as another, although all molecules do not have the same speed.

The pressure exerted by the gas is due to molecular collisions with the walls of the container. These collisions are assumed to be completely elastic, so that a molecule approaching a wall perpendicularly with momentum mv will recede from the wall with momentum $-mv$. The change of momentum per molecule per collision will therefore be $-2mv$. If we calculate the rate at which molecules strike a wall and multiply this by the change of momentum per molecule per collision, we shall have the rate of change of momentum which, by Newton's second law, is the force exerted by the wall on the gas. Dividing by the area A of the wall, the pressure may then be obtained. The pressure calculated in this way may then be compared with pressure measured experimentally, i.e., the pressure expressed by the ideal gas equation. If the two expressions agree, the assumptions of the kinetic theory are confirmed.

In general, a molecule near the center of the container will undergo many collisions with other molecules before it arrives at a wall. For a given density of molecules (i.e., a given number of molecules per unit volume), there exists an average distance that a molecule may traverse before it collides with another molecule. This is called its *mean free path*. Imagine a plane situated near a wall of the containing vessel at a distance much less than the mean free path. Between this plane and the wall all molecules moving in any direction with a component toward the wall will reach the wall without undergoing an appreciable number of collisions with other molecules on the way. In this space, let

$v_1 =$ a velocity component perpendicular to the wall,

$N_1 =$ the number of molecules per unit volume which have the velocity component v_1,

$t =$ the average time it takes such a molecule to reach the wall.

Then the number of molecules striking the wall in time t is equal to

$$\frac{N_1}{2} Av_1t,$$

since only half have velocity components directed *toward* the wall. Each of these molecules undergoes a change of momentum upon collision equal to $-2mv_1$. Therefore, the rate of change of momentum of these molecules equals

$$\frac{(N_1/2)Av_1t \times (-2mv_1)}{t}$$

and, by Newton's second law, this must represent the force exerted by the wall on these molecules. From Newton's third law, however, this is equal in magnitude but opposite in direction to the force exerted *on* the wall. The pressure, therefore, due to the collision of these molecules only is equal to

$$p_1 = \frac{(N_1/2)Av_1t \times (2mv_1)}{At}$$

or

$$p_1 = N_1mv_1^2.$$

Consider now another group of molecules, N_2 per unit volume, that have a different velocity component v_2 perpendicular to the wall. Their collisions with the wall will give rise to an additional pressure

$$p_2 = N_2mv_2^2.$$

The total pressure p due to all the molecules is therefore equal to

$$p = N_1mv_1^2 + N_2mv_2^2 + N_3mv_3^2 + \cdots, \qquad (19\text{–}10)$$

where all possible values of the velocity component perpendicular to the wall are taken into account.

If we regard the direction perpendicular to the wall as that of the x-axis, we may define an average of the squares of the x-components of velocity by the expression

$$\overline{v_x^2} = \frac{N_1v_1^2 + N_2v_2^2 + N_3v_3^2 + \cdots}{N},$$

in which N represents the total number of molecules per unit volume. Substituting this value of $\overline{v_x^2}$ into the expression for the pressure, Eq. (19–10), we get

$$p = Nm\overline{v_x^2}. \qquad (19\text{–}11)$$

If v is the magnitude of the velocity of any one molecule, then v may be expressed in terms of its x-, y-, and z-components, as follows:

$$v^2 = v_x^2 + v_y^2 + v_z^2.$$

Averaging over all the molecules, we get

$$\overline{v^2} = \overline{v_x^2} + \overline{v_y^2} + \overline{v_z^2}.$$

But the properties of the gas are uniform throughout the container. The average of the squares of the velocity components in any one direction is the same as that for any other direction. Therefore

$$\overline{v_x^2} = \overline{v_y^2} = \overline{v_z^2}$$

and

$$\overline{v^2} = 3\overline{v_x^2}.$$

Substituting this result in Eq. (19–11), we get finally

$$p = \tfrac{1}{3}Nm\overline{v^2}. \tag{19-12}$$

If **N** is the total number of molecules in the container of volume V, then $N = \mathbf{N}/V$ and

$$p = \frac{1}{3}\frac{\mathbf{N}}{V}\,m\overline{v^2}$$

or

$$pV = \tfrac{2}{3}\mathbf{N} \times \tfrac{1}{2}m\overline{v^2}. \tag{19-13}$$

The kinetic energy of a single molecule is $\tfrac{1}{2}mv^2$. The average kinetic energy per molecule is therefore $\tfrac{1}{2}m\overline{v^2}$. We have already come to the conclusion that molecular kinetic energy is somehow connected with temperature, so let us assume, in the case of an ideal gas, that

$$\tfrac{1}{2}m\overline{v^2} = \tfrac{3}{2}kT, \tag{19-14}$$

where k is a universal constant, known as *Boltzmann's constant*. It follows therefore that

$$pV = \tfrac{2}{3}\mathbf{N} \times \tfrac{3}{2}kT,$$

$$pV = \mathbf{N}kT. \tag{19-15}$$

We have therefore derived a relation among pressure, volume, and temperature (an equation of state) of an ideal gas from the laws of mechanics with the aid of the assumptions that:

(1) An ideal gas consists of identical, "rigid sphere," completely elastic molecules.

(2) The molecules move with uniform linear motion between impacts.

(3) The molecules exert no forces on one another, except during impact.

(4) The average kinetic energy per molecule is proportional to the kelvin temperature.

Comparing Eq. (19–15) with the experimental equation of state of an ideal gas,

$$pV = nRT,$$

we see that they are of the same form. Our assumptions are therefore justified. To make both equations identical, we must have

$$\mathbf{N}k = nR$$

or

$$k = \frac{R}{\mathbf{N}/n}.$$

The ratio of the number of molecules $\mathbf{N}$ to the number of moles n is the number of molecules per mole, or *Avogadro's number* N_0. Thus

$$k = \frac{R}{N_0}.$$

Avogadro's number may be measured in a variety of ways, one of which will be encountered when the conduction of electricity in liquids is studied. The latest value is

$$N_0 = 6.02 \times 10^{23} \frac{\text{molecules}}{\text{mole}}.$$

It follows, then, that Boltzmann's constant is

$$k = \frac{R}{N_0} = \frac{8.31 \times 10^7 \text{ ergs/mole·deg}}{6.02 \times 10^{23} \text{ molecules/mole}}$$

or

$$k = 1.38 \times 10^{-16} \frac{\text{erg}}{\text{molecule·deg}}.$$

Since there are no attractive forces among the molecules of an ideal gas, these molecules have no potential energy. The internal energy U of an ideal gas is therefore entirely kinetic. Since the average kinetic energy per molecule is $\frac{3}{2}kT$, we have

$$U = \tfrac{3}{2}\mathbf{N}kT$$

or

$$\boxed{U = \tfrac{3}{2}nRT,} \qquad (19\text{--}16)$$

which says that *the internal energy of an ideal gas is proportional to the kelvin temperature* and depends on temperature only, independent of the pressure or of the volume. It must be emphasized that Eq. (19–16) is of *very restricted validity*. It holds only for an aggregate of rigid, "billiard-ball" molecules which exert no forces on one another, and which do not rotate, vibrate, or dissociate. Equation (19–16) will therefore be expected to break down at high pressures when the average intermolecular distance is small, and also at high temperatures where molecules vibrate, dissociate, or undergo electronic rearrangements. We *cannot* infer from Eq. (19–16) that at absolute zero the kinetic energy of the molecules equals zero, because long before absolute zero is approached condensation takes place, and Eq. (19–16) breaks down.

It is shown in advanced textbooks that the energy of a substance in a condensed phase is a very complicated function of the temperature, in no way resembling Eq. (19–16). This function has the property that, as the temperature approaches zero, *the energy does not approach zero,* but approaches a constant value, known as the *zero-point energy.* In the case of helium at low temperature, the zero-point energy is so large that the molecules of liquid cannot get close enough together to form a solid, unless the pressure is raised to about 25 atmospheres. In the absence of this high pressure, helium remains a liquid down to absolute zero.

19–5 Specific heats of an ideal gas. The temperature of a gas may be raised under a variety of conditions. The volume may be kept constant, or the pressure may be kept constant, or both may be allowed to vary in some arbitrary manner. In each of these cases, the amount of heat necessary to cause unit rise of temperature in unit mass is different. In other words, a gas has many different heat capacities. Only two, however, are of practical use, namely, those at constant volume and at constant pressure.

Let us choose as a convenient unit of mass the number of grams equal to the molecular weight, that is, a mole. The corresponding heat capacity is called the *molar heat capacity,* represented by C_v. If we have n moles of an ideal gas with a molar heat capacity at constant volume C_v and we raise its temperature at constant volume from T_1 to T_2, then the heat transferred is $nC_v(T_2 - T_1)$ and the work done is zero. From the first law we get

$$nC_v(T_2 - T_1) = U_2 - U_1 + 0. \qquad (19\text{–}17)$$

If the same amount of the same gas were heated at constant pressure p until the temperature changed the same amount, then the heat transferred would be $nC_p(T_2 - T_1)$, where C_p is the molar heat capacity at constant pressure. In this process, however, the gas would expand, say, from volume V_1 to V_2 and an amount of work $p(V_2 - V_1)$ would be done. Therefore, using the first law,

$$nC_p(T_2 - T_1) = U_2' - U_1' + p(V_2 - V_1). \qquad (19\text{–}18)$$

Now U_1 and U_1' are the internal energies, respectively, of an ideal gas at the same temperature T_1 but at different pressures. Since the energy of an ideal gas is a function of temperature only, $U_1 = U_1'$, and similarly, $U_2 = U_2'$.

Subtracting Eq. (19–17) from Eq. (19–18) we get

$$n(C_p - C_v)(T_2 - T_1) = p(V_2 - V_1). \qquad (19\text{–}19)$$

But

$$pV_1 = nRT_1,$$

and

$$pV_2 = nRT_2,$$

so that

$$p(V_2 - V_1) = nR(T_2 - T_1).$$

Substituting this result in Eq. (19–19), we get

$$n(C_p - C_v)(T_2 - T_1) = nR(T_2 - T_1),$$

or finally

$$\boxed{C_p - C_v = R.} \qquad (19\text{–}20)$$

This equation shows that the molar heat capacity at constant pressure of an ideal gas is always larger than that at constant volume, the difference being the universal gas constant R. Of course R must be expressed in the same units as C_p and C_v, usually cal/mole C°. Since $R = 8.31$ joules/mole C° and 4.19 joules = 1 cal,

$$R = \frac{8.31}{4.19} = 1.99 \ \frac{\text{cal}}{\text{mole C°}},$$

or very nearly 2 cal/mole C°.

Equation (19–20) is strictly true only for an ideal gas but is very nearly true for real gases at moderate pressures. Measured values of C_p and C_v are given in Table 19–3 for some real gases at low pressures, and the difference is seen to be very nearly 2 cal/mole·C°.

In the last column of Table 19–3 are listed the values of the ratio C_p/C_v denoted by the Greek letter γ (gamma). It is seen that γ is 1.67 for monatomic gases, and is very nearly 1.40 for the so-called permanent diatomic gases. There is no simple regularity for polyatomic gases.

Solids and liquids also expand when heated, if free to do so, and hence perform work. The coefficients of volume expansion of solids and liquids are, however, so much smaller than those of gases that the external work is small. The internal energy of a solid or liquid *does* depend on its volume as well as its temperature, and this must be considered when evaluating the difference between specific heats of solids or liquids. It turns out that here also $C_p > C_v$, but the difference is small and is not expressible as simply as that for a gas. Because of the large stresses set up when

TABLE 19–3

MOLAR HEAT CAPACITIES OF GASES AT LOW PRESSURE

Type of gas	Gas	C_p, cal/mole·C°	C_v, cal/mole·C°	$C_p - C_v$	$\gamma = C_p/C_v$
Monatomic	He	4.97	2.98	1.99	1.67
"	A	4.97	2.98	1.99	1.67
Diatomic	H_2	6.87	4.88	1.99	1.41
"	N_2	6.95	4.96	1.99	1.40
"	O_2	7.03	5.04	1.99	1.40
"	CO	6.97	4.98	1.99	1.40
Polyatomic	CO_2	8.83	6.80	2.03	1.30
"	SO_2	9.65	7.50	2.15	1.29
"	H_2S	8.37	6.2	2.1	1.34

solids or liquids are heated and *not* allowed to expand, most heating processes involving them take place at constant pressure, and hence C_p is the quantity usually measured for a solid or liquid.

19–6 Adiabatic compression or expansion of an ideal gas. When an ideal gas is compressed adiabatically, the work done on the gas serves to increase the internal energy. Since the internal energy is a function of the temperature only, the temperature therefore rises. Conversely, in an adiabatic expansion of an ideal gas, the temperature decreases.

In Fig. 19–5, the heavy curves represent adiabatic curves on a p-V diagram. The dashed curves represent isotherms for comparison. The adiabatic curves, at any point, have a somewhat steeper slope than the isothermal curve passing through the same point. That is, as one follows along an adiabatic from right to left (compression process) the curve continually cuts across isotherms of higher and higher temperatures, in agreement with the fact that the temperature continually increases in an adiabatic compression. It can be shown that the equation of an adiabatic curve for an ideal gas is

$$pV^\gamma = \text{constant} \quad \text{(Adiabatic)}, \qquad (19\text{–}21)$$

where γ is the ratio of the heat capacities listed in the last column of Table 19–3. Equation (19–21) may be rewritten in the more useful form

$$p_1 V_1^\gamma = p_2 V_2^\gamma \quad \text{(Adiabatic)}, \qquad (19\text{–}22)$$

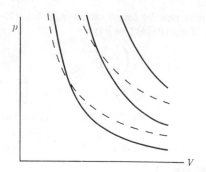

FIG. 19–5. Adiabatic curves (full lines) vs. isothermal curves (dashed lines).

where *any* unit of pressure may be used, provided it holds for *both* p_1 and p_2 and any unit of volume for both V_1 and V_2.

The states traversed by an ideal gas undergoing an adiabatic expansion or compression may be described by a relation between T and V just as well as by one between p and V. If we substitute for p in Eq. (19–21) the value given by the ideal gas equation, we get

$$\frac{nRT}{V} \cdot V^\gamma = \text{constant,}$$

or

$$\boxed{TV^{\gamma-1} = \text{constant,}} \tag{19–23}$$

or

$$T_1 V_1^{\gamma-1} = T_2 V_2^{\gamma-1}. \tag{19–24}$$

Both T_1 and T_2 must be expressed either on the kelvin scale or on the rankine scale. V_1 and V_2 must, of course, be expressed in the same units.

EXAMPLE.   The compression ratio of a diesel engine, V_1/V_2, is about 15. If the cylinder contains air at 15 lb/in² (absolute) and 60°F ($= 520$°R) at the start of the compression stroke, compute the pressure and temperature at the end of this stroke. Assume that air behaves like an ideal gas and that the compression is adiabatic. The value of γ for air is 1.40.

From Eq. (19–22),

$$p_2 = p_1 (V_1/V_2)^\gamma.$$

Or,

$$\log p_2 = \log p_1 + \gamma \log \frac{V_1}{V_2} = \log 15 + 1.4 \log 15 = 1.176 + 1.646 = 2.822.$$

$$\therefore p_2 = 663 \text{ lb/in}^2.$$

The temperature may now be found either from Eq. (19–24) or by the ideal gas law. Thus, from Eq. (19–24), we have

$$T_2 = T_1 \left(\frac{V_1}{V_2}\right)^{\gamma-1},$$

$$\log T_2 = \log T_1 + (\gamma - 1) \log \frac{V_1}{V_2}$$

$$= \log 520 + (1.4 - 1) \log 15$$

$$= 2.716 + 0.470 = 3.186,$$

$$T_2 = 1535°R = 1075°F.$$

Or, from the ideal gas law,

$$T_2 = T_1 \times \frac{p_2 V_2}{p_1 V_1} = 520 \times \frac{663 \times 1}{15 \times 15} = 1535°R.$$

19–7 Liquefaction of gases. An ideal gas, if compressed isothermally, remains a gas no matter how great a pressure is applied to it; the volume decreases continually with increasing pressure according to Boyle's law. All real gases, however, become liquids when the pressure is increased sufficiently (provided the temperature is below a value known as the critical temperature of the gas).

The difference between the behavior of an ideal and a real gas in an isothermal compression is illustrated in Fig. 19–6(a) and (b). Imagine the gases to be contained within two similar cylinders, each provided with a piston and a pressure gauge. The volume at each stage of the compression process is proportional to the distance of the piston from the closed end of the cylinder, and the pressure at each stage may be read from the gauge. Several stages of the compression are illustrated in each part of the figure, and corresponding pressures and volumes are plotted in the p-V diagrams. Each gas is initially at the same pressure and volume (point a), and the temperature of each is held constant throughout by the removal of heat.

As the piston in (a) is forced to the left, the reading of the pressure gauge rises steadily, and the relation between p and V is the familiar Boyle's law. As the volume of the real gas is decreased, in Fig. 19–6(b), the pressure rises at first along the curve ab in a manner not very different from that of the ideal gas. When point b is reached, however, a sharp break occurs in the curve, and the volume continues to decrease *without further increase of pressure*. At the same time, drops of liquid begin to appear on the walls of the cylinder. In other words, the process of *liquefaction* or *condensation* begins at point b.

As the volume is further reduced, from b to c and d, the quantity of liquid in the cylinder increases and the quantity of gas decreases. At point e, all the substance has been converted into the liquid phase. Of

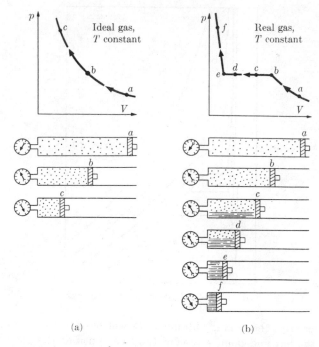

Fig. 19–6. Isothermal compression of (a) an ideal gas, (b) a real gas.

course, during the transition from b to e, it was necessary to remove from the substance its heat of condensation.

Since liquids are nearly incompressible, a very large pressure increase is necessary to reduce the volume below that at point e. That is, the curve rises nearly vertically from e to f, having a very small inclination toward the left.

As an example, if the cylinder in part (b) of the figure had initially contained one gram of steam at 100°C, at a pressure of about $\frac{1}{2}$ atm and a volume of about 3000 cm^3 (point a), condensation would begin when the pressure had increased to 1 atm and the volume decreased to 1670 cm^3 (point b). The pressure would remain constant at 1 atm from b to e, while the volume decreased from 1670 cm^3 to 1 cm^3. 539 cal would have to be removed during the condensation process. To produce a further decrease in volume of 0.001 cm^3, it would be necessary to increase the pressure to about 20 atm (point f).

If the experiment illustrated in Fig. 19–6(b) is repeated, starting at higher and higher temperatures, it is found that greater and greater pressures must be exerted on the gas before condensation begins. Figure

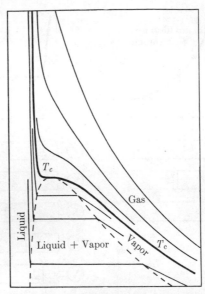

FIG. 19–7. Isotherms of a real gas.

19–7 illustrates the curves obtained. It will be seen that point b moves toward the left and point e toward the right until at the particular temperature lettered T_c in Fig. 19–7 the two points coincide. Above this temperature there is no straight horizontal portion to the curve. In other words, there is no stage in the compression process at which the substance separates into two distinct portions, one of which is a gas while the other is a liquid. The temperature T_c is called the *critical* temperature, and it is now evident why a gas must first be cooled below its critical temperature before it can be liquefied by compression.

It is customary to refer to a gas below its critical temperature as a *vapor*, although this distinction is not rigidly adhered to. Critical temperatures of some common gases are given in Table 19–4.

The dotted line in Fig. 19–7 divides the p-V plane into three regions. At all values of p, V, and T underneath this line, the substance is partly in the liquid and partly in the vapor phase. At the right of the curve it is a vapor or gas, at the left of the curve it is a liquid.

An examination of Fig. 19–7 shows that at any given temperature below the critical temperature there is one pressure and one pressure only at which the substance can exist in either the liquid or the vapor phase, or in both phases simultaneously. This is the pressure corresponding to the horizontal portion of the isothermal curve for that particular temperature. If the pressure is any higher than that at the horizontal

TABLE 19–4

CRITICAL TEMPERATURES, PRESSURES, AND VOLUMES

Substance	Critical temperature (°C)	Critical pressure (atm)	Critical volume (cm³/gm)
Ammonia	132	112	4.25
Argon	−122	48	1.88
Carbon dioxide	31	73.0	2.17
Helium	−268	2.26	14.4
Hydrogen	−240	12.8	32.3
Oxygen	−119	49.7	2.33
Sulfur dioxide	157	77.7	1.92
Water	374	218	3.14

portion, the substance can only be a liquid. If the pressure is any lower, it can only be a vapor. Precisely at this pressure both liquid and vapor can exist together. The pressure at which a liquid and its vapor can exist in equilibrium, at any given temperature, is called the *vapor pressure* at that temperature. A vapor whose pressure and temperature are those corresponding to the horizontal portion of any of the curves in Fig. 19–7 is called a *saturated vapor*. A saturated vapor may also be defined as one which is in equilibrium with its liquid.

From the straight portions of the curves of Fig. 19–7, one can read off a series of vapor pressures and their corresponding temperatures. If these are plotted as in Fig. 19–8, one obtains the *vapor pressure curve* of the substance. All vapor pressure curves are similar in form to that of Fig. 19–8, rising with a continually increasing slope and ending at the critical point. An abridged table of the vapor pressure of water is given in Table 19–5 in the next section.

Reference to Table 19–4 will show that the critical temperatures of carbon dioxide, ammonia, and sulfur dioxide are higher than "room temperature." Hence these gases can be liquefied at room temperature without precooling, simply by increasing the pressure. Oxygen, nitrogen, or hydrogen, however, must evidently be precooled below room temperature before they can be liquefied. The Linde process for producing liquid air (or liquid oxygen or nitrogen) will be described briefly.

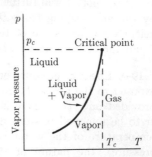

FIG. 19–8. Vapor pressure vs. temperature.

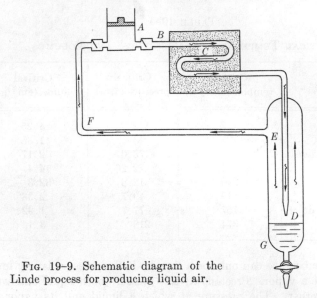

FIG. 19–9. Schematic diagram of the
Linde process for producing liquid air.

In Fig. 19–9, compressor A maintains a continuous circulation of air
as shown by the arrows. At B, the air leaving the compressor is at high
pressure and high temperature. It enters cooling coils C, where it is
cooled by air or water, and, still at high pressure, escapes through the
small orifice or nozzle D, performing a *throttling* process (see Section
18–10). If air were an ideal gas, no temperature change would result
from a throttling process. Real gases, however, undergo marked temperature changes in such a process, and if not too hot to begin with,
are cooled in passing through the orifice. The pressure in E and F is kept
low by the pump, and the cooled air passes up through E and F and
repeats the cycle. The cooled air in E, circulating around the incoming
air in D, cools it still further, hence an even lower temperature is reached
by the air escaping from D, until eventually the temperature falls sufficiently so that some of the air liquefies as it leaves the nozzle. The
liquid air collects at G, where it may be drawn off.

19–8 Effect of pressure on boiling and freezing points. A pan of water
exposed to the air of the room will evaporate, whatever its temperature,
provided only that there is opportunity for the vapor to diffuse away,
or to be removed in some manner from above the water surface. If the
temperature of the water is increased to 100°C (at normal atmospheric
pressure), the nature of the evaporation process changes completely.
Vapor is formed not only at the liquid surface but throughout the entire
volume of the liquid, which becomes violently agitated by the bubbles

TABLE 19–5

VAPOR PRESSURE OF WATER (ABSOLUTE)

| t, °C | Vapor pressure | | t_F, °F |
	mm of mercury	lb/in^2	
0	4.58	0.0886	32
5	6.51	0.126	41
10	8.94	0.173	50
15	12.67	0.245	59
20	17.5	0.339	68
40	55.1	1.07	104
60	149	2.89	140
80	355	6.87	176
100	760	14.7	212
120	1490	28.8	248
140	2710	52.4	284
160	4630	89.6	320
180	7510	145	356
200	11650	225	392
220	17390	336	428

of vapor which rise through it and break at the surface. What distinguishes this violent process of *boiling* from the slow evaporation which goes on at temperatures below the boiling point?

It will be recalled that every liquid has a certain *vapor pressure* which depends on the temperature of the liquid. If, keeping the temperature constant, an attempt is made to increase the pressure *above* the vapor pressure, the vapor immediately condenses. The water in a vessel open to the atmosphere is subjected to atmospheric pressure. Say that the temperature of the water is 80°C. Its vapor pressure, from Table 19–5, is then 355 mm of mercury or 6.87 lb/in^2. Hence if a small bubble of vapor should chance to form within the liquid, where it is subjected to a pressure of 760 mm or 14.7 lb/in^2, it would immediately collapse under the pressure and condense.

Suppose now the temperature of the liquid is increased to 100°C. At this temperature the vapor pressure is 760 mm or 14.7 lb/in^2. Hence bubbles of vapor can form at this temperature, and if the temperature were to increase only slightly above 100°C, the entire mass of water would change to the vapor phase *if its heat of vaporization could be supplied to it*. What actually happens is that the water does so change as fast as heat is supplied. As long as any liquid water remains, the temperature cannot rise above 100°C and all the heat supplied is used to produce a *change of phase* rather than an *increase in temperature*.

If the external pressure is suddenly increased above 14.7 lb/in², boiling immediately ceases, since the pressure is higher than the vapor pressure of water at 100°C. Assuming that heat is still supplied to the water, its temperature increases until the vapor pressure equals the applied pressure, when boiling commences again.

It is evident that under an external pressure less than atmospheric, boiling will take place at a temperature below 100°C. From Table 19–5, if the pressure is reduced to 0.339 lb/in², water will boil at room temperature (20°C).

> *The boiling point of a liquid is that temperature at which the vapor pressure of the liquid is equal to the external pressure.*

Freezing points as well as boiling points are affected by external pressure. The freezing point of a substance like water, which expands on solidifying, is *lowered* by an increase in pressure. The reverse is true for substances which contract on solidifying. The change in the freezing point temperature is much smaller than is that of the boiling point; an increase of one atmosphere lowers the freezing point of water by only about 0.007°C.

The lowering of the freezing point of water (or the melting point of ice) can be demonstrated by passing a loop of fine wire over a block of ice and hanging a weight of a few pounds from each end of the loop. Suppose that the main body of the ice is at 0°C and at atmospheric pressure. The temperature of the small amount of ice directly under the wire decreases until it achieves the melting point appropriate to the pressure under the wire. During this increase of pressure and decrease of temperature, a small amount of melting takes place. The water thus formed is squeezed out from under the wire and, coming to the top of the wire where the pressure is atmospheric, it refreezes and liberates heat which passes through the wire and serves to melt the next bit of ice below the wire.

The wire thus sinks farther and farther into the block, eventually cutting its way completely through, but leaving a solid block of ice behind it. This phenomenon is known as *regelation* (refreezing). Since heat is conducted from the top to the bottom of the wire while the wire is cutting through the ice, the greater the thermal conductivity of the wire, the faster will the wire cut through the ice. Even a perfectly conducting wire would not cut through the ice very rapidly, however, because of the very low thermal conductivity of the water film which is always present beneath the wire.

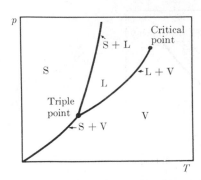

FIG. 19–10. *p-T* diagram.

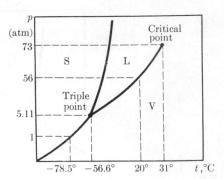

FIG. 19–11. *p-t* diagram of CO_2.
(Not to a uniform scale.)

19–9 The triple point. The vapor pressure curve of Fig. 19–8 can be considered to represent the pressure and temperature at which a change of phase from liquid to vapor will occur, or as the pressure and temperature at which both phases can remain in equilibrium with each other. There exist similar curves representing the pressure and temperature at which solid and liquid can be in equilibrium, and at which solid and vapor can be in equilibrium. These curves are shown in Fig. 19–10, and they intersect at a common point, called the *triple point*, at which all three phases can exist simultaneously.

The three curves in Fig. 19–10 divide the *p-T* plane into three regions. At any point (i.e., any pair of values of *p* and *T*) within one of these regions, the substance can exist in one phase only: solid, liquid, or vapor. Along each line, two phases can exist together, while only at the triple point can all three phases coexist.

For example, the triple-point temperature of CO_2 is −56.6°C, and the triple-point pressure is 5.11 atm. It is evident from Fig. 19–11 (not to a uniform scale) that at atmospheric pressure CO_2 can exist only as a solid or a vapor. Hence solid CO_2 (dry ice) transforms directly to CO_2 vapor when open to the atmosphere, without passing through the liquid state. This direct transition from solid to vapor is called *sublimation*. Liquid CO_2 can exist only at a pressure greater than 5.11 atm. The steel tanks in which CO_2 is commonly stored contain liquid and vapor. The pressure in these tanks is the vapor pressure of CO_2 at the temperature of the tank. If the latter is 20°C, the vapor pressure is about 56 atm or 830 lb/in².

While most substances increase in volume in the change of phase from solid to liquid, there are a few for which the reverse is true. Water, of course, is one of the latter. For such a substance an *increase* of pressure

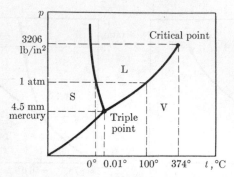

FIG. 19–12. p-t diagram of H_2O. (Not to a uniform scale.)

produces a *lowering* of the freezing point, as shown in Fig. 19–12. This effect was mentioned earlier in connection with regelation.

19–10 Humidity. Atmospheric air is a mixture of gases, consisting of about 80% nitrogen, 18% oxygen, and small amounts of carbon dioxide, water vapor, and other gases. The mass of water vapor per unit volume is called the *absolute humidity*. The total pressure exerted by the atmosphere is the sum of the pressures exerted by its component gases. These pressures are called the *partial pressures* of the components. It is found that the partial pressure of each of the component gases of a gas mixture is very nearly the same as would be the actual pressure of that component alone if it occupied the same volume as does the mixture, a fact known as *Dalton's law*. That is, each of the gases of a gas mixture behaves independently of the others. The partial pressure of water vapor in the atmosphere is ordinarily a few millimeters of mercury.

It should be evident that the partial pressure of water vapor at any given air temperature can never exceed the vapor pressure of water at that particular temperature. Thus at 10°C, from Table 19–5, the partial pressure cannot exceed 8.94 mm, or at 15°C it cannot exceed 12.67 mm. If the concentration of water vapor, or the absolute humidity, is such that the partial pressure equals the vapor pressure, the vapor is said to be *saturated*. If the partial pressure is less than the vapor pressure, the vapor is *unsaturated*. The ratio of the partial pressure to the vapor pressure at the same temperature is called the *relative humidity*, and is usually expressed as a percentage.

$$\text{Relative humidity (\%)} = 100 \times \frac{\text{partial pressure of water vapor}}{\text{vapor pressure at same temperature}}.$$

The relative humidity is 100% if the vapor is saturated and zero if no water vapor at all is present.

EXAMPLE. The partial pressure of water vapor in the atmosphere is 10 mm of mercury and the temperature is 20°C. Find (a) the relative humidity, and (b) the absolute humidity.

(a) From Table 19–5, the vapor pressure at 20°C is 17.5 mm of mercury. Hence

$$\text{Relative humidity} = \frac{10}{17.5} \times 100 = 57\%.$$

(b) Consider any volume V. From Dalton's law, the partial pressure of the water vapor present in this volume is the pressure that the water vapor would exert if it occupied the entire volume alone at 20°C. Using the ideal gas law,

$$pV = nRT,$$

we have

$$\frac{n}{V} = \frac{p}{RT} = \frac{10 \text{ mm}/(760 \text{ mm/atm})}{0.082 \text{ liter·atm/mole·deg} \times 293 \text{ deg}}$$

$$= 0.000548 \frac{\text{mole}}{\text{liter}}$$

Since the molecular weight of water is $M = 18$ gm/mole, and $1 \text{ m}^3 = 10^6 \text{ cm}^3 = 10^3$ liters, we get

$$\frac{m}{V} = \frac{nM}{V} = \frac{0.000548 \times 18}{10^{-3}} = 9.86 \frac{\text{gm}}{\text{m}^3}.$$

Since the water vapor in the atmosphere is saturated when its partial pressure equals the vapor pressure at the air temperature, saturation can be brought about either by increasing the water vapor content or by lowering the temperature. For example, let the partial pressure of water vapor be 10 mm when the air temperature is 20°C, as in the preceding example. Saturation, or 100% relative humidity, could be attained either by introducing enough more water vapor (keeping the temperature constant) to increase the partial pressure to 17.5 mm, *or by lowering the temperature* to 11.4°C, at which, by interpolation from Table 19–5, the vapor pressure is 10 mm.

If the temperature were to be lowered *below* 11.4°C, the vapor pressure would be less than 10 mm. The partial pressure would then be higher than the vapor pressure and enough vapor would condense to reduce the partial pressure to the vapor pressure at the lower temperature. It is this process which brings about the formation of clouds, fog, and rain. The phenomenon is also of frequent occurrence at night when the earth's surface becomes cooled by radiation. The condensed moisture is called *dew*. If the vapor pressure is so low that the temperature must fall below 0°C before saturation exists, the vapor condenses into ice crystals in the form of frost.

The temperature at which the water vapor in a given sample of air becomes saturated is called the *dew point*. Measuring the temperature of the dew point is the most accurate method of determining relative humidity. The usual method is to cool a metal container having a bright, polished surface, and to observe its temperature when the surface becomes clouded with condensed moisture. Suppose the dew point is observed in this way to be 10°C, when the air temperature is 20°C. We then know that the water vapor in the air is saturated at 10°C, hence its partial pressure, from Table 19–5, is 8.94 mm, equal to the vapor pressure at 10°C. The pressure necessary for saturation at 20°C is 17.5 mm. The relative humidity is therefore

$$\frac{8.94}{17.5} \times 100 = 51\%.$$

A simpler but less accurate method of determining relative humidity employs a *wet-and-dry bulb thermometer*. Two thermometers are placed side by side, the bulb of one being kept moist by a wick dipping in water. The lower the relative humidity, the more rapid will be the evaporation from the wet bulb, and the lower will be its temperature below that of the dry bulb. The relative humidity corresponding to any pair of wet-and-dry bulb temperatures is read from tables.

The *hair hygrometer* makes use of the fact that human hair absorbs or gives up moisture from the air in an amount which varies with relative humidity, and changes its length slightly with moisture content. Several strands of hair are wrapped around a small pivoted shaft to which is attached a pointer. The hair is kept taut by a light spring, and changes in its length cause the shaft to rotate and move the pointer over a scale.

19–11 Thermodynamic surfaces. The equation of state of a substance is a relation among the three variables, p, V, and T. If these quantities are laid off on three mutually perpendicular axes, the equation of state defines a *surface* in the p-V-T space. All possible states of the substance are represented by points on this surface, and all processes through which the substance may be carried are represented by lines in the surface. An isothermal process is a line in the surface at all points of which T is constant; in other words, it is the intersection of the surface with a plane perpendicular to the temperature axis. Similarly, processes at constant pressure or volume are intersections of the surface with planes perpendicular to the pressure or volume axes. Such a surface is called a thermodynamic surface, although variables other than p, V, and T are often used.

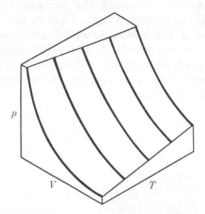

FIG. 19–13.　p-V-T surface of an ideal gas.

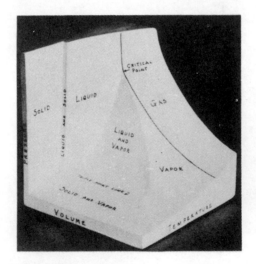

FIG. 19–14.　p-V-T surface of a real substance.　(Not to a uniform scale.)

Figure 19–13 illustrates the simplest of all p-V-T surfaces, that of an ideal gas. A few isotherms are indicated by the heavy lines. When this surface is viewed in a direction perpendicular to the p-V plane, the isotherms appear as in Fig. 19–2.

Figure 19–14 is a photograph of the p-V-T surface of a real substance, not to a uniform scale. When viewed perpendicular to the p-V plane, the isotherms appear as in Fig. 19–7. The triple "point" is actually not a point but a line, since, although the pressure and temperature are fixed at that point, the volume is not. That is, the volume depends on the relative masses of the substance which are in each phase. If, for example, the substance is mostly in the vapor phase, with only small amounts of solid and liquid present, the volume will be large. The surface is not constructed to scale because of the large volume changes involved in changes of phase.

Problems

(Assume all gases to be ideal.)

19–1. A tank contains 1.5 ft³ of nitrogen at an absolute pressure of 20 lb/in² and a temperature of 40°F. What will be the pressure if the volume is increased to 15 ft³ and the temperature raised to 440°F?

19–2. A tank having a capacity of 2 ft³ is filled with oxygen which has a gauge pressure of 60 lb/in² when the temperature is 47°C. At a later time it is found that because of a leak the gauge pressure has dropped to 50 lb/in² and the temperature has decreased to 27°C. Find (a) the mass of the oxygen in the tank under the first set of conditions, (b) the amount of oxygen that has leaked out.

19–3. A flask of volume 2 liters, provided with a stopcock, contains oxygen at 300°K and atmospheric pressure. The system is heated to a temperature of 400°K, with the stopcock open to the atmosphere. The stopcock is then closed and the flask cooled to its original temperature. (a) What is the final pressure of the oxygen in the flask? (b) How many grams of oxygen remain in the flask?

19–4. A barrage balloon whose volume is 20,000 ft³ is to be filled with hydrogen at atmospheric pressure. If the hydrogen is stored in cylinders of volume 2 ft³ at an absolute pressure of 200 lb/in², how many cylinders are required?

19–5. A bubble of air rises from the bottom of a lake, where the pressure is 3.03 atm, to the surface, where the pressure is 1 atm. The temperature at the bottom of the lake is 7°C and the temperature at the surface is 27°C. What is the ratio of the size (i.e., the volume) of the bubble as it reaches the surface to the size of the bubble at the bottom?

19–6. (a) Two gm of nitrogen at 27°C occupy a volume of 2 liters. What is the pressure? (b) If the pressure is doubled and the temperature raised to 127°C, calculate the final volume.

19–7. A liter of helium under a pressure of 2 atm and at a temperature of 27°C is heated until both pressure and volume are doubled. (a) What is the final temperature? (b) How many grams of helium are there?

19–8. A flask contains 1 gm of oxygen at an absolute pressure of 10 atm and at a temperature of 47°C. At a later time it is found that because of a leak the pressure has dropped to $\frac{5}{8}$ of its original value and the temperature has decreased to 27°C. (a) What is the volume of the flask? (b) How many grams of oxygen leaked out between the two observations?

19–9. Give an example of some process in which no heat is added to or removed from a system, but the temperature of the system decreases. If this is not possible, state why.

19–10. Give an example of some process in which heat is added to an object without changing its temperature.

19–11. Ten liters of air at atmospheric pressure are compressed isothermally to a volume of 2 liters. Show the process on a p-V diagram, carefully plotting the points. Approximately how much work is done by the gas during the compression? Find the answer directly from your p-V diagram.

19–12. The submarine Squalus sank at a point where the depth of water was 240 ft. The temperature at the surface is 27°C and at the bottom it is 7°C. The density of sea water may be taken as 2 slugs/ft². (a) If a diving bell in a form of a circular cylinder 8 ft high, open at the bottom and closed at the top, is lowered to this depth, to what height will the water rise within it when it reaches the bottom? (b) At what gauge pressure must compressed air be supplied to the bell while on the bottom to expel all the water from it?

19–13. A bicycle pump is full of air at an absolute pressure of 15 lb/in². The length of stroke of the pump is 18 inches. At what part of the stroke does air begin to enter a tire in which the gauge pressure is 40 lb/in²? Assume the compression to be isothermal.

19–14. A vertical cylindrical tank 1 m high has its top end closed by a tightly fitting frictionless piston of negligible weight. The air inside the cylinder is at an absolute pressure of 1 atm. The piston is depressed by pouring mercury on it slowly. How far will the piston descend before mercury spills over the top of the cylinder? The temperature of the air is maintained constant.

19–15. A barometer is made of a tube 90 cm long and of cross section 1.5 cm². Mercury stands in this tube to a height of 75 cm. The room temperature is 27°C. A small amount of nitrogen is introduced into the evacuated space above the mercury and the column drops to a height of 70 cm. How many grams of nitrogen were introduced?

19–16. A large tank of water has a hose connected to it, as shown in Fig. 19–15. The tank is sealed at the top and has compressed air between the

water surface and the top. When the water height h_2 is 10 ft, the gauge pressure p_1 is 15 lb/in². Assume that the air above the water surface expands isothermally and that water weighs 64 lb/ft³. (a) What is the velocity of flow out of the hose when $h_2 = 10$ ft? (b) What is the velocity of flow of the hose when h_2 has decreased to 8 ft? Neglect friction.

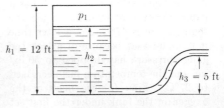

FIGURE 19–15

19–17. The volume of an ideal gas is 4 liters, the pressure 2 atm, and the temperature is 300°K. The gas first expands at constant pressure to twice its original volume, it is then compressed isothermally to its original volume, and finally cooled at constant volume to its original pressure. (a) Show the process in a p-V diagram. (b) Compute the temperature during the isothermal compression. (c) Compute the maximum pressure. (d) Explain how to find the net work done by the gas in the process.

19–18. Ten cubic feet of air initially at 140°F expand at a constant gauge pressure of 20 lb/in² to a volume of 50 ft³, and then expand further adiabatically to a final volume of 80 ft³ and a final gauge pressure of 3 lb/in². Sketch the process in a p-V diagram.

19–19. The cylinder of a pump compressing air from atmospheric pressure into a very large tank at 60 lb/in² gauge pressure is 10 inches long. (a) At what position in the stroke will air begin to enter the tank? Assume the compression to be adiabatic. (b) If the air is taken into the pump at 27°C, what is the temperature of the compressed air?

19–20. At the beginning of the compression stroke, the cylinder of a diesel engine contains 48 in^3 of air at atmospheric pressure and a temperature of 27°C. At the end of the stroke, the air has been compressed to a volume of 3 in^3, and the gauge pressure has increased to 600 lb/in^2. Compute the temperature, (a) in degrees kelvin, (b) degrees celsius, (c) degrees fahrenheit.

19–21. Ten liters of air at atmospheric pressure is compressed isothermally to a volume of 2 liters and is then allowed to expand adiabatically to a volume of 10 liters. Show the process in a p-V diagram.

19–22. An ideal gas is contained in a cylinder closed with a movable piston. The initial pressure is 1 atm and the initial volume is 1 liter. The gas is heated at constant pressure until the volume is doubled, then heated at constant volume until the pressure is doubled, and finally expanded adiabatically until the temperature drops to its initial value. Show the process in a p-V diagram.

19–23. An ideal gas at a pressure of 1 atm is heated at constant pressure until its volume is doubled, then heated at constant volume until its pressure is doubled, and finally allowed to expand isothermally until its pressure drops to 1 atm. Show the process in a p-V diagram.

19–24. Two moles of oxygen are initially at a temperature of 27°C and volume 20 liters. The gas is expanded first at constant pressure until the volume has doubled, and then adiabatically until the temperature returns to the original value. (a) What is the total increase in internal energy? (b) What is the final volume?

19–25. Make two plots for a real gas, one showing pressure as a function of volume, and the other showing pressure as a function of temperature. Show on each graph the region in which the substance exists as (a) a gas or vapor, (b) a liquid, (c) a solid. Show also the triple point and the critical point.

19–26. (a) What is the relative humidity on a day when the temperature is 68°F and the dew point is 41°F? (b) What is the partial pressure of water vapor in the atmosphere? (c) What is the absolute humidity, in gm/m^3?

19–27. The temperature in a room is 40°C. A can is gradually cooled by adding cold water. At 10°C the surface of the can clouds over. What is the relative humidity in the room?

19–28. A pan of water is placed in a sealed room of volume 60 m^3 and at a temperature of 27°C. (a) What is the absolute humidity in gm/m^3 after equilibrium has been reached? (b) If the temperature of the room is then increased 1 C°, how many more grams of water will evaporate?

19–29. (a) What is the dew point temperature on a day when the air temperature is 20°C and the relative humidity is 60%? (b) What is the absolute humidity, in gm/m^3?

19–30. The volume of a closed room, kept at a constant temperature of 20°C, is 60 m^3. The relative humidity in the room is 10%. If a pan of water is brought into the room, how many grams will evaporate?

19–31. An air conditioning system is required to increase the relative humidity of 10 ft^3 of air per second from 30% to 65%. The air temperature is

Molecular Data

N_0 = Avogadro's number = 6.02×10^{23} molecules/mole,

Mass of a hydrogen atom = 1.66×10^{-24} gm,

Mass of a nitrogen molecule = $28 \times 1.66 \times 10^{-24}$ gm,

Mass of an oxygen molecule = $32 \times 1.66 \times 10^{-24}$ gm,

Diameter of a typical molecule = 3×10^{-8} cm.

68°F. How many pounds of water are needed per hour?

19-32. Calculate Boltzmann's constant $k = R/N_0$ in ergs per molecule per degree.

19-33. Consider an ideal gas at 0°C and at 1 atm pressure. Imagine each molecule to be, on the average, at the center of a small cube. (a) What is the length of an edge of this small cube? (b) How does this distance compare with the diameter of a molecule?

19-34. A mole of liquid water occupies a volume of 18 cm³. Imagine each molecule to be, on the average, at the center of a small cube. What is the length of an edge of this small cube? How does this distance compare with the diameter of a molecule?

19-35. The velocity of sound in air at 27°C is about 1100 ft/sec. Compare this with the velocity of a nitrogen molecule at the same temperature.

19-36. (a) Compute the total random translational kinetic energy of the molecules in one mole of oxygen gas at a temperature of 27°C. (b) What is the velocity of a projectile having the same mass as one mole of oxygen if its translational kinetic energy equals the random kinetic energy of the molecule in part (a)?

19-37. At what temperature is the velocity of an oxygen molecule equal to the velocity of a hydrogen molecule at a temperature of 27°C?

CHAPTER 20

THE SECOND LAW OF THERMODYNAMICS

20-1 Introduction to the second law. The dominating feature of an industrial society is its ability to utilize, whether for wise or unwise ends, sources of energy other than the muscles of men or animals. Except for water power, where mechanical energy is directly available, most energy supplies are in the form of fuels such as coal or oil, where the energy is stored as internal energy. The process of combustion releases the internal energy and converts it to heat. In this form the energy may be utilized for heating habitations, for cooking, or for maintaining a furnace at high temperature in order to carry out other chemical or physical processes. But to operate a machine, or to propel a vehicle or a projectile, the heat must be converted to mechanical energy, and one of the problems of the mechanical engineer is to carry out this conversion with the maximum possible efficiency.

There is only one type of process in which internal energy can be converted directly to mechanical energy, and that is when the chemical substances can be combined in an electrolytic cell. All other methods involve the intermediate step of transforming internal energy into heat. The changes may be represented schematically by

$$\text{Internal energy} \rightarrow \text{Heat} \rightarrow \text{Mechanical energy}$$

The process represented by

$$\text{Internal energy} \rightarrow \text{Heat}$$

presents few difficulties. The most common example is, of course, the combustion of coal, oil, or gas. The problem then reduces to

$$\text{Heat} \rightarrow \text{Mechanical energy}$$

It is evident in the first place that this transformation always requires the services of some sort of *engine*, such as a steam engine, gasoline engine, or diesel engine.

At first sight the problem does not seem difficult, since we know that 1 Btu = 778 ft·lb, and it appears that every Btu of thermal energy should provide us with 778 ft·lb of mechanical energy. A pound of coal, for instance, develops about 13,000 Btu when burned, and might be expected to provide $13,000 \times 778$ ft·lb of mechanical work. Actual steam engines, however, furnish only from about 5% to about 30% of this value. What becomes of the remaining 70% to 95%?

Stack and friction losses account for only a small part, by far the largest part appearing as heat rejected in the exhaust. No one has ever constructed a heat engine which does not throw away in its exhaust a relatively large fraction of the heat supplied to it, and it is safe to say that no one ever will. The impossibility of constructing an engine which with no other outstanding changes will convert a given amount of heat *completely* into mechanical work is a fundamental law of Nature, known as *the second law of thermodynamics*. The first law, it will be recalled, is a statement of the principle of conservation of energy, and merely imposes the restriction that one can obtain *no more* than 778 ft·lb of mechanical work from every Btu of heat. It does not in itself restrict the fraction of a given amount of heat which an engine can convert into mechanical energy. The second law goes beyond the first, and states that 100% conversion is not possible by any form of engine. Of course, for that fraction of the heat supplied to it which an engine *does* convert to mechanical form, the equivalence expressed by the first law must hold true.

A young French engineer, Sadi Carnot, was the first to approach the problem of the efficiency of a heat engine from a truly fundamental standpoint. Improvements in steam engines, up to the time of Carnot's work in 1824, had either been along the lines of better mechanical design or, if more basic improvements had been made, they had come about by chance or inspiration and had not been guided by any knowledge of basic principles. Carnot's contribution was a "theoretical" one, but it had more influence on the development of our industrial society in the 19th Century than the work of any of the "practical" men who had preceded him in this field.

Briefly, what Carnot did was to disregard the details of operation of a heat engine and focus attention on its truly significant features. These are, first, the engine is supplied with energy, in the form of heat, at a relatively high temperature. Second, the engine performs mechanical work. Third, the engine rejects heat at a lower temperature. In Carnot's time the caloric theory of heat as an indestructible fluid was still generally accepted. It is difficult to ascertain from Carnot's published articles exactly what his beliefs were as to the nature of work and heat, largely because of his failure to give *precise* definitions of the terms used. But although Carnot himself may have intuitively understood the problem, most scientists of his time pictured the flow of heat through an engine, from a higher to a lower temperature, as analogous to the flow of water through a water wheel or turbine from a higher to a lower elevation. In any time interval, equal amounts of water enter the turbine and are discharged from it, but in the process some mechanical energy is abstracted from the water. Carnot believed that a similar process took place in a heat engine—some mechanical energy was abstracted from the heat but the amount of heat rejected by the engine in any time interval was equal to that delivered to the engine. We know now that this idea is incorrect, and that the heat rejected by the engine is less than the heat supplied to it by the amount that has been converted to mechanical work. In spite of his erroneous concept of the nature of heat, Carnot did in fact obtain the correct expression for the maximum efficiency of any heat engine operating between two given temperatures.

Since it is only heat and work that are of primary concern in a heat engine, we consider for simplicity an engine working in *closed cycles*. That is, the material that expands against a piston is periodically brought back to its initial condition so that in any one cycle the change in internal energy of this material, called the *working substance*, is zero. The condensing type of steam engine actually does operate in this way; the exhaust steam is condensed and forced back into the boiler so that the working substance (in this case, water) is used over and over again. The working substance then merely serves to transfer heat from one body to another and, in virtue of its changes in volume, to convert some of the heat to mechanical work.

The energy transformations in a heat engine are conveniently represented schematically by the *flow diagram* of Fig. 20–1. The engine itself is represented by the circle. The heat Q_2 supplied to the engine is proportional to the cross section of the incoming "pipeline" at the top of the diagram. The cross section of the outgoing pipeline at the bottom is proportional to that portion of the heat, Q_1, which is rejected as heat in the exhaust. The branch line to the right represents that portion of the heat supplied which the engine converts to mechanical work, W. Since the working substance is periodically returned to its initial state and the change in its internal energy in any number of complete cycles is zero, it follows from the first law of thermodynamics that

$$W = Q_2 - Q_1.$$

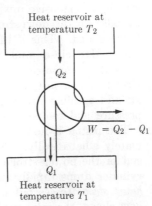

FIG. 20–1. Schematic flow diagram of a heat engine.

That is, the mechanical work done equals the difference between the heat supplied and the heat rejected. (For convenience, W, Q_2, and Q_1 are all considered positive.)

The *thermal efficiency* E of the engine is the ratio of work output to heat input. The output is the mechanical work W. The exhaust heat is not considered a part of the output. The input is the heat Q_2. Hence

$$E = \frac{\text{Work output}}{\text{Heat input}} \rightarrow \frac{W}{Q_2},$$

$$\boxed{E = \frac{Q_2 - Q_1}{Q_2}.} \tag{20-1}$$

In terms of the flow diagram, the most efficient engine is the one for which the branch pipeline representing the work obtained is as large as possible, and the exhaust pipeline representing the heat rejected is as small as possible, for a given incoming pipeline or quantity of heat supplied.

We shall now consider, without going into the mechanical details of their construction, the internal combustion engine, the diesel engine, and the steam engine.

20-2 The internal combustion engine. The common internal combustion engine is of the four-cycle type, so called because four processes take place in each cycle. Starting with the piston at the top of its stroke, an explosive mixture of air and gasoline vapor is drawn into the cylinder on the downstroke, the inlet valve being open and the exhaust valve closed. This is the *intake* stroke. At the end of this stroke the inlet valve closes and the piston rises, performing an approximately adiabatic compression of the air-gasoline mixture. This is the *compression* stroke. At or near the top of this stroke a spark ignites the mixture of air and gasoline vapor, and combustion takes place very rapidly. The pressure and temperature increase at nearly constant volume.

The piston is now forced down, the burned gases expanding approximately adiabatically. This is the *power stroke* or *working stroke*. At the end of the power stroke the exhaust valve opens. The pressure in the cylinder drops rapidly to atmospheric and the rising piston on the *exhaust stroke* forces out most of the remaining gas. The exhaust valve now closes, the inlet valve opens, and the cycle is repeated.

For purposes of computation, the internal combustion cycle is approximated by the *air standard* or *Otto* cycle illustrated in Fig. 20-2.

Starting at point a, air at atmospheric pressure is compressed adiabatically in a cylinder to point b, heated at constant volume to point c, allowed to expand adiabatically to point d, and cooled at constant volume to point a, after which the cycle is repeated. Line ab corresponds to the compression stroke, bc to the explosion, cd to the working stroke, and da to the exhaust of an internal combustion engine. V_1 and V_2, in Fig. 20–2, are respectively the maximum and minimum volumes of the air in the cylinder. The ratio

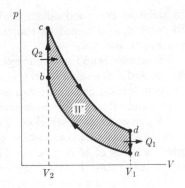

Fig. 20–2. p-V diagram of the Otto cycle.

V_1/V_2 is called the *compression ratio*, and is about 7 for an internal combustion engine.

The work output in Fig. 20–2 is represented by the shaded area enclosed by the figure $abcd$. The heat *input* is the heat supplied at constant volume along the line bc. The exhaust heat is removed along da. No heat is supplied or removed in the adiabatic processes ab and cd.

The heat input and the work output can be computed in terms of the compression ratio, assuming air to behave like an ideal gas. The result is

$$\text{Eff}(\%) = 100 \left(1 - \frac{1}{(V_1/V_2)^{\gamma-1}} \right),$$

where γ is the ratio of the specific heats. For a compression ratio of 7 and a value of $\gamma = 1.4$, the efficiency is about 54%. It will be seen that the higher the compression ratio, the higher the efficiency. Friction effects, turbulence, loss of heat to cylinder walls, etc., have been neglected. All these effects reduce the efficiency of an actual engine below the figure given above.

20–3 The diesel engine. In the diesel cycle, air is drawn into the cylinder on the intake stroke and compressed adiabatically on the compression stroke to a sufficiently high temperature so that fuel oil injected at the end of this stroke burns in the cylinder without requiring ignition by a spark. The combustion is not as rapid as in the gasoline engine, and the first part of the power stroke proceeds at essentially constant pressure. The remainder of the power stroke is an adiabatic expansion. This is followed by an exhaust stroke which completes the cycle.

The idealized air-diesel cycle is shown in Fig. 20–3. Starting at point a, air is compressed adiabatically to point b, heated at constant pressure to point c, expanded adiabatically to point d, and cooled at constant volume to point a.

Since there is no fuel in the cylinder of a diesel engine on the compression stroke, pre-ignition cannot occur and the compression ratio V_1/V_2 may be much higher than that of an internal combustion engine. A value of 15 is typical. The *expansion* ratio V_1/V_3 may be about 5. Using these values, and taking $\gamma = 1.4$, the efficiency of the air-diesel cycle is about 56%. Hence somewhat higher efficiencies are possible than for the Otto cycle. Again, the actual efficiency of a real diesel must be smaller than the value given above.

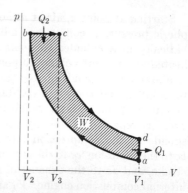

Fig. 20–3. p-V diagram of the diesel cycle.

20–4 The steam engine. The condensing type of steam engine performs the following sequence of operations. Water is converted to steam in the boiler, and the steam thus formed is superheated above the boiler temperature. Superheated steam is admitted to the cylinder, where it expands against a piston; connection is maintained to the boiler for the first part of the working stroke, which thus takes place at constant pressure. The inlet valve is then closed and the steam expands adiabatically for the rest of the working stroke. The adiabatic cooling causes some of the steam to condense. The mixture of water droplets and steam (known as "wet" steam) is forced out of the cylinder on the return stroke and into the condenser, where the remaining steam is condensed into water. This water is forced into the boiler by the feed pump, and the cycle is repeated.

An idealized cycle (called the rankine cycle) which approximates the actual steam cycle is shown in Fig. 20–4. Starting with liquid water at low pressure and temperature (point a), the water is compressed adiabatically to point b at boiler pressure. It is then heated at constant pressure to its boiling point (line bc), converted to steam (line cd), superheated (line de), expanded adiabatically (line ef), and cooled and condensed (along fa) to its initial condition.

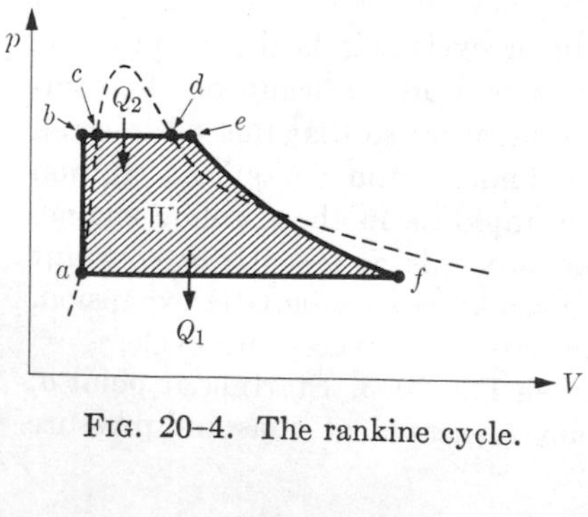

Fig. 20–4. The rankine cycle.

The efficiency of such a cycle may be computed in the same way as was done in the previous examples, by finding the quantities of heat taken in and rejected along the lines *be* and *fa*. Assuming a boiler temperature of 417°F (corresponding to a pressure of 300 lb/in²), a superheat of 63°F above this temperature (480°F), and a condenser temperature of 102°F, the efficiency of a rankine cycle is about 32%. Efficiencies of actual steam engines are, of course, considerably lower.

20–5 The second law of thermodynamics. Our experience with actual engines therefore leads us to the second law of thermodynamics, which may be stated rigorously as follows:

It is impossible to construct an engine that, operating in a cycle, will produce no effect other than the extraction of heat from a source and the conversion of this heat completely into work.

If the second law were not true, it would be possible to drive a steamship across the ocean by extracting heat from the ocean, or to run a power plant by extracting heat from the surrounding air. It should be noted that neither of these "impossibilities" violates the first law of thermodynamics. After all, both the ocean and the surrounding air contain an enormous store of internal energy which, in principle, may be extracted in the form of a flow of heat. There is nothing in the first law to preclude the possibility of converting this heat completely into work. The second law, therefore, is not a deduction from the first but stands by itself as a separate law of nature, referring to an aspect of nature different from that contemplated by the first law. The first law denies the possibility of creating or destroying energy; the second denies the possibility of utilizing energy in a particular way.

The fact that work may be dissipated completely into heat, whereas heat may not be converted entirely into work, expresses an essential one-sidedness of nature. All natural, spontaneous processes may be studied in the light of the second law, and in all such cases, this peculiar one-sidedness is found. Thus, heat always flows spontaneously from a hotter to a colder body; gases always seep through an opening spontaneously from a region of high pressure to a region of low pressure; gases and liquids left by themselves always tend to mix, not to unmix. Salt dissolves in water but a salt solution does not separate by itself into pure salt and pure water. Rocks weather and crumble; iron rusts; people grow old. These are all examples of *irreversible* processes that take place naturally in only one direction and, by their one-sidedness, express the second law of thermodynamics.

Irreversible, natural processes may be regarded from another point of view. A piece of pure salt and a volume of pure water represent an orderly arrangement of molecules. The solution of the salt in the water involves an increase in molecular disorder. If all the molecules of gas in a container were in one corner of the container, that would constitute an orderly arrangement. The uniform distribution throughout the container which actually exists is a much more disorderly arrangement. The sand that results from the weathering of rocks over a long period of time represents a greater disorder than the original well-formed rocks. Thus, the one-sidedness of nature may be redescribed by stating that *there is a tendency in nature to proceed toward a state of greater molecular disorder.*

20–6 The refrigerator. A refrigerator may be considered to be a heat engine operated in reverse. That is, a heat engine takes in heat from a *high* temperature source, converts a part of the heat into mechanical work output, and rejects the difference as heat in the exhaust at a *lower* temperature. A refrigerator takes in heat at a *low* temperature, the compressor supplies mechanical work *input*, and the sum is rejected as heat at a *higher* temperature.

The flow diagram of a refrigerator is given in Fig. 20–5. In terms of the processes in a household mechanical refrigerator, Q_1 represents the heat removed from the refrigerator by the cooling coils within it, W the work done by the motor, and Q_2 the heat delivered to the external cooling coils and removed by circulating air or water. It follows from the first law that

$$Q_2 = Q_1 + W.$$

That is, the circulating air or water must absorb both the heat "pumped" out of the refrigerator and the heat equivalent of the work done by the motor.

From an economic point of view, the best refrigeration cycle is one that removes the greatest amount of heat Q_1 from the refrigerator, for

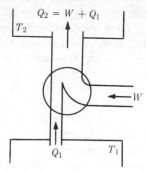

FIG. 20–5. Schematic flow diagram of a refrigerator.

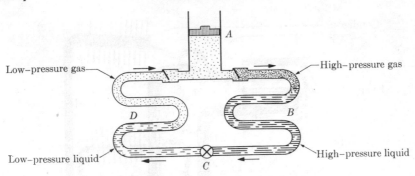

FIG. 20–6. Principle of the mechanical refrigeration cycle.

the least expenditure of mechanical work W. We therefore define the *coefficient of performance* (rather than the efficiency) of a refrigerator as the ratio Q_1/W, and since $W = Q_2 - Q_1$,

$$\text{Coefficient of performance} = \frac{Q_1}{Q_2 - Q_1}. \qquad (20\text{--}2)$$

The principles of the common refrigeration cycle are illustrated schematically in Fig. 20–6. Compressor A delivers gas (CCl_2F_2, NH_3, etc.) at high temperature and pressure to coils B. Heat is removed from the gas in B by water or air cooling, resulting in condensation of the gas to a liquid, still under high pressure. The liquid passes through the throttling valve or expansion valve C, emerging as a mixture of liquid and vapor at a lower temperature. In coils D, heat is supplied that converts the remaining liquid into vapor which enters compressor A to repeat the cycle. In a domestic refrigerator, coils D are placed in the ice compartment, where they cool the refrigerator directly. In a larger refrigerating plant, these coils are usually immersed in a brine tank and cool the brine, which is then pumped to the refrigerating rooms.

A simplified diagram of the so-called *gas refrigerator* is given in Fig. 20–7. In the generator, a solution of ammonia in water is heated by a small gas flame. Ammonia is driven out of solution and ammonia vapor rises in the liquid lift tube, carrying with it some of the water in the same way that water is raised in the central tube of a coffee percolator. This water collects in the separator, from which point it flows back through the absorber, while the ammonia vapor rises to the condenser. Here the ammonia vapor is liquefied, its heat of condensation being removed by air circulating around the cooling vanes. The liquid ammonia then flows into the evaporator, located in the cooling unit of the refrigerator,

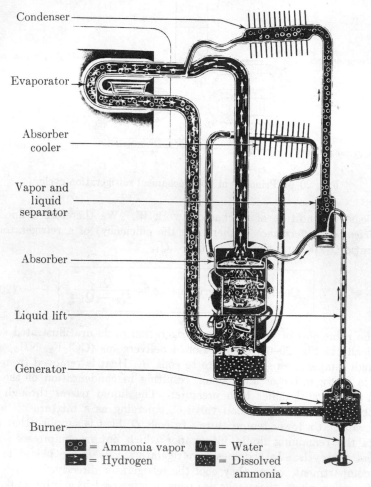

Condenser

Evaporator

Absorber cooler

Vapor and liquid separator

Absorber

Liquid lift

Generator

Burner

○○○ = Ammonia vapor   ○○○ = Water
→ = Hydrogen   ⬚ = Dissolved ammonia

FIG. 20–7. Simplified diagram of the gas refrigerator. (Courtesy of Servel-Electrolux.)

where it evaporates and in so doing absorbs heat from its surroundings. The ammonia vapor continues on to the absorber, where it dissolves in the water returning from the separator. The ammonia-water solution then flows to the generator, completing the cycle.

The absorber and evaporator also contain hydrogen gas which is maintained in circulation by a convection process, brought about by the fact that the mixture of ammonia and hydrogen in the tube at the extreme left is denser than the pure hydrogen in the tube leading from the top of the absorber. This current of hydrogen, entering at the top of the evaporator, sweeps the ammonia vapor out of the evaporator and aids in rapid evaporation. Since ammonia is much more readily soluble in water than is hydrogen, most of the ammonia is dissolved in the water trickling down through the absorber, while the hydrogen passes upward through the absorber.

It is necessary that heat be removed from the absorber as well as from the condenser because heat is liberated when ammonia vapor dissolves in water. This is accomplished by the auxiliary circuit made up of the cooling coils around the absorber, and the absorber cooler.

If no work were needed to operate a refrigerator, the coefficient of performance (heat extracted divided by work done) would be infinite. Coefficients of performance of actual refrigerators vary from about 2 to about 6. Experience shows that work is always needed to transfer heat from a colder to a hotter body. This negative statement leads to another statement of the second law of thermodynamics, namely:

It is impossible to construct a refrigerator that, operating in a cycle, will produce no effect other than the transfer of heat from a cooler to a hotter body.

At first sight, this and the previous statement of the second law appear to be quite unconnected, but it can be shown that they are in all respects equivalent. Any device that would violate one statement would violate the other.

20–7 The Carnot cycle. Although their efficiencies differ from one another, none of the heat engines which have been described has an efficiency of 100%. The question still remains open as to what is the maximum attainable efficiency, given a supply of heat at one temperature and a reservoir at a lower temperature for cooling the exhaust. An idealized engine which can be shown to have the maximum efficiency under these conditions was invented by Carnot and is called a *Carnot engine*. The *Carnot cycle*, shown in Fig. 20–8, differs from the Otto and diesel cycles in that it is bounded by two *isothermals* and two adiabatics. Thus all the heat input is supplied at a *single* high temperature and all the heat output is rejected at a *single* lower temperature. (Compare with Figs. 20–2 and 20–3, in which the temperature is different at all points of the lines *bc* and *da*.)

This, however, is not the only feature of the Carnot cycle. There are no "one-way" processes in the Carnot cycle, such as explosions or throttling processes. The isothermal and adiabatic processes of the Carnot cycle may be imagined to proceed in either direction. In the direction shown

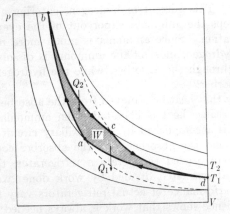

FIG. 20-8. The Carnot cycle.

in Fig. 20-8, heat Q_2 goes in, heat Q_1 goes out, and work W is done by the engine. The arrows in the figure could be reversed, in which case the cycle would be a refrigeration cycle. Then heat Q_2 would go out, heat Q_1 would go in, and work W would have to be done on the refrigerator.

Suppose an engine (not a Carnot engine) were to operate between a source of heat at some temperature and a reservoir of heat at a lower temperature, thereby delivering to the outside an amount of work W. Suppose this work W were used to operate a Carnot refrigerator which extracted heat from the colder reservoir and delivered it to the warmer source. It can be shown that if the first engine were more efficient than the Carnot engine that would result by operating the Carnot refrigerator backward, then the net effect would be a violation of the second law of thermodynamics. Proceeding along these lines, it has been proved that:

No engine operating between two given temperatures can be more efficient than a Carnot engine operating between the same two temperatures,

and also:

All Carnot engines operating between the same two temperatures have the same efficiency, irrespective of the nature of the working substance.

20-8 The kelvin temperature scale. It was shown in the beginning of this chapter that the efficiency of any engine is equal to

$$E = \frac{W}{Q_2} = \frac{Q_2 - Q_1}{Q_2} = 1 - \frac{Q_1}{Q_2}.$$

If, therefore, the efficiencies of all Carnot engines operating between the same two temperatures are the same, irrespective of the working substance, the ratio Q_1/Q_2 must depend only on the two temperatures and on nothing else. Lord Kelvin proposed that this fact be used to define a temperature scale which would be independent of the properties of any particular substance, unlike the gas thermometer scale described in Chapter 15.

The kelvin temperatures of the reservoir and the source between which a Carnot engine operates are defined by the relation

$$\boxed{\frac{Q_1}{Q_2} = \frac{T_1}{T_2},}$$ (20–3)

where Q_1/Q_2 is the ratio of the heats rejected and absorbed, and T_1/T_2 is the ratio of the kelvin temperatures of the reservoir and the source.

At first thought it might seem that the ratio of two kelvin temperatures would be impossible to measure, since a Carnot engine is an ideal engine, quite impossible to construct. The situation, however, is not so bad as it seems. The ratio of two kelvin temperatures is the ratio of two heats that are transferred during two isothermal processes bounded by the same two adiabatics. The two adiabatic boundaries may be located experimentally, and the heats transferred during two isothermal "nearly reversible" processes can be measured with considerable precision. As a matter of fact, this is one of the methods used in measuring temperatures below 1°K.

To complete the definition of the kelvin scale we proceed, as in Chapter 15, to assign the arbitrary value of 273.16°K to the temperature of the triple point of water T_3. For a Carnot engine operating between reservoirs at the temperatures T and T_3, we have

$$\frac{Q}{Q_3} = \frac{T}{T_3}$$

or

$$\boxed{T = 273.16°\text{K} \, \frac{Q}{Q_3} \, .}$$ (20–4)

Comparing this with the corresponding expression for the ideal gas temperature, namely,

$$273.16°\text{K} \lim_{p_3 \to 0} \left(\frac{p}{p_3}\right)_{\text{constant volume}},$$

it is seen that, in the kelvin scale, Q plays the role of a "thermometric property." This does not, however, have the objection attached to a coordinate of an arbitrarily chosen thermometer, inasmuch as the behavior of a Carnot engine is independent of the nature of the working substance.

Suppose we temporarily denote the temperature that is measured with a gas thermometer by the symbol T'. Then, using the ideal gas equation $pV = nRT'$, we may compute the heat rejected, Q_1, and the heat absorbed, Q_2, when an ideal gas undergoes a Carnot cycle. The result of this calculation is that

$$\frac{Q_1}{Q_2} = \frac{T'_1}{T'_2},$$

where T'_1 and T'_2 are the gas temperatures of the reservoir and source respectively. This, however, is exactly the same as the defining equation of the ratio of two kelvin temperatures. Therefore, since the temperature of the triple point of water is the same on both scales, we conclude that the gas temperature and the kelvin temperature are identical.

Now, the efficiency of a Carnot engine rejecting heat Q_1 to a reservoir at kelvin temperature T_1 and absorbing heat Q_2 from a source at kelvin temperature T_2 is, as usual,

$$E = 1 - \frac{Q_1}{Q_2}.$$

But, by definition of the kelvin scale,

$$\frac{Q_1}{Q_2} = \frac{T_1}{T_2}.$$

Therefore, the efficiency of a Carnot engine is

$$\boxed{E(\text{Carnot}) = 1 - \frac{T_1}{T_2}.} \tag{20-5}$$

Equation (20–5) points the way to the conditions which a real engine, such as a steam engine, must fulfill to approach as closely as possible the maximum attainable efficiency. These conditions are that the intake temperature T_2 must be made as high as possible and the exhaust temperature T_1 as low as possible.

The exhaust temperature cannot be lower than the lowest temperature available for cooling the exhaust. This is usually the temperature of the air, or perhaps of river water if this is available at the plant. The only recourse then is to raise the boiler temperature T_2. Since the vapor pressure of all liquids increases rapidly with increasing temperature, a limit is set by the mechanical strength of the boiler. Another possibility is to use, instead of water, some liquid with a lower vapor pressure. Successful experiments in this direction have been made with mercury vapor replacing steam. At a boiler temperature of 200°C, at which the pressure in a steam boiler would be 225 lb/in², the pressure in a mercury boiler is only 0.35 lb/in².

20–9 Absolute zero. It follows from Eq. (20–4) that the heat transferred isothermally between two given adiabatics decreases as the temperature decreases. Conversely, the smaller the value of Q, the lower the corresponding T. The smallest possible value of Q is zero, and the corresponding T is absolute zero. *Thus, if a system undergoes a reversible isothermal process without transfer of heat, the temperature at which this process takes place is called absolute zero.* In other words, at absolute zero, an isotherm and an adiabatic are identical.

It should be noted that the definition of absolute zero holds for all substances and is therefore independent of the peculiar properties of any one arbitrarily chosen substance. Furthermore, the definition is in terms of purely macroscopic concepts. No reference is made to molecules or to molecular energy. Whether absolute zero may be achieved experimentally is a question of some interest and importance. To achieve temperatures below 4.2°K at which ordinary helium (mass number 4) liquefies, it is necessary to lower the vapor pressure by pumping away the vapor as fast as possible. The lowest temperature that has ever been reached in this way is 0.7°K, and this required larger pumps and larger pumping tubes than are usually employed in low-temperature laboratories. With the aid of the light isotope of helium (mass number 3) which liquefies at 3.2°K, vigorous pumping will yield a temperature of about 0.3°K. Still lower temperatures may be achieved magnetically, but it becomes apparent that, the closer one approaches absolute zero, the more difficult it is to go farther. It is generally accepted as a law of Nature that, although absolute zero may be approached as close as we please, it is impossible actually to reach the zero of temperature. This is known as the *"unattainability statement of the third law of thermodynamics."*

PROBLEMS

20-1. The efficiency of an Otto cycle is 50% and $\gamma = 1.50$. What is the compression ratio?

20-2. A Carnot engine whose high-temperature reservoir is at 127°C takes in 100 cal of heat at this temperature in each cycle, and gives up 80 cal to the low temperature reservoir. Find the temperature of the latter reservoir.

20-3. A Carnot engine whose low temperature reservoir is at 7°C has an efficiency of 40%. It is desired to increase the efficiency to 50%. By how many degrees must the temperature of the high-temperature reservoir be increased?

20-4. A Carnot engine is operated between two heat reservoirs at temperatures of 400°K and 300°K. (a) If in each cycle the engine receives 1200 cal of heat from the reservoir at 400°K, how many calories does it reject to the reservoir at 300°K? (b) If the engine is operated in reverse, as a refrigerator, and receives 1200 cal of heat from the reservoir at 300°K, how many calories does it deliver to the reservoir at 400°K? (c) How many calories would be produced if the mechanical work required to operate the refrigerator in part (b) were converted directly to heat?

20-5. What is the efficiency of an engine which operates by taking an ideal monatomic gas through the following cycle? Let $C_v = 3$ cal/mole·C°. (a) Start with n moles at p_0, V_0, T_0. (b) Change to $2p_0$, V_0 at constant volume. (c) Change to $2p_0$, $2V_0$ at constant pressure. (d) Change to p_0, $2V_0$ at constant volume. (e) Change to p_0, V_0 at constant pressure.

20-6. A Carnot refrigerator takes heat from water at 0°C and discards it to the room at a temperature of 27°C. 100 kgm of water at 0°C are to be changed to ice at 0°C. (a) How many calories of heat are discarded to the room? (b) What is the required work in joules?

20-7. A cylinder contains air at a pressure of 2 atm. The volume is 3 liters and the temperature is 300°K. The air is carried through the following processes:

(1) Heated at constant pressure to 500°K.

(2) Cooled at constant volume to 250°K.

(3) Cooled at constant pressure to 150°K.

(4) Heated at constant volume to 300°K.

(a) Show each process on a p-V diagram, giving the numerical values of p and V at the end of each process. (b) Calculate the net work done by the gas.

20-8. For the data in Problem 20-7 find (a) the number of moles of air in the cylinder. (b) For air $C_p = 7$ cal/mole·deg and $C_V = 5$ cal/mole·deg. Find the total heat input to the cylinder in processes (1) and (4). Express the answer in calories. (c) What is the efficiency of this device as a heat engine?

20-9. (a) What is the coefficient of performance of a Carnot refrigerator which removes heat from a reservoir at -10°C and delivers heat to a reservoir at 30°C? (b) How many kwh of energy would have to be supplied to the refrigerator to remove from the low-temperature reservoir an amount of heat equal to that required to melt 100 lb of ice? (c) What would be the cost of this energy, at 5 cents/kwh?

CHAPTER 21

WAVE MOTION

21-1 Propagation of a disturbance in a medium. Imagine a medium consisting of a large number of particles, each connected or coupled to its neighbors by *elastic* material. If one end of the medium is disturbed or displaced in any way, the displacement will not occur immediately at all other parts of the medium. The original displacement will give rise to an elastic force in the material adjacent to it, then the next particle will be displaced, and then the next, and so on. In other words, *the displacement will be propagated along the medium with a definite speed.*

In Fig. 21-1(a) the medium is a spring, or just a wire under tension. If the left end is given a small displacement in a direction perpendicular to the medium, this transverse displacement will occur at successive

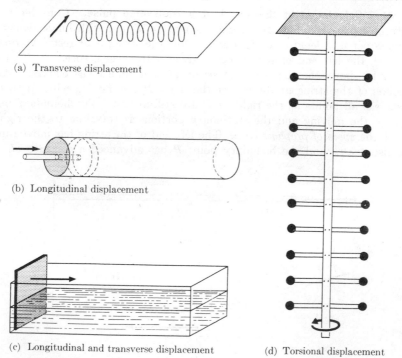

(a) Transverse displacement

(b) Longitudinal displacement

(c) Longitudinal and transverse displacement

(d) Torsional displacement

Fig. 21-1. Propagation of disturbances.

intervals of time at each coil of the spring and there will result the propagation of a *transverse pulse* along the spring.

In Fig. 21–1(b) the medium is to be regarded as either a liquid or a gas contained in a tube closed at the right end with a rigid wall and at the left end with a movable piston. If the piston is moved slightly toward the right, a *longitudinal pulse* will be propagated through the medium in the tube.

In Fig. 21–1(c) the medium is a liquid contained in a trough. The horizontal motion of a flat piece of wood at the left end will provide a displacement of the liquid which is both longitudinal and slightly transverse, and this disturbance will travel along the medium.

In Fig. 21–1(d) the medium is a set of "dumbbells" connected to a steel strip. A slight rotation of the lowest dumbbell constitutes a *torsional displacement* which will be propagated up the medium with a finite speed.

It will be shown in the next section that the speed of a pulse produced by a *small* displacement depends only on certain physical properties *of the medium itself* and not on the rapidity of the original displacement.

21–2 Calculation of the speed of a transverse pulse.
Consider the string depicted in Fig. 21–2, under a tension T and with linear density (mass per unit length) μ. In Fig. 21–2(a) the string is at rest. At time $t = 0$, the left end of the string is given a transverse speed v. Figure 21–2(b) shows the shape of the string after a time t has elapsed. All points of the string at the left of the point P are moving with speed v, whereas all points at the right of P are still at rest. The boundary between the moving and the stationary portions is traveling to the right with the *speed of propagation* u. The left end of the string has moved up a distance vt, and the boundary point P has advanced a distance ut.

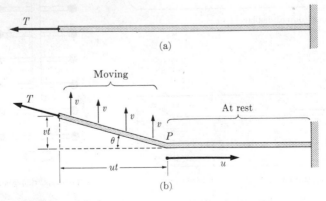

FIG. 21–2. Propagation of a transverse disturbance in a string.

The speed of propagation u can be calculated by setting the transverse impulse (transverse force × time) equal to the change of transverse momentum of the moving portion (mass × transverse velocity). The transverse component of the force T is $T \sin \theta$. If the angle θ is very small, $\sin \theta$ is very nearly equal to $\tan \theta$, and hence

$$\sin \theta = \tan \theta = \frac{vt}{ut} = \frac{v}{u}.$$

Hence

$$\text{Transverse impulse} = (T \sin \theta) \cdot t = T \frac{v}{u} t.$$

The mass of the moving portion is the product of the mass per unit length μ and the length ut. Hence

$$\text{Transverse momentum} = \mu utv.$$

Applying the impulse-momentum theorem, we get

$$T \frac{v}{u} t = \mu utv,$$

and therefore

$$\boxed{u = \sqrt{T/\mu}. \quad \text{(Transverse)}} \qquad (21\text{--}1)$$

Thus it is seen that the velocity of propagation of a transverse pulse in a string depends only on the tension and the mass per unit length.

In numerical applications of Eq. (21–1), attention must be paid to the units employed. With cgs units, T must be expressed in dynes and μ in grams per centimeter. With mks units, T must be in newtons and μ in kilograms per meter. Finally, in engineering units, T must be in pounds and μ in slugs per foot. The corresponding units of velocity will then be, respectively, centimeters per second, meters per second, and feet per second.

EXAMPLE. Calculate the velocity of a transverse pulse in a string under a tension of 20 lb if the string weighs 0.003 lb/ft.

$$T = 20 \text{ lb},$$

$$\mu = \frac{0.003}{32} \frac{\text{lb/ft}}{\text{ft/sec}^2},$$

$$u = \sqrt{\frac{20 \text{ lb} \times 32 \text{ ft/sec}^2}{0.003 \text{ lb/ft}}} = 461 \frac{\text{ft}}{\text{sec}}.$$

21–3 Calculation of the speed of a longitudinal pulse. Figure 21–3 shows a fluid (liquid or gas) of density ρ in a tube of cross-sectional area A and under a pressure p. In Fig. 21–3(a) the fluid is at rest. At time $t = 0$, the piston at the left end of the tube is set in motion toward the right with a speed v. Figure 21–3(b) shows the fluid after a time t has elapsed. All portions of the fluid at the left of point P are moving with speed v, whereas all portions at the right of P are still at rest. The boundary between the moving and the stationary portions travels to the right with the speed of propagation u. The piston has moved a distance vt and the boundary has advanced a distance ut. As for a transverse disturbance in a string, the speed of propagation can be computed from the impulse-momentum theorem.

The quantity of fluid set in motion in time t is that originally occupying a volume of length ut and of cross-sectional area A. The mass of this fluid is therefore ρutA and the longitudinal momentum it has acquired is

$$\text{Longitudinal momentum} = \rho utAv.$$

We next compute the increase of pressure Δp in the moving fluid. The original volume of the moving fluid, Aut, has been decreased by an amount Avt. From the definition of bulk modulus B (see Chapter 10),

$$B = \frac{\text{change in pressure}}{\text{fractional change in volume}} = \frac{\Delta p}{Avt/Aut}.$$

Therefore

$$\Delta p = B\,\frac{v}{u}.$$

The pressure in the moving fluid is therefore $p + \Delta p$, and the force exerted on it by the piston is $(p + \Delta p)A$. The *net* force on the moving

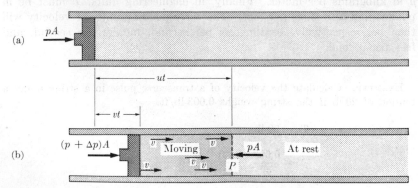

Fig. 21–3. Propagation of a longitudinal disturbance in a fluid confined in a tube.

fluid [see Fig. 21–3(b)] is ΔpA, and the longitudinal impulse is

$$\text{Longitudinal impulse} = \Delta pAt = B\,\frac{v}{u}\,At.$$

Applying the impulse-momentum theorem, we get

$$B\,\frac{v}{u}\,At = \rho utAv,$$

and therefore

$$\boxed{u = \sqrt{B/\rho}. \quad \text{(Longitudinal)}} \tag{21-2}$$

The speed of propagation of a longitudinal pulse in a fluid therefore depends only on the bulk modulus and density of the medium.

When a solid bar is struck a blow at one end, the situation is somewhat different from that of a fluid confined in a tube of constant cross section, since the bar will expand slightly sidewise when it is compressed longitudinally. It can be shown by the same type of reasoning as that just given that the velocity of a longitudinal pulse in the bar is given by

$$\boxed{u = \sqrt{Y/\rho}, \quad \text{(Longitudinal)}} \tag{21-3}$$

where Y is Young's modulus, defined in Chapter 10.

21–4 The motion of a wave. Up to this point we have considered the simplest type of disturbance that could be imparted to a medium, namely, a single transverse or longitudinal displacement. Suppose now that one end of a medium is forced to vibrate periodically, the displacement y (either transverse or longitudinal) varying with the time according to the equation of simple harmonic motion:

$$y = A \cos 2\pi ft.$$

During half a cycle, a displacement in one direction is propagated through the medium, and during the other half, a displacement in the opposite direction is caused to proceed. The resulting continuous train of disturbances traveling with a speed depending on the properties of the medium is called a *wave*.

To fix our ideas, suppose that one end of a stretched string is forced to vibrate periodically in a transverse direction with simple harmonic motion of amplitude A, frequency f, and period $T = 1/f$. For the present we shall assume the string to be long enough so that any effects at the

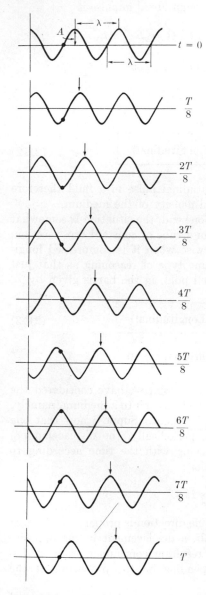

far end need not be considered. A *continuous train* of transverse sinusoidal waves then advances along the string. The shape of a portion of the string near the end, at intervals of $\frac{1}{8}$ of a period, is shown in Fig. 21–4 for a total time of one period. The string is assumed to have been vibrating for a sufficiently long time so that the shape of the string is sinusoidal for an indefinite distance from the driven end. It will be seen from the figure that the wave form advances steadily toward the right, as indicated by the short arrow pointing to one particular wave crest, while any one point on the string (see the black dot) oscillates about its equilibrium position with simple harmonic motion. It is important to distinguish between the motion of the *wave form*, which moves with constant velocity u along the string, and the motion of *a particle of the string*, which is simple harmonic and transverse to the string.

The distance between two successive maxima (or between any two successive points in the same phase) is the *wavelength* of the wave and is denoted by λ. Since the wave form, traveling with constant velocity u, advances a distance of one wavelength in a time interval of one period, it follows that $u = \lambda T$, or

$$u = f\lambda. \qquad (21\text{–}4)$$

That is, *the velocity of propagation equals the product of frequency and wavelength.*

Fig. 21–4. A sinusoidal transverse wave traveling toward the right, shown at intervals of $\frac{1}{8}$ of a period.

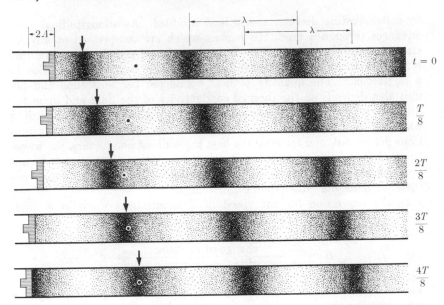

FIG. 21–5. A sinusoidal longitudinal wave traveling toward the right shown at intervals of ⅛ of a period.

To understand the mechanics of a longitudinal wave, consider the long tube filled with a fluid and provided with a plunger at the left end, as shown in Fig. 21–5. The dots represent particles of the fluid. Suppose the plunger is forced to undergo a simple harmonic vibration parallel to the direction of the tube. During a part of each oscillation, a region whose pressure is above the equilibrium pressure is formed. Such a region is called a *condensation* and is represented by closely spaced dots. Following the production of a condensation, a region is formed in which the pressure is lower than the equilibrium value. This is called a *rarefaction* and is represented by widely spaced dots. The condensations and rarefactions move to the right with constant velocity u. The motion of a single particle of the medium, shown by a heavy black dot, is simple harmonic, parallel to the direction of propagation.

The wavelength is the distance between two successive condensations or two successive rarefactions, and the same fundamental equation, $u = f\lambda$, holds in this, as in all types of waves.

21–5 Adiabatic character of a longitudinal wave. It is a familiar fact that compression of a fluid causes a rise in its temperature unless heat is withdrawn in some way. Conversely, an expansion is accompanied by a temperature decrease unless heat is added. As a longitudinal wave advances through a fluid, the regions which are compressed at any instant are slightly warmer than those that are expanded. The condition is present, therefore, for the conduction of heat from a condensation to a rarefaction. The quantity of heat conducted per unit time and per unit area depends on the thermal conductivity of the fluid and upon the distance between a condensation and its adjacent rarefaction (half a wavelength). Now for ordinary frequencies, say from 20 to 20,000 vibrations per second, and for even the best known heat conductors, the wavelength is too large and the thermal conductivity too small for an appreciable amount of heat to flow. The compressions and rarefactions are therefore *adiabatic* rather than isothermal.

In the expression for the speed of a longitudinal wave in a fluid, $u = \sqrt{B/\rho}$, the bulk modulus B is defined by the relation

$$B = \frac{\text{change of pressure}}{\text{change of volume per unit volume}}.$$

The change in volume produced by a given change of pressure depends upon whether the compression (or expansion) is adiabatic or isothermal. There are therefore two bulk moduli, the adiabatic bulk modulus B_{ad} and the isothermal bulk modulus. The rigorous expression for the speed of a longitudinal wave should therefore be written

$$u = \sqrt{B_{ad}/\rho}. \tag{21-5}$$

In the case of an ideal gas, the relation between pressure p and volume V during an adiabatic process is given by Eq. (19–21),

$$pV^\gamma = \text{constant},$$

where γ is the ratio of the heat capacity at constant pressure to the heat capacity at constant volume. It can be shown with the aid of the calculus that

$$B_{ad} = \gamma p. \quad \text{(Ideal gas)} \tag{21-6}$$

Therefore

$$u = \sqrt{\gamma p/\rho}. \quad \text{(Ideal gas)} \tag{21-7}$$

But, for an ideal gas,

$$\frac{p}{\rho} = \frac{RT}{M},$$

where R is the universal gas constant and M the molecular weight. Therefore

$$u = \sqrt{\gamma RT/M}, \quad \text{(Ideal gas)} \quad (21\text{–}8)$$

and since for a given gas, γ, R, and M are constants, we see that the velocity of propagation is proportional to the square root of the absolute temperature.

Let us use Eq. (21–8) to compute the velocity of longitudinal waves in air. The mean molecular weight of air is 28.8, $\gamma = 1.40$, and $R = 8.31 \times 10^7$ ergs/mole·deg. Let $T = 300°$K. Then

$$u = \sqrt{\frac{1.40 \times 8.31 \times 10^7 \text{ dynes·cm/mole·deg} \times 300 \text{ deg}}{28.8 \text{ gm/mole}}}$$

$$= 34{,}800 \frac{\text{cm}}{\text{sec}} = 348 \frac{\text{m}}{\text{sec}} = 1140 \frac{\text{ft}}{\text{sec}}.$$

This is in good agreement with the measured velocity at this temperature.

Longitudinal waves in air give rise to the sensation of sound. The ear is sensitive to a range of sound frequencies from about 20 to about 20,000 cycles/sec. From the relation $u = f\lambda$, the corresponding wavelength range is from about 56 ft, corresponding to a 20-cycle note, to about 0.056 ft or 5/8 inch, corresponding to 20,000 cycles/sec.

21–6 Mathematical representation of a wave. Suppose that a sinusoidal wave (either transverse or longitudinal) is advancing toward the right in a medium which extends indefinitely in the x-direction. At any given time t, the displacement y of a particle depends on its position, or its coordinate x.

For example, in Fig. 21–4, where we have arbitrarily set $t = 0$ at an instant when the shape of the string is a cosine curve, the transverse displacement y at this instant is given by

$$y = A \cos \frac{2\pi}{\lambda} x \quad (t = 0). \quad (21\text{–}9)$$

It can be seen from this equation, and from the top graph of Fig. 21–4, that $y = A$ when $x = 0$, $x = \lambda$, $x = 2\lambda$, etc. When this equation is plotted, it gives rise to a graph of the *wave form*, as shown in Fig. 21–6.

Every particle of the medium, on the other hand, oscillates with simple harmonic motion. For example, the displacement of the particle at the left end of the string in Fig. 21–4 is given by

$$y = A \cos \frac{2\pi}{T} t \quad (x = 0). \quad (21\text{–}10)$$

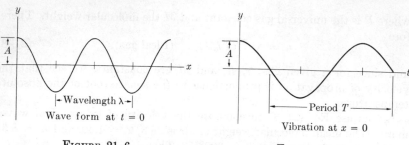

FIGURE 21-6   FIGURE 21-7

When this equation is plotted, we obtain a graph of the *vibration*, shown in Fig. 21–7.

We see, therefore, that the displacement y of a particle depends both on the position of the particle and on the time. In other words, y *is a function of two independent variables*, x and t. This function must have the property that when t is constant y will vary with the cosine of $2\pi x/\lambda$, as in Eq. (21–9), and when x is constant y will vary with the cosine of $2\pi t/T$, as in Eq. (21–10). Such a function is

$$y = A \cos 2\pi \left(\frac{t}{T} - \frac{x}{\lambda}\right). \tag{21-11}$$

This expression represents a sinusoidal wave (transverse or longitudinal) traveling in the *positive* x-direction. For the negative x-direction one merely replaces the minus sign in the parentheses by a plus sign.

A graph of Eq. (21–11) would be a surface for the same reason that a graph of the relation between p, V, and T for water is a thermodynamic surface. It is customary in plotting Eq. (21–11) to make two plane graphs, either

1. (a) the wave form at one moment and (b) the wave form at a known time later, or

2. (a) the wave form at a moment and (b) the vibration at a point.

Problems

21-1. A steel wire 2 m long has a mass of 20 gm and is stretched with a tension of 1000 newtons. What is the velocity of propagation of a transverse wave in the wire?

21-2. One end of a horizontal string is attached to a prong of an electrically driven tuning fork whose frequency of vibration is 240 vib/sec. The other end passes over a pulley and supports a weight of 6 lb. The linear weight density of the string is 0.0133 lb/ft. (a) What is the speed of a transverse wave in the string? (b) What is the wavelength?

21-3. A metal wire has the following properties: coefficient of linear expansion $= 1.5 \times 10^{-5}(C°)^{-1}$, Young's modulus $= 2.0 \times 10^{12}$ dynes/cm^2, density $= 9.0$ gm/cm^3. At each end are rigid supports. If the tension is zero at 20°C, what will be the speed of a transverse wave at 8°C.

21-4. A metal wire of density 20 slugs/ft^3 with a Young's modulus equal to 15×10^6 lb/in^2 is stretched between rigid supports. At one temperature the speed of a transverse wave is found to be 657 ft/sec. When the temperature is raised 100 F°, the speed decreases to 536 ft/sec. What is the coefficient of linear expansion?

21-5. A steel pipe 200 ft long is struck at one end. A person at the other end hears two sounds as a result of two longitudinal waves, one in the pipe and the other in the air. What is the time interval between the two sounds? Take Young's modulus of steel to be 30×10^6 lb/in^2.

21-6. What must be the stress (F/A) in a stretched wire of a material whose Young's modulus is Y in order that the velocity of longitudinal waves shall equal 10 times the velocity of transverse waves?

21-7. The velocity of longitudinal waves in water is approximately 1450 m/sec at 20°C. Compute the adiabatic compressibility $(1/B_{ad})$ of water and compare with the isothermal compressibility listed in Table 10-2.

21-8. Provided the amplitude is sufficiently great, the human ear can respond to longitudinal waves over a range of frequencies from about 20 vib/sec to about 20,000 vib/sec. Compute the wavelengths corresponding to these frequencies (a) for waves in air, (b) for waves in water. (See Problem 21-7.)

21-9. At a temperature of 27°C, what is the velocity of longitudinal waves in (a) argon, (b) hydrogen? Compare with the velocity in air at the same temperature.

21-10. What is the difference between the velocities of longitudinal waves in air at −3°C and at 57°C?

21-11. The sound waves from a loudspeaker spread out nearly uniformly in all directions when their wavelength is large compared with the diameter of the speaker. When the wavelength is small compared with the diameter of the speaker, much of the sound energy is concentrated in the forward direction. For a speaker of diameter 10 inches, compute the frequency for which the wavelength of the sound waves, in air, is (a) 10 times the diameter of the speaker, (b) equal to the diameter of the speaker, (c) 1/10 the diameter of the speaker.

21-12. Show that Eq. (21-11) may be written

$$y = A \cos \frac{2\pi}{\lambda} (x - ut).$$

21-13. A traveling transverse wave on a string is represented by the equation in Problem 21-12. Let $A = 1$ in., $\lambda = 2$ in., and $u = \frac{1}{4}$ in./sec. (a) At time $t = 0$, compute the transverse displacement y at $\frac{1}{4}$-inch intervals of x(i.e., at $x = 0$, $x = \frac{1}{4}$ in., $x = \frac{1}{2}$ in., etc.) from $x = 0$ to $x = 4$ inches. Show the results in a graph. This is the shape of the string at time $t = 0$. (b) Repeat the calculations, for the same values of x, at times $t = 1$ sec, $t = 2$ sec, $t = 3$ sec, and $t = 4$ sec. Show on the same graph the shape of the string at these instants. In what direction is the wave traveling?

21-14. The equation of a transverse traveling wave on a string is

$$y = 2 \cos [\pi(0.5x - 200t)],$$

where x and y are in cm and t is in sec. (a) Find the amplitude, wavelength, frequency, period, and velocity of propagation. (b) Sketch the shape of the string at the following values of t: 0, 0.0025, and 0.005 sec. (c) If the mass per unit length of the string is 5 gm/cm, find the tension.

FIGURES 21–8 and 21–9

To use these diagrams, cut a slit about $4\frac{1}{4}''$ long and about $\frac{1}{16}''$ wide in a card. Place the card over the diagram and move it vertically with constant velocity. The portions of the curves that appear in the slit will correspond to the oscillations of the particles in a longitudinal traveling wave in Fig. 21–8, and to a longitudinal stationary wave in Fig. 21–9.

FIGURE 21–8

FIGURE 21–9

CHAPTER 22

VIBRATING BODIES

22-1 Boundary conditions for a string. Let us now consider what will happen when a wave pulse or wave train, advancing along a stretched string, arrives at the end of the string. If fastened to a rigid support, the end must evidently remain at rest. The arriving pulse exerts a force on the support, and the reaction to this force "kicks back" on the string and sets up a *reflected* pulse traveling in the reverse direction. At the opposite extreme from a rigidly fixed end would be one which was perfectly free—a case of no great importance here (it may be realized by a string hanging vertically) but which is of interest since its analogue does occur in other types of waves. At a free end the arriving pulse causes the string to "overshoot" and a reflected wave is also set up. The conditions which must be satisfied at the ends of the string are called *boundary conditions*.

The multiflash photograph of Fig. 22-1 shows the reflection of a pulse at a fixed end of a string. (The camera was tipped vertically while the photographs were taken so that successive images lie one under the other. The "string" is a rubber tube and it sags somewhat.) It will be seen that the pulse is reflected with its displacement and its velocity both reversed.

FIG. 22-1. A pulse starts in the upper left corner and is reflected from the fixed end of the string at the right.

414

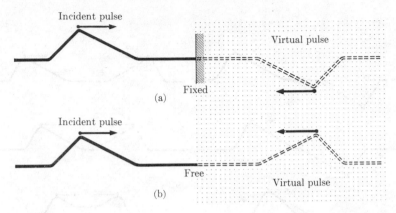

Fig. 22–2. Description of reflection of a pulse (a) at a fixed end of a string, and (b) at a free end, in terms of an imaginary "virtual" pulse.

When reflection takes place at a free end, the direction of the velocity is reversed but the direction of the displacement is unchanged.

It is helpful to think of the process of reflection in the following way. Imagine the string to be extended indefinitely beyond its actual terminus. The actual pulse can be considered to continue on into the imaginary portion as though the support were not there, while at the same time a "virtual" pulse, which has been traveling in the imaginary portion, moves out into the real string and forms the reflected pulse. The nature of the reflected pulse depends on whether the end is fixed or free. The two cases are shown in Fig. 22–2.

The displacement at a point where the actual and virtual pulses cross each other is the algebraic sum of the displacements in the individual pulses. Figures 22–3 and 22–4 show the shape of the end of the string for both types of reflected pulses. It will be seen that Fig. 22–3 corresponds to a free end and Fig. 22–4 to a fixed end. In the latter case, the incident and reflected pulses combine in such a way that the displacement of the end of the string is always zero.

22–2 Stationary waves in a string. When a continuous train of waves arrives at a fixed end of a string, a continuous train of reflected waves appears to originate at the end and travel in the opposite direction. Provided the elastic limit of the string is not exceeded and the displacements are sufficiently small, the actual displacement of any point of the string is the algebraic sum of the displacements of the individual waves, a fact which is called the *principle of superposition*. This principle is extremely important in all types of wave motion and applies not only to

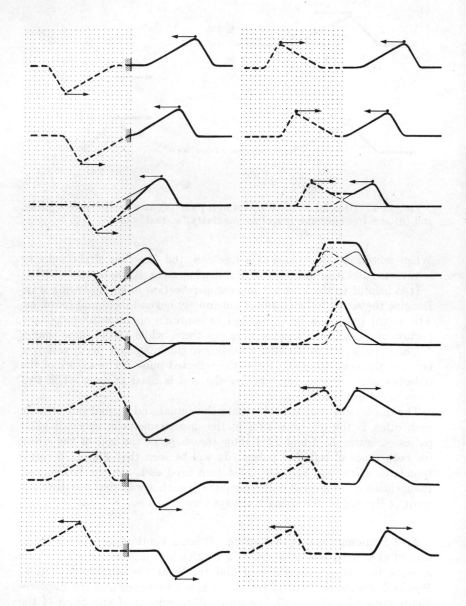

FIG. 22–3. Reflection at a free end.   FIG. 22–4. Reflection at a fixed end.

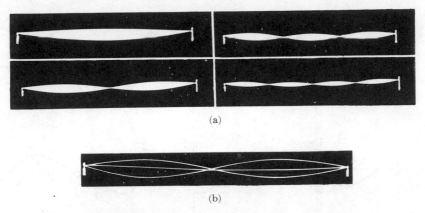

FIG. 22–5. (a) Standing waves in a stretched string (time exposure). (b) Multiflash photograph of a standing wave, with nodes at the center and at the ends.

waves in a string but to sound waves in air, to light waves, and, in fact, to wave motion of any sort. The general term *interference* is applied to the effect produced by two (or more) sets of wave trains which are simultaneously passing through a given region.

The appearance of the string in these circumstances gives no evidence that two waves are traversing it in opposite directions. If the frequency is sufficiently great so that the eye cannot follow the motion, the string appears subdivided into a number of segments as in the time exposure photograph of Fig. 22–5(a). A multiflash photograph of the same string, in Fig. 22–5(b), indicates a few of the instantaneous shapes of the string. At any instant (except those when the string is straight) its shape is a sine curve, but whereas in a traveling wave the amplitude remains constant while the wave progresses, here the wave form remains fixed in position (longitudinally) while the amplitude fluctuates. Certain points known as the *nodes* remain always at rest. Midway between these points, at the *loops* or *antinodes*, the fluctuations are a maximum. The vibration as a whole is called a *stationary* wave.

To understand the formation of a stationary wave, consider the four separate graphs of wave form at four instants $\frac{1}{8}$ of a period apart, shown in Fig. 22–6. The system of short dashed curves represents a wave traveling to the right. The system of long dashed curves represents a wave of the same velocity, same wavelength, and same amplitude traveling to the left. The heavy curves represent the resultant wave form, obtained by applying the principle of superposition, that is, by adding displacements. At those places on the string marked N, the resultant

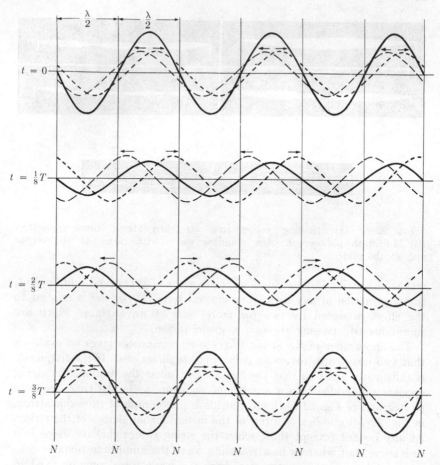

Fig. 22–6. The formation of a stationary wave.

displacements are always zero. These are the nodes. Midway between the nodes, the vibrations have the largest amplitude. These are the anti-nodes. It is evident from the figure that

$$\left\{\begin{array}{c} \text{Distance between adjacent nodes} \\ \text{or} \\ \text{Distance between adjacent antinodes} \end{array}\right\} = \frac{\lambda}{2}.$$

The equation of a standing wave may be obtained by adding the displacements of two waves of equal amplitude, period, and wavelength, but traveling in opposite directions. Thus if

$$y_1 = A \cos 2\pi \left(\frac{t}{T} - \frac{x}{\lambda} \right) \qquad \text{(positive x-direction)},$$

$$y_2 = A \cos 2\pi \left(\frac{t}{T} + \frac{x}{\lambda} \right) \qquad \text{(negative x-direction)},$$

then

$$y_1 + y_2 = A \left[\cos 2\pi \left(\frac{t}{T} - \frac{x}{\lambda} \right) + \cos 2\pi \left(\frac{t}{T} + \frac{x}{\lambda} \right) \right].$$

Introducing the expressions for the cosine of the sum and difference of two angles and combining terms, we obtain

$$y_1 + y_2 = [2A \cos 2\pi f t] \cos \frac{2\pi x}{\lambda}. \qquad (22\text{–}1)$$

The shape of the string at each instant is, therefore, a cosine curve whose amplitude (the expression in brackets) varies with time.

22–3 Vibration of a string fixed at both ends. Thus far we have been discussing a long string fixed at one end and have considered the stationary waves set up near that end by interference between the incident and reflected waves. Let us next consider the more usual case, that of a string fixed at both ends. A continuous train of sine or cosine waves is reflected and re-reflected, and since the string is fixed at both ends, both ends must be nodes. Since the nodes are one-half a wavelength apart, the length of the string may be $\lambda/2$, $2(\lambda/2)$, $3(\lambda/2)$, or, in general, any integral number of half-wavelengths. Or, to put it differently, if one considers a particular string of length L, stationary waves may be set up in the string by vibrations of a number of different frequencies, namely, those which give rise to waves of wavelengths $2L/1$, $2L/2$, $2L/3$, etc.

From the relation $f = u/\lambda$, and since u is the same for all frequencies, the possible frequencies are

$$\frac{u}{2L}, \qquad 2\,\frac{u}{2L}, \qquad 3\,\frac{u}{2L}, \cdots$$

The lowest frequency, $u/2L$, is called the *fundamental* frequency f_1 and the others are the *overtones*. The frequencies of the latter are, therefore, $2f_1$, $3f_1$, $4f_1$, and so on. Overtones whose frequencies are integral multiples of the fundamental are said to form a *harmonic series*. The fundamental is the *first harmonic*. The frequency $2f_1$ is the *first overtone* or the *second harmonic*, the frequency $3f_1$ is the *second overtone* or the *third harmonic*, and so on.

We can now see an important difference between a spring-mass system and a vibrating string. The former has but one natural frequency, while the vibrating string has an infinite number of natural frequencies, the fundamental and all the overtones. If a body suspended from a spring is pulled down and released, only one frequency of vibration will ensue. If a string is initially distorted so that its shape is the same as *any one* of the possible harmonics, it will vibrate, when released, at the frequency of that particular harmonic. But when a piano string is struck, not only the fundamental, but many of the overtones are present in the resulting vibration. The fundamental frequency of the vibrating string is $f_1 = u/2L$, where $u = \sqrt{T/\mu}$. It follows that

$$f_1 = \frac{1}{2L}\sqrt{T/\mu}. \tag{22-2}$$

Stringed instruments afford many examples of the implications of this equation. For example, all such instruments are "tuned" by varying the tension T, an increase of tension increasing the frequency or pitch, and vice versa. The inverse dependence of frequency on length L is illustrated by the long strings of the bass section of the piano or the bass viol compared with the shorter strings of the piano treble or the violin. One reason for winding the bass strings of a piano with wire is to increase the mass per unit length μ, so as to obtain the desired low frequency without resorting to a string which is inconveniently long.

22–4 Demonstration of the harmonic series in a vibrating string. We have seen that a string is capable of vibrating at a number of different frequencies. That it may vibrate with many different frequencies *at the same time* may be demonstrated very graphically with the aid of the apparatus depicted in Fig. 22–7. A metal string is stretched between two metal posts which are in turn connected to a "step-up" transformer. The secondary of the transformer is then connected to those plates of a cathode-ray oscilloscope which impart vertical motion to the electron beam. If the string is made to oscillate in a magnetic field, an alternating current will be set up whose frequency is exactly the same as that of the string. With proper adjustment of the oscilloscope, this alternating current may be caused to give rise to figures on the screen such as those shown.

Suppose that one small magnet is placed over the center of the string [Fig. 22–7(a)] and the string is plucked near the center so that this part of the string vibrates perpendicular to the magnetic lines of force. The figure on the oscilloscope shows the fundamental frequency.

Placing one magnet $\frac{1}{4}$ of the way along the string and another magnet *with its polarity reversed* at the $\frac{3}{4}$ mark [Fig. 22–7(b)], and plucking the

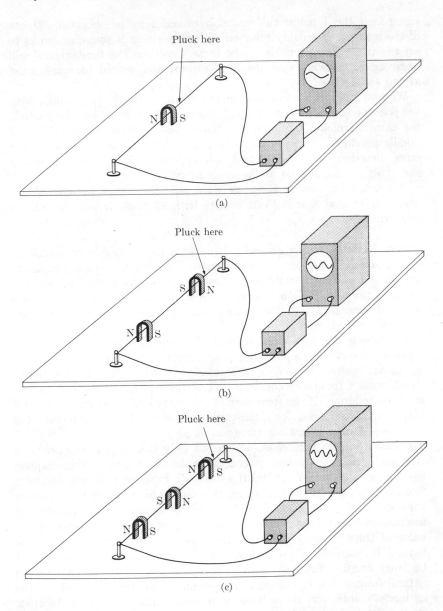

Fig. 22–7. Demonstration of the harmonics present in the vibration of a plucked string.

string near the $\frac{1}{4}$ point, the second harmonic may be obtained. If one of the magnets is quickly reversed while the string is sounding, so as to set the two magnetic fields in the same direction, the fundamental will occur again, showing that the fundamental and second harmonic exist at the same time.

We now place three magnets on the string at the $\frac{1}{6}$, $\frac{1}{2}$, $\frac{5}{6}$ points, with the polarity shown in Fig. 22–7(c). Plucking the string near the $\frac{1}{6}$ point, the third harmonic is obtained. While the string is vibrating, if the middle magnet is reversed so as to make all the magnets point in the same direction, the fundamental will appear. Thus the fundamental and third harmonic exist at the same time.

Proceeding in this manner, we may pick up higher harmonics and demonstrate that a string can vibrate with all these frequencies at the same time.

22–5 Resonance. In general, whenever a body capable of oscillating is acted on by a periodic series of impulses having a frequency equal to one of the natural frequencies of oscillation of the body, the body is set into vibration with a relatively large amplitude. This phenomenon is called *resonance*, and the body is said to *resonate* with the applied impulses.

A common example of mechanical resonance is provided by pushing a swing. The swing is a pendulum with a single natural frequency depending on its length. If a series of regularly spaced pushes is given to the swing, with a frequency equal to that of the swing, the motion may be made quite large. If the frequency of the pushes differs from the natural frequency of the swing, or if the pushes occur at irregular intervals, the swing will hardly execute a vibration at all.

Unlike a simple pendulum, which has only one natural frequency, a stretched string (and other systems to be discussed later in this chapter) has a large number of natural frequencies. Suppose that one end of a stretched string is fixed while the other is moved back and forth in a transverse direction. The amplitude at the driven end is fixed by the driving mechanism. Stationary waves will be set up in the string, whatever the value of the frequency f. If the frequency is not equal to one of the natural frequencies of the string, the amplitude at the antinodes will be fairly small. However, if the frequency is equal to *any one* of the natural frequencies, the string is in resonance and the amplitude at the antinodes will be very much larger than that at the driven end. In other words, although the driven end is not a node, it lies much closer to a node than to an antinode when the string is in resonance. In Fig. 22–5(a), the right end of the string was fixed and the left end was forced to oscillate vertically with small amplitude. Stationary waves of relatively large amplitude resulted when the frequency of oscillation of the left end was equal to the fundamental frequency or to any of the first three overtones.

A bridge or, for that matter, any structure, is capable of vibrating with certain natural frequencies. If the regular footsteps of a column of soldiers were to have a frequency equal to one of the natural frequencies of a bridge which the soldiers are crossing, a vibration of dangerously large amplitude might result. Therefore, in crossing a bridge, a column of soldiers is ordered to break step.

Tuning a radio is an example of electrical resonance. By turning a dial, the natural frequency of an alternating current in the receiving circuit is made equal to the frequency of the waves broadcast by the desired station. Optical resonance may also take place between atoms in a gas at low pressure and light waves from a lamp containing the same atoms. Thus light from a sodium lamp may cause the sodium atoms in a glass bulb to glow with characteristic yellow sodium light.

The phenomenon of resonance may be demonstrated with the aid of the longitudinal waves set up in air by a vibrating plate or tuning fork. If two identical tuning forks are placed some distance apart and one is struck, the other will be heard when the first is suddenly damped. Should a small piece of wax or modeling clay be put on one of the forks, the frequency of that fork will be altered enough to destroy the resonance.

22–6 Interference of longitudinal waves. The phenomenon of interference between two longitudinal waves in air may be demonstrated with the aid of the apparatus depicted in Fig. 22–8. A wave emitted by an electrically driven diaphragm S is sent into a metal tube, where it divides into two waves, one following the constant path SAR, the other the path SBR, which may be varied by sliding the tube B to the right. Suppose the frequency of the source is 1100 vibrations per second. Then

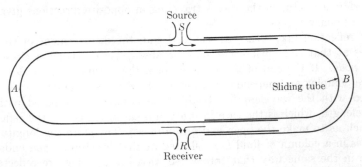

FIG. 22–8. Apparatus for demonstrating interference of longitudinal waves.

the wavelength $\lambda = u/f = 1$ ft. If both paths are of equal length, the two waves will arrive at R at the same time and the vibrations set up by both waves will be in phase. The resulting vibration will have an amplitude equal to the sum of the two individual amplitudes and the phenomenon of *reinforcement* may be detected either with the ear at R or with the aid of a microphone, amplifier, and loudspeaker.

Now suppose the tube B is moved out a distance of three inches, thereby making the path SBR 6 inches longer than the path SAR. The right-hand wave will have traveled a distance $\lambda/2$ greater than the left-hand wave, and the vibration set up at R by the right-hand wave will therefore be in opposite phase to that set up by the left-hand wave. The consequent interference is shown by the marked reduction in sound at R.

If the tube B is now pulled out another 3 inches, so that the *path difference*, SBR minus SAR, is one foot (one wavelength), the two vibrations at R will again reinforce each other. Thus

$$\left.\begin{matrix}\text{Reinforcement takes place} \\ \text{when the path difference}\end{matrix}\right\} = 0,\ \lambda,\ 2\lambda,\ \text{etc.}$$

$$\left.\begin{matrix}\text{Interference takes place} \\ \text{when the path difference}\end{matrix}\right\} = \frac{\lambda}{2},\ \frac{3\lambda}{2},\ \frac{5\lambda}{2},\ \text{etc.}$$

An acoustical interferometer of this sort is of value only in demonstrating the phenomenon of interference. Optical interferometers, however, whose principles of operation are the same, have many practical uses in physical optics.

22–7 Stationary longitudinal waves.

Longitudinal waves traveling along a tube of finite length are reflected at the ends of the tube in much the same way that transverse waves in a string are reflected at its ends. Interference between the waves traveling in opposite directions gives rise to stationary waves.

If reflection takes place at a closed end, the displacement of the particles at that end must necessarily be always zero. Hence a closed end is a *node*. If the end of the tube is open, the nature of the reflection is more complex and depends on whether the tube is wide or narrow compared with the wavelength. If the tube is narrow compared with the wavelength, which is the case in most musical instruments, the reflection is such as to make the open end an *antinode*. Therefore the longitudinal waves in a column of fluid are reflected at the closed and open ends of a tube in the same way that transverse waves in a string are reflected at fixed and free ends respectively.

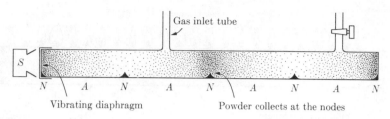

Gas inlet tube

S

N \ A N A N \ A N A N

Vibrating diaphragm   Powder collects at the nodes

FIG. 22–9. Kundt's tube for determining the velocity of sound in a gas. The dots represent the density of the gas molecules at an instant when the pressure at the displacement nodes is a maximum or a minimum.

The reflections at the openings where the instrument is blown are found to be such that an antinode is located at or near the opening. The effective length of the air column of a wind instrument is thus less definite than the length of a string fixed at its ends.

Stationary longitudinal waves in a column of gas may be demonstrated conveniently with the aid of the apparatus shown in Fig. 22–9, known as Kundt's tube. A glass tube a few feet long is closed at one end with glass and at the other with a flexible diaphragm. The gas to be studied is admitted to the tube at a known temperature and at atmospheric pressure. A powerful source of longitudinal waves S, whose frequency may be varied, causes vibration of the flexible diaphragm. A small amount of light powder or cork dust is sprinkled uniformly along the tube.

When a frequency is found at which the air column is in resonance, the amplitude of the stationary waves becomes large enough for the gas particles to sweep the cork dust along the tube, at all points where the gas is in motion. The powder therefore collects at the displacement nodes, where the gas remains at rest. Sometimes a wire running along the axis of the tube is maintained at a dull red heat by an electric current, and the nodes show themselves as hot points compared with the antinodes.

With careful manipulation and with a good variable frequency source, a fair determination of the velocity of the wave may be obtained with Kundt's tube. Since, in a stationary wave, the distance between two adjacent nodes is one-half a wavelength, the wavelength λ is obtained by measuring the distance between alternate clumps of powder. Knowing the frequency f, the velocity u is then

$$u = f\lambda.$$

A constant frequency source may be used if the vibrating element is a piston which may be moved along the tube until resonance is obtained.

At a displacement node, the pressure variations above and below the average are a maximum, whereas at an antinode, there are no pressure

Gas flames

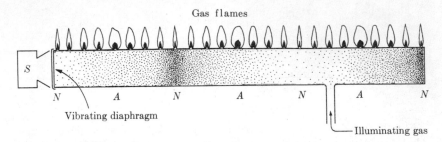

Vibrating diaphragm

Illuminating gas

FIG. 22–10. The variations in gas pressure are greatest at the displacement nodes. The dots represent the density of the gas molecules at an instant when the pressure at the displacement nodes is a maximum or a minimum.

variations. This may be understood easily when it is realized that two small masses of gas on opposite sides of a node are vibrating in *opposite phase*. Thus, when they approach each other, the pressure at the node is a maximum, and when they recede from each other, the pressure at the node is a minimum. Two small masses of gas, however, on opposite sides of an antinode vibrate *in phase*, and hence give rise to no pressure variations at the antinode. This may be demonstrated in the case of illuminating gas with the aid of the apparatus shown in Fig. 22–10. At the nodes, where the harmonic variations of gas pressure are greatest, the flames are blue and stiff. At the antinodes, where the variations of gas pressure are small, the flames are yellow and yielding.

22–8 Vibrations of organ pipes. If one end of a pipe is open and a stream of air is directed against an edge, vibrations are set up and the tube resonates at its natural frequencies. As in the case of a plucked string, the fundamental and overtones exist at the same time. In the

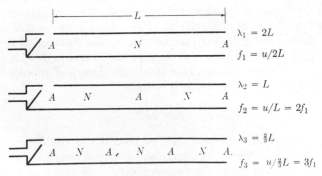

FIG. 22–11. Modes of vibration of an open organ pipe.

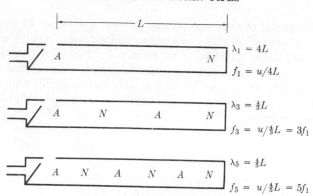

FIG. 22–12. Modes of vibration of a closed organ pipe.

case of an open pipe, the fundamental frequency f_1 corresponds to an antinode at each end and a node in the middle, as shown at the top of Fig. 22–11. Succeeding diagrams of Fig. 22–11 show two of the overtones, which are seen to be the second and third harmonics. *In an open pipe the fundamental frequency is $u/2L$ and all harmonics are present.*

The properties of a closed pipe are shown in the diagrams of Fig. 22–12. The fundamental frequency is seen to be $u/4L$, which is one-half that of an open pipe of the same length. In the language of music, the pitch of a closed pipe is one octave lower than that of an open pipe of equal length. From the remaining diagrams of Fig. 22–12, it may be seen that the second, fourth, etc., harmonics are missing. Hence, *in a closed pipe, the fundamental frequency is $u/4L$ and only the odd harmonics are present.*

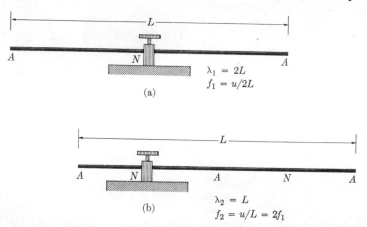

FIG. 22–13. Modes of vibration of a rod.

22–9 Vibrations of rods and plates. A rod may be set in longitudinal vibration by clamping it at some point and stroking it with a chamois skin that has been sprinkled with rosin. In Fig. 22–13(a) the rod is clamped in the middle, and consequently when it is stroked near the end, a stationary wave is set up with a node in the middle and antinodes at each end, exactly the same as the fundamental mode of an open organ pipe. The fundamental frequency of the rod is then $u/2L$, where u is the velocity of a longitudinal wave in the rod. Since the velocity of a longitudinal wave in a solid is much greater than that in air, a rod has a higher fundamental frequency than an open organ pipe of the same length.

By clamping the rod at a point $\frac{1}{4}$ of its length from one end, as shown in Fig. 22–13(b), the second harmonic may be produced.

If a stretched flexible membrane, such as a drumhead, is struck a blow, a two-dimensional pulse travels outward from the struck point and is reflected and re-reflected at the boundary of the membrane. If some point of the membrane is forced to vibrate periodically, continuous trains of waves travel along the membrane. Just as with the stretched string, stationary waves can be set up in the membrane and each of these waves has a certain natural frequency. The lowest frequency is the fundamental and the others are overtones. In general, when the membrane is vibrating, a number of overtones are present.

The nodes of a vibrating membrane are lines (nodal lines) rather than points. The boundary of the membrane is evidently one such line. Some of the other possible nodal lines of a circular membrane are shown in Fig. 22–14, with the modes of vibration arranged in order of increasing frequency. The natural frequency of each mode is given in terms of the

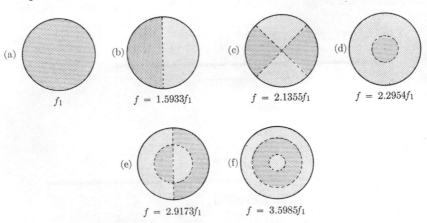

FIG. 22–14. Possible modes of vibration of a membrane, showing nodal lines. The frequency of each is given in terms of the fundamental frequency, f_1.

fundamental f_1. It will be noted that the frequencies of the overtones are *not* integral multiples of f_1. That is, they are not harmonics.

The restoring force in a vibrating flexible membrane arises from the tension with which it is stretched. A metal plate, if sufficiently thick, will vibrate in a similar way, the restoring force being produced by bending stresses in the plate. The study of vibrations of membranes and plates is of importance in connection with the design of loud-speaker diaphragms and the diaphragms of telephone receivers and microphones.

PROBLEMS

22-1. Two transverse cosine waves, each of amplitude 1 inch and wavelength 2 inches, travel in opposite directions in a string with a speed of $\frac{1}{4}$ inch/sec. Construct graphs of the shape of the string at the following times: $t = 0$, $t = 2$ sec, $t = 4$ sec.

22-2. The equation of a transverse wave in a stretched string is

$$y = 4 \cos 2\pi \left(\frac{t}{0.02} - \frac{x}{400} \right),$$

where y and x are in centimeters and t is in seconds. (a) Is the wave a traveling wave or a standing wave? (b) What is the amplitude of the wave? (c) What is its wavelength? (d) What is its velocity of propagation? (e) What is its frequency?

22-3. A steel piano wire 50 cm long, of mass 5 gm, is stretched with a tension of 400 newtons. (a) What is the frequency of its fundamental mode of vibration? (b) What is the number of the highest overtone that could be heard by a person who can hear frequencies up to 10,000 cycles/sec?

22-4. A steel wire of length $L = 100$ cm and density $\rho = 8$ gm/cm^3 is stretched tightly between two rigid supports. Vibrating in its fundamental mode, the frequency is $f = 200$ cycles per sec. (a) What is the velocity of transverse waves on this wire? (b) What is the longitudinal stress in the wire (in dynes/cm^2)? (c) If the maximum acceleration at the mid-point of the wire is 80,000 cm/sec^2, what is the amplitude of vibration at the mid-point?

22-5. A stretched string is observed to vibrate with a frequency of 30 cycles per second in its fundamental mode when the supports are 60 cm apart. The amplitude at the antinode is 3 cm. The string has a mass of 30 gm. (a) What is the velocity of propagation of a transverse wave in the string? (b) Compute the tension in the string.

22-6. Suppose the piano wire in Problem 22-3 is set vibrating at twice its fundamental frequency. (a) What is the wavelength of transverse waves in the wire? (b) What is the wavelength, in air, of the sound waves emitted by the wire?

22-7. A standing wave of frequency 1100 vibrations per second in a column of methane at 20°C produces nodes that are 20 cm apart. What is the ratio of the heat capacity at constant pressure to that at constant volume?

22-8. An aluminum weight is hung from a steel wire. The fundamental frequency for transverse stationary waves on the wire is 300 cycles/sec. The weight is then immersed in water so that one-half of its volume is submerged. What is the new fundamental frequency?

22–9. Stationary waves are set up in a Kundt's tube by the longitudinal vibration of an iron rod one meter long, clamped at the center. If the frequency of the iron rod is 2480 vibrations per second and the powder heaps within the tube are 6.9 cm apart, (a) what is the velocity of the waves in the iron rod, and (b) in the gas?

22–10. The speed of a longitudinal wave in a mixture of helium and neon at 300°K was found to be 758 m/sec. What is the composition of the mixture?

22–11. The atomic weight of iodine is 127. A stationary wave in iodine vapor at 400°K produces nodes that are 6.77 cm apart when the frequency is 1000 vib/sec. Is iodine vapor monatomic or diatomic?

22–12. A copper rod 1 m long, clamped at the $\frac{1}{4}$ point, is set in longitudinal vibration and is used to produce stationary waves in a Kundt's tube containing air at 300°K. Heaps of cork dust within the tube are found to be 4.95 cm apart. What is the velocity of longitudinal waves in copper?

22–13. Find the fundamental frequency and the first four overtones of a 6-inch pipe (a) if the pipe is open at both ends, (b) if the pipe is closed at one end. (c) How many overtones may be heard by a person having normal hearing for each of the above cases?

22–14. A long tube contains air at a pressure of 1 atm and temperature 77°C. The tube is open at one end and closed at the other by a movable piston. A tuning fork near the open end is vibrating with a frequency of 500 cycles/sec. Resonance is produced when the piston is at distances 18.0, 55.5, and 93.0 cm from the open end. (a) From these measurements, what is the velocity of sound in air at 77°C? (b) From the above result, what is the ratio of the specific heats γ for air?

22–15. An organ pipe A of length 2 ft, closed at one end, is vibrating in the first overtone. Another organ pipe B of length 1.35 ft, open at both ends, is vibrating in its fundamental mode. Take the velocity of sound in air as 1120 ft/sec. Neglect end corrections. (a) What is the frequency of the tone from A? (b) What is the frequency of the tone from B?

22–16. A plate cut from a quartz crystal is often used to control the frequency of an oscillating electrical circuit. Longitudinal standing waves are set up in the plate with displacement antinodes at opposite faces. The fundamental frequency of vibration is given by the equation

$$f_1 = \frac{2.87 \times 10^5}{s},$$

where f_1 is in cycles/sec and s is the thickness of the plate in cm. (a) Compute Young's modulus for the quartz plate. (b) Compute the thickness of plate required for a frequency of 1200 kilocycles/sec. (1 kilocycle = 1000 cycles.) The density of quartz is 2.66 gm/cm³.

CHAPTER 23

ACOUSTICAL PHENOMENA

23–1 Pressure variations in a sound wave. We shall limit ourselves in this chapter to the consideration of longitudinal waves only, and in particular to those which, when striking the ear, give rise to the sensation of sound. Such waves, within the frequency range from 20 to 20,000 vibrations per second, are called, for simplicity, *sound waves*.

The reception of a sound wave by the ear gives rise to a vibration of the air particles at the eardrum with a definite frequency and a definite amplitude. This vibration may also be described in terms of the variation of air pressure at the same point. The air pressure rises above atmospheric pressure and then sinks below atmospheric pressure with simple harmonic motion of the same frequency as that of an air particle. The maximum amount by which the pressure differs from atmospheric pressure is called the *pressure amplitude*. It can be proved that the pressure amplitude is proportional to the displacement amplitude.

Measurements of sound waves show that the maximum pressure variations in the loudest sounds which the ear can tolerate are of the order of magnitude of 280 dynes/cm^2 (above and below atmospheric pressure of about 1,000,000 dynes/cm^2). The corresponding maximum displacement for a frequency of 1000 vibrations per second is about a thousandth of a centimeter. The displacement amplitudes, even in the loudest sounds, are therefore extremely small.

The maximum pressure variations in the *faintest* sound of frequency 1000 vibrations per second are only about 2×10^{-4} dyne/cm^2. The corresponding displacement amplitude is about 10^{-9} cm. By way of comparison, the wavelength of yellow light is 6×10^{-5} cm, and the diameter of a molecule about 10^{-8} cm. It will be appreciated that the ear is an extremely sensitive organ.

23–2 Intensity. From a purely geometrical point of view, that which is propagated by a traveling wave is the *wave form*. From a physical viewpoint, however, something else is propagated by a wave, namely, *energy*. The most outstanding example, of course, is the energy supply of the earth, which reaches us from the sun via electromagnetic waves. The *intensity I* of a traveling wave is defined as *the time average rate at which energy is transported by the wave per unit area* across a surface perpendicular to the direction of propagation. More briefly, the intensity is the average power transported per unit area.

We have seen that the power developed by a force equals the product of force times velocity. Hence the power per unit area in a sound wave equals the product of the excess pressure (force per unit area) times the *particle* velocity. Averaging over one cycle, it can be proved that

$$ I = \frac{P^2}{2\rho u}, \tag{23-1} $$

where P is the pressure amplitude, ρ is the average density of the air, and u is the velocity of the sound wave. It will be noted that the *intensity* is proportional to the *square of the amplitude*, a result which is true for any sort of wave motion.

The intensity of a sound wave of pressure amplitude $P = 280$ dynes/cm^2 (roughly, the loudest tolerable sound) is

$$ I = \frac{(280 \text{ dynes/cm}^2)^2}{2 \times 1.22 \times 10^{-3} \text{ gm/cm}^3 \times 3.46 \times 10^4 \text{ cm/sec}} $$

$$ = 940 \text{ ergs/sec·cm}^2 = 94 \times 10^{-6} \text{ watt/cm}^2.* $$

The pressure amplitude of the faintest sound wave which can be heard is about 0.0003 dyne/cm^2 and the corresponding intensity is about 10^{-16} watt/cm^2.

The total power carried across a surface by a sound wave equals the product of the intensity at the surface times the surface area, if the intensity over the surface is uniform. The average power developed as sound waves by a person speaking in an ordinary conversational tone is about 10^{-5} watt, while a loud shout corresponds to about 3×10^{-2} watt. Since the population of the city of New York is about six million persons, the acoustical power developed if all were to speak at the same time would be about 60 watts, or enough to operate a moderate-sized electric light. On the other hand, the power required to fill a large auditorium with loud sound is considerable. Suppose the intensity over the surface of a hemisphere 20 meters in radius is 10^{-4} watt/cm^2. The area of the surface is about 25×10^6 cm^2. Hence the acoustic power output of a speaker at the center of the sphere would have to be

$$ 10^{-4} \times 25 \times 10^6 = 2500 \text{ watts} $$

or 2.5 kilowatts. The electrical power input to the speaker would need to be considerably larger, since the efficiency of such devices is not very high.

---

* The "watt/cm^2" is a hybrid unit, neither cgs nor mks. We shall retain it to conform with general usage in acoustics.

TABLE 23-1

NOISE LEVELS DUE TO VARIOUS SOURCES

(Representative values)

Source or description of noise	Noise level, db
Threshold of pain	120
Riveter	95
Elevated train	90
Busy street traffic	70
Ordinary conversation	65
Quiet automobile	50
Quiet radio in home	40
Average whisper	20
Rustle of leaves	10
Threshold of hearing	0

23-3 Intensity level and loudness. Because of the large range of intensities over which the ear is sensitive, a logarithmic rather than an arithmetic intensity scale is convenient. Accordingly, the *intensity level β* of a sound wave is defined by the equation

$$\beta = 10 \log \frac{I}{I_0}, \tag{23-2}$$

where I_0 is an arbitrary reference intensity which is taken as 10^{-16} watt/cm^2, corresponding roughly to the faintest sound which can be heard. Intensity levels are expressed in *decibels*, abbreviated db.*

If the intensity of a sound wave equals I_0 or 10^{-16} watt/cm^2, its intensity level is zero. The maximum intensity which the ear can tolerate, about 10^{-4} watt/cm^2, corresponds to an intensity level of 120 db. Table 23-1 gives the intensity levels in db of a number of familiar noises. It is taken from a survey made by the N. Y. City Noise Abatement Commission.

The intensity of a sound wave is a purely objective or physical attribute of a wave, and can be measured by acoustical apparatus without

---

* Originally, a scale of intensity levels in *bels* was defined by the relation

Intensity level $= \log I/I_0$.

This unit proved rather large and hence the decibel, one-tenth of a bel, has come into general use. The unit is named in honor of Alexander Graham Bell.

making use of the hearing sense of a human observer. However, if we listen to a sound wave whose intensity is gradually increased, the sensation which we describe as *loudness* increases also. The term loudness is reserved to refer to this sensation, and since it is a sensation or a subjective attribute of a sound wave, loudness cannot be measured by physical apparatus. Nevertheless, it is possible to establish a numerical scale of loudness sensation. It is found that while an increase of intensity results in an increase of the loudness sensation, loudness is by no means proportional to intensity. That is, a sound of intensity 10^{-6} watt/cm^2 is not one hundred times as loud as one of intensity 10^{-8} watt/cm^2. Rather, the loudness sensation is more nearly, although not directly, proportional to the logarithm of the intensity or to the *intensity level*. In other words, the loudness sensation produced by a sound wave of intensity level 60 db exceeds the loudness sensation produced by the same type of wave of intensity level 40 db, by approximately the same amount as the sensation produced by the 40-db wave exceeds that produced by a wave of intensity level 20 db.

The preceding discussion holds only for the comparison of the physiological effects produced by the *same type of wave* at various intensities. It may break down completely when comparing waves of different types. For example, it is possible to create one wave of one frequency only and another wave of many frequencies, so that both waves have exactly the same intensity level. The two waves, however, may give rise to entirely different sensations of loudness.

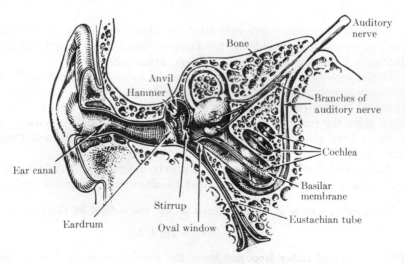

Fig. 23-1. Diagrammatic section of the right ear.

23–4 The ear and hearing. Figure 23–1 is a semidiagrammatic section of the right ear. The scale of the inner ear has been exaggerated to show details. Sound waves traveling down the ear canal strike the eardrum. A linkage of three small bones, the hammer, anvil, and stirrup, transmits the vibrations to the oval window. The oval window in turn transmits them to the inner ear, which is filled with fluid. The terminals of the auditory nerve, of which there are about 30,000 in each ear, are distributed along the basilar membrane which divides the spiral channel or cochlea into two canals. The 30,000 nerve terminals actually occupy an area only about 30 millimeters long and $\frac{1}{3}$ of a millimeter wide, a remarkable feat of engineering.

A great deal of work has been done in recent years, notably by Dr. Harvey Fletcher of the Bell Telephone Laboratories, on the processes by which the sound waves set up in the cochlea are picked up by the nerve endings. To represent the process graphically, the cochlea is drawn as a conventionalized spiral (Fig. 23–2). Each division along the spiral refers to a so-called "patch" of 1% of the nerve endings (about 300 terminals).

The width of the blackened strip in Fig. 23–3 shows the extent to which the corresponding nerve patches are stimulated by a 200-cycle tone at an intensity level of 90 db. Diagrams of this sort are called *auditory patterns.* Although the response of the ear to a pure tone is not localized at any one point, notes of lower frequency stimulate chiefly those patches near the inner portion of the spiral, and vice versa. When listening to a street noise or a symphony orchestra, all portions of the cochlea will be stimulated to a greater or lesser extent.

The range of frequencies and intensities to which the ear is sensitive is conveniently represented by a diagram like that of Fig. 23–4, which is a graph of the *auditory area* of a person of good hearing. The height

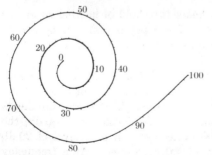

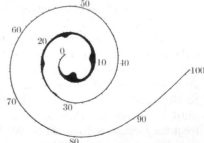

FIG. 23–2.　Conventionalized diagram of the cochlea. (Courtesy of Dr. Harvey Fletcher.)

FIG. 23–3.　Auditory pattern of a 200-cycle tone at an intensity level of 90 db. (Courtesy Dr. Harvey Fletcher.)

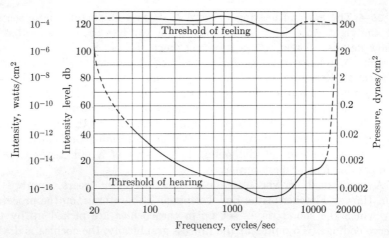

F‍IG. 23-4.   Auditory area between threshold of hearing and threshold of feeling. (Courtesy of Dr. Harvey Fletcher.)

of the lower curve at any frequency represents the intensity level of the faintest pure tone of that frequency which can be heard. It will be seen from the diagram that the ear is most sensitive to frequencies between 2000 and 3000 cycles/sec where the *threshold of hearing*, as it is called, is about −5 db. The height of the upper curve at any frequency corresponds to the intensity level of the loudest pure tone of that frequency which can be tolerated. At intensities above this curve, which is called the *threshold of feeling*, the sensation changes from one of hearing to discomfort or even pain. The height of the upper curve is approximately constant at a level of about 120 db for all frequencies. Every pure tone which can be heard may be represented by a point lying somewhere in the area between these two curves.

Only about 1% of the population has a threshold of hearing as low as the bottom curve in Fig. 23-4; 50% of the population can hear pure tones of a frequency of 2500 cycles when the intensity level is about 8 db, and 90% when the level is 20 db.

It was stated earlier that the frequency range of the ear is from about 20 to about 20,000 cycles/sec and the intensity range from about 10^{-16} to 10^{-4} watt/cm^2, or zero to 120 db. We see now that these statements must be qualified. That is, for a loud tone of intensity level 80 db, the frequency range is from 20 to 20,000 cycles/sec, but at a level of 20 db it is only from about 200 to about 15,000 cycles/sec. At a frequency of 1000 cycles/sec the range of intensity level is from about 3 db to about 120 db, whereas at 100 cycles/sec it is only from 30 db to 120 db.

Sounds which are not pure tones are not associated with any one fre-

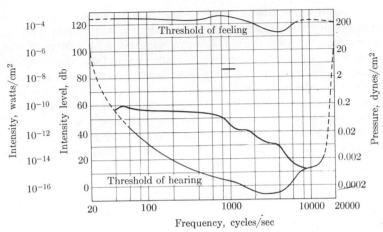

FIG. 23–5. Spectrogram of street noise. (Courtesy of Dr. Harvey Fletcher.)

quency and hence cannot be represented by a single point on the diagram. A sound such as that from a musical instrument, consisting of a mixture of a relatively few frequencies (the fundamental and overtones), can be represented by a set of points, each point giving the intensity and frequency of one particular overtone. A sound such as a street noise, while it cannot be considered as made up of a fundamental and overtones, can nevertheless be represented on the diagram in the following way. The sound is picked up by a microphone and sent through an electrical network which selects a narrow range of frequencies and measures the average intensity within this range. By repeating the process at a large number of frequencies throughout the audible range, a series of points is obtained which can be plotted. A continuous curve drawn through them is called the *spectrogram* of the sound. A typical spectrogram of street noise is shown in Fig. 23–5.

The term "spectrogram" is borrowed from optics. The process just described is entirely analogous to the optical one of dispersing a beam of light waves into a spectrum by means of a prism and measuring the intensity at a number of points throughout the spectrum. The light emitted by a gas in an electrical discharge is a mixture of waves of a number of definite frequencies and corresponds to the sound emitted by a musical instrument. Most light beams, however, are a mixture of all frequencies and are therefore the optical analog of noise.

The total intensity level of a noise can be found from its spectrogram by an integration process. There are also instruments known as noise meters which measure the level directly. The level of the street noise in Fig. 23–5 is about 85 db and is shown by the short heavy line.

23–5 Quality and pitch. A string that has been plucked or a plate that has been struck, if allowed to vibrate freely, will vibrate with many frequencies at the same time. It is a rare occurrence for a body to vibrate with only one frequency. A carefully made tuning fork struck lightly on a rubber block may vibrate with only one frequency, but in the case of musical instruments, the fundamental and many harmonics are usually present at the same time. The impulses that are sent from the ear to the brain give rise to one net effect which is characteristic of the instrument. Suppose, for example, the sound spectrum of a tone consisted of a fundamental of 200 vibrations per second and harmonics 2, 3, 4, and 5, all of different intensity, whereas the sound spectrum of another tone consisted of exactly the same frequencies but with a different intensity distribution. The two tones would sound different; they are said to differ in *quality*.

Adjectives used to describe the quality of musical tones are purely subjective in character, such as reedy, golden, round, mellow, tinny, etc. *The quality of a sound is determined by the number of overtones present*

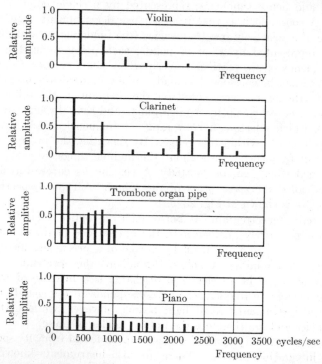

FIG. 23–6. Sound spectra of some musical instruments. (Courtesy of Dr. Harvey Fletcher.)

and their respective intensities. The sound spectra of various musical instruments are shown in Fig. 23-6.

Another subjective attribute of a musical sound that is described with the aid of the adjectives high, medium, low, etc., is called the *pitch.* It is a simple matter to explain the pitch of a sound produced by a wave of only one frequency. If we take a set of tuning forks differing in size and cause each one to sound its fundamental only, then it becomes apparent that the greater the frequency, the higher the pitch. The situation, however, is very much more complicated when the sound is produced by a wave of many frequencies. If the fundamental is considerably more intense than any of the overtones, then the pitch is determined by the frequency of the fundamental. But this is not always the case. It is possible to construct a tone consisting of many frequencies whose pitch corresponds to a frequency that actually does not exist in the tone itself.

23-6 Beats. Stationary waves in an air column have been cited as one example of interference. They arise when two wave trains of the same amplitude and frequency are traveling through the same region in opposite directions. We now wish to consider another type of interference which results when two wave trains of equal amplitude but slightly different frequency travel through the same region. Such a condition exists when two tuning forks of slightly different frequency are sounded simultaneously or when two piano wires struck by the same key are slightly "out of tune."

Let us consider some one point of space through which the waves are simultaneously passing. The displacements due to the two waves separately are plotted as a function of the time on graph (a) in Fig. 23-7. If the total extent of the time axis represents one second, the graphs correspond to frequencies of 16 vibrations per second and of 18 vibrations per second. Applying the principle of superposition to find the resultant vibration, we get graph (b), where it is seen that the amplitude varies

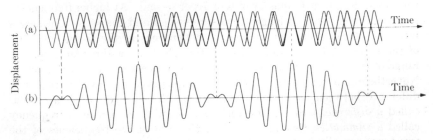

FIG. 23-7. Beats are fluctuations in amplitude produced by two sound waves of slightly different frequency.

with the time. These variations of amplitude give rise to variations of loudness which are called *beats*. Two strings may be tuned to the same frequency by tightening one of them while sounding both until the beats disappear.

The production of beats may be treated mathematically as follows. The displacements due to the two waves passing simultaneously through some one point of space may be written

$$y_1 = A \cos 2\pi f_1 t, \qquad y_2 = A \cos 2\pi f_2 t.$$

(The amplitudes are assumed equal.)

By the principle of superposition, the resultant displacement is

$$y = y_1 + y_2 = A [\cos 2\pi f_1 t + \cos 2\pi f_2 t],$$

and, since

$$\cos a + \cos b = 2 \cos \frac{a+b}{2} \cos \frac{a-b}{2},$$

this may be written

$$y = \left[2A \cos 2\pi \left(\frac{f_1 - f_2}{2} \right) t \right] \cos 2\pi \frac{f_1 + f_2}{2} t.$$

The resulting vibration can then be considered to be of frequency $(f_1 + f_2)/2$, or the average frequency of the two tones, and of amplitude given by the expression in brackets. The amplitude therefore varies with time at a frequency $(f_1 - f_2)/2$. If f_1 and f_2 are nearly equal, this term is small and the amplitude fluctuates very slowly. When the amplitude is large, the sound is loud, and vice versa. A beat, or a maximum of amplitude, will occur when $\cos 2\pi t (f_1 - f_2)/2$ equals 1 or -1. Since each of these values occurs once in each cycle, the number of beats per second is twice the frequency $(f_1 - f_2)/2$, or *the number of beats per second equals the difference of the frequencies.*

23–7 Combination tones. Beats between two tones can be detected by the ear up to a beat frequency of 6 or 7 per second. At higher frequencies, individual beats can no longer be distinguished and the sensation merges into one of *consonance* or *dissonance* depending on the frequency ratio of the tones. A beat frequency, even though it lies within the frequency range of the ear, is not interpreted by the ear as a tone of that frequency. Nevertheless, a tone can be heard of frequency equal to the frequency difference between two others sounded simultaneously. Such a tone is called a *difference* tone. Although not as easy to recognize, a frequency called a *summation* tone and equal to the sum of the frequencies of the two tones can also be heard. The general term applied to both difference tones and summation tones is *combination* tones.

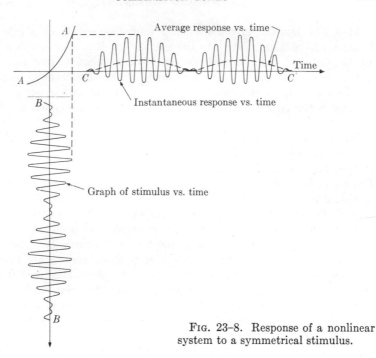

Fɪɢ. 23–8. Response of a nonlinear system to a symmetrical stimulus.

Combination tones are similar to beats but are due to the nature of the hearing mechanism. The ear is one of a number of devices whose response is said to be *nonlinear*. A vacuum tube operated on the curved portion of its characteristic is another. Figure 23–8 illustrates the situation schematically. The response to a given stimulus is represented by the curved line AA. (In a vacuum tube the "response" would be the plate current and the "stimulus" the grid potential.) The curve BB extending vertically downward represents the displacement of the air at a point through which two waves of different frequency are passing simultaneously. The response to this stimulus is obtained by projecting upward from every point of this curve to the curve AA and then projecting across. It will be seen that because of the curvature (or nonlinearity) of AA, the response curve CC is not symmetrical but has an "average" upward sweep indicated by the dotted line. Hence, if the graph represents the motion of the eardrum, it is seen that the latter will vibrate at a frequency equal to the beat frequency or the difference in frequencies of the two tones. This vibration is superposed on the much higher frequency of the individual waves in the tone. Note carefully that if the response curve AA were *linear*, the curve CC would be symmetrical and no such motion of the eardrum would ensue.

23–8 The Doppler effect. When a source of sound, or a listener, or both, are in motion relative to the air, the pitch of the sound, as heard by the listener, is in general not the same as when source and listener are at rest. The most common example is the sudden drop in pitch of the sound from an automobile horn as one meets and passes a car proceeding in the opposite direction. This phenomenon is called the *Doppler effect.*

We shall consider only the special case in which the velocities of listener and source, v_L and v_S, lie along the line joining them. Since these velocities may be in the same or opposite directions, and the listener may be either ahead of or behind the source, a convention of signs is required. We shall take the positive directions of v_L and v_S as that *from* the position of the listener *to* the position of the source. The velocity of propagation of sound waves, u, will always be considered positive.

In Fig. 23–9, a listener L is at the left of a source S. The positive direction is then from left to right, and both v_L and v_S are positive in the diagram. The sound source is at point a at time $t = 0$ and at point b at time t. The outer circle represents the wave surface emitted at time $t = 0$. This surface (in free space) is a sphere with center at a, and is traveling radially outward at all points with velocity u. (The fact that the wave originated at a *moving* source does not affect its velocity after leaving the source. The wave velocity u is a property of the *medium* only; the waves forget about the source as soon as they leave it.) The

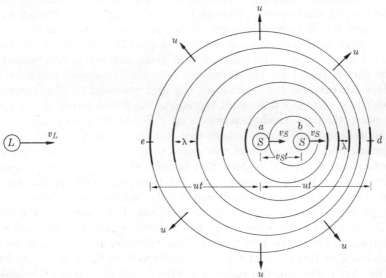

FIG. 23–9. Wave surfaces emitted by a moving source.

radius of this sphere (the distance ea or ad) is therefore ut. The distance ab equals v_St, so

$$eb = (u + v_S)t, \qquad bd = (u - v_S)t.$$

In the time interval between $t = 0$ and $t = t$, the number of waves emitted by the source is f_St, where f_S is the frequency of the source. In front of the source these waves are crowded into the distance bd, while behind the source they are spread out over the distance eb. The wavelength in front of the source is therefore

$$\lambda = \frac{(u - v_S)t}{f_St} = \frac{u - v_S}{f_S},$$

while the wavelength behind the source is

$$\lambda = \frac{(u + v_S)t}{f_St} = \frac{u + v_S}{f_S}.$$

The waves approaching the moving listener L have a velocity of propagation relative to him, given by $u + v_L$. The frequency at which he encounters these waves is

$$f = \frac{u + v_L}{\lambda} = \frac{u + v_L}{(u + v_S)/f_S},$$

or

$$\frac{f}{u + v_L} = \frac{f_S}{u + v_S}, \qquad (23\text{-}3)$$

which expresses the frequency f as heard by the listener in terms of the frequency f_S of the source. It is unnecessary to derive equations for other special cases if consistent use is made of the sign convention given above. See the following examples.

If the medium in which the waves are traveling has a velocity v_M parallel to the line joining listener and source, then

$$\frac{f}{u + v_L - v_M} = \frac{f_S}{u + v_S - v_M}.$$

EXAMPLE.   Let $f_S = 1000$ cycles/sec, $u = 1000$ ft/sec. The wavelength of the waves emitted by a stationary source is then $u/f_S = 1.00$ ft.

(a) What are the wavelengths ahead of and behind the moving source in Fig. 23-9 if its velocity is 100 ft/sec?

In front of the source,

$$\lambda = \frac{u - v_S}{f_S} = \frac{1000 - 100}{1000} = 0.90 \text{ ft.}$$

Behind the source,

$$\lambda = \frac{u + v_S}{f_S} = \frac{1000 + 100}{1000} = 1.10 \text{ ft.}$$

(b) If the listener L in Fig. 23-9 is at rest and the source is moving away from him at 100 ft/sec, what is the frequency as heard by the listener? Since $v_L = 0$ and $v_S = 100$ ft/sec,

$$f = f_S \frac{u}{u + v_S} = 1000 \frac{1000}{1000 + 100} = 909 \frac{\text{cycles}}{\text{sec}}.$$

(c) If the source in Fig. 23-9 is at rest and the listener is moving toward the left at 100 ft/sec, what is the frequency as heard by the listener? The positive direction (from listener to source) is still from left to right, so

$$v_L = -100 \frac{\text{ft}}{\text{sec}}, \qquad v_S = 0,$$

$$f = f_S \frac{u + v_L}{u} = 1000 \frac{1000 - 100}{1000} = 900 \frac{\text{cycles}}{\text{sec}}.$$

Thus while the frequency as heard by the listener is less than the frequency f_S both when the source moves away from the listener and when the listener moves away from the source, the decrease in frequency is not the same for the same velocity of recession.

The Doppler effect is not, of course, confined to sound waves. Light waves are emitted as a result of electronic rearrangements in atoms, and presumably the frequency of these light sources is the same whether a given atom is on the earth or in a star. The wavelength of the light from certain stars is found to be slightly longer, and from other stars slightly shorter, than that from the same atoms in a source on the earth. The inference is that the stars are moving toward or away from the earth, and their velocity can be computed from the observed wavelength difference. Even in a gas discharge tube in the laboratory, the atoms are not at rest, but are flying about with relatively large velocities. Hence the light from such a source, resulting from a given atomic process, is a mixture of waves with a slight "spread" of wavelengths. Another interesting example is the reflection of radar waves from a moving object such as a plane or an automobile. The wavelength of the reflected waves is increased if the object is moving toward the source, decreased if it is moving away from the source. The same phenomenon occurs when underwater sound waves (sonar) are reflected by a moving submarine.

TABLE 23–2

FREQUENCY RELATIONS IN THE MAJOR DIATONIC SCALE
AND IN THE EQUALLY TEMPERED SCALE

	Do	Re	Mi	Fa	Sol	La	Ti	Do'	Re'
Frequency relations	Middle C	D	E	F	G	A	B	C'	D'
1 Octave, key of C	1							2	
2 Major triad, key of C	4		5		6			(8)	
3 Major triad, key of F				4		5		6	
4 Major triad, key of G		(3)			4		5		6
5 Diatonic scale, key of C	264	297	330	352	396	440	495	528	594
6	9/8 whole	10/9 whole	16/15 half	9/8 whole	10/9 whole	9/8 whole	16/15 half	9/8 whole	
7 Equally tempered scale suitable for all keys	261.6	293.7	329.6	349.2	392.0	440	493.9	523.3	587.4
8	$\sqrt[6]{2}$	$\sqrt[6]{2}$	$\sqrt[12]{2}$	$\sqrt[6]{2}$	$\sqrt[6]{2}$	$\sqrt[6]{2}$	$\sqrt[12]{2}$	$\sqrt[6]{2}$	

23–9 Musical intervals and scales. If certain musical tones are produced in succession, an untrained listener, as well as an accomplished musician, recognizes a relationship among them. Such relations are described in musical language by words such as octave, major third, minor third, etc. The listener recognizes something basic in these intervals, and experimental measurement of the fundamental frequencies of the separate tones discloses that they bear simple whole-number ratios to one another. Thus, the fundamental frequencies of middle C of the piano and its *octave* above, C′, are to each other as 1 to 2. Another basic set of tones is obtained by playing C, E, G. These constitute what is known as a *major triad*, and the frequencies are found to be proportional to 4, 5, and 6.

Starting at middle C of the piano, and playing only the white notes toward the right, it is possible to find, within only nine notes, three major triads. These are shown in Table 23–2, and enable one to calculate the frequencies of all the notes, once one of them has been chosen arbitrarily. By international agreement, the frequency of the A above middle C is chosen to be 440 vibrations per second. The frequencies of all the notes, shown in row 5 of Table 23–2, are those that correspond to the *major diatonic scale* of the key of C. The frequency ratios of adjacent notes are seen to be either 9/8, 10/9, or 16/15. The interval between two tones whose frequencies bear the ratio 9/8 or 10/9 are called *whole tones*, whereas the interval between two notes of frequency ratio 16/15 is a *half tone*.

If a major diatonic scale were constructed starting at D instead of at C, four new notes would be needed for a perfect diatonic scale. If all possible musical keys were to be provided for, 72 notes would be needed for each octave. To avoid this tremendous complication, what is known as the *equally tempered scale* has been devised (used by J. S. Bach and probably earlier musicians). In this scheme there are 12 half-tone intervals in every range of an octave, adjacent notes a half tone apart bearing the constant ratio of the twelfth root of 2, i.e., 1.05946. Simple as this scheme is, it results in no one scale being exactly diatonic. Since the ratios of the diatonic scale were originally selected to suit the preferences of the ear (being made up of three sets of major triads, each of which constitutes a harmonious combination), this means that music which makes use of the equally tempered scale is not quite so pleasant to the ear. The difference, however, is apparently slight to any but the most critical.

PROBLEMS

23-1. (a) If the pressure amplitude in a sound wave is tripled, by how many times is the intensity of the wave increased? (b) By how many times must the pressure amplitude of a sound wave be increased in order to increase the intensity by a factor of 16 times?

23-2. (a) Two sound waves, one in air and one in water, are equal in intensity. What is the ratio of the pressure amplitude of the wave in water to that of the wave in air? (b) If the pressure amplitudes of the waves are equal, what is the ratio of their intensities?

23-3. (a) Relative to the arbitrary reference intensity of 10^{-16} watt/cm^2, what is the intensity level in db of a sound wave whose intensity is 10^{-10} watt/cm^2? (b) What is the intensity level of a sound wave in air whose pressure amplitude is 2 dynes/cm^2?

23-4. (a) Show that if β_1 and β_2 are the intensity levels in db of sounds of intensities I_1 and I_2 respectively, the difference in intensity levels of the sounds is

$$\beta_2 - \beta_1 = 10 \log \frac{I_2}{I_1}.$$

(b) Show that if P_1 and P_2 are the pressure amplitudes of two sound waves, the difference in intensity levels of the waves is

$$\beta_2 - \beta_1 = 20 \log \frac{P_2}{P_1}.$$

(c) Show that if the reference level of intensity is $I_0 = 10^{-16}$ watt/cm^2, the intensity level of a sound of intensity I is

$$\beta = 160 + 10 \log I.$$

23-5. Two loud-speakers, A and B, radiate sound uniformly in all directions. The output of acoustic power from A is 8×10^{-4} watt, and from B it is 13.5×10^{-4} watt. Both loud-speakers are vibrating in phase at a frequency of 173 cycles/sec. (a) Determine the difference in phase of the two signals at a point C along the line joining A and B, 3 m from B and 4 m from A. (b) Determine the intensity at C from speaker A if speaker B is turned off, and the intensity at C from speaker B if speaker A is turned off. (c) With both speakers on, what is the intensity and intensity level at C?

23-6. The intensity due to a number of independent sound sources is the sum of the individual intensities. How many db greater was the intensity level when all five of the quintuplets cried simultaneously than when a single one cried? How many more crying babies would be required to produce a further increase in the intensity level of the same number of db?

23-7. A window whose area is 1 m^2 opens on a street where the street noises result in an intensity level, at the window, of 60 db. How much "acoustic power" enters the window via the sound waves?

23-8. (a) What are the upper and lower limits of intensity level of a person whose auditory area is represented by the graph of Fig. 23-4? (b) What are the highest and lowest frequencies he can hear when the intensity level is 40 db?

23-9. Two whistles, A and B, each have a frequency of 500 cycles/sec. A is stationary and B is moving toward the right (away from A) at a velocity of 200 ft/sec. An observer is between the two whistles, moving toward the right with a velocity of 100 ft/sec. Take the velocity of sound in air as 1100 ft/sec. (a) What is the frequency from A as heard by the observer? (b) What is the frequency from B as heard by the observer? (c) What is the beat frequency heard by the observer?

23-10. A railroad train is traveling at 100 ft/sec in still air. The frequency of the note emitted by the locomotive whistle is 500 cycles/sec. What is the wavelength of the sound waves (a) in front of the locomotive, and (b) behind it? What would be the frequency of the sound heard by a stationary listener (c) in front of, (d) behind the locomotive? What frequency would be heard by a passenger on a second train traveling at 50 ft/sec and (e) approaching the first, (f) receding from the first? (g) How is each of the preceding answers altered if a wind of velocity 30 ft/sec is blowing in the same direction as that in which the first locomotive is traveling?

23-11. Compare the frequencies heard by a listener under the following circumstances: (a) A listener in still air moves with a velocity of 100 ft/sec directly toward a stationary source emitting sound waves of a frequency 1000 cycles/sec. (b) The listener remains at rest while the source moves directly toward him at 100 ft/sec.

23-12. A man stands at rest in front of a large smooth wall. Directly in front of him, between him and the wall, he holds a vibrating tuning fork of frequency f_0 cycles/sec. He now moves the fork toward the wall with a velocity v. How many beats per sec will he hear between the sound waves reaching him directly from the fork, and those reaching him after being reflected from the wall? Represent the velocity of sound in air by V. For a numerical example, let $f_0 = 400$ cycles/sec and $v = 4$ ft/sec.

23-13. A source of sound waves S, emitting waves of frequency 1000 cycles/sec, is traveling toward the right in still air with a velocity of 100 ft/sec. At the right of the source is a large smooth reflecting surface moving toward the left with a velocity of 400 ft/sec. (a) How far does an emitted wave travel in 0.01 sec? (b) What is the wavelength of the emitted waves in front of (i.e., at the right of) the source? (c) How many waves strike the reflecting surface in 0.01 sec? (d) What is the velocity of the reflected waves? (e) What is the wavelength of the reflected waves?

CHAPTER 24

COULOMB'S LAW

24–1 Electric charges. It was known to the ancient Greeks as far back as 600 B.C. that amber, rubbed with wool, acquired the property of attracting light objects. In describing this property today, we say that the amber is *electrified*, or possesses an *electric charge*, or is *electrically charged*. These terms are derived from the Greek word *elektron*, meaning amber. It is possible to impart an electric charge to any solid material by rubbing it with any other material. Thus, an automobile becomes charged by virtue of its motion through the air; an electric charge is developed on a sheet of paper moving through a printing press; a comb is electrified in passing through dry hair. Actually, intimate contact is all that is needed to give rise to an electric charge. Rubbing merely serves to bring many points of the surfaces into good contact.

In lecture demonstrations hard rubber and fur are commonly used. If, after it is rubbed with fur, a rubber rod is placed in a dish containing tiny pieces of tissue paper, many of these will at first cling to the rod, but after a few seconds they will fly off. The initial attraction will be explained in Chapter 27; the subsequent repulsion is due to a force that is found to exist whenever two bodies are electrified in the same way. Suppose two small, very light pith balls are suspended near each other by fine silk threads. At first they will be attracted to an electrified rubber rod and will cling to it. A moment later, they will be repelled by the rubber and will also repel each other.

A similar experiment performed with a glass rod that has been rubbed with silk gives rise to the same result. Pith balls electrified by contact with such a glass rod are repelled not only by the glass rod but by each other. On the other hand, a pith ball that has been in contact with electrified rubber, when placed near one that has been in contact with electrified glass, is found to be attracted. We are therefore led to the conclusion that there are two kinds of electric charge—that possessed by hard rubber after being rubbed with fur, called a *negative charge*, and that possessed by glass after being rubbed with silk, called a *positive charge*. The words *negative* and *positive* are merely convenient labels, having no mathematical connotations whatever. As a matter of fact, as we shall see presently, a negatively charged body has acquired something extra, whereas a positively charged body has lost some of the same thing.

The experiments on pith balls described in the preceding paragraph lead to the fundamental results that (1) like charges repel, (2) unlike charges attract.

These repulsive or attractive forces, of electrical origin, exist in addition to the gravitational force of attraction and, in most situations with which we shall deal, are so much larger than the gravitational force that the latter may be completely neglected.

Suppose a rubber rod is rubbed with fur and then touched to a suspended pith ball. Both the rubber and the pith ball are negatively charged. If the fur is now brought near the pith ball, the ball will be attracted, indicating that the fur is positively charged. It follows that when rubber is rubbed with fur, opposite charges appear on the two materials. This is found to happen whenever any substance is rubbed with any other substance. Thus glass becomes positive, while the silk with which the glass was rubbed becomes negative. This suggests strongly that electric charges are not generated or created, but that the process of acquiring an electric charge consists of transferring something from one body to another, so that one body has an excess and the other a deficiency of that something. It was not until the end of the nineteenth century that this "something" was found to consist of very small, light pieces of negative electricity, known today as *electrons*.

Electrons are one of the fundamental constituents of matter. Once the electrical structure of atoms is made clear, electrical phenomena are much easier to understand. Consequently, instead of adopting a historical point of view from now on, we shall first study atomic structure and then use this knowledge in introducing further electrical effects.

24–2 Atomic structure. The word *atom* is derived from the Greek *atomos*, meaning indivisible. It is scarcely necessary to point out that the term is inappropriate. All atoms are more or less complex arrangements of subatomic particles, and there are many methods of splitting off some of these particles, either singly or in groups. The most spectacular example, of course, is the disruption of an atomic nucleus in the process of nuclear fission.

The subatomic particles, the building blocks out of which atoms are constructed, are of three different kinds: the negatively charged *electron*, the positively charged *proton*, and the neutral *neutron*. The negative charge of the electron is of the same magnitude as the positive charge of the proton and no charges of smaller magnitude have ever been observed. The charge of a proton or an electron is the ultimate, natural unit of charge.

The subatomic particles are arranged in the same general way in all atoms. The protons and neutrons always form a closely packed group called the *nucleus*, which has a net positive charge due to the protons. The diameter of the nucleus, if we think of it as a sphere, is of the order of 10^{-12} cm. Outside the nucleus, but at relatively large distances from it, are the electrons, whose number is equal to the number of protons within the nucleus. If the atom is undisturbed, and no electrons are removed from the space around the nucleus, the atom as a whole is electrically neutral. If, on the other hand, one or more electrons have been removed, the remaining positively charged structure is called a positive *ion*. A negative ion is an atom which has gained one or more extra electrons. The process of losing or gaining electrons is called *ionization*.

In the atomic model proposed by the Danish physicist Niels Bohr in 1913, the electrons were pictured as whirling about the nucleus in circular or elliptical orbits. We now believe this model is not entirely correct, but it is still useful in visualizing the structure of an atom. The diameters of the electronic orbits, which determine the size of an atom as a whole, are of the order of 2 or 3 × 10^{-8} cm, or about ten thousand times as great as the diameter of the nucleus. A Bohr atom is a solar system in miniature, with electrical forces taking the place of gravitational forces. The positively charged central nucleus corresponds to the sun, while the electrons, moving around the nucleus under the electrical force of its attraction for them, correspond to the planets moving around the sun under the influence of its gravitational attraction.

The masses of a proton and a neutron are nearly equal, and the mass of each is about 1840 times as great as that of an electron. Practically all the mass of an atom, therefore, is concentrated in its nucleus. Since one mole of monatomic hydrogen consists of 6.02 × 10^{23} particles (Avogadro's number) and its mass is 1.008 gm, the mass of a single hydrogen atom is

$$\frac{1.008 \text{ gm}}{6.02 \times 10^{23}} = 1.67 \times 10^{-24} \text{ gm} = 1.67 \times 10^{-27} \text{ kgm.}$$

The hydrogen atom is the sole exception to the rule that all atoms are constructed of three kinds of subatomic particles. The nucleus of a hydrogen atom is a single proton, outside of which there is a single electron. Hence out of the total mass of the hydrogen atom, 1/1840 part is the mass of the electron and the remainder is the mass of a proton. Then to three significant figures,

$$\text{mass of electron} = \frac{1.67 \times 10^{-24}}{1840} = 9.11 \times 10^{-28} \text{ gm}$$

$$= 9.11 \times 10^{-31} \text{ kgm,}$$

$$\text{mass of proton} = 1.67 \times 10^{-24} \text{ gm} = 1.67 \times 10^{-27} \text{ kgm,}$$

and since the masses of a proton and a neutron are nearly equal,

$$\text{mass of neutron} = 1.67 \times 10^{-24} \text{ gm} = 1.67 \times 10^{-27} \text{ kgm.}$$

The next element beyond hydrogen is helium. Its nucleus consists of two protons and two neutrons, and it has two extranuclear electrons. When these two electrons are absent, the doubly charged helium ion, which is the helium nucleus itself, is often called an *alpha particle*, or *α*-particle. The next element, lithium, has three protons in its nucleus and has thus a nuclear charge of three units. In the un-ionized state the lithium atom has three extranuclear electrons. Each element has a different number of nuclear protons and therefore a different positive nuclear charge. In the table of elements listed in the back of this book, known as the *periodic table*, each element occupies a box with which is associated a number, called the *atomic number*. *The atomic number represents the number of nuclear protons or, in the undisturbed state, the number of extra-nuclear electrons.*

In addition to the forces of attraction or repulsion between protons and electrons, which depend only on the separation of the particles, other forces are found to exist between them which depend on their relative motion. It is these forces which are responsible for *magnetic* phenomena. For many years, the apparent force of repulsion or attraction between a pair of bar magnets was explained on the theory that there existed magnetic entities similar to electric charges and called "magnetic poles." It is a familiar fact, however, that magnetic effects are also observed around a wire in which there is a current. But a current is simply a motion of electric charge, and it appears now that all magnetic effects come about as a result of the relative motion of electric charges. Hence magnetism and electricity are not two separate subjects, but are related phenomena arising from the properties of electric charges.

24–3 Charging by contact. The atoms of ordinary matter, as stated in the preceding section, contain equal numbers of electrons and protons. Hence ordinary matter does not exhibit electrical effects and is said to be electrically *neutral* or *uncharged*. If by some means the balance between electrons and protons is upset, that is, if a body has an excess or deficiency of electrons, it is said to be *charged* and will be spoken of as a *charged body* or, for brevity, simply as a *charge*. There are many ways in which the normal balance between positive and negative charges can be altered. The oldest, historically, is the phenomenon of charging by friction, as described in Section 24–1. When rubber and fur are brought into contact, there is a spontaneous transfer of electrons from the fur to the rubber. The rubber therefore acquires an excess of electrons and becomes negatively charged, while the fur, having lost some electrons, is positively charged. Measurements show that the charge acquired by the rubber when it is brought into contact with the fur is exactly equal and opposite to that acquired by the fur. There is thus no *creation* of electric charge

Fig. 24–1. The leaf electroscope.

in the charging process, but simply a *transfer* of electrons from one body to another.

A charged pith ball may be used as a test body to determine whether or not a second body is charged. A more sensitive test is afforded by the *leaf electroscope* (Fig. 24–1). Two strips of thin gold leaf or aluminum foil *A* are fastened at the end of a metal rod *B* which passes through a support *C* of rubber, amber, or sulfur. The surrounding case *D* is provided with windows through which the leaves can be observed and which serve to protect them from air currents. When the knob of the electroscope is touched by a charged body, the leaves acquire charges of the same sign and repel each other, their divergence being a measure of the quantity of charge they have received.

If one terminal of a "B" battery of a few hundred volts potential difference is connected to the knob of an electroscope and the other terminal to the electroscope case, the leaves will diverge just as if they had been charged from a body electrified by contact. There is no difference between the "kinds" of charge given the leaves in the two processes and, in general, there is no distinction between "static electricity" and "current electricity." The term "current" refers to a flow of charge, while "electrostatics" is concerned for the most part with interactions between charges at rest. The charges themselves in either case are those of electrons or protons.

24-4 Conductors and insulators.

Let one end of a copper wire be attached to the knob of an electroscope, its other end being supported by a glass rod as in Fig. 24-2. If a charged rubber rod is touched to the far end of the wire, the electroscope leaves will immediately diverge. There has, therefore, been a transfer of charge along or through the wire, and the wire is called a *conductor*. If the experiment is repeated, using a silk thread or rubber band in place of the wire, no such deflection of the electroscope occurs and the thread or rubber is called an *insulator* or *dielectric*. The motion of charge through a material substance will be studied in more detail in Chapter 28, but for our present purposes it is sufficient to state that most substances fall into one or the other of the two classes above. Conductors permit the passage of charge through them, while insulators do not.

Metals in general are good conductors, while nonmetals are insulators. The positive valency of metals and the fact that they form positive ions in solution indicate that the atoms of a metal will part readily with one or more of their outer electrons. Within a metallic conductor such as a copper wire, a few outer electrons become detached from each atom and can move freely throughout the metal. These are called *free* electrons. The positive nuclei and the remainder of the electrons remain fixed in position. Within an insulator, on the other hand, there are none (or at any rate very few) of these free electrons.

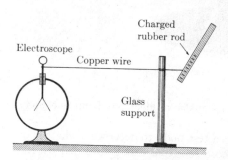

Fig. 24-2. Copper is a conductor of electricity.

The phenomenon of charging by contact is not limited to rubber and fur, or indeed to insulators in general. Any two dissimilar substances exhibit the effect to a greater or less extent, but evidently a conductor must be supported on an insulating handle or the charges developed on it will at once leak away.

24-5 Charging a metal by induction.

In charging a leaf electroscope by contact with, say, a rubber rod that has been rubbed with fur, some of the extra electrons on the rubber are transferred to the electroscope, leaving the rubber with a smaller negative charge. After a while, the rubber rod will have to be recharged if it is to be used over and over again. There is, however, another way to use the rubber rod to charge other bodies, in which the rubber may impart a charge of opposite sign, and lose none of its own charge in the process. This is called *charging by induction*, and

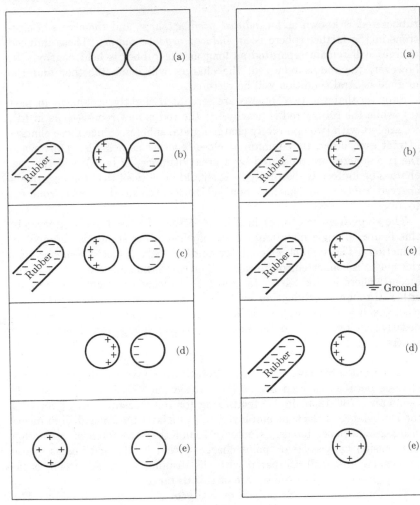

Fig. 24-3. By induction, equal and opposite charges are obtained on two metal spheres.

Fig. 24-4. Charging a single metal sphere by induction.

is explained with reference to Fig. 24-3. In part (a) of this figure are depicted schematically two neutral metal spheres in contact. It is understood that both metal spheres are supported on insulating stands. When a negatively charged rubber rod is brought *close* to one of the spheres, but without touching it, as in (b), some of the free electrons in the metal spheres are repelled. The deficiency of electrons in the sphere nearer the

rubber rod is known as an *induced positive charge*, and the excess of electrons in the farther sphere is an *induced negative charge*. These induced
charges will remain separated as long as the rubber is held nearby. If,
however, the rod is removed, the charges will come together and the
original neutral condition will be restored.

Suppose that the two spheres are separated slightly, as shown in part
(c), while the rubber rod is nearby. If the rod is now removed, as in (d),
we are left with two oppositely charged metal spheres. Since these charges
attract each other, they remain as close together as possible. Only when
the two spheres are separated by a great distance, as in (e), will the two
charges be uniformly distributed. It should be noticed that the negatively
charged rubber rod has lost none of its charge in the steps from (a)
to (e).

The steps from (a) to (e) in Fig. 24–4 should be self-explanatory. In
this figure, a single metal sphere (on an insulating stand) is charged by
induction. The symbol lettered "ground" in part (c) simply means that
the sphere is connected to the earth. The earth thus takes the place of the
second sphere in Fig. 24–3. In step (c), electrons are repelled to ground
either through a conducting wire, or along the moist skin of a person
who touches the sphere with his finger. The earth thus acquires a
negative charge equal to the induced positive charge remaining on the
sphere.

24–6 Coulomb's law. The first quantitative investigation of the law
of force between charged bodies was carried out by Charles Augustin de
Coulomb (1736–1806) in 1784, utilizing for the measurement of forces a
torsion balance of the type employed 13 years later by Cavendish in measuring gravitational forces. Coulomb found that the force of attraction
or repulsion between two "point charges," that is, charged bodies whose
dimensions are small compared with the distance r between them, is inversely proportional to the square of this distance.

The force also depends on the quantity of charge on each body. The
net charge of a body might be described by a statement of the excess number of electrons or protons in the body. In practice, however, the charge
of a body is expressed in terms of a unit much larger than the charge of
an individual electron or proton. We shall use the letter q or Q to represent the charge of a body, postponing for the present the definition of the
unit charge.

The concept of quantity of charge was not clearly appreciated in
Coulomb's time and no unit of charge or method of measuring it had been
devised. Thus, although Coulomb did not state his conclusions in this
form, his experiments showed that the force between two point charges
q and q' is proportional to the product of these charges. The complete

expression for the force between two point charges is therefore

$$F \propto \frac{qq'}{r^2} \tag{24-1}$$

or

$$F = k \frac{qq'}{r^2}, \tag{24-2}$$

where k is a proportionality constant whose magnitude depends on the units in which F, q, q', and r are expressed. Equation (24-2) is the mathematical statement of what is known today as *Coulomb's law: The force of attraction or repulsion between two point charges is directly proportional to the product of the charges and inversely proportional to the square of the distance between them.*

The best verification of Coulomb's law lies in the correctness of many conclusions which have been drawn from it, rather than on direct experiments with point charges which cannot be made with high precision.

If there is matter in the space between the charges, the net force acting on each is altered because charges are "induced" in the molecules of the intervening medium. This effect will be described later on. As a practical matter, the law can be used as it stands for point charges in air, since even at atmospheric pressure the effect of the air is to alter the force from its value in vacuum by only about one part in two thousand.

The same law of force holds whatever may be the sign of the charges q and q'. If the charges are of like sign the force is a repulsion, if the charges are of opposite sign the force is an attraction. Forces of the same magnitude, but in opposite directions, are exerted on each of the charges.

24–7 Rutherford's nuclear atom. In nature, the nearest thing to a truly geometrical point charge is the positively charged nucleus of an atom, and we have direct experimental evidence that the force of repulsion between a pair of atomic nuclei obeys Coulomb's law. The experiments were performed not for the primary purpose of verifying this law, but to learn, if possible, how the positive and negative electricities are arranged within an atom, and it was these very experiments that first showed the atom to consist of a small, massive nucleus, surrounded by electrons. The experiments were carried out in 1910–11 by Sir Ernest Rutherford and two of his students, Hans Geiger and Ernest Marsden, at Cambridge, England.

The electron had been "discovered" in 1897 by Sir J. J. Thomson, and by 1910 its mass and charge were quite accurately known. It had also been well established that, with the sole exception of hydrogen, all atoms contain more than one electron. Thomson had proposed an atomic model consisting of a relatively large sphere of positive charge (about 2 or

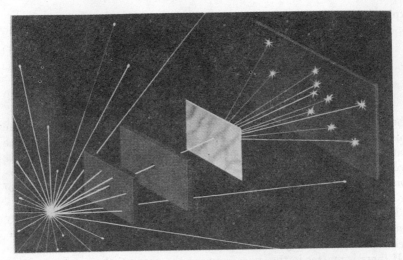

FIG. 24–5. The scattering of alpha particles by a thin metal foil.

3×10^{-8} cm in diameter) within which were embedded, like plums in a pudding, the electrons.

What Rutherford and his co-workers did was to project other particles at the atoms under investigation, and from observations of the way in which the projected particles were deflected or *scattered*, they drew conclusions about the distribution of charge within the atoms at which the particles had been projected. Fortunately, a supply of projectiles was available. In certain radioactive disintegrations, there are emitted alpha particles (or α-particles). These particles, which we now know are the nuclei of helium atoms, are ejected with velocities of the order of 10^9 cm/sec. The normal helium atom has two electrons. Its nucleus, the α-particle, therefore has a double positive charge and consists of two protons and two neutrons. Because of the tremendous speeds of α-particles, they are capable of traveling several centimeters in air, or a few tenths or hundredths of a millimeter through solids, before they are brought to rest by collisions.

The experimental setup is shown schematically in Fig. 24–5. A radioactive source at the left emits α-particles. Thick lead screens stop all particles except those in a narrow beam defined by small holes. The beam then passes through a thin metal foil (gold, silver, and copper were used) and strikes a plate coated with zinc sulfide. A momentary flash or scintillation can be observed on the screen whenever it is struck by an α-particle, and the number of particles that have been deflected through any angle from their original direction can therefore be determined.

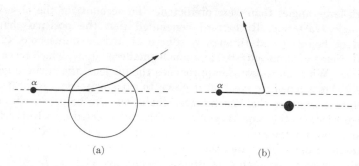

(a)   (b)

FIG. 24–6. (a) Alpha particle scattered through a small angle by the Thomson atom. (b) Alpha particle scattered through a large angle by the Rutherford nuclear atom.

According to the Thomson model, the atoms of a solid are packed together like marbles in a box. The experimental fact that an α-particle can pass right through a sheet of metal foil forces one to conclude, if this model is correct, that the α-particle is capable of actually penetrating the spheres of positive charge. Granted that this is possible, we can compute the deflection it would undergo. The Thomson atom is electrically neutral, so outside the atom no force would be exerted on the α-particle. Within the atom, the electrical force would be due in part to the electrons and in part to the sphere of positive charge. However, the mass of an α-particle is about 7400 times that of an electron, and from momentum considerations it follows that the α-particle can suffer only a negligible scattering as a consequence of forces between it and the much less massive electrons. It is only interactions with the positive charge, which makes up most of the atomic mass, that can deviate the α-particle.

The electrical force on an α-particle within a sphere of positive charge is like the gravitational force on a mass point within a sphere, except that gravitational forces are attractive, while the force between two positive charges is a repulsion. The gravitational intensity within a sphere is zero at the center and increases linearly with distance from the center, because that part of the mass of the sphere lying *outside* any radius exerts no force at interior points. The α-particle is therefore *repelled* from the center of the sphere with a force proportional to its distance from the center, and its trajectory can be computed for any initial direction of approach such as that in Fig. 24–6(a). On the basis of such calculations, Rutherford predicted the number of α-particles that should be scattered at any angle with their original direction.

The experimental results did not agree with the calculations based on the Thomson atom. In particular, many more particles were scattered through large angles than were predicted. To account for the observed large-angle scattering, Rutherford concluded that the positive charge, instead of being spread through a sphere of atomic dimensions (2 or 3×10^{-8} cm) was concentrated in a much smaller volume, which he called a *nucleus*. When an α-particle approaches the nucleus, the entire nuclear charge exerts a repelling effect on it down to extremely small separations, with the consequence that much larger deviations can be produced. Figure 24-6(b) shows the trajectory of an α-particle deflected by a Rutherford nuclear atom, for the same original path as that in part (a) of the figure.

Rutherford again computed the expected number of particles scattered through any angle, assuming an inverse square law of force between the α-particle and the nucleus of the scattering atom. Within the limits of experimental accuracy, the computed and observed results were in agreement down to distances of approach of about 10^{-12} cm. We may therefore say that these experiments verify the Coulomb law for "point" charges, and at the same time indicate that the size of the nucleus is about 10^{-12} cm.

Every serious student of physics should read Rutherford's account of these researches in the *Philosophical Magazine*, **21**, 669 (1911).

24-8 Systems of units. The equations of mechanics can be written more simply if the units of force, mass, and acceleration are chosen of such magnitude that *unit force* imparts *unit acceleration* to *unit mass*. A similar simplification in some of the equations of electricity and magnetism can be attained if this procedure is adopted with regard to Coulomb's law, that is, if the units of force, distance, and quantity of charge are so chosen that two *unit charges* attract (or repel) with *unit force* when separated by *unit distance*. When this is done, the proportionality constant in Coulomb's law is equal to unity.

While some of the common systems of electrical units are set up in this way, there are others in which the units of force, distance, and charge are defined independently of Coulomb's law, with the consequence that the proportionality constant is not equal to unity and must be carried along in all equations which derive from this law.

At the present time, the formulation of the equations of electricity and magnetism is in a stage of transition, with no general agreement on symbols or terminology. One may choose a half-dozen books or articles at random, and find a different system of notation in each. All have something in their favor, and no matter what system we were to adopt in this book the reader would be certain to encounter other systems in his more advanced study and in his reference to material already published.

For many years, the equations of electrostatics have been written using units of the *electrostatic* system, while equations relating to magnetic phenomena used the *electromagnetic* system. Units of the same quantity are not of the same magnitude in the two systems. For example, the electromagnetic unit of charge is 3×10^{10} times as great as the electrostatic unit. Furthermore, the units of the *practical* system, such as the familiar volt, ampere, and ohm, are different from those in both of the above systems. Hence it has been customary to carry along three sets of units and the necessary factors for converting from one to the other.

The mechanical units in both the electrostatic and the electromagnetic systems are those of the cgs system, i.e., the gram, centimeter, dyne, etc. It was pointed out comparatively recently, however, that, with a few minor changes, the units of the familiar practical system would fit nicely into a single system adapted to both electricity and magnetism if, instead of the cgs units, one adopted the mks mechanical units, i.e., the kilogram, meter, newton, etc. There is little doubt that this mks system, in one form or another, will eventually receive world-wide adoption and for that reason it is the one we shall use in this book. When, if ever, general agreement is attained on the precise form the equations should take, it is safe to say they will differ from ours only in the symbols and names used for various quantities, and perhaps in the location of the factor 4π.

Although we shall refer to it only occasionally, some familiarity with the electrostatic system is necessary because of the large number of books, articles, and reference tables already in existence in which this system is used. In the electrostatic system, forces are expressed in dynes, distances in centimeters, and the unit of charge is chosen of such magnitude that the proportionality constant in Coulomb's law is equal to unity. This law, with $k = 1$, then *defines* the unit charge in this system. This unit is called *one statcoulomb*, the prefix "stat" being applied in general to quantities in the electrostatic system. *One statcoulomb* may accordingly be defined as *that charge which repels an equal charge of the same sign with a force of one dyne when the charges are separated by one centimeter*, the charges being carried by bodies whose dimensions are small compared with one centimeter. Coulomb's law takes the simple form

$$F = \frac{qq'}{r^2}. \qquad (24\text{–}3)$$

In the mks system, forces are expressed in newtons and distances in meters. Quantity of charge is defined not by Coulomb's law, but in terms of the unit of current, the ampere. (See Section 33–2.) The mks unit of charge is called *one coulomb* and is defined as the quantity of charge which in one second crosses a section of a conductor in which there is a constant current of one ampere. The coulomb is very nearly 3×10^9 times as large as the statcoulomb. (The precise value is

1 coulomb = 2.99790×10^9 statcoulombs.)

The coulomb is a relatively large quantity of charge and for many purposes the *microcoulomb* (1 μ coulomb = 10^{-6} coulomb) is a unit of more convenient size.

The "natural" unit of electric charge is the charge carried by an electron or proton. The most precise measurements which have been made up to the present time find this charge to be

$$e = 1.601864 \times 10^{-19} \text{ coulomb}$$
$$= 4.80223 \times 10^{-10} \text{ statcoulomb}.$$

One statcoulomb therefore represents the aggregate charge carried by 2.08×10^9 electrons, or about two billion electrons, and one coulomb the charge of about 6×10^{18} electrons. By way of comparison, the total population of the earth is estimated to be about 2×10^9 persons, while on the other hand, a cube of copper one centimeter on a side contains about 8×10^{22} free electrons.

Since the units of force, charge, and distance, in the mks system, are defined independently of Coulomb's law, the numerical value of the proportionality constant k in this system must be found by experiment. In principle, the experiment would consist of measuring the force, in newtons, between two point charges whose charges had been measured in coulombs, at a measured separation expressed in meters. Equation (24–2) could then be solved for k. In practice, the magnitude of k is determined indirectly. The best value to date is, numerically,

$$k = 8.98742 \times 10^9.$$

For most purposes, the approximation $k = 9 \times 10^9$ is sufficiently accurate.

In any system of units, the units of k are those of force $\times$ distance^2 $\div$ charge^2. Hence in the electrostatic system

$$k = 1 \frac{\text{dyne·cm}^2}{\text{statcoulomb}^2},$$

and in the mks system,

$$k = 9 \times 10^9 \frac{\text{newtons·m}^2}{\text{coulomb}^2}.$$

For the purpose of avoiding the appearance of the factor 4π in other equations derived from Coulomb's law, and which are used more frequently than is Coulomb's law itself, we now define a new constant ϵ_0 by the relation

$$\epsilon_0 = \frac{1}{4\pi k},$$

or

$$k = \frac{1}{4\pi\epsilon_0},$$

and write Coulomb's law as

$$F = \frac{1}{4\pi\epsilon_0} \frac{qq'}{r^2}. \qquad\qquad (24\text{--}4)$$

From the numerical value of k given above it follows that in the mks system

$$\epsilon_0 = \frac{1}{4\pi k} = \frac{1}{4\pi \times 9 \times 10^9} = 8.85 \times 10^{-12} \frac{\text{coulomb}^2}{\text{newtons·m}^2},$$

while the factor $1/4\pi\epsilon_0$ is

$$\frac{1}{4\pi\epsilon_0} = k = 9 \times 10^9 \frac{\text{newtons·m}^2}{\text{coulomb}^2}.$$

EXAMPLE. Compute the electrostatic force of repulsion between two α-particles at a separation of 10^{-11} cm, and compare with the force of gravitational attraction between them.

Each α-particle has a charge of $+2e$, or $2 \times 1.60 \times 10^{-19}$ coul $= 3.20 \times 10^{-19}$ coul. The force of repulsion at a separation of 10^{-11} cm or 10^{-13} m is

$$F = \frac{1}{4\pi\epsilon_0} \frac{qq'}{r^2}$$

$$= 9 \times 10^9 \frac{\text{n·m}^2}{\text{coul}^2} \times \frac{3.2 \times 10^{-19} \text{ coul} \times 3.2 \times 10^{-19} \text{ coul}}{(10^{-13} \text{ m})^2}$$

$$= 9.18 \times 10^{-2} \text{ newton,}$$

and since 1 newton $= 10^5$ dynes,

$$F = 9180 \text{ dynes.}$$

This is a sizeable force, equal to the weight of nearly 10 grams!

The mass of an α-particle (2 protons + 2 neutrons) is

$$4 \times 1.67 \times 10^{-24} \text{ gm} = 6.68 \times 10^{-24} \text{ gm}$$

$$= 6.68 \times 10^{-27} \text{ kgm.}$$

The gravitational constant G (see Chapter 5) is

$$G = 6.67 \times 10^{-11} \frac{\text{n·m}^2}{\text{kgm}^2}.$$

The force of gravitational attraction is

$$F = G \frac{mm'}{r^2}$$

$$= 6.67 \times 10^{-11} \frac{\text{n·m}^2}{\text{kgm}^2} \times \frac{6.68 \times 10^{-27} \text{kgm} \times 6.68 \times 10^{-27} \text{kgm}}{(10^{-13} \text{ m})^2}$$

$$= 2.97 \times 10^{-37} \text{ n.}$$

The gravitational force is evidently negligible in comparison with the electrostatic force.

PROBLEMS

$$(\epsilon_0 = 8.85 \times 10^{-12} \text{ coul}^2/\text{n·m}^2, \qquad k = 9 \times 10^9 \text{ n·m}^2/\text{coul}^2)$$

24-1. A point charge of $+24$ statcoul is placed 6 cm from a second point charge of -12 statcoul. (a) What force is exerted on each charge? (b) What is the resultant force on a charge of $+3$ statcoul placed midway between them? (c) At what point must the $+3$ statcoul charge be placed for the resultant force on it to vanish?

24-2. How many excess electrons must be placed on each of two small spheres spaced 3 cm apart if the force of repulsion between the spheres is to be 10^{-19} n?

24-3. (a) A point charge of $+80$ statcoulombs is 5 cm from a point charge of -60 statcoulombs. What force, in dynes, is exerted on each charge by the other? (b) A point charge of $+14.4$ statcoulombs is 4 cm from the positive charge in part (a) and 3 cm from the negative charge. What is the resultant force exerted on it?

24-4. It will be shown in the next chapter that when a conducting sphere 1 cm in radius, in air, is given a charge of more than about 3×10^{-8} coulomb, the air around the sphere becomes conducting and the charge "leaks" away. Use the figure above as the maximum charge a sphere of this radius can retain, in air, and compute the maximum force between two such spheres at a center-to-center distance of 10 cm.

24-5. Each of two small spheres is positively charged, the combined charge totaling 26 statcoul. What is the charge on each sphere if they are repelled with a force of 3 dynes when placed 4 cm apart?

24-6. Point charges of 2×10^{-9} coul are situated at each of three corners of a square whose side is 0.20 m. What would be the magnitude and direction of the resultant force on a point charge of -1×10^{-9} coul if it were placed (a) at the center of the square? (b) at the vacant corner of the square?

24-7. 6.02×10^{23} atoms of monatomic hydrogen have a mass of one gram. How far would the electron of a hydrogen atom have to be removed from the nucleus for the force of attraction to equal the weight of the atom?

24-8. Radium decomposes radioactively to form radon (atomic number 86) by emitting an α-particle from its nucleus. (a) What is the force of repulsion between the radon nucleus and the α-particle when the distance between them is 5×10^{-11} cm? (b) What is the acceleration of the α-particle at this distance?

24-9. One gram of monatomic hydrogen contains 6.02×10^{23} atoms, each atom consisting of a positively-charged nucleus and a single outer electron. If all the electrons in one gram of hydrogen could be concentrated at the north pole of the earth and all the nuclei concentrated at the south pole, what would be the force of attraction between them, in tons? The polar radius of the earth is 6357 km.

24-10. Rutherford's experiments showed that Coulomb's law held for the force of repulsion of two nuclei, down to a separation of about 10^{-12} cm. The gold nucleus consists of 118 neutrons and 79 protons, and the helium nucleus (an α-particle) consists of two neutrons and two protons. (a) What is the force of repulsion, in newtons, between a gold nucleus and an α-particle at a separation of 10^{-12} cm? (b) Find the acceleration of an α-particle when acted on by this force.

24–11. Two very small spheres, each weighing 3×10^{-5} n, are attached to silk fibres 5×10^{-2} m long and hung from a common point. When the spheres are given equal quantities of negative charge, each supporting fibre makes an angle of 30° with the vertical. Find the magnitude of the charges.

24–12. In the Bohr model of the hydrogen atom, an electron revolves in a circular orbit around a nucleus consisting of a single proton. If the radius of the orbit is 5.28×10^{-9} cm, find the number of revolutions of the electron per second. The force of electrostatic attraction between proton and electron provides the centripetal force.

24–13. Two charges of $+10^{-9}$ coul each are 8 cm apart in air. Find the magnitude and direction of the force exerted by these charges on a third charge of $+5 \times 10^{-11}$ coul that is 5 cm distant from each of the first two charges.

24–14. Two small metal-coated balls of mass 14 gm each are held at the ends of silk threads 70 cm long. The other ends of the threads are fastened at a common point. Charges are placed on the balls and they come to equilibrium at a distance of 10 cm from each other. If the charge on one ball is -0.04 μcoul, what is the charge on the other ball?

CHAPTER 25

THE ELECTRIC FIELD

25-1 The electric field. Figure 25-1(a) represents two positively charged bodies A and B, between which there is an electrical force of repulsion, **F**. Like the force of gravitational attraction, this force is of the action-at-a-distance type, making itself felt without the presence of any material connection between A and B. No one knows "why" this is possible—it is an experimental fact that charged bodies behave in this way. It is useful, however, to think of each of the charged bodies as modifying the state of affairs in the space around it, so that this state is different in some way from whatever it may be when the charged bodies are not present. Thus, let body B be removed. Point P, Fig. 25-1(b), is the point of space at which B was formerly located. The charged body A is said to produce or set up an *electric field* at the point P, and if the charged body B is now placed at P, one considers that a force is exerted on B *by the field*, rather than by body A directly. Since a force would be experienced by body B at all points of space around body A, the whole of space around A is an electric field.

One can equally well consider that body B sets up a field, and that a force is exerted on body A by the field of B.

The experimental test for the existence of an electric field at any point is simply to place a charged body, which will be called a *test charge*, at the point. If a force (of electrical origin) is exerted on the test charge, then an electric field exists at the point.

An electric field is said to exist at a point if a force of electrical origin is exerted on a charged body placed at the point.

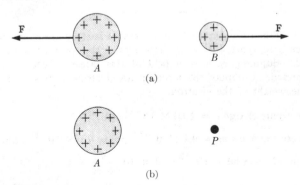

Fig. 25-1. The space around a charged body is an electric field.

Whether or not the force is of electrical origin can be determined by comparing the forces on the test body when it is charged and when it is uncharged. Any force that may be observed when the test body is charged, and which did not exist when it was uncharged, is a force of electrical origin.

Since force is a vector quantity, the electric field is a vector quantity also, having both magnitude and direction. The *magnitude* of the field at any point, represented by E, is defined as *the quotient obtained when the force F on a test charge placed at the point is divided by the quantity of charge q' on the test charge.* In other words, the magnitude of an electric field is the *force per unit charge.*

The *direction* of an electric field at any point is *the direction of the force on a positive test charge placed at the point.* The force on a negative charge, such as an electron, is therefore opposite to the direction of the field. Therefore

$$\mathbf{E} = \frac{\mathbf{F}}{q'}. \tag{25-1}$$

We shall refer to the electric field vector at a point as the *electric intensity* at the point. Several other terms are commonly used, for example, electric field strength, electric field intensity, or merely field intensity. In the mks system, where forces are expressed in newtons and charges in coulombs, the unit of electric intensity is *one newton per coulomb.* Other units in which electric intensity may be expressed will be defined later.

Equation (25–1) may be written

$$\mathbf{F} = q'\mathbf{E}.$$

That is, the force exerted on a charge q' at a point where the electric intensity is $\mathbf{E}$ equals the product of the electric intensity and the charge.

EXAMPLE 1. When the terminals of a 100-volt battery are connected to two parallel plates 1 cm apart, the electric intensity in the space between the plates is 10^4 n/coul. Suppose we have a field of this intensity whose direction is vertically upward. Compute the force on an electron in this field and compare with the weight of the electron.

Electronic charge $e = 1.60 \times 10^{-19}$ coul.

Electronic mass $m = 9.1 \times 10^{-28}$ gm $= 9.1 \times 10^{-31}$ kgm.

$F_{elec} = eE = 1.60 \times 10^{-19}$ coul $\times 10^4 \, \dfrac{\text{n}}{\text{coul}} = 1.60 \times 10^{-15}$ n.

$F_{grav} = mg = 9.1 \times 10^{-31}$ kgm $\times 9.8 \, \dfrac{\text{n}}{\text{kgm}} = 8.9 \times 10^{-30}$ n.

The ratio of the electrical to the gravitational force is therefore

$$\frac{1.60 \times 10^{-15} \text{ n}}{8.9 \times 10^{-30} \text{ n}} = 1.8 \times 10^{14}!$$

It will be seen that the gravitational force is negligible.

EXAMPLE 2. If released from rest, what velocity will the electron of Example 1 acquire while traveling 1 cm? What will then be its kinetic energy? How long a time is required?

The force is constant, so the electron moves with a constant acceleration of

$$a = \frac{F}{m} = \frac{eE}{m} = \frac{1.60 \times 10^{-15} \text{ n}}{9.1 \times 10^{-31} \text{ kgm}} = 1.8 \times 10^{15} \frac{\text{m}}{\text{sec}^2}.$$

Its velocity after traveling 1 cm or 10^{-2} m is

$$v = \sqrt{2ax} = \sqrt{2 \times 1.8 \times 10^{15} \text{ m/sec}^2 \times 10^{-2} \text{ m}} = 6.0 \times 10^6 \frac{\text{m}}{\text{sec}}.$$

Its kinetic energy is

$$\tfrac{1}{2}mv^2 = \tfrac{1}{2} \times 9.1 \times 10^{-31} \text{ kgm} \times \left(6.0 \times 10^6 \frac{\text{m}}{\text{sec}}\right)^2 = 1.6 \times 10^{-17} \text{ joule}.$$

The time is

$$t = \frac{v}{a} = \frac{6.0 \times 10^6 \text{ m/sec}}{1.8 \times 10^{15} \text{ m/sec}^2} = 3.3 \times 10^{-9} \text{ sec}.$$

EXAMPLE 3. If the electron of Example 1 is projected into the field with a horizontal velocity, find the equation of its trajectory (Fig. 25–2).

The direction of the field is upward in Fig. 25–2, so the force on the electron is downward. The initial velocity is along the positive x-axis. The x-acceleration is zero, the y-acceleration is $-(eE/m)$. Hence, after a time t,

$$x = v_0 t,$$

$$y = -\frac{1}{2}\frac{eE}{m}t^2.$$

Elimination of t gives

$$y = -\frac{eE}{2mv_0^2}x^2,$$

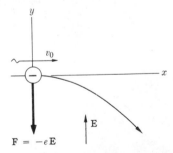

FIG. 25–2. Trajectory of an electron in an electric field.

which is the equation of a parabola. The motion is the same as that of a body projected horizontally in the earth's gravitational field. The deflection of electrons by an electric field is used to control the direction of an electron stream in many electronic devices such as the cathode-ray oscilloscope.

25–2 Calculation of electric intensity. The preceding section describes an experimental method of measuring the electric intensity at a point. The method consists of placing a test charge at the point, measuring the force on it, and taking the ratio of the force to the charge. The electric intensity at a point may also be computed from Coulomb's law if the magnitudes and positions of all charges contributing to the field are known. Thus to find the magnitude of the electric intensity at a point of space P, at a distance r from a point charge q, imagine a test charge q' to be placed at P. The force on the test charge, by Coulomb's law, is

$$F = \frac{1}{4\pi\epsilon_0} \frac{qq'}{r^2},$$

and hence the electric intensity at P is

$$E = \frac{F}{q'} = \frac{1}{4\pi\epsilon_0} \frac{q}{r^2}.$$

The direction of the field is away from the charge q if the latter is positive, toward q if it is negative.

If a number of point charges q_1, q_2, etc., are at distances r_1, r_2, etc., from a given point P, as in Fig. 25–3, each exerts a force on a test charge q' placed at the point, and the resultant force on the test charge is the vector sum of these forces. The resultant electric intensity at the point is the vector sum of the individual electric intensities,

$$\boxed{\mathbf{E} = \mathbf{E}_1 + \mathbf{E}_2 + \cdots.} \qquad (25\text{–}2)$$

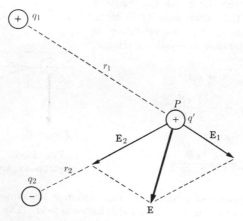

FIG. 25–3. The resultant electric intensity at point P is the vector sum of intensities $\mathbf{E}_1$ and $\mathbf{E}_2$.

EXAMPLE. Point charges q_1 and q_2 of $+12 \times 10^{-9}$ and -12×10^{-9} coul respectively are placed 10 cm apart, as in Fig. 25–4. Compute the electric intensities due to these charges at points a, b, and c.

At point a, the vector due to the positive charge is directed toward the right and its magnitude is

$$9 \times 10^9 \frac{\text{n·m}^2}{\text{coul}^2} \times \frac{12 \times 10^{-9} \text{ coul}}{(0.06 \text{ m})^2} = 3.00 \times 10^4 \frac{\text{n}}{\text{coul}}.$$

The vector due to the negative charge is also directed toward the right and its magnitude is

$$9 \times 10^9 \frac{\text{n·m}^2}{\text{coul}^2} \times \frac{12 \times 10^{-9} \text{ coul}}{(0.04 \text{ m})^2} = 6.75 \times 10^4 \frac{\text{n}}{\text{coul}}.$$

Hence at point a,

$$E_a = (3.00 + 6.75) \times 10^4 \frac{\text{n}}{\text{coul}} = 9.75 \times 10^4 \frac{\text{n}}{\text{coul}}, \text{ toward the right.}$$

At point b, the vector due to the positive charge is directed toward the left and its magnitude is

$$9 \times 10^9 \frac{\text{n·m}^2}{\text{coul}^2} \times \frac{12 \times 10^{-9} \text{ coul}}{(0.04 \text{ m})^2} = 6.75 \times 10^4 \frac{\text{n}}{\text{coul}}.$$

The vector due to the negative charge is directed toward the right and its magnitude is

$$9 \times 10^9 \frac{\text{n·m}^2}{\text{coul}^2} \times \frac{12 \times 10^{-9} \text{ coul}}{(0.14 \text{ m})^2} = 0.55 \times 10^4 \frac{\text{n}}{\text{coul}}.$$

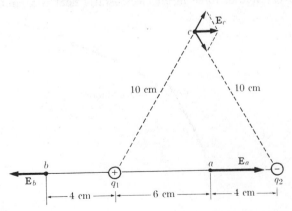

FIG. 25–4. Electric intensity at three points, a, b, and c, in the field set up by charges q_1 and q_2.

Hence at point b,

$$E_b = (6.75 - 0.55) \times 10^4 \, \frac{\text{n}}{\text{coul}} = 6.20 \times 10^4 \, \frac{\text{n}}{\text{coul}}, \text{ toward the left.}$$

At point c, the magnitude of each vector is

$$9 \times 10^9 \, \frac{\text{n·m}^2}{\text{coul}^2} \times \frac{12 \times 10^{-9} \, \text{coul}}{(0.1 \, \text{m})^2} = 1.08 \times 10^4 \, \frac{\text{n}}{\text{coul}}.$$

The directions of these vectors are shown in the figure, and their resultant E_c is easily seen to be

$$E_c = 1.08 \times 10^4 \, \frac{\text{n}}{\text{coul}}, \text{ toward the right.}$$

25–3 Lines of force. The concept of lines of force was introduced by Michael Faraday (1791–1867) as an aid in visualizing electric (and magnetic) fields. A *line of force* (in an electric field) is *an imaginary line drawn in such a way that its direction at any point* (i.e., the direction of its tangent) *is the same as the direction of the field at that point.* (See Fig. 25–5.) Since, in general, the direction of a field varies from point to point, lines of force are usually curves.

Figure 25–6 shows some of the lines of force around a single positive charge; around two equal charges, one positive and one negative; and around two equal positive charges. The direction of the resultant intensity at every point in each diagram is along the tangent to the line of force passing through the point. Arrowheads on the lines indicate the direction in which the tangent is to be drawn.

No lines of force originate or terminate in the space surrounding a charge. Every line of force in an electrostatic field is a continuous line

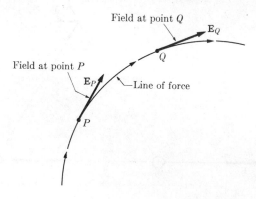

Fig. 25–5. The direction of the electric intensity at any point is tangent to the line of force through that point.

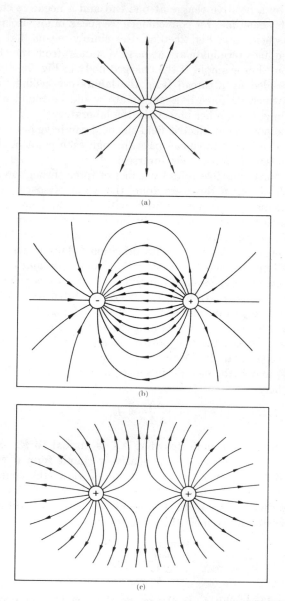

(a)

(b)

(c)

Fig. 25–6. The mapping of an electric field with the aid of lines of force.

terminated by a positive charge at one end and a negative charge at the other. While sometimes for convenience we speak of an "isolated" charge and draw its field as in Fig. 25–6(a), this simply means that the charges on which the lines terminate are at large distances from the charge under consideration. For example, if the charged body in Fig. 25–6(a) is a small sphere suspended by a thread from the laboratory ceiling, the negative charges on which its force lines terminate would be found on the walls, floor, or ceiling, or on other objects in the laboratory.

At any one point in an electric field the field can have but one direction. Hence only one line of force can pass through each point of the field. In other words, lines of force never intersect.

It is, of course, possible to draw a line of force through every point of an electric field, but if this were done, the whole of space and the entire surface of a diagram would be filled with lines, and no individual line could be distinguished. By suitably limiting the number of force lines which one draws to represent a field, the lines can be used to indicate the magnitude of a field as well as its direction. This is accomplished by spacing the lines in such a way that *the number per unit area crossing a surface at right angles to the direction of the field is at every point proportional to the electric intensity.* In a region where the intensity is large, such as that between the positive and negative charges of Fig. 25–6(b), the lines of force are closely spaced, whereas in a region where the intensity is small, such as that between the two positive charges of Fig. 25–6(c), the lines are widely separated. If ΔN lines cross perpendicularly a small element of area ΔA, and if the electric intensity at the center of the element of area is E, then

$$\frac{\Delta N}{\Delta A_n} \propto E,$$

where the subscript n indicates that ΔA is normal to E. Many of the equations of electrostatics take a relatively simple form if we make this proportionality into an equation and choose ϵ_0 as the constant of proportionality. Thus, let us arbitrarily space the electric lines of force in such a way that, at any point, the number of lines per unit area and the electric intensity are connected by the relation

$$\boxed{\frac{\Delta N}{\Delta A_n} = \epsilon_0 E.} \tag{25–3}$$

To understand why ϵ_0 is chosen as the constant of proportionality, consider the lines of force issuing from a positive point charge q, as shown in Fig. 25–6(a). Imagine a spherical surface of arbitrary radius r surrounding this point charge and concentric with it. The magnitude of the electric intensity at all points of the surface of this sphere is

$$E = \frac{1}{4\pi\epsilon_0} \frac{q}{r^2}.$$

The number of lines per unit area is therefore the same at all points of the surface and is given by

$$\epsilon_0 E = \frac{1}{4\pi} \frac{q}{r^2}.$$

Also, since the direction of E is radially outward, the lines of force cross the surface at right angles. The total area A_n of the spherical surface is $4\pi r^2$, so the total number of lines N crossing the surface is

$$N = \epsilon_0 E A_n = q.$$

We therefore see that if the spacing of the lines of force is chosen so that the number per unit area equals $\epsilon_0 E$, the total number of lines issuing from a positive point charge q is exactly equal to q.

25–4 Gauss' law. It was shown in the preceding section that the total number of lines of force N crossing a spherical surface of arbitrary radius having a positive point charge q at its center is numerically equal to q. It should be evident from an examination of Fig. 25–6(a) that the same number of lines will cross a closed surface of any shape enclosing the point charge. Had the charge in Fig. 25–6(a) been negative, the lines of force would have crossed a surface enclosing the charge in an inward direction. If a closed surface is constructed anywhere in the field in such a way that it does *not* enclose the charge, some lines will cross it in an inward direction and these same lines will later cross it in an outward direction (the reader can construct his own diagram). The *net* number of lines crossing the surface in an outward direction is therefore zero.

Gauss' law is a generalization of the conclusions above, applying to a closed surface of any shape in the field set up by any arbitrary distribution of charges, positive or negative. Expressed in terms of lines of force, this law states that the net number of lines of force crossing any closed surface in an outward direction is equal to the net positive charge enclosed within the surface.

$$N = \Sigma q. \tag{25–4}$$

The practical utility of the law arises from the fact that the net number of lines of force, N, can be expressed in terms of the electric intensity at the surface. For a surface of arbitrary shape, in the field set up by an arbitrary charge distribution, lines of force do not in general cross the surface at right angles and the intensity varies in magnitude from point

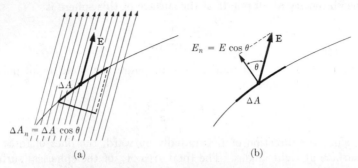

FIG. 25-7. The number of lines of force crossing an area ΔA is $\epsilon_0 E_n \, \Delta A$.

to point of the surface. Figure 25-7(a) shows the lines that cross a typical element of area ΔA. The electric intensity at the center of the element is **E**. The projection of this element at right angles to the lines is $\Delta A_n = \Delta A \cos \theta$, and the number of lines crossing it is

$$\Delta N = \epsilon_0 E \, \Delta A_n = \epsilon_0 E \, \Delta A \cos \theta.$$

Inspection of the diagram shows that those lines, and only those lines, that cross ΔA_n also cross ΔA. Now let us write the preceding equation as

$$\Delta N = \epsilon_0 \, (E \cos \theta) \, \Delta A.$$

But $E \cos \theta$ [see Fig. 25-7(b)] is the magnitude of the component of **E** normal to ΔA, or E_n, so when lines cross a surface in an arbitrary direction, the number of lines crossing an element of the surface equals the product of ϵ_0, the component E_n of electric intensity normal to the element, and the area of the element, ΔA.

$$\Delta N = \epsilon_0 E_n \, \Delta A.$$

Now imagine the surface enclosing the distributed charge to be divided into a number of elements of area ΔA_1, ΔA_2, etc. Let E_{n1}, E_{n2}, etc., represent the normal components of electric intensity at the centers of these elements. The numbers of lines crossing the elements are then $\Delta N_1 = \epsilon_0 E_{n1} \, \Delta A_1$, $\Delta N_2 = \epsilon_0 E_{n2} \, \Delta A_2$, etc., and the total number of lines crossing the entire surface is

$$\begin{aligned}
N &= \Delta N_1 + \Delta N_2 + \cdots \\
&= \epsilon_0' \, (E_{n1} \, \Delta A_1 + E_{n2} \, \Delta A_2 + \cdots) \\
&= \epsilon_0 \sum E_n \, \Delta A.
\end{aligned} \tag{25-5}$$

Having expressed N in terms of E_n, we may now combine Eqs. (25–4) and (25–5) to obtain

$$\epsilon_0 \sum E_n\, \Delta A = \sum q, \qquad\qquad (25\text{–}6)$$

where $\sum q$ is the net positive charge enclosed within the surface. The relation above is *Gauss' law*.

It should be noted that although $\sum q$ includes only the net positive charge *within* the closed surface, the electric intensity **E** is the resultant field due to *all* charges, *both inside and outside the surface*. Note also that the concept of lines of force has dropped out of the final result; the quantities of physical interest are E and $\sum q$. Lines of force provide a useful method of visualizing the electric intensity but their "reality" must not be over-emphasized.

Gauss' law is very useful in dealing with charges and charge distributions that are simple enough to give rise to electric fields which possess some degree of symmetry. In such cases one can find a closed surface consisting of a number of parts of simple geometrical shape, such that over each part of the surface the normal component of E is either zero or is constant and normal to the surface. Then, if sufficient information is given about E, we can calculate $\sum q$ or, conversely, if $\sum q$ is known we can calculate E. A number of illustrations are given in the following sections.

The general proof of Gauss' law is not complicated but is rather long and will not be given. Basically, however, the law is a consequence of the fact that the field of a single point charge follows an inverse square law, and the best experimental proof that this law is correct lies in the great accuracy with which conclusions drawn from Gauss' law are found to be verified.

EXAMPLE. Figure 25–8 is a schematic diagram of a number of charged bodies, showing a few of the force lines of their field, and the traces with the plane of the diagram of four closed surfaces, A, B, C, and D. The actual field, and the closed surfaces, are, of course, three-dimensional. Each $+$ and $-$ sign represents one coulomb.

The number of lines crossing each surface can be found by inspection. Consider first surface A. Four lines leave it and four lines enter it. No line can terminate within the surface, since there is no charge within it. The net number of lines crossing the surface in an outward direction (zero) equals the net charge within the surface (also zero).

Consider next surface B, which encloses 7 units of positive charge. The surface is intersected at 11 points, at 9 of which the lines cross it in an outward direction and at 2 of which the crossing is inward. The net number of lines crossing in an outward direction is $9 - 2 = 7$, and the positive charge within the surface is seven coulombs.

Similar analyses of surfaces C and D are left as an exercise.

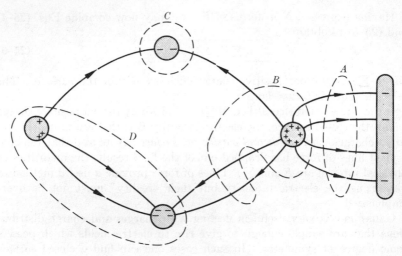

FIG. 25-8. Gauss' law.

25-5 Conclusions from Gauss' law concerning the charge within a conductor. A conductor is a material within which there are free charges, that is, charges which are free to move provided a force is exerted on them by an electric field. If by any means an electric field is maintained within a conductor, there will be a continuous motion of its free charges. (This motion is called a current.) On the other hand, if there is no field within a conductor there will be no motion of its free charges.* We may now reverse the reasoning and conclude that if the charges in a conductor are known to be at rest, the field within the conductor must be zero. With the help of this fact and Gauss' law we may now show that when a conductor is charged, the *excess* charge is confined entirely to the surface of the conductor.

Figure 25-9(a) represents a solid conductor of irregular shape, to which has been given an excess charge q. Construct a surface (shown dotted in the figure and known as a *Gaussian surface*) lying in the material of the conductor, just inside its surface. According to Gauss' law, the net number of lines of force crossing this surface in an outward direction equals the net positive charge enclosed by the surface. But if the charges are at rest, the electric intensity at all points within the conductor is zero. The number of lines crossing the dotted surface is therefore zero and, from

---

* The free electrons within a metal share in the thermal energy of the molecules, but their thermal motion is a random one like that of the molecules in a gas and does not result in a net transfer of charge across any surface. For our present purposes this random electronic motion may be ignored.

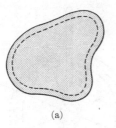 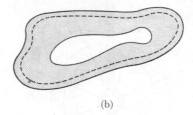

(a)   (b)

FIG. 25–9. Application of Gauss' law to a conductor.

Gauss' law, the net charge within this surface is zero also. All the excess charge on the conductor must therefore lie *outside* the dotted surface. But this surface is only an infinitesimal distance inside the actual surface of the conductor. Hence all the excess charge on the conductor lies on its surface.

The fact that an electric charge, that is, an excess or deficiency of electrons, resides only on the surface of a conductor is seen to be a consequence of Gauss' law. Although we have given no proof of Gauss' law, it should be emphasized that the proof rests upon the inverse square law of attraction or repulsion among electric charges. As a matter of fact, starting with the contention that a charge resides on the surface, it is possible to derive the inverse square law. If like charges repelled one another with a force inversely proportional, say, to the cube of the separation, the charges on conductors would not be found on the surface only.

If the conductor is not solid but is hollow, as in Fig. 25–9(b), the same result holds true. Provided there are no charges within the cavity, the electric intensity in the cavity is zero and there are no charges on the inner wall of the conductor. The fact that the field within a closed conductor is zero is the basis of what is known as electrical or electrostatic *shielding*. Any device such as an electroscope can be isolated from the influence of other charges by surrounding it by a conductor. An interesting experiment is to surround an electroscope by a shield of wire mesh. The shield may be connected directly to one terminal of a static machine, and the electroscope will show practically no deflection when the machine is in operation. The wire mesh is not a continuous closed surface, but its shielding is nearly as effective as if it were.

Consider next an uncharged hollow conducting sphere with a small hole in its surface through which a body with a charge $+q$ may be introduced into the cavity, as shown in Fig. 25–10(a). At first the electric field set up by the charged body penetrates the walls of the hollow sphere, and a momentary rearrangement of the charges within the walls takes place. A negative induced charge appears on the inner surface of the sphere, and a positive charge is induced on the outer surface, as shown in Fig. 25–10(b).

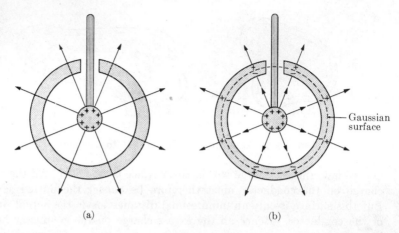

(a)   (b)

FIG. 25-10. Induced charges on the inner and outer surfaces of a hollow conductor.

Imagine a spherical Gaussian surface drawn within the material of the walls of the hollow sphere, as in Fig. 25-10(b). Except for the small part of the Gaussian surface within the hole, the electric field at the Gaussian surface is zero, since motion of all charges has ceased. Therefore $\sum q$ within the Gaussian surface is zero, and the induced negative charge $-q$ on the inner surface of the hollow sphere is equal to the positive charge $+q$ of the body that was introduced into the cavity. Since the hollow sphere was originally uncharged, the positive charge on its outer surface is equal to the charge q within the cavity.

If the small charged body is moved around within the cavity, the *distribution* of induced charge on the inner surface changes but its magnitude remains the same. If, however, the charged body is touched to the inner wall of the hollow sphere, its positive charge will be completely neutralized by the equal induced negative charge on the inner wall, and the small body will therefore lose all of its original charge. An equal positive charge will be found on the outside wall of the hollow sphere.

Now that the outer surface of the hollow sphere is charged, suppose that the small body is withdrawn, recharged, and again introduced into the cavity. Using the same Gaussian surface, we may show that again there is an induced charge on the inner wall, equal in magnitude to that of the charge q on the small body but of opposite kind. Since the *total* charge on the hollow sphere is not altered, the positive charge on its outer surface increases by an amount q. If the small body is again touched to the inner wall, its charge will again be neutralized. Therefore by touching a charged body to the *inner* wall of a hollow conducting sphere, the charge on the body may, in effect, be *completely* transferred to the outer surface of the hollow sphere, no matter what charge already resides on this outer surface. This fact, which is the underlying principle of the Van de Graaff generator, will be discussed quantitatively in the next chapter after the concept of potential has been introduced.

25–6 Conclusions from Gauss' law concerning the field outside a charged conductor. In the preceding section we used Gauss' law to arrive at a conclusion about $\sum q$, starting with information about **E**. In this section we shall use Gauss' law in the reverse manner: starting with a given charge distribution, we shall calculate the magnitude of E at any point in the neighborhood of this charge distribution.

Field around a charged sphere. Let the inner circle of Fig. 25–11 represent the intersection of the plane of the paper with a conducting sphere of radius a. Suppose a positive charge q is uniformly distributed on the surface of the sphere. By symmetry, the electric lines of force are equally spaced and are directed radially outward. Construct as a Gaussian surface a sphere of radius r, shown by the dotted circle in Fig. 25–11. Since the lines of force cross this surface normally, the total number of lines of force crossing it in an outward direction is the product of ϵ_0, the electric intensity E at the surface, and the area of the surface, $4\pi r^2$. Since the quantity of charge enclosed within the surface is q, Gauss' law becomes

$$\epsilon_0 E \times 4\pi r^2 = q,$$

or

$$E = \frac{1}{4\pi\epsilon_0}\frac{q}{r^2},$$

which is exactly the same expression as that given in Section 25–2 for the intensity at a distance r from a *point* charge q.

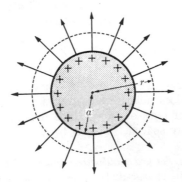

Fig. 25–11. Gaussian surface for a charged sphere.

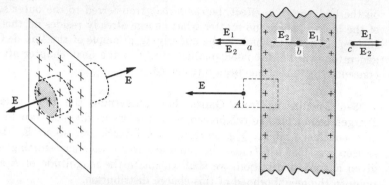

FIG. 25–12. Gaussian surface in the   FIG. 25–13. Electric field inside and
form of a cylinder for finding the field   outside a charged conducting plate.
of an infinite plane sheet of charge.

Therefore, *the field outside a uniformly charged conducting sphere is the same as though all of the charge were concentrated at the center of the sphere.* The field inside the sphere is zero.

The preceding equation also gives the electric intensity at points in the space between two concentric spherical conductors.

Field of an infinite plane sheet of charge. To solve this problem, construct the Gaussian surface shown by dotted lines in Fig. 25–12, consisting of a cylinder whose ends have an area A and whose walls are perpendicular to the sheet of charge. By symmetry, since the sheet is infinite, the electric intensity E is the same on both sides of the surface, is uniform, and is directed normally away from the sheet of charge. No lines of force cross the side walls of the cylinder, that is, the component of E normal to these walls is zero. At the ends of the cylinder the normal component of E is equal to E. The expression $\epsilon_0 \sum E_n \, \Delta A$, calculated over the entire surface of the cylinder, therefore reduces to $2\epsilon_0 EA$. If σ is the charge per unit area in the plane sheet, the net positive charge within the Gaussian surface is σA. Hence

$$2\epsilon_0 EA = \sigma A, \qquad E = \frac{\sigma}{2\epsilon_0}.$$

Note that the magnitude of the field is independent of the distance from the plate and does not decrease inversely with the square of the distance. In terms of lines of force, these remain everywhere straight, parallel, and uniformly spaced. This is because the plate was assumed infinitely large.

Field of an infinite charged conducting plate. When a metal plate is given a net charge, this charge distributes itself over the entire outer surface of the plate, and if the plate is of uniform thickness and is infinitely large (or if we are not too near the edges of a finite plate), the charge per unit area is uniform and is the same on both surfaces. Hence the field of such a charged plate arises from the superposition of the fields of *two* sheets of charge, one on each surface of the plate. By symmetry, the field is perpendicular to the plate, directed away from it if the plate has a positive charge, and is uniform. The magnitude of the electric intensity at any point can be found from Gauss' law or by using the results already derived for a sheet of charge.

Figure 25–13 shows a portion of a large charged conducting plate. Let σ represent the charge per unit area in the sheet of charge on *either* surface. At point a, outside the plate at the left, the component of electric intensity E_1, due to the sheet of charge on the left face of the plate, is directed toward the left and its magnitude is $\sigma/2\epsilon_0$. The component E_2 due to the sheet of charge on the right face of the plate is also toward the left and its magnitude is also $\sigma/2\epsilon_0$. The magnitude of the resultant intensity E is therefore

$$E = E_1 + E_2 = \frac{\sigma}{2\epsilon_0} + \frac{\sigma}{2\epsilon_0} = \frac{\sigma}{\epsilon_0}.$$

At point b, inside the plate, the two components of electric intensity are in opposite directions and their resultant is zero, as it must be in any conductor in which the charges are at rest. At point c the components again add and the magnitude of the resultant is σ/ϵ_0, directed toward the right.

To derive these results from Gauss' law, consider the cylinder shown by dotted lines. Its end faces are of area A and one lies inside and one outside the plate. The field inside the conductor is zero. The field outside, by symmetry, is perpendicular to the plate, so the normal component of $\mathbf{E}$ is zero over the walls of the cylinder and is equal to $\mathbf{E}$ over the outside end face. Hence, from Gauss' law,

$$\epsilon_0 E A = \sigma A, \qquad E = \frac{\sigma}{\epsilon_0}.$$

Field just outside any charged conductor. Consider a portion of a charged conductor, such as that shown in Fig. 25–14. The charge, of course, resides on the surface of the conductor and is at rest. If we assume that the electric intensity $\mathbf{E}$ just outside the surface makes an angle ϕ with the normal to the surface, as shown at the left of the diagram, then the vector $\mathbf{E}$ may be resolved into components perpendicular and parallel to the surface. Under the influence of the parallel component, $E \sin \phi$, charges would move along the surface of the conductor. But since the charges are at rest, the component $E \sin \phi$ is zero and the field is normal to the surface. Hence lines of force intersect the surface of any charged conductor at right angles, when the charges on the conductor are at rest. In general,

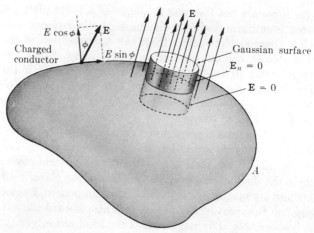

FIG. 25-14. The field outside a charged conductor is perpendicular to the surface and, at points near the conductor, is equal to σ/ϵ_0.

the lines will change their direction as we move away from the surface, depending on the location of other charges in the vicinity. (If the conductor is carrying a current, the charges within it are not at rest and lines of force do not intersect it at right angles.)

To calculate the magnitude of the electric intensity just outside the conductor, construct a Gaussian surface in the form of a small cylinder, one of whose end faces, of area A, lies within the conductor, while the other lies just outside. The electric intensity is zero at all points of the surface within the conductor. Outside the conductor, the normal component of $\mathbf{E}$ is zero at the side walls of the cylinder (since we have shown that $\mathbf{E}$ is normal to the conductor), while over the end faces the normal component of $\mathbf{E}$ is equal to $\mathbf{E}$. Hence, from Gauss' law,

$$\epsilon_0 E A = \sigma A,$$

$$\boxed{E = \frac{\sigma}{\epsilon_0}.} \qquad (25\text{--}7)$$

This agrees with the result already obtained for the field at points outside an infinite charged conducting plate, and it shows that, whatever the shape of a conductor, when the field at any point due to *all* of the charges on its surface is taken into account, the components just cancel one another at internal points and give rise to a field of magnitude σ/ϵ_0 at points just outside the surface. For a plate with parallel faces, as in Fig. 25-13, it is easy to see how this cancellation or addition is brought about.

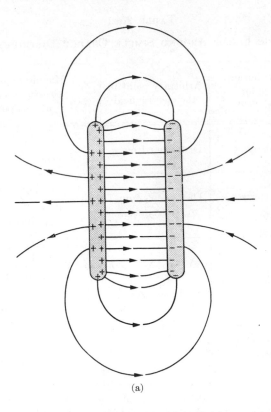

(a)

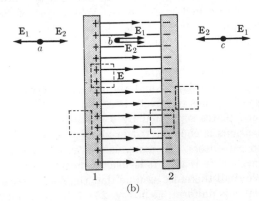

(b)

FIG. 25–15. Electric field between oppositely charged parallel plates.

TABLE 25-1

ELECTRIC FIELDS AROUND SIMPLE CHARGE DISTRIBUTIONS

Charge distribution responsible for the electric field	Arbitrary point in the electric field	Magnitude of the electric intensity at this point
Single point charge q	Distance r from q	$E = \dfrac{1}{4\pi\epsilon_0} \cdot \dfrac{q}{r^2}$
Several point charges, $q_1, q_2, \ldots$	Distance r_1 from q_1, r_2 from $q_2 \ldots$	$E = \dfrac{1}{4\pi\epsilon_0}\left(\dfrac{q_1}{r_1^2} + \dfrac{q_2}{r_2^2} + \cdots\right)$ (vector sum)
Charge q uniformly distributed on the surface of a conducting sphere of radius a	(a) Outside, $r > a$ (b) Inside, $r < a$	(a) $E = \dfrac{1}{4\pi\epsilon_0} \cdot \dfrac{q}{r^2}$ (b) $E = 0$
Two equally and oppositely charged conducting plates with charge per unit area σ	Any point between plates	$E = \dfrac{\sigma}{\epsilon_0}$

Field between oppositely charged parallel plates. When two plane parallel conducting plates, having the size and spacing shown in Fig. 25-15, are given equal and opposite charges, the field between and around them is approximately as shown in Fig. 25-15(a). While most of the charge accumulates at the opposing faces of the plates and the field is essentially uniform in the space between them, there is a small quantity of charge on the outer surfaces of the plates and a certain spreading or "fringing" of the field at the edges of the plates.

As the plates are made larger and the distance between them diminished, the fringing becomes relatively less. Such an arrangement of two oppositely charged plates separated by a distance small compared with their linear dimensions is encountered in many pieces of electrical equipment, notably in capacitors. In many instances the fringing is entirely negligible, and even if it is not, it is usually neglected for simplicity in computation. We shall therefore assume that the field between two oppositely charged plates is uniform, as in Fig. 25-15(b), and that the charges are distributed uniformly over the opposing surfaces.

The electric intensity at any point can be considered either as the resultant of that due to two sheets of charge of opposite sign, or it may be found from Gauss' law. Thus at points a and c in Fig. 25-15(b), the components $\mathbf{E}_1$ and $\mathbf{E}_2$ are each of magnitude $\sigma/2\epsilon_0$ but are oppositely directed, so their resultant is zero. At any point b between the plates the components are in the same direction and their resultant is σ/ϵ_0. It is left as an exercise to show that the same results follow from applying Gauss' law to the surfaces shown by dotted lines.

The results obtained so far are summarized in Table 25-1.

25-7 The Millikan oil-drop experiment.

We have now developed the theory of electrostatics to a point where one of the classical experiments of all time can be described—the measurement of the charge of an individual electron by Robert Andrews Millikan.

Millikan's apparatus is shown in Fig. 25-16. A and B are two accurately parallel horizontal metal plates. Oil is sprayed in fine droplets from an atomizer above the upper plate, and a few of the droplets are allowed to fall through a small hole in this plate. A beam of light is directed between the plates and a telescope set up with its axis transverse to the light beam. The oil drops, illuminated by the light beam, appear like tiny bright stars when viewed through the telescope, falling slowly under the combined influence of their weight, the buoyant force of the air, and the viscous force opposing their motion.

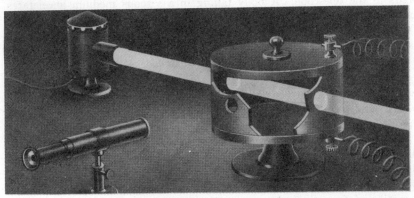

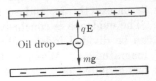

Fig. 25-16. Millikan's oil-drop experiment.

It is found that the oil droplets in the spray from an atomizer are electrically charged, presumably because of frictional effects. This charge is usually negative, meaning that the drops have acquired one or more excess electrons. If now the upper plate is positively charged and the lower plate negatively charged, the region between the plates becomes a uniform electric field. By adjusting the electric intensity, the force exerted on a negatively charged drop by the field may be made just equal to the weight of the drop less the buoyant force of the air, so that the drop can be held stationary between the plates. When the field has been adjusted to this value, we have

$$qE = \text{weight} - \text{buoyant force}$$

$$= \tfrac{4}{3}\pi a^3 g(\rho - \rho'), \tag{25-8}$$

where q is the charge of the drop, E the electric intensity, g the acceleration due to gravity, a the radius of the drop, ρ its density, and ρ' the density of air. Hence, if E, g, a, ρ, and ρ' are known, the charge may be found.

The radii of the drops are about 10^{-5} cm, much too small to be measured directly. Millikan devised an extremely ingenious method for determining these radii. When the field is removed, the drop falls slowly and its rate of fall may be measured by timing it as it passes reference cross hairs in the telescope. A body falling in a viscous medium accelerates until a terminal velocity is reached such that the net downward force (weight minus buoyant force) equals the viscous force as given by Stokes' law:

$$\tfrac{4}{3}\pi a^3 g(\rho - \rho') = 6\pi \eta a v, \tag{25-9}$$

where η is the viscosity of the medium and v the terminal velocity. Since g, ρ, ρ', and η are known and v may be measured, a can be found. Hence q can be computed from Eq. (25–8).

During the course of experiments carried on over the period 1909–1913, Millikan and his co-workers measured the charges of some thousands of drops, with the following remarkable result. Every drop observed was found to have a charge equal to some small integral multiple of a basic quantity of (negative) charge e. That is, drops were observed having charges of e, or exactly $2e$ or exactly $3e$, and so forth, but never such values as $0.76e$ or $2.49e$. The evidence is conclusive that electric charge is not something which can be divided indefinitely, but that it exists in nature only in units of magnitude e. When a drop is observed with charge e, we conclude it has acquired one extra electron, if its charge is $2e$, it has two extra electrons, and so on.

Measurements of the electronic charge by Millikan's method are still being carried on in a number of laboratories. The best results to date give*

$$e = 1.6065 \times 10^{-19} \text{ coulomb}$$

$$= 4.8130 \times 10^{-10} \text{ statcoulomb.}$$

The brief description above cannot do justice to Millikan's work. For a more complete description of his experiments see Millikan's book, *Electrons (+ and −)* . . . .

25–8 Dielectric strength. An insulator, or dielectric, is a substance within which there are no (or at least relatively few) charged particles free to move continuously under the influence of an electric field. For every dielectric there exists, however, a certain limiting electric intensity above which the substance loses its insulating properties and becomes a conductor. The maximum electric intensity which a dielectric can withstand without breakdown is called its *dielectric strength*. For example, the dielectric strength of air at atmospheric pressure is about 3×10^6 n/coul, while that of glass is two or three times as great.

Since the maximum electric intensity that can exist in air at atmospheric pressure without breakdown is about 3×10^6 n/coul, the maximum charge per unit area on the surface of a conductor in air can be computed from Eq. (25–7), setting $E = 3 \times 10^6$. One finds

$$\sigma = \epsilon_0 E = 8.85 \times 10^{-12} \frac{\text{coul}^2}{\text{n·m}^2} \times 3 \times 10^6 \frac{\text{n}}{\text{coul}} = 27 \times 10^{-6} \frac{\text{coul}}{\text{m}^2}.$$

Hence the maximum *total* charge that can be retained by a metal sphere 1 cm in radius in air is

$$q = 4\pi a^2 \sigma = 3.3 \times 10^{-8} \text{ coul.}$$

It is of interest to compare this charge with the total charge of all the free electrons in the sphere. Assume the sphere to be of copper, of density 8.8 gm/cm^3. Its volume is $4\pi a^3/3$ or 4.2 cm^3, its mass is 37 gm, and it therefore contains $37/63 = 0.59$ mole of copper, or 3.5×10^{23} atoms. If each atom contributes one free electron, of charge 1.6×10^{-19} coul, the total free electronic charge is 5.6×10^4 coul. Hence an excess charge of 3.3×10^{-8} coul means an excess (or deficiency) of only about one free electron in 10^{12}. The sphere may be "highly charged," but the proportional change in its normal electron population is negligible.

* This figure differs slightly from that quoted in Section 24–8, which is based on the results of *all* measurements of e, including those made by other methods.

Actually, the conditions under which a spark will jump from one conductor to another in air are much more complex than is implied by the simple statement that the electric intensity cannot exceed 3×10^6 n/coul. The size and shape of the conductors, their separation, and many other factors must be considered. A text on the conduction of electricity in gases should be consulted for further details.

PROBLEMS

$$(\epsilon_0 = 8.85 \times 10^{-12} \text{ coul}^2/\text{n·m}^2, \qquad k = 9 \times 10^9 \text{ n·m}^2/\text{coul}^2)$$

25–1. A small object carrying a charge of -5×10^{-9} coul experiences a downward force of 20×10^{-9} n when placed at a certain point in an electric field. (a) What is the electric intensity at the point? (b) What would be the magnitude and direction of the force acting on an α-particle placed at the point?

25–2. What must be the charge on a particle of mass 2 gm for it to remain stationary in space when placed in a downward directed electric field of intensity 500 n/coul?

25–3. The electric intensity in the region between the deflecting plates of a certain cathode-ray oscilloscope is 30,000 n/coul. (a) What is the force on an electron in this region? (b) What is the acceleration of an electron when acted on by this force?

25–4. A uniform electric field exists in the region between two oppositely charged plane parallel plates. An electron is released from rest at the surface of the negatively charged plate and strikes the surface of the opposite plate, 2 cm distant from the first, in a time interval of 1.5×10^{-8} sec. (a) Find the electric intensity. (b) Find the velocity of the electron when it strikes the second plate.

25–5. In Fig. 25–17, an electron is projected along the axis midway between the plates of a cathode-ray tube with an initial velocity of 2×10^7 m/sec. The uniform electric field between the plates has an intensity of 20,000 n/coul and is upward. (a) How far below the axis has the electron moved when it reaches the end of the plates? (b) At what angle with the axis is it moving as it leaves the plates? (c) How far below the axis will it strike the fluorescent screen S?

25–6. An electron is projected with an initial velocity $v_0 = 10^7$ m/sec into the uniform field between the parallel plates in Fig. 25–18. The direction of the field is vertically downward, and the field is zero except in the space between the plates. The electron enters the field at a point midway between the plates. If the electron just misses the upper plate as it emerges from the field, find the magnitude of the electric intensity.

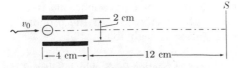

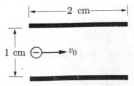

FIGURE 25–17   FIGURE 25–18

25-7. An electron is projected into a uniform electric field of intensity 5000 n/coul. The direction of the field is vertically upward. The initial velocity of the electron is 10^7 m/sec, at an angle of 30° above the horizontal. (a) Find the maximum distance the electron rises vertically above its initial elevation. (b) After what horizontal distance does the electron return to its original elevation? (c) Sketch the trajectory of the electron.

25-8. In a rectangular coordinate system a charge of 25×10^{-9} coul is placed at the origin of coordinates, and a charge of -25×10^{-9} coul is placed at the point $x = 6$ m, $y = 0$. What is the electric intensity at (a) $x = 3$ m, $y = 0$; (b) $x = 3$ m, $y = 4$ m?

25-9. A charge of 16×10^{-9} coul is fixed at the origin of coordinates, a second charge of unknown magnitude is at $x = 3$ m, $y = 0$, and a third charge of 12×10^{-9} coul is at $x = 6$ m, $y = 0$. What is the magnitude of the unknown charge if the resultant field at $x = 8$ m, $y = 0$ is 20.25 n/coul directed to the right?

25-10. In a rectangular coordinate system, two positive point charges of 10^{-8} coulomb each are fixed at the points $x = +0.1$ m, $y = 0$, and $x = -0.1$ m, $y = 0$. Find the magnitude and direction of the electric intensity at the following points: (a) the origin; (b) $x = 0.2$ m, $y = 0$; (c) $x = 0.1$ m, $y = 0.15$ m; (d) $x = 0$, $y = 0.1$ m.

25-11. Same as Problem 10, except that one of the point charges is positive and the other negative.

25-12. How many excess electrons must be added to an isolated spherical conductor 10 cm in diameter to produce a field just outside the surface whose intensity is 1.3×10^{-3} n/coul?

25-13. The plates in the cathode-ray tube of Problem 5 have a width of 3 cm.

What is the total number of lines of force between the two plates? Neglect end effects.

25-14. The maximum charge that can be retained by one of the spherical terminals of a large Van de Graaff generator is about 10^{-3} coulomb. Assume a positive charge of this magnitude, distributed uniformly over the surface of a sphere in otherwise empty space. (a) Compute the magnitude of the electric intensity at a point outside the sphere, 5 m from its center. (b) If an electron were released at this point, what would be the magnitude and direction of its initial acceleration?

25-15. (a) What is the electric intensity in the field of a gold nucleus, at a distance of 10^{-12} cm from the nucleus? (See Problem 24-10.) (b) What is the electric intensity in the field of a proton, at a distance of 5.28×10^{-9} cm from the proton? (See Problem 24-12.)

25-16. A uniformly charged conducting sphere of 0.4 m diameter has a surface charge density of $8 \,\mu\text{coul}/\text{m}^2$. What is the total number of lines of force leaving the surface of the sphere?

25-17. The charge density on the surface of a conducting sphere is 8.85×10^{-7} coul/m^2, and the electric intensity 2 m from the surface of the sphere is 3.6×10^4 n/coul. Determine the radius of the sphere.

25-18. The electric intensity in the region between a pair of oppositely charged plane parallel plates, each 100 cm^2 in area, is 10 n/coul. What is the charge on each plate? Neglect edge effects.

25-19. A small sphere whose mass is 0.1 gm carries a charge of 3×10^{-10} coulomb and is attached to one end of a silk fiber 5 cm long. The other end of the fiber is attached to a large vertical conducting plate which has a surface charge of 25×10^{-6} coul/m^2. Find the angle which the fiber makes with the vertical.

25–20. Using Gauss' law show that the electric field at a distance r from a long thin straight wire carrying a charge per unit length of λ coul/m is given by $E = \lambda/2\pi\epsilon_0 r$. [Hint: Take as a Gaussian surface a cylinder concentric with the wire, of unit length and radius r.]

25–21. Prove that the electric field outside an infinitely long cylindrical conductor with a uniform surface charge is the same as if all the charge were on the axis. Let R represent the radius of the cylinder and take as a Gaussian surface a coaxial cylinder of radius r, where $r > R$.

25–22. A coaxial cable consists of an inner cylindrical conductor of radius R_1 and an outer coaxial cylinder of inner radius R_2. The inner cylinder has a uniform positive charge λ per unit length, and the outer cylinder has an equal negative charge. With the aid of Gauss' law, calculate the electric intensity (a) at any point between the two cylinders, and (b) at any external point. Assume the cable to be infinitely long.

25–23. A charged oil drop, in a Millikan oil-drop apparatus, is observed to fall through a distance of 1 mm in a time of 27.4 sec, in the absence of any external field. The same drop can be held stationary in a field of 2.37×10^4 n/coul. How many excess electrons has the drop acquired? The viscosity of air is 180×10^{-7} n · sec/m^2. The density of the oil is 824 kgm/m^3, and the density of air is 1.29 kgm/m^3.

25–24. An oil droplet of mass 3×10^{-11} gm and of radius 2×10^{-4} cm carries 10 excess electrons. What is its terminal velocity (a) when falling in a region in which there is no electric

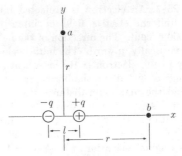

FIGURE 25–19

field? (b) When falling in an electric field whose intensity is 3×10^5 n/coul directed downward? The viscosity of air is 180×10^{-7} n · sec/m^2. Neglect the buoyant force of the air.

25–25. An "electric doublet" or "electric dipole" consists of a pair of electric charges of equal magnitude and opposite sign, as in Fig. 25–19. (a) Prove that the electric intensity set up by the doublet at point a is parallel to the x-axis and is approximately

$$E = \frac{1}{4\pi\epsilon_0} \frac{ql}{r^3} \quad \text{when } r \gg l.$$

(b) Prove that the electric intensity at b is also parallel to the x-axis and is approximately

$$E = \frac{1}{4\pi\epsilon_0} \frac{2ql}{r^3} \quad \text{when } r \gg l.$$

25–26. Suppose that positive charge is uniformly distributed throughout a spherical volume of radius R, the charge per unit volume being ρ. (a) Use Gauss' law to prove that the electric intensity inside the volume, at a distance r from the center, is

$$E = \frac{\rho r}{3\epsilon_0}.$$

(b) What is the electric intensity at a point outside the spherical volume at a distance r from the center? (c) Compare the answers to (a) and (b) when $r = R$.

CHAPTER 26

POTENTIAL

26-1 Electrical potential energy. When a body is lifted from the surface of the earth, the system composed of earth and body has a property that did not exist before. In falling back to the earth, the body may compress a spring, or lift another body, or turn an electric generator, etc. In other words, the work done in separating two parts of a system which attract each other (earth and body) can be recovered. These ideas have been discussed in Chapter 7, and lead to the concept of gravitational potential energy. The work done to separate the body from the earth increases the gravitational potential energy of the system, and when the two parts come together, this gravitational potential energy is liberated and can be converted into other forms of energy.

Precisely the same ideas may be applied to any system composed of bodies that attract each other. The attraction need not necessarily be gravitational. Work must be done to separate a positive from a negative charge, and this work can be recovered when the two charges are allowed to approach each other. Unlike gravitational forces, which are always attractive, the electrical force between two positive or two negative charges is a repulsion. This does not alter the situation except that work must be done to bring two like charges together. The work then may be recovered when the charges are allowed to separate. When two unlike charges are separated, or when two like charges are brought together, the electrical potential energy of the system is increased and the change of electrical potential energy is defined as the work done to effect the separation or the approach.

Consider a small test body with a positive charge q' and of negligible mass in the electric field produced by a positive point charge q, shown in Fig. 26-1. We wish to calculate the work of the electric force when the charge q' is moved from any point a to any other point b along any path connecting these points. Let us subdivide the path into a number of small linear displacements such as $a \rightarrow 1$, $1 \rightarrow 2$, etc., which taken together in sufficient number may be made to approach the actual curved path as closely as we please. In the first step, from $a \rightarrow 1$, the test charge q' is acted on by a force $q'\mathbf{E}$ which makes an angle θ with the line Δs. Since the component of $q'\mathbf{E}$ along the line of Δs has a direction opposite that of the displacement Δs, the work of the electric force is

$$\Delta W_{a \rightarrow 1} = -(q'E \cos \theta) \, \Delta s.$$

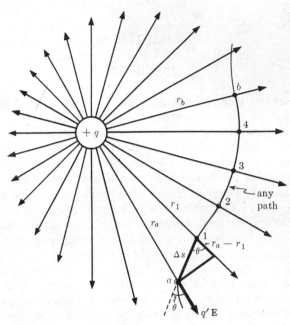

FIG. 26-1. Work done in transferring a small positive test charge q' from point a to point b along any path in the electric field of a positive charge q.

In moving from a to 1, the magnitude of E varies from the value

$$E_a = \frac{1}{4\pi\epsilon_0} \frac{q}{r_a^2} \text{ (at point } a\text{)}$$

to

$$E_1 = \frac{1}{4\pi\epsilon_0} \frac{q}{r_1^2} \text{ (at point 1).}$$

Since points a and 1 are very close together, these two forces do not differ appreciably, and we may replace the actual variable intensity E by an average value

$$E = \frac{1}{4\pi\epsilon_0} \frac{q}{r_a r_1} \text{ (average between } a \text{ and 1).}$$

Also, it is clear from Fig. 26-1 that

$$\Delta s \cos \theta = r_a - r_1.$$

Therefore, since $\Delta W = -(q'E)(\Delta s \cos \theta)$,

$$\Delta W_{a \to 1} = -\frac{q'}{4\pi\epsilon_0}\frac{q}{r_a r_1}(r_a - r_1),$$

or

$$\Delta W_{a \to 1} = -\frac{q'q}{4\pi\epsilon_0}\left(\frac{1}{r_1} - \frac{1}{r_a}\right).$$

In similar manner,

$$\Delta W_{1 \to 2} = -\frac{q'q}{4\pi\epsilon_0}\left(\frac{1}{r_2} - \frac{1}{r_1}\right),$$

$$\Delta W_{2 \to 3} = -\frac{q'q}{4\pi\epsilon_0}\left(\frac{1}{r_3} - \frac{1}{r_2}\right),$$

$$\Delta W_{3 \to 4} = -\frac{q'q}{4\pi\epsilon_0}\left(\frac{1}{r_4} - \frac{1}{r_3}\right),$$

and

$$\Delta W_{4 \to b} = -\frac{q'q}{4\pi\epsilon_0}\left(\frac{1}{r_b} - \frac{1}{r_4}\right).$$

When these equations are added, the sum of the left-hand members becomes the total work $W_{a \to b}$, whereas in the sum of the right-hand members, the terms $1/r_1$, $1/r_2$, $1/r_3$, and $1/r_4$ cancel, leaving

$$W_{a \to b} = -\frac{q'q}{4\pi\epsilon_0}\left(\frac{1}{r_b} - \frac{1}{r_a}\right). \tag{26–1}$$

As the number of subdivisions is increased, the path $a \to b$ is more closely approximated, so that Eq. (26–1) is a rigorous result.

Since the result depends only on the initial and final distances of the points a and b from the charge q, it follows that the work is the same for *any* path between these points (or between any pair of points at the distances r_a and r_b from the charge q). Also, if the test charge is returned from point b to point a along any path, the work done to move it from a to b can be completely recovered. The electric force is therefore a *conservative* force (see Chapter 7) and we are justified in defining an *electric potential energy*, according to the same principles that were developed in Chapter 7 in connection with gravitational potential energy. The term $(1/4\pi\epsilon_0)(qq'/r_a)$ represents the potential energy at a distance r_a from the charge q, and the term $(1/4\pi\epsilon_0)(qq'/r_b)$ represents its potential energy at a distance r_b. Since the distances r_a and r_b are arbitrary, the potential energy of a point charge q' at any distance r from a point charge q is

$$\text{P.E.} = \frac{1}{4\pi\epsilon_0}\frac{qq'}{r}. \tag{26–2}$$

Now suppose the field is set up by some arbitrary distribution of charges. These can always be subdivided, in imagination, into a number of point charges q_1, q_2, ... Let r_1, r_2, . . . represent the distances from these charges to a test charge q' at point a, in Fig. 26–2. Since energy is a scalar quantity, the total potential energy of the test charge q' is the *algebraic* sum of its potential energies with respect to all the other charges.

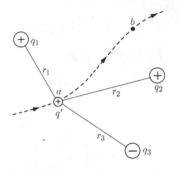

$$(\text{P.E.})_a = \frac{1}{4\pi\epsilon_0}\, q' \left(\frac{q_1}{r_1} + \frac{q_2}{r_2} + \cdots\right)$$

$$= \frac{1}{4\pi\epsilon_0}\, q'\sum \frac{q}{r}. \qquad (26\text{–}3)$$

Fig. 26–2. The potential energy of the test charge q' at point a is

$$\frac{q'}{4\pi\epsilon_0}\left(\frac{q_1}{r_1} + \frac{q_2}{r_2} - \frac{q_3}{r_3}\right).$$

At a second point b, the potential energy is given by the same expression except that r_1, r_2, . . . now represent the distances from the respective charges to point b. The work of the electric force in moving the test charge from a to b along any path is equal to the negative of the difference between its potential energies at b and at a.

We see from Eq. (26–3) that the "reference level" of electrical potential energy, at which the potential energy is zero, is that at which all the distances r_1, r_2, . . . are infinite. That is, the potential energy of the test charge is zero when it is very far removed from all the charges setting up the field. (This is the most convenient reference level for most electrostatic problems. When dealing with electrical circuits, other reference levels are more convenient, which simply means that a constant term is added to the potential energy. This is not of importance, since it is only *differences* in potential energy that are of practical significance.) It follows that *the potential energy of a test charge at any point in an electric field is equal to the negative of the work of the electric force when the test charge is brought from a reference level, often taken at infinity, to the point in question.*

26–2 Potential. The *potential* at a point in an electric field is defined as the ratio of the potential energy of a test charge at the point to the magnitude of the charge, or as *the potential energy per unit charge.* (This is in exact analogy with the definition of the electric intensity at a point as the *force* per unit charge.) The potential at a point is considered to have a value even though there may be no charge at the point. We place (in imagination) a test charge at the point, compute its potential energy, and take the ratio of potential energy to charge. It must be assumed that the original charge distribution is not altered by the introduction of the test charge, which will be the case if the test charge is sufficiently small.

Potential will be represented by the letter V, or by V_a or V_b, for example, if we wish to call attention to the fact that it refers to a specific point a or b.

$$\text{Potential at point } a = V_a = \frac{\text{P.E. of charge } q' \text{ at point } a}{q'}. \quad (26\text{–}4)$$

It follows from this definition that the potential energy of a charge q' at a point a in an electric field where the potential is V_a is the product of the potential at the point and the charge q'.

$$\text{P.E. of charge } q' \text{ at point } a = q' V_a. \quad (26\text{–}5)$$

Since energy is a scalar quantity, potential is a scalar also. It has magnitude but not direction, and in this respect differs from electric intensity, which is a vector.

From its definition as potential energy per unit charge, potential is expressed in the mks system in *joules per coulomb*. A potential of one joule per coulomb is called *one volt*. The volt is named in honor of Alessandro Volta (1745–1827), an Italian scientist. He was the inventor of the "voltaic pile," the first electric cell. The volt may be defined as follows:

The potential at a point in an electrostatic field is one volt if one joule of work per coulomb is done against electrical forces when a charge is brought from infinity to the point.

An alternative definition is:

The potential at a point in an electrostatic field is one volt if the ratio of the potential energy of a charge at the point to the magnitude of the charge, is one joule per coulomb.

One one-thousandth of a volt is called one *millivolt* (mv), and one one-millionth of a volt is called a *microvolt* (μv). One thousand volts is a *kilovolt* (kv), and one million volts is a *megavolt* (Mv).

We have shown that the potential energy of a test charge q' at a distance r from a single point charge q is

$$\text{P.E.} = \frac{1}{4\pi\epsilon_0} \frac{qq'}{r}.$$

It follows that the potential V at this distance is

$$V = \frac{\text{P.E.}}{q'} = \frac{1}{4\pi\epsilon_0} \frac{q}{r}. \tag{26-6}$$

The potential is in volts if q is in coulombs and r in meters. The distance r is always considered positive, but the charge q may be positive or negative. The potential therefore has the same sign as the charge q.

When the field is set up by a number of point charges, then from Eq. (26–3),

$$V = \frac{1}{4\pi\epsilon_0} \sum \frac{q}{r}. \quad \text{(Algebraic sum)} \tag{26-7}$$

EXAMPLE 1. Point charges of $+12 \times 10^{-9}$ coul and -12×10^{-9} coul are placed 10 cm apart, as in Fig. 26–3. Compute the potentials at points a, b, and c.

We must evaluate the *algebraic* sum $(1/4\pi\epsilon_0)\sum(q/r)$ at each point. At point a, the potential due to the positive charge is

$$9 \times 10^9 \frac{\text{n·m}^2}{\text{coul}^2} \times \frac{12 \times 10^{-9} \text{ coul}}{0.06 \text{ m}} = 1800 \frac{\text{n·m}}{\text{coul}} = 1800 \frac{\text{joules}}{\text{coul}} = 1800 \text{ volts},$$

and the potential due to the negative charge is

$$9 \times 10^9 \frac{\text{n·m}^2}{\text{coul}^2} \times \frac{-12 \times 10^{-9} \text{ coul}}{0.04 \text{ m}} = -2700 \frac{\text{joules}}{\text{coul}} = -2700 \text{ volts}.$$

Hence

$$V_a = 1800 \text{ volts} - 2700 \text{ volts} = -900 \text{ volts} = -900 \frac{\text{joules}}{\text{coul}}.$$

At point b, the potential due to the positive charge is $+2700$ volts and that due

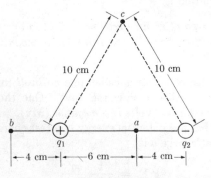

FIGURE 26–3

to the negative charge is -770 volts. Hence

$$V_b = 2700 \text{ volts} - 770 \text{ volts} = 1930 \text{ volts} = 1930 \, \frac{\text{joules}}{\text{coul}}.$$

At point c the potential is

$$V_c = 1080 \text{ volts} - 1080 \text{ volts} = 0.$$

EXAMPLE 2. Compute the potential energy of a point charge of $+4 \times 10^{-9}$ coul if placed at the points a, b, and c in Fig. 26–3.

$$\text{P.E.} = qV.$$

Hence at point a,

$$\text{P.E.} = qV_a = 4 \times 10^{-9} \text{ coul} \times \left(-900 \, \frac{\text{joules}}{\text{coul}} \right) = -36 \times 10^{-7} \text{ joule.}$$

At point b,

$$\text{P.E.} = qV_b = 4 \times 10^{-9} \text{ coul} \times 1930 \, \frac{\text{joules}}{\text{coul}} = 77 \times 10^{-7} \text{ joule.}$$

At point c,

$$\text{P.E.} = qV_c = 0.$$

(All relative to a point at infinity.)

26–3 Potential difference.

The difference between the potential at two points in an electrostatic field is called the *potential difference* between the points. Since potentials are expressed in volts, potential differences are in volts also. *The potential difference between points b and a is one volt if one joule of work per coulomb is done against electrical forces when a charge is moved from point a to point b.*

Point b is said to be at a higher potential than point a if work is done against electrical forces when a positive charge is moved from a to b. That is, b is at a higher potential than a if the potential energy of a *positive* charge is greater at b than it is at a.

The concept of potential difference is an extremely important one, both in electrostatics and in electric circuits. Electrical engineers commonly refer to it as "voltage."

For example, the potential difference between the terminals of a common automobile storage battery is about 6 volts, the terminal at the higher potential being designated by a $+$ sign, that at the lower potential by a $-$ sign. The $+$ terminal is positively charged, the $-$ terminal negatively charged. There exists, therefore, an electric field in the space around and between the battery terminals, and the statement that the potential difference between the terminals is 6 volts simply means that if one were to move a positively charged body from the negative to the positive terminal (say by transporting a small positively charged metal sphere attached to an insulating handle from one point to the other), the work done against the electrical forces of the field between the terminals would be 6 joules per coulomb of charge transported.

The potential difference between two points, say a and b, or p and q, will be abbreviated from $V_a - V_b$ or $V_p - V_q$ to V_{ab} or V_{pq}:

$$V_{ab} \equiv V_a - V_b, \qquad V_{pq} \equiv V_p - V_q, \text{ etc.}$$

If this difference is a positive quantity, the first point (a or p) is at a *higher* potential than the second (b or q), and external work must be done to move positive charge *from b to a*, or *from q to p*. Conversely, if the difference is negative, the second point is at a higher potential than the first. Also, since $V_{ab} \equiv V_a - V_b$, and $V_{ba} \equiv V_b - V_a$, it follows that

$$V_{ab} \equiv -V_{ba}.$$

This simply means that if work must be done against the field to move positive charge from b to a, work can be obtained from the field when positive charge is allowed to move from a to b.

Differences of potential may be measured by electroscopes, electrometers, and voltmeters. If the knob of a leaf electroscope is connected to a body at one potential and the case of the instrument to a body at a different potential, the divergence of the electroscope leaves is a rough measure of the potential difference between the bodies. Since there is no simple relation between the divergence of its leaves and the potential difference, the leaf electroscope is rarely used in quantitative work, some form of electrometer being preferred. The familiar pivoted coil voltmeter also measures the potential difference between its terminals, but being a current-operated instrument, it is not suitable for purely electrostatic measurements.

EXAMPLE 1. What is the potential difference or voltage between points a and b in Fig. 26–3? (Refer to the example at the end of the preceding section.) Between b and a? Between b and c? How much work would be required to move a point charge of $+4 \times 10^{-9}$ coul from a to b, in the absence of friction and with no increase in kinetic energy? From c to a?

The potential difference between points a and b is $V_a - V_b$ or V_{ab}.

$$V_{ab} \equiv V_a - V_b = -900 \text{ volts} - 1930 \text{ volts} = -2830 \text{ volts},$$

$$V_{ba} \equiv V_b - V_a = 1930 \text{ volts} - (-900 \text{ volts}) = +2830 \text{ volts},$$

$$V_{bc} \equiv V_b - V_c = 1930 \text{ volts} - 0 = +1930 \text{ volts}.$$

The work required to take a charge q from a to b is qV_{ba}.

$$W_{a \to b} = qV_{ba} = 4 \times 10^{-9} \text{ coul} \times 2830 \text{ volts} = 113 \times 10^{-7} \text{ joule},$$
$$W_{c \to a} = qV_{ac} = 4 \times 10^{-9} \text{ coul} \times (-900 \text{ volts}) = -36 \times 10^{-7} \text{ joule}.$$

EXAMPLE 2. By symmetry, the electric intensity $\mathbf{E}$ between two oppositely charged, closely spaced parallel plates is uniform and perpendicular to the plates. What is the potential difference between the plates (see Fig. 26-4)?

A test charge q' experiences a force $q'E$ which is constant in magnitude and in direction. The work of this force is therefore

$$q'(V_a - V_b) = q'Ed$$

or

$$E = V_{ab}/d, \qquad (26\text{-}8)$$

where d is the distance between the plates. The electric intensity therefore equals the potential difference between the plates divided by the distance between them. Equation (26-8) is a more useful expression for the electric intensity between parallel plates than the equation $E = \sigma/\epsilon_0$, since the potential difference V_{ab} can be determined experimentally more readily than the surface charge per unit area.

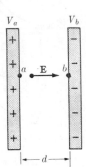

FIGURE 26-4

26-4 Potential of a charged spherical conductor.
The electric intensity *outside* a charged spherical conductor is the same as though all of the charge on the conductor were concentrated at its center. It follows that the potential at points outside the conductor is given by the same expression as that for a point charge, namely,

$$V = \frac{1}{4\pi\epsilon_0} \frac{q}{r}, \qquad (26\text{-}9)$$

where r is equal to or greater than the radius of the sphere. At points *inside* the sphere the electric intensity is zero. Therefore the potential is the same at all internal points and is equal to the potential at the surface, namely,

$$V = \frac{1}{4\pi\epsilon_0} \frac{q}{a}, \qquad (26\text{-}10)$$

where a is the radius of the sphere. Hence Eq. (26-9) gives the potential at points outside and Eq. (26-10) the potential at points inside the sphere.

Figure 26-5 shows a sphere of radius a having a positive charge q, together with graphs of the electric intensity E and the potential V at points along a line through the center of the sphere.

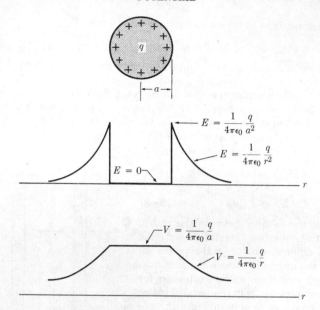

FIG. 26-5. Electric intensity E and potential V at points inside and outside a charged spherical conductor.

It has been shown previously that the maximum charge that can be retained by a conductor in air is limited by the fact that the air itself becomes conducting at an electric intensity of about 3×10^6 volts/m. In general, if E_m represents the upper limit of electric intensity, the maximum charge that can be retained by a spherical conductor in air is

$$q_m = 4\pi\epsilon_0 a^2 E_m.$$

Hence the maximum *potential* to which a spherical conductor in air can be raised, from Eq. (26-10), is

$$V_m = aE_m.$$

For a sphere one centimeter in radius, $V_m = 0.01 \times 3 \times 10^6 = 30,000$ volts, and no amount of "charging" could raise the potential of a sphere of this size, in air, higher than about 30,000 volts.

It is this fact which necessitates the use of such large spherical terminals on high voltage machines. If we make $a = 2$ meters, then

$$V_m = 2 \times 3 \times 10^6 = 6 \text{ million volts.}$$

At the other extreme is the effect produced by sharp points, a point being a portion of a surface of very small radius of curvature. Since the maximum potential is directly proportional to the radius, even relatively small potentials applied to sharp points in air will produce sufficiently high fields just outside the point to result in ionization of the surrounding air.

26–5 The energy principle.   Many problems in mechanics can be greatly simplified with the help of energy considerations. For example, the velocity of a body sliding down a frictionless surface of any arbitrary shape can be found by setting the increase in the kinetic energy of the body equal to the decrease in its gravitational potential energy.   The principle of conservation of energy is, of course, equally applicable to the motion of an electron, an ion, or any charged body in an electric field. In practically all cases of interest the gravitational force on a charge is so small in comparison with the electrical force that gravitational potential energy is negligible. However, every charged particle in an electric field has electrical potential energy which arises from the work done in moving it against electrical forces, just as gravitational potential energy arises from the work done in lifting a body against gravitational forces.

We may state the work-energy relation in the same way that we did in mechanics. Thus, in the absence of friction, if a charge q is transferred from point 1 to point 2,

$$\left\{ \begin{matrix} \text{Work of the non-} \\ \text{conservative forces} \end{matrix} \right\} + \left\{ \begin{matrix} \text{Work of the} \\ \text{electric force} \end{matrix} \right\} = \left\{ \begin{matrix} \text{Change in kinetic} \\ \text{energy} \end{matrix} \right\},$$

or

$$W' - q(V_2 - V_1) = E_{k2} - E_{k1}.$$

If W' is zero, then

$$q(V_1 - V_2) = \tfrac{1}{2}mv_2^2 - \tfrac{1}{2}mv_1^2.$$

EXAMPLE. A simple type of vacuum tube known as a diode consists essentially of two electrodes within a highly evacuated enclosure. One electrode, the cathode, is maintained at a high temperature and emits electrons from its surface. A potential difference of a few hundred volts is maintained between the cathode and the other electrode, known as the anode or plate, with the anode at the higher potential. Suppose that in a certain diode the plate potential is 250 volts above that of the cathode, and an electron is emitted from the cathode with no initial velocity. What is its velocity when it reaches the anode?

Let V_k and V_p represent the cathode and anode potentials, respectively, and let the charge on the electron be e. Since e is negative, the electron goes from the cathode where the potential is lower to the anode where the potential is higher. Hence the *decrease* in electrical potential energy is $-e(V_k - V_p)$ or eV_{pk}, and

$$eV_{pk} = \tfrac{1}{2}mv_p^2 - \tfrac{1}{2}mv_k^2.$$

Since $v_k = 0$,

$$v_p = \sqrt{2eV_{pk}/m}$$

$$= \sqrt{\frac{2 \times 1.6 \times 10^{-19} \text{ coul} \times 250 \text{ joules/coul}}{9.1 \times 10^{-31} \text{ kgm}}}$$

$$= 9.4 \times 10^6 \left(\frac{\text{joules}}{\text{kgm}}\right)^{1/2}$$

$$= 9.4 \times 10^6 \left(\frac{\text{n·m}}{\text{kgm}}\right)^{1/2}$$

$$= 9.4 \times 10^6 \left(\frac{\text{kgm·m}^2/\text{sec}^2}{\text{kgm}}\right)^{1/2}$$

$$= 9.4 \times 10^6 \frac{\text{m}}{\text{sec}}.$$

Note that the shape or separation of the electrodes need not be known. The final velocity depends only on the difference of potential between the cathode and the anode. Of course, the time of transit from cathode to anode depends on the geometry of the tube.

26–6 Equipotential surfaces. The potential distribution in an electric field may be represented graphically by *equipotential surfaces*. An equipotential surface is one at all points of which the potential has the same value. While an equipotential surface may be constructed through every point of an electric field, it is customary to show only a few of the equipotentials in a diagram.

Since the potential energy of a charged body is the same at all points of a given equipotential surface, it follows that no (electrical) work is needed to move a charged body over such a surface. Hence the equipotential surface through any point must be at right angles to the direction of the field at that point. If this were not so, the field would have a component lying in the surface and work would have to be done against electrical forces to move a charge in the direction of this component. The lines of force and the equipotential surfaces thus form a mutually perpendicular network. In general, the lines of force of a field are curves and the equipotentials are curved surfaces. For the special case of a uniform field, where the lines of force are straight and parallel, the equipotentials are parallel planes perpendicular to the lines of force.

It has been shown that the lines of force at the surface of a charged conductor are at right angles to the conductor if the charges on it are at rest. Hence the surface of such a conductor is an equipotential. Furthermore, since the field within a charged conductor is zero, the entire interior of the conductor is an equipotential *volume*, at the same potential as the surface of the conductor.

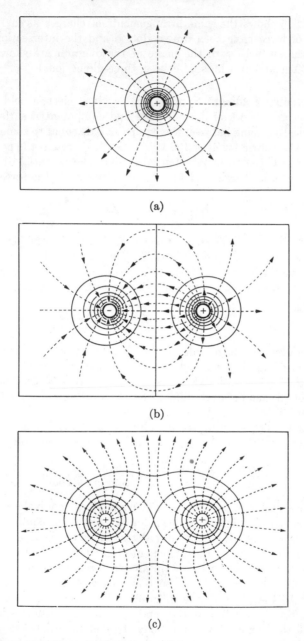

(a)

(b)

(c)

Fig. 26–6.   Equipotential surfaces (solid lines) and lines of force (dotted lines) in the neighborhood of point charges.

Figure 26–6 shows the same arrangements of charges as in Fig. 25–6. The lines of force have been drawn dotted and the intersections of the equipotential surfaces with the plane of the diagram are shown by the full lines. The actual field is, of course, three-dimensional.

26–7 Potential gradient. Suppose that a given electric field has been mapped by its network of lines of force and equipotential surfaces, with the (electrical) spacing between the equipotentials equal to some constant difference ΔV such as 1 volt or 100 volts. Let Δs represent the perpendicular distance between two equipotentials. Since the potential difference is the work per unit charge, and the electric intensity is the force per unit charge,

$$\Delta V = E \, \Delta s, \quad \text{or} \quad \Delta s = \frac{\Delta V}{E}.$$

That is, the greater the electric intensity E, the smaller the perpendicular distance Δs between the equipotentials. The equipotentials are therefore crowded close together in a strong field and are more widely separated in a weak field. Another way of saying the same thing is to write

$$E = \frac{\Delta V}{\Delta s}, \tag{26–11}$$

which expresses the magnitude of the electric intensity in terms of the difference of potential per unit distance in a direction perpendicular to the equipotentials. The ratio $\Delta V / \Delta s$ is called the *potential gradient,* just as the ratio of the temperature difference to the distance is called the temperature gradient.

Potential gradient is expressed in volts per meter, while electric intensity or force per unit charge is expressed in newtons per coulomb. However,

$$\frac{\text{volts}}{\text{m}} = \frac{\text{joules/coul}}{\text{m}} = \frac{\text{n·m}}{\text{coul·m}} = \frac{\text{n}}{\text{coul}},$$

so that the volt/meter and the newton/coulomb are equivalent units.

The geometrical relations between lines of force and equipotential surfaces afford a graphical method for determining the charge distribution and electric intensity in an arrangement of conductors where it would be difficult, if not impossible, to obtain an exact analytic expression for the desired result. Figure 26–7 is a sectional view of a long conductor perpendicular to the plane of the diagram. We know that the surface of the conductor is an equipotential, and also that at distances large compared with the dimensions of the body the equipotentials are cylindrical surfaces, since at a sufficiently great distance the body may be considered a line charge. Traces of the equipotentials may then be sketched, starting

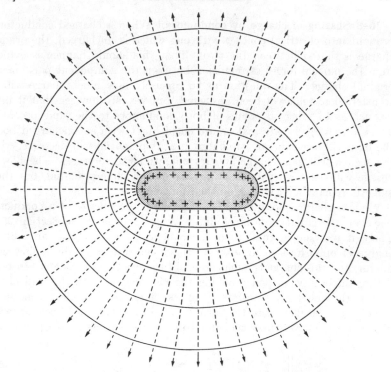

Fig. 26–7. Equipotential surfaces (solid lines) and lines of force (dotted lines) about a conductor of irregular shape.

with one just outside the body and gradually altering the shape so that the trace approaches a circle. It will be found that the smaller the radius of curvature of the surface, the more closely must the equipotentials be spaced. The closest spacing occurs near the curved ends and the greatest spacing is outside the flat surfaces. The electric intensity is therefore greatest near the ends.

The lines of force may next be sketched in, making them everywhere perpendicular to the equipotentials, of which the surface of the conductor is one, and spacing them more closely together the smaller the separation of the equipotentials.

Finally, since the electric intensity just outside a surface is proportional to the surface density of charge, it follows that the surface density is greatest at the curved ends and least at the flat surfaces.

Note that although the surface density of charge is far from uniform over the surface of a body of irregular shape, the *potential* is necessarily constant over the entire surface.

26–8 Sharing of charge by conductors. When a charged conductor is brought into electrical contact with one which is uncharged, the original charge is shared between the two. That this should happen is evident from the mutual forces of repulsion between the component parts of the original charge. The question as to precisely how much charge will be transferred has not yet been answered, but we can now see that it must be such as to bring all points of both conductors to the same potential. Thus if a charged body makes *external* contact with an uncharged body, the first will lose some of its charge and its potential will decrease, while the second will gain charge and its potential will increase. The flow of charge will cease when both bodies are at the same potential, but there will still remain some charge on the first body.

When a charged body makes contact with the *interior* of a conductor, however, the situation is quite different, as emphasized in Section 25–5. There it was shown that, as a consequence of Gauss' law, an induced charge of opposite sign appears on the inner surface of the hollow conductor, and this charge is independent of the position of the charged body within the cavity. Upon touching the charged body to the wall of the cavity, the first body transfers *all* of its charge to the hollow conductor, in spite of the fact that the latter may have originally been charged. This experiment was first performed by Faraday using an ice pail as the

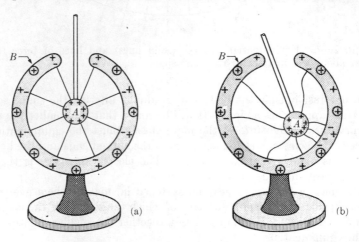

Fig. 26–8. Body A, with charge $+q_A$ introduced into a hollow spherical conductor B with an original charge $+q_B$ (indicated by the symbol $\oplus$). (a) When A is at the center, the field around it is symmetrical and the induced negative charge $-q_A$ is distributed evenly on the inner surface of the hollow sphere. (b) When A is off-center, the field around it is asymmetrical and the induced negative charge $-q_A$ is distributed unevenly on the inner surface of the hollow sphere.

hollow conductor, and it is known today as Faraday's ice-pail experiment.

To study this experiment in more detail, consider the large hollow metal sphere B shown in Fig. 26–8(a) with an original positive charge q_B indicated by positive signs with circles around them. Let us neglect the thickness of the walls and call the radius of the sphere r_B. Let an opening be made in the walls large enough to admit a small metal sphere A of radius r_A and with a positive charge q_A.

When A is at the center of B and the small effect due to the small opening in B is neglected, the positive charge on A and the equal induced negative charge on the interior surface of B are *evenly distributed*, and the electric field between these two charges is symmetrical and radial. By Gauss' law, the field between A and B is due only to the charge on A, and at a distance r from the center of A, is given by

$$E = \frac{q_A}{4\pi\epsilon_0} \cdot \frac{1}{r^2}.$$

The potential difference between A and B is therefore

$$V_A - V_B = \frac{q_A}{4\pi\epsilon_0}\left(\frac{1}{r_A} - \frac{1}{r_B}\right). \tag{26–12}$$

This equation expresses two important facts:

(1) $V_A - V_B$ is positive, or A is at a *higher* potential than B.

(2) $V_A - V_B$ depends *only* on q_A, and is thus independent of the original charge residing on B.

If A and B are connected by a conductor, electricity will flow from A to B until $V_A - V_B = 0$, or, from Eq. (26–12), until $q_A = 0$. This leads to the conclusion that *all* of the charge on A is transferred to B, *regardless of the initial value of B's charge and potential*. This is the principle of the Van de Graaff generator, described in the next section.

When body A is off center, as shown in Fig. 26–8(b), the positive charge on A and the equal induced negative charge on the interior wall of B are unevenly distributed. The electric field between A and B is quite asymmetrical and cannot be expressed in simple mathematical form. The difference of potential $V_A - V_B$ is *still positive*, however, but with a value smaller than that which existed when A was at the center, and furthermore, $V_A - V_B$ still depends *only* on q_A, regardless of the original charge and potential of B.

26–9 The Van de Graaff generator. The Van de Graaff generator makes use of the principle described in the preceding section, namely, that if a charged conductor is brought into *internal* contact with a second hollow conductor, *all* of its charge transfers to the hollow conductor no matter how high the potential of the latter may be. Thus, were it not for insulation difficulties, the charge, and hence the potential, of a hollow conductor could be raised to any desired value by successively adding charges to it by internal contact. Actually, since the conductor must be supported in some way, its maximum potential will be limited to that at which the rate of leakage of charge from it through its supports or through the surrounding air equals the rate at which charge is delivered to it.

The Van de Graaff generator is shown schematically in Fig. 26–9 and a photograph of the installation at M.I.T. in Fig. 26–10. Referring to Fig. 26–9, A is a hollow spherical conductor supported on an insulating hollow column B. A belt C passes over pulleys D, the lower pulley being driven by a motor while the upper one is an idler. Terminal E, which consists of a number of sharp points projecting from a horizontal rod, is maintained at a negative potential of some tens of thousands of volts relative to ground by the auxiliary source F. Terminal G, similarly constructed, is maintained at a positive potential with respect to the spherical terminal A. The air around the points becomes ionized and a "spray" of ions is repelled from each set of points, negative ions from E and positive ions from G. Some of these attach themselves to the surface of the moving belt, so that the upward moving half becomes negatively and the other half positively charged. The ion current at terminals E and G is adjusted

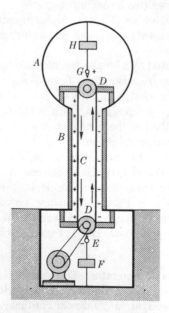

Fig. 26–9. Schematic diagram of a Van de Graaff generator.

Fig. 26–10. Photograph of the Van de Graaff generator at the Massachusetts Institute of Technology. The column at the left houses an installation like that in Fig. 26–9. (Courtesy of M.I.T. News Service.)

so that, first, the charge carried toward either terminal is neutralized and, second, an equal charge of opposite sign is deposited on the belt.

The right-hand column in Fig. 26–10 encloses a giant x-ray tube some 20 ft long. The sphere at the top of this column houses the cathode of the tube. Electrons are driven down the tube by the potential difference between spheres and ground (about 2.5 million volts) and strike a metal anode mounted in a chamber below ground level. The anode then becomes a source of x-rays of short wavelength and great penetrating power.

PROBLEMS

26–1. A particle carrying a charge of $+3 \times 10^{-9}$ coul is urged to the left by an electric field. A mechanical force moves it to the right from point a to point b, performing 6×10^{-5} joule of work, and at the same time increasing the kinetic energy of the particle by 4.5×10^{-5} joule. What is the difference of potential between points a and b?

26–2. A charge of 2.5×10^{-8} coul is placed in an upwardly directed uniform electric field whose intensity is 5×10^4 n/coul. How much work is done against the field when the charge is moved (a) 45 cm to the right? (b) 80 cm down? (c) 260 cm at an angle of $45°$ upward from the horizontal?

26–3. (a) Show that n/coul is equivalent dimensionally to volts/m. (b) Two parallel plates have a difference of potential of 2000 volts. What is the smallest distance the plates can be brought together without the air between them breaking down, if the dielectric strength of air is 3×10^6 n/coul?

26–4. A small sphere of mass 0.2 gm hangs by a thread between two parallel vertical plates 5 cm apart. The sphere holds a charge of 6×10^{-9} coul. What difference of potential between the plates will cause the thread to assume an angle of $30°$ with the vertical?

26–5. In an apparatus for measuring the electronic charge e by Millikan's method, an electric intensity of 6.34×10^4 volts/m is required to just support a charged oil drop. If the plates are 1.5 cm apart, what potential difference between them is required?

26–6. In the Bohr model of the hydrogen atom a single electron revolves around a single proton in a circle of radius 5.28×10^{-9} cm. (a) What is the electrostatic potential energy of the atom? (b) Through what potential difference would an electron have to be accelerated to gain this amount of energy?

26–7. Two parallel plates 4 cm apart have a difference of potential of 1600 volts. An electron is released from the negative plate at the same instant that a proton is released from the positive plate. (a) How far from the positive plate will they pass each other? (b) How do their velocities compare as they strike the opposite plates? (c) How do their energies compare when they strike the opposite plates?

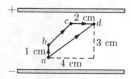

FIGURE 26–11

26–8. The work done in moving a unit charge between two points in an electric field (and therefore the difference of potential) is independent of the path taken between the points. Calculate the work done in moving a charge of $+2 \times 10^{-4}$ coul from a to d in Fig. 26–11, (a) along the straight line ad, (b) along $abcd$. The intensity of the electric field is 400 n/coul.

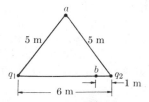

FIGURE 26–12

26–9. In Fig. 26–12, $q_1 = +25 \times 10^{-9}$ coul and $q_2 = -25 \times 10^{-9}$ coul. (a) What is the potential at point a? (b) How much work must be done on a charge of -8×10^{-9} coul to move it from point a to point b?

26–10. (a) Prove that when a particle of constant mass and charge is accelerated from rest in an electric field, its final velocity is proportional to the square root of the potential difference through which it is accelerated. (b) Find the magnitude of the proportionality constant if the particle is an electron, the velocity is in m/sec, and the potential difference is in volts. (c) At velocities much greater than $\frac{1}{10}$ of the velocity of light, the mass of a body becomes appreciably larger than its "rest mass" and cannot be considered constant. (The velocity of light is 3×10^8 m/sec.) Through what voltage must an electron be accelerated, assuming no change in its mass, to acquire a velocity $\frac{1}{10}$ that of light? (d) What would be the velocity of a deuteron, accelerated through the same voltage? Express the velocity as a fraction of the velocity of light.

26–11. The potential at a certain distance from a point charge is 600 volts, and the electric field is 200 n/coul. (a) What is the distance to the point charge? (b) What is the magnitude of the charge?

26–12. Two point charges whose magnitudes are $+20 \times 10^{-9}$ coul and -12×10^{-9} coul are separated by a distance of 5 cm. An electron is released from rest between the two charges, 1 cm from the negative charge, and moves along the line connecting the two charges. What is its velocity when it is 1 cm from the positive charge?

26–13. An electron volt is a unit of energy equal to the kinetic energy acquired by an electron in accelerating through a potential difference of one volt. (a) What potential difference is required to give an alpha particle an energy of 10^5 ev? (b) What is then the velocity of the alpha particle? The mass of the alpha particle is 6.68×10^{-27} kgm.

26–14. A vacuum diode consists of a cylindrical cathode 0.05 cm in radius, mounted coaxially within a cylindrical anode 0.45 cm in radius. The potential of the anode is 300 volts above that of the cathode. An electron leaves the surface of the cathode with zero initial velocity. Find its velocity when it strikes the anode.

26–15. Two point charges, $q_1 = +40 \times 10^{-9}$ coulomb and $q_2 = -30 \times 10^{-9}$ coulomb, are 10 cm apart. Point A is midway between them, point B is 8 cm from q_1 and 6 cm from q_2. Find (a) the potential at point A; (b) the potential at point B; (c) the work required to carry a charge of 25×10^{-9} coulomb from point B to point A.

26–16. Three equal point charges of 3×10^{-7} coul are placed at the corners of an equilateral triangle whose side is one meter. What is the potential energy of the system? Take as zero potential energy the energy of the three charges when they are infinitely far apart.

26–17. A vacuum triode may be idealized as follows. A plane surface (the cathode) emits electrons with negligible initial velocities. Parallel to the cathode and 3 mm away from it is an open grid of fine wire at a potential of 18 volts above the cathode. A second plane surface (the anode) is 12 mm beyond the grid and is at a potential of 15 volts above the cathode. Assume that the plane of the grid is an equipotential surface, and that the potential gradient between cathode and grid, and between grid and anode, are uniform. Assume also that the structure of the grid is sufficiently open for electrons to pass through it freely. (a) Draw a diagram of potential *vs.* distance, along a line from cathode to anode. (b) With what velocity will electrons strike the anode?

26–18. Suppose the potential difference between the spherical terminal of a Van de Graaff generator and the point at which charges are sprayed onto the upward moving belt is 2 million volts. If the belt delivers negative charge to the sphere at the rate of 2×10^{-3} coul/sec and removes positive charge at the same rate, what horsepower must be expended to drive the belt against electrical forces?

CHAPTER 27

CAPACITANCE. PROPERTIES OF DIELECTRICS

27–1 Capacitors. If a number of charged conductors are in the vicinity of one another, the potential of each is determined not only by its own charge but by the magnitude and sign of the charges on the other conductors and by their shapes, sizes, and locations. For example, the potential of a positively charged sphere is lowered if a second, negatively charged sphere is brought near the first.

An important special case arises in practice when two conductors in the same vicinity are given equal amounts of charge of opposite sign. This is usually accomplished by connecting the conductors, both initially uncharged, to the terminals of a battery, which results in a transfer of charge from one conductor to the other. Such an arrangement of two conductors is called a *capacitor*. The fact that each conductor is in the vicinity of another carrying a charge of opposite sign makes possible the transfer of relatively large quantities of charge from one conductor to the other, with relatively small differences of potential.

The capacitance C of a capacitor is defined as the ratio of the charge Q on either conductor to the potential difference V_{ab} between the conductors:

$$C = \frac{Q}{V_{ab}}. \tag{27–1}$$

The net charge on the capacitor as a whole, of course, is zero, and "the charge on a capacitor" is understood to mean the charge on *either* conductor, without regard to sign. We see from its definition that capacitance is expressed in *coulombs per volt*. Since one volt is equivalent to one joule per coulomb, one coulomb per volt is equivalent to one (coul)^2/joule. A capacitance of one coulomb per volt is called one *farad* (in honor of Michael Faraday). That is, *the capacitance of a capacitor is one farad* if one coulomb is transferred from one conductor to the other, per volt of potential difference between the conductors.

A capacitor is represented by the symbol

Capacitors find many applications in electrical circuits. A capacitor is used to eliminate sparking when a circuit containing inductance is suddenly opened. The ignition system of every automobile engine contains a capacitor for this purpose. Capacitors are used in radio circuits for tuning, and for "smoothing" the rectified current delivered by the power supply. The efficiency of alternating current power transmission can often be increased by the use of large capacitors.

The term "condenser" has long been used for the piece of apparatus we have described as a "capacitor." But "capacitor" is to be preferred, because nothing is actually "condensed" in a "condenser," and also because of the corresponding usage of the terms resistance and resistor. That is, a resistor is a device that has resistance, and a capacitor is a device that has capacitance.

27–2 The parallel plate capacitor. The most common type of capacitor consists of two conducting plates parallel to each other and separated by a distance which is small compared with the linear dimensions of the plates (see Fig. 27–1). Practically the entire field of such a capacitor is localized in the region between the plates, as shown. There is a slight "fringing" of the field at its outer boundary, but the fringing becomes relatively less as the plates are brought closer together. If the plates are sufficiently close, the fringing may be neglected, the field between the plates is uniform, and the charges on the plates are uniformly distributed over their opposing surfaces. This arrangement is known as a *parallel plate capacitor*.

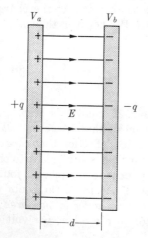

FIG. 27–1. Parallel plate capacitor.

Let us assume first that the plates are in vacuum. It has been shown that the magnitude of the electric intensity between a pair of closely spaced parallel plates in vacuum is

$$E = \frac{1}{\epsilon_0}\sigma = \frac{1}{\epsilon_0}\frac{Q}{A},$$

where A is the area of each plate and Q is the charge on *either* plate. Since the electric intensity or potential gradient between the plates is uniform, the potential difference between the plates is

$$V_{ab} = Ed = \frac{1}{\epsilon_0}\frac{Qd}{A},$$

where d is the separation of the plates. Hence the capacitance of a parallel plate capacitor in vacuum is

$$C = \frac{Q}{V_{ab}} = \epsilon_0\frac{A}{d}. \tag{27–2}$$

Since ϵ_0, A, and d are constants for a given capacitor, the capacitance is a constant independent of the charge on the capacitor, and is directly proportional to the area of the plates and inversely proportional to their separation. If mks units are used, A is to be expressed in square meters and d in meters. The capacitance C will then be in farads.

As an example, let us compute the area of the plates of a one-farad parallel plate capacitor if the separation of the plates is one millimeter and the plates are in vacuum.

$$C = \epsilon_0 \frac{A}{d},$$

$$A = \frac{Cd}{\epsilon_0} = \frac{1 \text{ farad} \times 10^{-3} \text{ m}}{8.85 \times 10^{-12} \text{ coul}^2/\text{n·m}^2} = 1.13 \times 10^8 \text{ m}^2.$$

This corresponds to a square 10,600 meters, or 34,600 ft, or about $6\frac{1}{2}$ miles on a side!

Since the farad is such a large unit of capacitance, units of more convenient size are the *microfarad* ($1 \ \mu\text{f} = 10^{-6}$ farad), and the *micro-microfarad* ($1 \ \mu\mu\text{f} = 10^{-12}$ farad). For example, a common radio set contains in its power supply several capacitors whose capacitances are of the order of ten microfarads, while the capacitances of the tuning capacitors are of the order of a few hundred micro-microfarads.

Variable capacitors whose capacitance may be varied at will (between limits) are widely used in the tuning circuits of radio receivers. These are

Fig. 27–2. Variable air capacitor. (Courtesy of General Radio Company.)

usually air capacitors of relatively small capacitance and are constructed of a number of fixed parallel metal plates connected together and constituting one "plate" of the capacitor, while a second set of movable plates also connected together forms the other "plate" (Fig. 27–2). By rotating a shaft on which the movable plates are mounted, the second set may be caused to interleave the first to a greater or lesser extent. The effective area of the capacitor is that of the interleaved portion of the plates only.

A variable capacitor is represented by the symbol

While parallel plate capacitors are the simplest and cheapest to construct, capacitors consisting of concentric spheres and of coaxial cylinders are sometimes used in standards laboratories, since the corrections for the "fringing" fields can be made more readily and the capacitance can be accurately calculated from the dimensions of the apparatus. Problems involving a spherical and a cylindrical capacitor will be found at the end of the chapter.

EXAMPLE. The plates of a parallel plate capacitor are 5 mm apart and 2 m^2 in area. The plates are in vacuum. A potential difference of 10,000 volts is applied across the capacitor. Compute (a) the capacitance, (b) the charge on each plate, and (c) the electric intensity in the space between them.

(a)
$$C = \epsilon_0 \frac{A}{d}$$

$$= 8.85 \times 10^{-12} \frac{coul^2}{n \cdot m^2} \times \frac{2 \text{ m}^2}{5 \times 10^{-3} \text{ m}}$$

$$= 3.54 \times 10^{-9} \frac{coul^2}{n \cdot m}.$$

But

$$\frac{coul^2}{n \cdot m} = \frac{coul^2}{joule} = \frac{coul}{joule/coul} = \frac{coul}{volt} = farad,$$

so

$$C = 3.54 \times 10^{-9} \text{ farad}.$$

(b) The charge on the capacitor is

$$Q = C V_{ab} = 3.54 \times 10^{-9} \frac{coul}{volt} \times 10^4 \text{ volts}$$

$$= 3.54 \times 10^{-5} \text{ coul}.$$

(c) The electric intensity is

$$E = \frac{\sigma}{\epsilon_0} = \frac{Q}{\epsilon_0 A} = \frac{3.54 \times 10^{-5} \text{ coul}}{8.85 \times 10^{-12} \text{ (coul}^2/\text{n·m}^2) \times 2 \text{ m}^2}$$

$$= 20 \times 10^5 \frac{\text{n}}{\text{coul}}.$$

Or, since the electric intensity equals the potential gradient,

$$E = \frac{V_{ab}}{d} = \frac{10^4 \text{ volts}}{5 \times 10^{-3} \text{ m}} = 20 \times 10^5 \frac{\text{volts}}{\text{m}}.$$

Of course, the newton/coulomb and the volt/meter are equivalent units.

27–3 Capacitors in series and in parallel. Circuits often contain two or more capacitors. Consider the three capacitors connected as in Fig. 27–3, where it is possible to proceed from point a to point d along only one path, $abcd$. When this is the case, the capacitors are said to be connected in *series* between points a and d. In Fig. 27–4, on the other hand, it is possible to go from a to b along three different paths, and the capacitors are said to be connected in *parallel* between points a and b.

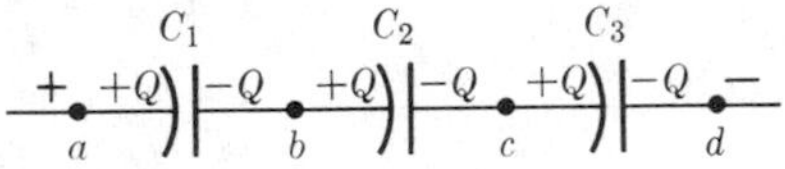

FIG. 27–3. Capacitors in series. The charge on each capacitor is the same.

The capacitance of a capacitor is defined as the ratio of the charge Q on either plate to the potential difference between the capacitor terminals. The charge Q may be described as the charge displaced past any point of the external circuit in the process of charging the capacitor.

The *equivalent* capacitance of a capacitor network is similarly defined as the ratio of the displaced charge to the potential difference between the terminals of the network. Hence the method of computing the equivalent capacitance of a network is to assume a potential difference between the terminals of the network, compute the corresponding charge, and take the ratio of the charge to the potential difference.

Let the capacitances of the three capacitors in Fig. 27–3 be C_1, C_2,

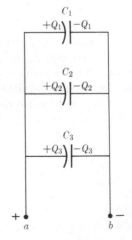

FIG. 27–4. Capacitors in parallel. The potential difference across each capacitor is the same.

and C_3, and suppose that the terminals a and d are maintained at a potential difference V_{ad}. If the left plate of capacitor 1 receives a charge $+Q$, an equal negative charge $-Q$ will be induced on the right plate. At the same time, a charge $+Q$ appears on the left plate of capacitor 2, since the conductor consisting of the right plate of capacitor 1, the left plate of capacitor 2, and the wire connecting them was originally uncharged and is insulated from the rest of the circuit. Thus each capacitor receives a charge of *magnitude* Q on each of its plates. Then

$$Q = C_1 V_{ab}, \qquad Q = C_2 V_{bc}, \qquad Q = C_3 V_{cd},$$

and

$$V_{ad} = V_{ab} + V_{bc} + V_{cd}.$$

Let C represent the *equivalent* capacitance of the arrangement, that is, the capacitance of the single capacitor that would become charged with the same charge Q when the potential difference across its terminals is V_{ad}. Then

$$V_{ad} = \frac{Q}{C}$$

and

$$\frac{Q}{C} = \frac{Q}{C_1} + \frac{Q}{C_2} + \frac{Q}{C_3},$$

whence

$$\frac{1}{C} = \frac{1}{C_1} + \frac{1}{C_2} + \frac{1}{C_3}. \qquad (27\text{--}3)$$

That is, when any number of capacitors are connected in series, the reciprocal of the equivalent capacitance equals the sum of the reciprocals of the individual capacitances.

Next, let a potential difference V_{ab} be applied across the terminals a and b of the parallel network in Fig. 27–4. The potential difference across each capacitor is then V_{ab}, but the charges on each are different. Thus

$$Q_1 = C_1 V_{ab}, \qquad Q_2 = C_2 V_{ab}, \qquad Q_3 = C_3 V_{ab}.$$

The total charge Q on the parallel network is

$$Q = Q_1 + Q_2 + Q_3.$$

Again defining the equivalent capacitance C as that of a single capacitor which would acquire the same total charge Q with the same potential difference V_{ab}, we have

$$Q = C V_{ab}$$

and hence

$$CV_{ab} = C_1 V_{ab} + C_2 V_{ab} + C_3 V_{ab}$$

or

$$\boxed{C = C_1 + C_2 + C_3.}\tag{27–4}$$

Hence when any number of capacitors are connected in parallel, the equivalent capacitance equals the sum of the individual capacitances.

EXAMPLE. Refer to Fig. 27–5. If point b is grounded and point a is maintained at a potential of $+1200$ volts, find the charge on each capacitor and the potential of point c.

The 4-μf and the 2-μf capacitors are in parallel, and are hence equivalent to a single capacitor of capacitance

$$C_4 = 4 \ \mu\text{f} + 2 \ \mu\text{f} = 6 \ \mu\text{f}.$$

This equivalent capacitor is in series with the 3-μf capacitor. Hence the equivalent capacitance C of the network is

$$\frac{1}{C} = \frac{1}{C_1} + \frac{1}{C_4} = \frac{1}{3 \ \mu\text{f}} + \frac{1}{6 \ \mu\text{f}} = \frac{1}{2 \ \mu\text{f}}$$

or

$$C = 2 \ \mu\text{f}.$$

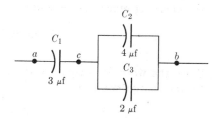

FIG. 27–5. Simple network of capacitors.

The charge on the equivalent capacitor is

$$Q = C V_{ab} = 2 \times 10^{-6} \text{ farad} \times 1200 \text{ volts} = 2.4 \times 10^{-3} \text{ coul.}$$

This must equal the charge on the 3-μf capacitor, and the sum of the charges on the 4-μf and 2-μf capacitors. Now

$$V_{ac} = \frac{Q_1}{C_1} = \frac{2.4 \times 10^{-3} \text{ coul}}{3 \times 10^{-6} \text{ farad}} = 800 \text{ volts,}$$

$$V_{ac} \equiv V_a - V_c = 800 \text{ volts,} \quad V_a = 1200 \text{ volts,} \quad \therefore V_c = 400 \text{ volts}$$

and

$$V_{cb} \equiv V_c - V_b = 400 \text{ volts} - 0 = 400 \text{ volts.}$$

Hence

$$Q_2 = C_2 V_{cb} = 4 \times 10^{-6} \text{ farad} \times 400 \text{ volts} = 1.6 \times 10^{-3} \text{ coul,}$$

$$Q_3 = C_3 V_{cb} = 2 \times 10^{-6} \text{ farad} \times 400 \text{ volts} = 0.8 \times 10^{-3} \text{ coul,}$$

$$Q_2 + Q_3 = (1.6 + 0.8) \times 10^{-3} \text{ coul} = 2.4 \times 10^{-3} \text{ coul.}$$

27–4 Energy of a charged capacitor. The process of charging a capacitor consists of transferring charge from the plate at lower potential to the plate at higher potential. The charging process therefore requires the expenditure of energy. Imagine the charging process to be carried out by starting with both plates completely uncharged, and then repeatedly removing small positive charges from one plate and transferring them to the other plate. At a stage of this process when the total quantity of charge transferred has reached an amount q, the potential difference between the plates is

$$V_{ab} = \frac{q}{C}.$$

That is, the potential difference is proportional to the charge. Since the charge varied from zero to a quantity Q, the potential difference must have varied linearly from zero to Q/C. The average potential difference during the charging process is therefore

$$V_{ab} \text{ (average)} = \frac{1}{2}\frac{Q}{C}.$$

Since the work W is equal to the average potential difference multiplied by the charge, we have

$$W = \frac{1}{2}\frac{Q}{C}Q,$$

or

$$W = \frac{1}{2}\frac{Q^2}{C}. \tag{27–5}$$

Since the farad is equivalent to the coul^2/joule, the energy is expressed in joules when Q is in coulombs and C in farads.

Since $V_{ab} = Q/C$, Eq. (27–5) is equivalent to

$$W = \tfrac{1}{2}CV_{ab}^2 = \tfrac{1}{2}QV_{ab}, \tag{27–6}$$

where V_{ab} now represents the potential difference across the capacitor when its charge is Q.

EXAMPLE. A 1-μf capacitor is charged to 100 volts and a 2-μf capacitor to 200 volts. They are then connected in parallel, positive plate to positive plate. Determine the initial and final energies and account for the difference.

The initial energy of the 1-μf capacitor is

$$(W_1)_i = \tfrac{1}{2}C_1V_1^2 = \tfrac{1}{2} \times 10^{-6} \text{ farad} \times 10^4 \text{ volts} = 0.005 \text{ joule},$$

and the initial energy of the 2-μf capacitor is

$$(W_2)_i = \tfrac{1}{2}C_2 V_2^2 = \tfrac{1}{2} \times 2 \times 10^{-6} \text{ farad} \times 4 \times 10^4 \text{ volts} = 0.04 \text{ joule.}$$

The total initial energy of both capacitors is

$$(W_1 + W_2)_i = 0.005 \text{ joule} + 0.04 \text{ joule} = 0.045 \text{ joule.}$$

When the two capacitors are connected in parallel, $+$ to $+$, the resulting combination has a capacitance C_f of 3 μf and a charge Q_f equal to the sum of the two separate charges. Thus,

$$Q_f = Q_1 + Q_2 = C_1 V_1 + C_2 V_2$$

$$= 1 \times 10^{-6} \text{ farad} \times 100 \text{ volts} + 2 \times 10^{-6} \text{ farad} \times 200 \text{ volts}$$

$$= 5 \times 10^{-4} \text{ coul.}$$

The final energy of the combination is therefore

$$W_f = \frac{1}{2}\frac{Q_f^2}{C_f} = \frac{(5 \times 10^{-4} \text{ coul})^2}{2 \times 3 \times 10^{-6} \text{ farad}} = 0.0417 \text{ joule.}$$

The final energy is seen to be less than the initial energy, the difference being the energy that must have been converted into another form. If the connecting wires that were used to make the parallel combination were extremely thin (large resistance), the energy was converted into heat. If, on the other hand, these wires were quite thick (negligible resistance), much of the energy was radiated in the form of radio waves.

27-5 Dielectric coefficient. Permittivity. Most capacitors utilize a solid, nonconducting material or *dielectric* between their plates. A common type is the paper and foil capacitor, in which strips of metal foil form the plates and a sheet of paper impregnated with wax is the dielectric. By rolling up such a capacitor, a capacitance of several microfarads can be obtained in a relatively small volume. The "Leyden jar," constructed by cementing metal foil over a portion of the inside and outside surfaces of a glass jar, is essentially a parallel plate capacitor with the glass forming the dielectric.

Electrolytic capacitors utilize as their dielectric an extremely thin layer of nonconducting oxide between a metal plate and a conducting solution. Because of the small thickness of the dielectric, electrolytic capacitors of relatively small dimensions may have a capacitance of the order of 50 μf.

The function of a solid dielectric between the plates of a capacitor is threefold. First, it solves the mechanical problem of maintaining two large metal sheets at an extremely small separation but without actual

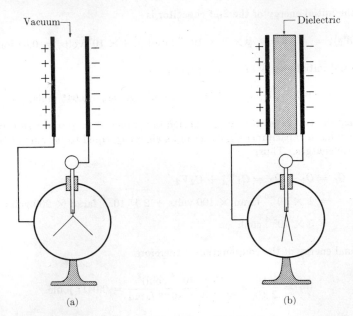

Fig. 27-6. Effect of a dielectric between the plates of a parallel plate capacitor. (a) With a given charge, the potential difference is V_0. (b) With the same charge, the potential difference V is smaller than V_0.

contact. Second, since its dielectric strength is larger than that of air, the maximum potential difference which the capacitor can withstand without breakdown is increased. Third, it is found that the capacitance of a capacitor of given dimensions is several times larger with a dielectric separating its plates than if the plates were in vacuum. This effect can be demonstrated as follows. Figure 27-6(a) illustrates a parallel plate capacitor whose plates have been given equal and opposite charges of magnitude Q. The plates are assumed to be in vacuum and the potential difference V_0 between the plates is indicated by an electroscope. If a sheet of dielectric, such as glass, bakelite, or hard rubber, is now inserted between the plates as in Fig. 27-6(b), just filling the space between them, the potential difference is observed to decrease to a smaller value V. If the dielectric is removed, the potential difference returns to its original value, showing that the original charges on the plates were not affected by insertion of the dielectric.

The original capacitance of the capacitor, C_0, was

$$C_0 = \frac{Q}{V_0}.$$

TABLE 27–1

DIELECTRIC COEFFICIENT K

$(\epsilon_0 = 8.85 \times 10^{-12} \text{ coul}^2/\text{n}\cdot\text{m}^2)$

Material	t, °C	K
Vacuum		1
Glass	25	5–10
Mica	25	3–6
Hevea rubber	27	2.94
Neoprene	24	6.70
Bakelite	27	5.50
	57	1.80
	88	18.2
Plexiglas	27	3.40
Polyethylene	23	2.25
Vinylite	20	3,18
	47	3.60
	76	3.92
	96	6.60
	110	9.9
Teflon	22	2.1
Germanium	20	16
Strontium titanate	20	310
Titanium dioxide (rutile)	20	173($\perp$), 86($\parallel$)
Water	25	78.54
Glycerin	25	42.5
Liquid ammonia	−77.7	25
Benzene	20	2.284
Air (1 atm)	20	1.00059
Air (100 atm)	20	1.0548

The capacitance C with the dielectric between the plates was

$$C = \frac{Q}{V}.$$

Since Q does not change and V is observed to be less than V_0, it follows that C is greater than C_0.

The ratio of C to C_0 is called the *dielectric coefficient* of the material, K.

$$K = \frac{C}{C_0}. \tag{27–7}$$

Since C is always greater than C_0, the dielectric coefficient of all dielectrics is greater than unity.   Some illustrative values are given in Table 27–1.   For a vacuum, of course, $K = 1$, and K for air is so nearly equal to 1 that for most purposes an air capacitor is equivalent to one in vacuum, and the original measurement of V_0 in Fig. 27–6(a) could have been made with the plates in air instead of in a vacuum.

With a vacuum (or air) between its plates, the electric intensity E_0 in the region between the plates of a parallel plate capacitor is

$$E_0 = \frac{V_0}{d} = \frac{\sigma}{\epsilon_0}.$$

The observed reduction in potential difference, when a dielectric is inserted between the plates, implies a reduction in the electric intensity, which in turn implies a reduction in the charge per unit area.   Since no charge has leaked off the plates, such a reduction could be caused only by charge of opposite sign appearing on the two surfaces of the dielectric. That is, the dielectric surface adjacent to the positive plate must have an induced negative charge and that adjacent to the negative plate an induced positive charge of equal magnitude, as shown in Fig. 27–7. If σ_i is the magnitude of induced charge per unit area on the surfaces of the dielectric, the electric intensity in the dielectric is

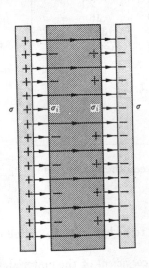

$$E = \frac{V}{d} = \frac{\sigma - \sigma_i}{\epsilon_0}. \qquad (27\text{–}8)$$

But

$$K = \frac{C}{C_0} = \frac{Q/V}{Q/V_0} = \frac{V_0}{V} = \frac{E_0}{E}$$
$$= \frac{\sigma}{\sigma - \sigma_i}, \qquad (27\text{–}9)$$

and therefore
$$\sigma - \sigma_i = \frac{\sigma}{K}. \qquad (27\text{–}10)$$

Substituting Eq. (27–10) into Eq. (27–8), we get

$$E = \frac{\sigma}{K\epsilon_0}. \qquad (27\text{–}11)$$

The product $K\epsilon_0$ is called the *permittivity* of the dielectric and is represented by ϵ.

Fig. 27–7. Induced charges on the faces of a dielectric in an external field.

$$\boxed{\epsilon = K\epsilon_0.} \qquad (27\text{–}12)$$

TABLE 27–2

PARALLEL PLATE CAPACITOR

With vacuum	With dielectric
$C_0 = \epsilon_0 \dfrac{A}{d}$	$C = \epsilon \dfrac{A}{d}$
$E_0 = \dfrac{\sigma}{\epsilon_0}$	$E = \dfrac{\sigma}{\epsilon} = \dfrac{\sigma - \sigma_i}{\epsilon_0}$
$K = 1$	$K = \dfrac{\epsilon}{\epsilon_0} = \dfrac{\sigma}{\sigma - \sigma_i}$
$V_0 = E_0 d$	$V = Ed$

The electric intensity within the dielectric may therefore be written

$$E = \frac{\sigma}{\epsilon}. \tag{27–13}$$

Also,

$$C = KC_0 = K\epsilon_0 \frac{A}{d},$$

and the capacitance of a parallel plate capacitor with a dielectric between its plates is therefore

$$\boxed{C = \epsilon \frac{A}{d}.} \tag{27–14}$$

In empty space, where $K = 1$, $\epsilon = \epsilon_0$, and therefore ϵ_0 may be described as the "permittivity of empty space" or the "permittivity of a vacuum." Since K is a pure number, the units of ϵ and ϵ_0 are evidently the same, $coul^2/n \cdot m^2$. Some representative values of K are listed in Table 27–1, and the properties of a parallel plate capacitor in vacuum and with a dielectric between its plates are compared in Table 27–2.

EXAMPLE. The parallel plates in Fig. 27–6 have an area of 2000 cm² or 2×10^{-1} m², and are 1 cm or 10^{-2} m apart. The original potential difference between them, V_0, is 3000 volts, and it decreases to 1000 volts when a sheet of dielectric is inserted between the plates. Compute (a) the original capacitance C_0, (b) the charge Q on each plate, (c) the capacitance C after insertion of the dielectric, (d) the dielectric coefficient K of the dielectric, (e) the permittivity ϵ of the dielectric, (f) the induced charge Q_i on each face of the dielectric, (g) the original electric intensity E_0 between the plates, (h) the electric intensity E after insertion of the dielectric.

(a) $C_0 = \epsilon_0 \dfrac{A}{d} = 8.85 \times 10^{-12} \dfrac{\text{coul}^2}{\text{n·m}^2} \times \dfrac{2 \times 10^{-1}\,\text{m}^2}{10^{-2}\,\text{m}} = 17.7 \times 10^{-11}\ \text{farad.}$

(b) $Q = C_0 V_0 = 17.7 \times 10^{-11}\ \text{farad} \times 3 \times 10^3\ \text{volts} = 53.1 \times 10^{-8}\ \text{coul.}$

(c) $C = \dfrac{Q}{V} = \dfrac{53.1 \times 10^{-8}\ \text{coul}}{10^3\ \text{volts}} = 53.1 \times 10^{-11}\ \text{farad.}$

(d) $K = \dfrac{C}{C_0} = \dfrac{53.1 \times 10^{-11}\ \text{farad}}{17.7 \times 10^{-11}\ \text{farad}} = 3.$

The dielectric coefficient could also be found from Eq. (27–9),

$$K = \frac{V_0}{V} = \frac{3000\ \text{volts}}{1000\ \text{volts}} = 3.$$

(e) $\qquad \epsilon = K\epsilon_0 = 3 \times 8.85 \times 10^{-12} \dfrac{\text{coul}^2}{\text{n·m}^2}$

$$= 26.6 \times 10^{-12} \frac{\text{coul}^2}{\text{n·m}^2}.$$

(f) $\qquad\qquad Q_i = A\sigma_i, \qquad Q = A\sigma,$

$$\sigma - \sigma_i = \frac{\sigma}{K}, \qquad \sigma_i = \sigma\left(1 - \frac{1}{K}\right),$$

$Q_i = Q\left(1 - \dfrac{1}{K}\right) = 53.1 \times 10^{-8}\ \text{coul}\,(1 - \tfrac{1}{3}) = 35.4 \times 10^{-8}\ \text{coul.}$

(g) $\qquad\qquad E_0 = \dfrac{V_0}{d} = \dfrac{3000\ \text{volts}}{10^{-2}\,\text{m}} = 3 \times 10^5\ \dfrac{\text{volts}}{\text{m}}.$

(h) $\qquad\qquad E = \dfrac{V}{d} = \dfrac{1000\ \text{volts}}{10^{-2}\,\text{m}} = 1 \times 10^5\ \dfrac{\text{volts}}{\text{m}},$

or

$$E = \frac{\sigma}{\epsilon} = \frac{Q}{A\epsilon} = \frac{53.1 \times 10^{-8}\ \text{coul}}{2 \times 10^{-1}\,\text{m}^2 \times 26.6 \times 10^{-12}\ \text{coul}^2/\text{n·m}^2} = 1 \times 10^5\ \frac{\text{volts}}{\text{m}},$$

or

$$E = \frac{\sigma - \sigma_i}{\epsilon_0} = \frac{Q - Q_i}{A\epsilon_0} = \frac{(53.1 - 35.4) \times 10^{-8}\ \text{coul}}{2 \times 10^{-1}\,\text{m}^2 \times 8.85 \times 10^{-12}\ \text{coul}^2/\text{n·m}^2}$$

$$= 1 \times 10^5\ \frac{\text{volts}}{\text{m}},$$

or, from Eq. (27-9),

$$E = \frac{E_0}{K} = \frac{3 \times 10^5 \text{ volts/m}}{3} = 1 \times 10^5 \frac{\text{volts}}{\text{m}}.$$

27-6 Induced charges on a dielectric. The charges induced on the surface of a dielectric sphere in an external field afford an explanation of the
attraction of an *uncharged* pith ball or bit of paper by a charged rod of
rubber or glass. When the external field is uniform, the net *force* on the
sphere is zero, since the forces on the positive and negative induced charges
are equal and opposite. However, if the field is *non*uniform, the induced
charges are in regions where the electric intensity is different and the force
in one direction is not equal to that in the other.

Figure 27-8 shows an uncharged dielectric sphere B in the radial field
of a positive charge A. The induced positive charges on B experience a
force toward the right, while the force on the negative charges is toward
the left. Since the negative charges are closer to A and therefore in a
stronger field than are the positive, the force toward the left exceeds that
toward the right, and B, although its net charge is ʼzero, experiences a
resultant force toward A. The sign of A's charge does not affect the conclusion, as may readily be seen. Furthermore, the effect is not limited
to dielectrics—a conducting sphere would be similarly attracted.

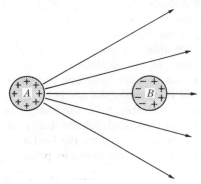

Fig. 27-8. An uncharged dielectric sphere B in the radial field of a positive
charge A.

More general arguments based on energy considerations show that a
dielectric body in a nonuniform field always experiences a force urging it
from a region where the field is weak toward a region where it is stronger,
provided the dielectric coefficient of the body is greater than that of the
medium in which it is immersed. If the dielectric coefficient is less, the
reverse is true.

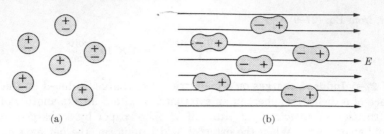

FIG. 27–9. Behavior of nonpolar molecules in the absence and in the presence of an electric field.

27–7 Molecular theory of induced charges on a dielectric. When a *conductor* is placed in an electric field, the free electrons within it undergo a displacement as a result of the forces exerted on them by the field. We have seen that in the final steady state the conductor has an induced charge on its surface, distributed in such a way that the field of this induced charge neutralizes the original field at all internal points and the net electric intensity within the conductor is reduced to zero. A *dielectric*, however, contains no free electrons. How, then, is it possible for an induced charge to appear on the surfaces of a dielectric when it is inserted in the electric field between the plates of a charged capacitor?

The molecules of a dielectric may be classified as either *polar* or *nonpolar*. A nonpolar molecule is one in which the "centers of gravity" of the positive nuclei and the electrons normally coincide, while a polar molecule is one in which they do not. Symmetrical molecules like H_2, N_2, and O_2 are nonpolar. In the molecules N_2O and H_2O, on the other hand, both nitrogen atoms or both hydrogen atoms lie on the same side of the oxygen atom, and these molecules are polar.

Under the influence of an electric field, the charges of a nonpolar molecule become displaced, as indicated schematically in Fig. 27–9. The molecules are said to become *polarized* by the field and are called *induced dipoles*. When a nonpolar molecule becomes polarized, restoring forces

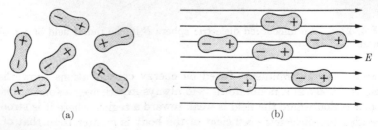

FIG. 27–10. Behavior of polar molecules in the absence and in the presence of an electric field.

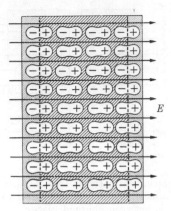

FIG. 27–11. Polarization of a dielectric in an electric field gives rise to thin layers of bound charges on the surfaces.

come into play on the displaced charges, pulling them together much as if they were connected by a spring. Under the influence of a given external field, the charges separate until the restoring force is equal and opposite to the force exerted on the charges by the field. Naturally, the restoring forces vary in magnitude from one kind of molecule to another, with corresponding differences in the displacement produced by a given field.

When a dielectric consists of polar molecules or *permanent dipoles*, these dipoles are oriented at random when no external field is present, as in Fig. 27–10(a). Under the action of an electric field, some degree of orientation takes place. The stronger the field, the greater the number of dipoles pointing in the direction of the field, as shown in Fig. 27–10(b).

Whether the molecules of a dielectric are polar or nonpolar, the net effect of an external field is substantially the same as shown in Fig. 27–11. Within the two extremely thin surface layers indicated by dotted lines there is an excess charge, negative in one layer and positive in the other. It is these layers of charge which give rise to the apparent induced charge on the surfaces of a dielectric, which (per unit of area) was represented by σ_i in Section 27–5. The charges are not free, but each is bound to a molecule lying in or near the surface. Within the remainder of the dielectric the net charge per unit volume remains zero.

The four parts of Fig. 27–12 illustrate the behavior of a sheet of dielectric when inserted in the field between a pair of oppositely charged plane parallel plates. Part (a) shows the original field. Part (b) is the situation after the dielectric has been inserted but before any rearrangement of charges has occurred. Part (c) shows by dotted lines the field set up in

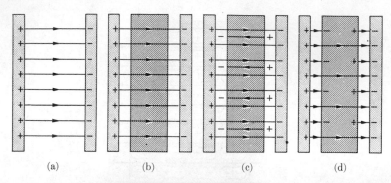

(a)   (b)   (c)   (d)

FIG. 27–12. (a) Electric field between two charged plates. (b) Introduction of a dielectric. (c) Induced surface charges and their field. (d) Resultant field when a dielectric is between charged plates.

the dielectric by its induced surface charges. This field is opposite to the original field but, since the charges in the dielectric are not free to move indefinitely, their displacement does not proceed to such an extent that the induced field is equal in magnitude to the original field. The field in the dielectric is therefore *weakened* but not reduced to zero, as it would be in the interior of a conductor.

The resultant field is shown in Fig. 27–12(d). Some of the lines of force leaving the positive plate penetrate the dielectric; others terminate on the induced charges on the faces of the dielectric.

PROBLEMS

27-1. A capacitor has a capacitance of 8.5 μf. How much charge must be removed to lower the potential difference of its plates by 50 volts?

27-2. Three capacitors having capacitances of 8, 8, and 4 μf are connected in series across a 12-volt line. (a) What is the charge on the 4-μf capacitor? (b) What is the total energy of all three capacitors? (c) The capacitors are disconnected from the line and reconnected in parallel with the positively charged plates connected together. What is the voltage across the parallel combination? (d) What is the energy of the combination?

27-3. The capacitance of all the capacitors shown in Fig. 27-13 are in μf. (a) What is the equivalent capacitance between x and y? (b) If the charge on the 5-μf capacitor is 120 μcoul, what is the potential difference between x and a?

each capacitor, (c) the final energy of the system, (d) the decrease in energy when the capacitors are connected.

27-6. A 1-μf capacitor and a 2-μf capacitor are connected in series across a 1200-volt supply line. (a) Find the charge on each capacitor and the voltage across each. (b) The charged capacitors are disconnected from the line and from each other, and reconnected with terminals of like sign together. Find the final charge on each and the voltage across each.

27-7. A 1-μf capacitor and a 2-μf capacitor are connected in parallel across a 1200-volt supply line. (a) Find the charge on each capacitor and the voltage across each. (b) The charged capacitors are then disconnected from the line and from each other, and reconnected with terminals of unlike sign together. Find the final charge on each and the voltage across each.

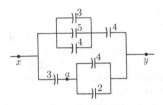

FIGURE 27-13

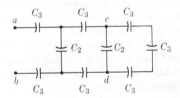

FIGURE 27-14

27-4. A 500-μf capacitor is charged to 120 volts. How many calories are produced on discharging the capacitor if all of the energy goes into heating the wire?

27-5. A 20-μf capacitor is charged to a potential difference of 1000 volts. The terminals of the charged capacitor are then connected to those of an uncharged 5-μf capacitor. Compute (a) the original charge of the system, (b) the final potential difference across

27-8. In Fig. 27-14, each capacitance $C_3 = 3$ μf and each capacitance $C_2 = 2$ μf. (a) Compute the equivalent capacitance of the network between points a and b. (b) Compute the charge on each of the capacitors nearest a and b, when $V_{ab} = 900$ volts. (c) With 900 volts across a and b, compute V_{cd}.

27-9. The capacitance of a variable radio capacitor can be changed from 50 μμf to 950 μμf by turning the dial from 0° to 180°. With the dial set at 180° the capacitor is connected to a 400-volt battery. After charging, the capacitor is disconnected from the battery and the dial is turned to 0°. (a) What is the charge on the capacitor? (b) What is the potential difference across the capacitor when the dial reads 0°? (c) What is the energy of the capacitor in this position? (d) How much work is required to turn the dial, if friction is neglected?

27–10. An air capacitor, consisting of two closely spaced parallel plates, has a capacitance of 1000 $\mu\mu f$. The charge on each plate is 1 microcoulomb. (a) What is the potential difference between the plates? (b) If the charge is kept constant, what will be the potential difference between the plates if the separation is doubled? (c) How much work is required to double the separation?

27–11. (a) The permittivity of diamond is 1.46×10^{-10} coul^2/n · m^2. What is the dielectric coefficient of diamond? (b) What is the dielectric coefficient of a metal?

27–12. Two parallel plates of 100 cm^2 area are given equal and opposite charges of 10^{-7} coul. The space between the plates is filled with a dielectric material, and the electric intensity within the dielectric is 3.3×10^5 volts/m. (a) What is the dielectric coefficient of the dielectric? (b) What is the total induced charge on either face of the dielectric?

27–13. Two parallel plates have equal and opposite charges. When the space between the plates is evacuated, the electric intensity is 2×10^5 volts/m. When the space is filled with dielectric, the electric intensity is 1.2×10^5 volts/m. What is the induced charge density on the surface of the dielectric?

27–14. A potential difference of 100 volts exists between the plates of a parallel plate capacitor in which the dielectric is air. (a) What will be the difference in potential between the plates if a dielectric sheet having a dielectric coefficient of 2.5 is inserted between the plates, the charge on the plates remaining constant? (b) With the air dielectric the capacitance of the capacitor was 100 μf. What is the energy in the capacitor for both dielectrics? (c) Assume that there is no friction between the dielectric and the plates. How much work would be required to withdraw the dielectric from the plates?

27–15. A parallel plate capacitor is to be constructed using as a dielectric rubber, having a dielectric coefficient of 3 and a dielectric strength of 2×10^5 volts/cm. The capacitor is to have a capacitance of 0.15 μf and must be able to withstand a maximum potential difference of 6000 volts. What is the minimum area the plates of the capacitor may have?

27–16. A capacitor consists of two parallel plates of area 25 cm^2 separated by a distance of 0.2 cm. The material between the plates has a dielectric coefficient of 5. The plates of the capacitor are connected to a 300-volt battery. (a) What is the capacitance of the capacitor? (b) What is the charge on either plate? (c) What is the energy in the charged capacitor?

27–17. Two oppositely charged conducting plates, having numerically equal quantities of charge per unit area, are separated by a dielectric 5 mm thick, of dielectric coefficient 3. The resultant electric intensity in the dielectric is 10^6 volts/m. Compute: (a) the free charge per unit area on the conducting plates, (b) the induced charge per unit area on the surfaces of the dielectric.

27-18. The paper dielectric, in a paper and foil capacitor, is 0.005 cm thick. Its dielectric coefficient is 2.5 and its dielectric strength is 50×10^6 volts/m. (a) What area of paper, and of tinfoil, is required for a 0.1 μf capacitor? (b) If the electric intensity in the paper is not to exceed one-half the dielectric strength, what is the maximum potential difference that can be applied across the capacitor?

27-19. A spherical capacitor consists of an inner metal sphere of radius r_a supported on an insulating stand at the center of a hollow metal sphere of inner radius r_b. There is a charge $+Q$ on the inner sphere and a charge $-Q$ on the outer. (a) What is the potential difference V_{ab} between the spheres?

(b) Prove that the capacitance is

$$C = 4\pi\epsilon_0 \frac{r_b r_a}{r_b - r_a}.$$

27-20. A coaxial cable consists of an inner solid cylindrical conductor of radius r_a supported by insulating disks on the axis of a thin-walled conducting tube of inner radius r_b. The two cylinders are oppositely charged with a charge λ per unit length. The potential difference V_{ab} between the conductors is

$$V_{ab} = \frac{2\lambda}{4\pi\epsilon_0} \ln \frac{r_b}{r_a}.$$

Prove that the capacitance of a length l of the cable is

$$C = l \frac{2\pi\epsilon_0}{\ln (r_b/r_a)}.$$

Neglect any effect of the supporting disks.

CHAPTER 28

CURRENT AND RESISTANCE

28-1 Current. In purely electrostatic problems such as those considered in the preceding chapters, one is concerned chiefly with the forces between charges, the final, steady-state distribution of charge brought about by these forces, and the motion of charged particles in empty space. We are next to discuss the motion of charge in a conductor when an electric field is maintained within the conductor. This motion constitutes a *current*.

A conductor, it will be recalled, is a material within which there are "free" charges which will move when a force is exerted on them by an electric field. The free charges in a *metallic* conductor are negative electrons. The free charges in an *electrolyte* are ions, both positive and negative. A *gas* under the proper conditions, as in a neon sign or a fluorescent lamp, is also a conductor and its free charges are positive and negative ions and negative electrons.

We have seen that when an isolated conductor is placed in an electric field the charges within the conductor rearrange themselves so as to make the interior of the conductor a field-free region throughout which the potential is constant. The motion of the charges in the rearranging process constitutes a current, but it is of short duration only and is called a *transient* current. If we wish to maintain a continuous current in a conductor, we must continuously maintain a field, i.e. a potential gradient, within it. If the field is always in the same direction, even though it may fluctuate in magnitude, the current is called *direct*. If the field reverses direction periodically, the flow of charge reverses also and the current is *alternating*. Direct and alternating currents are abbreviated to d-c and a-c respectively.

A number of electrical devices, which we shall discuss in detail later, have the property of maintaining their terminals continuously at different potentials. The most familiar of these are the dry cell, the storage battery, and the generator. If the ends of a wire are connected to the terminals of any one of these devices, a potential gradient or an electric field will be maintained within the wire and there will be a continuous motion of charge through it. To be specific, if the ends of a copper wire one meter long are connected to the terminals of a 6-volt storage battery, a potential gradient or electric field of intensity 6 volts/m or 6 n/coul is established and maintained along the wire.

536

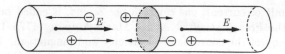

FIG. 28–1. Negative charges crossing a section from right to left are equivalent to positive charges crossing from left to right.

When there is an electric field in a conductor the *free* charges within it are set in motion, positive charges moving in the same direction as the field, negative charges in the opposite direction. Figure 28–1 shows a portion of a conductor within which there is an electric field of intensity E. A few positive and negative free charges are also shown. In a given time interval a certain number of positive charges cross the shaded section from left to right, while negative charges cross it from right to left. Let q_+ represent the total positive charge crossing the section, and q_- the total negative charge crossing in the same time. The effect of positive charge crossing the section is to increase the net positive charge at the right of the section. But since *removal* of *negative* charge is equivalent to *addition* of *positive* charge, the negative charge crossing from right to left also increases the net positive charge at the right of the section. Therefore the total increase in positive charge q at the right of the section equals the *sum* of q_+ and q_-:

$$q = q_+ + q_-.$$

For example, if 4 coul of positive charge cross from left to right and 2 coul of negative charge cross from right to left, the total increase in positive charge at the right of the section is

$$q = 4 \text{ coul} + 2 \text{ coul} = 6 \text{ coul}.$$

The result is the same as if 6 coul of positive charge had crossed the section from left to right.

The *current* at the section, represented by the symbol i, is defined as the total rate of transfer of positive charge across the section, or as the total positive charge crossing per unit time. Thus, in the example above, if the time interval was 2 sec, the current was

$$i = \frac{6 \text{ coul}}{2 \text{ sec}} = 3 \frac{\text{coul}}{\text{sec}}.$$

The rate at which charge is transported across a section of the wire, or q/t, is called the current in the wire.

$$\boxed{i = \frac{q}{t}.}$$ (28–1)

The mks unit of current, *one coulomb per second*, is called one *ampere*, in honor of the French scientist André Marie Ampere (1775–1836), who developed many of the concepts of electricity and magnetism. Small currents are more conveniently expressed in milliamperes (ma) (1 milliampere $= 10^{-3}$ amp) or in microamperes (μa) (1 microampere $= 10^{-6}$ amp).

Since a current is a flow of charge, the common expression "flow of current" should be avoided, since literally it means "flow of flow of charge."

It might seem logical to define the *direction* of a current as the direction of motion of the free charges. We immediately come up against the difficulty, however, that in an electrolytic or gaseous conductor free charges of both signs are in motion in opposite directions. Whichever direction is assigned to the current, we would find charges moving in the opposite direction. Since some convention must be adopted, it has been agreed to speak of the direction of a current as if the carriers were all positive charges. In a *metallic* conductor, it is only the negative charges or free electrons which are mobile. Hence the entire current in a metallic conductor arises from the motion of negative charges, and *in a metallic conductor the electrons move in the opposite direction to the conventional current*. From now on we shall adopt this convention, and indeed shall often speak of the current in a metal as though it arose from the motion of positive charges alone.

The current in a conductor can be expressed in terms of the velocity of the moving charges as follows. Consider a conductor of cross-sectional area A in which positively charged particles are moving from left to right, as in Fig. 28–2. Suppose there are n particles per unit volume, all moving with velocity v. In a time interval t, each advances a distance vt. The number of particles crossing any section such as that shaded is equal to the number contained in a portion of the conductor of length vt and of volume vAt. This number is $nvAt$, and if the charge on each is e, the total charge crossing the section is

$$q = nevAt.$$

The current is therefore

$$i = \frac{q}{t} = nevA. \tag{28–2}$$

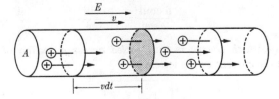

FIGURE 28–2

In general, if any number of different kinds of charged particles are present, in different concentrations and moving with different velocities, the total charge crossing a section is

$$q = At(n_1 e_1 v_1 + n_2 e_2 v_2 + \cdots)$$

and the current is

$$i = \frac{q}{t} = A\sum nev. \tag{28-3}$$

All the *nev* products will have the same sign, since charges of opposite sign move in opposite directions.

If the charges in a conductor were perfectly free to move indefinitely, they would accelerate under the influence of the applied field, their velocities would continuously increase, and the current would continuously increase. This is not observed to happen; the current remains constant so long as the electric field is constant. This can be explained by assuming that after a momentary acceleration a moving particle collides with one of the fixed particles in the conductor and is slowed down or brought to rest, after which it again accelerates, and so on. It thus moves with a certain average velocity, called the *drift* velocity, which must be interpreted as the velocity v in the preceding equations. The collisions with the fixed particles result in a transfer of energy to them which increases their energy of vibration and results in the development of heat. This production of heat in a current-carrying conductor is discussed further in Chapter 29.

Let us estimate the drift velocity of the free electrons in a conductor. Consider a copper conductor of cross-sectional area 1 cm^2 or 10^{-4} m^2 in which the current is 200 amp. Previous calculations have shown that there are in copper about 8.5×10^{28} free electrons per cubic meter, on the assumption that each copper atom contributes two free electrons. Then

$$v = \frac{i}{enA}$$

$$= \frac{200 \text{ coul/sec}}{1.6 \times 10^{-19} \text{ (coul/electron)} \times 8.5 \times 10^{28} \text{ (electrons/m}^3) \times 10^{-4} \text{ m}^2}$$

$$= 1.47 \times 10^{-4} \frac{\text{m}}{\text{sec}},$$

or about 0.015 cm/sec. The drift velocity is therefore quite small.

The drift velocity of the free electrons should not be confused with the velocity of propagation of an electromagnetic wave along the conductor (discussed in Chapter 37), which, if the conductor is in vacuum, is the same as the velocity of light, that is, 3×10^8 mi/sec or 186,000 mi/sec.

28–2 The complete circuit. When the ends of a wire are connected to two points maintained at fixed, but different, potentials, such as the terminals of a cell or generator, there will be a current in the wire but the potential of each point of the wire remains constant in time. Consider any short element of the wire bounded by two transverse planes and shown shaded in Fig. 28–3. If the electrons in the wire are moving from left to right, negative charge is entering the element at its left face and leaving it at its right face. The quantity of charge entering the element in any time interval must be exactly equal to that leaving, for if it were not, the quantity of charge in the element, and hence the potential of the element, would change. We conclude that the current must be the same at both faces of the element, and therefore must be the same at *all* sections of the wire. In this respect a flow of electrons is like the flow of an incompressible fluid.

Fig. 28–3. Electric charge entering and leaving a small element of a wire.

The conducting wire and the cell or generator to which its ends are connected are said to form a complete circuit or a *closed circuit*. An electrolytic cell is represented by the symbol ⊣⊢ and a generator by ⊸Ⓞ⊶, the + sign denoting the terminal which is normally at the higher potential. Figure 28–4 is a diagram of such a closed circuit. The arrow indicates the direction of the conventional current. The electrons in the wire circulate in the opposite direction. The positive ions within the cell move in the same direction as the conventional current, the negative ions in the opposite direction.

A number of cross sections of the circuit are indicated by dotted lines. The current is the same at all these sections, including the one through the cell. Current is not something which squirts out of the positive ter-

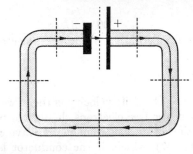

Fig. 28–4. A closed circuit consisting of an electrolytic cell and a wire.

minal of a cell and gets all used up by the time it reaches the negative terminal. A steady current can exist only in a closed circuit equivalent to that of Fig. 28–4. If the wire is disconnected from the cell at either end, or if a break is made at any other point of the circuit, the current immediately ceases. The circuit is then said to be *open*.

Note carefully that the direction of the conventional current is "from plus to minus" *in the external circuit only*. Within the cell, the direction is from minus to plus.

28–3 Resistivity, resistance, and Ohm's law. The current i in a given conductor depends on the electric intensity E in the conductor. In a pure metal, the current is directly proportional to the electric intensity. For other materials, the relation between i and E is more complicated. In any case, we can define a property of a conductor called its *resistivity*, ρ, as the ratio of the electric intensity to the current per unit cross-sectional area:

$$\rho = \frac{E}{i/A}.$$
$$(28\text{–}4)$$

Let V_a and V_b be the potentials at two points on a conductor separated by a length L. The electric intensity E in the conductor then equals the potential gradient $(V_a - V_b)/L$. Hence we can write Eq. (28–4) as

$$\rho = \frac{V_a - V_b}{iL/A},$$

or

$$i = \frac{V_a - V_b}{\rho L/A}.$$
$$(28\text{–}5)$$

The electrical *conductivity* of a material, σ, is defined as the reciprocal of the resistivity ρ. In terms of σ, we can write Eq. (28–5) in the form

$$i = \sigma A \frac{V_a - V_b}{L}.$$

It is then exactly analogous to the equation of steady-state heat conduction,

$$H = KA \frac{t_2 - t_1}{L}.$$

The electrical current i corresponds to the heat current H, the electrical conductivity σ to the thermal conductivity K, and the potential gradient $(V_a - V_b)/L$ to the temperature gradient $(t_2 - t_1)/L$.

The relation between the conduction of electricity and the conduction of heat is more than a mere mathematical analogy. The free electrons which are the carriers of charge in electrical conduction also play an important role in the conduction of heat, and hence a correlation can be expected between electrical and thermal conductivity. It is a familiar fact that good electrical conductors, such as the metals, are good conductors of heat, while poor electrical conductors are also poor conductors of heat.

The quantity $\rho L/A$ is called the *resistance R* of the conductor:

$$R = \frac{\rho L}{A}. \tag{28-6}$$

In terms of resistance, Eq. (28–5) becomes

$$i = \frac{V_a - V_b}{R} = \frac{V_{ab}}{R}. \tag{28-7}$$

If the current per unit area in a conductor is directly proportional to E, the resistivity ρ of the conductor is a constant and, therefore, for a conductor of given length L and area A, the resistance R is a constant also, independent of i and E. That is, for such a conductor, the current i is

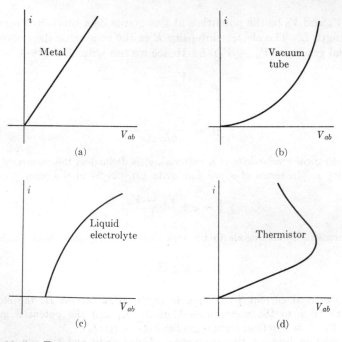

FIG. 28–5. Four examples of the relation between current and potential difference. (a) A metal, where R is constant. (b) A vacuum tube, where R decreases. (c) An electrolyte (liquid), where R increases. (d) A thermistor, where R is first constant and then decreases.

directly proportional to the potential difference V_{ab} or is a *linear* function of V_{ab}. The conductor is called a *linear* conductor; Fig. 28–5(a) is a graph of i vs. V_{ab} for such a conductor.

This direct proportionality between the current in a metallic conductor and the potential difference between its terminals was discovered experimentally by the German scientist Georg Simon Ohm (1789–1854), and is known as *Ohm's law*.

From Eq. (28–7), the resistance R of any electrical device can be defined as the ratio of the potential difference between its terminals to the current through it:

$$R = \frac{V_{ab}}{i}. \tag{28–8}$$

The graphs in Fig. 28–5(b), (c), and (d) illustrate the behavior of *non-linear* conductors, where Ohm's law is not obeyed. In part (b) the resistance decreases with V_{ab}, in part (c) it increases, and in (d) it is first constant and then decreases.

The unit of resistance, from Eq. (28–8), is the *volt per ampere*. A resistance of one volt per ampere is called one *ohm*. That is, *the resistance of a conductor is one ohm if the potential difference between the terminals of the conductor is one volt when the current in the conductor is one ampere.*

The Greek letter Ω (omega) is used to designate a resistance in ohms. Thus a resistance of 4.5 volts/amp or 4.5 ohms is written

$$4.5 \ \Omega.$$

Large resistances are more conveniently expressed in megohms (1 megohm $= 10^6$ ohms) and small resistances in microhms (1 microhm $= 10^{-6}$ ohm).

Resistance units constructed to introduce into a circuit lumped resistances large compared with those of leads and contacts are called *resistors*. A resistor is represented by the symbol ⌇⌇⌇.

Portions of a circuit of negligible resistance are shown by straight lines.

An adjustable resistor is called a *rheostat*. A common type is constructed by winding resistance wire on a porcelain or enamel tube, and making connections to one end and to a sliding contact. A rheostat is represented by ⌇⌇ or simply ⌇⌇ .

28–4 Standard resistors. The ohm as defined in the preceding section (i.e., the resistance of a conductor in which the current is one ampere when the potential difference between its terminals is one volt) is known as the *absolute ohm*. For practical convenience, the ohm has been defined by international agreement in terms of a physical standard. At the time of its adoption, in 1908, this *international ohm* was believed to be identical

FIG. 28–6. Standard resistor. (Courtesy of Leeds and Northrup.)

with the absolute ohm. Later measurements have shown the two to differ slightly, the best value at present being

$$1 \text{ int. ohm} = 1.00048 \text{ abs. ohm.}$$

The international ohm is defined as the resistance offered to an unvarying electric current by a column of mercury at the temperature of melting ice, 14.4521 gm in mass, of a constant cross-sectional area and 106.300 cm in length.

The international standard consists of a mercury column in a glass tube and is obviously not suited for a working standard in the laboratory. So-called "standard resistors" are, however, available commercially with resistances ranging from 0.001 ohm to 10,000 ohms, accurate to within a few hundredths of one percent. They are constructed of wire, usually manganin because of its low temperature coefficient of resistivity, and are mounted in a metal case through which oil can be circulated to maintain constant temperature (see Fig. 28–6). Heavy "current terminals" are provided for leading the current into and out of the resistor, together with a pair of "potential terminals" between which the resistance has its specified value and which are used for measuring the potential difference across the resistor.

28–5 Calculation of resistance. The resistance of a homogeneous conductor of constant cross section is given by Eq. (28-6):

$$R = \frac{\rho L}{A}.$$

The resistance is proportional to the length of the conductor and inversely proportional to its cross section. If the conductor is of unit length and unit cross section, the ratio L/A is unity and the resistance R and the resistivity ρ are numerically equal. Hence the resistivity of a material is numerically equal to the resistance of a specimen of the material of unit length and unit cross-sectional area.

In the mks system, where the unit of length is the meter and the unit of area the square meter, the unit of resistivity is one *ohm·meter*. The resistivity of a material in ohms·meter is numerically equal to the resistance, in ohms, between opposite faces of a cube of the material one meter on a side.

If the centimeter is used as a unit of length and the square centimeter as a unit of area, resistivities are expressed in *ohms·centimeter*.

In engineering work it is customary to express the length of a conductor in feet and its cross-sectional area in circular mils.* The resistivity of a material in terms of these units is expressed in ohms·circular mil per foot, usually abbreviated to the "mil·foot" resistivity. The mil·foot resistivity is numerically equal to the resistance in ohms of a wire of circular cross section, one foot long and one one-thousandth of an inch in diameter.

It is evident from the significance of resistivity that materials having large resistivities are poor conductors or good insulators. Conversely, substances of small resistivity are good conductors. No perfect insulator ($\rho = \infty$) exists, nor does a perfect conductor† ($\rho = 0$). There is, however, a wide difference in the resistivities of different materials, so that in general they can be grouped into two classes, conductors and insulators. See Table 28–1.

The resistivity of a pure metal in a definite crystalline state and at a definite temperature is a quantity characteristic of the metal. Changes

---

* A circular mil (abbreviated CM) is a unit of *area*, equal to the area of a circle whose diameter is one one-thousandth of an inch or one mil. Since the areas of two circles are proportional to the squares of their diameters, the area of any circle in circular mils is equal to the square of its diameter in mils:

$$\text{area (in CM)} = [D \text{ (in mils)}]^2.$$

Since most wires are circular in cross section, the use of a unit of area which is itself circular eliminates the factor π in calculations of area.

It follows at once from its definition that

$$1 \text{ CM} = \frac{\pi}{4{,}000{,}000} \text{ square inches.}$$

† At extremely low temperatures, near absolute zero, some conductors lose the last vestige of resistance, a phenomenon known as *superconductivity*. A current once started in such a conductor will continue of itself for hours or even days.

TABLE 28-1

RESISTIVITIES AND TEMPERATURE COEFFICIENTS
(Approximate values near room temperature)

Material	ρ (ohm·meter)*	$\alpha_0(°C^{-1})$
Aluminum	2.63×10^{-8}	0.0039
Brass	$6-8 \times 10^{-8}$	0.0020
Carbon	3500×10^{-8}	-0.0005
Constantan (Cu 60, Ni 40)	49×10^{-8}	$+0.000002$
Copper (commercial annealed)	1.72×10^{-8}	0.00393
Iron	10×10^{-8}	0.0050
Lead	22×10^{-8}	0.0043
Manganin (Cu 84, Mn 12, Ni 4)	44×10^{-8}	0.000000
Mercury	94×10^{-8}	0.00088
Nichrome	100×10^{-8}	0.0004
Silver	1.47×10^{-8}	0.0038
Tungsten	5.51×10^{-8}	0.0045
Amber	5×10^{14}	
Bakelite	$2 \times 10^5 - 2 \times 10^{14}$	
Glass	$10^{10} - 10^{14}$	
Hard rubber	$10^{13} - 10^{16}$	
Mica	$10^{11} - 10^{15}$	
Quartz (fused)	75×10^{16}	
Sulfur	10^{15}	
Wood	$10^8 - 10^{11}$	

* Multiply ρ in ohm·m by 10^2 to get ρ in ohm·cm; by 6.02×10^8 to get ρ in the mil·foot system.

in the crystalline structure due to heat treatment or mechanical strain, or impurities alloyed with the metal even in minute quantities, may have a pronounced effect on its resistivity. For example, the resistivity of commercial annealed copper at 20°C is 1.72×10^{-8} ohm·m, that of hard drawn copper is 1.77×10^{-8} ohm·m.

Hydrostatic pressure applied to a metal modifies its resistivity very slightly. The resistivity of bismuth is increased if the bismuth is in a magnetic field, and this change in resistivity affords a convenient method for measuring such fields. The resistivity of the metal selenium is decreased when the metal is illuminated. The light liberates photoelectrons within the metal, rendering it a better conductor.

The resistivity of all conducting materials is affected by their temperature. A plot of resistivity vs. temperature, for a metallic conductor, is given in Fig. 28–7. The curve may be satisfactorily represented by an equation of the form

$$\rho = \rho_0 + at + bt^2 + \cdots,\qquad(28\text{–}9)$$

where ρ_0 is the resistivity at 0°C; a, b, etc., are constants characteristic of a particular material; and t is the celsius temperature. For temperatures which are not too great, the terms in t^2 and higher powers may be neglected and we may write

$$\rho = \rho_0 + at.\qquad(28\text{–}10)$$

It is convenient to put Eq. (28–10) in the form

$$\rho = \rho_0 + \frac{\rho_0 at}{\rho_0}$$

or

$$\rho = \rho_0(1 + \alpha_0 t),\qquad(28\text{–}11)$$

where

$$\alpha_0 = \frac{a}{\rho_0} = \frac{\rho - \rho_0}{\rho_0 t}.$$

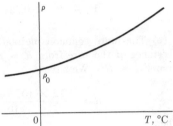

Fig. 28–7. Variation of resistivity of a metal with temperature.

The quantity α_0 is called the *temperature coefficient of resistivity* and is the fractional increase in resistivity per degree increase in temperature. Its units are $\deg^{-1}$ or "reciprocal degrees."

Since the resistance of a given conductor is proportional to its resistivity, Eq. (28–11) may also be written

$$R = R_0(1 + \alpha_0 t),\qquad(28\text{–}12)$$

where R_0 is the resistance at 0°C and R is the resistance at t°C.

The resistivities of nonmetals decrease with increasing temperature, and their temperature coefficients of resistivity are negative. Electrolytes also have negative temperature coefficients of resistivity. In other words, they conduct more readily at high temperatures, which is probably because their decreased viscosity affords less opposition to the transport of ions through them. The temperature coefficients of resistivity of some common materials are listed in Table 28–1.

EXAMPLE 1. What is the electric intensity in the copper conductor used as an example in Section 28–1?

From Eq. (28–4), the electric intensity E is

$$E = \frac{\rho i}{A}.$$

From Table 28–1, the resistivity of copper is 1.72×10^{-8} ohm·m. Therefore,

$$E = \frac{1.72 \times 10^{-8}\ \text{ohm·m} \times 200\ \text{amp}}{10^{-4}\ \text{m}^2} = 0.0344\ \frac{\text{volt}}{\text{m}}.$$

EXAMPLE 2. What is the potential difference between two points on the above wire 100 m apart?

(a) Since the electric intensity or potential gradient is 0.0344 volt/m, the potential difference between two points 100 m apart is

$$V_a - V_b = 0.0344\ \frac{\text{volt}}{\text{m}} \times 100\ \text{m} = 3.44\ \text{volts}.$$

(b) The more common method of solution would be to first compute the resistance of the wire from $R = \rho L/A$ and then find the potential difference from $V_{ab} = Ri$. We have

$$R = \frac{1.72 \times 10^{-8}\ \text{ohm·m} \times 100\ \text{m}}{10^{-4}\ \text{m}^2} = 0.0172\ \text{ohm}.$$

Then

$$V_{ab} = 0.0172\ \text{ohm} \times 200\ \text{amp} = 3.44\ \text{volts},$$

which is the same as the previous answer.

28–6 Measurement of current, potential difference, and resistance.
Currents are measured by instruments called *galvanometers* or *ammeters*. The most common type makes use of the interaction between a current-carrying conductor and a magnetic field and is described in Chapter 32. For our present purposes it is sufficient to know that such instruments exist.

To measure the current at a point such as *a, b,* or *c* in Fig. 28–8(a), the circuit must be opened and the ammeter inserted at that point so

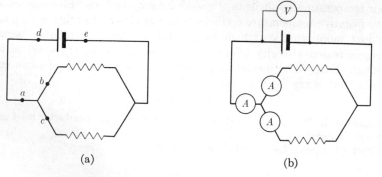

(a)   (b)

FIG. 28–8. Ammeter and voltmeter connections.

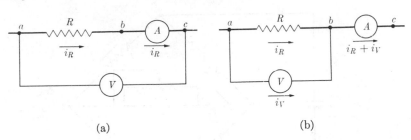

FIG. 28-9. Ammeter-voltmeter methods of measuring resistance.

that the current to be measured passes *through* the ammeter, as in Fig. 28-8(b).   An ammeter is a low resistance instrument, representative values being a few hundredths or thousandths of an ohm.

The potential difference between two points of a circuit might be measured with an electroscope or electrometer.   It is more convenient, however, to use some type of *voltmeter*, the construction of which is described more fully in Chapter 32.   Most voltmeters, unlike electroscopes and electrometers, are current-operated.   The voltmeter terminals are connected to the points between which the potential difference is to be measured.   Figure 28-8(b) shows a voltmeter V connected so as to measure the potential difference between the terminals of the cell.   If the details of its construction are disregarded, a voltmeter may be treated as a resistor which automatically indicates the potential difference between its terminals.   Typical resistances, for a 100-volt instrument, are from 10,000 to 100,000 ohms.

The resistance of a conductor is the ratio of the potential difference between its terminals to the current in it.   The most straightforward method of measuring resistance is therefore to measure these two quantities and divide one by the other.   The ammeter-voltmeter method for so doing is illustrated in Fig. 28-9.   In circuit (a) the ammeter measures the current i_R in the resistor, but the voltmeter reads V_{ac} and not the potential difference V_{ab} between the terminals of the resistor.   In circuit (b) the voltmeter reads V_{ab}, but the ammeter reads the *sum* of the currents in the resistor and in the voltmeter.   Hence, whichever circuit is used, corrections must be made to the reading of one meter or the other, unless these corrections can be shown to be negligible.

28-7 The Wheatstone bridge.   The Wheatstone bridge circuit, shown in Fig. 28-10, is widely used for the rapid and precise measurement of resistance.   It was invented in 1843 by the English scientist Charles Wheatstone. M, N, and P are adjustable resistors which have been previously calibrated, and X represents the unknown resistance.   To use the bridge, switches K_1 and K_2 are closed and the resistance of P is adjusted until

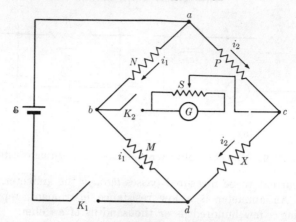

FIG. 28–10. Wheatstone bridge circuit.

the galvanometer G shows no deflection. Points b and c must then be at the same potential or, in other words, the potential drop from a to b equals that from a to c. Also, the drop from b to d equals that from c to d. Since the galvanometer current is zero, the current in M equals that in N, say i_1, and the current in P equals that in X, say i_2. Then, since $V_{ab} = V_{ac}$, it follows that

$$i_1 N = i_2 P,$$

and since $V_{bd} = V_{cd}$,

$$i_1 M = i_2 X.$$

When the second equation is divided by the first, we find

$$X = \frac{M}{N} P.$$

Hence if M, N, and P are known, X can be computed. The ratio M/N is usually set at some integral power of 10, such as 0.01, 1, 100, etc., for simplicity in computation.

During preliminary adjustments, when the bridge may be far from balance and V_{bc} large, the galvanometer must be protected by the shunt S. A resistor whose resistance is large compared with that of the galvanometer is permanently connected across the galvanometer terminals. When the sliding contact is at the left end of the resistor, none of the current in the path between b and c passes through the galvanometer. In a position such as that shown, that portion of the resistor at the right of the sliding contact is in series with the galvanometer, and this combination is shunted by that portion of the resistor at the left of the contact. Hence only a fraction of the current passes through the galvanometer. With the

Fig. 28–11. Portable Wheatstone bridge. (Courtesy of Leeds and Northrup.)

sliding contact at the right of the resistor, all the current passes through the galvanometer except the small fraction bypassed by the resistor. The galvanometer is therefore fully protected when the contact is at the left end of the resistor, and practically full galvanometer sensitivity is attained when the contact is at the right end.

If any of the resistances are inductive, the potentials V_b and V_c may attain their final values at different rates when K_1 is closed, and the galvanometer, if connected between b and c, would show an initial deflection even though the bridge were in balance. Hence K_1 and K_2 are frequently combined in a double key which closes the battery circuit first and the galvanometer circuit a moment later, after the transient currents have died out.

Portable bridges are available having a self-contained galvanometer and dry cells. The ratio M/N can be set at any integral power of 10 between 0.001 and 1000 by a single dial switch, and the value of R adjusted by four dial switches. Figure 28–11 is a photograph of such a bridge.

28–8 Joule's law. The electronic motion in a conductor may be described as a series of accelerations, each of which is terminated by a collision with one of the fixed particles of the conductor. The electrons gain kinetic energy in the free paths between collisions, and give up to the fixed particles, in each collision, the same amount of energy they have gained. The energy acquired by the fixed particles (which are "fixed" only in the sense that their *mean* position does not change) increases their amplitude of vibration. In other words, it is converted to heat.

To derive the expression for the rate of development of heat in a conductor, we first work out the general expression for the power input to any portion of an electric circuit. The rectangle in Fig. 28–12 represents a portion of a circuit in which there is a (conventional) current i from left to right. V_a and V_b are the potentials at terminals a and b. The nature of the circuit between a and b is immaterial—it may be a conductor, motor, generator, battery, or any combination of these. The power input, as we shall show, depends only on the magnitudes and relative directions of the current and the terminal potential difference.

In a time interval t, a quantity of charge $q = it$ enters the portion of the circuit under consideration at terminal a, and in the same time an equal quantity of charge leaves at terminal b. There has thus been a transfer of charge q from a potential V_a to a potential V_b. The energy W

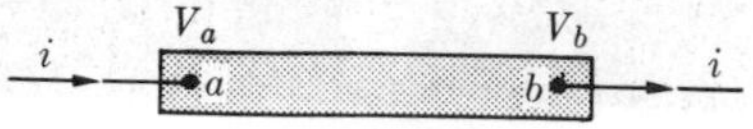

FIG. 28–12. Transfer of charge in a portion of a circuit.

given up by the charge is

$$W = q(V_a - V_b) = itV_{ab},$$

and the *rate* at which energy is given up, or the power input P, is

$$P = \frac{W}{t} = iV_{ab}. \tag{28-13}$$

That is, the power is equal to the product of the current and the potential difference. If the current is in amperes or coul/sec and the potential difference in volts or joules/coul, the power is in joules/sec or watts, since

$$\text{amp} \times \text{volts} = \frac{\text{coul}}{\text{sec}} \times \frac{\text{joules}}{\text{coul}} = \frac{\text{joules}}{\text{sec}} = \text{watts}.$$

Equation (28-13) is a perfectly general relation that holds whatever the nature of the circuit elements between a and b. We shall return to it later on.

In the special case in which the circuit between a and b is a pure resistance R, all the energy supplied is converted to heat, and in this special case the potential difference V_{ab} is given by

$$V_{ab} = iR.$$

Hence

$$P = iV_{ab} = i \times iR,$$

or

$$P = i^2 R. \tag{28-14}$$

To bring out more explicitly that in this special case the energy appears as heat, we may set $P = H$, where H is the heat developed in unit time. Equation (28-14) then becomes

$$H = i^2 R. \tag{28-15}$$

If the conductor is linear, i.e., if R is a constant independent of i, Eq. (28-15) states that *the rate of development of heat is directly proportional to the square of the current*. This fact was discovered experimentally by Joule in the course of his measurements of the mechanical equivalent of heat, and is known as *Joule's law*. Of course, it is a law only in the same sense as is Ohm's law; that is, it expresses a special property of certain materials rather than a general property of all matter. A material which obeys Ohm's law necessarily obeys Joule's law also, and the two are not independent relations.

If in Eq. (28–15) the resistance is expressed in ohms and the current in amperes, the rate of development of heat is in joules/sec or watts, since

$$\text{amp}^2 \times \text{ohms} = \text{amp}^2 \times \frac{\text{volts}}{\text{amp}} = \text{amp} \times \text{volts} = \text{watts}.$$

This can readily be converted to cal/sec from the relation 1 calorie = 4.186 joules.

Notice that the rate of development of heat in a conductor is not the same thing as the rate of increase of temperature of the conductor. The latter depends on the heat capacity of the conductor and the rate at which heat can escape from the conductor by conduction, convection, and radiation. The rate of loss of heat increases as the temperature of the conductor increases, and the temperature of a current-carrying conductor will rise until the rate of loss of heat equals the rate of development of heat, after which the temperature remains constant. Thus when the circuit is closed through an incandescent lamp, the temperature of the filament rises rapidly until the rate of heat loss (chiefly by radiation) equals the rate of development of heat, i^2R. On the other hand, a fuse is constructed so that when the current in it exceeds a certain predetermined value, the fuse melts before its final equilibrium temperature can be attained.

PROBLEMS

28–1. A silver wire 1 mm in diameter carries a charge of 90 coul in 1 hr and 15 min. Silver contains 5.8×10^{22} free electrons per cm^3. (a) What is the current in the wire? (b) What is the drift velocity of the electrons in the wire?

28–2. When a sufficiently high potential difference is applied between two electrodes in a gas, the gas ionizes, electrons moving toward the positive electrode and positive ions toward the negative electrode. (a) What is the current in a hydrogen discharge tube if in each second 4×10^{18} electrons and 1.5×10^{18} protons move in opposite directions past a cross section of the tube? (b) What is the direction of the current?

28–3. A vacuum diode can be approximated by a plane cathode and a plane anode, parallel to each other and 5 mm apart. The area of both cathode and anode is 2 cm^2. In the region between cathode and anode the current is carried solely by electrons. If the electron current is 50 ma, and the electrons strike the anode surface with a velocity of 1.2×10^7 m/sec, find the number of electrons per cubic millimeter in the space just outside the surface of the anode.

28–4. The belt of a Van de Graaff generator is one meter wide and travels with a speed of 25 m/sec. (a) Neglecting leakage, at what rate in coul/sec must charge be sprayed on one face of the belt to correspond to a current of 10^{-4} amp into the collecting sphere? (b) Compute the surface charge per unit area on the belt.

28–5. In the Bohr model of the hydrogen atom the electron makes about 0.6×10^{16} rev/sec around the nucleus.

What is the average current at a point on the orbit of the electron?

28–6. A wire 100 m long and 2 mm in diameter has a resistivity of 4.8×10^{-8} ohm·m. (a) What is the resistance of the wire? (b) A second wire of the same material has the same weight as the 100-meter length, but twice its diameter. What is its resistance?

28–7. (a) The following measurements of current and potential difference were made on a resistor constructed of Nichrome wire:

i (amp)	V_{ab} (volts)
0.5	2.18
1.0	4.36
2.0	8.72
4.0	17.44

Make a graph of V_{ab} as a function of i. Does the Nichrome obey Ohm's law? What is the resistance of the resistor, in ohms?

(b) The following measurements were made on a "thyrite" resistor.

i (amp)	V_{ab} (volts)
0.5	4.76
1.0	5.81
2.0	7.05
4.0	8.56

Make a graph of V_{ab} as a function of i. Does "thyrite" obey Ohm's law? What is the resistance of the resistor?

28–8. An aluminum bar 2.5 m long has a rectangular cross section 1 cm by 5 cm. (a) What is its resistance? (b) What would be the length of an iron wire 15 mm in diameter having the same resistance?

28–9. An electrical power line using No. 4 copper wire has a resistance of 0.248 ohm per 1000 ft and carries a current of 30 amp. If the potential at a point on the line is 250 volts, what is the potential at a point 5 miles farther along the line in the direction of the current?

28–10. A solid cube of brass has a mass of 68.8 gm. What is its resistance between opposite faces?

28–11. The two parallel plates of a capacitor have equal and opposite charges Q. The dielectric has a dielectric coefficient K and a resistivity ρ. Show that the "leakage" current carried by the dielectric is given by the relationship $i = Q/K\epsilon_0\rho$.

28–12. The international ampere is based on electrochemical measurements and equals 0.9998 abs. amp. One international volt is equivalent to how many absolute volts?

28–13. (a) Show that the relationship $R_0 = R(1 - \alpha t)$ holds approximately if α and t are small. (b) What is the resistance of a Nichrome wire at 0°C whose resistance is 100.00 ohms at 12°C? (c) What is the resistance of a carbon rod at 30°C whose resistance is 0.0150 ohm at 0°C?

28–14. The resistance of a coil of copper wire is 200 ohms at 20°C. What is its resistance at 50°C?

28–15. A toaster using a Nichrome heating element operates on 120 volts. When it is switched on at 0°C it car-

ries an initial current of 1.5 amp. A few seconds later the current reaches the steady value of 1.33 amp. What is the final temperature of the element? The average value of the temperature coefficient of Nichrome over the temperature range = 0.00045 (C°)$^{-1}$.

28–16. A resistor develops heat at the rate of 40 watts when the potential difference across its ends is 60 volts. What is its resistance?

28–17. A motor operating on 120 volts draws a current of 2 amp. If heat is developed in the motor at the rate of 9 cal/sec, what is its efficiency?

28–18. No. 18 B and S rubber-covered copper wire has a diameter of 1.024 mm and an allowable carrying capacity of 3 amp. How many watts are dissipated per meter when the wire carries this current?

28–19. A "660-watt" electric heater is designed to operate from 120-volt lines. (a) What is its resistance? (b) What current does it draw? (c) What is the rate of development of heat, in cal/sec? (d) If the line voltage drops to 110 volts, what power does the heater take, in watts? (Assume the resistance constant. Actually, it will change somewhat because of the change in temperature.)

28–20. Express the rate of development of heat in a resistor in terms of (a) potential difference and current, (b) resistance and current, (c) potential difference and resistance.

CHAPTER 29

DIRECT-CURRENT CIRCUITS

29–1 Electromotive force. We have shown in the preceding chapter that in order to have a current in a conductor, an electric field must be maintained in the conductor. We have also shown that a continuous energy input is necessary to maintain the current, the energy being converted to heat in the conductor. The development of heat in a conductor is an "irreversible" process in the thermodynamic sense. That is, while energy is conserved in the process, the heat developed cannot be reconverted to electrical energy except under the restrictions imposed by the second law of thermodynamics.

We now wish to consider another type of energy transformation, one which is reversible in the thermodynamic sense. Devices in which such reversible transformations occur are the storage battery, the generator, and the motor. (There are other devices also, but they need not concern us at present.) Consider a storage battery which is operating the starting motor of an automobile. The internal energy of the materials in the battery is decreasing, and is converted to mechanical form available at the shaft of the starter motor. After the automobile engine starts, the starting motor is disconnected and the generator sends a reversed, charging current through the storage battery. The chemical reactions in the battery then proceed in the reversed direction, and internal energy is developed at the expense of mechanical work that must be done by the automobile engine to drive the generator. Hence, depending on the direction of the current through it, we may have in the storage battery either of these transformations:

$$\text{Internal energy} \rightarrow \text{electrical energy},$$

$$\text{Electrical energy} \rightarrow \text{internal energy}.$$

As contrasted with the *irreversible* conversion of electrical energy into heat via i^2R heating in a resistor, the conversion of electrical energy into internal energy in a storage battery is *reversible* in the sense that the internal energy can be completely recovered and converted to electrical form, with no outstanding changes in other bodies.*

---

* The fact that the recovery is not 100% in an actual storage battery under the conditions in which it is used does not vitiate the possibility of complete recovery under the proper conditions.

557

The mechanism of energy transformations in a motor or generator will be discussed in more detail in succeeding chapters. It will suffice for the present to state that in these devices we have conversion from electrical to mechanical (rather than internal) energy or vice versa, and that the conversion may be 100% in either direction.

Any device in which a reversible transformation between electrical energy and some other form of energy can take place is called a *seat of electromotive force*.

The magnitude of the electromotive force of a seat may be defined quantitatively as the energy converted from electrical to nonelectrical form, or vice versa (exclusive of energy converted irreversibly to heat), per unit of charge passing through the seat. More briefly, electromotive force may be defined as the *work per unit charge*. Electromotive force will be represented by the symbol ε, and is often abbreviated to emf.* Hence if q is the charge crossing a section through the seat in time t, and W is the energy transformed in this time, the emf is

$$\varepsilon = \frac{W}{q}. \tag{29-1}$$

Since electromotive force is work per unit charge, the unit of emf in the mks system is *one joule per coulomb*. This is the same as the unit of potential and has been abbreviated to one volt. Hence emf's can be expressed in volts. It should be noted, however, that although emf and potential are expressible in the same unit, they relate to different concepts. The distinction will be made clearer as we proceed.

The work done by the seat in time t is

$$W = \varepsilon q, \tag{29-2}$$

and the rate of doing work, or the power, is

$$P = \frac{W}{t} = \varepsilon \frac{q}{t} = \varepsilon i. \tag{29-3}$$

For example, the emf of the common automobile storage battery is about 6 volts or 6 joules/coul. This means that for every coulomb passing across a section through the battery (or across any section of a circuit to which the battery is connected) 6 joules of internal energy are converted to electrical form if the battery is discharging, or 6 joules of internal

---

* The use of the word "force" in connection with this concept is unfortunate, since an emf is not a force but work per unit charge. It has been suggested that "electromotance" would be a better term.

energy are developed at the expense of electrical energy if the battery is being charged. If the current in the battery is 10 amp, or 10 coul/sec, the rate of energy conversion is

$$P = \mathcal{E}i = 6 \text{ volts} \times 10 \text{ amp}$$

$$= 6 \frac{\text{joules}}{\text{coul}} \times 10 \frac{\text{coul}}{\text{sec}}$$

$$= 60 \frac{\text{joules}}{\text{sec}} = 60 \text{ watts.}$$

29-2 The circuit equation. Let us consider now a simple circuit (Fig. 29-1) in which a resistor of resistance R is connected by leads of negligible resistance to the terminals of a seat of emf such as a dry cell or storage battery. Let i represent the current in the circuit. When a number of circuit elements are connected as in Fig. 29-1 so as to provide only a single conducting path, they are said to be *in series*. Other types of connection will be considered later.

One minor point should be clarified at the start. Points p and a, in Fig. 29-1(a), are connected by a resistanceless conductor. The potential difference between two points of a conductor equals the product of the current and the resistance between the points. But since the resistance between p and a is zero, the potential difference between them is also zero or, in other words, points p and a are at the same potential. Hence p and a and, in fact, all points of the conductor connecting them, are *electrically* equivalent and separate letters need not be assigned to them. The same is evidently true of points b and q. The circuit is therefore relettered in Fig. 29-1(b).

If the direction of the current in the resistor is from a toward b, the potential V_a is higher than the potential V_b. The + sign at the terminal a of the cell indicates this fact.

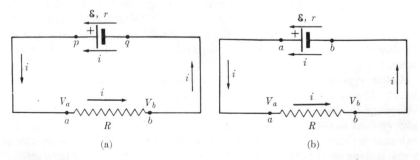

(a)   (b)

FIG. 29-1. A seat of emf connected in series with a resistor by means of resistanceless connecting wires.

Although, strictly speaking, emf is not a vector quantity, it is useful to assign to it a direction (or better, a sense). We shall arbitrarily consider the direction or sense of an emf to be from the $-$ toward the $+$ terminal of the seat, within the seat. This directed emf is indicated by an arrow in Fig. 29–1.

We now set down the expressions for the rates of energy transformation in the various parts of the circuit. Heat is developed in the external resistor at a rate Ri^2. It is also found, as might be expected, that every seat of emf has resistance. This is called the *internal resistance* of the seat and we shall represent it by r. Hence the rate of development of heat in the cell is ri^2. The sum of Ri^2 and ri^2 is the rate at which energy is given up by the circulating charge in the form of heat, and the seat of emf must supply energy at an equal rate. Then, from Eq. (29–3),

$$\mathcal{E}i = Ri^2 + ri^2. \tag{29–4}$$

After canceling and rearranging terms, we get

$$\boxed{i = \frac{\mathcal{E}}{R + r}.} \tag{29–5}$$

The principle of conservation of energy therefore leads to this exceedingly useful relation between the current, the emf, and the resistance in a simple series circuit. It may be called the "circuit equation."

Consider next a circuit that contains a seat of emf within which work is done *by* the circulating charge. Examples are a motor, where the work done by the charge appears as mechanical energy, or a storage battery being "charged," where the work appears as internal energy. Figure 29–2 represents a circuit in which a motor, represented by the symbol $-\!\!\mathrm{o}\!\!-$ is being run by a battery. A resistance R is included for generality.

The current in the motor is directed from right to left, or from b to c. Since the circulating charge gives up energy in passing through the motor, the potential V_b must be higher than the potential V_c. Hence a $+$ sign is attached to terminal b of the motor and the sense of its emf is from c toward b.

Let us represent the emf of the motor by $\mathcal{E}'$ and its internal resistance by r'. From the definition of electromotive force, the rate of conversion of energy to mechanical form by the motor is $\mathcal{E}'i$, and the rate of conversion to heat in the motor is $r'i^2$. The rates of development of heat in the external resistor and in the battery are Ri^2 and ri^2. The rate at which work is done on the circulating charge by the battery is $\mathcal{E}i$. Therefore

$$\mathcal{E}i = \mathcal{E}'i + r'i^2 + Ri^2 + ri^2$$

and

$$i = \frac{\mathcal{E} - \mathcal{E}'}{R + r + r'}, \quad (29\text{-}6)$$

or

$$i = \frac{\sum \mathcal{E}}{\sum R}. \quad (29\text{-}7)$$

This equation is evidently a generalization of Eq. (29–5) and may be stated: the current (in a series circuit) equals the algebraic sum of the emf's in the circuit divided by the sum of the resistances in the circuit.

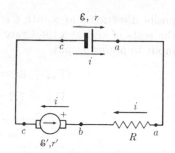

FIG. 29–2. A series circuit with two seats of emf.

It is necessary that a convention of sign be adopted when using Eq. (29–7). The simplest rule is to select an arbitrary direction around the circuit (clockwise or counterclockwise) as positive. Then currents and emf's are positive if they are in the direction selected, negative if in the opposite direction. Resistances are always considered positive. In writing Eq. (29–6), the clockwise direction was considered positive. If the opposite direction had been considered positive, the same equation would have been obtained with the signs of i, $\mathcal{E}$, and $\mathcal{E}'$ all reversed.

The *relative* directions of current and emf in the two seats in Fig. 29–2 lead to the following generalizations. When the current in a seat of emf is in the *same* direction as the emf, as it is in the battery, work is done *on* the circulating charge at the expense of energy of some other form. When the current in a seat of emf is *opposite* in direction to the emf, as in the motor, work is done *by* the circulating charge and energy of some other form appears. The emf in the latter case is often called a *back electromotive force*.

29–3 Potential difference between points in a circuit. We next deduce the general expression for the difference in potential between any two points in a series circuit. Figure 29–3 shows a portion of such a circuit in which the direction of the current i is from a toward b. The rate at which the circulating charge gives up energy to the portion of the circuit between a and b is iV_{ab}. In other words, this is the power input to this portion of the circuit, supplied by the seat or seats of emf in the remainder of the circuit (not shown). Power is also supplied *by* the first seat of emf (since i and $\mathcal{E}$ are in the same direction) at a rate $\mathcal{E}i$. Power is supplied *to* the second seat of emf (i and $\mathcal{E}'$ are in op-

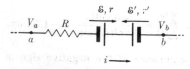

FIG. 29–3. Portion of a circuit with two seats of emf.

posite directions) at a rate $\mathcal{E}'i$. Heat is developed in the resistor and in the seats of emf at a total rate $(R + r + r')i^2$. Then, if we equate power input to power output,

$$iV_{ab} + \mathcal{E}i = \mathcal{E}'i + (R + r + r')i^2,$$

$$V_{ab} = (R + r + r')i - (\mathcal{E} - \mathcal{E}'), \qquad (29\text{–}8)$$

$$\boxed{V_{ab} = \sum Ri - \sum\mathcal{E}.} \qquad (29\text{–}9)$$

This is the desired general expression for the potential difference $V_{ab} \equiv V_a - V_b$ between any two points a and b of a series circuit.

Careful attention must be paid to algebraic signs. The direction from a toward b is always considered positive. Then currents and emf's are positive if their direction is from a toward b, negative if their direction is from b toward a. Resistances are always positive. The potential difference V_{ab} is positive if a is at a higher potential than b, negative if b is at a higher potential than a. It will be seen that the signs in Eq. (29–8) are consistent with these conventions.

Equation (29–9) reduces, of course, to the familiar relation $V_{ab} = Ri$ for the special case where a and b are the terminals of a pure resistance. It also contains implicitly the general circuit equation, Eq. (29–7). That is, if points a and b coincide,

$$V_{ab} = 0 = \sum Ri - \sum\mathcal{E}, \quad \text{and} \quad i = \frac{\sum\mathcal{E}}{\sum R}.$$

EXAMPLE 1. Given that, in Fig. 29–4, $\mathcal{E}_1 = 12$ volts, $r_1 = 0.2$ ohm, $\mathcal{E}_2 = 6$ volts, $r_2 = 0.1$ ohm, $R_3 = 1.4$ ohms, $R_4 = 2.3$ ohms, compute (a) the current in the circuit, in magnitude and direction, and (b) the potential difference V_{ac}.

(a) It seems obvious that the current will be clockwise, since $\mathcal{E}_1 > \mathcal{E}_2$. However, to illustrate that one need not rely on intuition to find its direction, let us assume the counterclockwise direction to be positive. Then

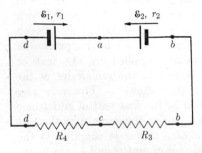

FIGURE 29–4

$$\sum\mathcal{E} = -12 \text{ volts} + 6 \text{ volts} = -6 \text{ volts},$$

$$\sum R = 4 \text{ ohms} = 4 \frac{\text{volts}}{\text{amp}},$$

$$i = \frac{\sum\mathcal{E}}{\sum R} = \frac{-6 \text{ volts}}{4 \text{ volts/amp}} = -1.5 \text{ amp}.$$

The significance of the negative sign is that the current is in the negative, or clockwise, direction. Had we assumed the clockwise direction to be positive, we would have obtained

$$\sum \varepsilon = 12 \text{ volts} - 6 \text{ volts} = +6 \text{ volts,}$$

$$\sum R = 4 \text{ ohms}, \qquad i = \frac{6 \text{ volts}}{4 \text{ ohms}} = +1.5 \text{ amp.}$$

So the same numerical value is obtained in either case, and the direction of the current need not be known in advance.

(b) The potential difference between a and c is $V_{ac} = \sum Ri - \sum \varepsilon$. We can proceed from a to c by two paths, and either may be used to compute V_{ac}. Let us first use path abc. We have already shown that the current is clockwise. The direction of the current in the path abc is from a toward c, hence i is positive and

$$\sum Ri = (0.1 \text{ ohm} + 1.4 \text{ ohms})(+1.5 \text{ amp}) = +2.25 \text{ volts.}$$

The direction of ε_2 is from b toward a, so

$$\sum \varepsilon = -6 \text{ volts.}$$

Hence

$$V_{ac} = +2.25 \text{ volts} - (-6 \text{ volts}) = +8.25 \text{ volts,}$$

and since

$$V_{ac} \equiv V_a - V_c,$$

$$V_a - V_c = 8.25 \text{ volts}, \qquad V_a = V_c + 8.25 \text{ volts.}$$

That is, the potential at point a is 8.25 volts above that at point c.

If we proceed from a to c along path adc, the current term has a negative sign, since its direction is from c toward a. Hence

$$\sum Ri = (0.2 \text{ ohm} + 2.3 \text{ ohms})(-1.5 \text{ amp}) = -3.75 \text{ volts.}$$

The direction of ε_1 is from c toward a, so

$$\sum \varepsilon = -12 \text{ volts.}$$

Hence

$$V_{ac} = -3.75 \text{ volts} - (-12 \text{ volts}) = +8.25 \text{ volts,}$$

and the same answer is obtained whichever path is used.

EXAMPLE 2. In practically all circuits, whether power distribution systems or small units such as radio amplifiers, one or more points of the circuit are connected to the earth or to "ground." In contrast to the reference level of potential used in general field theory (that of a point at infinity), when dealing with circuits the potential of the grounded points is assumed to be zero and the potential of any other point of the circuit is expressed relative to this reference level. Consider the simple circuit in Fig. 29–5, grounded at point b. Compute the potentials of points a and c.

The current in the circuit is

$$i = \frac{\sum \mathcal{E}}{\sum R} = \frac{10 \text{ volts}}{5 \text{ ohms}} = 2 \text{ amp},$$

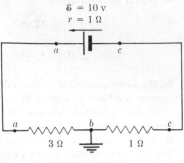

and its direction is counterclockwise.
The potential differences V_{ab} and V_{bc} are

$$V_{ab} = Ri = 3 \text{ ohms} \times 2 \text{ amp}$$

$$= 6 \text{ volts} = V_a - V_b,$$

$$V_{bc} = Ri = 1 \text{ ohm} \times 2 \text{ amp}$$

$$= 2 \text{ volts} = V_b - V_c.$$

FIGURE 29–5

Since $V_b = 0$, it follows that

$$V_a = +6 \text{ volts}, \qquad V_c = -2 \text{ volts}.$$

That is, point a is 6 volts *above* ground and point c is 2 volts *below* ground. The potential difference V_{ac} can now be found by subtraction.

$$V_{ac} \equiv V_a - V_c = 6 \text{ volts} - (-2 \text{ volts}) = +8 \text{ volts}.$$

As a check, we may proceed from a to c through the cell, obtaining

$$V_{ac} = \sum Ri - \sum \mathcal{E} = 1 \text{ ohm} \times (-2 \text{ amp}) - (-10 \text{ volts}) = +8 \text{ volts}.$$

29–4 Terminal voltage of a seat of emf. It is convenient to develop the special form of Eq. (29–9) when points a and b are the terminals of a seat of electromotive force. There can be but two possibilities, shown in Fig. 29–6(a) and (b), namely, when the current and emf are in the same or opposite directions. Let us agree that point a shall always refer to the

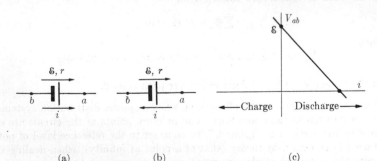

Fɪɢ. 29–6. (a) Current and emf in the same direction. (b) Current and emf in opposite directions. (c) Graph of terminal voltage of a seat of emf vs. current.

+ terminal and point b to the − terminal of the seat. Then, since the direction from a to b in Eq. (29–9) is always positive, both ε and i in Fig. 29–6(a) are negative and

$$V_{ab} = V_{+-} = \sum Ri - \sum \varepsilon = -ri - (-\varepsilon) = \varepsilon - ri.$$

In Fig. 29–6(b), ε is negative but i is positive. Hence

$$V_{ab} = V_{+-} = ri - (-\varepsilon) = \varepsilon + ri.$$

The potential difference *between the + and − terminals* of a seat of emf is therefore equal to the emf of the seat, diminished by the product of the internal resistance and the current when emf and current are in the same direction, and increased by this product when the two are in opposite directions. (In the latter case we have a seat of back emf.) When the current in a seat of emf is zero, the terminal voltage equals the electromotive force. Therefore the emf of a seat may be found experimentally by measuring its terminal voltage on open circuit.

The terminal voltage as a function of current is represented graphically in the voltage-current diagram of Fig. 29–6(c). When the current is zero, the terminal voltage equals the emf ε. When current and emf are in the same direction (discharge), the terminal voltage is less than the emf. When they are in opposite directions (charge), the terminal voltage is greater than the emf. When the seat is short-circuited (zero *external* resistance), the terminal voltage is zero. What is the significance of the portion of the graph where the current is greater than the short-circuit current and the terminal voltage is negative? How could the current be made greater than the short-circuit current?

If the terminal voltage is measured with the common type of voltmeter, care must be taken that the current in the circuit does not result in any appreciable lowering of the terminal voltage below the emf. Figure 29–7 shows a cell of emf ε and internal resistance r with a voltmeter of resistance R_V connected to its terminals. Since the voltmeter provides a conducting path, we have a closed circuit as soon as it is connected to the cell. The current in the circuit is

$$i = \frac{\varepsilon}{R_V + r}.$$

The terminal voltage is

$$V_{ab} = \varepsilon - ri = \varepsilon - r\frac{\varepsilon}{R_V + r}$$
$$= \varepsilon\left(\frac{1}{1 + r/R_V}\right).$$

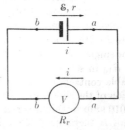

Fig. 29–7. Measurement of the terminal voltage of a seat of emf by means of a voltmeter.

If $R_V \gg r$, the term in parentheses is nearly unity, and the voltmeter reading (V_{ab}) is nearly equal to the emf. It is evident, therefore, that a voltmeter should be a high-resistance instrument.

29–5 The potentiometer. The potentiometer is an instrument which can be used to measure the emf of a seat without drawing any current from the seat. It also has a number of other useful applications. Essentially, it balances an unknown potential difference against an adjustable, measurable potential difference.

The principle of the potentiometer is shown schematically in Fig. 29–8. A resistance wire ab is permanently connected to the terminals of a seat of emf $\mathcal{E}_1$. A sliding contact c is connected through the galvanometer G

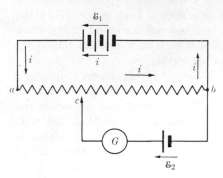

to a second cell whose emf $\mathcal{E}_2$ is to be measured. Contact c is moved along the wire until a position is found at which the galvanometer shows no deflection. (This necessitates that $V_{ab} \geq \mathcal{E}_2$.) If we then write the expressions for V_{cb} for both paths between these points, and remember that there is no current in the lower path,

(upper path) $\qquad V_{cb} = iR_{cb},$

(lower path) $\qquad V_{cb} = \mathcal{E}_2.$

FIG. 29–8. Principle of the potentiometer.

Hence iR_{cb} is *exactly* equal to the emf $\mathcal{E}_2$, and $\mathcal{E}_2$ can be computed if i and R_{cb} are known. No correction need be made for the "ir" term, since the current in $\mathcal{E}_2$ is zero.

In practice, the simple potentiometer circuit is modified as shown in Fig. 29–9. The following description relates specifically to the Leeds and Northrup student-type potentiometer. Still other refinements are introduced in high-precision instruments. Figures 29–9(a) and (b) are photographs of the instrument. Figure 29–9(c) is a circuit diagram.

The single slide wire of Fig. 29–8 is replaced by sixteen resistors $R_1, R_2, R_3, \ldots,$ R_{15}, R_{16} in series, each of resistance 10 ohms. R_{16} alone is a slide wire. The movable contacts c and b may include any whole number of resistors plus any fraction of the slide wire. The potentiometer is always to be used with a current of 0.010 amp in the upper circuit. The potential difference across each 10-ohm resistor is therefore 0.100 volt, and the instrument may be calibrated to read volts directly.

To ensure that the current in the upper circuit has its proper value, switch S is first thrown in the "up" position, connecting the standard cell of known

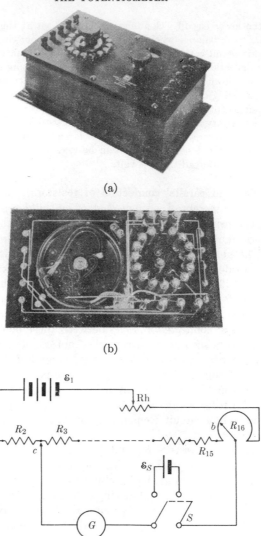

FIG. 29–9 (a) External view of student potentiometer. (b) Inside view of student potentiometer. (c) Circuit diagram of student potentiometer. (Courtesy of Leeds and Northrup.)

emf $\mathcal{E}_S$ in the lower circuit. Contacts c and b are set at the points where the circuit *should* be in balance when the current in the upper circuit has its correct value, and this circuit is then adjusted by the rheostat Rh until the galvanometer G shows no deflection. Then, without changing the setting of Rh, switch S is thrown to the "down" position and the galvanometer current is again brought to zero by adjusting c and b. The unknown emf $\mathcal{E}_2$ may then be read directly from the positions of c and b.

During preliminary adjustments a protective resistor is inserted *in series* with the galvanometer to prevent damage both to it and to the standard cell.

The potentiometer described above can be read to within 10^{-4} volt. High-precision instruments read to 10^{-6} volt.

29–6 Series and parallel connection of resistors.

Most electrical circuits consist not merely of a single seat of emf and a single external resistor, but comprise a number of emf's, resistors, or other elements such as capacitors, motors, etc., interconnected in a more or less complicated manner. The general term applied to such a circuit is a *network*. We shall next consider a few of the simpler types of network.

Figure 29–10 illustrates four different ways in which three resistors having resistances R_1, R_2, and R_3 might be connected between points a and b. In part (a), the resistors provide only a single path between the points, and are said to be connected in *series* between these points. Any number of circuit elements such as resistors, cells, motors, etc., are similarly said to be in series with one another between two points if connected as in (a) so as to provide only a single path between the points.

The resistors in Fig. 29–10(b) are said to be in *parallel* between points a and b. Each resistor provides an alternative path between the points, and any number of circuit elements similarly connected are in parallel with one another.

In Fig. 29–10(c), resistors R_2 and R_3 are in parallel with each other, and this combination is in series with the resistor R_1. In Fig. 29–10(d), R_2 and R_3 are in series, and this combination is in parallel with R_1.

It is always possible to find a single resistor which could replace a combination of resistors in any given circuit and leave unaltered the potential difference between the terminals of the combination and the current in the rest of the circuit. The resistance of this single resistor is called the *equivalent* resistance of the combination. If any one of the networks in Fig. 29–10 were replaced by its equivalent resistance R, we could write

$$V_{ab} = Ri \qquad \text{or} \qquad R = \frac{V_{ab}}{i},$$

where V_{ab} is the potential difference between the terminals of the network and i is the current at the point a or b. Hence the method of computing an equivalent resistance is to assume a potential difference V_{ab}

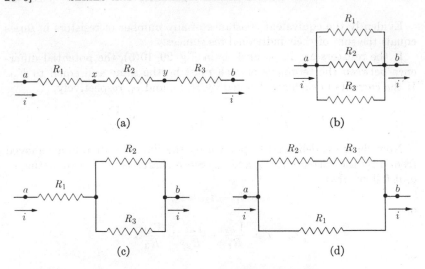

FIG. 29–10. Four different ways of connecting three resistors.

across the actual network, compute the corresponding current i (or vice versa), and take the ratio of one to the other. The simple series and parallel connections of resistors are sufficiently common so that it is worth while to develop formulas for these two special cases.

If the resistors are in series, as in Fig. 29–10(a), the current in each must be the same and equal to the line current i. Hence

$$V_{ax} = iR_1, \qquad V_{xy} = iR_2, \qquad V_{yb} = iR_3,$$

$$V_{ax} + V_{xy} + V_{yb} = i(R_1 + R_2 + R_3).$$

But

$$V_{ax} = V_a - V_x, \qquad V_{xy} = V_x - V_y, \qquad V_{yb} = V_y - V_b,$$

$$V_{ax} + V_{xy} + V_{yb} = V_a - V_b = V_{ab}.$$

Hence

$$V_{ab} = i(R_1 + R_2 + R_3),$$

and

$$\frac{V_{ab}}{i} = R_1 + R_2 + R_3.$$

But V_{ab}/i is, by definition, the equivalent resistance R. Therefore

$$\boxed{R = R_1 + R_2 + R_3.} \qquad (29\text{–}10)$$

Evidently the equivalent resistance of any number of resistors in series equals the sum of their individual resistances.

If the resistors are in parallel, as in Fig. 29–10(b), the potential difference between the terminals of each must be the same and equal to V_{ab}. If the currents in each are denoted by i_1, i_2, and i_3, respectively,

$$i_1 = \frac{V_{ab}}{R_1}, \qquad i_2 = \frac{V_{ab}}{R_2}, \qquad i_3 = \frac{V_{ab}}{R_3}.$$

Now charge is delivered to point a by the line current i, and removed from a by the currents i_1, i_2, and i_3. Since charge is not accumulating at a, it follows that

$$i = i_1 + i_2 + i_3,$$

or

$$i = \frac{V_{ab}}{R_1} + \frac{V_{ab}}{R_2} + \frac{V_{ab}}{R_3},$$

or

$$\frac{i}{V_{ab}} = \frac{1}{R_1} + \frac{1}{R_2} + \frac{1}{R_3}.$$

Since

$$\frac{i}{V_{ab}} = \frac{1}{R},$$

then

$$\boxed{\frac{1}{R} = \frac{1}{R_1} + \frac{1}{R_2} + \frac{1}{R_3}.} \qquad (29\text{–}11)$$

Evidently, for any number of resistors in parallel, the *reciprocal* of the equivalent resistance equals the *sum of the reciprocals* of their individual resistances.

For the special case of two resistors in parallel,

$$\frac{1}{R} = \frac{1}{R_1} + \frac{1}{R_2} = \frac{R_2 + R_1}{R_1 R_2} \qquad \text{and} \qquad R = \frac{R_1 R_2}{R_1 + R_2}.$$

Also, since $V_{ab} = i_1 R_1 = i_2 R_2$,

$$\frac{i_1}{i_2} = \frac{R_2}{R_1},$$

and the currents carried by two resistors in parallel are inversely proportional to their resistances.

The equivalent resistances of the networks in Figs. 29–10(c) and (d) could be found by the same general method, but it is simpler to consider them as combinations of series and parallel arrangements. Thus in (c) the combination of R_2 and R_3 in parallel is first replaced by its equivalent

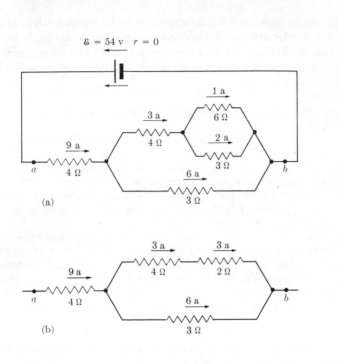

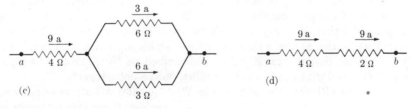

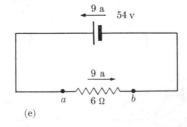

FIG. 29–11. Successive stages in the reduction of a network to a single equivalent resistance.

resistance, which then forms a simple series combination with R_1. In (d), the combination of R_2 and R_3 in series forms a simple parallel combination with R_1. Not all networks, however, can be reduced to simple series-parallel combinations, and special methods must be used for handling such networks.

————————

EXAMPLE. Compute the equivalent resistance of the network in Fig. 29–11, and find the current in each resistor.

Successive stages in the reduction to a single equivalent resistance are shown in parts (b) to (e) of the figure. For simplicity, the seat of emf has been omitted from all except the first and last diagrams. The 6-ohm and the 3-ohm resistor in parallel in (a) are equivalent to the single 2-ohm resistor which replaces them in (b). In (c) the 4- and the 2-ohm resistors in series are replaced by their equivalent 6-ohm resistor. Repetition of this process leads to the single equivalent 6-ohm resistor in (e).

We now work back up the series of diagrams and compute the currents. In the simple series circuit of (e) the current is $i = \sum \mathcal{E}/\sum R = 54$ volts/6 ohms $=$ 9 amp. Since the 6-ohm resistor in (e) replaces the 4-ohm and the 2-ohm resistors in series, the current in each of these in (d) is also 9 amp. In (c), the current in the 4-ohm resistor remains 9 amp but the currents in the 6-ohm and 3-ohm resistors divide as shown. Repetition of the process gives the current distribution in (a).

29–7 Networks containing seats of emf. The arrangement of two or more seats of emf is not uniquely described by the statement that the seats are in series or parallel. Two cells in series, for example, might be connected either as in Fig. 29–12(a) or (b). The connection in (a) is denoted as "series aiding"; that in (b) as "series opposing." A combination such as that in Fig. 29–12(c) is described as "in parallel, like poles together," and that in (d) as "in parallel, unlike poles together."

Note that although the cells in Fig. 29–12(c) and (d) are in parallel as far as the rest of the circuit is concerned, each of these arrangements in itself forms a closed circuit with the cells in series opposing in the first

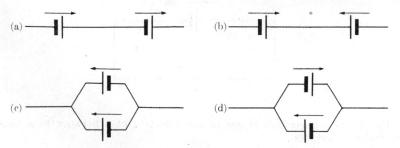

FIG. 29–12. Four ways of connecting two seats of emf.

case and in series aiding in the second. Hence the terms "series" and "parallel" are not mutually exclusive, nor do they by themselves completely describe a network. Very frequently a more explicit statement is required.

The expression for the current in a *series* circuit containing a number of seats of emf either aiding or opposing can be written

$$i = \frac{\sum \mathcal{E}}{R + \sum r}.$$

It is obvious that the equivalent emf is the algebraic sum of the individual emf's, and the equivalent internal resistance is the arithmetic sum of the internal resistances.

When any number of seats whose emf's are *equal* are connected in parallel with like poles together, as in Fig. 29–12(c), the equivalent emf is equal to that of a single seat, and the equivalent internal resistance is computed by the usual method for resistances in parallel. When the seats are of unequal emf, or are connected as in Fig. 29–12(d), the problem becomes more complicated and more general methods for handling it are required.

29–8 Kirchhoff's rules. Networks in which the resistors are not in simple series or parallel groupings, or in which there are seats of emf in parallel paths, cannot in general be solved by the method of equivalent resistances. Two rules, first formally stated by Gustav Robert Kirchhoff (1824–1887), enable such problems to be handled systematically.

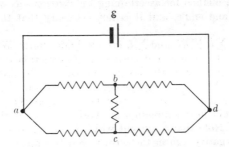

Fig. 29–13. Circuit illustrating branch points and loops.

We first define two terms. A *branch point* is a point of a network at which three (or more) conductors are joined. A *loop* is any closed conducting path. For example, points a, b, c, and d in Fig. 29–13 are branch points, and paths $abca$, $abdca$, $abcd\mathcal{E}a$, etc., are loops.

Kirchhoff's rules may be stated as follows:

Point rule: The algebraic sum of the currents toward any branch point of a network is zero:

$$\sum i = 0.$$

Loop rule: The algebraic sum of the emf's in any loop of a network equals the algebraic sum of the Ri products in the same loop:

$$\sum \mathcal{E} = \sum Ri.$$

The first rule merely states formally that no charge accumulates at a branch point of the network. The second rule follows from the generalized expression for the potential difference between two points of a circuit, $V_{ab} = \sum Ri - \sum \mathcal{E}$. This equation was developed for a simple series circuit in which the current was the same at all points. The currents in various parts of a loop will, in general, differ from one another, and the term $\sum Ri$ must be understood to mean the sum of the products of each resistance and the current *in that particular resistance*. Then, if one continues completely around a loop so that the second point coincides with the first, the potential difference is zero, and $\sum \mathcal{E} = \sum Ri$.

The first step in applying Kirchhoff's rules is to assign a magnitude and direction to all unknown currents and emf's, and a magnitude to all unknown resistances. These, as well as the known quantities, are represented in a diagram with directions carefully shown. The solution is then carried through on the basis of the assumed directions. If, in the numerical solution of the equations, a negative value is found for a current or an emf, its correct direction is opposite to that assumed. The correct *numerical* value is obtained in any case. Hence the rules provide a method for ascertaining the *directions* as well as the magnitudes of currents and emf's, and it is not necessary that these directions be known in advance.

The expressions $\sum i$, $\sum Ri$, and $\sum \mathcal{E}$ are algebraic sums. When applying the point rule, a current is considered positive if its direction is toward a branch point, negative if away from the point. (Of course, the opposite convention may also be used.) When applying the loop rule, some direction around the loop (i.e., clockwise or counterclockwise) must be chosen as the positive direction. All currents and emf's in this direction are positive, those in the opposite direction are negative. Note that a current which has a positive sign in the point rule may have a negative sign in the term in which it appears in the loop rule. Note also that the direction around the loop which is considered positive is immaterial, the result of choosing the opposite direction being merely to obtain the same equation with signs reversed. There is a tendency to assume that the "correct" direction to consider positive is that of the current in the loop, but in general such a choice is not possible, since the currents in some elements of a loop may be clockwise and in other elements, counterclockwise. These and other points will be illustrated by examples.

In complicated networks, where a large number of unknown quantities may be involved, it is sometimes puzzling to know how to obtain a sufficient number of independent equations to solve for the unknowns. The following rules are useful:

(1) If there are n branch points in the network, apply the point rule at $n - 1$ of these points. Any points may be chosen. Application of the point rule at the nth point does not lead to an independent relation.

(2) Imagine the network·to be separated into a number of simple loops, like the pieces of a jigsaw puzzle. Apply the loop rule to each of these loops.

EXAMPLE. Let the magnitudes and directions of the emf's and the magnitudes of the resistances in Fig. 29–14(a) be given. Solve for the current in each branch of the network.

Assign a direction and a letter to each unknown current. The assumed directions are entirely arbitrary. Note that the currents in R_3, R_1, and $\mathcal{E}_1$ are the same, and hence require only a single letter. The same is true for the currents in $\mathcal{E}_2$, R_2, and R_6.

The branch points are lettered a, b, c, and d.

$$\text{At point } a, \qquad i_1 + i_2 - i_3 = 0.$$

$$\text{At point } b, \qquad -i_1 - i_4 - i_6 = 0.$$

$$\text{At point } c, \qquad i_4 + i_5 - i_2 = 0.$$

Since there are four branch points, there are only three independent "point" equations. If the point rule is applied at the fourth point, d, one finds

$$i_6 + i_3 - i_5 = 0.$$

But if the first three equations are added, the result is

$$-i_6 - i_3 + i_5 = 0,$$

which is the same equation. Hence no new information is found by going to point d. We have, however, secured a check on the first three equations.

In Fig. 29–14(b) the circuit is shown cut up into its "jigsaw" sections. Let us consider the clockwise direction positive in each loop. The loop rule then furnishes the following equations:

$$-\mathcal{E}_1 - \mathcal{E}_5 = i_1 R_1 + i_1 r_1 - i_2 r_5 - i_4 R_4 + i_1 R_3,$$

$$+\mathcal{E}_2 + \mathcal{E}_5 = i_3 r_2 + i_3 R_2 + i_3 R_6 + i_5 R_5 + i_2 r_5,$$

$$+ \mathcal{E}_4 = i_4 R_4 - i_5 R_5 - i_6 r_4 - i_6 R_7,$$

and one has six independent equations to be solved for the six unknown currents.

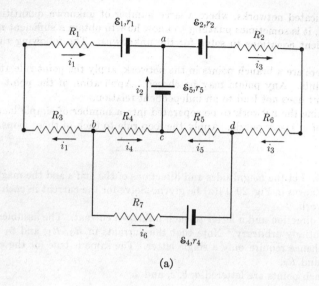

(a)

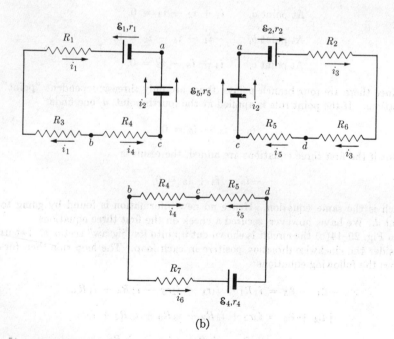

(b)

FIG. 29-14. (a) Diagram of a circuit arranged for the application of Kirchhoff's laws. (b) Same circuit cut up into loops.

29–9 Power. Since our analysis of circuits has been developed from considerations of energy and power, little can be added under this heading except by way of summary.

The power input to any portion of a circuit between points a and b is given by

$$P = iV_{ab}. \qquad (29\text{–}12)$$

The power is expressed in watts when i is in amperes and V_{ab} in volts. Current is considered positive if its direction is from a toward b in the portion of the circuit considered. If the power input as computed by this equation has a negative sign, which will be the case if the current is from b toward a or if $V_a < V_b$, the portion of the circuit considered is actually supplying power to the remainder of the circuit and the magnitude of P represents the *power output*. Equation (29–12) is independent of the nature of the circuit between a and b, that is, the circuit may consist of resistors, motors, batteries, etc., arranged in any way.

If the circuit between a and b comprises resistance only, then $V_{ab} = Ri$ and

$$P = iV_{ab} = Ri^2 = H.$$

That is, the power input equals the rate of development of heat.

The rate of energy conversion in a seat of emf is equal to $\mathcal{E}i$. If $\mathcal{E}$ and i are in the same direction, electrical energy is developed at the expense of some other form. If $\mathcal{E}$ and i are in opposite directions (a seat of back emf), some other form of energy is developed at the expense of electrical energy.

————

EXAMPLE. Figure 29–15 shows a battery and a resistor in series. The current in the circuit is

$$i = \frac{12 \text{ volts}}{5.5 \text{ ohms} + 0.5 \text{ ohm}} = 2 \text{ amp}.$$

Point b is at a higher potential than point a, and

$$V_{ba} = iR = 2 \text{ amp} \times 5.5 \text{ ohms} = 11 \text{ volts},$$

or

$$V_{ba} = \mathcal{E} - iR = 12 \text{ volts} - (2 \text{ amp} \times 0.5 \text{ ohm}) = 11 \text{ volts},$$

and

$$V_{ab} = -V_{ba} = -11 \text{ volts}.$$

Consider first that part of the circuit within the upper dotted rectangle. The

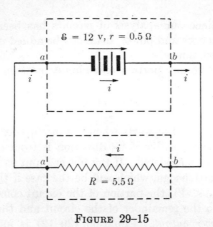

FIGURE 29–15

direction of the current through it is from a to b. Hence the power *input* to this portion is

$$\text{Power input} = iV_{ab} = 2 \text{ amp} \times (-11 \text{ volts}) = -22 \text{ watts}.$$

The minus sign means that this is actually a power output.

In the lower rectangle, the direction of the current is from b to a. Hence,

$$\text{Power input} = iV_{ab} = (-2 \text{ amp}) \times (-11 \text{ volts}) = +22 \text{ watts},$$

and power is supplied to this part of the circuit.

As a check, since the energy supplied to the resistor is converted to heat,

$$\frac{dH}{dt} = i^2R = (2 \text{ amp})^2 \times 5.5 \text{ ohms} = 22 \text{ watts}.$$

The rate of conversion of nonelectrical to electrical energy in the seat of emf is

$$P = \mathcal{E}i = 12 \text{ volts} \times 2 \text{ amp} = 24 \text{ watts}.$$

The rate of development of heat in the seat of emf is

$$i^2r = (2 \text{ amp})^2 \times 0.5 \text{ ohm} = 2 \text{ watts}.$$

The power output is therefore 24 watts — 2 watts = 22 watts, as previously computed.

To sum up:

The battery converts nonelectrical to electrical energy at the rate of 24 joules per second, or 24 watts.

The rate of heating in the battery is 2 watts.

The rate at which energy is supplied to the rest of the circuit by the battery is 24 — 2, or 22 watts.

This energy is transformed to heat in the resistor at the rate of 22 watts.

29–10 Measurement of power and energy. The power supplied to (or by) the device X in Fig. 29–16(a) may be measured by the ammeter and voltmeter connected as shown, correction being made, if necessary, for the fact that the ammeter reads the sum of the current in X and the voltmeter current. If meter corrections are neglected, the power in watts supplied to X is given by the product of the ammeter reading in amperes and the voltmeter reading in volts.

The *wattmeter* is a single instrument which performs the combined functions of ammeter and voltmeter in Fig. 29–16(a) and indicates the power directly. It consists of a coil with a pointer attached, pivoted so that it can swing in the magnetic field of a second fixed coil, and restrained by a hairspring whose restoring torque is proportional to the angle of deflection. The deflecting torque on the pivoted coil is jointly proportional to the current in it and to the magnetic field set up by the fixed coil. The latter is proportional to the current in the fixed coil. Hence if the fixed coil (with a suitable shunt) is connected as is the ammeter in Fig. 29–16(a), the current in it is proportional to the line current and its magnetic field is proportional to this current. If the pivoted coil (with suitable series resistance) is connected as is the voltmeter in Fig. 29–16(a), the current in it is proportional to the potential difference between the terminals of X. The deflecting torque is therefore proportional to the product of the current and the potential difference, or to the power supplied to X. Under the influence of this torque, the coil rotates to a position where the restoring torque equals the deflecting torque, and since the restoring torque is proportional to the angle of deflection, the latter is proportional to the power.

A wattmeter is provided with four terminals, two corresponding to an ammeter and two to a voltmeter. Connections are made as in Fig. 29–16(b).

The *watt-hour meter* indicates the total *energy* supplied to (or by) a device, rather than the *rate* of supply of energy, or power. Essentially, it

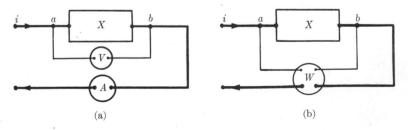

Fig. 29–16. (a) Voltmeter-ammeter method of measuring power. (b) A wattmeter.

is a small motor whose angular velocity is proportional to the power consumed. That is,

$$\omega = kp,$$

where ω is the instantaneous angular velocity, p the instantaneous power, and k is a constant of proportionality. The angular displacement θ in any time interval is therefore proportional to the energy supplied in the time interval.

The arrangement of dials in the familiar watt-hour meter found in most homes is simply a revolution counter for recording the total angular displacement of the meter. The dials are commonly calibrated to include the proportionality constant and indicate the energy directly in kilowatt-hours.

PROBLEMS

29–1. The internal resistance of a dry cell increases gradually with age, even though the cell is not used. The emf, however, remains fairly constant at about 1.5 volts. Dry cells are often tested for age at the time of purchase by connecting an ammeter directly across the terminals of the cell and reading the current. The resistance of the ammeter is so small that the cell is practically short-circuited. (a) The short-circuit current of a fresh No. 6 dry cell is about 30 amp. Approximately what is the internal resistance? (b) What is the internal resistance if the short-circuit current is only 10 amp? (c) The short-circuit current of a 6-volt storage battery may be as great as 1000 amp. What is its internal resistance?

29–2. An immersion heater has a resistance of 50 ohms and carries a current of 2.5 amp. What is the final temperature of 1500 gm of water initially at 20°C if the water absorbs all the heat given off by the heater during an interval of 3 minutes?

29–3. A closed series circuit consists of a 12-volt battery, a 3.7-ohm resistor, and a switch. The internal resistance of the battery is 0.3 ohm. The switch is opened. What would a high-resistance voltmeter read when placed (a) across the terminals of the battery, (b) across the resistor, (c) across the switch? Repeat (a), (b), and (c) for the case when the switch is closed.

29–4. In the circuit in Fig. 29–17, find (a) the rate of conversion of internal energy to electrical energy within the battery, (b) the rate of development of heat in the battery, (c) the rate of development of heat in the external resistor.

29–5. A battery of emf $\mathcal{E}$ and internal resistance r is connected to an external resistance R. Prove that the power delivered to the external resistor is given by

$$P = \mathcal{E}^2 \frac{R}{(R + r)^2}.$$

Choose for R successive values from 0 to $2r$ in steps of $0.2r$. Plot $R/(R + r)^2$ as a function of R and infer from the graph the condition that must exist for maximum power to be delivered to the external resistor.

29–6. In the circuit of Fig. 29–18, what is the charge on the 2-μf capacitor?

29–7. The power supplied to a motor is 180 watts at its rated voltage of 60 volts. (a) What series resistance should be used if the motor is to operate from a 110-volt line? (b) What power should the resistor be able to dissipate?

12 v, 1 Ω

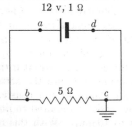

FIGURE 29–17

48 v, 1 Ω

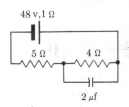

FIGURE 29–18

29–8. A single layer cylindrical coil is wound of insulated wire 2 m long, successive windings touching each other. The insulation can withstand a maximum potential difference of 750 volts. What is the maximum diameter the coil may have to avoid breakdown between successive windings if a potential difference of 12,000 volts is applied across the ends of the coil?

29–9. (a) In the circuit shown in Fig. 29–19, what is the potential at point a? (b) What value resistor must be inserted in the circuit at c to make $V_a = 7.5$ volts? (c) A battery has an internal resistance of 1 Ω. What emf must it have to make $V_a = 2$ volts when the battery is inserted in the circuit at c? [The resistor of part (b) is removed.]

29–12. The potential difference across the terminals of a battery is 8.5 volts when there is a current of 3 amp in the battery from the negative to the positive terminal. When the current is 2 amp in the reverse direction, the potential difference becomes 11 volts. (a) What is the internal resistance of the battery? (b) What is the emf of the battery?

29–13. (a) What is the potential at point a in the circuit of Fig. 29–21? (b) What is the terminal voltage of the 4-volt battery? (c) A battery of emf 17 volts and internal resistance 1 ohm is inserted in the circuit at d, its positive terminal being the grounded side. What is now the difference of potential between the terminals of the 4-volt battery?

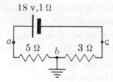

FIGURE 29–19

29–10. The external circuit of a battery has a resistance of 3 ohms and carries a current of 5 amp. When 5 ohms are added to the external circuit the current drops to 2.5 amp. (a) What is the emf of the battery? (b) What is its external resistance?

29–11. In the circuit of Fig. 29–20, calculate (a) V_{ag}, (b) V_{dg}, (c) V_{ch}.

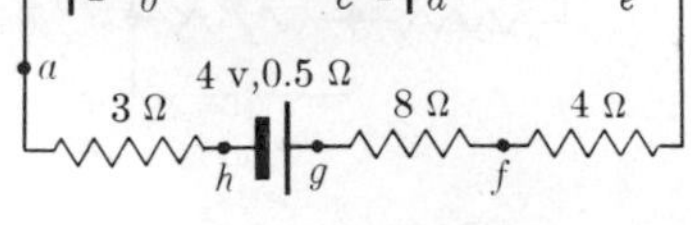

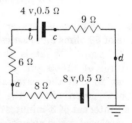

FIGURE 29–21

29–14. A storage battery whose emf is 12 volts and whose internal resistance is 0.1 ohm (internal resistances of commercial storage batteries are actually only a few thousandths of an ohm) is to be charged from a 112-volt d-c supply. (a) Should the + or the − terminal of the battery be connected to the + side of the line? (b) What will be the charging current if the battery is connected directly across the line? (c) Compute the resistance of the series resistor required to limit the current to 10 amp. With this resistor in the circuit, compute (d) the poten-

FIGURE 29–20

tial difference between the terminals of the battery, (e) the power taken from the line, (f) the power wasted as heat in the series resistor, (g) the *useful* power input to the battery.

29–15. Figure 29–22 represents a d-c generating plant G supplying electrical power to a distant factory along a transmission line. The terminal voltage of the generator, V_{ba}, is 230 volts, and the line current is 50 amp. The resistances of the wires bc and ad are 0.1 ohm each. Point a is grounded. (a) What is the potential at point b? (b) What is the iR drop in each wire? (c) What is the potential at point c? (d) What is the potential at point d? (e) What is the line voltage at the load, that is, V_{cd}? (f) Show in a diagram how voltmeters should be connected to measure the potential differences in parts (b) and (e). (g) Compute the power output of the generator, the power loss in the line, and the power delivered to the factory. (h) Suppose the terminal voltage at the generator were doubled and the power delivered to the factory kept constant. Find the power output of the generator and the power loss in the line.

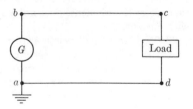

FIGURE 29–22

29–16. A 100-volt battery has an internal resistance of 5 ohms. (a) What is the reading of a voltmeter having a resistance of 500 ohms when placed across the terminals of the battery? (b) What maximum value may the ratio r/R_v have if the error in the reading of the emf of a battery is not to exceed 5%?

29–17. When switch S is open, the voltmeter V, connected across the terminals of the dry cell in Fig. 29–23, reads 1.52 volts. When the switch is closed the voltmeter reading drops to 1.37 volts and the ammeter reads 1.5 amp. Find the emf and internal resistance of the cell. Neglect meter corrections.

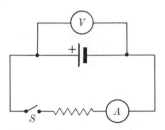

FIGURE 29–23

29–18. In Fig. 29–24 is shown a potentiometer set up to measure the emf of cell x. B is a battery whose emf is approximately 3 volts and whose internal resistance is unknown. St is a standard cell of 1.0183 volts emf. The switch is set at point 2, placing the standard cell in the galvanometer circuit. When the tap b is 0.36 of the distance from a to c the galvanometer G reads zero. (a) What is the difference of potential across the entire length of resistor ac? (b) The switch is then set

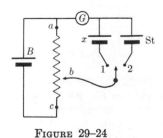

FIGURE 29–24

at point 1 and a new zero reading of the galvanometer obtained when b is 0.47 of the distance from a to c. What is the emf of cell x?

29–19. In Fig. 29–25 the "potentiometer" is a resistor with a movable tap. The galvanometer has a resistance of 90 ohms. P has a resistance of 75 ohms. At what point should the movable tap be placed if the current in the galvanometer is to be 1/3 the current in line bc?

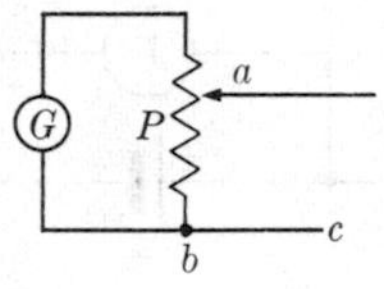

FIGURE 29–25

29–20. Prove that when two resistors are connected in parallel the equivalent resistance of the combination is always smaller than that of either resistor.

29–21. (a) Calculate the equivalent resistance of the circuit of Fig. 29–26 between x and y. (b) What is the potential difference between x and a if the current in the 8-ohm resistor is 0.5 amp?

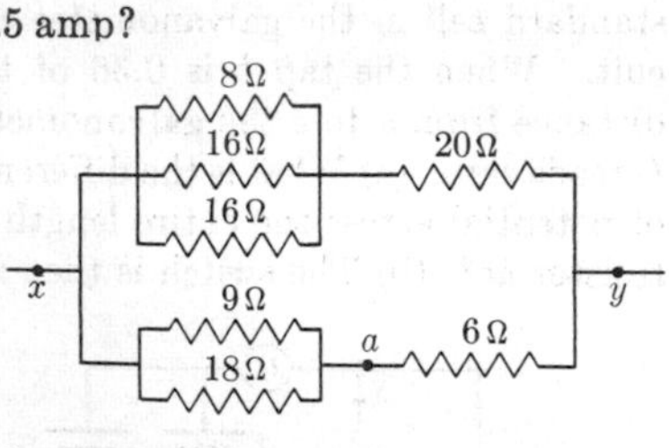

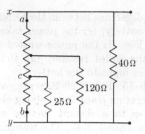

FIGURE 29–26

29–22. (a) The long resistor between a and b in Fig. 29–27 has a resistance of 300 ohms and is tapped at the one-third points. What is the equivalent resistance between x and y? (b) The

FIGURE 29–27

potential difference between x and y is 320 volts. What is the potential difference between b and c?

29–23. The three resistors in Fig. 29–28 each have a resistance of 2 ohms and can dissipate a maximum of 18 watts without becoming excessively heated. What is the maximum power the circuit can dissipate?

FIGURE 29–28

29–24. Two lamps marked "60 watts, 120 volts" and "40 watts, 120 volts" are connected in series across a 120-volt line. What power is consumed in each lamp? Assume that the resistance of the filaments does not vary with current.

29–25. Three equal resistors are connected in series. When a certain potential difference is applied across the combination the total power consumed is 10 watts. What power would be consumed if the three resistors were connected in parallel across the same potential difference?

29–26. (a) The power rating of a 10,000-ohm resistor is 2 watts. (The power rating is the maximum power the resistor can safely dissipate as heat without too great a rise in temperature.) What is the maximum allowable

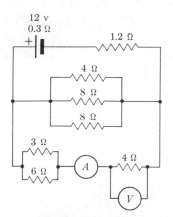

FIGURE 29–29

potential difference across the terminals of the resistor? (b) A 20,000-ohm resistor is to be connected across a potential difference of 300 volts. What power rating is required? (c) It is desired to connect a resistance of 1000 ohms across a potential difference of 200 volts. A number of 10-watt, 1000-ohm resistors are available. How should they be connected?

29–27. (a) Find the equivalent resistance of the external circuit in Fig. 29–29. (b) Find the readings of the ammeter A and the voltmeter V.

29–28. The resistance of a certain galvanometer is 30 ohms. (a) What resistance in shunt (i.e., in parallel) with the galvanometer will reduce the equivalent resistance to 10 ohms? (b) If the potential difference between the galvanometer terminals is 100 mv, find the current in the galvanometer and in the shunt.

29–29. In Fig. 29–30, find (a) the current in the battery, (b) the current in each resistor, (c) the potential difference between points a and b.

29–30. (a) Find the resistance of the network in Fig. 29–31, between the terminals a and b. (b) What potential difference between a and b will result in a current of 1 amp in the 4-ohm resistor?

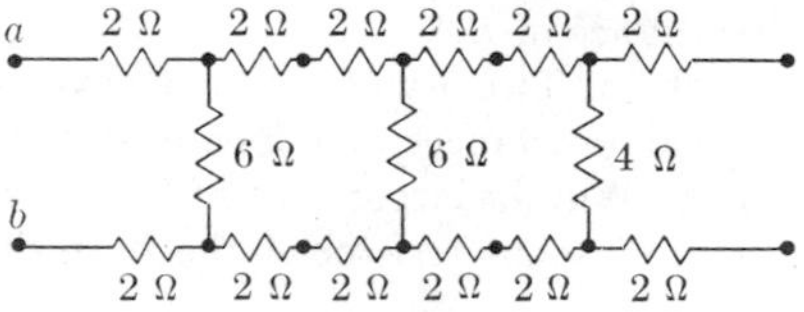

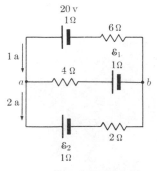

FIGURE 29–31

29–31. Two resistors A and B are in parallel with one another and in series with a 200-ohm resistor and a dry cell whose emf is 1.5 volts and whose internal resistance is negligible. The resistance of A is 100 ohms. When B

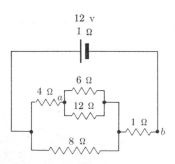

FIGURE 29–30

FIGURE 29–32

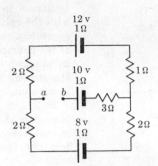

FIGURE 29–33

is disconnected from A, an additional resistance of 50 ohms must be inserted in the circuit in order to keep the current through A unchanged. Find the resistance of B.

29–32. Two 6-volt batteries have internal resistances of 0.3 ohm and 0.6 ohm. Will the larger current be carried by a 0.4-ohm resistor if the batteries are connected across it in series or in parallel?

29–33. Find the emf's $\mathcal{E}_1$, and $\mathcal{E}_2$ in the circuit of Fig. 29–32, and the potential difference between points a and b.

29–34. (a) Find the potential difference between points a and b in Fig. 29–33. (b) If a and b are connected, find the current in the 12-volt cell.

CHAPTER 30

ELECTROCHEMISTRY AND THERMOELECTRICITY

30–1 Electrolysis. In 1833, Michael Faraday observed that pure water was almost a perfect insulator, whereas aqueous solutions of certain substances were electrically conducting. If two electrodes of some metal such as platinum are dipped into a beaker of distilled water, and one electrode is connected to the positive terminal of a d-c source, the other to the negative, practically no current is observed. A small amount of an acid such as sulfuric acid (H_2SO_4) or a base such as sodium hydroxide (NaOH), or a salt such as common table salt, sodium chloride (NaCl), when dissolved in the water, provides a solution whose resistance is sufficiently low for the current to be appreciable. The resistance of the solution depends markedly on the concentration and upon the temperature. Solutions of most organic compounds such as sugar, however, are not electrically conducting.

A solution which conducts an electric current is called an *electrolyte*. The conduction phenomenon, which, as we shall see, is attended by secondary chemical effects, is called *electrolysis*. The vessel which holds the electrolyte and the electrodes is called an *electrolytic cell*. The most striking effects that accompany electrolysis are the chemical reactions that take place at the electrodes. Thus, with platinum electrodes in dilute sulfuric acid, hydrogen is formed and liberated as bubbles of gas at the negative electrode, whereas oxygen is formed and liberated as bubbles of gas at the positive electrode. These gases may be collected, dried, and weighed, and the first quantitative measurements made by Faraday consisted in noting

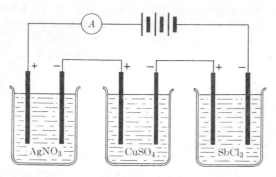

Fig. 30–1. Deposition of silver (Ag), copper (Cu), and antimony (Sb), simultaneously. The same quantity of electricity is transferred through each cell.

587

the substances that formed at both electrodes and measuring their respective masses, after a known current had existed for a known time.

Imagine three electrolytic cells, all equipped with platinum electrodes (to avoid complications that might result if the electrodes themselves were chemically active and were attacked by the materials formed at their surfaces), but with different aqueous solutions as electrolytes, as shown in Fig. 30–1. Connecting them in series ensures that the current is the same in all cells. Experiment shows that silver is deposited on the negative electrode of the left-hand cell, copper on the negative electrode of the middle cell, and antimony on the negative electrode of the right-hand cell. Let us suppose that the current has been maintained for such a time that a quantity of electricity equal to 96,500 coul has been transferred through each cell. When the three electrodes are removed and the mass of material on each is measured, the following results are obtained:

$$\text{Silver:} \quad 108 \text{ gm} = \frac{108}{1} \text{ gm,}$$

$$\text{Copper:} \quad 31.8 \text{ gm} = \frac{63.6}{2} \text{ gm,}$$

$$\text{Antimony:} \ 40.7 \text{ gm} = \frac{122}{3} \text{ gm.}$$

These fractions have a simple interpretation. The numerators are the atomic weights of the respective elements, and the denominators are their respective valences. A mass equal to the atomic weight divided by the valence is called an *equivalent weight*. The quantity of electricity equal to 96,500 coul (more exactly, 96,519) is called one *faraday, F*. Faraday's law of electrolysis is, therefore, that *the number of gram-equivalent weights of a substance deposited, liberated, dissolved, or reacted at an electrode is equal to the number of faradays of electricity transferred through the electrolyte.*

If a current I is maintained for a time t, then the number of faradays of electricity transferred is It/F. If a mass m of a substance of atomic weight M and of valence j is deposited, then the number of gram-equivalents is mj/M. Faraday's law may therefore be written

$$\boxed{\frac{mj}{M} = \frac{It}{F}.} \qquad (30\text{--}1)$$

30–2 Mechanism of electrolytic conduction. The flow of electricity through an electrolyte was first explained by Svante Arrhenius (1859–1928). The fundamental ideas of his original theory are still of value today, although details have changed. A solution of an acid, a base, or a salt consists in part of electrically charged particles called *ions*. Ions are positively or negatively charged atoms or groups of atoms (radicals). Thus in a water solution of silver nitrate there are positively charged silver ions Ag^+, consisting of silver atoms each of which has lost its outermost or valence electron, and nitrate ions NO_3^-, consisting of one nitrogen and three oxygen atoms as a stable group to which an extra electron has been added.

In a copper sulfate solution there are doubly positively charged copper ions Cu^{++}, consisting of copper atoms that have lost their two valence electrons, and also doubly negatively charged sulfate ions SO_4^{--}. Similarly, an antimony chloride solution contains trebly charged antimony ions Sb^{+++}, consisting of antimony atoms which have lost their three valence electrons, and, for each antimony ion, three singly negatively charged chlorine ions Cl^-, which are chlorine atoms that have gained an extra electron. Notice that these solutions are, on the whole, electrically neutral, since the total positive charge equals the total negative charge.

When positive and negative electrodes exist at different places in the solution, the positive ions migrate slowly toward the negative electrode, and the negative ions toward the positive electrode, but not necessarily with the same speed. Ionic speeds are quite small, of the order of a few hundred-thousandths of a centimeter per hour. The current in a solution, therefore, consists of opposite motions of oppositely charged ions, in contrast with a current in a metallic conductor, where only electrons flow from minus to plus. The motion of positive particles in one direction constitutes a current of the same sign as the motion of negative particles in the other direction. Due to the difference in speeds of the two kinds of ions, the positive ions carry, in general, a different proportion of the current from that carried by the negative ions.

A solid crystal of NaCl consists of a cubic arrangement of positive sodium and negative chlorine ions, not atoms. The ions are held together by electrostatic attraction and are not free to move throughout the crystal. They merely execute vibratory motion about their equilibrium positions, the kinetic energy of such motion depending on the temperature of the crystal. The important question that arises at this point is why an ionic substance dissolved in water gives rise to ions which are not tightly bound to one another, but are so weakly attracted that they are free to move under the action of a weak electric field. The answer lies in the dielectric properties of water or, in other words, the polar properties of water molecules.

Each water molecule is a small dipole, that is, its positive and negative charges do not coincide. We may represent these dipoles in an exaggerated manner by oval-shaped structures, as shown in Fig. 30–2. Clustering around a positive sodium ion will be a number of water molecules with their negative ends near the sodium ion. In a similar manner, the positive

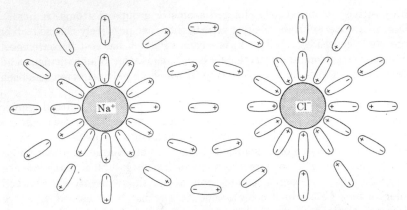

FIG. 30–2. The force of attraction between a positive and a negative ion is weakened by the presence of the induced charges of the polar water molecules.

ends of some other water molecules will cluster around the chlorine ion. The force *on the chlorine ion* is the resultant of three forces: (1) that due to the positive induced charge on the water molecules around it, (2) that due to the sodium ion, and (3) that due to the ring of induced charge on the water molecules around the sodium ion. All other charges throughout the diagram are neutralized by opposite charges nearby.

(1) The positive induced charges surrounding the chlorine ion are symmetrically distributed and exert no net force on the chlorine ion.

(2) The force exerted by the sodium ion is

$$\frac{q_{Na^+} \times q_{Cl^-}}{4\pi\epsilon_0 r^2}.$$

(3) The force exerted by the induced charge $q_{\overline{i}}$ around the sodium ion is

$$\frac{q_{\overline{i}} \times q_{Cl^-}}{4\pi\epsilon_0 r^2}.$$

The resultant force is therefore

$$\frac{(q_{Na^+} - q_{\overline{i}}) \times q_{Cl^-}}{4\pi\epsilon_0 r^2}.$$

But, from Eq. (27–10),

$$q_{Na^+} - q_{\overline{i}} = \frac{q_{Na^+}}{K},$$

where K is the dielectric coefficient. Since for water $K = 81$, it follows that the force of attraction between the two ions is reduced to 1/81 of its value in a vacuum.

According to this explanation, the ions of dissolved ionic substances should be free in any solvent of high dielectric coefficient. This is indeed the case. Electrolytic conduction is quite good when substances are dissolved in methyl alcohol ($K = 35$) and in liquid ammonia ($K = 22$). In media of low dielectric coefficient, such as benzene ($K = 2$), the ions of dissolved ionic substances remain bound, so that the conductivity is low.

Pure water ionizes to a slight extent. Only a very small fraction of the water molecules dissociate into hydrogen ions H^+ (protons) and hydroxyl ions OH^-. The hydrogen ion attaches itself to a water molecule to form a hydronium ion $(H_3O)^+$, so that the dissociation of water may be represented thus:

$$H_2O + H_2O \rightarrow (H_3O)^+ + OH^-.$$

Although there are about 10^{16} hydronium and hydroxyl ions present in a liter of pure water, these are not enough to give rise to an appreciable current when a moderate potential difference is applied across two platinum electrodes. This number, however, is ample to give rise to electrode reactions, and indeed when hydroxyl and sulfate ions migrate to a positive electrode under a small electric field, the hydroxyl ions discharge upon the electrode and the sulfate ions do not.

30–3 The determination of Avogadro's number. The number of molecules of a substance whose mass in grams is numerically equal to its molecular weight is called Avogadro's number N_0. When this mass of substance (called a *gram-mole*) is in the form of a gas at one atmosphere pressure and at 0°C, it always occupies a volume of 22,400 cubic centimeters. Therefore, if sufficient gas is admitted to a chamber to occupy a volume of 22,400 cm^3 at 1 atm and 0°C, the mass of this gas is its molecular weight, and this method is often used to determine molecular weights. If the molecular weight is divided by Avogadro's number, the mass of each individual molecule may be found. Faraday's law, in conjunction with Millikan's value of the electronic charge, provides us with one possible method of calculating Avogadro's number.

Consider the electrolysis of silver nitrate, resulting in the deposition of metallic silver on the cathode. Every silver ion that arrives at the negative electrode receives an electronic charge before it adheres as a neutral silver atom. If a mass of silver equal to the atomic weight is deposited, it follows that N_0 silver atoms must have been transported. The total electric charge transferred is then $N_0 e$, where e is the electronic charge. But the total charge is one faraday of electricity, $F = 96,519$ coulombs. We have, therefore,

$$N_0 e = F. \tag{30–2}$$

Substituting the numerical values of F and e, we find

$$N_0 = \frac{96{,}519 \text{ coul/faraday}}{1.6019 \times 10^{-19} \text{ coul/electron}}$$

$$= 6.0254 \times 10^{23} \frac{\text{electrons}}{\text{faraday}}$$

$$= 6.0254 \times 10^{23} \frac{\text{molecules}}{\text{mole}}.$$

30–4 The electrolysis of water. A dilute solution of sulfuric acid consists of molecules of H_2O, hydronium ions H_3O^+, sulfate ions SO_4^{--}, and a very much smaller number of hydroxyl ions OH^-. If platinum electrodes are introduced and a moderate potential difference established across them, the hydronium ions migrate toward the negative electrode, and both hydroxyl and sulfate ions toward the positive electrode.

At the negative electrode, the hydronium ion combines with an electron to form a neutral molecule of water and a neutral hydrogen atom, and then two hydrogen atoms combine to form a hydrogen molecule, according to the scheme

$$2(H_3O)^+ + 2(e^-) \rightarrow 2H_2O + H_2.$$

The hydrogen molecules are liberated as bubbles of gas.

At the positive electrode, it is believed that the hydroxyl ions are discharged but the sulfate ions are not. The mechanism of discharge of the hydroxyl ions is represented by the following scheme:

$$2(OH)^- \rightarrow \tfrac{1}{2}O_2 + H_2O + 2(e^-),$$

and the oxygen molecules are liberated as bubbles of gas.

Whether these ionic reactions at the electrodes are correct or not, the experimental facts are that hydrogen and oxygen are liberated and the sulfuric acid remains unchanged. The net effect of the electrolysis is therefore the chemical reaction represented by the chemical "equation"

$$H_2O \rightarrow H_2 + \tfrac{1}{2}O_2.$$

Since the gases are liberated at the same temperature and pressure, and the volume of hydrogen is double that of oxygen, it follows that there are twice as many molecules of hydrogen as of oxygen.

The dissociation of water into hydrogen and oxygen may also be caused to take place in the gaseous phase at a very high temperature. If this is done, energy must be supplied in the form of heat, and the reaction is called an *endothermic reaction*. In the electrolysis of water the energy is supplied as electrical energy instead of exclusively as heat. In this case the reaction is termed *endergic*.

Many chemical reactions are *exothermic*, that is, they involve the liberation of heat. We shall see in a later section how such reactions may be used to generate electrical energy, in which case they may be referred to as *exergic*.

After the electrolysis of water has taken place for a while, suppose the electrodes are disconnected from the source and are connected to a galvanometer. A momentary current in the opposite direction will be observed, indicating that a back emf existed for a short while. This counter emf arises from the fact that one electrode is coated with hydrogen and the other with oxygen. The combination of two dissimilar substances in an electrolyte constitutes a galvanic cell, which will be discussed in the next few sections. Let us accept for the moment the experimental fact that such cells exist and let us denote the back emf present during the electrolysis of water by $\mathcal{E}$. We may estimate the *theoretical* value of $\mathcal{E}$ by considering the energy necessary to convert one mole of liquid water into one mole of hydrogen and one-half mole of oxygen, first by a purely thermal method, and then by the electrolytic method.

(1) *Thermal dissociation of* H_2O. Imagine 1 mole of liquid water (18 gm) at room temperature and at atmospheric pressure. To convert this into water vapor at the same temperature and pressure requires

$$18 \text{ gm} \times 590 \, \frac{\text{cal}}{\text{gm}} \times 4.19 \, \frac{\text{joule}}{\text{cal}} = 44{,}500 \text{ joules}$$

of heat. Purely chemical measurements of the heat of reaction for the dissociation of one mole of water vapor yield the value 242,000 joules. Therefore to convert one mole of liquid water into hydrogen and oxygen requires a total amount of heat equal to 286,500 joules.

(2) *Electrolytic dissociation of* H_2O. To convert one mole of liquid H_2O into hydrogen and oxygen electrolytically, a quantity of electricity equal to $2 \times 96{,}500$ coul must be transferred through a seat of emf $\mathcal{E}$. This requires an amount of electrical energy equal to $2 \times 96{,}500 \, \mathcal{E}$ joules. Some heat is also extracted from the surroundings, but the quantity is small and may be neglected as a first approximation.

Equating the two amounts of energy given in (1) and (2), we have

$$2 \times 96{,}500 \, \mathcal{E} = 286{,}500$$

or

$$\mathcal{E} = 1.49 \text{ volts.}$$

Actually, it takes about 1.7 volts to carry out the electrolysis of water at low current density between platinum electrodes. The excess is called *overvoltage* and is believed in this case to be due to the dissipation of energy attendant upon formation and release of bubbles.

30–5 Electrode potentials. We have seen that the deposition of hydrogen gas and oxygen gas on the platinum electrodes of an electrolytic cell gives rise to a back emf which must be overcome if the current is to be maintained. Let us consider another situation in which the electrodes react with the materials deposited on them. Suppose two electrodes made of lead are immersed in dilute sulfuric acid. Hydrogen is liberated at the negative electrode, as it would be if the electrode were made of platinum, but the oxygen liberated at the positive electrode now combines with the lead to form lead dioxide PbO_2. After a while, if the source is removed and a galvanometer substituted, a reverse current will be observed, indicating a back emf. Measurement shows this emf to be about 2 volts.

Under suitable conditions, two dissimilar materials and an electrolyte may be so arranged that the emf is not merely transitory, but may remain fairly constant while current is delivered to an outside circuit. Such an arrangement is called a *voltaic cell* or a *galvanic cell*, after Volta and Galvani, who first studied them. A galvanic cell may be considered the reverse of an electrolytic cell.

As a first step in the understanding of a galvanic cell, consider what happens when a zinc plate is dipped in pure water. Zinc ions immediately go into solution. The chemical equation for the process may be written as follows:

$$Zn \rightarrow Zn^{++} + 2e^-.$$

From a somewhat oversimplified point of view one may imagine that the attractive forces of the water molecules exceed the cohesive forces which hold the zinc ions in their crystalline lattice. In the absence of other effects, a steady flow of ions into solution would occur, but since every positive ion which goes into solution leaves two electrons behind, the plate immediately acquires a negative potential with respect to the solution. As a consequence, the ions in solution are attracted by the zinc plate, and a certain fraction is captured by the plate and neutralized. The greater the negative charge on the plate, the greater the tendency of the positive ions to return to the plate. At equilibrium, the rates of flow and of return are equal and the potential of the plate is just sufficient to produce a reverse reaction equal to the forward reaction. This potential is called the *electrode potential* and its numerical value is of considerable importance in electrochemical processes.

The presence of more zinc ions in the solution increases the reverse reaction rate and the electrode potential decreases to a lower equilibrium value. It is therefore evident that the equilibrium potential of the zinc with respect to the solution depends on the concentration of the zinc ions around it. Since the two reaction rates are influenced to a different degree by the temperature of the system, the electrode potential varies with temperature.

TABLE 30–1

STANDARD ELECTRODE POTENTIALS

Electrode	Electrode reaction	Electrode potential (volts)
Li, Li$^+$	$Li \rightleftharpoons Li^+ + e^-$	3.045
Na, Na$^+$	$Na \rightleftharpoons Na^+ + e^-$	2.714
Al, Al^{+++}	$Al \rightleftharpoons Al^{+++} + 3e^-$	1.70
Zn, Zn^{++}	$Zn \rightleftharpoons Zn^{++} + 2e^-$	0.763
Fe, Fe^{++}	$Fe \rightleftharpoons Fe^{++} + 2e^-$	0.440
Ni, Ni^{++}	$Ni \rightleftharpoons Ni^{++} + 2e^-$	0.250
Sn, Sn^{++}	$Sn \rightleftharpoons Sn^{++} + 2e^-$	0.136
H$_2$, H$_3$O$^+$	$H_2 + 2H_2O \rightleftharpoons 2H_3O^+ + 2e^-$	0.000
Cu, Cu^{++}	$Cu \rightleftharpoons Cu^{++} + 2e^-$	-0.337
Ag, Ag$^+$	$Ag \rightleftharpoons Ag^+ + e^-$	-0.7991
Hg, Hg^{++}	$Hg \rightleftharpoons Hg^{++} + 2e^-$	-0.860
O$_2$, H$_2$O	$6H_2O \rightleftharpoons O_2 + 4H_3O^+ + 4e^-$	-1.23
Cl$_2$, Cl$^-$	$2Cl^- \rightleftharpoons Cl_2 + 2e^-$	-1.360
Au, Au$^+$	$Au \rightleftharpoons Au^+ + e^-$	-1.50

The magnitude of the electrode potential at a standard temperature with a standard concentration of ions around it is a measure of the extent to which a metal will go into solution. The greater the number of ions that leave the metal and go into solution, the greater the electrode potential. Conversely, the electrode potential is a measure of the inability of an ion to discharge on an electrode and adhere to it. In this connection, it is often referred to as the *discharge potential*. In the electrolysis of water, the discharge potential of SO_4^{--} is so much larger than that of OH^- that, with the current density commonly employed, only the OH^- ion discharges at the positive electrode. Similarly, in a solution of NaCl in water the magnitude of the discharge potential of Na^+ is so much larger than that of H^+ that only H^+ is discharged at the negative electrode.

To measure the absolute value of an electrode potential it would be necessary to measure the difference of potential between the electrode in question and another electrode *at the same potential as that of the solution*. In practice this is not feasible. Relative values, however, may be obtained with the aid of a standard electrode, arbitrarily chosen. The standard reference electrode is the *normal hydrogen electrode* consisting of platinum covered with adsorbed hydrogen and hydrogen gas and immersed in an acid solution containing a standard concentration of H^+ ions. If this electrode is combined at 25°C with a series of other electrodes surrounded by a standard concentration of their respective ions, a relative scale of electrode potentials may be obtained. This scale is given in Table 30–1.

Roughly speaking, the metals at the top of the table tend to part with ions easily, but the ions do not discharge readily on them. Those at the bottom do not easily send ions into solution, but the ions readily discharge on the electrodes.

30–6 Electrolytic refining of metals. One of the most important industrial applications of electrolysis is in the refining of metals. The process is carried out in an electrolytic cell where the positive electrode is the metal containing impurities, and the negative electrode is a sheet of pure metal. The electrolyte consists of a solution of some salt of the metal. During electrolysis, only the pure metal will be plated on the negative electrode. The impurities either go into solution and do not discharge on the negative electrode, or do not go into solution at all but drop to the bottom as a sludge.

Copper is a convenient example. The electrolyte is an aqueous solution of copper sulfate. The positive electrode consists of a plate of impure copper, the impurities consisting of, say, nickel and silver. The negative electrode is a plate of pure copper. When the potential difference across the cell is about 0.2 volt, the nickel goes into solution because its electrode potential is higher than that of copper, but, for the same reason, nickel ions are not discharged at the negative electrode. They therefore remain in solution. The silver does not go into solution at all because its electrode potential is lower than that of copper.

30–7 Galvanic cells. When a single electrode is placed in a solution, it evidently forms a single seat of emf. The introduction of a second electrode completes a galvanic cell. The emf of the cell is determined in part by the difference between the emf's arising at the electrodes. These emf's depend upon the nature of the electrodes, upon the ionic concentrations around them, upon the temperature, and, in special cases, upon the pressure. There is an additional source of emf in some cells. Just as a difference of potential arises between an electrode and a solution, potential differences may also occur at the junction between one solution and another. This effect is particularly marked when a concentrated solution is in contact with a dilute solution and the positive and negative ions are of such a nature that they diffuse with a considerable difference in velocities. One of the most interesting of such cells is that in which both electrodes are of the same material and only the concentrations of the ions about the electrodes are different. Such cells are called *concentration cells*, and are important in the study of corrosion.

It was emphasized by Langmuir in 1916, by Butler in 1924, and again by Gurney in 1936 that the emf's of some cells other than concentration cells may be due in part to another factor not connected with electrode potentials or liquid junction potentials. This factor is the *contact potential* (or Volta potential) that exists between any two dissimilar metals in air or in a vacuum. If two different metals touch for a short while (or are connected by a wire) and are then separated, they are found to be charged, and the potential difference between them is found to be of the order of 1 or 2 volts. The role that this plays in the establishment of the emf of a galvanic cell has been generally overlooked by electrochemists. The subject, however, is very complicated and requires for proper discussion some of the modern ideas of quantum mechanics applied to metals. We shall therefore limit ourselves to the description of a few important cells, and state the facts without insisting on any one theoretical interpretation.

30–8 The Daniell cell. One of the simplest practical sources of electrical energy is the Daniell cell. It contains a zinc electrode immersed in a solution of zinc ions (Zn^{++}) and a copper electrode in a solution of bivalent copper ions (Cu^{++}). Negative ions are also present but need not be considered for the moment. In some cases the two solutions are separated by a porous cup and in others by gravity. The latter type of cell is called a "gravity cell" and is illustrated in Fig. 30–3. The maximum voltage is obtained by preparing the cell with a minimum concentration of zinc ions in the upper layer and a saturated solution of copper ions in the lower. The saturation of the copper solution is maintained by an excess of solid crystals of copper sulfate in the bottom.

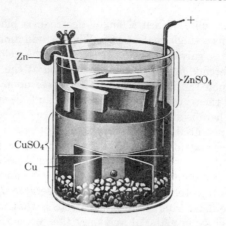

FIG. 30–3. The Daniell cell.

As current is drawn, zinc goes into solution and copper is deposited on the copper electrode. The concentration of zinc ions in the upper part of the cell increases; therefore the emf gradually declines with time. Electrons flow in the external circuit from the zinc to the copper. To prevent copper ions from diffusing upward to the zinc electrode, it is advantageous to keep the external circuit of a Daniell cell closed at all times. The Daniell cell has a high internal resistance, and works best when operating continuously in a closed circuit of moderately high resistance.

The net chemical effect of the discharge of a Daniell cell is the disappearance of Zn and Cu^{++}, and the appearance of Zn^{++} and Cu, which may be represented by the chemical "equation"

$$Zn + Cu^{++} \rightarrow Zn^{++} + Cu.$$

It is a simple matter to cause this reaction to take place in a purely chemical manner, quite apart from a Daniell cell. Thus, if zinc powder is shaken in a solution of copper sulfate, all the zinc will dissolve (i.e., become ions in solution) and all the copper ions will become metal atoms, provided the original amounts of the two substances are chosen properly. During this reaction, heat is liberated; that is, the reaction is *exothermic*. The Daniell cell is therefore seen to be a device for converting the energy released during a chemical reaction into electrical energy.

30–9 Polarization. In the transfer of electricity through any cell, electrolytic or galvanic, there is a theoretical emf that may be calculated by thermodynamic methods similar to those used previously in the case of the electrolysis of water, or with the aid of a table of electrode potentials. In operating a cell, however, the emf is always different from this theoretical value, due to the phenomenon of polarization. (This is not to be confused with the polarization of a dielectric!)

The simplest kind of polarization occurs when the ionic concentration around an electrode is altered by the passage of current. Thus, if the current density in a copper refining cell or in a Daniell cell is raised momentarily to a high value, the concentration of copper ions around the copper plate drops to a low value and, simultaneously, the concentration of metal ions around the other electrode rises sharply. The result is an increase in the potential difference of the copper refining cell, or a decrease in the emf of the Daniell cell.

Polarization always results in "loss," that is, more energy necessary to operate electrolytic cells and less energy obtained from galvanic cells. Many cells, especially those in which gaseous products are formed at one or both of the electrodes, exhibit polarization even at low current densities. *In the limit of vanishingly low current density, the difference between the theoretical emf and the actual emf required because of polarization is called overvoltage.*

When gases are formed at the electrodes, another serious situation arises. The presence of the gas increases the resistance between the electrode and the solution, thereby increasing the internal resistance of the cell.

There are various ways in which the polarization of a cell may be reduced. If it is due to a temporary impoverishment of ions near one electrode and a temporary enrichment of ions near the other electrode, vigorous stirring will help to reduce polarization. Alternatively, if the cell is left on open circuit for a while, the natural diffusion of ions toward regions of lower concentration will accomplish the same purpose. When the polarization of a galvanic cell is due to the collection of bubbles of gas on an electrode, a chemical agent known as a *depolarizer* may be used to react with the gas to form water.

30–10 The dry cell. The dry cell is the most convenient small portable source of electrical energy. The positive pole is a rod of carbon and the negative pole is of metallic zinc. The ordinary fluid is replaced by a paste containing zinc chloride and ammonium chloride. As a depolarizer, manganese dioxide is added. Although many high voltage dry batteries are built in layers, single cells are usually cylindrical, the zinc being in the form of a closed can with the carbon electrode in the center. The paste occupies the space between and the top is sealed with a layer of pitch or wax. As the cell discharges, metallic zinc changes to bivalent zinc ions at the negative pole. At the positive pole ammonium ions are believed to interact with the manganese dioxide by the reaction

$$2NH_4^+ + 2e^- + MnO_2 \rightarrow 2NH_3 + MnO + H_2O.$$

The open circuit emf of a freshly prepared dry cell lies between 1.5 and 1.6 volts, depending on conditions at the electrodes. As current is drawn, the terminal voltage falls, since the depolarization is slow. If the cell is allowed to stand for a short time, the depolarization reaction "catches up" and the terminal voltage increases to nearly its original value. After extensive use, the internal resistance increases until the cell becomes useless. This effect is believed to be due to depletion of the manganese dioxide.

30–11 The lead storage battery. The cells of a lead storage battery in the fully charged state consist of sets of positive plates of lead dioxide and sets of negative plates of metallic lead. The materials are coated on grids of metallic lead and are prepared in a highly porous form so that the electrolyte gains full access to the plates over a maximum surface area. Separation is maintained by the use of treated wood or glass fiber spacers. The electrolyte is sulfuric acid of specific gravity 1.31 at 80°F. The emf is 2.1 volts per cell. As charge passes through a cell, reactions occur at the plates. At the positive plate lead is reduced from the quadrivalent state to the divalent state by the reaction

$$PbO_2 + SO_4^{--} + 4H^+ + 2e^- \rightarrow PbSO_4 + 2H_2O.$$

Since lead sulfate is poorly soluble, it adheres to the plate as it is formed. At the negative plate sulfate ions are neutralized by the reaction

$$Pb + SO_4^{--} \rightarrow PbSO_4 + 2e^-.$$

Again the sulfate adheres to the plate. When the battery is discharged, both plates have been almost entirely converted to lead sulfate. The loss of sulfate ions from the electrolyte causes the specific gravity to be lowered so that in the discharged condition it reaches 1.16. Under these conditions the open circuit emf is approximately 1.75 volts per cell.

At low temperatures the open circuit emf of the lead storage battery falls somewhat, as it does for other electrochemical reactions. The most important effect, however, is the decreasing ion mobility within the battery at low temperatures. This appears as an increased internal resistance. Thus the terminal voltage drops abnormally when current is drawn. As a result of the combined low temperature effects, the cranking ability of an automobile storage battery at 0°C is only about 40% of its value at 80°C.

30–12 Standard cells. A number of cells have been devised which are extremely stable, maintaining a fixed emf over long periods of time. Probably the most common of these is the saturated Weston cell. It contains an electrode of mercury in contact with a paste of mercurous sulfate, and

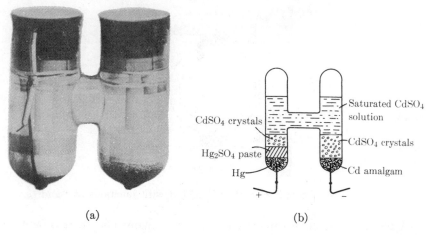

(a)   (b)

Fig. 30–4. (a) A Weston standard cell. (Courtesy of Weston Electrical Instrument Corporation.) (b) Diagram of a Weston cell.

an electrode of cadmium amalgam in contact with a saturated solution of cadmium sulfate, as shown in Fig. 30–4. The construction is such that the passage of small amounts of charge in either direction has a negligible effect on the internal condition of the cell. The emf of the saturated Weston cell is affected by the temperature, not only through the temperature variation of the electrode emf's, but also because the concentration of saturated cadmium sulfate changes slightly with temperature. The change, however, is small, and the Weston cell is almost universally used to calibrate a potentiometer.

30–13 Thermoelectricity. We have seen how an emf may be produced and maintained in a circuit by means of chemical reactions. In 1826 Thomas Johann Seebeck (1770–1831) discovered that an emf could be produced by purely thermal means in a circuit composed of two different metals A and B whose junctions are maintained at different temperatures, as shown schematically in Fig. 30–5. The two metals constitute a *thermocouple*, and the emf in the circuit is called a *thermal* emf, or a *Seebeck* emf. When the temperature of the reference junction t_R is kept constant, the Seebeck emf $\mathcal{E}_{AB}$ is found to be a function of the temperature t of the test junction. This fact enables the thermocouple to be used as a thermometer, as described in Section 15–2, and this is its main use today. The advantage of a thermocouple thermometer is that, because its heat capacity is small, the test junction comes quite rapidly to thermal equilibrium with the system whose temperature is to be measured. It therefore follows temperature changes easily.

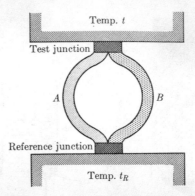

Fig. 30–5. Thermocouple of metals A and B with junctions at t and t_R.

A *thermopile* is an instrument consisting of many fine thermocouples connected in series, so that the total emf is the sum of the separate emf's. In conjunction with a high sensitivity galvanometer, a thermopile is an extremely sensitive device for detecting and measuring radiant energy. The reference junctions are covered, while the test junctions are blackened and exposed to the radiant energy. Thermopiles are used to measure the radiation from stars and are commonly employed to investigate the distribution of energy in those portions of a spectrum beyond the limits of a photographic plate.

The Seebeck emf arises from the fact that the density of free electrons in a metal differs from one metal to another and, in a given metal, depends on the temperature. When two different metals are connected to form a junction, electrons diffuse from one into the other. The junction acts as a seat of emf, and if there is current from one metal to the other, energy is either liberated or absorbed. The transfer of energy is in the form of a flow of heat between the junction and its surroundings. It is known as the *Peltier heat*, after its discoverer, Jean C. A. Peltier, a French physicist. Experiment has shown that the Peltier heat transferred at any junction is proportional to the quantity of electricity crossing the junction, and that it reverses its direction of flow when the electric current is reversed. The number of joules of heat absorbed or liberated at a junction of metals A and B per coulomb of electricity transferred is called the *Peltier emf* π_{AB}. Thus

$$\pi_{AB} = \frac{\text{Peltier heat (joules)}}{Q \text{ (coulombs)}}. \tag{30–3}$$

It is found that π_{AB} depends not only on the nature of the two metals, but also on the temperature of the junction, and that it is independent of any other junction that may be present.

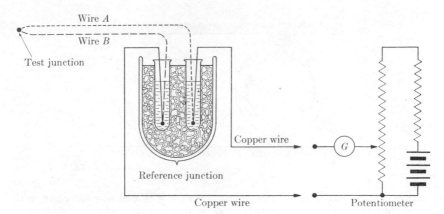

FIG. 30-6. Thermocouple of wires A and B with a reference junction consisting of two junctions with copper, connected to a potentiometer.

In a single wire whose ends are maintained at different temperatures, the free electron density varies from point to point. Each element of a wire of nonuniform temperature is therefore a seat of emf, a discovery made by Sir William Thomson (Lord Kelvin). When a current is maintained in a wire of nonuniform temperature, heat is liberated or absorbed at all points of the wire, and this *Thomson heat* is proportional to the quantity of electricity passing the section of wire and to the temperature difference between the ends of the section. If a small length of wire A has a temperature difference Δt, the number of joules of heat absorbed or liberated in this length of wire per coulomb of electricity transferred is called the *Thomson emf*, written $\sigma_A \, \Delta t$. Thus

$$\sigma_A \, \Delta t = \frac{\text{Thomson heat (joules)}}{Q \text{ (coulombs)}} \, . \qquad (30\text{--}4)$$

Experiment has shown that the Thomson heat is also reversible, and depends on the nature of the wire and on the average temperature of the portion of the wire under consideration. The coefficient σ_A is sometimes called the "specific heat of electricity."

To connect a thermocouple to a measuring instrument, it is necessary to break the thermocouple circuit at some point and introduce a third metal, thereby creating two new junctions. It can be shown that no disturbing effects are produced, provided both new junctions are maintained at the same temperature. The correct procedure for connecting a thermocouple to a potentiometer is shown in Fig. 30-6.

Consider the two thermocouples depicted in Fig. 30-7, one composed of metals A and C and the other of metals B and C. It is an important

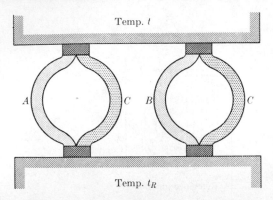

Fig. 30–7. Two separate thermocouples, each with one wire the same, with junctions at the same temperature. $\mathcal{E}_{AB} = \mathcal{E}_{AC} - \mathcal{E}_{BC}$.

fact that the emf of a thermocouple AB is the difference between the emf's of two thermocouples AC and BC when the junction temperatures are the same. This fact enables us to tabulate convenient numbers from which the thermal emf of any thermocouple may be computed. Thus, if M is any metal and L is lead, experiment shows that the thermal emf $\mathcal{E}_{ML}$ depends on the temperature t of the test junction, when $t_R = 0°C$, according to the equation

$$\mathcal{E}_{ML} = at + \tfrac{1}{2}bt^2, \tag{30-5}$$

provided t is no more than a few hundred degrees. The constants a and b are given for various metals M in Table 30–2.

EXAMPLE. Find the emf of a copper-iron thermocouple when $t_R = 0°C$. We write

$$\mathcal{E}_{CuFe} = \mathcal{E}_{CuPb} - \mathcal{E}_{FePb},$$

and using Eq. (30–5),

$$\mathcal{E}_{CuFe} = (a_{CuPb} - a_{FePb})t + \tfrac{1}{2}(b_{CuPb} - b_{FePb})t^2.$$

Using Table 30–2,

$$\mathcal{E}_{CuFe} = (2.76 - 16.6)\,\frac{\mu V}{deg}\,t + \tfrac{1}{2}(0.012 + 0.030)\,\frac{\mu V}{deg^2}\,t^2$$

$$= -13.8\,\frac{\mu V}{deg}\,t + 0.021\,\frac{\mu V}{deg^2}\,t^2.$$

At $t = 100°C$,

$$\mathcal{E}_{CuFe} = -1.17\ mv,$$

where the minus sign indicates that the direction of the current is from iron to copper at the junction at 100°C.

TABLE 30–2

CONSTANTS IN THE EQUATION
$$\mathcal{E}_{ML} = at + \tfrac{1}{2}bt^2 \ (t_R = 0°\text{C})$$

Metal M (L = lead)	$a \left(\dfrac{\mu\text{v}}{\deg}\right)$	$b \left(\dfrac{\mu\text{v}}{\deg^2}\right)$
Aluminum .	-0.47	0.003
Bismuth	-43.7	-0.47
Copper	2.76	0.012
Gold	2.90	0.0093
Iron	16.6	-0.030
Nickel	19.1	-0.030
Platinum	-1.79	-0.035
Silver	2.50	0.012
Steel	10.8	-0.016

The graphs of Fig. 30–8 show the emf of a copper-iron thermocouple as a function of the temperature of the test junction t for three different values of the temperature of the reference junction t_R. It will be seen that, at any value of t, the slope is the same for the three curves, and is therefore independent of t_R.

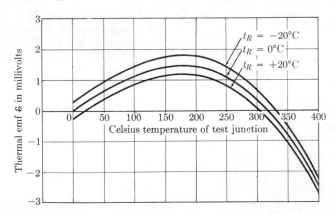

FIG. 30–8. Thermal emf of a copper-iron thermocouple as a function of the temperature of the test junction, for three different values of the temperature of the reference junction.

PROBLEMS

(Atomic weights are given below the symbols for the elements in the periodic table in the appendix.)

30-1. What current would be required to deposit 4.5 gm of zinc from a solution of $ZnCl_2$ in 20 min?

30-2. The international ampere is defined as that unvarying current which in one second will deposit 0.001118 gm of silver from a solution of $AgNO_3$. Determine from this definition the value of the faraday.

30-3. How many faradays of electricity are required to deposit 159 gm of copper from a solution of $CuSO_4$?

30-4. (a) What mass of silver will be deposited by a current of 4 amp in 3 hr from a solution of $AgNO_3$? (b) How many silver atoms are deposited?

30-5. A thin rectangular plate 4 cm × 3 cm is to be plated on both sides with gold to a thickness of 0.001 cm. How long must a current of 1.5 amp be maintained through the plating solution?

30-6. What is the mutual force of repulsion between two electrons separated by a distance of 10^{-5} cm in glycerin?

30-7. What mass of copper is deposited in a Daniell cell when used for one hour to run a small motor that draws one ampere?

30-8. A copper refining cell has two parallel plate electrodes 1 m square and 5 cm apart. The resistivity of the solution is 1.2 ohm·cm. Calculate the resistance of the cell.

30-9. Two electrolytic tanks are arranged in series, one containing a solution of $CuSO_4$, the other $AgNO_3$. How much silver will be deposited during the time that 4.8 gm of copper are deposited?

30-10. Calculate the volumes of the gaseous products at 0°C and 1 atm pressure liberated during the electrolysis of water for one hour with a current of 5 amp.

30-11. In the silver plating of a spoon, a current of 0.1 amp is maintained for 2 hr. What is the thickness of the silver plate deposited if the surface area of the spoon is 150 cm^2?

30-12. A potential difference of 3 volts is established across a copper electroplating cell. How much does it cost to deposit 500 gm of copper if the price of electrical energy is 1.5 cents per kwh?

30-13. Using Table 30-2, compute for a copper-nickel thermocouple the thermal emf when $t = 100°C$.

30-14. It is desired to construct a bismuth-silver thermopile that will develop a thermal emf of 1 μv when $t = 0.001°C$, t_R being 0°C. How many separate thermocouples must be connected in series?

CHAPTER 31

THE MAGNETIC FIELD

31–1 Magnetism. The first magnetic phenomena to be observed were undoubtedly those associated with so-called "natural" magnets, rough fragments of an ore of iron found near the ancient city of Magnesia (whence the term "magnet"). These natural magnets have the property of attracting to themselves unmagnetized iron, the effect being most pronounced at certain regions of the magnet known as its *poles*. It was known to the Chinese as early as 121 A.D. that an iron rod, after being brought near a natural magnet, would acquire and retain this property of the natural magnet, and that such a rod when freely suspended about a vertical axis would set itself approximately in the north-south direction. The use of magnets as aids to navigation can be traced back at least to the eleventh century.

The study of magnetic phenomena was confined for many years to magnets made in this way. Not until 1819 was there shown to be any connection between electrical and magnetic phenomena. In that year the Danish scientist Hans Christian Oersted (1770–1851) observed that a pivoted magnet (a compass needle) was deflected when in the neighborhood of a wire carrying a current. Twelve years later, after attempts extending over a period of several years, Faraday found that a momentary current existed in a circuit while the current in a nearby circuit was being started or stopped. Shortly afterward followed the discovery that the motion of a magnet toward or away from the circuit would produce the same effect. Joseph Henry (1797–1878), an American scientist who later became the first director of the Smithsonian Institution, had anticipated Faraday's discoveries by about twelve months, but since Faraday was the first to publish his results he is usually assigned the credit for them. The work of Oersted thus demonstrated that magnetic effects could be produced by moving electric charges, and that of Faraday and Henry that currents could be produced by moving magnets.

It is believed at the present time that all so-called magnetic phenomena arise from forces between electric charges in motion. That is, moving charges exert "magnetic" forces on one another, over and above the purely "electrical" or "electrostatic" forces given by Coulomb's law. We shall therefore begin the subject of magnetism with a study of the forces between moving charges and postpone the question of magnetic poles until a later chapter, where they will be discussed in connection with the magnetic properties of matter in general.

607

Since the electrons in atoms are in motion about the atomic nuclei, and since each electron appears to be in continuous rotation about an axis passing through it, all atoms can be expected to exhibit magnetic effects and, in fact, such is found to be the case. The possibility that the magnetic properties of matter were the result of tiny atomic currents was first suggested by Ampere in 1820. Not until recent years has the verification of these ideas been possible.

As with electrostatic forces, the medium in which the charges are moving may have a pronounced effect on the observed magnetic forces between them. In the present chapter we shall assume the charges or conductors to be in otherwise empty space. For all practical purposes the results will apply equally well to charges and conductors in air.

31–2 The magnetic field. Induction. Instead of dealing directly with the forces exerted on one moving charge by another, it is found more convenient to adopt the point of view that a moving charge sets up in the space around it a *magnetic field,* and that it is this field which exerts a force on another charge moving through it. The magnetic field around a moving charge exists in addition to the electrostatic field which surrounds the charge whether it is in motion or not. A second charged particle in these combined fields experiences a force due to the electric field whether it is in motion or at rest. The magnetic field exerts a force on the particle only if it is in motion.

A magnetic field is said to exist at a point if a force (over and above any electrostatic force) *is exerted on a moving charge at the point.*

The electric field set up by moving charges or by currents is, in many instances, so small that the electrostatic force on a moving charge can be neglected in comparison with the magnetic force.

There are two aspects to the problem of computing the magnetic force between moving charges. The first is that of finding the magnitude and direction of the magnetic field at a point, given the data on the moving charges that set up the field. The second is to find the magnitude and direction of the force on a charge moving in a given field. We shall take up the latter aspect of the problem first. That is, let us accept for the present the fact that moving charges and currents do set up magnetic fields, and study the laws that determine the force on a charge moving through the field.

The cathode-ray tube is a convenient experimental device for studying, at least in a qualitative way, the behavior of moving charges in a magnetic field. At one end of this tube is an electron gun which shoots out a narrow electron beam at a speed that can be controlled and calculated. At the other end is a fluorescent screen which emits light at the point where the electron beam strikes it. Let us suppose that our cathode-ray tube is small, that it is not surrounded by iron, and that it can be carried around the room easily. If the spot of light is always in the same place on the screen as we move the tube, we may conclude that there is no detectable magnetic field. If, on the other hand, as we move the tube around the room, the spot of light changes its position by virtue of the deflection of the electron beam, we conclude that we are in a magnetic field. Since the cathode-ray tube is imagined to be small, rotating the tube about any axis through its center, without shifting the position of its center, will provide information concerning the magnetic field in a small region at the center or, roughly, the magnetic field at a point.

At a given point in a magnetic field, the electron beam will, in general, be deflected. By rotating the cathode-ray tube, however, there will be found one direction in which no deflection takes place. *The direction of motion of a charge on which a magnetic field exerts no force is defined as the direction of the magnetic field.* (The sense of the field will be defined later.)

Having determined the direction (but not the sense) of the magnetic field, let us now place the cathode-ray tube so that the electron beam moves in a plane perpendicular to this direction. Experiment shows that a deflection always takes place in such a manner as to indicate a force acting in this plane, but at right angles to the velocity of the electron beam. That is, *when the velocity of the moving charge is perpendicular to the magnetic field, the force is perpendicular to both the magnetic field and the velocity.* The magnitude of this force is found to be directly proportional to the velocity. If the velocity v of the moving charge is not perpendicular to the direction of the magnetic field, but makes an angle ϕ with the field, then the velocity vector v may be resolved into two components: $v \cos \phi$ in the direction of the field, and $v \sin \phi$ perpendicular to the field. In this general case, *the force acting on the moving charge is perpendicular to both the magnetic field and to $v \sin \phi$, and has a magnitude proportional to $v \sin \phi$,* as shown in Fig. 31–1.

It is possible to conceive of a positive ion tube, with a positive ion source at one end and a detector at the other, so that deflection of the positive ion beam may be observed when the tube is placed in various positions in a magnetic field. By using different positive ions, it is possible to measure the force acting on positive charges of different magnitudes. Thus, with hydrogen ions (protons), the force on singly charged positive ions may be measured, and with other gases under proper conditions, forces on doubly and trebly charged positive ions may be measured. Experiment shows in all cases that *the force acting on a charge moving in a magnetic field is proportional to the magnitude of the charge.*

From these experimental observations we may define a vector quantity **B** known as the *magnetic induction*, which characterizes a magnetic field in the same way that the vector **E** characterizes an electric field. The magni-

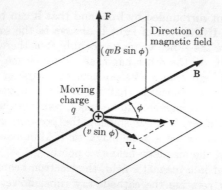

Fig. 31–1. The magnetic force **F** acting on a charge q moving with velocity **v** is perpendicular to both the magnetic field and to $v \sin \phi$.

tude of the magnetic induction B at any point is defined as

$$B = \frac{F}{qv \sin \phi},$$ (31–1)

where q is the magnitude of the charge, v its velocity, ϕ the angle between v and the direction of the magnetic field, and F the force acting on a moving charge at the point.

When F is expressed in newtons, q in coulombs, and v in meters per second, B is said to be in *webers per square meter*. Thus, *one weber per square meter is the magnetic induction of a magnetic field in which one coulomb of charge, moving with a component of velocity perpendicular to the field* ($v_\perp = v \sin \phi$) *equal to one meter per second, is acted on by a force of one newton.* Hence,

$$1 \, \frac{\text{weber}}{\text{m}^2} = 1 \, \frac{\text{newton}}{\text{coul·m/sec}}$$

or, since one coulomb per second equals one ampere,

$$1 \, \frac{\text{weber}}{\text{m}^2} = 1 \, \frac{\text{newton}}{\text{amp·m}}.$$

In the cgs system, B is measured in *maxwells per square centimeter*, or in *gauss*. It can be shown that

$$1 \text{ gauss} = 1 \, \frac{\text{maxwell}}{\text{cm}^2} = 10^{-4} \, \frac{\text{weber}}{\text{m}^2},$$

or

$$1 \, \frac{\text{weber}}{\text{m}^2} = 10^4 \text{ gauss}.$$

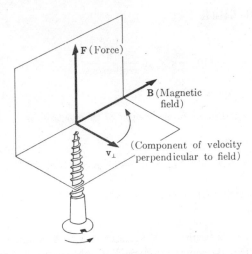

Fig. 31–2.   The vectors $v_\perp$, **B**, and **F** form a mutually perpendicular set. If you rotate the vector $v_\perp$ toward the vector **B**, the vector **F** will point in the direction of advance of a right-hand screw.

The largest values of magnetic induction that can be produced in the laboratory are of the order of 10 w/m^2 or 100,000 gauss, while in the magnetic field of the earth the induction is only a few hundred-thousandths of a weber per square meter, or a few tenths of a gauss.

Up to this point we have defined the magnitude of the magnetic induction and its direction, but not its sense. The definition of the magnetic induction vector **B** may now be completed by specifying that *when the moving charge is positive*, the three vectors $v_\perp$, **B**, and **F** form a mutually perpendicular set, as shown in Fig. 31–2. The relation among their magnitudes is

$$F = v_\perp Bq,$$

whereas the relation among their directions may be kept in mind by the *right-hand screw rule*, which provides that *the direction of the force is the direction of advance of a right-hand screw when rotated from $v_\perp$ toward B.* (The direction of the force on a negative charge is opposite that on a positive charge.)

EXAMPLE. An electron is projected into a magnetic field of flux density $B = 10$ w/m^2 = 10 n/(coul·m/sec) with a velocity of 3×10^7 m/sec in a direction at right angles to the field. Compute the magnetic force on the electron and compare with the weight of the electron.

The magnetic force is

$$F = v_\perp Bq$$

$$= 3 \times 10^7 \, \frac{m}{sec} \times 10 \, \frac{n}{coul \cdot m/sec} \times 1.6 \times 10^{-19} \, coul$$

$$= 4.8 \times 10^{-11} \, n.$$

The gravitational force, or the weight of the electron, is

$$F = mg$$

$$= 9 \times 10^{-31} \, kgm \times 9.8 \, \frac{m}{sec^2} = 8.8 \times 10^{-30} \, n.$$

The gravitational force is therefore negligible in comparison with the magnetic force.

31–3 Lines of induction. Magnetic flux. A magnetic field, like an electric field, can be represented by lines called *lines of induction,* whose direction at every point is that of the magnetic induction vector. By convention, the number of these lines per unit area normal to the direction is made equal to the magnitude of the induction. The unit of induction was chosen to be one weber per square meter so that one weber would equal one line of induction. Similarly, in the cgs system, the unit of induction was chosen to be one maxwell per square centimeter so that one maxwell would equal one line.

In a uniform magnetic field, where the magnetic induction vector has a constant magnitude and direction at all points, the lines of induction are straight and equally spaced. If the pole pieces of an electromagnet are large and close together, there is a region between the poles where the magnetic field is approximately uniform. The lines of induction of various magnetic fields are shown in some of the figures in Chapter 33.

The total number of lines of induction threading through a surface is called the *magnetic flux* through the surface and is denoted by Φ (phi). In the special case where **B** is uniform and normal to a finite area A,

$$\Phi = BA. \tag{31–2}$$

Since B is in w/m^2 and A is in m^2, the flux is in *webers*. Since the induction B at a point equals the flux per unit area, it is often referred to as the *flux density.*

31–4 Orbits of charged particles in magnetic fields. It is often necessary to represent pictorially a magnetic field perpendicular to the plane of the paper (or of the blackboard) directed either toward or away from the reader. This is usually done with a number of dots or crosses. The dots may be thought of as representing the points of arrows directed toward the reader, the crosses as the tail feathers of arrows directed away from the reader.

Let a positively charged particle at point O in a uniform magnetic field of flux density $\mathbf{B}$ be given a velocity $\mathbf{v}$ in a direction at right angles to the field (Fig. 31–3). The right-hand screw rule shows that an upward force $\mathbf{F}$, of magnitude vBq, is exerted on the particle at this point. Since the force is at right angles to the velocity, it will not affect the magnitude of this velocity but will merely alter its direction. At points such as P and Q the directions of force and velocity will have changed as shown, the magnitude of the force remaining constant since the magnitudes of $\mathbf{v}$, $\mathbf{B}$, and q are constant. The particle therefore moves under the influence of a force whose magnitude is constant but whose direction is always at right angles to the velocity of the particle. The orbit of the particle is therefore a circle described with constant tangential speed v, the force $\mathbf{F}$ being the centripetal force. Since

$$\text{Centripetal acceleration} = \frac{v^2}{R},$$

we have, from Newton's second law,

$$vBq = m\,\frac{v^2}{R}$$

and the radius of the circular orbit is

$$R = \frac{mv}{Bq}. \qquad (31\text{–}3)$$

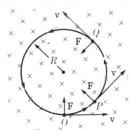

FIG. 31–3. The orbit of a charged particle in a uniform magnetic field is a circle when the initial velocity is perpendicular to the field.

If the direction of the initial velocity is not perpendicular to the field, the particle moves in a helix.

31–5 The cyclotron. The cyclotron is an instrument developed in 1931 by Drs. Ernest O. Lawrence and M. Stanley Livingston at the University of California at Berkeley, for the purpose of securing a beam of charged atomic particles traveling at high speed. Despite its size and complexity, the basic theory of its operation is quite simple.

The heart of the cyclotron is a pair of metal chambers shaped like the halves of a pillbox that has been cut along one of its diameters. (See Fig. 31–4.) These hollow chambers, referred to as "dees" or "D's" because of their shape, have their diametric edges parallel and slightly separated from each other. A source of ions—the positively charged nuclei of heavy hydrogen (deuterons) are commonly used—is located near the midpoint of the gap between the dees. The latter are connected to the terminals

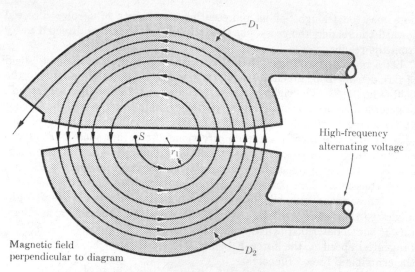

FIG. 31–4. Schematic diagram of a cyclotron.

of an electric circuit of the same sort as that used in a radio transmitter. The potential between the dees is thus caused to alternate rapidly, some millions of times per second, so the electric field in the gap between the dees is directed first toward one and then toward the other. But because of the electrical shielding effect of the dees, the space within each is a region of zero electric field.

The two dees are enclosed within, but insulated from, a somewhat larger cylindrical metal container from which the air is exhausted, and the whole apparatus is placed between the poles of a powerful electromagnet which provides a magnetic field whose direction is perpendicular to the ends of the cylindrical container.

Consider an ion of charge $+q$ and mass m, emitted from the ion source S at an instant when D_1 in Fig. 31–4 is positive. The ion is accelerated by the electric field in the gap between the dees and enters the (electric) field-free region within D_2 with a speed, say, of v_1. Since its motion is at right angles to the magnetic field, it will travel in a circular path of radius

$$r_1 = \frac{mv_1}{Bq}.$$

If now, in the time required for the ion to complete a half-circle, the *electric* field has reversed so that its direction is toward D_1, the ion will again be accelerated as it crosses the gap between the dees and will enter D_1 with a greater velocity v_2. It therefore moves in a half circle of larger radius within D_1 to emerge again into the gap.

The angular velocity ω of the ion is

$$\omega = \frac{v}{r} = B \frac{q}{m}.$$

Hence the angular velocity is *independent of the speed of the ion and of the radius of the circle* in which it travels, depending only on the magnetic induction and the charge-to-mass ratio (q/m) of the ion. If, therefore, the electric field reverses at regular intervals, each equal to the time required for the ion to make a half revolution, the field in the gap will always be in the proper direction to accelerate an ion each time the gap is crossed. It is this feature of the motion, the independence of time of rotation on radius, which makes the cyclotron feasible, since the regularly timed reversals are accomplished automatically by the "radio" circuit to which the dees are connected.

The path of an ion is a sort of spiral, composed of semicircular arcs of progressively larger radius, connected by short segments along which the radius is increasing. If R represents the outside radius of the dees and v_{max} the speed of the ion when traveling in a path of this radius,

$$v_{max} = BR \frac{q}{m},$$

and the corresponding kinetic energy of the ion is

$$\frac{1}{2}mv_{max}^2 = \frac{1}{2}m\left(\frac{q}{m}\right)^2 B^2 R^2.$$

The potential difference V which would be required to produce the same kinetic energy in a single step, as in the Van de Graaff generator, can be found from

$$\tfrac{1}{2}mv_{max}^2 = qV,$$

or

$$V = \frac{1}{2} \frac{q}{m} B^2 R^2. \tag{31–4}$$

If the ions are deuterons,

$$\frac{q}{m} = 4.8 \times 10^7 \frac{coul}{kgm}.$$

In the M.I.T. cyclotron, B is about 1.8 w/m^2 and $R = 0.48$ m. Hence

$$V = \tfrac{1}{2} \times 4.8 \times 10^7 \times (1.8)^2 \times (0.48)^2$$
$$= 18 \times 10^6 \text{ volts, or 18 million volts,}$$

and the deuterons have the same speed as if they had been accelerated through a potential difference of 18 million volts.

(a)

(b)

FIG. 31–5. The M.I.T. cyclotron.

Figure 31–5(a) is a photograph of the M.I.T. cyclotron, and Fig. 31–5(b) shows the dees removed from the gap between the poles of the electromagnet. The cover of the outer vacuum chamber has been removed in this photograph. The bar in the gap between the dees supports the ion source. Accelerated particles can be brought out of the chamber through a thin foil window in the short tube at the lower right.

The cyclotron operates successfully only with relatively massive particles such as protons or deuterons. It cannot be used to accelerate electrons for the following reason. In order that a particle shall remain in phase with the alternating electric field, its angular velocity, Bq/m, must remain constant. Now although q and B are constants, the same is not true of the mass m. The latter increases with increasing velocity because of relativistic effects. For a given energy, the velocity of an electron is much greater than that of a more massive proton or deuteron and the relativistic increase of mass is correspondingly more pronounced. For example, the mass of a 2-million volt electron is about five times its rest mass, while the mass of a 2-million volt deuteron differs from its rest mass by only about 0.01 percent. Hence electrons very quickly get out of phase with the electric field and do not arrive at the gap between the dees at the proper times to be accelerated. This difficulty does not arise in a generator of the Van de Graaff type, and it can also be surmounted by a device called a *betatron*, described in Section 34–4.

Even with protons or deuterons, the relativistic increase of mass sets an upper limit of about 30 million volts to the equivalent voltage through which these particles can be accelerated in a cyclotron. This limit can be increased to several hundred million volts in the *frequency modulated cyclotron*, where the frequency of alternation of the electric field is decreased as a particle spirals out from the center, at the same rate that the angular velocity decreases because of increasing mass. Of course the frequency cannot be decreased indefinitely. It is alternately decreased and increased and a burst of particles is accelerated during each interval of decreasing frequency.

31–6 Measurement of e/m. The charge-to-mass ratio of an electron, e/m, was first measured by Sir J. J. Thomson in 1897 at the Cavendish Laboratory in Cambridge, England. The apparatus used by Thomson was a glass tube having the form shown in Fig. 31–6, from which most of the air had been evacuated. A potential difference of a few thousand volts is maintained between anode A and cathode C. The few positive ions which are always present in a gas, caused by radioactivity or cosmic radiation, are accelerated toward the cathode by the electric field in the anode-cathode space. When these rapidly moving ions strike the cathode, they liberate electrons from its surface and these electrons accelerate

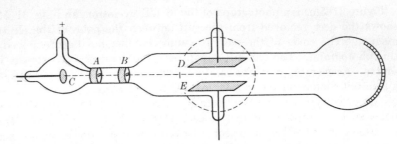

FIG. 31-6. Apparatus of J. J. Thomson to measure the ratio e/m of electrons.

in the opposite direction toward the anode A. Occasional collisions between them and the residual gas atoms maintain the supply of positive ions. This mechanism of releasing electrons from a surface is called "secondary emission."

At the time these experiments were being performed the nature of the electron stream was not known, and the particles composing it (if they were particles at all) were simply called *cathode rays*.

Most of the electrons emitted at the cathode are stopped by the anode, but a narrow beam passes through the slit in the anode and through a second slit in the metal plug B. The end of the tube is coated on the inside with a fluorescent material and the point of impact of the electron stream appears as a bright luminous spot. Except for the mechanism of electron emission, the tube is essentially the same as that now used in cathode-ray oscillographs and television receivers.

The tube is provided with two metal plates D and E between which a vertical electric field can be set up, and by means of an external electromagnet a magnetic field can be established, perpendicular to the plane of the diagram, within the region indicated by the dotted circle. If the electric field is upward, and if there is no magnetic field, the electron stream will be deflected downward as it passes between the plates, and its deflection can be observed on the fluorescent screen. If a magnetic field only is present, directed out from the plane of the diagram, the electron stream will be deflected upward. By the proper adjustment of the combined electric and magnetic fields, the deflection can be made zero. Under these conditions the electric force Ee on an electron in the region of "crossed fields" is equal and opposite to the magnetic force vBe.

$$Ee = vBe \qquad \text{or} \qquad v = \frac{E}{B}, \qquad (31\text{-}5)$$

from which the velocity of the electrons can be found.

Now let the electric field be cut off. The electron stream then moves through the magnetic field in a circular arc, the radius of this arc being, as we have seen, $R = mv/eB$. Hence

$$\frac{e}{m} = \frac{v}{RB},$$

and, combining with Eq. (31–5), we obtain

$$\frac{e}{m} = \frac{E}{RB^2}.$$

The radius R can be deduced from the displacement of the fluorescent spot, the extent of the magnetic field, and the distance from the field to the screen, and hence e/m can be found.

Many modifications of Thomson's original method have been used to determine e/m. The most precise value to date is

$$\frac{e}{m} = 1.7589 \times 10^{11} \frac{\text{coul}}{\text{kgm}}.   \tag{31–6}$$

In one sense these experiments of Thomson constituted the "discovery" of the electron, although they measured only the ratio of the electronic charge to its mass and the charge on an individual electron was not determined until 12 years later by Millikan. If the assumption is made that the electronic charge is numerically equal to the charge on a hydrogen ion, the mass of an electron can be computed from this charge and the charge-to-mass ratio. On the basis of this assumption Thomson concluded that the mass of an electron was only about 1/1860 as great as that of a hydrogen atom, the lightest particle which had hitherto been known. The way was thus opened for the study of subatomic particles and the structure of the "indivisible" atoms, a subject which has dominated the field of experimental physics during the present century.

It should be mentioned that Thomson and one of his pupils, H. A. Wilson, pointed the way for Millikan's later measurements of the electronic charge when they attempted to measure this quantity by determining the *total* charge on a cloud of water droplets. Millikan's great contribution was his success in making measurements on a single isolated droplet.

If we insert in Eq. (31–6) the value of e based on Millikan's measurements, we find for the mass of an electron,

$$m = 9.1072 \times 10^{-31} \text{ kgm} = 9.1072 \times 10^{-28} \text{ gm.}$$

Now the mass of a hydrogen atom is

$$\frac{1.00813}{6.0254 \times 10^{23}} = 1.6731 \times 10^{-24} \text{ gm.}$$

Hence the electronic mass is only 1/1836 as great as the mass of a hydrogen atom.

31-7 The mass spectrograph. As another illustration of the motion of charged particles in electric and magnetic fields we shall describe briefly one type of *mass spectrograph*. The mass spectrograph is an instrument similar in principle to Thomson's apparatus for measuring the charge-to-mass ratio of an electron, but is used for determining the masses of positively charged ions. The first apparatus was designed by Thomson, but many modifications and improvements have been made by other investigators, notably Aston in England, and Dempster and Bainbridge in this country.

A mass spectrograph designed by Bainbridge is illustrated schematically in Fig. 31-7. S_1 and S_2 are metal plates in each of which is a narrow slit whose long dimension is perpendicular to the plane of the diagram. Plate S_1 is maintained at a potential of a few thousand volts above S_2. Positive ions produced in the space above S_1 pass through the slit in this plate and are accelerated toward S_2 by the electric field. We shall consider only singly charged ions, that is, those that have lost one electron and hence have a positive charge of magnitude e. Not all ions, however, have the same velocity when they go through the slit S_1, and hence their velocities will differ when they emerge from S_2.

The next stage in the apparatus is a "velocity filter" which selects only those ions having a predetermined velocity. An electric field, directed from left to right, is maintained between the plates P_1 and P_2, together with a magnetic field perpendicular to the plane of the diagram. A third slit S_3 is placed below the plates P_1 and P_2. Only those ions can pass through the slit S_3 which are undeviated by the crossed electric and magnetic fields between S_2 and S_3, that is, only those whose velocity is such that the magnetic force on them is just balanced by the electric force, or

$$Ee = vBe$$

and

$$v = \frac{E}{B}.$$

In the region below S_3 there is also a magnetic field $\mathbf{B}'$ perpendicular to the plane of the figure, but no electric field. In this region an ion moves in a circular path of radius

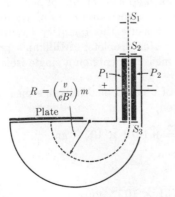

FIG. 31-7. Bainbridge's mass spectrograph, utilizing a velocity selector.

$$R = \frac{mv}{eB'} = \left(\frac{v}{eB'}\right) m.$$

The velocity filter ensures that all ions in this region have the same velocity. Hence the ratio v/eB' is the same for all ions, and the radius R is directly proportional to the mass of the ion, m. Ions of different mass travel in different semicircular paths and strike a photographic plate after having made one-half a revolution. The emulsion on the plate is rendered developable when struck by the ions, just as it is by exposure to light. Since the long dimensions of the slits are at right angles to the plane of the figure, the semicircular paths are like curved ribbons or tapes, and each path produces a line on the plate at the point where it strikes. The distance of any line from the slit S_3 is twice the radius in which that particular ion moves and, since the radii are proportional to the masses, equal mass differences appear as equal separations of lines on the developed photographic plate. The apparatus spreads the beam of ions into a "mass spectrum," much as a prism spreads a beam of light into a spectrum; hence the name "mass spectrograph."

The mass spectrograph is used chiefly for the study of *isotopes*. The term refers to atoms that have the same atomic number but differ in mass. Since the atomic number equals the number of electrons in the atom, and the *chemical* properties of an atom depend only on the number and arrangement of its electrons, isotopes cannot be separated by chemical means, but of course they are separated by the mass spectrograph. The differences in mass arise from different numbers of neutrons in the nucleus.

Most elements as they occur in Nature are mixtures of isotopes. Oxygen, for example, always occurs as a mixture of three isotopes. The most abundant (relative abundance $= 99.76\%$) is arbitrarily assigned an atomic weight of exactly 16.0000. The other two, relative to the first, have atomic weights of 17.0045 (relative abundance $= 0.04\%$) and 18.005 (relative abundance $= 0.20\%$). The average atomic weight is therefore not exactly 16.0000, but slightly larger. (The chemists, however, assign the value of exactly 16.0000 to this average, so the physical and chemical scales of atomic weights are not exactly the same.) As another example, chlorine, whose atomic weight is 35.46, is a mixture of 75.4% of an isotope of atomic weight 34.980 and 24.6% of an isotope of atomic weight 36.978, all on the physical scale.

The nearest integer to the atomic weight of an isotope is called its *mass number* and is written as a superscript. The number of extranuclear electrons, or the number of protons in the nucleus, is written below and to the left of the chemical symbol. Thus oxygen is a mixture of $_8O^{16}$, $_8O^{17}$, and $_8O^{18}$, while chlorine is a mixture of $_{17}Cl^{35}$ and $_{17}Cl^{37}$.

The masses of both the proton and the neutron, on the physical scale, are very nearly unity. Since an oxygen atom contains eight electrons, its nucleus must contain eight protons. Therefore all the isotopes of oxygen have eight protons in the nucleus, but $_8O^{16}$ has eight neutrons, $_8O^{17}$ nine neutrons, and $_8O^{18}$ ten neutrons.

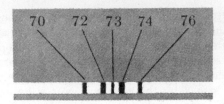

FIG. 31–8. The mass spectrum of germanium, showing the isotopes of mass numbers 70, 72, 73, 74, 76. (Courtesy of Dr. K. T. Bainbridge.)

Figure 31–8 is a reproduction of a plate showing the isotopes of germanium as they are separated by a mass spectrograph. The numbers are the mass numbers of the isotopes.

31–8 Force on a current-carrying conductor. When a current-carrying conductor lies in a magnetic field, magnetic forces are exerted on the moving electrons within the conductor. These forces are transmitted to the material of the conductor and hence the conductor as a whole experiences a force, or torque, or both. The electric motor and the moving coil galvanometer both depend for their operation on the torque exerted on a current-carrying loop in a magnetic field.

Figure 31–9 represents a portion of a straight conductor of length l and cross section A, within which there is a current i. A magnetic field of flux density **B** is perpendicular to the conductor. Since the force on the conductor as a whole is the resultant of the forces on the moving charges within it, let us express the current in the conductor in terms of the number of moving charges per unit volume, n, the charge q on each, and their velocity v. This relation has been shown to be

$$i = nqvA.$$

The magnitude of the force on each charge, say f, is

$$f = vBq.$$

The number of charges in the length l is

$$N = nlA.$$

The resultant force F is therefore

$$F = fN = (vBq)(nlA),$$

and since $i = nqvA$, this can be written

$$F = iBl.$$

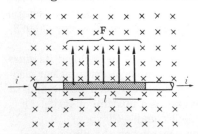

FIG. 31–9. Force on a straight conductor of length l at right angles to a magnetic field of flux density **B** directed away from the reader.

If the conductor makes an angle ϕ with the magnetic field, the force is $iBl \sin \phi$, or if $i \sin \phi$ is designated by the symbol $i_\perp$, we have finally

$$F = i_\perp Bl.$$ (31–7)

To find the direction of the force on a current-carrying conductor placed in a magnetic field we may use the same right-hand screw rule that was used in the case of a moving positive charge. Rotate a right-hand screw from the direction of $i_\perp$ toward **B** and the direction of advance will be the direction of **F**.

31–9 Force and torque on a complete circuit. The net force and torque on a complete circuit in a magnetic field can be found from Eq. (31–7). Three simple cases will be analyzed.

Rectangular loop. In Fig. 31–10 there is shown a rectangular loop of wire the lengths of whose sides are a and b. The normal to the plane of the loop makes an angle α with the direction of a uniform magnetic field. The loop is pivoted about an axis OO, and it carries a current i. (Provision must be made for leading the current into and out of the loop, or for inserting a seat of emf. This is omitted from the diagram for simplicity.)

Sides cd and ef of the loop are perpendicular to the field. Hence equal and opposite forces of magnitude

$$F = iBa$$

are exerted on them, vertically upward on cd, vertically downward on ef.

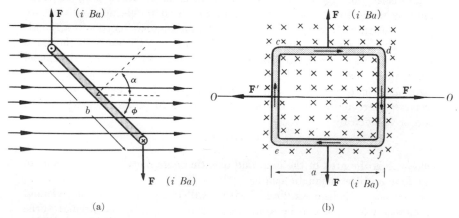

(a)   (b)

Fig. 31–10. Rectangular loop of wire carrying a current in a uniform magnetic field.

Sides *ce* and *df* make an angle ϕ with the field. Equal and opposite forces of magnitude

$$F' = iBb \sin \phi$$

are exerted on them, to the right on *df* and to the left on *ce*. [These forces are in reality distributed along each side of the loop. They are shown as single forces in Fig. 31–10(b).]

The resultant *force* on the loop is evidently zero, since the forces on opposite sides are equal and opposite. The resultant *torque*, however, is not zero, since the forces on sides *cd* and *ef* constitute a couple of moment

$$\Gamma = iBa \times b \sin \alpha. \qquad (31\text{–}8)$$

The couple is a maximum when $\alpha = 90°$ or when the plane of the coil is parallel to the field, and it is zero when $\alpha = 0$ and the plane of the coil is perpendicular to the field. The position of stable equilibrium is that in which side *cd* is uppermost.

Since *ab* is the area of the coil, A, Eq. (30–8) may be written

$$\Gamma = iBA \sin \alpha.$$

If the coil is a closely wound one having N turns, then evidently

$$\boxed{\Gamma = NiBA \sin \alpha.} \qquad (31\text{–}9)$$

Circular loop. If we replace a circular loop by a very large number of small rectangular loops, then the sum of the areas of the rectangular loops may be made to approach the area of the circular one as closely as we please. Furthermore, the boundary of the rectangular loops will approximate the circular loop with any desired accuracy. Currents in the same sense in all the rectangular loops will give rise to forces which will cancel at all points except on the boundary. It can therefore be proved quite rigorously that, *not only for a circular loop, but for a loop of any shape whatever*, carrying a current i in a magnetic field of flux density B, the torque is given by

$$\Gamma = iBA \sin \alpha,$$

where A is the area of the loop and α is the angle between the normal to the loop and the magnetic field.

Solenoid. A helical winding of wire is called a *solenoid*. If the solenoid is closely wound, it can be approximated by a number of circular turns lying in planes at right angles to its long axis. The total torque acting on a solenoid in a magnetic field is simply the sum of the torques on the individual turns. Hence for a solenoid of N turns in a uniform field of flux density B,

$$\Gamma = NiBA \sin \alpha,$$

where α is the angle between the axis of the solenoid and the direction of the field.

The torque is a maximum when the induction is parallel to the planes of the individual turns or perpendicular to the long axis of the solenoid. The effect of this torque, if the solenoid is free to turn, is to rotate it into a position in which each turn is perpendicular to the field and the axis of the solenoid is parallel to the field.

Although little has been said thus far regarding permanent magnets, everyone will probably recognize that the behavior of the solenoid as described above is the same as that of a bar magnet or compass needle, in that both the solenoid and the magnet will, if free to turn, set themselves with their axes parallel to a magnetic field. The behavior of a bar magnet or compass is usually explained by ascribing the torque on it to magnetic forces exerted on "poles" at its ends. We see, however, that no such interpretation is demanded in the case of the solenoid. May it not be, therefore, that the whirling electrons in a bar of magnetized iron are equivalent to the current in the windings of a solenoid, and that the observed torque arises from the same cause in both instances? We shall return to this question later.

PROBLEMS

31-1. The magnetic induction or flux density B in a certain region is 2 w/m^2 and its direction is that of the positive x-axis in Fig. 31-11. (a) What is the magnetic flux across the surface *abcd* in Fig. 31-11? Express the answer in webers and in maxwells. (b) What is the magnetic flux across the surface *becf*? (c) What is the magnetic flux across the surface *aefd*?

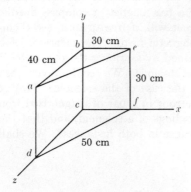

FIGURE 31-11

31-2. Each of the lettered circles at the corners of the cube in Fig. 31-12 represents a positive charge q moving with a velocity of magnitude v in the directions indicated. The region in the figure is a uniform magnetic field of flux density B, parallel to the x-axis and directed toward the right. Copy the figure, find the magnitude and direction of the force on each charge, and show the force on your diagram.

31-3. The electron in a hydrogen atom executes uniform circular motion around the proton with a speed of 2.2×10^6 m/sec in an orbit of radius 5.3×10^{-11} m. (a) If the hydrogen atom is placed in a magnetic field whose flux density equals 0.1 w/m^2, with the plane of its orbit perpendicular to the field, calculate the ratio of the electrostatic force between electron and proton to the magnetic force on the electron. (b) How will the magnetic force affect the motion of the electron?

31-4. A particle having a mass of 0.5 gm carries a charge of 2.5×10^{-8} coul. The particle is given an initial horizontal velocity of 6×10^4 m/sec. What is the magnitude and direction of the minimum magnetic field that will keep the particle moving in a horizontal direction?

31-5. A deuteron travels in a circular path of radius 40 cm in a magnetic field of flux density 1.5 w/m^2. (a) Find the speed of the deuteron. (b) Find the time required for it to make one-half a revolution. (c) Through what potential difference would the deuteron have to be accelerated to acquire this velocity?

31-6. An electron at point A in Fig. 31-13 has a velocity v_0 of 10^7 m/sec. Find (a) the magnitude and direction of the magnetic induction that will cause the electron to follow the semicircular path from A to B; (b) the time required for the electron to move from A to B.

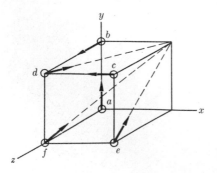

FIGURE 31-12

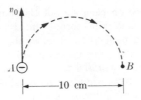

FIGURE 31-13

31-7. A particle carries a charge of 4×10^{-9} coul. When it moves with a velocity v_1 of 3×10^4 m/sec at 45° above the x-axis in the xy-plane a uniform magnetic field exerts a force F_1 along the z-axis. When the particle moves with a velocity v_2 of 2×10^4 m/sec along the z-axis there is a force F_2 of 4×10^{-5} newton exerted on it along the x-axis. What is the magnitude and direction of the magnetic field? (See Fig. 31-14.)

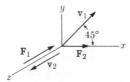

FIGURE 31-14

31-8. An electron moves in a circular path of radius 1.2 cm perpendicular to a uniform magnetic field. The velocity of the electron is 10^6 m/sec. What is the total magnetic flux encircled by the orbit?

31-9. An electron and an alpha particle both move in circular paths in a magnetic field with the same tangential velocity. Compare the number of revolutions they make per second. The mass of the alpha particle is 6.68×10^{-27} kgm.

31-10. The magnetic induction in a cyclotron which is accelerating protons is 1.5 w/m². (a) How many times per second should the potential across the dees reverse? (b) The maximum radius of the cyclotron is 0.35 m. What is the maximum velocity of the proton? (c) Through what potential difference would the proton have to be accelerated to give it the maximum cyclotron velocity?

31-11. (a) What is the velocity of a beam of electrons when the simultaneous influence of an electric field of intensity 34×10^4 volts/m and a magnetic field of flux density 2×10^{-3} w/m², both fields being normal to the beam and to each other, produces no deflection of the electrons? (b) Show in a diagram the relative orientation of the vectors v, E, and B. (c) What is the radius of the electron orbit when the electric field is removed?

31-12. The electric field between the plates of the velocity selector in a Bainbridge mass spectrograph is 1200 volts/cm and the magnetic induction in both magnetic fields is 0.6 w/m². A stream of singly charged neon ions moves in a circular path of 7.28 cm radius in the magnetic field. Determine the mass number of the neon isotope.

31-13. A singly charged Li^7 ion has a mass of 1.16×10^{-23} gm. It is accelerated through a potential difference of 500 volts and then enters a magnetic field of flux density 0.4 w/m², moving perpendicular to the field. What is the radius of its path in the magnetic field?

31-14. Suppose the electric intensity between the plates P_1 and P_2 in Fig. 31-7 is 150 volts/cm, and the magnetic induction in both magnetic fields is 0.5 w/m². If the source contains the three isotopes of magnesium, $_{12}Mg^{24}$, $_{12}Mg^{25}$, and $_{12}Mg^{26}$, and the ions are singly charged, find the distance between the lines formed by the three isotopes on the photographic plate. Assume the atomic weights of the isotopes equal to their mass numbers.

31-15. The cube in Fig. 31-15, of sides 0.5 m, is in a uniform magnetic field of 0.6 w/m². The wire *abcde* carries a current of 4 amp in the direction indicated. Determine the magnitude and direction of the force acting on lengths *ab, bc, cd*, and *de*.

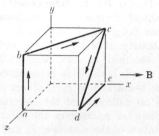

FIGURE 31-15

31-16. The plane of a rectangular loop of wire 5 cm × 8 cm is parallel to a magnetic field whose flux density is 0.15 w/m². (a) If the loop carries a current of 10 amp, what torque acts on it? (b) What is the maximum torque that can be obtained with the same total length of wire carrying the same current in this magnetic field?

31-17. The rectangular loop in Fig. 31-16 is pivoted about the *y*-axis and carries a current of 10 amp in the direction indicated. (a) If the loop is in a uniform magnetic field of flux density 0.2 w/m², parallel to the *x*-axis, find

the force on each side of the loop, in dynes, and the torque in dyne·cm required to hold the loop in the position shown. (b) Same as (a) except the field is parallel to the *z*-axis. (c) What torque would be required if the loop were pivoted about an axis through its center, parallel to the *y*-axis?

31-18. A circular coil of wire 8 cm in diameter has 12 turns and carries a current of 5 amp. The coil is in a field where the magnetic induction is 0.60 w/m². (a) What is the maximum torque on the coil? (b) In what position would the torque be one-half as great as in (a)?

31-19. What is the maximum torque on a galvanometer coil 5 × 12 cm, of 600 turns, when carrying a current of 10^{-5} amp in a field where the flux density is 0.10 w/m²?

31-20. The rectangular loop of wire in Fig. 31-17 has a mass of 0.1 gm per centimeter of length, and is pivoted about side *ab* as a frictionless axis. The current in the wire is 10 amp in the direction shown. (a) Find the magnitude and sense of the magnetic field, parallel to the *y*-axis, that will cause the loop to swing up until its plane makes an angle of 30° with the *yz*-plane. (b) Discuss the case where the field is parallel to the *x*-axis.

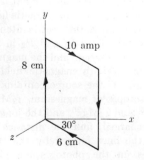

FIGURE 31-16

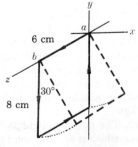

FIGURE 31-17

CHAPTER 32

GALVANOMETERS, AMMETERS, AND VOLTMETERS.
THE DIRECT-CURRENT MOTOR

32–1 The galvanometer. Any device used for the detection or measurement of current is called a galvanometer, and the majority of such instruments depend for their action on the torque exerted on a coil in a magnetic field. The earliest form of galvanometer was simply the apparatus of Oersted, namely, a compass needle placed below the wire in which the current was to be measured. Wire and needle were both aligned in the north-south direction with no current in the wire. The deflection of the needle when a current was sent through the wire was then a measure of the current. The sensitivity of this form of galvanometer was increased by winding the wire into a coil in a vertical plane with the compass needle at its center, and instruments of this type were developed by Lord Kelvin in the 1890's to a point where their sensitivity is scarcely exceeded by any available at the present time.

Practically all galvanometers used today, however, are of the D'Arsonval moving coil or pivoted coil type, in which the roles of magnet and coil are interchanged. The magnet is made much larger and is stationary, while the moving element is a light coil swinging in the field of the magnet.* The construction of a moving coil galvanometer is illustrated in Fig. 32–1. The magnetic field of a horseshoe magnet whose poles are designated by N and S is concentrated in the vicinity of the coil C by the soft iron cylinder A. The coil consists of from 10 to 20 turns, more or less, of insulated copper wire wound on a rectangular frame and suspended by a fine conducting wire or thin flat strip F which provides a restoring torque when the coil is deflected from its normal position, and which also serves as one current lead to the coil. The other terminal of the coil is connected to the loosely wound spiral S which serves as the second lead, but which exerts a negligible control on the coil.

When a current is maintained in the coil, horizontal and oppositely directed side-thrusts are exerted on its vertical sides, producing a couple about a vertical axis through its center. The coil rotates in the direction of this couple and eventually comes to rest in such a position that the restoring torque exerted by the upper suspension equals the deflecting

---

* The magnetic field surrounding a permanent magnet is discussed more fully in Chapter 35. For our present purposes, we may take it for granted that in the region between the magnet poles of Fig. 32–1 there does exist a field whose general direction is from N to S.

629

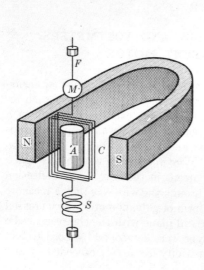

FIG. 32–1. Construction of the   FIG. 32–2. D'Arsonval galvanome-
D'Arsonval galvanometer.   ter. (Courtesy of Leeds and Northrup.)

torque due to the side-thrust. The angle of deflection is observed with
the aid of a beam of light reflected from a small mirror M cemented to
the upper suspension, the light beam serving as a weightless pointer. Since
light incident on the mirror is reflected at an angle of reflection equal
to the angle of incidence, rotation of the mirror through an angle θ deflects
the light beam through an angle 2θ. It is standard practice to observe the
reflected beam on a scale at a distance of one meter from the galvanometer.

The *current sensitivity* of a galvanometer is defined as the current in the
galvanometer coil required to produce a displacement of the reflected
light beam through one millimeter, on a scale one meter distant from the
galvanometer. Typical current sensitivities range from 0.01 microampere
(10^{-8} amp) to 0.0001 microampere (10^{-10} amp) per mm division at one
meter. Figure 32–2 is a photograph of a high-sensitivity galvanometer.

With a given current in the galvanometer coil the deflection is proportional to the flux density, to the number of turns in the coil, and to
its breadth, and is inversely proportional to the torque constant k ($\Gamma =$
$-k\theta$) of the upper suspension. On the other hand, increasing the number
of turns and the breadth of the coil, and decreasing the torque constant
of the suspension, all increase the period of swing and hence make the
instrument slow in coming to its final equilibrium position. In practice,
a compromise must be made between sensitivity and time of swing.

Because of the geometry of the field in which the moving coil swings, the deflections of a D'Arsonval galvanometer are not directly proportional to the current in the galvanometer coil except for relatively small angles. Hence these instruments are used chiefly as *null* instruments, that is, in connection with circuits such as those of a Wheatstone bridge or a potentiometer, in which other circuit elements are adjusted so that the galvanometer current is zero.

32–2 The pivoted coil galvanometer. The pivoted coil galvanometer, while essentially the same in principle as the D'Arsonval instrument, differs from the latter in two respects. One is that the moving coil, instead of being suspended by a fine fiber, is pivoted between two jewel bearings. The instrument may hence be used in any position and is much more rugged and conveniently portable. The second difference is that the permanent magnetic field is modified by the use of soft iron pole pieces attached to the permanent magnet as shown in Fig. 32–3, so that the coil swings in a field which is everywhere radial. The side-thrusts on the coil are therefore always perpendicular to the plane of the coil, and the angular deflection of the coil is directly proportional to the current in it. The restoring torque is provided by two hairsprings, which serve also as current leads. A length of aluminum tubing, flattened at its tip in a vertical plane, serves as a pointer.

The frictional torque of the jewel bearings, while small, is greater than that of a supporting fiber. Since the deflecting and restoring torques must both be considerably larger than the friction torque, pivoted coil instruments cannot be made as sensitive as the D'Arsonval type. The smallest currents which can be read on such an instrument are of the order of magnitude of 0.1 microampere.

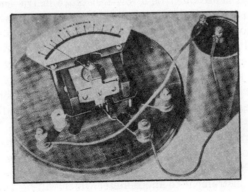

Fig. 32–3. Pivoted coil galvanometer, modified for use as an ammeter or a voltmeter. Series resistor may be seen at left. (Courtesy of Houghton Mifflin Company.)

In addition to the double pivot type, many other modifications are in use. For example, the coil may rest on a single pivot with some gain in sensitivity but with a sacrifice in ruggedness.

32–3 Ammeters and voltmeters.

The coil of a pivoted coil galvanometer is deflected because of the interaction between the field of the permanent magnet and the current in the coil. We shall assume that the deflection is proportional to this current. Since the coil and associated leads are metallic conductors obeying Ohm's law, the current in the coil is directly proportional to the potential difference between the terminals of the instrument. Hence the deflection of the instrument is proportional to the potential difference between its terminals as well as to the current through it, and it may be calibrated and used to measure either this potential difference or the current.

For example, suppose that the resistance of the coil and leads of a pivoted coil galvanometer is 20 ohms, and that the galvanometer deflects full-scale with a current in the coil of 10 ma or 0.010 amp. The potential difference between the terminals, with a current of 0.010 amp, is

$$V = iR = 0.010 \text{ amp} \times 20 \text{ ohms} = 0.20 \text{ volt.}$$

The scale of the instrument could therefore be calibrated to read either from zero to 0.010 amp, or from zero to 0.20 volt. Then if in some particular circuit the pointer were deflected by one-half the full-scale amount, one could conclude that the current through the instrument was 0.005 amp, and also that the potential difference between the terminals of the instrument was 0.10 volt.

It has been explained earlier that an ammeter must be inserted in series in a circuit and hence must be a low-resistance instrument, while a voltmeter, which is connected in parallel between the points whose potential difference is to be measured, needs to have a relatively high resistance. The physical limitations imposed on the size of the pivoted coil prevent the use of either very large wire, to obtain a low resistance, or a very large number of turns to obtain a high resistance. However, by inserting a low-resistance shunt in parallel with the pivoted coil, or a resistor of high resistance in series with it, any galvanometer may be modified to serve as an ammeter or a voltmeter.

As an illustration, consider the pivoted coil galvanometer described in the preceding example, whose resistance was 20 ohms and which deflected full-scale with a current of 0.010 amp through it. Suppose it is desired to convert this instrument to an ammeter which will be deflected full-scale by a current of 10 amp. The coil and its shunt are shown schematically in Fig. 32–4. The line current is assumed to be 10.0 amp. Since the

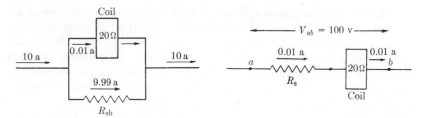

FIG. 32–4. Conversion of a galva- nometer to an ammeter with the aid of a shunt.

FIG. 32–5. Conversion of a galva- nometer to a voltmeter with the aid of a series resistor.

instrument is to deflect full scale with this line current, the current through the coil must be 0.010 amp. Hence the current in the shunt is

$$10 \text{ amp} - 0.010 \text{ amp} = 9.99 \text{ amp}.$$

Since the currents are inversely proportional to the resistances,

$$\frac{0.01}{9.99} = \frac{R_{\text{sh}}}{20}$$

and R_{sh}, the required shunt resistance, is 0.0200 ohm (to three significant figures).

The resistance R of the ammeter as a whole is

$$\frac{1}{R} = \frac{1}{R_{\text{coil}}} + \frac{1}{R_{\text{sh}}} = \frac{1}{20 \text{ ohms}} + \frac{1}{0.02 \text{ ohm}},$$

$$R = 0.020 \text{ ohm},$$

so that one has a low-resistance instrument which at the same time re- quires 10 amp for full-scale deflection. The shunt is ordinarily enclosed within the case of the instrument, although in some instances external shunts are provided.

Suppose next that it is desired to modify the same galvanometer for use as a voltmeter which will deflect full scale with 100 volts across its terminals. The coil and its series resistor are shown in Fig. 32–5. Assume that $V_{ab} = 100$ volts. The current in the moving coil must then be 0.010 amp. Hence

$$0.010 \text{ amp} = \frac{100 \text{ volts}}{(R_{\text{s}} + 20 \text{ ohms})},$$

and R_{s}, the required series resistance, is 9980 ohms.

The resistance of the voltmeter as a whole is 10,000 ohms, and one has a high-resistance instrument which draws only 0.010 amp with a potential difference of 100 volts between its terminals.

32–4 The ballistic galvanometer. A ballistic galvanometer is used for measuring the *quantity of charge* displaced by a current of short duration, as for example in the charging or discharging of a capacitor. While any moving coil galvanometer can be used ballistically, instruments designed specifically for the purpose have coils with somewhat larger moments of inertia, and suspensions with somewhat smaller torque constants, than are found in instruments designed primarily for current measurement.

The angular impulse exerted on a galvanometer coil during the passage of a transient current produces an equal angular momentum of the coil. The coil then proceeds to swing until its initial kinetic energy has been converted to potential energy of the suspension. The maximum angle of throw is observed, and this can be shown to be proportional to the quantity of charge which passed through the coil. Notice that the process is entirely analogous to that which takes place when a ballistic pendulum is struck by a bullet.

32–5 The dynamometer. The D'Arsonval galvanometer and its modifications are suitable for the measurement of direct currents and potential differences only. If alternating current is sent through the coil of such an instrument, the direction of the torque reverses with each reversal of current, and since the moment of inertia of the moving element is too large for it to follow alternations at the commercial frequency of 60 cycles/sec or higher, the instrument shows no deflection.

One method of obtaining a steady deflection with an alternating current is to employ a *dynamometer* type of movement, in which the moving coil is deflected, not by the field of a permanent magnet, but by the field of a second fixed coil. If the current in the second coil alternates at the same frequency as that in the moving coil, the magnetic field reverses whenever the current in the moving coil reverses and the deflecting torque, although pulsating, is always in the same direction. The moving element then assumes a position in which the restoring torque equals the *average* deflecting torque. The same type of movement is used in the *wattmeter*.

32–6 The direct-current motor. The direct-current motor is illustrated schematically in Fig. 32–6. The armature, A, is a cylinder of soft steel laminated to minimize eddy current losses (see Section 34–9) and mounted on a shaft so that it can rotate about its axis. Embedded in longitudinal slots in the surface of the armature are a number of copper conductors C. Current is led into and out of these conductors through graphite brushes making contact with a segmented cylinder on the shaft called the commutator (not shown in Fig. 32–6). The commutator is an automatic switching arrangement which maintains the currents in the conductors in the directions shown in the figure, whatever the position of the armature.

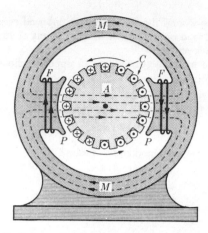

FIG. 32–6. Schematic diagram of a direct-current motor.

The current in the field coils F,F sets up a magnetic field which because of the shape of the pole pieces P,P is essentially radial in the gap between them and the armature. The motor frame M,M provides a path for the magnetic field. Some of the lines of induction are indicated by the dotted lines in the figure.

Application of the right-hand screw rule shows that with the relative directions of field and armature currents as shown, the side-thrust on each conductor is such as to produce a counterclockwise torque on the armature. When the motor is running, the armature develops mechanical energy at the expense of electrical energy. It must therefore be a seat of back emf. This is an "induced" emf and is discussed further in Chapter 34. The field windings, however, are static and behave like a pure resistance.

If the armature and the field windings are connected in series we have a *series* motor; if they are connected in parallel, a *shunt* motor. In some motors the field windings are in two parts, one in series with the armature and the other in parallel with it; the motor is then *compound*. The three corresponding electrical circuits are shown in Fig. 32–7.

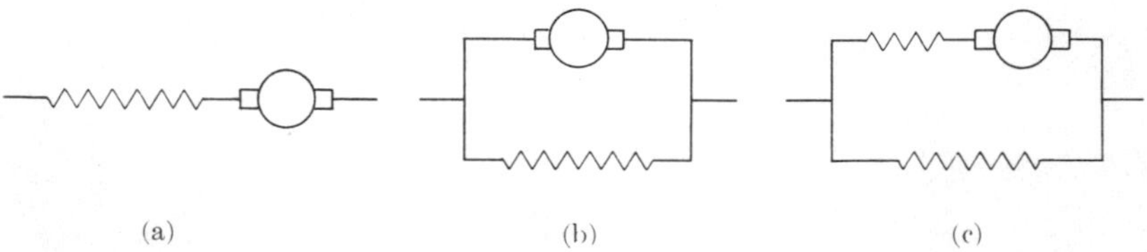

(a)   (b)   (c)

FIG. 32–7. Three ways of connecting the armature and field coils of a d-c motor. (a) Series, (b) shunt, (c) compound.

EXAMPLE. A series-wound d-c motor has an internal resistance of 0.2 ohm. When running at full load on a 120-volt line, a current of 40 amp is drawn.

(a) What is the back emf?

Since the back emf and the current are in opposite directions, the terminal voltage (line voltage) is

$$V_{ab} = \mathcal{E} + ri,$$

$$120 \text{ volts} = \mathcal{E} + 0.2 \text{ ohm} \times 40 \text{ amp},$$

$$\mathcal{E} = 112 \text{ volts}.$$

(b) What is the power delivered to the motor?

$$P = iV_{ab}$$
$$= 40 \text{ amp} \times 120 \text{ volts}$$
$$= 4800 \text{ watts}.$$

(c) What is the rate of generation of heat in the motor?

$$P = i^2R$$
$$= (40 \text{ amp})^2 \times 0.2 \text{ ohm}$$
$$= 320 \text{ watts}.$$

(d) What is the mechanical power developed?

Mechanical power = total power — rate of production of heat.

4800 watts — 320 watts = 4480 watts.

The mechanical power may also be calculated from the relation

Mechanical power = back emf × current
$$= 112 \text{ volts} \times 40 \text{ amp} = 4480 \text{ watts}.$$

PROBLEMS

32–1. A 1-ma meter has a resistance of 33 ohms. (a) What value of resistor should be used, and how should it be connected to convert it into a meter reading 1 amp full scale? 10 amps full scale? (b) What maximum power must these resistors be able to dissipate?

32–2. A 50-ma meter has a resistance of 12 ohms. (a) What resistance multiplier is required to convert it into a meter reading 10 volts full scale? (b) If the actual resistance of the multiplier used is 2% greater than required, what is the percentage error in the full-scale reading of the 10-volt meter?

32–3. The coil of a pivoted coil galvanometer has 50 turns and encloses an area of 6 cm². The magnetic induction in the region in which the coil swings is 100 gauss and is radial. The torsional constant of the hairsprings is $k = 0.1$ dyne·cm/deg. Find the angular deflection of the coil for a current of 1 ma.

32–4. The resistance of a galvanometer coil is 25 ohms and the current required for full-scale deflection is 20 ma. (a) Show in a diagram how to convert the galvanometer to an ammeter reading 5 amp full scale, and compute the shunt resistance. (b) Show how to convert the galvanometer to a voltmeter reading 150 volts full scale, and compute the series resistance.

32–5. The 0.01-amp meter A in Fig. 32–8 has a resistance of 4 ohms. What must be the values of the resistors R_1, R_2, and R_3, connected as shown in the diagram, to convert the meter to one having the ranges 0.1 amp, 1 amp, and 5 amp?

32–6. An 0.2-amp meter has a moving coil consisting of 120 turns of wire. In repairing the meter 5 turns of wire were removed. How has the range of the meter been affected?

32–7. Figure 32–9 shows the internal wiring of a "three-scale" voltmeter whose binding posts are marked +, 3 v, 15 v, 150 v. The resistance of the moving coil, R_G, is 15 ohms, and a current of 1 ma in the coil causes it to deflect full scale. Find the resistances R_1, R_2, R_3, and the over-all resistance of the meter on each of its ranges.

32–8. A certain d-c voltmeter is said to have a resistance of "one thousand ohms per volt." What current, in milliamperes, is required for full-scale deflection?

32–9. An ammeter reads 5 amp when connected across an unknown potential difference. A 10-ohm resistor is then inserted in series with the meter across the same potential difference, and the current drops to 3.5 amp. (a) What is the resistance of the ammeter? (b) What is the value of the unknown potential difference?

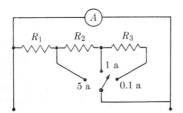

FIGURE 32–8

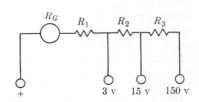

FIGURE 32–9

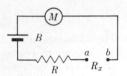

FIGURE 32–10

32–10. The circuit of a common type of ohmmeter is shown in Fig. 32–10. *M* is a 1-ma meter having a resistance of 100 ohms. The battery *B* has an emf of 3 volts and negligible internal resistance. *R* is so chosen that when the terminals *a* and *b* are shorted ($R_x = 0$) the meter reads full scale. When *a* and *b* are open ($R_x = \infty$) the meter reads zero. All intermediate values of R_x will be indicated by currents between 0 and 1 ma. (a) What should be the value of the resistor *R*? (b) What current would indicate a resistance R_x of 600 ohms? (c) What resistance R_x would be indicated when the meter reads 0.5 ma?

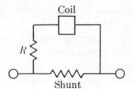

FIGURE 32–11

32–11. The resistance of the coil of a pivoted coil galvanometer is 10 ohms, and a current of 0.02 amp causes it to deflect full scale. It is desired to convert this galvanometer to an ammeter reading 10 amp full scale. The only shunt available has a resistance of 0.03 ohm. What resistance *R* must be connected in series with the coil? (See Fig. 32–11.)

32–12. A 150-volt voltmeter has a resistance of 20,000 ohms. When con-

nected in series with a large resistance *R* across a 110-volt line, the meter reads 5 volts. Find the resistance *R*. (This problem illustrates one method of measuring large resistances.)

32–13. A potential difference of 110 volts is placed across the 12,000-ohm resistor *ab*. The voltmeter *V* has a resistance of 6000 ohms, and point *c* is $\frac{1}{4}$ of the distance from *a* to *b*. What is the reading of the voltmeter? (See Fig. 32–12.)

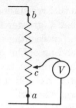

FIGURE 32–12

32–14. A voltmeter having a resistance of 1000 ohms is placed across the terminals of an unknown resistor, the two being inserted in series with an ammeter. When the ammeter reads 0.02 amp the voltmeter indicates 4 volts. What is the resistance of the unknown resistor?

32–15. A 600-ohm resistor and a 400-ohm resistor are connected in series across a 90-volt line. A voltmeter across the 600-ohm resistor reads 45 volts. (a) Find the voltmeter resistance. (b) Find the reading of the same voltmeter if connected across the 400-ohm resistor.

32–16. In Fig. 32–13, point *a* is maintained at a constant potential above ground. $R_1 = 20,000$ ohms, $R_2 = R_3 = 10,000$ ohms. A 150-volt voltmeter whose resistance is 15,000 ohms reads 45 volts when connected between point *c* and ground. (a) What was the potential of point *c* above

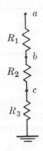

FIGURE 32-13

ground before the voltmeter was connected? (b) What is the potential of point a above ground?

32–17. A ballistic galvanometer is calibrated by discharging through it a 6-μf capacitor which had been charged by a potential difference of 24 volts. The galvanometer deflection is 18 scale divisions. A second capacitor is charged by a potential difference of 16 volts. If it causes a deflection of the galvanometer of 5 scale divisions, what is its capacitance?

32–18. A shunt motor has an armature resistance of 0.5 ohm and a field resistance of 150 ohms. When the motor is connected across a 110-volt line the back emf in the armature is 106 volts. (a) What is the current in the armature? (b) What is the total current in the motor? (c) What is the power input to the motor?

32–19. The ranges of a "three-scale" voltmeter (see Problem 32–7) are 1.5 v, 3 v, and 15 v. The resistance of the meter between its 15-volt terminals (i.e. between the $+$ terminal and the terminal marked 15 v) is 1500 ohms. (a) What is the resistance between the 1.5 v terminals and between the 3 v terminals? (b) When a cell is connected across the 1.5 v terminals the meter reads 1.42 volts; when the same cell is connected across the 3 v ter-

minals the meter reads 1.48 volts. Compute the emf and internal resistance of the cell.

32–20. Two 150-volt voltmeters, one of resistance 15,000 ohms and the other of resistance 150,000 ohms, are connected in series across a 120-volt d-c line. Find the reading of each voltmeter.

32–21. The voltmeter V in Fig. 32–14 reads 117 volts and the ammeter A reads 0.130 amp. The resistance of the voltmeter is 9000 ohms and the resistance of the ammeter is 0.015 ohm. Compute (a) the resistance R; (b) the power input to R.

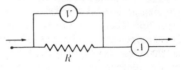

FIGURE 32-14

32–22. The resistance of the moving coil of the galvanometer G in Fig. 32–15 is 25 ohms and it deflects full scale with a current of 0.010 amp. Find the magnitudes of the resistances R_1, R_2, and R_3, to convert the galvanometer to a multirange ammeter deflecting full scale with currents of 10 amp, 1 amp, and 0.1 amp.

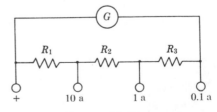

FIGURE 32-15

32–23. Find the efficiency of a certain motor from the following data, given on its name plate: 5 hp, 230 volts, 18 amp, 1200 rpm.

32–24. In a shunt-wound d-c motor the resistance of the field coils is 150 ohms and the resistance of the armature is 2 ohms. When a difference of potential of 120 volts is applied to the brushes, and the motor is running at full speed delivering mechanical power, the current supplied to it is 4.5 amp. (a) What is the current in the field coils? (b) What is the current in the armature? (c) What is the back emf developed by the motor? (d) How much mechanical power is developed by this motor?

32–25. A shunt-wound d-c motor is running at normal speed and developing 2 hp. The current in the armature is 7.0 amp when the impressed voltage is 220 volts. (a) What is the back emf of the motor? (b) At what rate is heat developed in the armature?

32–26. Figure 32–16 is a diagram of a shunt-wound d-c motor, operating from 120-volt d-c mains. The resistance of the field windings, R_f, is 240 ohms. The resistance of the armature, R_a, is 3 ohms. When the motor is running the armature develops a back emf $\mathcal{E}$ in the direction of the arrow. The motor

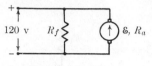

FIGURE 32–16

draws a current of 4.5 amp from the line. Compute (a) the field current, (b) the armature current, (c) the back emf $\mathcal{E}$, (d) the rate of development of heat in the field windings, (e) the rate of development of heat in the armature, (f) the power input to the motor, (g) the efficiency of the motor, if friction and windage losses amount to 50 watts.

32–27. Refer to the shunt motor in Problem 32–26. Assume that the given data apply when the motor is rotating at 1800 rpm, and that the back emf is proportional to the angular velocity. Assume also that friction and windage losses are constant. (a) As the result of an increased load on the motor its angular velocity decreases to 1700 rpm. What power does it now draw from the line? (b) What power does it deliver to the load? (c) At what angular velocity, in rpm, will the motor run when the external load is removed completely?

CHAPTER 33

MAGNETIC FIELD OF A CURRENT

33-1 Magnetic field of a current element. An electric charge in motion sets up, in the space around it, a magnetic field. A second charge, moving in a magnetic field, experiences a force. The two preceding chapters were devoted to the second aspect of the problem, that is, to the forces on moving charges or current-carrying conductors in magnetic fields. The existence of the field was taken for granted. In this chapter we return to the first part of the problem and correlate the magnitude and direction of a magnetic field with the motion of the charged particles responsible for it. In practice, the moving charges setting up a magnetic field are most commonly those constituting the current in a conductor. We shall therefore begin by discussing the magnetic field around a conductor in which there is a current.

The first recorded observations of magnetic fields set up by currents were those of Oersted, who discovered that a pivoted compass needle, beneath a wire in which there was a current, set itself with its long axis perpendicular to the wire. Later experiments by Biot and Savart, and by Ampere, led to a relation by means of which we can compute the

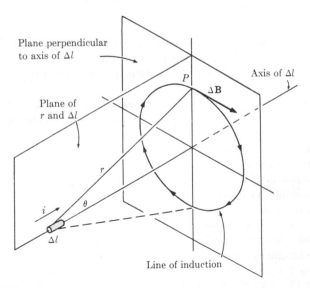

FIG. 33-1. Magnetic field due to a current element.

flux density at any point of space around a circuit in which there is a current.

The circuit is to be divided, in imagination, into short elements of length Δl, one of which is shown in Fig. 33–1. The moving charges in each element set up a field at all points of space, and the field of the entire circuit, at any point, is the resultant of the infinitesimal fields of all the elements of the circuit. The direction of the infinitesimal field $\Delta \mathbf{B}$ set up at point P by the element of length Δl is shown in Fig. 33–1. The vector $\Delta \mathbf{B}$ lies *in* a plane perpendicular to the axis of Δl, and is itself *perpendicular* to the plane determined by Δl and the line joining P and Δl. It follows that the lines of induction, to which the vectors are tangent, are circles lying in planes perpendicular to the axis of the element. The direction of these lines is clockwise when viewed along the direction of the conventional current in Δl. The direction may also be described as that in which a right-hand screw would have to be rotated in order that it should advance in the direction of the current.

Another useful rule is to grasp the element (in imagination) in the right hand with the extended thumb pointing in the direction of the current. The fingers then encircle the element in the direction of the flux lines.

The magnitude of ΔB is given by the following relation,

$$\Delta B = k' \frac{i \, \Delta l \sin \theta}{r^2}, \tag{33–1}$$

where r is the distance between Δl and the point P, and θ is the angle between r and Δl. This equation is often called *Ampere's formula*, or *Ampere's law*, but it should be credited to Biot, who first proposed it in 1820.

The factor k' in Eq. (33–1) is a proportionality constant whose magnitude, like that of the constant k in Coulomb's law, depends on the choice of units. If the units of flux density, current, and length are independently defined, then k' must be found by experiment. On the other hand, some arbitrary value may be assigned to k' and to the units of any two of the quantities in Eq. (33–1) and this equation may then be used to define the unit of the third quantity. The latter procedure is the one that is actually adopted. In the mks system, k' is set equal to exactly 10^{-7} weber per ampere·meter, and Eq. (33–1) (or more precisely, an equation derived from it) is used to define the unit of current, the ampere. In the electromagnetic system, k' is set equal to unity, and Eq. (33–1) then defines the unit current in this system, the abampere.

For the sake of eliminating the factor 4π from other equations derived from the Biot law, and which are used more frequently than is the law itself, it is convenient to define a new proportionality constant μ_0 by the equation

$$\frac{\mu_0}{4\pi} = k', \qquad \mu_0 = 4\pi k'.$$

This procedure is analogous to replacing the proportionality constant k in Coulomb's law by the term $1/4\pi\epsilon_0$. To four significant figures,

$$\mu_0 = 4\pi k' = 12.57 \times 10^{-7}\ \frac{\text{w}}{\text{amp·m}},$$

$$\frac{\mu_0}{4\pi} = 10^{-7}\ \frac{\text{w}}{\text{amp·m}}.$$

The Biot law then becomes

$$\Delta B = \frac{\mu_0}{4\pi}\ \frac{i\,\Delta l \sin\theta}{r^2}. \tag{33-2}$$

It follows from this equation that the flux density ΔB due to a current element is zero at all points on the axis of the element, since $\sin\theta = 0$ at all such points. At a given distance r from the element the flux density is a maximum in a plane passing through the element perpendicular to its axis, since $\theta = 90°$ and $\sin\theta = 1$ at all points in such a plane.

The expression for the resultant flux density at any point of space, due to a complete circuit, is obtained by forming the vector sum of all the values of ΔB due to all the elementary current elements. Thus

$$B = \frac{\mu_0}{4\pi}\ i\left(\frac{\Delta l_1 \sin\theta_1}{r_1^2} + \frac{\Delta l_2 \sin\theta_2}{r_2^2} + \cdots\right). \quad \text{(Vector sum)} \tag{33-3}$$

Except in certain special cases, the evaluation of Eq. (33–3) is an elaborate mathematical problem. We shall be concerned in this book with three important simple applications: (1) the flux density at any point near a very long straight wire carrying a current, (2) the flux density at the center of a circular loop, and (3) the flux density at a point near the center of a solenoid, or helix.

If there is matter in the space around a circuit, the flux density at a point will be due not entirely to currents in conductors, but in part to the magnetization of this matter. The magnetic properties of matter are discussed more fully in a later chapter. However, unless iron or some of the ferromagnetic materials are present, this effect is so small that, while strictly speaking Eq. (33–2) holds only for conductors in vacuum, as a practical matter it can be used without correction for conductors in air, or in the vicinity of any nonferromagnetic material.

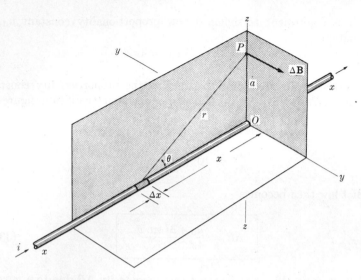

FIG. 33–2. Magnetic field set up by the current in an element Δx of a long straight conductor.

33–2 Magnetic field of a long straight conductor. Consider a point at a perpendicular distance a from a long straight wire carrying a current i, as shown in Fig. 33–2. If the wire is very long compared with the distance a, and the operations indicated in Eq. (33–3) are carried out, the following simple result is obtained:

$$B = \frac{\mu_0}{2\pi} \frac{i}{a}. \tag{33–4}$$

This relation was deduced from experimental observations by Biot and Savart before Eq. (33–2) had been discovered. It is called the Biot-Savart law.

Unlike the electric field around a charged wire, which is radial, the lines of magnetic induction are *circles* concentric with the wire and lying in planes perpendicular to it. It will also be noted that each line of induction is a *closed* line, and that in this respect lines of induction differ from the lines of force in an electric field which terminate on positive or negative charges. This property of lines of induction is true whatever the geometry of the circuit setting up the field—every line of induction closes on itself.

A portion of the magnetic field around a long straight conductor is shown in the cutaway view in Fig. 33–3.

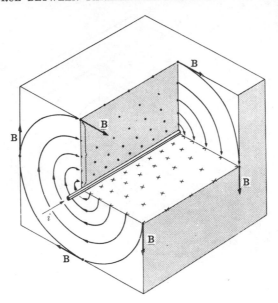

FIG. 33–3. Magnetic field around a long straight conductor.

33–3 Force between parallel conductors. The ampere. Figure 33–4 shows a portion of two long straight parallel conductors separated by a distance a and carrying currents i and i' respectively in the same direction. Since each conductor lies in the magnetic field set up by the other, each will experience a force. The diagram shows some of the lines of induction set up by the current in the lower conductor. The magnitude of the **B**-vector at the upper conductor is

$$B = \frac{\mu_0}{4\pi} \frac{2i}{a}.$$

From Eq. (31–7), the force on a length l of the upper conductor is

$$F = iBl = \frac{\mu_0}{4\pi} l \frac{2ii'}{a},$$

and the force per unit length is therefore

$$\frac{F}{l} = \frac{\mu_0}{4\pi} \frac{2ii'}{a}.$$

The right-hand screw rule shows that the direction of the force on the upper conductor is downward. There is an equal and opposite force per unit length on the lower conductor, as may be seen by considering the

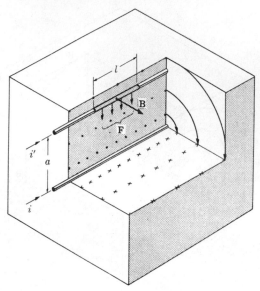

FIG. 33–4. Parallel conductors carrying currents in the same direction attract each other.

field around the upper conductor, or by Newton's third law. Hence the conductors attract one another.

If the direction of either current is reversed, the forces reverse also. Parallel conductors carrying currents in opposite directions repel one another.

The fact that two straight parallel conductors exert forces of attraction or repulsion on one another is made the basis of the definition of the ampere in the mks system. The ampere is defined as follows:

One ampere is that unvarying current which, if present in each of two parallel conductors of infinite length and one meter apart in empty space, causes each conductor to experience a force of exactly 2×10^{-7} newton per meter of length.

It follows from this definition and the preceding equation that the numerical value of μ_0 in the rationalized mks system is exactly $4\pi \times 10^{-7}$ or, to four significant figures,

$$\mu_0 = 12.57 \times 10^{-7} \frac{weber}{amp \cdot m}.$$

Now the coulomb is defined in terms of the ampere as the quantity of charge that in one second crosses a section of a circuit in which there is a constant current of one ampere. It follows that the unit of charge in the mks system is defined in terms of the force between *moving* charges, as contrasted with the electrostatic system in which the statcoulomb is defined in terms of the electrostatic force between charges.

From the definition above, the ampere can be established, in principle, with the help of a meter stick and a spring balance. For the practical standardization of the ampere, coils of wire are used instead of straight wires and their separation is made only a few centimeters. The complete instrument, which is capable of measuring currents with a high degree of precision, is called a *current balance*.

33–4 Field at the center of a circular turn. Figure 33–5 represents a circular turn of wire. The radius of the turn is a and the current in it is i. Of course a seat of emf is necessary to maintain the current, and one may either imagine the turn cut and a small seat of emf inserted, or consider that current is led into and out of the turn through two long straight wires side by side. The currents in the straight wires are in opposite directions and annul one another's magnetic effects.

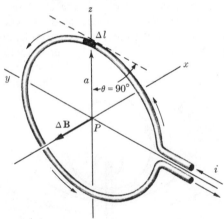

Fig. 33–5. Field at the center of a circular turn.

Let us imagine the circular loop to be divided into a large number of elements of lengths Δl_1, Δl_2, and so on. A typical element of length Δl is shown in Fig. 33–5, where it can be seen that all elements are at the same distance a from the point P at the center, and each element makes a right angle with the line joining it to P. The vectors $\Delta \mathbf{B}_1$, $\Delta \mathbf{B}_2$, etc., due to each element are all in the same direction. Equation (33–3), namely,

$$B = \frac{\mu_0}{4\pi} i \left(\frac{\Delta l_1 \sin \theta_1}{r_1^2} + \frac{\Delta l_2 \sin \theta_2}{r_2^2} + \cdots \right),$$

becomes a simple scalar equation with $\sin \theta_1 = 1$, $\sin \theta_2 = 1$, etc., and $r_1 = a$, $r_2 = a$, etc. Hence

$$B = \frac{\mu_0}{4\pi} \frac{i}{a^2} (\Delta l_1 + \Delta l_2 + \cdots).$$

But $\Delta l_1 + \Delta l_2 + \cdots$ is simply the circumference of the turn, $2\pi a$. Therefore

$$B = \frac{\mu_0}{2} \frac{i}{a}. \tag{33-5}$$

If instead of a single turn, as in Fig. 33-5, one has a coil of N closely spaced turns all of essentially the same radius, each turn contributes equally to the field and Eq. (33-5) becomes

$$B = \frac{\mu_0}{2} \frac{Ni}{a}. \tag{33-6}$$

Some of the lines of induction surrounding a circular turn and lying in a plane through the axis are shown in Fig. 33-6. In reality, of course, the field is three-dimensional, and it may be visualized by imagining the plane to be rotated about the axis x-x. Each line of induction is a closed line.

It was pointed out in Chapter 31 that a loop of wire of any shape and carrying a current is acted on by a torque when placed in an external

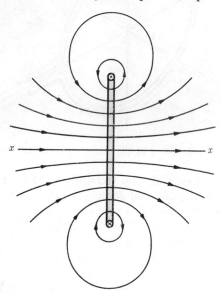

FIG. 33-6. Lines of induction surrounding a circular turn.

magnetic field. The final position of equilibrium was seen to be one in which the plane of the loop was perpendicular to the external field. Now we see that this position is such that, within the area enclosed by the loop, the induction of the loop's own field is in the same direction as that of the external field. In other words, a loop, if free to·turn, will set itself in such a plane that the flux passing through the area enclosed by it has its maximum possible value. This is found to be true in all instances and is a useful general principle. For example, if a current is sent through an irregular loop of flexible wire in an external magnetic field, the loop will assume a circular form with its plane perpendicular to the field and with its own flux adding to that of the field. The same conclusion can, of course, be drawn by analyzing the side thrusts on the elements of the conductor.

33–5 Ampere's law.

Ampere's law is a useful relation that is closely analogous to Gauss' law. The latter, it will be recalled, is a relation between the normal component of electric intensity at points on a closed surface and the net charge enclosed by the surface. Ampere's law is a relation between the tangential component of magnetic induction at points on a closed curve and the net current through the area bounded by the curve.

Consider first a long straight wire carrying a current i away from the reader, and a closed curve consisting of a circle of radius r with center at the wire, as in Fig. 33–7. We have shown that the magnitude of the magnetic induction vector at a point at a distance r from a long straight wire is

$$B = \frac{\mu_0}{2\pi}\frac{i}{r},$$

and that its direction is tangent to a circle passing through the point and concentric with the wire. In Fig. 33–7, Δs is an element of the circle, and in this special case the tangential component of **B** is equal to **B** itself. We now multiply the tangential component of **B** by the length of arc Δs, and sum these products along the entire circumference of the circle.

$$\sum B_t\,\Delta s = \sum B\,\Delta s = B\sum \Delta s$$

$$= \frac{\mu_0}{2\pi}\frac{i}{r} \times 2\pi r = \mu_0 i,$$

or

$$\frac{1}{\mu_0}\sum B_t\,\Delta s = i.$$

Hence in this special case the quantity $(1/\mu_0)\sum B_t\,\Delta s$ equals the current through the area enclosed by the closed curve.

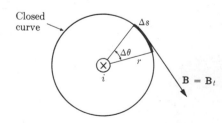

FIGURE 33–7

It is not difficult to show that if any number of long straight conductors pass through a plane curve, normal to the plane, that $(1/\mu_0)\sum B_t\,\Delta s$ equals the *algebraic* sum of the currents in the conductors, currents away from the reader being considered positive, those toward the reader negative, and $\mathbf{B}_t$ being considered positive if it is clockwise, negative if counterclockwise. It is not as simple to prove that the same result is true in general, whether or not the closed curve lies in a plane and whether or not the conductors are straight. We shall have to say that "it can be shown" to be perfectly general that

$$\frac{1}{\mu_0}\sum B_t\,\Delta s = \sum i \qquad\qquad (33\text{--}7)$$

for any closed curve. Equation (33–7) is the mathematical statement of Ampere's law. Like Gauss' law, it can be used to compute $\mathbf{B}$ in cases where by symmetry we can see that $\mathbf{B}$ has the same magnitude at all points of a closed curve of simple shape, and is everywhere tangent to the curve.

33–6 Field of a solenoid and of a toroid. The flux density produced at any point by a current in a solenoidal or a toroidal winding is simply the resultant of the flux densities set up at that point by each turn of the winding. Making use of Eq. (33–3), it can be shown that the flux density B at any point on the axis of a closely wound solenoid, not too near either

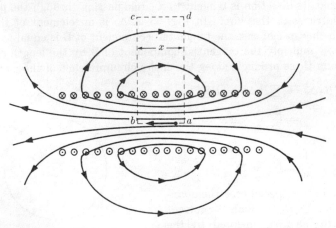

FIG. 33–8. Lines of induction surrounding a solenoid. The dotted rectangle *abcd* is used to compute the flux density B in the solenoid from Ampere's law.

end, is given by the equation

$$B = \mu_0 \frac{Ni}{l}, \tag{33-8}$$

where N is the total number of turns and l is the length of the solenoid. The complete field is shown in Fig. 33–8. The radius of the cylinder on which the wire is wound is of no consequence provided the radius is small compared with the length.

The result above can easily be derived with the help of Ampère's law. We select as a closed path the dotted rectangle $abcd$ in Fig. 33–8. Side ab, of length x, is parallel to the axis of the solenoid. Sides bc and da are to be taken very long so that side cd is far from the solenoid and the field at this side is negligibly small. If the solenoid itself is also very long, and the rectangle is not too near either end, the field is at right angles to the sides bc and da, in one direction within the solenoid and in the opposite direction outside it.

By symmetry, the flux density $\mathbf{B}$ along side ab is parallel to this side and is constant, so that for this side $B_t = \mathbf{B}$ and

$$\frac{1}{\mu_0} \sum B_t \, \Delta s = \frac{1}{\mu_0} Bx.$$

Along sides bc and da, $B_t = 0$ since $\mathbf{B}$ is perpendicular to these sides; and along side cd, $B_t = 0$ also since $\mathbf{B} = 0$. The sum around the entire closed path therefore reduces to the expression above.

Let N be the total number of turns of the solenoid and l its total length. The number of turns per unit length is then N/l and the number of turns in a length x, or the number of turns passing through the closed path, is Nx/l. The current in each turn is i, so the total current through the path is

$$\sum i = \frac{Nxi}{l}.$$

Hence from Ampère's law,

$$\frac{1}{\mu_0} Bx = \frac{Nxi}{l}$$

and

$$B = \mu_0 \frac{Ni}{l},$$

which is Eq. (33–8). Since side ab does not necessarily lie on the axis of the solenoid, the flux density is uniform over the entire cross section.

A winding such as that in Fig. 33–9 is called a *toroid*. We next use Ampère's law to compute the flux density set up by a current in a toroidal winding, shown in a sectional view in Fig. 33–10. By symmetry, the direc-

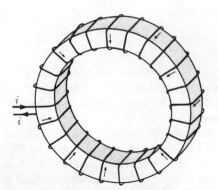

FIG. 33–9. A toroid.

tion of **B** at any point is tangent to a circle passing through the point and having its center at the center O of the toroid, and the magnitude of **B** is the same at all points of any such circle.

Consider any closed path in the form of a circle with center at O, such as the dotted paths lettered 1, 2, and 3. Let l be the length of the path (the circumference of the circle). Then since $B_t = B =$ constant along any of these paths,

$$\frac{1}{\mu_0} \sum B_t \, \Delta s = \frac{1}{\mu_0} Bl.$$

Path 1 lies within the space enclosed by the windings of the toroid. Every turn of the winding passes once through the area bounded by this path, so that for path 1

$$\sum i = Ni.$$

Then from Ampere's law,

$$\frac{1}{\mu_0} Bl = Ni,$$

and the flux density within the core of the toroid is

$$B = \mu_0 \frac{Ni}{l},$$

which has the same form as Eq. (33–8). The flux density is *not* uniform over a cross section of the core, because the path length l is larger at the outer side of the section than at the inner side. However, if the radial thickness t of the core is small compared with the radius R, the flux density varies only slightly across a section.

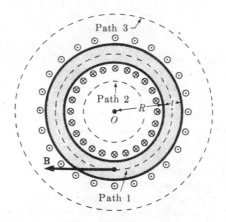

Fig. 33–10. Closed paths (dotted circles) used to compute the flux density B set up by a current in a toroidal winding. The field is zero at all points except those within the space enclosed by the windings.

Now consider paths 2 and 3. There is no current through the area bounded by path 2, so for this path

$$\frac{1}{\mu_0} Bl = \sum i = 0$$

and

$$B = 0.$$

Each turn of the winding passes *twice* through the area bounded by path 3, carrying equal currents in opposite directions. The *net* current through the area is therefore zero, also, and

$$\frac{1}{\mu_0} Bl = \sum i = 0,$$

$$B = 0.$$

The flux density is therefore zero at all points except within the core, and a closely wound toroidal winding produces no *external* magnetic field. This is of importance when it is desired that the magnetic field of a winding of wire should not affect other circuits in its vicinity.

The equations derived above for the flux density in a closely wound solenoidal or toroidal winding are strictly correct only for a winding in vacuum. For most practical purposes, they can be used for a winding in air, or on a core of any nonferromagnetic material. We shall show in Chapter 35 how they are modified if the core is of iron.

PROBLEMS

33–1. A long straight wire, carrying a current of 200 amp, runs through a cubical wooden box, entering and leaving through holes in the centers of opposite faces as in Fig. 33–11. The length of each side of the box is 20 cm. Consider an element of the wire 1 cm long at the center of the box. Compute the magnitude of the magnetic induction ΔB produced by this element at the points lettered a, b, c, d, and e in Fig. 33–11. Points a, c, and d are at the centers of the faces of the cube, point b is at the midpoint of one edge, and point e is at a corner. Copy the figure and show by vectors the directions and relative magnitudes of the field vectors.

33–2. The wire in Fig. 33–12 carries a current of 8 amp. The cubical box has sides 25 cm in length. Determine the fields at P due to elements of the wire at a, b, and c, each of 0.5 cm length.

33–3. A long straight wire carries a current of 10 amp along the z-axis, as shown in Fig. 33–13. A uniform magnetic field whose flux density is 10^{-6} w/m^2 is directed parallel to the x-axis. What is the resultant magnetic field at the following points: (a) $x = 0$, $y = 2$ m, (b) $x = 2$ m, $y = 0$, (c) $x = 0$, $y = -0.5$ m?

33–4. A long straight wire carries a current of 1.5 amp. An electron travels with a velocity of 5×10^6 cm/sec par-

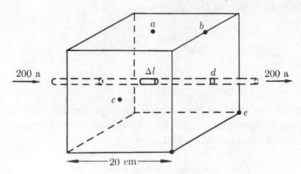

FIGURE 33–11

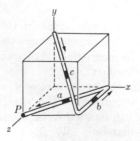

FIGURE 33–12

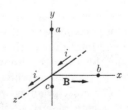

FIGURE 33–13

allel to the wire, 10 cm from it, and in the same direction as the current. What force does the magnetic field of the current exert on the moving electron?

33–5. Two long straight wires, A and B, are arranged in a vertical plane 10 cm apart as in Fig. 33–14. B carries a current of 6 amp into the plane of the paper. (a) What must be the magnitude and direction of the current in A for the resultant field at point a, 5 cm under A, to be zero? (b) What is then the resultant field at b, 5 cm above B, and at c, 6 cm from A and 8 cm from B?

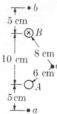

FIGURE 33–14

rests on the surface of a table. (See Fig. 33–15.) Another wire CD vertically above the first is 100 cm long and is free to slide up and down on the two vertical metal guides C and D. The two wires are connected through the sliding contacts and carry a current of 50 amp. The mass of the wire CD is 0.05 gm/cm. To what equilibrium height will the wire CD rise, assuming the magnetic force on it to be due wholly to the current in the wire AB?

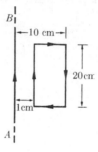

FIGURE 33–16

33–6. Two long straight wires are spaced 40 cm between centers. The current in each wire is 20 amp. Compute the magnetic flux density at a point in the plane of the wires and midway between them.

33–7. Two long parallel wires are hung by cords of 4 cm length from a common axis. The wires have a mass of 50 gm/m and carry the same current in opposite directions. What is the current if the cords hang at an angle of 30° with the vertical?

33–8. A long horizontal wire AB

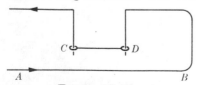

FIGURE 33–15

33–9. The long straight wire AB in Fig. 33–16 carries a current of 20 amp. The rectangular loop whose long edges are parallel to the wire carries a current of 10 amp. Find the magnitude and direction of the resultant force exerted on the loop by the magnetic field of the wire.

33–10. A closely wound coil has a diameter of 40 cm and carries a current of 2.5 amp. How many turns does it have if the magnetic induction at the center of the coil is 1.26×10^{-4} w/m²?

33–11. A closely wound coil of 100 turns, 5 cm in radius, carries a current of 2 amp. Compute the magnetic flux density at the center of the coil.

33–12. A coaxial cable consists of a small solid conductor supported by insulating disks on the axis of a thin-walled tube. If the central conductor and the tube carry equal currents in opposite directions, find the magnetic flux density (a) at points outside the axial conductor but inside the tube, and (b) at points outside the tube. (Use Ampere's law.)

33–13. A solenoid is 10 cm long and is wound with two layers of wire. The inner layer consists of 50 turns, the outer layer of 40 turns. The current is 3 amp, in the same direction in both layers. What is the magnetic induction at a point near the center of the solenoid?

33–14. A solenoid of length 20 cm and radius 2 cm is closely wound with 200 turns of wire. The current in the winding is 5 amp. Compute the magnetic induction at a point near the center of the solenoid.

33–15. A wooden ring whose mean diameter is 10 cm is wound with a closely spaced toroidal winding of 500 turns. Compute the flux density at a point on the mean circumference of the ring when the current in the windings is 0.3 amp.

CHAPTER 34

INDUCED ELECTROMOTIVE FORCE

34–1 Motional electromotive force. Our present-day large scale production and distribution of electrical energy would not be economically feasible if the only seats of emf available were those of chemical nature, such as dry cells. The development of electrical engineering as we now know it began with Faraday and Henry, who independently and at nearly the same time discovered the principles of induced emf's and the methods by which mechanical energy can be converted directly to electrical energy.

Figure 34–1 represents a conductor of length l in a uniform magnetic field, perpendicular to the plane of the diagram and directed away from the reader. If the conductor is set in motion toward the right with a velocity **v**, perpendicular both to its own length and to the magnetic field, every charged particle within it experiences a force **F** of magnitude vBq directed along the length of the conductor. The direction of the force on a negative charge is from a toward b in Fig. 34–1, while the force on a positive charge is from b toward a.

The state of affairs within the conductor is therefore the same as if it had been inserted in an electric field of intensity vB whose direction was from b toward a. The free electrons in the conductor will move in the

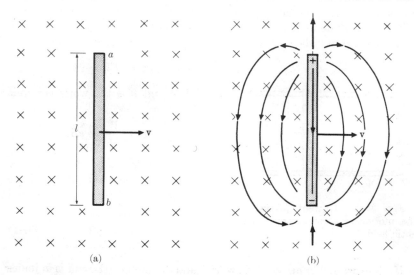

FIG. 34–1. Conductor moving in a uniform magnetic field.

direction of the force acting on them until the accumulation of excess charges at the ends of the conductor establishes an electrostatic field such that the resultant force on every charge within the conductor is zero. The general nature of this electrostatic field is indicated in Fig. 34–1(b). The upper end of the wire acquires an excess positive charge, and the lower end an excess negative charge.

That such a separation of charge actually takes place in a conductor moving in a magnetic field was shown by Barnet, who carried out experiments equivalent to cutting the rod at its center while it was still in motion, and then bringing it to rest. The upper half was found to be positively charged and the lower half negatively charged.

Imagine now that the moving conductor slides along a stationary U-shaped conductor as in Fig. 34–2. There is no magnetic force on the charges within the stationary conductor, but since it lies in the electrostatic field surrounding the moving conductor, a current will be established within it, the direction of this current (in the conventional sense) being counterclockwise, or from b toward a. As a result of this current the excess charges at the ends of the moving conductor are reduced, the electrostatic field within the moving conductor is weakened, and the magnetic forces cause a further displacement of the free electrons within it from a toward b. As long as the motion of the conductor is maintained there will, therefore, be a continual displacement of electrons clockwise around the circuit, or a conventional current in a counterclockwise direction. The moving conductor corresponds to a seat of electromotive force, and is said to have *induced* within it a *motional electromotive force*.

The magnitude of this emf can be found as follows. When a charge q moves from b to a through a distance l, the work of the force F is

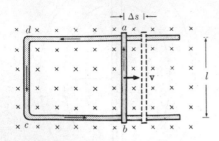

FIG. 34–2. Current produced by the motion of a conductor in a magnetic field.

$$W = Fl = vBql.$$

The emf ε is the work per unit charge, so

$$\varepsilon = \frac{W}{q} = vBl.$$

If the velocity of the conductor makes an angle ϕ with the field, we must replace v by $v_\perp = v \sin \phi$, and

$$\boxed{\varepsilon = v_\perp Bl.} \qquad (34\text{–}1)$$

If v is expressed in m/sec, B in w/m^2, and l in meters, the emf is in joules per coulomb or volts, as may readily be verified. The direction of ε is

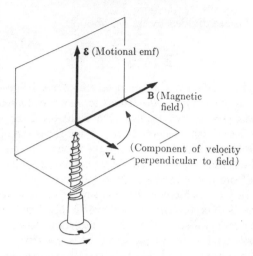

FIG. 34–3. The vectors $\mathbf{v}_\perp$, $\mathbf{B}$, and $\mathcal{E}$ form a mutually perpendicular set. If you rotate the vector $\mathbf{v}_\perp$ toward the vector $\mathbf{B}$, the direction of $\mathcal{E}$ will be that in which a right-hand screw will advance.

given, as usual, by the right-hand screw rule: rotate a right-hand screw from the direction of $v_\perp$ toward B, and the direction of advance will be the direction of the emf as shown in Fig. 34–3.

EXAMPLE. The induction B in the region between the pole faces of an electromagnet is 0.5 w/m². Find the induced emf in a straight conductor 10 cm long, perpendicular to B, and moving perpendicular both to B and its own length with a velocity of 1 m/sec.

The induced emf is

$$\mathcal{E} = vBl$$
$$= 1\ \frac{\text{m}}{\text{sec}} \times 0.5\ \frac{\text{w}}{\text{m}^2} \times 0.10\ \text{m} = 0.05\ \text{volt}.$$

34–2 The Faraday law. The induced emf in the circuit of Fig. 34–2 may be considered from another viewpoint. While the conductor moves toward the right a distance Δs, the cross-sectional area of the closed circuit $abcd$ increases by

$$\Delta A = l\Delta s,$$

and the change in flux through the circuit is

$$\Delta \Phi = B\Delta A = Bl\Delta s.$$

When both sides are divided by Δt, we obtain

$$\frac{\Delta \Phi}{\Delta t} = \frac{\Delta s}{\Delta t} \, Bl = vBl.$$

But the product vBl equals the induced emf $\mathcal{E}$, so the preceding equation states that *the induced emf in the circuit is numerically equal to the rate of change of the magnetic flux through it.* The right-hand screw convention of sign is usually used with this equation. If one faces the circuit, an emf is considered positive if it results in a conventional current in a clockwise direction, and $\Delta \Phi / \Delta t$ is considered positive if there is an increase in the flux directed away from the observer. (Then a decrease in flux away from the observer is negative, an increase in flux toward the observer is negative, and a decrease in flux toward the observer is positive.) In Fig. 34–2 the current is counterclockwise so the emf is negative, while the flux is away from the observer and is increasing so $\Delta \Phi / \Delta t$ is positive. A study of other possibilities shows that $\mathcal{E}$ and $\Delta \Phi / \Delta t$ always have opposite signs. Hence we write the equation

$$\mathcal{E} = -\frac{\Delta \Phi}{\Delta t}. \tag{34–2}$$

If the magnetic flux through a conductor changes a finite amount from a value Φ_0 to a value Φ in a time t, the *average* emf is therefore given by

$$\mathcal{E}_{\text{avg}} = -\frac{\Phi - \Phi_0}{t}.$$

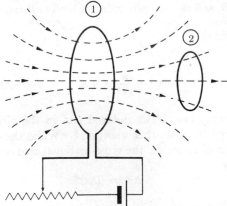

Fig. 34–4. As the current in circuit 1 is varied, the magnetic flux through circuit 2 changes.

Equation (34–2) is known as *Faraday's law*. As it stands, it appears to be merely an alternative form of Eq. (34–1) for the emf in a moving conductor. It turns out, however, that the relation has a much deeper significance than might be expected from its derivation. That is, it is found to apply to many circuits through which the flux is caused to vary even though there is no motion of any part of the circuit and hence no emf directly attributable to a force on a moving charge.

Suppose, for example, that two loops of wire are located as in Fig. 34–4. A current in circuit 1 sets up a magnetic field whose magnitude at all points is proportional to this current. A part of this flux passes through circuit 2, and if the current in circuit 1 is increased or decreased, the flux through circuit 2 will also vary. Circuit 2 is not moving in a magnetic field and hence no "motional" emf is induced in it, but there is a change in the flux through it, and it is found experimentally that an emf appears in circuit 2 of magnitude $\mathcal{E} = d\Phi/dt$.

In a situation such as that shown in Fig. 34–4 it is evident that no one portion of circuit 2 can be considered the seat of emf; the entire circuit constitutes the seat.

The problem cannot be reduced to one of a "motional" emf by saying that the flux lines set up by the current in circuit 1 move outward as the current in this circuit is increased and in doing so "cut" the conductor of circuit 2. There is no way of identifying one specific line of flux and saying that at a certain instant some one line passes through circuit 2, while a moment later the same line lies outside the circuit. The lines of flux are a figment of the imagination, in spite of the lines we draw to represent them, and it is meaningless to speak of a line as moving with a certain velocity. As the current in circuit 1 is increased the number of lines per square meter at every point increases, but the new lines are created in the process of increasing the current and did not get where they are by moving from somewhere else.

Another example may illustrate this point even more strikingly. Suppose we set up a magnetic field within the toroidal winding of Fig. 34–5,

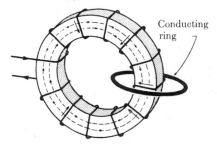

Conducting ring

FIG. 34–5. An emf is induced in the ring when the flux in the toroid varies.

link the toroid with a conducting ring, and vary the current in the winding of the toroid. We have shown that the flux lines set up by a current in a toroidal winding are wholly confined to the space enclosed by the winding, so that not only is the ring not *moving* in a magnetic field, it is not even *in* a magnetic field. However, lines of flux do pass through the area bounded by the ring, and their number changes as the current in the windings changes. Equation (34–2) predicts an induced emf in the ring and we find by experiment that the emf actually exists. In case the reader has not identified the apparatus in Fig. 34–5 from the way it has been described, it may be pointed out that it is merely a transformer with a one-turn secondary, so that the phenomenon we are now discussing is the basis of the operation of every transformer.

To sum up, then, an emf is induced in a circuit whenever the flux through the circuit varies with time. The flux may be caused to vary in two ways, (1) by the motion of a conductor in a constant magnetic field where the circuit is not deformed during the motion as in Fig. 34–2, or (2) by a change in the magnitude of the flux through a stationary circuit as in Fig. 34–4 or 34–5. For case (1), the emf may be computed either from

$$\varepsilon = vBl$$

or from

$$\varepsilon = -\frac{\Delta\Phi}{\Delta t}.$$

For case (2), the emf may be computed only by

$$\varepsilon = -\frac{\Delta\Phi}{\Delta t}.$$

If we have a coil of N turns and the flux varies at the same rate through each, the induced emf's in the turns are in series, and the total emf is

$$\boxed{\varepsilon = -N\frac{\Delta\Phi}{\Delta t}.}$$

EXAMPLE. With a certain current in circuit 1 of Fig. 34–4, a flux of 5×10^{-4} w links with circuit 2. When circuit 1 is opened the flux falls to zero in 0.001 sec. What average emf is induced in circuit 2?

The average rate of decrease of flux in circuit 2 is

$$\frac{\Delta\Phi}{\Delta t} = \frac{5 \times 10^{-4}\ \text{w}}{0.001\ \text{sec}} = 0.5\ \frac{\text{w}}{\text{sec}}.$$

The average induced emf is therefore 0.5 volt.

34-3 Lenz's law. H. F. E. Lenz (1804–64) was a German scientist who, without knowledge of the work of Faraday and Henry, duplicated many of their discoveries nearly simultaneously. The law which goes by his name is a useful rule for predicting the direction of an induced current. It states:

The direction of an induced current is such as to oppose the cause producing it.

The "cause" of the current may be the motion of a conductor in a magnetic field, or it may be the change of flux through a stationary circuit. In the first case, the direction of the induced current in the moving conductor is such that the direction of the side-thrust exerted on the conductor by the magnetic field is opposite in direction to its motion. The motion of the conductor is therefore "opposed."

In the second case, the current sets up a magnetic field of its own which within the area bounded by the circuit is (a) *opposite* to the original field if this is *increasing*, but (b) is in the *same* direction as the original field if the latter is *decreasing*. Thus it is the *change in flux* through the circuit (not the flux itself) which is "opposed" by the induced current.

Lenz's law follows directly from the principle of the conservation of energy, for, if an induced current were in such a direction as to aid the cause producing it, an induced current once started would increase indefinitely and be self-sustaining.

In order for there to be an induced current, we must have a closed circuit. If a conductor does not form a closed circuit, then we mentally complete the circuit between the ends of the conductor and use Lenz's law to determine the direction of the current. The polarity of the ends of the open-circuited conductor may then be deduced.

34-4 The betatron. The magnetic induction accelerator, or betatron, is a recent addition to the family of instruments designed for the purpose of accelerating charged particles to high speeds. It was invented in 1941 by Donald W. Kerst of the University of Illinois. Kerst's original apparatus was capable of accelerating electrons to energies of 2 million electron-volts. A second machine constructed by the General Electric Company developed 20 million-volt electrons, and in 1945 a third model was completed which can accelerate electrons to an energy of 100 million electron-volts. The following description refers to the 100 million-volt machine.

An evacuated toroidal or doughnut-shaped glass tube of elliptical cross section, 74 inches in outside diameter and 58 inches in inside diameter, is placed horizontally in an air gap between the pole faces of an electromagnet. Alternating current at a frequency of 60 cycles/sec is sent through the windings of the electromagnet so that the magnetic flux

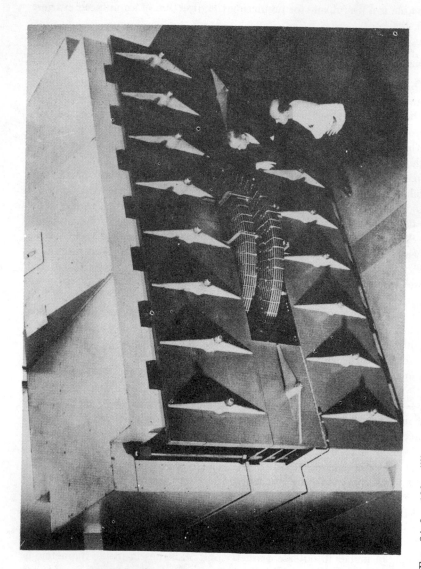

FIG. 34-6.   100 million-volt induction electron accelerator.   (Courtesy of General Electric Company.)

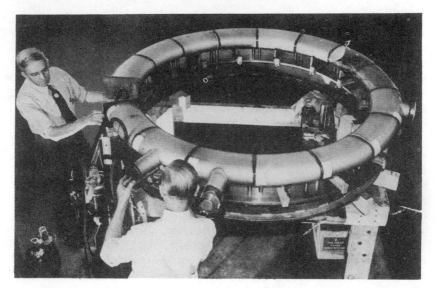

Fig. 34–7. Assembling the huge vacuum tube of the betatron. (Courtesy of General Electric Company.)

through the plane of the toroid reverses from a maximum in one direction to a maximum in the opposite direction in 1/120 sec. Electrons accelerated through approximately 50,000 volts by an electron gun are shot tangentially into the tube and are caused by the magnetic field to circle around within the tube in an orbit 66 inches in diameter. In each revolution they are accelerated through the same voltage (about 400 volts) as would be induced in a single turn of wire through which the flux varied at the same rate. The accelerator may be compared to an ordinary transformer, with the usual high voltage secondary winding of many turns replaced by the electrons in the evacuated tube. The electrons are accelerated by the *changing* magnetic field and at the same time are forced to move in a circular orbit by the *existence* of the magnetic field. The velocity acquired is so great that an electron may make 250,000 revolutions in the time required for the flux to increase from zero to its maximum value. Since each revolution is equivalent to an acceleration through 400 volts, the final energy is 250,000 × 400 or 100 million electron-volts.

At any desired stage in the accelerating process an additional surge or pulse of current may be sent through the magnet coils. This causes the electrons to spiral out of their circular path and strike a target, which then becomes a source of x-rays of extremely short wavelength and great penetrating power.

Note that the relativistic increase of mass with velocity, which prevents the acceleration of electrons in a cyclotron, does not preclude their acceleration in this apparatus, since they gain their final energy in less than one cycle of the varying field and do not have to remain in phase with the field for a large number of cycles.

Figure 34–6 is a front view of the accelerator. Figure 34–7 is a photograph showing the lower portion of the electromagnet, one of the energizing coils, and the vacuum tube.

34–5 Induced emf in a rotating coil. The principle of the present-day form of dynamo is illustrated in Fig. 34–8. A closely wound rectangular coil *abcd* of N turns rotates about an axis OO which is perpendicular to a uniform magnetic field of flux density **B**. The terminals of the coil are connected to *slip rings S-S* concentric with the axis of the coil and rotating with it, but insulated from each other. Brushes bearing against these rings connect the coil to the external circuit. The magnetic field of a commercial dynamo is provided by an electromagnet, and the coil itself is wound on an iron cylinder or *armature*. (The assembly of coil plus cylinder is also referred to as the armature.)

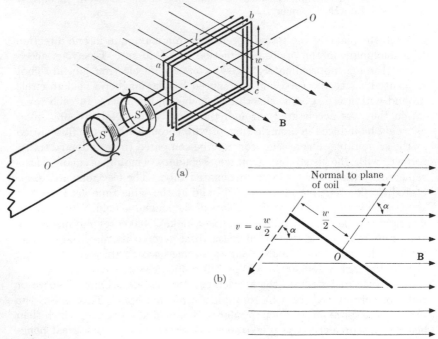

Fɪɢ. 34–8. Principle of the dynamo.

The magnitude of the emf induced in the coil of Fig. 34–8 may be computed either from the rate of change of flux through the coil, or from the velocities of its sides transverse to the magnetic field.

If w is the width and l the length of the coil, the tangential velocity of sides ab and cd is

$$v = \omega \frac{w}{2}.$$

The component of this velocity perpendicular to the lines of force is

$$v \sin \alpha = \omega \frac{w}{2} \sin \alpha.$$

The motional emf in the sides ab and cd is

$$\varepsilon = vBl \sin \alpha = \tfrac{1}{2} Bl\omega w \sin \alpha.$$

(There is no motional emf in the sides bc and da. Why not?) Since these emf's are in series aiding, the net emf in N turns is

$$\varepsilon = NBlw\omega \sin \alpha,$$

and since $lw = A$,

$$\varepsilon = NBA\omega \sin \alpha. \tag{34–3}$$

It is easy to show that Eq. (34–3) applies to a coil of any shape, rotating about an axis perpendicular to a uniform magnetic field.

From Eq. (34–3) the emf is a maximum when the plane of the coil is parallel to the field, and zero when it is perpendicular to the field. This is in agreement with the fact that in the parallel position the sides ab and cd are moving normally to the field, while in the perpendicular position

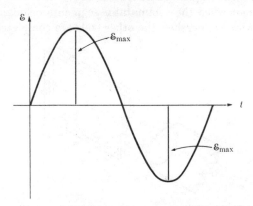

FIG. 34–9. Graph of the alternating emf induced in the coil of Fig. 34–8.

their motion is parallel to the field. The maximum emf is

$$\mathcal{E}_{max} = NBA\omega.$$

Hence Eq. (34–3) can be written

$$\mathcal{E} = \mathcal{E}_{max} \sin \alpha.$$

If ω is constant,

$$\alpha = \omega t \qquad \text{or} \qquad \alpha = 2\pi f t$$

and hence

$$\mathcal{E} = \mathcal{E}_{max} \sin \omega t = \mathcal{E}_{max} \sin 2\pi f t, \tag{34–4}$$

which brings out explicitly the dependence of the instantaneous emf on the time t. A graph of Eq. (34–4) is given in Fig. 34–9. The rotating coil is the simplest form of *alternating-current generator* or *alternator*.

34–6 The direct-current generator. A coil of wire rotating in a magnetic field develops, as we have seen, a sinusoidal alternating emf. A unidirectional emf may be obtained by connecting each terminal of the coil to one side of a split ring or *commutator* (see Fig. 34–10). At the instant when the emf in the coil reverses, the connections to the external circuit are interchanged, and the emf between the terminals, although pulsating, is always in the same direction, as shown in Fig. 34–11.

If it is desired to generate an emf that is not only unidirectional but also practically constant, a first step might be to wind a large number of coils on the generator armature, bringing the terminals of each coil out to its own pair of small commutator segments. The brushes would thus make connection to each coil during a short period when the emf in that coil was near its maximum value. The emf in the external circuit would thus have only a very slight ripple. This method, however, is very wasteful because, at the moment when the commutator segments belonging to one coil are in contact with the brushes, the other coils are completely inactive.

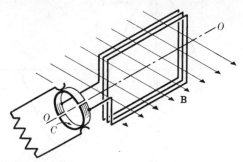

FIG. 34–10. Split ring, or commutator, for unidirectional emf.

To avoid this, a large number of conductors are set in slots in the armature and connected in series in such a way that the entire armature is a closed coil with a net emf equal to zero. Connections are made to commutator segments (whose number is one-half that of the conductors) so that at any moment the emf across the brushes is the resultant of the emf's in half the conductors. With enough conductors, this emf is not only unidirectional but also practically constant. The connections are complicated and properly belong in a text on d-c machinery.

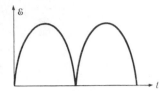

FIG. 34–11. Graph of the unidirectional pulsating emf in the external circuit of Fig. 34–10.

We are now in a position to understand why the armature of a motor is a seat of back emf, a fact which was stated without proof in Chapter 28. A motor armature is simply a coil (or coils) in continuous rotation in a magnetic field. The armature is forced to rotate by the side-thrust on the current maintained in it by the external seat of emf to which its terminals are connected. The fact that it does rotate results in the generation of an emf within it, opposite to the external emf. Every motor is therefore necessarily a generator also.

34–7 Search coil method of measuring magnetic flux. A useful experimental method of measuring the flux density at a point in a magnetic field will now be described. The apparatus consists of a ballistic galvanometer connected by flexible leads to the terminals of a small, closely wound coil called a *search coil* or a *snatch coil*. Assume first, for simplicity, that the search coil is placed with its plane perpendicular to a magnetic field of flux density B. If the area enclosed by the coil is A, the flux Φ through it is $\Phi = BA$. Now if the coil is quickly given a one-quarter turn about one of its diameters so that its plane becomes parallel to the field, or if it is quickly snatched from its position to another where the field is known to be zero, the flux through it decreases rapidly from BA to zero. During the time that the flux is decreasing, an emf of short duration is induced in the coil and a "kick" is imparted to the ballistic galvanometer. The maximum deflection of the galvanometer is noted.

The galvanometer current at any instant is

$$i = \frac{\varepsilon}{R},$$

where R is the combined resistance of galvanometer and search coil, ε is the instantaneous induced emf, and i the instantaneous current.

Since

$$\mathcal{E} = -N \frac{\Delta \Phi}{\Delta t},$$

$$i = -\frac{N}{R} \frac{\Delta \Phi}{\Delta t},$$

and

$$i \, \Delta t = -\frac{N}{R} \Delta \Phi = \frac{N}{R} (\Phi - 0).$$

But $i \, \Delta t = q$, so that

$$\Phi = \frac{Rq}{N}, \tag{34-5}$$

and

$$B = \frac{\Phi}{A} = \frac{Rq}{NA}. \tag{34-6}$$

The maximum deflection of a ballistic galvanometer is proportional to the quantity of charge displaced through it (see Section 32–4). Hence, if this proportionality constant is known, q may be found, and from q one may obtain Φ and B.

Strictly speaking, while this method gives correctly the total flux through the coil, it is only the *average* flux density over the area of the coil which is measured. However, if the area is sufficiently small, this approximates closely the flux density at, say, the center of the coil.

The preceding discussion assumed the plane of the coil to be initially perpendicular to the direction of the field. If one is "exploring" a field whose direction is not known in advance, the same apparatus may be used to find the direction by performing a series of experiments in which the coil is placed at a given point in the field in various orientations, and snatched out of the field from each orientation. The deflection of the galvanometer will be a maximum for the particular orientation in which the plane of the coil was perpendicular to the field. Thus the magnitude and direction of an unknown field can both be found by this method.

Since the search coil is permanently connected to the galvanometer terminals, the galvanometer will be highly damped and must either be calibrated with the search coil connected, or the corrections mentioned in the next section must be applied.

34–8 Galvanometer damping. Suppose a ballistic galvanometer is connected as in Fig. 34–12(a) to measure the quantity of charge on a capacitor. Let the switch S be closed momentarily, allowing the capacitor to discharge through the galvanometer, and then immediately opened. The surge of charge starts the galvanometer coil swinging and, since it is rotating in a magnetic field, an emf is induced in it. The current through

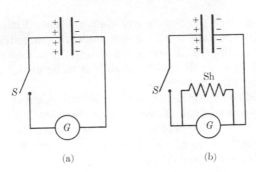

Fig. 34–12. Discharge of a capacitor through a ballistic galvanometer.

it is zero, however, since the switch has been opened and there is no closed circuit. The motion of the coil is controlled solely by the suspension and friction. If the latter were entirely absent, the coil would oscillate indefinitely with angular harmonic motion.

Now let the shunt resistor Sh in Fig. 34–12(b) be connected across the galvanometer terminals and the experiment repeated. The motion of the galvanometer will be affected for two reasons. First, a part of the discharge current of the capacitor will be bypassed by the shunt, and the impulse imparted to the coil will be correspondingly less. Second, the galvanometer and shunt now form a closed circuit even when switch S is opened, so that there will now be a current in the swinging coil. The side-thrusts on this current give rise to a torque on the coil, and from Lenz's law the direction of this torque is such as to oppose the motion of the coil and aid in bringing it to rest. From the energy standpoint, a part of the kinetic energy of the swinging coil becomes converted to heat developed by the induced currents. The motion of the coil is accordingly *damped harmonic*.

It should be evident that the smaller the shunt resistance, the larger will be the induced current and the greater the damping. With a sufficiently small shunt resistance the motion ceases to be oscillatory; the galvanometer makes but one swing and returns slowly to its zero position. The particular resistance for which the motion just ceases to be oscillatory is called the *critical external damping resistance (CXDR)*, and when shunted by its $CXDR$ the galvanometer is said to be *critically damped*. With more resistance it is *underdamped* and with less it is *overdamped*.

Since the presence of damping reduces the maximum swing of a ballistic galvanometer, the simple theory in Chapter 32, which assumes that all the initial kinetic energy of the coil is converted to potential energy of the suspension, must be extended if damping is present. The complete analysis shows that the quantity of charge displaced is still proportional to the maximum angle of swing, although with a modified proportionality constant. However, if the galvanometer is calibrated with the same external resistance as that with which it is to be used, the modified constant is automatically determined.

In many pivoted coil instruments, such as portable ammeters and voltmeters, the necessary amount of damping is "built in" to the moving coil, so to speak, by winding this coil on a light aluminum frame. The frame itself then forms a closed circuit, and the currents induced in this circuit quickly bring the swinging coil to rest.

34–9 Eddy currents. Thus far we have considered only instances in which the currents resulting from induced emf's were confined to well-defined paths provided by the wires and apparatus of the external circuit. In many pieces of electrical equipment, however, one finds masses of metal moving in a magnetic field or located in a changing magnetic field, with the result that induced currents circulate throughout the volume of the metal. Because of their general circulatory nature, these are referred to as *eddy currents*.

Consider a disk rotating in a magnetic field perpendicular to the plane of the disk but confined to a limited portion of its area, as in Fig. 34–13(a). Element Ob is moving across the field and has an emf induced in it. Elements Oa and Oc are not in the field and hence are not seats of emf. They do, however, in common with all other elements located outside the field, provide return conducting paths along which positive charges displaced along OB can return from b to O. A general eddy current circulation is therefore set up in the disk somewhat as sketched in Fig. 34–13(b).

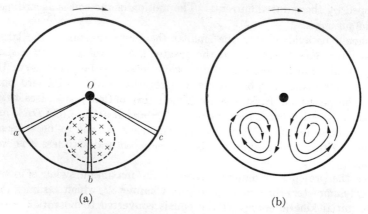

(a)

(b)

FIG. 34–13. Eddy currents in a rotating disk.

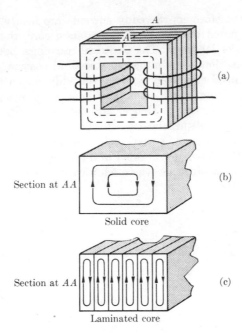

Fɪɢ. 34–14. Reduction of eddy currents by use of a laminated core.

Application of the screw rule or of Lenz's law shows that the currents in the neighborhood of radius Ob experience a side-thrust which opposes the motion of the disk, while the return currents, since they lie outside the field, do not experience such a thrust. The interaction between the eddy currents and the field therefore results in a braking action on the disk. The apparatus finds some technical applications and is known as an "eddy current brake."

As a second example of eddy currents, consider the core of an alternating-current transformer, shown in Fig. 34–14. The alternating current in the transformer windings sets up an alternating flux within the core, and an induced emf develops in the secondary windings because of the continual change in flux through them. The iron core, however, is also a conductor, and any section such as that at $A–A$ can be thought of as a number of closed conducting circuits, one within the other. The flux through each of these circuits is continually changing, so that there is an eddy current circulation in the entire volume of the core, the lines of flow lying in planes perpendicular to the flux. These eddy currents are very undesirable both because of the large i^2R heating which they produce, and because of the flux which they themselves set up.

In all actual transformers the eddy currents are nearly, although not completely, eliminated by the use of a *laminated* core, that is, one built up of thin sheets or laminae. The electrical resistance between the surfaces of the laminations (due either to a natural coating of oxide or to an insulating varnish) effectively confines the eddy currents to individual laminae. The resulting length of path is greatly increased, with consequent increase in resistance. Hence, although the induced emf is not altered, the currents and their heating effects are minimized.

In open core transformers or spark coils a bundle of iron wires is often used as a core. Powdered iron formed into a core under high pressure is also used in small transformers where eddy current loss must be kept to an absolute minimum.

PROBLEMS

34-1. The cube in Fig. 34-15, 1 meter on a side, is placed in a uniform magnetic field of flux density $0.2 \ w/m^2$ directed along the x-axis. Wires A, C, and D move in the directions indicated, each at the rate of 50 cm/sec. Determine the emf induced in each wire.

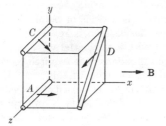

FIGURE 34-15

34-2. A slender rod one meter long rotates about an axis through one end and perpendicular to the rod, with an angular velocity of 2 rev/sec. The plane of rotation of the rod is perpendicular to a uniform magnetic field of $0.5 \ w/m^2$ flux density. What emf is induced across the ends of the rod?

34-3. A conducting rod AB in Fig. 34-16 makes contact with the metal rails CA and DB. The apparatus is in a uniform magnetic field of flux density 500 milliwebers/in², perpendicular to the plane of the diagram. (a) Find the magnitude and direction of the emf

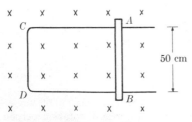

FIGURE 34-16

induced in the rod when it is moving toward the right with a velocity of 4 m/sec. (b) If the resistance of the circuit $ABCD$ is 0.2 ohm (assumed constant), find the force required to maintain the rod in motion. Neglect friction. (c) Compare the rate at which mechanical work is done by the force (Fv) with the rate of development of heat in the circuit (i^2R).

34-4. Figure 34-17 is a side view of the same rod and metal rails as in Fig. 34-16, except that the magnetic induction makes an angle of 60° with the plane of the loop $ABCD$. Find the induced emf. The flux density is 500 milliwebers/m² and the velocity of the rod is 4 m/sec toward the right.

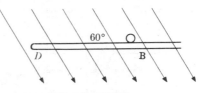

FIGURE 34-17

34-5. A closely wound rectangular coil of 50 turns has dimensions of 12 cm × 25 cm. The plane of the coil is rotated from a position where it makes an angle of 45° with a magnetic field of flux density $2 \ w/m^2$ to a position perpendicular to the field in time $t = 0.1$ sec. What is the average emf induced in the coil?

34-6. A coil of 1000 turns enclosing an area of 20 cm² is rotated from a position where its plane is perpendicular to the earth's magnetic field to one where its plane is parallel to the field, in 0.02 sec. What average emf is induced if the flux density of the earth's magnetic field is $6 \times 10^{-5} \ w/m^2$?

34-7. A flat square coil of 10 turns has sides of length 12 cm. The coil rotates in·a magnetic field whose flux density is 0.025 w/m². (a) What is the angular velocity of the coil if the maximum emf produced is 20 mv? (b) What is the average emf at this velocity?

34-8. A cardboard tube is wound with two windings of insulated wire as in Fig. 34-18. Terminals a and b of winding A may be connected to a seat of emf through a reversing switch.

State whether the induced current in the resistor R is from left to right, or from right to left, in the following circumstances: (a) the current in winding A is from a to b and is increasing; (b) the current is from b to a and is decreasing; (c) the current is from b to a and is increasing.

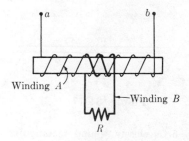

FIGURE 34-18

34-9. A solenoid has 96 turns of wire, a length of 8 cm, a cross-sectional area of 6 cm², and carries a current of 0.25 amp. A "secondary" of 2 turns is wound around the solenoid. When a switch is opened the magnetic field of the solenoid becomes zero in 0.05 sec. What emf is induced in the 2 turns?

34-10. Using Lenz's law, determine the direction of the current in resistor ab of Fig. 34-19 when (a) switch S is opened, (b) coil B is brought closer to coil A, (c) the resistance of R is decreased.

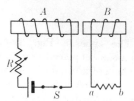

FIGURE 34-19

34-11. The orbit of an electron in a betatron is a circle of radius R. Suppose the electron is revolving in this orbit with a tangential velocity v. (a) What flux density is required to maintain the electron in this orbit if the magnitude of its velocity is constant? (b) If the flux density is uniform over the plane of the orbit, and is increasing at a rate $\Delta B/\Delta t$, what is the equivalent voltage accelerating the electron in each revolution?

34-12. In the diagram of the toroidal tube of the betatron, Fig. 34-20, a magnetic field is directed into the plane of the diagram and is increasing. An electron is moving clockwise. (a) Show that the emf induced around the electron's orbit is such as to accelerate the electron. (b) Show that the increasing radial force on the electron due to the magnetic field tends to prevent the electron from going to larger orbits.

FIGURE 34-20

34-13. A rectangular coil of wire rotates with its axis of rotation perpendicular to a magnetic field whose flux density is 0.60 w/m² [see Fig. 34–8(a)]. The coil is 6 cm × 8 cm and has 250 turns. (a) At what speed must the coil rotate to generate an average emf of 100 volts during each quarter revolution? (b) What is the maximum emf at this speed?

34–14. Assume a rectangular coil of wire having 10 turns with dimensions of 20 cm × 30 cm to be rotating at a constant speed of 600 rpm in a magnetic field in which the flux density is 0.10 w/m². The axis of rotation is perpendicular to the field. Find the maximum emf produced.

34–15. A coil of 5 turns has dimensions 9 cm × 7 cm. It rotates at the rate of 15π rad/sec in a uniform magnetic field whose flux density is 0.8 w/m². (a) What maximum emf is induced in the coil? (b) What is the emf 1/90 sec after it reaches the value of zero? (c) Sketch a curve of $\mathcal{E}$ vs. t for one rotation of the coil, and on the same graph, a curve of $\mathcal{E}$ vs. t if the angular velocity of the coil is doubled.

34–16. A circular turn of wire 4 cm in radius rotates with an angular velocity of 1800 rpm about a diameter which is perpendicular to a uniform magnetic field of flux density 0.5 w/m². What is the instantaneous induced emf in the turn when the plane of the turn makes an angle of 30° with the direction of the flux?

34–17. A closely wound search coil has an area of 4 cm², 160 turns, and a resistance of 50 ohms. It is connected to a ballistic galvanometer whose re-

sistance is 30 ohms. When the coil is rotated quickly from a position parallel to a uniform magnetic field to one perpendicular to the field, the galvanometer indicates a charge of 4×10^{-5} coul. What is the flux density of the field?

34–18. A solenoid 50 cm long and 8 cm in diameter is wound with 500 turns. A closely wound coil of 20 turns of insulated wire surrounds the solenoid at its midpoint, and the terminals of the coil are connected to a ballistic galvanometer. The combined resistance of coil, galvanometer, and leads is 25 ohms. (a) Find the quantity of charge displaced through the galvanometer when the current in the solenoid is quickly decreased from 3 amp to 1 amp. (b) Draw a sketch of the apparatus, showing clearly the directions of winding of the solenoid and coil, and of the current in the solenoid. What is the direction of the current in the coil when the solenoid current is decreased?

34–19. The cross-sectional area of a closely wound search coil having 20 turns is 1.5 cm² and its resistance is 4 ohms. The coil is connected through leads of negligible resistance to a ballistic galvanometer of resistance 16 ohms. Find the quantity of charge displaced through the galvanometer when the coil is pulled quickly out of a region where $B = 1.8$ w/m² to a point where the magnetic field is zero. The plane of the coil, when in the field, made an angle of 90° with the magnetic induction.

CHAPTER 35

MAGNETIC PROPERTIES OF MATTER

35–1 Introduction. In the preceding chapters we have discussed the magnetic fields set up by moving charges or by currents in conductors, when the charges or conductors are in air (or, strictly speaking, in a vacuum). However, pieces of technical equipment such as transformers, motors, and generators, which make use of the magnetic fields set up by a current, always incorporate iron or an iron alloy in their structures, both for the purpose of increasing the magnetic flux and for confining it to a desired region. Furthermore, by the use of permanent magnets, as in galvanometers or permanent magnet speakers, magnetic fields can be produced without any apparent circulation of charge.

We therefore turn next to a consideration of the magnetic properties which make iron and a few other ferromagnetic materials so useful. We shall find that magnetic properties are not confined to ferromagnetic materials but are exhibited (to a much smaller extent, to be sure) by *all* substances. From the standpoint of the electrical engineer, the ferromagnetic materials are of the greatest interest, but a study of the magnetic properties of other materials is of importance also, affording as it does another means of gaining an insight into the nature of matter in general.

The existence of the magnetic properties of a substance can be demonstrated by supporting a small spherically shaped specimen by a fine thread and placing it near the poles of a powerful electromagnet. If the specimen is of iron or one of the *ferromagnetic* substances, it will be attracted into the strong part of the magnetic field. Not so familiar is the fact that any substance whatever will be influenced by the field, although to an extent which is extremely small compared with a substance like iron. Some substances will, like iron, be forced into the strong part of the field, while others will be urged to move toward the weak part of the field. The first type is called *paramagnetic;* the second, *diamagnetic.* All substances, including liquids and gases, fall into one or the other of these classes. Liquids and gases must, of course, be enclosed within some sort of container, and due allowance must be made for the properties of the container as well as those of the medium (usually air) in which the specimens are immersed.

35–2 Magnetic permeability. In Chapter 27, our formulation of the properties of a dielectric substance was based on a specimen in the form of a flat slab, inserted in the field between oppositely charged parallel plates.

The electric field is wholly confined to the region between the plates if their separation is small, and therefore a flat slab between the plates will completely occupy all points of space at which an electric field exists. A specimen of this shape is not as well suited for a study of magnetic effects, however, since lines of magnetic induction are closed lines and there is no way of producing a magnetic field which is confined to the region between two closely spaced surfaces. The magnetic field within a closely spaced toroidal winding, however, is wholly confined to the space enclosed by the winding. We shall accordingly use such a field on which to base our discussion of magnetic properties, the specimen being in the form of a ring on whose surface the wire is wound. Such a specimen is often called a *Rowland ring* after J. H. Rowland, who made much use of it in his experimental and theoretical work on electricity and magnetism. The winding of wire around the specimen is called the *magnetizing winding*, and the current in the winding, the *magnetizing current*.

The magnetic flux density within the space enclosed by a toroidal winding *in vacuum* is (see Section 33–6)

$$B_0 = \mu_0 \frac{Ni}{l}. \tag{35–1}$$

Suppose now that the same coil is wound on a Rowland ring, and that a second winding is placed on the ring as in Fig. 35–1, with its terminals connected to a ballistic galvanometer. The flux density within the ring may be measured, as explained in Section 34–7, by opening switch S and quickly reducing the magnetizing current to zero. If this is done, the flux

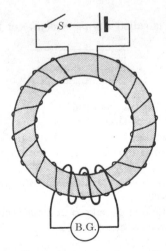

FIG. 35–1.   Magnetic specimen in the form of a ring with a toroidal winding.

density computed from the ballistic galvanometer deflection will not agree with that computed from Eq. (35–1). If the core is made of a ferromagnetic material, the measured flux density will be tremendously larger; if made of a paramagnetic material, very slightly larger; and if made of a diamagnetic material, it will be very slightly smaller than the calculated value. The differences in the two latter cases are, in fact, so small that this method is not a practical one for investigating these substances, but its principle is simpler than that of other methods, so we shall ignore experimental difficulties.

Let B represent the flux density in a material ring and B_0 the flux density in a "ring of vacuum." The ratio of B to B_0 is called the *relative permeability* of the material and is represented by K_m:

$$K_m = \frac{B}{B_0}.$$

(35–2)

K_m is $\begin{cases} \text{equal to 1 for a vacuum,} \\ \text{slightly larger than 1 for paramagnetic materials,} \\ \text{slightly smaller than 1 for diamagnetic materials,} \\ \text{often much larger than 1 for ferromagnetic materials.} \end{cases}$

Substituting for B_0 its value $\mu_0 Ni/l$, we get

$$B = K_m \mu_0 \frac{Ni}{l}.$$

The product $K_m \mu_0$ is called the *permeability* of the material and is denoted by μ:

$$\mu = K_m \mu_0.$$

(35–3)

μ is $\begin{cases} \text{equal to } \mu_0 \text{ for a vacuum,} \\ \text{slightly greater than } \mu_0 \text{ for paramagnetic materials,} \\ \text{slightly smaller than } \mu_0 \text{ for diamagnetic materials,} \\ \text{often much larger than } \mu_0 \text{ for ferromagnetic materials.} \end{cases}$

The unit in which μ is expressed is the same as that for μ_0, namely, webers per ampere·meter.

The expression for the flux density B in a material substance in the form of a Rowland ring may now be written

$$B = \mu \frac{Ni}{l}.$$

(35–4)

The reader's attention is called to the close parallelism between dielectric and magnetic quantities with regard to definitions, terminology, and symbolism, as shown in the table below.

COMPARISON OF DIELECTRIC AND MAGNETIC QUANTITIES

Dielectric	Magnetic
Dielectric coefficient $K = C/C_0$	Relative permeability $K_m = B/B_0$
Permittivity $\epsilon = K\epsilon_0$	Permeability $\mu = K_m\mu_0$

35–3 Magnetic intensity. The magnetic properties of matter can easily be measured and calculated when the substance is fashioned into the form of a ring, because the magnetic field set up by a current in the magnetizing winding is then confined wholly to the interior of the ring. No lines of magnetic induction pass through the surface of the material to the space outside. When magnetic materials are cylindrical or U-shaped, as is often the case, lines of induction cross the surface at certain regions which are called *poles*. Those regions where lines of induction emerge from the body are called north-seeking poles, and the regions where lines of induction enter the body are called south-seeking poles. Some of the properties of magnetic poles are discussed further later on in the chapter.

A current-carrying wire or a moving charge is acted on by a force when in the neighborhood of a magnetic pole. Thus magnetic fields can be produced both by currents in conductors and by magnetic poles. To develop the subject of magnetism with sufficient generality to account for both of these magnetic effects, a new magnetic vector **H** is defined and called the *magnetic intensity*. The complete expression for **H** contains two terms, one of which expresses the effect of currents in conductors, the other that of magnetic poles. In the case of a Rowland ring, where there are no magnetic poles, the second term is zero.

The term expressing the effect of currents in conductors is given by an expression that is the same as the Biot law, Eq. (33–2), except for the factor μ_0.

$$\Delta H = \frac{1}{4\pi} \frac{i\,\Delta l \sin\theta}{r^2}. \tag{35–5}$$

(See Fig. 33–1 for the meaning of the symbols in this equation. The direction of the Δ**H** vector is the same as that of Δ**B**.) The magnetic intensity H in the material of a Rowland ring is therefore

$$H = \frac{Ni}{l}. \quad \text{(Rowland ring)} \tag{35–6}$$

Notice that the magnetic intensity does *not* depend on the material of which the ring is constructed.

It follows from Eq. (35–6) that magnetic intensity is expressed in *amperes per meter*, or ampere-turns per meter if one wishes to include the factor N in the units. Like magnetic induction, the magnitude and direction of H can be represented by lines of magnetic force. The direction of the magnetic intensity vector at any point is tangent to the line of magnetic force passing through the point. Within a Rowland ring the lines of magnetic force have the same shape as the lines of magnetic induction, although this is not always the case.

Since in a Rowland ring $B = \mu Ni/l$ and $H = Ni/l$, it follows that $B = \mu H$, or

$$\mu = \frac{B}{H}. \tag{35–7}$$

In rigorous treatments of the subject of magnetism, the vector **H** is defined before the permeability μ, and Eq. (35–7) is used to *define* the permeability. Hence this equation applies in *all* instances, although we have derived it only for a special case. At any point in empty space, $\mu = \mu_0$ and

$$H = \frac{B}{\mu_0}. \qquad \text{(Empty space)} \tag{35–8}$$

EXAMPLE. A Rowland ring, made of iron, of mean circumferential length 30 cm and cross section 1 cm^2, is wound uniformly with 300 turns of wire. Ballistic galvanometer measurements made with a search coil around the ring, as in Fig. 35–1, show that when the current in the windings is 0.032 amp, the flux in the ring is 2×10^{-6} weber. Compute (a) the flux density in the ring, (b) the magnetic intensity, (c) the permeability, (d) the relative permeability.

(a) Flux density $B = \dfrac{\Phi}{A} = \dfrac{2 \times 10^{-6}\,\text{w}}{10^{-4}\,\text{m}^2} = 2 \times 10^{-2}\,\dfrac{\text{w}}{\text{m}^2}.$

(b) Magnetic intensity $H = \dfrac{Ni}{l} = \dfrac{300 \times 0.032\,\text{amp}}{0.30\,\text{m}} = 32\,\dfrac{\text{amp}}{\text{m}}.$

(c) Permeability $\mu = \dfrac{B}{H} = \dfrac{2 \times 10^{-2}\,\text{w/m}^2}{32\,\text{amp/m}} = 6250 \times 10^{-7}\,\dfrac{\text{w}}{\text{amp·m}}.$

(d) Relative permeability $K_m = \dfrac{\mu}{\mu_0} = \dfrac{6250 \times 10^{-7}\,\text{w/amp·m}}{12.57 \times 10^{-7}\,\text{w/amp·m}} = 498.$

35–4 Ferromagnetism. The flux density in a Rowland ring of iron may be hundreds or even thousands of times as great as that due to the magnetizing current alone. Furthermore, the flux density B is not a linear function of the magnetic intensity H or, in other words, the permeability μ is not a constant. To complicate matters even further, the permeability depends on the past history (magnetically speaking) of the iron, a phenomenon known as *hysteresis*. In fact, a flux may exist in the iron even in the absence of any external field; when in this state the iron is called a *permanent magnet*.

Any substance which exhibits the properties above is called *ferromagnetic*. Iron, nickel, cobalt, and gadolinium are the only ferromagnetic elements, but a number of alloys whose components are not ferromagnetic also show these effects.

Because of the complicated relation between the flux density B and the magnetic intensity H in a ferromagnetic material, it is not possible to express B as an analytic function of H. Instead, the relation between these quantities is either given in tabular form or is represented by a graph of B vs. H, called the *magnetization curve* of the material.

The magnetization curve of a specimen of annealed iron is shown in Fig. 35–2 in the curve labeled B vs. H. The permeability μ, equal to the ratio of B to H, can be found at any point of the curve by dividing the flux density B, at the point, by the corresponding magnetic intensity

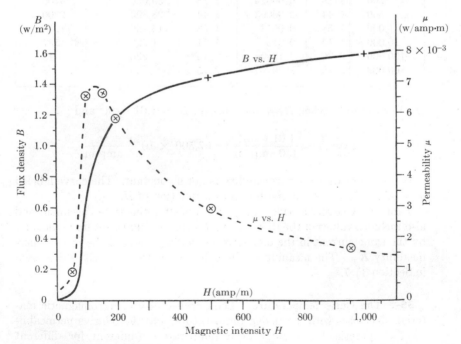

FIG. 35–2. Magnetization curve and permeability curve of annealed iron

TABLE 35–1

MAGNETIC PROPERTIES OF ANNEALED IRON

Magnetic intensity	Total flux density	Flux density due to current in windings	Flux density due to electronic currents	Permeability	Relative permeability
H, amp-turns/m	B, w/m^2	B_0, w/m^2	$B - B_0$, w/m^2	$\mu = B/H$, w/amp·m	$K_m = \mu/\mu_0$
0	0	0	0	$3{,}100 \times 10^{-7}$	250
10	0.0042	0.000013	0.0042	4,200	330
20	0.010	0.000025	0.010	5,000	400
40	0.028	0.000050	0.028	7,000	560
50	0.043	0.000063	0.043	8,600	680
60	0.095	0.000078	0.095	16,000	1270
80	0.45	0.000104	0.45	56,000	4500
100	0.67	0.00013	0.67	67,000	5300
150	1.01	0.00019	1.01	67,500	5350
200	1.18	0.00025	1.18	59,000	4700
500	1.44	0.00063	1.44	28,800	2300
1,000	1.58	0.0013	1.58	15,800	1250
10,000	1.72	0.013	1.71	1,720	137
100,000	2.26	0.13	2.13	226	18
800,000	3.15	1.00	2.15	39	3.1

H. For example, when $H = 150$ amp/m, $B = 1.01$ w/m^2 and

$$\mu = \frac{B}{H} = \frac{1.01 \text{ w/m}^2}{150 \text{ amp/m}} = 67{,}500 \times 10^{-7} \; \frac{\text{w}}{\text{amp·m}}.$$

It is evident that the permeability is not a constant. The curve labeled μ vs. H in Fig. 35–2 is a graph of μ as a function of H.

Table 35–1 covers a wider range of values for the same specimen, and also includes values of the flux density B_0 that would be set up in vacuum by the same current in the magnetizing windings, and of the relative permeability K_m. The meaning of the column headed $B - B_0$ is discussed in Section 35–7.

35–5 The Curie temperature. The permeability of ferromagnetic materials decreases with increasing temperature, and the relative permeability falls practically to unity at a temperature (different for different materials) called the *Curie temperature*. Above the Curie temperature,

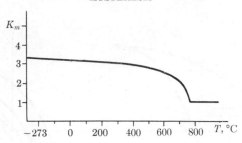

FIG. 35–3. Relative permeability of a sample of iron under a constant magnetic intensity of 800,000 ampere·turns/meter. The Curie temperature is about 760°C.

iron is paramagnetic but not ferromagnetic. In Fig. 35–3 there is shown the temperature variation of the relative permeability of a sample of iron. H is kept constant at 800,000 amp/m. The Curie temperature is about 760°C for this sample.

35–6 Hysteresis. A magnetization curve such as that in Fig. 35–2 expresses the relation between the flux density B in a ferromagnetic material and the corresponding magnetic intensity H, *provided the sample is initially unmagnetized and the magnetic intensity is steadily increased from zero.* Thus in Fig. 35–4, if the magnetizing current in the windings of an unmagnetized ring sample is steadily increased from zero until the magnetic intensity H corresponds to the abscissa Oe, the flux density B is given by the ordinate Of. If, starting from the same unmagnetized state, the magnetic intensity is first increased from zero to Og and then *decreased* to Oe, the magnetic state of the sample follows the path $Oabc$. The flux density, when the magnetic intensity has been reduced to Oe, is represented by the ordinate Oh rather than Of. If the magnetizing current is now reduced to zero, the curve continues to point d, where the flux density is Od.

The flux density in the sample is seen to depend not on the magnetic intensity alone, but on the magnetic history of the sample as well. It has a magnetic "memory," so to speak, and "remembers" that it has been magnetized to point b even after the magnetizing current has been cut off. At point d it has become a *permanent magnet*. This behavior of the ma-

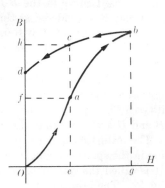

FIG. 35–4. Graph showing hysteresis.

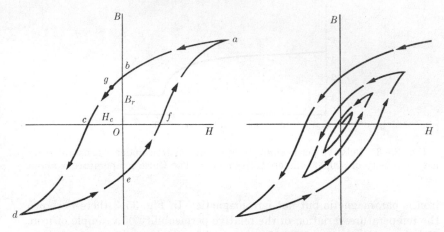

FIG. 35–5. Hysteresis loop.   FIG. 35–6. Successive hysteresis loops during the operation of demagnetizing a ferromagnetic sample.

terial, as evidenced by the fact that the *B-H* curve for decreasing *H* does not coincide with that for increasing *H*, is called *hysteresis*. The term means literally "to lag behind."

In many pieces of electrical apparatus, such as transformers and motors, masses of iron are located in magnetic fields whose direction is continually reversing. That is, the magnetic intensity *H* increases from zero to a certain maximum in one direction, then decreases to zero, increases to the same maximum but in the opposite direction, decreases to zero, and continues to repeat this cycle over and over. The flux density *B* within the iron reverses also, but in the manner indicated in Fig. 35–5, tracing out a closed curve in the *B-H* plane known as a *hysteresis loop*. Figure 35–4 may be considered as the start of such a hysteresis loop.

Positive values of *H* or *B* in Fig. 35–5 indicate that the respective directions of these quantities are, say, clockwise in a Rowland ring, while negative values mean that the directions are counterclockwise. The magnitude and direction of *H* are determined solely by the current in the winding, while those of *B* depend on the magnetic properties of the sample and its past history. Note that at points in the second and fourth quadrants, *B* and *H* are opposite in direction.

The ordinate *Ob* or *Oe* in Fig. 35–5 represents the flux density remaining in the specimen when the magnetic intensity has been reduced to zero. It is called the *retentivity* or *remanence* of the specimen and is designated by B_r. The abscissa *Oc* or *Of* represents the reversed magnetic intensity needed to reduce the flux density to zero after the specimen has been magnetized to saturation in the opposite direction, and it is called the *coercive force* or the *coercivity*, H_c. What is the permeability at points b, c, e, and f?

The magnetization curve Oab in Fig. 35-4 shows the sample initially unmagnetized. One may wonder how this can be accomplished, since cutting off the magnetizing current does not reduce the flux density in the material to zero. A sample may be demagnetized by reversing the magnetizing current a number of times, decreasing its magnitude with each reversal. The sample is thus carried around a hysteresis curve which winds more and more closely about the origin (see Fig. 35-6).

Hysteresis effects introduce a similar difficulty in measuring the flux in a sample. In the absence of hysteresis, the flux falls to zero when the magnetizing current is cut off, and a ballistic galvanometer connected to a search coil around the specimen indicates the flux previously present in the specimen. But since B does not become zero when H is reduced to zero, ballistic galvanometer deflections only indicate the *changes* in flux corresponding to changes in the magnetizing force. Hence in practice the complete hysteresis loop must be traced out in stepwise fashion, measuring the changes in flux accompanying changes in magnetizing current.

It is evidently desirable that a material for permanent magnets should have both a large retentivity so that the magnet will be "strong" and a large coercive force so that the magnetization will not be wiped out by stray external fields. Some typical values are given in Table 35-2. Alnico 5 is one of the most recently developed alloys for permanent magnets.

TABLE 35-2

RETENTIVITY AND COERCIVE FORCE OF PERMANENT
MAGNET MATERIALS

Material	Composition, %	B_r, w/m^2	H_c, amp/m
Carbon steel	98 Fe, 0.86 C, 0.9 Mn	0.95	3.6×10^3
Cobalt steel	52 Fe, 36 Co, 7 W, 3.5 Cr, 0.5 Mn, 0.7 C	0.95	18×10^3
Alnico 2	55 Fe, 10 Al, 17 Ni, 12 Co, 6 Cu	0.76	42×10^3
Alnico 5	51 Fe, 8 Al, 14 Ni, 24 Co, 3 Cu	1.25	44×10^3

Its superiority to carbon steel, which was the material used for many years, is evident.

One consequence of the phenomenon of hysteresis is the production of heat within a ferromagnetic material each time the material is caused to traverse its hysteresis loop. This heat results from a kind of internal friction as the magnetic domains within the material are reversed in direction. It can be shown that the heat developed per unit volume, in each cycle, is proportional to the area enclosed by the hysteresis loop. Hence if a ferromagnetic material is to be subjected to a field which is continually reversing its direction (the core of a transformer, for example), it is desirable that the hysteresis loop of the material shall be narrow to minimize heat losses. Fortunately, iron or iron alloys are available which combine high permeability with small hysteresis loss.

35–7 Ampere's theory of magnetism. The earliest speculations as to the origin of the magnetic properties of a piece of lodestone, or a permanent magnet, were that such a substance was composed of, or at least contained, a number of tiny particles each of which was endowed with two magnetic poles. The process of magnetizing a body consisted of aligning these elementary magnets with their like poles pointing the same way. When it was discovered that magnetic effects could also be produced by currents, Ampere proposed the theory that the magnetic properties of a body arose from a multitude of tiny closed current loops within the body. The currents in these loops were assumed to continue indefinitely as if there were no resistance. In an unmagnetized body the loops were oriented at random. The magnetizing process consisted of aligning these loops with their planes parallel to one another and with the currents all circulating in the same direction.

At the time the theory was proposed it was highly speculative, since no currents were known that would continue indefinitely without any source of emf and without the production of heat. We now believe the theory to be essentially correct, the elementary current loops consisting of electrons spinning about their own axes or revolving in orbits around nuclei.

Regardless of the origin of the current loops, a body in which the planes of all such loops are parallel to one another can be represented as in Fig. 35–7(a), where the loops are represented by small circles. At interior points the currents in adjacent loops are in opposite directions and cancel. The outer portions of the outside loops, however, are uncompensated and the entire assembly of loops is equivalent to a current circulating around the outside of the conductor, as in Fig. 35–7(b). These equivalent surface currents have essentially the same shape as would a magnetizing winding around the specimen. The flux they produce adds to the flux

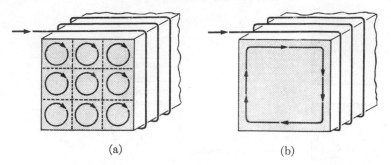

(a)　　　　　　　　　　　(b)

FIG. 35–7. (a) Alignment of atomic current loops. (b) Surface current equivalent to part (a).

produced by the current in an actual winding if the two circulate in the same direction, as in Fig. 35–7, or subtracts from it if they are in opposite directions.

We are now in a position to understand column 4 in Table 35–1. The difference $B - B_0$ between the actual flux density B and the flux density B_0 due to the current in the windings is attributed to the electronic currents in the iron. It will be seen that when H is small, practically all the flux is due to the electronic loop currents. Beyond the point where H is of the order of 1000 amp/m there is but little further increase in the flux density due to the electronic currents. In this region the iron is said to become *saturated*. Further increases in B are due almost wholly to increases in the magnetizing current.

For *paramagnetic* substances, the difference $B - B_0$ is a small positive quantity, proportional to H and decreasing as the temperature increases. For *diamagnetic* substances, $B - B_0$ is a small negative quantity also proportional to H but independent of the temperature. Thus in paramagnetic and ferromagnetic materials the electronic currents are in the same direction as those in the magnetizing winding, while in diamagnetic materials the two are in opposite directions.

35–8 Magnetic domains. In para- and diamagnetic materials, the flux density due to electronic loop currents is negligible compared with the applied field, while in ferromagnetic materials it may be thousands of times as great as the applied field. The conclusion is that in a ferromagnetic substance some aligning influence other than the applied field must act on the molecular magnets. This can only arise from the mutual interaction between the molecules, an effect which is negligible in a para- or diamagnetic substance. That such an effect must exist was first pointed out by Pierre Weiss in 1907.

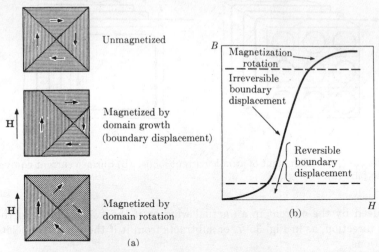

FIG. 35–8. Schematic diagram showing magnetization by domain growth and domain rotation.

Recent experimental and theoretical work has led to a fairly complete understanding of the nature of these interactions, but the problem is far from simple, and even a reasonably complete description would take us far beyond the scope of this book. It must suffice to state that there exist in ferromagnetic materials small regions called *domains*, in each of which, as a result of molecular interactions, the molecular magnetic moments are all aligned parallel to one another. In other words, each domain is spontaneously magnetized to saturation even in the absence of any external field. The directions of magnetization in different domains are not necessarily parallel to one another, so that in an unmagnetized specimen the resultant magnetization is zero. When the specimen is placed in a magnetic field the resultant magnetization may increase in two different ways, either by an increase in the volume of those domains which are favorably oriented with respect to the field at the expense of unfavorably oriented domains, or by the rotation of the direction of magnetization toward the direction of the field. These two methods are shown in Fig. 35–8(a).

In weak fields, the magnetization usually changes by means of domain boundary displacements so that the favorably oriented domains increase in size. In strong fields the magnetization usually changes by rotation of the direction of magnetization. The curve in Fig. 35–8(b) shows the regions in which each process is dominant. In small fields the changes are reversible. That is, the boundaries return to their original positions when the field is removed, and hysteresis effects are small. In stronger fields the changes are irreversible and the substance remains magnetized when the external field is removed.

The sizes of the domains can be studied by spreading a finely divided magnetic powder on the surface of the specimen, a technique first developed by F. H. Bitter. The powder particles collect along the boundaries between domains and may be examined under a microscope. The size of the domains may vary widely, depending on the size of the specimen and whether it is a single crystal or is polycrystalline. Typical values are from 10^{-6} to 10^{-2} cm^3, which means that a domain may contain from 10^{17} to 10^{21} molecules.

The Barkhausen effect, which is most pronounced along the steeply rising portion of the magnetization curve, is believed to be caused by the irregular motion of domain boundaries. If a rod of ferromagnetic material is surrounded by a search coil connected to an audio amplifier, and the rod is placed in a magnetic field that can be steadily increased or decreased, a crackling sound is heard from a speaker connected to the amplifier. As the domain boundaries change in size, each change induces a sudden short rush of current through the search coil and these surges are heard as noise from the speaker.

35–9 Magnetic poles. A ring sample of magnetic material simplifies the presentation of most of the concepts associated with the magnetic properties of matter for the reason that the magnetic field of such a ring is confined entirely to its interior. We consider next the magnetization of a body whose field extends to the region surrounding it. The most common examples are a compass needle, or a bar or horseshoe magnet.

Consider a specimen of ferromagnetic material placed in the uniform magnetic field shown in Fig. 35–9(a). As soon as the specimen is introduced, the field becomes greatly distorted. The field at any point is the resultant of the original uniform field and the field set up by the orientation of the magnetic domains [see Fig. 35–9(b)]. In picturesque language, we may say that the lines of induction "crowd" into the iron, leaving the field quite weak at certain places outside the iron. If a watch (whose steel parts will not function properly when magnetized) is completely surrounded by an iron case, very few lines of induction of an external magnetic field will pass through the watch, most of them crowding into the iron case. This is known as *magnetic shielding*.

Upon removing the iron specimen from the field, all of the flux due to the electronic loops will disappear if the iron shows no hysteresis. Usually, however, hysteresis is present and the iron becomes a permanent magnet, with a magnetic field shown in Fig. 35–9(c). If the flux density is measured at various points outside the specimen, it will be found to be quite small at points near the center, but large near the two ends. The magnetic field

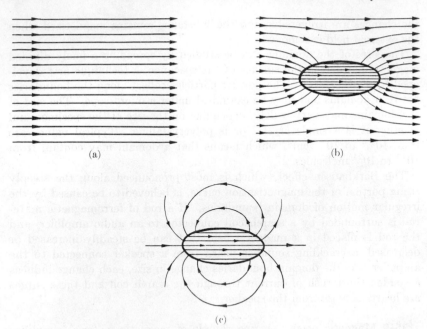

FIG. 35–9. (a) Original uniform magnetic field. (b) Field after insertion of specimen of iron. (c) Field of permanently magnetized specimen. The regions near the ends of the specimen, where most of the lines of induction enter or leave, are called *poles*.

set up in the space around the bar magnet appears as though the "cause" of the magnetism were concentrated on the ends. In fact, before the relations between electrical and magnetic effects were understood as well as they are today, it was assumed that the magnetism actually was due to "magnetic charges," or, as they were called, magnetic "poles." In spite of the fact that magnetic charges are no longer believed to exist, it is nevertheless convenient in many instances to make use of the magnetic pole concept and to compute the field of a magnetized body in terms of its poles rather than in terms of its electronic loop currents.

35–10 Torque on a bar magnet. It was shown in Section 31–9 that the torque acting on a closed loop of wire carrying a current i and enclosing an area a when placed with its plane parallel to a magnetic field of flux density B is given by

$$\Gamma = Bia.$$

Consider a strong bar magnet of length l and cross-sectional area A placed

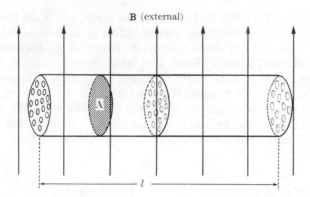

B (external)

FIG. 35–10. A strong bar magnet in a weak external field.

perpendicular to a weak external magnetic field, as shown in Fig. 35–10. Assume that all the electronic loops are aligned with their planes parallel to the field and that their alignment is not destroyed or affected by the field. If there are n loops per unit volume, there will be a total of nAl such loops, and if each loop encloses an area a, the resultant torque acting on all the loops will be

$$\Gamma = (Bia) \times (nAl) \tag{35–9}$$

$$= B \times (ianA) \times l. \tag{35–10}$$

The quantity in parentheses in (35–10) is of great importance. The product ia (current times area) is called the *magnetic moment* of a current loop. Multiplying it by the number of loops per unit volume, n, we get ian, which is the *magnetic moment per unit volume*, or *intensity of magnetization*. Finally, multiplying by the area A, we get a quantity that expresses the peculiar characteristics of the end faces or *poles*. We define the pole strength m of each of the end faces by the equation

$$m = ianA. \tag{35–11}$$

Since i is in amperes, a and A in square meters, and n is a pure number divided by a volume in cubic meters, the units of pole strength are *ampere-meters*.

Finally, substituting Eq. (35–11) in (35–10), we get for the torque on a bar magnet

$$\Gamma = Bml. \tag{35–12}$$

Since $ml = (ian) \times (Al) =$ magnetic moment per unit volume × volume of magnet, this quantity represents the total magnetic moment of the magnet.

If the external magnetic field is that of the earth, and if the bar magnet is free to swing in a horizontal plane, the effect of the torque Bml will be a rotation until the axis of the magnet is parallel to the horizontal component of the earth's field. When this takes place it is found that one pole always points in a northerly direction. This pole is known as the *north-seeking pole* of the magnet; the other is called the *south-seeking pole*. For brevity, these are usually called simply the north and south poles.

Equation (35–12) can be interpreted as follows. Suppose that on each pole of the magnet, of pole strength m, there is exerted a force

$$F = Bm, \qquad\qquad (35\text{–}13)$$

this force being in the same direction as **B** on a north pole, and opposite to **B** on a south pole (Fig. 35–11). Since the poles are separated by a distance l, the torque on the magnet is

$$\Gamma = Fl = Bml,$$

which is the same as Eq. (35–12).

We may therefore consider the torque as due either to (a) electronic loop currents, and compute it from the equation

$$\Gamma = B \times (ianA) \times l,$$

or to (b) forces on the poles of the magnet, and compute it from the equation

$$\Gamma = Bml.$$

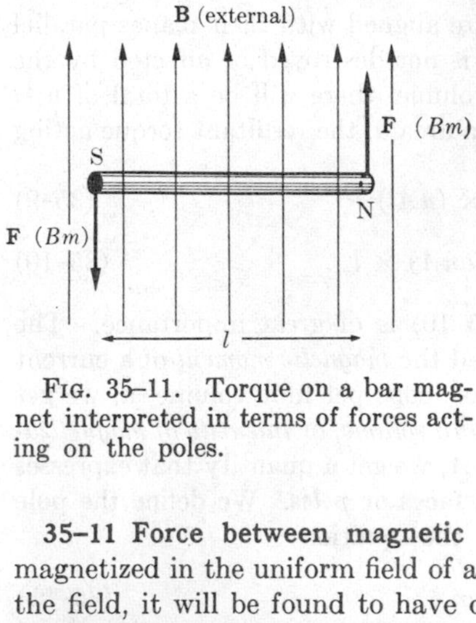

Fig. 35–11. Torque on a bar magnet interpreted in terms of forces acting on the poles.

35–11 Force between magnetic poles. If a long, thin iron bar is magnetized in the uniform field of a long solenoid and then removed from the field, it will be found to have only two poles, concentrated near the extreme ends. Since the end faces are small, we may regard them as points, or *point poles*. In the case of such a long bar magnet, the influence of the magnetic field of one pole on the other may be neglected. In the neighborhood of one pole, therefore, the field is radial with lines of induction that are straight lines radiating from the pole, as shown in Fig. 35–12(a), where the convention has been adopted that the field is *away* from a north pole. It is important to show that the magnitude of the magnetic induction at any point near one pole, but far from the other pole, varies inversely as the square of the distance from the near pole. To prove this, let us place a circular loop of wire of radius r so that the point pole is at the center, as

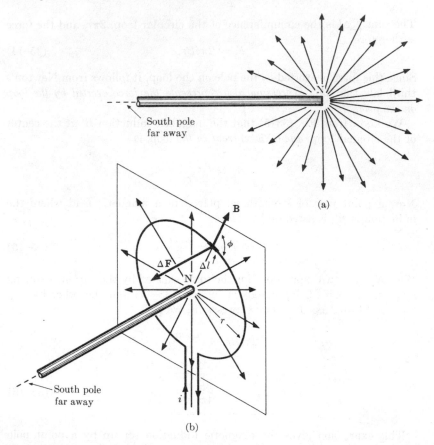

South pole
far away

(a)

B

φ

ΔF

Δl

N

r

South pole
far away

i

(b)

FIG. 35–12. (a) Radial magnetic field due to one pole of a long, thin bar magnet. (b) Circular loop of wire carrying a current and having a point pole at its center.

shown in Fig. 35–12(b). The orientation of the loop is arbitrary. A small element of length Δl, in which there is a current i, is in a magnetic field $\mathbf{B}$, *due to the pole.* The force $\mathbf{\Delta F}$ acting on the element is given by Eq. (31–7), or

$$\Delta F = iB\Delta l,$$

since the angle ϕ between $\mathbf{B}$ and Δl is 90°. The direction of the force $\mathbf{\Delta F}$ is perpendicular to the plane determined by $\mathbf{B}$ and Δl, that is, perpendicular to the plane of the coil. This is the direction of all the $\mathbf{\Delta F}$'s due to all the Δl's, and hence the total force is

$$F = iB\sum\Delta l.$$

The sum $\sum \Delta l$ is the circumference of the circular loop, $2\pi r$, and the force is therefore

$$F = 2\pi i B r. \tag{35-14}$$

Since this force is exerted *by* the pole *on* the loop, it follows from Newton's third law that *this expression also represents the force exerted by the loop on the pole.*

We know from Eq. (33–5) that the magnetic induction B' at the center of the circular loop, *due to the current in the loop,* is

$$B' = \frac{\mu_0}{2} \frac{i}{r}.$$

Now a point pole of strength m, placed in a magnetic field where the induction is B', is acted on by a force

$$F = B'm = \frac{\mu_0 i m}{2r}. \tag{35-15}$$

We now have two expressions for the force exerted by the current-carrying loop on the point pole, one given by Eq. (35–14) and the other by Eq. (35–15). Equating these two expressions, we get

$$2\pi i B r = \frac{\mu_0 i m}{2r},$$

or

$$\boxed{B = \frac{\mu_0}{4\pi} \frac{m}{r^2}.} \tag{35-16}$$

This expression gives the magnetic induction set up by a point pole of strength m, at a point whose distance from the pole is r. If we place at this point one pole of another long thin bar magnet of pole strength m', the force on this pole is

$$F = Bm',$$

or

$$\boxed{F = \frac{\mu_0}{4\pi} \frac{mm'}{r^2}.} \tag{35-17}$$

If the poles are alike, the force is a repulsion; if unlike, the force is an attraction.

This equation has the same form as Coulomb's law for the force between point charges, and it is often taken as the starting point from which one develops all "magnetic" equations. However, since we now believe that the magnetic effects of magnetized matter are actually due to its revolving or spinning electrons and that the "poles" of a magnetized body are only a convenient mathematical artifice, it seems preferable to base the magnetic equations on the general law of force between moving charges.

Finally, since we have shown that in a vacuum $H = B/\mu_0$, it follows from Eq. (35–16) that the magnetic intensity H in vacuum, due to a point pole of strength m, is

$$H = \frac{1}{4\pi} \frac{m}{r^2}. \tag{35–18}$$

The resultant magnetic intensity due to all poles present is the additional term in the definition of H that was mentioned in Section 35–3.

The reader can now appreciate that the magnetization of a cylindrical rod or a U-shaped magnet is a very complicated problem. Suppose a short iron rod, originally unmagnetized, is placed in a long solenoid. The magnetic intensity H, before the rod is inserted, is given by Ni/l. But as soon as the rod becomes magnetized, poles appear at its ends and a new component of H develops due to these poles. This component is opposite in direction to the original H (why?) and is called a *demagnetizing* field. If the magnetizing current in the solenoid is now reduced to zero, and if the iron shows hysteresis, the pole strength decreases to some extent but does not become zero. A component of H due to the poles remains, and since it is opposite in direction to the remanent flux density, the magnetic state of a permanent bar magnet is represented by a point on the hysteresis loop in the second quadrant, such as point g in Fig. 35–5.

EXAMPLE. In Fig. 35–13, a long straight conductor perpendicular to the plane of the paper carries a current i. A bar magnet having point poles of strength m at its ends lies in the plane of the paper. What is the magnitude and direction of the magnetic intensity **H** at point P?

The vectors $\mathbf{H}_i$, $\mathbf{H}_N$, and $\mathbf{H}_S$ represent the components of **H** due respectively to the current and to the N and S poles of the magnet. The component H_i is

$$H_i = \frac{1}{2\pi} \frac{i}{a}.$$

The components H_N and H_S are, respectively,

$$H_N = \frac{1}{4\pi} \frac{m}{b^2}, \qquad H_S = \frac{1}{4\pi} \frac{m}{c^2}.$$

The resultant of these three vectors is the magnetic intensity **H** at the point P.

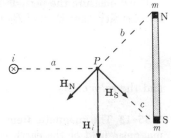

FIG. 35–13. Magnetic intensity components, at a point in space, due to magnet poles and to a current in a wire.

35–12 Oscillation of a bar magnet in a magnetic field. Figure 35–14 is a top view of a bar magnet in a horizontal field **B**. The magnet is pivoted at its center, either suspended by a supporting fiber or pivoted from below, as is a compass needle. The support is assumed to exert no torque on the magnet.

When the magnet is displaced from its equilibrium position by an angle θ, the restoring torque is

$$\Gamma = -Bm \times l \sin \theta,$$

where ml is the total magnetic moment of the bar magnet. The minus sign is introduced because we have a *restoring* torque.

If θ is small we may replace $\sin \theta$ by θ.

$$\Gamma = -Bml\theta.$$

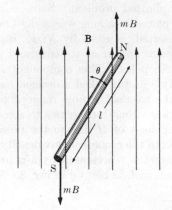

This is the condition necessary for angular harmonic motion, and the magnet therefore oscillates about its equilibrium position with a period

$$T = 2\pi \sqrt{\frac{I_0}{Bml}},$$

FIG. 35–14. Bar magnet pivoted at its center, vibrating in a uniform magnetic field.

where I_0 is the moment of inertia of the magnet about its center of gravity. The magnetic induction B can therefore be computed if the other factors are known.

If we measure the periods T_1 and T_2 at two points where the magnetic flux densities are B_1 and B_2 respectively, then

$$\frac{T_1}{T_2} = \sqrt{\frac{B_2}{B_1}},$$

and the *ratio* of B_2 to B_1 can be found without knowing I_0 or ml.

35–13 The magnetic field of the earth. To a first approximation, the magnetic field of the earth is the same as that outside a uniformly magnetized sphere. Figure 35–15 represents a section through the earth. The heavy vertical line is its axis of rotation, and the *geographic* north and south poles are lettered N_G and S_G. The direction of the (presumed) internal magnetization makes an angle of about 15° with the earth's axis.

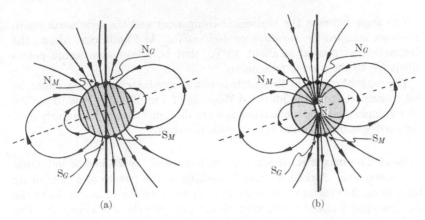

(a)   (b)

FIG. 35–15. Simplified diagram of the magnetic field of the earth.

The dotted line indicates the plane of the magnetic equator, and the letters N_M and S_M represent the so-called *magnetic* north and south poles. Note carefully that lines of induction emerge from the earth's surface over the entire southern magnetic hemisphere and enter its surface over the entire northern magnetic hemisphere. Hence if we wish to attribute the earth's field to magnetic poles we must assume, on the basis of this hypothesis about the earth's internal magnetic state, that magnetic *north* poles are distributed over the entire *southern* magnetic hemisphere, and magnetic *south* poles over the entire *northern* magnetic hemisphere. This can be very confusing. The north and south magnetic poles, considered as points on the earth's surface, are simply those points where the field is vertical. The former is located at latitude 70°N, longitude 96°W.

It is interesting to note that the same field at *external* points would result if the earth's magnetism were due to a short bar magnet near its center as in Fig. 35–15(b), with the south pole of the magnet pointing towards the north magnetic pole. The field within the earth is different in the two cases, but for obvious reasons experimental verification of either hypothesis is impossible.

Except at the magnetic equator, the earth's field is not horizontal. The angle which the field makes with the horizontal is called the *angle of dip* or the *inclination*. At Cambridge, Mass. (about 45°N lat.), the magnitude of the earth's field is about 5.8×10^{-5} w/m^2 and the angle of dip about 73°. Hence the horizontal component at Cambridge is about 1.7×10^{-5} w/m^2 and the vertical component about 5.5×10^{-5} w/m^2. In northern magnetic latitudes the vertical component is directed downward; in southern magnetic latitudes it is upward. The angle of dip is, of course, 90° at the magnetic poles.

The angle between the horizontal component and the true north-south direction is called the *variation* or *declination*. At Cambridge, Mass., the declination at present is about 15°W, that is, a compass needle points about 15° to the west of true north.

The magnetic field of the earth is not as symmetrical as one might be led to suspect from the idealized drawing of Fig. 35–15. It is in reality very complicated; the inclination and the declination vary irregularly over the earth's surface, and also vary with the time.

35–14 The magnetic circuit. As we have seen, every line of induction is a closed line. Although there is nothing in the nature of a flow along these lines, it is useful to draw an analogy between the closed paths of the flux lines and a closed conducting circuit in which there is a current. The region occupied by the magnetic flux is called a *magnetic circuit*, of which a Rowland ring is the simplest example. When the windings on such a ring are closely spaced over its surface, practically all the flux lines are confined to the ring [Fig. 35–16(a)]. Even if the winding is concentrated over only a small portion of the ring, as in Fig. 35–16(b), the permeability of the ring is so much greater than that of the surrounding air that most of the flux is still confined to the material of the ring. The small part which returns via an air path is called the *leakage flux* and is indicated by dotted lines.

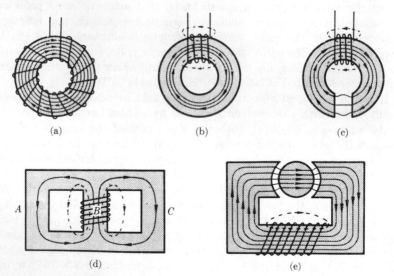

(a)   (b)   (c)

(d)   (e)

FIG. 35–16. Various magnetic circuits. (a) Rowland ring completely wound. (b) Rowland ring partially wound, showing leakage. (c) Fringing in an air gap. (d) Leakage in a transformer core. (e) Fringing and leakage in the core of a motor or generator.

If the ring contains an air gap, as in Fig. 35–16(c), there will be a certain amount of spreading or "fringing" of the flux lines at the air gap, but again most of the flux is confined to a well-defined path. This magnetic circuit may be considered to consist of the iron ring and the air gap "in series."

Figure 35–16(d) shows a section of a common type of transformer core. Here the magnetic circuit is divided, and sections A and C may be considered to be "in parallel" with each other, and in series with section B.

Figure 35–16(e) is the magnetic circuit of a motor or generator. The two air gaps are in series with the iron portion of the circuit.

One of the important problems in the design of apparatus in which there is a magnetic circuit is to compute the flux density which will result from a given current in a given winding on a given core or, conversely, to design a core and windings so as to produce a desired flux density. It is this problem which we are now to consider, although naturally many of the factors which arise in practice must be ignored for simplicity.

Consider first a closed ring (no air gap) of uniform cross section. We have shown that within the ring

$$B = \mu \frac{Ni}{l},$$

and since $\Phi = BA$,

$$\Phi = \mu \frac{NiA}{l},$$

or

$$\Phi = \frac{Ni}{l/\mu A}. \tag{35–19}$$

Now the resistance R of a conductor of uniform cross section A, length l, and resistivity ρ is given by

$$R = \rho \frac{l}{A},$$

or in terms of the conductivity σ ($\sigma = 1/\rho$),

$$R = \frac{l}{\sigma A}.$$

If such a conductor is connected to the terminals of a seat of emf of negligible internal resistance, the circuit equation becomes

$$I = \frac{\text{emf}}{l/\sigma A}.$$

The form of this equation is the same as that of Eq. (35–19), with current corresponding to magnetic flux, the quantity Ni corresponding to electromotive force, and $l/\mu A$ corresponding to resistance. In view of the close analogy, the numerator in Eq. (35–19) is called the *magnetomotive force*, and the denominator is called the *reluctance* of the magnetic circuit.

$$\text{Magnetomotive force (mmf)} = Ni, \qquad (35\text{–}20)$$

$$\text{Reluctance } (\mathfrak{R}) = \frac{l}{\mu A}, \qquad (35\text{–}21)$$

and Eq. (35–19) may be written

$$\Phi = \frac{\text{mmf}}{\mathfrak{R}}. \qquad (35\text{–}22)$$

Magnetomotive force is evidently expressed in *ampere-turns*, and reluctance in *ampere-turns per weber*. The reluctance of a magnetic circuit is the required number of ampere-turns, per weber of magnetic flux in the circuit.

The advantage of writing the expression for the flux in a magnetic circuit in the form of Eq. (35–22) is most apparent when one considers a circuit containing an air gap (or more generally, when the circuit is composed of sections of different permeabilities, lengths, and cross sections). It turns out that the *equivalent reluctance* of such a circuit may be found in the same way that one finds the equivalent resistance of a network of conductors. For example, a ring containing an air gap corresponds to two resistors in series and the equivalent reluctance of the circuit is the sum of the reluctances of ring and gap. The arms A and C of Fig. 35–16(d) are in parallel, and the reciprocal of their equivalent reluctance is the sum of the reciprocals of the reluctances of the arms individually. For a simple "series" magnetic circuit one has

$$\Phi = \frac{\text{mmf}}{\sum \mathfrak{R}} = \frac{\text{mmf}}{\sum (l/\mu A)} = \frac{\text{mmf}}{l_1/\mu_1 A_1 + l_2/\mu_2 A_2 + \cdots}, \qquad (35\text{–}23)$$

where l_1, l_2, etc., are the lengths of the various portions of the circuit, μ_1, μ_2, etc., the corresponding permeabilities, and A_1, A_2, etc., the cross-sectional areas.

The statements above are correct to a good approximation if the leakage flux is small.

EXAMPLE 1. The mean length of a Rowland ring is 50 cm and its cross section is 4 cm². Use the permeability curve of Fig. 35–2 to compute the magnetomotive force needed to establish a flux of 4×10^{-4} weber in the ring. What current is required if the ring is wound with 200 turns of wire?

The desired flux density B is

$$B = \frac{\Phi}{A} = \frac{4 \times 10^{-4}\ \text{w}}{4 \times 10^{-4}\ \text{m}^2} = 1\ \frac{\text{w}}{\text{m}^2}.$$

From Fig. 35–2, the permeability at this flux density is about 65×10^{-4} w/amp·m. Hence the reluctance $\mathfrak{R}$ is

$$\mathfrak{R} = \frac{l}{\mu A} = \frac{0.5\ \text{m}}{65 \times 10^{-4}\ (\text{w/amp·m}) \times 4 \times 10^{-4}\ \text{m}^2} = 1.92 \times 10^5\ \frac{\text{amp}}{\text{w}},$$

and since mmf $= \Phi\mathfrak{R}$, the required magnetomotive force is

$$\text{mmf} = 4 \times 10^{-4}\ \text{w} \times 1.92 \times 10^5\ (\text{amp/w}) = 77\ \text{amp-turns}.$$

If the ring is wound with 200 turns, the current required is 0.385 amp.

EXAMPLE 2. If an air gap one millimeter in length is cut in the ring, what current is required to maintain the same flux?

The reluctance of the air gap is

$$\mathfrak{R} = \frac{l}{\mu_0 A} = \frac{10^{-3}\ \text{m}}{12.57 \times 10^{-7}\ (\text{w/amp·m}) \times 4 \times 10^{-4}\ \text{m}^2} = 20 \times 10^5\ \frac{\text{amp}}{\text{w}}.$$

Neglecting the small change in length of the iron, its reluctance is the same as before, or 1.92×10^5 amp-turns/w. Thus the reluctance of the gap, although only 1 mm long, is ten times as great as that of the iron portion of the circuit. The reluctance of the entire circuit is now $(20 \times 10^5 + 1.92 \times 10^5)$ amp/w $= 22 \times 10^5$ amp/w. The number of ampere turns required is 880 and the corresponding current is 4.4 amp.

PROBLEMS

35–1. A Rowland ring having 500 turns of wire and a mean diameter of 12 cm carries a current of 0.3 amp. The relative permeability of the core is 600. (a) What is the flux density in the core? (b) What is the magnetic intensity? (c) What part of the flux density is due to electronic loop currents in the core?

35–2. Table 35–3 lists corresponding values of H and B for a specimen of commercial hot-rolled silicon steel, a material widely used in transformer cores. (a) Construct graphs of B and μ as functions of H, in the range from $H = 0$ to $H = 1000$ amp-turns/m. (b) What is the maximum permeability? (c) What is the initial permeability

TABLE 35–3

MAGNETIC PROPERTIES OF SILICON STEEL

Magnetic intensity H, amp-turns/m	Flux density B, w/m^2
0	0
10	0.050
20	0.15
40	0.43
50	0.54
60	0.62
80	0.74
100	0.83
150	0.98
200	1.07
500	1.27
1,000	1.34
10,000	1.65
100,000	2.02
800,000	2.92

($H = 0$)? (d) What is the permeability when $H = 800,000$ amp-turns/m?

35–3. Suppose a cylindrical bar magnet of Alnico 5, 1 cm in diameter and 10 cm long, is permanently and uniformly magnetized with a pole strength of 75 amp·m. (a) What is the magnetic moment of the magnet? (b) What is the torque exerted on the magnet when it is suspended in air at right angles to a magnetic field of flux density 1 mw/m^2? (c) Compare the magnitude of H in the above field with the coercive force of Alnico 5.

35–4. A solenoidal winding of 100 turns of wire is wound on a wooden rod of the same dimensions as the bar magnet in Problem 35–3. What current must be sent through the wire in order that the torque acting on the solenoid in an external field shall equal the torque on the bar magnet?

35–5. A bar magnet has a coercivity of 4×10^3 amp/m. It is desired to demagnetize it by inserting it inside a solenoid 12 cm long and having 60 turns. What current should be carried by the solenoid?

35–6. An electron moves on a horizontal line from east to west along the equator. What is the direction of the force exerted on it by the earth's magnetic field?

35–7. The poles of a long, thin magnet are 40 cm apart, and have a strength of 80 amp·m. What are the direction and magnitude of the magnetic intensity and of the magnetic induction at a point 30 cm from the south pole and 50 cm from the north pole?

35–8. What are the magnetic intensity and the magnetic induction at a point 20 cm from the magnet of Problem 35-7 and on the perpendicular bisector of the magnet?

35-9. A bar magnet 10 cm long has poles whose strength is 200 amp·m. It is placed parallel to a long wire carrying a 10-amp current and 5 cm from it. (a) What torque is exerted on the magnet? (b) Draw a diagram showing the direction of the torque on the magnet.

35-10. The two bar magnets of Fig. 35-17 each have poles whose strength is 80 amp·m. What resultant force is exerted on each by the other?

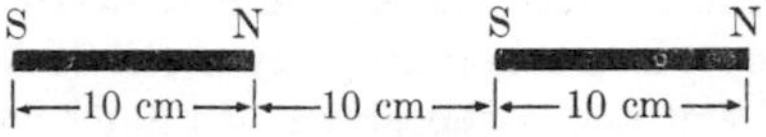

FIGURE 35-17

35-11. A bar magnet is 20 cm long and has poles of strength 60 amp·m. What is the magnetic intensity 10 cm from the north pole along the axis of the magnet?

35-12. The two magnets of Problem 35-10 are placed parallel to each other and 10 cm apart, like poles nearest each other. What is the resultant force on each magnet?

35-13. The horizontal component of the flux density of the earth's magnetic field at Cambridge, Mass., is 1.7×10^{-5} w/m². What is the horizontal component of the magnetic intensity?

35-14. A compass needle with a moment of inertia of 40 gm·cm² oscillates through a small angle in a horizontal plane with a period of 3.0 sec. What is its magnetic moment if the horizontal component of the flux density of the earth's magnetic field is 1.5×10^{-5} w/m² ? If the needle is moved to a different place where the period is 2.8 sec, what is the horizontal component of the flux density at this place?

35-15. A bar magnet has a moment of inertia of 0.2×10^{-4} kgm·m², with respect to an axis perpendicular to it at its center. The magnet has a length of 10 cm and poles of strength 4 amp·m. What will be the period of oscillation of the bar when suspended from its center in a magnetic field of 0.1 w/m²?

35-16. An iron Rowland ring has a mean circumferential length of 40 cm and an area of 5 cm². The ring is wound with 350 turns of wire and carries a current of 0.2 amp. (a) What is the magnetomotive force on the ring? (b) What is the magnetic intensity in the ring? (c) Using the permeability curve of Fig. 35-2, determine the permeability of iron at this value of magnetic intensity. (d) What is the reluctance of the magnetic circuit? (e) What is the total flux in the ring?

35-17. A Rowland ring has a cross section of 2 cm², a mean length of 30 cm, and is wound with 400 turns. Find the current in the winding that is required to set up a flux density of 0.1 w/m² in the ring (a) if the ring is of annealed iron (Table 35-1), (b) if the ring is of silicon steel (Problem 35-2). (c) Repeat the computations above if a flux density of 1.2 w/m² is desired.

35-18. A gap 0.5 mm wide is cut in the ring of Problem 35-16. (a) What is the reluctance of the magnetic circuit? (b) What is now the flux in the ring?

CHAPTER 36

INDUCTANCE AND CAPACITANCE

36–1 Self-inductance. We have shown that an emf is induced in a stationary circuit whenever the magnetic flux linking the circuit is increasing or decreasing. In the preceding examples, the source of the magnetic field has been considered to be independent of the circuit in which the induced emf appears. But whenever there is a current in any circuit, this current sets up a magnetic field which itself links with the circuit and which varies when the current varies. Hence any circuit in which there is a varying current has induced in it an emf because of the variation in its own magnetic field. Such an emf is called a *self-induced electromotive force*. For example, Fig. 36–1 shows in a schematic way a coil of N turns connected in series with a seat of emf and a rheostat and linked by Φ lines of induction. As the rheostat slider is moved the flux linking the coil varies and thus induces an emf in the circuit.

The number of flux linkages per unit current is called the *self-inductance* of the circuit, L.

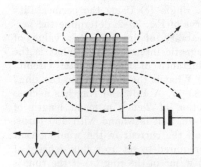

Fig. 36–1. A flux of Φ lines of induction linking a coil of N turns. When the current in the circuit changes, the flux changes also, and a self-induced emf appears in the circuit.

$$L = \frac{N\Phi}{i}. \qquad (36\text{–}1)$$

The unit of self-inductance is evidently the *weber-turn per ampere*. For brevity, one weber-turn per ampere is called one *henry*, in honor of Joseph Henry.

The self-inductance of a circuit depends on its size, shape, number of turns, etc. It also depends on the magnetic properties of any materials in which magnetic fields exist. For example, the self-inductance of a solenoid of given dimensions is much greater if it has an iron core than if it is in vacuum. If no *ferro*magnetic materials are present, the self-inductance is a constant, independent of the current, since then the flux density at any point is directly proportional to the current. When ferromagnetic materials are present, the self-inductance varies in a complicated way as the current varies because of the variations in permeability. For simplicity, we shall consider only circuits of constant self-inductance.

Equation (36–1) can be written

$$N\Phi = Li.$$

If Φ and i change with the time, then

$$N\frac{\Delta\Phi}{\Delta t} = L\frac{\Delta i}{\Delta t},$$

and since the self-induced emf $\mathcal{E}$ is

$$\mathcal{E} = -N\frac{\Delta\Phi}{\Delta t},$$

it follows that

$$\boxed{\mathcal{E} = -L\frac{\Delta i}{\Delta t}.} \qquad (36\text{–}2)$$

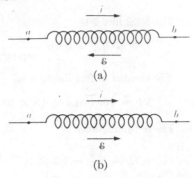

Fig. 36–2. Direction of a self-induced emf. (a) i increasing, $\mathcal{E}$ opposite to i, point a at a higher potential than b. (b) i decreasing, $\mathcal{E}$ and i in the same direction, b at higher potential than a. ($R = 0$.)

The self-inductance of a circuit may therefore be regarded also as *the self-induced emf per unit rate of change of current*. When $\mathcal{E}$ is expressed in volts and $\Delta i/\Delta t$ in amperes per second, L is in henrys. Hence *the self-inductance of a circuit is one henry if an emf of one volt is induced in the circuit when the current in the circuit changes at the rate of one ampere per second.*

A circuit or part of a circuit which has inductance is called an *inductor*. An inductor is represented by the symbol ⎯〇〇〇〇〇〇〇〇〇〇〇⎯.

The direction of a self-induced emf is found from Lenz's law. The "cause" of the emf is an increasing or decreasing current. If the current is increasing, the direction of the induced emf is opposite to that of the current. If the current is decreasing, the emf and the current are in the same direction. Thus it is the *change* in current, not the current itself, which is "opposed" by the induced emf (see Fig. 36–2).

EXAMPLE 1. Compute the self-inductance of the toroid in Fig. 33–9 if it is wound with 100 turns of wire on a form of mean circumference 20 cm, cross-sectional area 1 cm², and relative permeability $K_m = 1000$ (assumed constant).

Assume an arbitrary current i in the windings. The flux density B in the core is

$$B = \mu H = K_m\mu_0\frac{Ni}{l}$$

$$= \frac{1000 \times 4\pi \times 10^{-7}\ (\text{w/amp·m}) \times 100\ \text{turns} \times i}{0.20\ \text{m}}$$

$$= 0.63i\ \frac{\text{w}}{\text{amp·m}^2}.$$

The total flux Φ is

$$\Phi = BA = 0.63i \, \frac{\mathrm{w}}{\mathrm{amp \cdot m^2}} \times 10^{-4} \, \mathrm{m^2} = 6.3 \times 10^{-5} i \, \frac{\mathrm{w}}{\mathrm{amp}} \cdot$$

The number of flux linkages is

$$N\Phi = 100 \text{ turns} \times 6.3 \times 10^{-5} \, i \, \frac{\mathrm{w}}{\mathrm{amp}} = 6.3 \times 10^{-3} i \, \frac{\text{weber-turns}}{\mathrm{amp}} \cdot$$

The self-inductance is

$$L = \frac{N\Phi}{i} = 6.3 \times 10^{-3} \, \frac{\text{weber-turns}}{\mathrm{amp}} = 6.3 \times 10^{-3} \text{ henry.}$$

EXAMPLE 2. If the current in the coil above increases uniformly from zero to 1 amp in 0.1 sec, find the magnitude and direction of the self-induced emf.

$$\mathcal{E} = -L \, \frac{\Delta i}{\Delta t} = -6.3 \times 10^{-3} \, \mathrm{h} \times \frac{1 \text{ amp}}{0.1 \text{ sec}} = -0.063 \text{ volts.}$$

Since the current is increasing, the direction of this emf is opposite to that of the current.

36–2 Circuit containing inductance and resistance. An inductor in which there is an increasing current becomes a seat of emf whose direction is opposite to that of the current. As a consequence of this back emf, the current in an inductive circuit will not rise to its final value at the instant when the circuit is closed, but will grow at a rate which depends on the inductance and resistance of the circuit.

Figure 36–3 shows a series circuit consisting of a resistanceless inductor, a noninductive resistor, a battery of emf $\mathcal{E}$ and negligible internal resistance, and a switch S. At some instant after the switch is closed, let i represent the current in the circuit and $\Delta i/\Delta t$ its rate of increase. The potential difference across the inductor is*

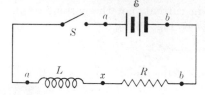

$$V_{ax} = L \, \frac{\Delta i}{\Delta t},$$

FIG. 36–3. Series circuit containing resistance and self-inductance (R-L circuit).

and that across the resistor is

$$V_{xb} = iR.$$

* If the current in Fig. 36–3 is increasing, the induced emf in the inductor is from right to left as in Fig. 36–2(a). The inductor then corresponds to a battery with its negative terminal at the right and its positive terminal at the left. Point a is therefore at a higher potential than point x, and V_{ax} is positive.

Since $\varepsilon = V_{ax} + V_{xb}$, it follows that

$$\varepsilon = L \frac{\Delta i}{\Delta t} + iR. \tag{36-3}$$

The rate of increase of current is therefore

$$\frac{\Delta i}{\Delta t} = \frac{\varepsilon - iR}{L} = \frac{\varepsilon}{L} - \frac{R}{L} i.$$

At the instant the circuit is first closed, $i = 0$ and the current starts to grow at the rate

$$\left(\frac{\Delta i}{\Delta t}\right)_{\text{initial}} = \frac{\varepsilon}{L}.$$

The greater the self-inductance L, the more slowly does the current start to increase.

As the current increases, the term Ri/L increases also, and hence the *rate* of increase of current becomes smaller and smaller. When the current reaches its final *steady-state* value I, its rate of increase is zero. Then

$$0 = \frac{\varepsilon}{L} - \frac{R}{L} I$$

and

$$I = \frac{\varepsilon}{R}.$$

That is, the final current does not depend on the self-inductance and is the same as it would be in a pure resistance R connected to a cell of emf ε.

The equation describing the increasing current (the solution of Eq. 36–3) is found to be

$$i = \frac{\varepsilon}{R} (1 - e^{-Rt/L}) = I(1 - e^{-Rt/L}). \tag{36-4}$$

When $t = 0$, the exponential term $e^{-Rt/L} = 1$ and the initial current is zero. As t increases, the exponential term approaches zero and the current approaches its steady-state value $I = \varepsilon/R$.

Figure 36–4(a) is a graph of Eq. (36–4). The instantaneous current i first rises rapidly, then increases more slowly and approaches asymptotically the final value $I = \varepsilon/R$. The *time constant* of the circuit is defined as the time at which $Rt/L = 1$, or when

$$t = \frac{L}{R}.$$

If L is expressed in henrys [1 henry = 1 volt/(amp/sec)] and R is in

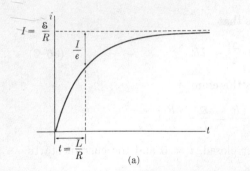

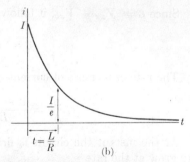

(a)   (b)

Fig. 36–4. (a) Growth of a current in a circuit containing inductance and resistance. (b) Decay of current in a circuit containing inductance and resistance.

ohms (1 ohm = 1 volt/amp), the time constant is in seconds. When $t = L/R$,

$$i = I\,(1 - e^{-1}) = I\,[1 - (1/2.718)] = I\,[1 - 0.369]$$
$$= 0.631\,I,$$

or about 63% of I.

For a circuit with a given resistance, this time is longer the larger the inductance, and vice versa. Thus although the graph of i vs. t has the same general shape whatever the inductance, the current rises rapidly to its final value if L is small, and slowly if L is large. For example, if $R = 100$ ohms and $L = 10$ henrys,

$$\frac{L}{R} = \frac{10\text{ h}}{100\text{ ohms}} = 0.1\text{ sec,}$$

and the current increases to about 63% of its final value in 0.1 sec. On the other hand, if $L = 0.01$ henry,

$$\frac{L}{R} = \frac{0.01\text{ h}}{100\text{ ohms}} = 10^{-4}\text{ sec,}$$

and only 10^{-4} sec is required for the current to increase to 63% of its final value.

If there is a steady current I in the circuit of Fig. 36–3 and the battery is short-circuited, the decay of the current depicted in Fig. 36–4(b) follows a curve which is the exact inverse of Fig. 36–4(a). The equation of the decaying current is

$$i = Ie^{-Rt/L}, \tag{36–5}$$

and the time constant, L/R, is the time for the current to decrease to $1/e$th of its original value.

EXAMPLE. An inductor of inductance 3 henrys and resistance 6 ohms is connected to the terminals of a battery of emf 12 volts and of negligible internal resistance. (a) Find the initial rate of increase of current in the circuit. (b) Find the rate of increase of current at the instant when the current is one ampere. (c) What is the instantaneous current 0.2 sec after the circuit is closed? (d) What is the final steady-state current?

(a) From Eq. (36–3),

$$\frac{\Delta i}{\Delta t} = \frac{\mathcal{E}}{L} - \frac{R}{L} i.$$

The initial current is zero. Hence the initial rate of increase of current is

$$\frac{\Delta i}{\Delta t} = \frac{\mathcal{E}}{L} = \frac{12 \text{ volts}}{3 \text{ h}} = 4 \frac{\text{amp}}{\text{sec}}.$$

(b) When $i = 1$ amp,

$$\frac{\Delta i}{\Delta t} = \frac{12 \text{ volts}}{3 \text{ h}} - \frac{6 \text{ ohms}}{3 \text{ h}} \times 1 \text{ amp} = 2 \frac{\text{amp}}{\text{sec}}.$$

(c) From Eq. (36–4),

$$i = \frac{\mathcal{E}}{R} (1 - e^{-Rt/L}) = \frac{12 \text{ volts}}{6 \text{ ohms}} (1 - e^{-6 \times 0.2/3}) = 2 \text{ amp} (1 - e^{-0.4})$$

$$= 2 \text{ amp} (1 - 0.672) = 0.65 \text{ amp}.$$

(d) The final steady-state current is

$$I = \frac{\mathcal{E}}{R} = \frac{12 \text{ volts}}{6 \text{ ohms}} = 2 \text{ amp}.$$

36–3 Energy associated with an inductor. When the circuit depicted in Fig. 36–3 is closed, the current rises from zero to its final value $I = \mathcal{E}/R$. During this time there is a back emf whose magnitude varies from the full line voltage $\mathcal{E}$ to zero. The variation, however, is not linear. At any moment the back emf is $L \Delta i/\Delta t$ and the current is i. The power input to the inductor is therefore also variable with an instantaneous value equal to

$$P = iL \frac{\Delta i}{\Delta t}. \qquad (36-6)$$

When the current has reached its final steady value I, $\Delta i/\Delta t = 0$ and the power input ceases. The energy that has been supplied to the inductor is used to establish the magnetic field around the inductor where it is "stored" as potential energy. When the switch is opened, the magnetic field collapses and the energy is returned to the circuit. It is this release of energy which maintains the arc often seen when a switch is opened in an inductive circuit.

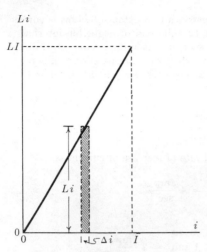

FIG. 36–5. Graph of Li against i, the area under which is the energy stored in the magnetic field around an inductor.

The energy stored in the field around an inductor carrying a steady current I may be calculated in a simple geometric manner with the aid of the graph shown in Fig. 36–5, where Li is plotted against i. Consider the narrow rectangle whose width is Δi (any small change in i), and whose height is the average ordinate Li. The area of this rectangle, shown in cross shading, is $Li \times \Delta i$. But from Eq. (36–6)

$$P\,\Delta t = Li \times \Delta i,$$

and $P\,\Delta t$ is the energy supplied to the inductor during the time interval in which the change Δi took place. The total energy W supplied to the inductor while the current rises from zero to the final value I is the sum of the areas of all such narrow rectangles, that is, the area under the straight line graph. This, however, is merely the area of a triangle of base I and altitude LI. Therefore the energy stored in the field around an inductor carrying a steady current I is

$$W = \tfrac{1}{2}LI^2. \tag{36–7}$$

The same amount of energy is released when the current falls to zero.

36–4 The induction coil. The changes in current that take place upon making or breaking a circuit containing resistance and inductance may be used to generate a high voltage in a neighboring circuit. A device used for this purpose is the so-called *induction coil* and is depicted schematically in Fig. 36–6.

When the switch S is closed, the current in the primary coil rises relatively slowly because the time constant L/R is large. When the magnetic field set up in the iron core is large enough, the iron armature is attracted, thereby breaking the circuit at the point marked G. Even though sparking takes place, the resistance of the air gap at G is relatively large and the time constant L/R is smaller than before. The current therefore decreases at a more rapid rate than that at which it rose. When the primary current is zero, the iron armature springs back, making contact at G, and

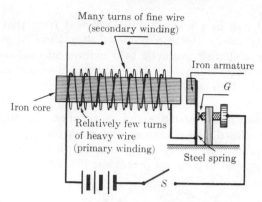

Many turns of fine wire
(secondary winding)

Iron armature

G

Iron core

Relatively few turns
of heavy wire
(primary winding)

Steel spring

S

FIG. 36–6. An induction coil with a mechanical interrupter.

the cycle is repeated, as shown in the upper curve of Fig. 36–7. The number of cycles per second depends on the frequency of vibration of the interrupter which, in turn, depends on the elasticity and inertia of the armature and spring.

Many turns of fine insulated wire are wound outside the primary winding. The changing magnetic flux set up by the changing primary current links with the turns of the secondary winding and induces in the secondary an emf proportional to the rate of change of flux and to the number of turns. Since this rate is larger on the "break" of the circuit than on the "make," the secondary voltage is much larger in one direction, as shown in the lower curve of Fig. 36–7.

The sparking that takes place across the gap at G usually results in excessive heating of the contacts. The contacts are therefore usually made of a metal of high melting point, such as platinum or tungsten. The energy of the spark derives from the energy stored in the magnetic field surrounding the primary. Instead of allowing this energy to become converted into heat exclusively, it is usually the practice to convert some of it into electrostatic energy of a capacitor that is connected across the contact points. With a capacitor connected across G, the current on the break

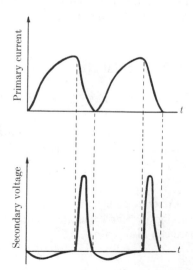

FIG. 36–7. Primary current and secondary voltage obtained with an induction coil.

of the circuit behaves in a manner quite different from that shown in the graphs of Fig. 36–7. Instead of descending steadily, it oscillates and the resulting oscillating magnetic field induces an oscillating emf in the secondary. Further analysis of this behavior is unnecessary at this point, but we shall return to it in the next chapter.

36–5 Circuit containing resistance and capacitance. When the switch S in Fig. 36–8 is closed, the charge on the capacitor does not increase instantaneously to its final value, but approaches this value in the same way as does the current in a circuit containing inductance and resistance.

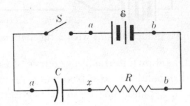

Fig. 36–8. Series circuit containing resistance and capacitance (R-C circuit).

Let q represent the charge on the capacitor at a certain instant after the switch S is closed, and i the current in the circuit at that instant. The instantaneous potential difference V_{ax} is then $V_{ax} = q/C$, and the potential difference V_{xb} is

$$V_{xb} = iR = R\frac{\Delta q}{\Delta t},$$

since $i = \Delta q/\Delta t$. But $\mathcal{E} = V_{ax} + V_{xb}$, so

$$\mathcal{E} = \frac{q}{C} + R\frac{\Delta q}{\Delta t}.$$

This equation has exactly the same form as Eq. (36–3) and therefore has the same solution, namely,

$$q = C\mathcal{E}(1 - e^{-t/RC}).$$

After a sufficiently long time has elapsed, the term $e^{-t/RC}$ becomes negligibly small and the charge q approaches the value $Q = C\mathcal{E}$. Hence we can also write

$$q = Q(1 - e^{-t/RC}). \tag{36–8}$$

Figure 36–9(a) is a graph of this equation. The charge approaches its final value asymptotically and an infinite time is required for the capacitor to become fully charged. The time constant of the circuit is equal to RC.

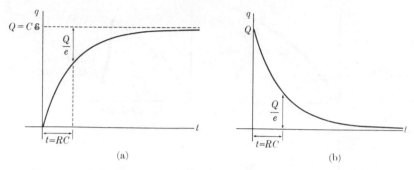

FIG. 36–9. Charge and discharge of a capacitor through a resistor.

For example, if $R = 1$ megohm $= 10^6$ ohms and $C = 1 \ \mu f = 10^{-6}$ farad, the time constant is 1 sec and the charge on the capacitor increases to 63% of its final value in 1 sec.

If the capacitor is originally charged and is then discharged through a resistance R, the charge decreases with time according to the relation

$$q = Qe^{-t/RC}, \tag{36–9}$$

as shown in Fig. 36–9(b). The time constant RC is the time for the charge to decrease to $1/e$th of its original value.

The curves in Fig. 36–9 also show the way in which the potential difference across the capacitor changes, since the potential difference is proportional to the charge.

36–6 The "sweep" circuit.   In the operation of a cathode-ray oscilloscope (see Fig. 38–22) an electron beam passes between two sets of metal plates on its way to a fluorescent screen, where it produces a bright spot of light.   Variations of potential on one set of plates cause horizontal motion of the electron beam, whereas variations of potential on the other set of plates cause vertical motion.   If the potential on the first set of plates is made to increase linearly with the time, and then to become zero almost instantaneously, repeating this cycle over and over again with any desired frequency, the electron beam will sweep horizontally in one direction across the fluorescent screen with uniform linear motion, return to the starting point, and repeat this motion with the same frequency. A simultaneous potential variation on the other set of plates that is repeated with the same frequency will give rise to a figure on the screen that appears to be stationary and which constitutes a graph with time plotted along the horizontal axis.   A circuit for creating a saw-tooth variation of potential such as that shown in Fig. 36–10(c) is called a *sweep circuit*.

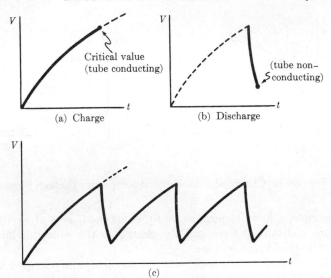

FIG. 36–10. (a) Slow increase of $\mathcal{E}$ (large time constant). (b) Rapid decrease of $\mathcal{E}$ (small time constant). (c) "Saw-tooth" voltage.

A convenient circuit for accomplishing this purpose is shown in Fig. 36–11. The three-element tube at the left is a small gas-filled *thyratron* which operates as follows. The tube is originally nonconducting. When switch S is closed, the capacitor C charges through the resistor R. Both C and R may be varied, and therefore the time constant RC may be adjusted to any desired value. When the potential difference V_{ab} across the capacitor reaches a critical value, shown in Fig. 36–10(a), the tube suddenly "breaks down" and becomes conducting. The capacitor discharges rapidly through the tube, the time constant RC being small because of the low resistance of the tube. The potential difference V_{ab} therefore decreases very quickly to a smaller value at which the thyratron is no longer conducting.

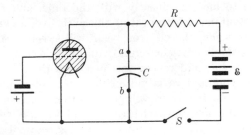

FIG. 36–11. Thyratron tube circuit for producing a "saw-tooth" voltage wave.

The cycle is then repeated, giving rise to the saw-tooth voltage across the capacitor as shown in Fig. 36–10(c). The number of cycles per second may be varied by changing either C or R. In practice, coarse changes in frequency are produced by changing C and fine adjustments by varying R.

36–7 Electrical oscillations.

When the discharge of a capacitor through a resistor was discussed in Section 36–5, the effect of inductance in the circuit was ignored. We now consider how the discharge is affected by inductance, taking up first a circuit in which the resistance is negligible.

Figure 36–12(a) represents schematically a charged capacitor, a switch, and an inductor of negligible resistance. At the instant when the circuit is closed, the capacitor starts to discharge through the inductor. At a later instant, represented in Fig. 36–12(b), the capacitor has completely discharged and the potential difference between its terminals (and those of the inductor) has decreased to zero. The current in the inductor has meanwhile established a magnetic field in the space around it. This magnetic field now decreases, inducing an emf in the inductor in the same direction as the current. The current therefore persists, although with diminishing magnitude, until the magnetic field has disappeared and the capacitor has been charged in the opposite sense to its initial polarity, as in Fig. 36–12(c). The process now repeats itself in the reversed direction, and in the absence of energy losses the charges on the capacitor will surge back and forth indefinitely. This process is called an *electrical oscillation*.

From the energy standpoint, the oscillations of an electrical circuit consist of a transfer of energy back and forth from the electric field of the capacitor to the magnetic field of the inductor, the total energy associated

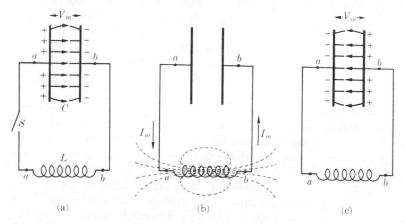

Fig. 36–12.   Energy transfer between electric and magnetic fields in an oscillating circuit (L-C circuit).

TABLE 36-1

OSCILLATION OF A MASS ON A SPRING COMPARED WITH THE
ELECTRICAL OSCILLATION IN AN L-C CIRCUIT

Mass on a spring	Circuit containing inductance and capacitance
Kinetic energy $= \frac{1}{2}mv^2$	Magnetic energy $= \frac{1}{2}Li^2$
Potential energy $= \frac{1}{2}kx^2$	Electrical energy $= \frac{1}{2}\frac{1}{C}q^2$
$\frac{1}{2}mv^2 + \frac{1}{2}kx^2 = \frac{1}{2}kA^2$	$\frac{1}{2}Li^2 + \frac{1}{2}\frac{1}{C}q^2 = \frac{1}{2}\frac{1}{C}Q^2$
$v = \pm\sqrt{k/m}\,\sqrt{A^2 - x^2}$	$i = \pm\sqrt{1/LC}\,\sqrt{Q^2 - q^2}$
$v = \dfrac{\Delta x}{\Delta t}$	$i = \dfrac{\Delta q}{\Delta t}$
$x = A\cos\sqrt{k/m}\,t$	$q = Q\cos\sqrt{1/LC}\,t$
$\quad = A\cos 2\pi ft$	$\quad = Q\cos 2\pi ft$
$v = -2\pi fA\sin 2\pi ft$	$i = -2\pi fQ\sin 2\pi ft$
$\quad = -v_{max}\sin 2\pi ft$	$\quad = -I\sin 2\pi ft$

with the circuit remaining constant. This is analogous to the transfer of energy in an oscillating mechanical system from kinetic to potential, and vice versa.

The frequency of the electrical oscillations of a circuit containing inductance and capacitance only (a so-called L-C circuit) may be calculated in exactly the same way as the frequency of oscillation of a body suspended from a spring. In the mechanical problem, a body of mass m is attached to a spring of force constant k. Let the body be displaced a distance A from its equilibrium position and released from rest at time $t = 0$. Then, as shown in the left column of Table 36-1, the kinetic energy of the system at any later time is $\frac{1}{2}mv^2$, its elastic potential energy is $\frac{1}{2}kx^2$, and the sum of these equals the initial energy of the system, $\frac{1}{2}kA^2$. The velocity v at any coordinate x is therefore $v = \pm\sqrt{k/m}\,\sqrt{A^2 - x^2}$. The velocity equals $\Delta x/\Delta t$, and the coordinate x as a function of t has been shown to be $x = A\cos(\sqrt{k/m})t = A\cos 2\pi ft$, where

$$f = \frac{1}{2\pi}\sqrt{k/m}.$$

In the electrical problem, a capacitor of capacitance C is given a charge Q and at time $t = 0$ is connected to the terminals of an inductor of self-inductance L. The magnetic energy of the inductor at any later time corresponds to the kinetic energy of the vibrating body and is given by $\frac{1}{2}Li^2$. The electrical energy of the capacitor corresponds to the elastic potential energy of the spring and is given by $\frac{1}{2}(1/C)q^2$, where q is the charge on the capacitor. The sum of these equals the initial energy of the system, $\frac{1}{2}(1/C)Q^2$. The current i, when the charge on the capacitor is q, is therefore $i = \sqrt{1/LC}\sqrt{Q^2 - q^2}$. The current $i = \Delta q/\Delta t$, and it varies with time in the same way as the coordinate x in the mechanical problem. That is, $q = Q\cos(\sqrt{1/LC})t = Q\cos 2\pi ft$. The frequency of the electrical oscillations is therefore

$$f = \frac{1}{2\pi}\sqrt{1/LC}. \tag{36–10}$$

The striking parallelism between the mechanical and electrical systems displayed in Table 36–1 is only one of many such examples in physics. So close is the parallelism between electrical and mechanical (and acoustical) systems that it has been found possible to solve complicated mechanical and acoustical problems by setting up analogous electrical circuits and measuring the currents and voltages which correspond to the desired mechanical and acoustical "unknowns."

The effect of resistance in an oscillatory circuit is to drain away the energy of the circuit and convert it to heat. Resistance, in other words, plays the same role in an electrical circuit as friction does in a mechanical system. Oscillations may be sustained in a circuit if some provision is made for returning energy at the same rate as it is removed. The most common method of doing this at present is to utilize the amplifying properties of a thermionic tube.

36–8 Propagation of a disturbance along a transmission line. In the circuits discussed thus far in this chapter, we have considered only so-called "lumped" capacitance and inductance, that is, the capacitance and inductance associated with assemblies of closely spaced parallel plates and with coils of wire. Actually, however, a certain amount of capacitance exists between the conductors that connect one lumped element with another, and these conductors also have a certain amount of self-inductance. Let us consider a long resistanceless transmission line consisting either of two parallel wires or a coaxial cable. The two wires, or the inner and outer conductors of the cable, constitute a capacitor whose capacitance, instead of being lumped, is *distributed* along the line. The capacitance per unit length C' of a coaxial cable in vacuum is (see Problem 27–20)

$$C' = \frac{2\pi\epsilon_0}{\ln r_b/r_a}, \tag{36–11}$$

where r_a and r_b are the radii of the inner and outer conductors. The capacitance per unit length of an open two-wire line is given by an expression of the same form.

The self-inductance per unit length L' of a coaxial cable in vacuum is (see Problem 36–2)

$$L' = \frac{\mu_0}{2\pi} \ln \frac{r_b}{r_a}. \tag{36–12}$$

An equation having the same form gives the self-inductance per unit length of an open two-wire line.

Let a generator of constant terminal voltage V be suddenly connected across one end of a long transmission line of either type. After a time interval t the state of the line is as depicted in Fig. 36–13, where the line is shown as a two-wire line. When the generator is first connected, electrons start flowing to the left at the left end of the upper wire and to the right at the left end of the lower. In other words, there is a conventional current i at the end of each conductor, to the right in the upper conductor and to the left in the lower. The electron drift velocity v can be calculated as in Section 28–1 and, as we have seen, it is quite small.

Because of the distributed self-inductance and capacitance of the line, the free electrons in the wires do not all start to move simultaneously at the instant the generator is first connected. At the end of a time interval t all those electrons at the left of the dotted line are in motion and all those at the right of this line are still at rest. The *boundary* between moving and stationary electrons advances to the right in both conductors, with a constant velocity c which we wish to compute.

The situation in Fig. 36–13 is closely analogous to that in a pipe containing a fluid, when a plunger at the left end of the pipe is suddenly set in motion to the right with a constant velocity v (see Chapter 21). The boundary plane between moving and stationary fluid advances to the right with the velocity of propagation $u = \sqrt{B/\rho}$.

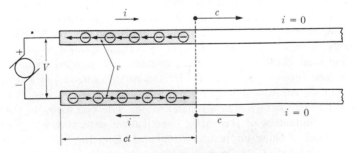

FIG. 36–13. Propagation of a disturbance along a transmission line, at a time t after a constant voltage V is impressed across one end.

First consider the portion of the line of length ct as an inductor. Its self-inductance L is $L'ct$, and since $N\Phi = Li$ and $N = 1$, it follows that

$$\Phi = L'cti.$$

The induced emf in this portion of the line is given by Φ/t, and this equals the generator voltage V if the line has no resistance. Therefore

$$V = L'ci. \tag{36–13}$$

Next consider the same portion of the line as a capacitor. Its capacitance C is $C'ct$ and the charge Q that it has acquired in time t is $Q = it$. Since $Q = CV$,

$$it = C'ctV,$$

and

$$i = C'cV. \tag{36–14}$$

Multiplying Eqs. (36–13) and (36–14) gives

$$Vi = L'C'c^2Vi,$$

and hence

$$c^2 = \frac{1}{L'C'}. \tag{36–15}$$

When the expressions for C' and L' from Eqs. (36–11) and (36–12) are inserted in this equation, we get

$$c^2 = \frac{1}{\mu_0/2\pi \ln r_b/r_a \times [2\pi\epsilon_0/(\ln r_b/r_a)]},$$

or

$$\boxed{c = \sqrt{1/\mu_0\epsilon_0}.} \tag{36–16}$$

Finally, inserting the numerical values of μ_0 and $\dot{\epsilon}_0$, we get

$$c = \sqrt{\frac{1}{\mu_0\epsilon_0}} = \sqrt{\frac{1}{4\pi \times 10^{-7}} \frac{\text{n·m}^2}{\text{coul}^2} \times 4\pi \times 9 \times 10^9 \frac{\text{coul}^2}{\text{n·sec}^2}}$$

$$= 3 \times 10^8 \frac{\text{m}}{\text{sec}}.$$

This is a remarkable result. The measured speed of light in a vacuum is also found to be 3×10^8 m/sec, which points strongly to the inference that light is electromagnetic in nature. We shall return to a further consideration of electromagnetic waves in general in the next chapter, but it is interesting to discover that the speed of propagation of a disturbance along a resistanceless transmission line in vacuum is equal to the speed of light.

Since the speed c is so large, the time required to charge completely a transmission line of ordinary length is very small indeed. Thus for a line 3000 km or 3×10^6 m long, the time for a disturbance to travel from one end to the other is only

$$t = \frac{3 \times 10^6 \text{ m}}{3 \times 10^8 \text{ m/sec}} = 10^{-2} \text{ sec.}$$

It is interesting to note that although the line was assumed to have no resistance, the charging current is the same as if it had a resistance R given by

$$R = \frac{V}{i}.$$

Since $V = L'ci$ and $i = C'c\,V$,

$$\frac{V}{i} = \frac{L'}{C'} \frac{i}{V},$$

and

$$R = \sqrt{L'/C'}. \tag{36-17}$$

This is called the *characteristic impedance* of the line. If a line of finite length is terminated at the far end by a resistance equal to its characteristic impedance, a disturbance is not reflected from the far end and the line appears to be infinitely long. With any other termination, however, reflection will take place just as a compressional pulse in a tube containing a fluid is reflected at the end of the tube.

EXAMPLE. What is the characteristic impedance of a coaxial cable consisting of an inner conductor of radius 0.50 mm mounted on the axis of a hollow cylindrical conductor of inner radius 5 mm? Neglect the resistance of the conductors and any effect of the supports of the inner conductor.

The self-inductance per unit length is

$$L' = \frac{\mu_0}{2\pi} \ln \frac{r_a}{r_b} = \frac{4\pi \times 10^{-7} \text{ h/m}}{2\pi} \ln \frac{5.0}{0.50}$$

$$= 2 \times 10^{-7} \times 2.3 \text{ h/m} = 4.6 \times 10^{-7} \text{ h/m.}$$

The capacitance per unit length is

$$C' = \frac{2\pi \epsilon_0}{\ln r_a/r_b} = \frac{2\pi \text{ f/m}}{4\pi \times 9 \times 10^9 \times \ln (5.0/0.50)} = 2.42 \times 10^{-11} \frac{\text{farad}}{\text{m}}.$$

Hence

$$R = \sqrt{\frac{L'}{C'}} = \sqrt{\frac{4.6 \times 10^{-7} \text{ h/m}}{2.42 \times 10^{-11} \text{ f/m}}}$$

$$= \sqrt{1.9 \times 10^4 \text{ h/f}} = 138 \text{ ohms.}$$

PROBLEMS

36-1. (a) Show that the two expressions for self-inductance, namely,

$$\frac{N\Phi}{i} \quad \text{and} \quad \frac{\mathcal{E}}{\Delta i/\Delta t},$$

have the same units. (b) Show that L/R and RC both have the units of time.

36-2. A coaxial cable consists of a small solid conductor of radius r_a supported by insulating disks on the axis of a thin-walled tube of inner radius r_b. Show that the self-inductance of a length l of the cable is

$$L = l\,\frac{\mu_0}{2\pi}\ln\frac{r_b}{r_a}.$$

Assume the inner and outer conductors to carry equal currents in opposite directions. (*Hint:* Use Ampere's law to find the flux density of any point in the space between the conductors. Write the expression for the flux $\Delta\Phi$ through a narrow strip of length l parallel to the axis, of width Δr, at a distance r from the axis of the cable and lying in a plane containing the axis. Integrate to find the total flux linking a current i in the central conductor.)

36-3. Two capacitors are charged in series by a 12-volt battery (Fig. 36-14). (a) What is the time constant of the charging circuit? (b) After being closed for the length of time determined in (a) the switch S is opened. What is the voltage across the 6-μf capacitor?

36-4. A coil has a resistance of 25 ohms and a time constant of 0.075 sec. What is its inductance?

36-5. The resistance of a 10-henry inductor is 200 ohms. The inductor is suddenly connected across a potential difference of 10 volts. (a) What is the final steady current in the inductor? (b) What is the initial rate of increase of current? (c) At what rate is the current increasing when its value is one-half the final current? (d) At what time after the circuit is closed does the current equal 99% of its final value? (e) Compute the current at the following times after the circuit is closed: 0, 0.025 sec, 0.05 sec, 0.075 sec, 0.10 sec. Show the results in a graph.

36-6. An inductor of resistance R and self-inductance L is connected in series with a noninductive resistor of resistance R_0 to a constant potential difference $\mathcal{E}$ (Fig. 36-15). (a) Find the expression for the potential difference V_{cb} across the inductor at any time t after switch S_1 is closed. (b) Let $\mathcal{E} = 20$ volts, $R_0 = 50$ ohms, $R = 150$ ohms, $L = 5$ henrys. Compute a few points, and construct graphs of V_{ac} and V_{cb} over a time interval from zero to twice the time constant of the circuit.

36-7. After the current in the circuit of Fig. 36-15 has reached its final steady value the switch S_2 is closed,

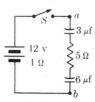

FIGURE 36-14

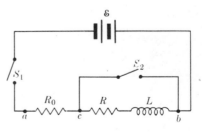

FIGURE 36-15

thus short-circuiting the inductor. What will be the magnitude and direction of the current in S_2, 0.01 sec after S_2 is closed?

36–8. Refer to the inductor in the example at the end of Section 36–2. (a) What is the power input to the inductor at the instant when the current in it is 0.5 amp? (b) What is the rate of development of heat at this instant? (c) What is the rate at which the energy of the magnetic field is increasing? (d) How much energy is stored in the magnetic field when the current has reached its final steady value?

36–9. A 10-μf capacitor is connected through a 1-megohm resistor to a constant potential difference of 100 volts. (a) Compute the charge on the capacitor at the following times after the connections are made: 0, 5 sec, 10 sec, 20 sec, 100 sec. (b) Compute the charging current at the same instants. (c) How long a time would be required for the capacitor to acquire its final charge if the charging current remained constant at its initial value? Compare with the time constant of the circuit. (d) Find the time required for the charge to increase from zero to 5×10^{-4} coul. (e) Construct graphs of the results of parts (a) and (b) for a time interval of 20 sec.

36–10. A capacitor of capacitance C is charged by connecting it through a resistance R to the terminals of a battery of emf $\mathcal{E}$ and of negligible internal resistance. (a) How much energy is supplied by the battery in the charging process? (b) What fraction of this energy appears as heat in the resistor?

36–11. Show that the unit of $\sqrt{L'/C'}$ is the ohm.

36–12. The maximum capacitance of a variable air capacitor is 35 $\mu\mu$f. (a) What should be the self-inductance of a coil to be connected to this capacitor if the natural frequency of the L-C circuit is to be 550×10^3 cycles/sec, corresponding to one end of the broadcast band? (b) The frequency at the other end of the broadcast band is 1550×10^3 cycles/sec. What must be the minimum capacitance of the capacitor if the natural frequency is to be adjustable over the range of the broadcast band?

36–13. Refer to Fig. 36–13. (a) At the instant shown in the diagram, how much energy has been supplied by the generator? (b) Show that this energy is shared equally by the magnetic field of the inductor and the electric field of the capacitor, and that the total energy equals the energy supplied.

CHAPTER 37

ALTERNATING CURRENTS AND ELECTROMAGNETIC WAVES

37-1 The alternating-current series circuit. A coil of wire, rotating with constant angular velocity in a uniform magnetic field, develops a sinusoidal alternating emf as explained in Section 34–5. This simple device is the prototype of the commercial alternating-current generator, or alternator, the field and armature structure of which are illustrated in Fig. 37–1. A number of pairs of poles are spaced around the inner circumference of the *stator*. As each conductor on the surface of the armature or *rotor* sweeps across the magnetic field, a motional emf is induced in it, in one direction as the conductor passes a north pole and in the opposite direction as it passes a south pole. The induced emf is therefore alternating, the number of complete cycles in each revolution equaling the number of *pairs* of poles. This multipole structure enables a sufficiently high frequency to be attained without an unduly high angular velocity of the rotor.

The induced emf of a commercial alternator may differ slightly from a purely sinusoidal form but, unless explicitly stated otherwise, we shall assume in this chapter that we have to do with an alternator which maintains between its terminals a sinusoidal potential difference given by

$$v = V_m \sin 2\pi ft, \qquad (37\text{-}1)$$

where v is the instantaneous potential difference, V_m the maximum potential difference, and f is the frequency, equal to the number of revolu-

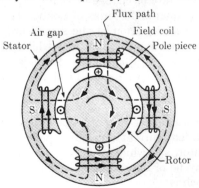

FIG. 37-1. Schematic diagram of a four-pole commercial alternating-current generator.

725

tions per second of the rotor multiplied by the number of pairs of poles. For many of the a-c generators in this country, $f = 60$ cycles/sec. The product $2\pi f$ is called the *angular* frequency and is represented by ω. For a simple two-pole generator, ω equals the actual angular velocity of the rotor in radians/sec.

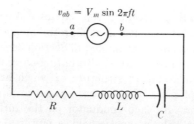

FIG. 37–2. Series circuit of a resistor, an inductor, and a capacitor.

We now proceed to investigate the current in a circuit when a sinusoidal alternating potential difference is maintained across its terminals. Let a series circuit composed of a resistor, an inductor, and a capacitor be connected to the terminals of an alternator as in Fig. 37–2. The instantaneous potential a and b equals the sum of the instantaneous potential differences across R, L, and C. That is

$$V_m \sin 2\pi ft = Ri + L\frac{\Delta i}{\Delta t} + \frac{q}{C},$$

where i, $\Delta i/\Delta t$, and q are respectively the instantaneous current, its rate of change, and the charge on the capacitor. Since the instantaneous current i is equal to the rate of change of charge $\Delta q/\Delta t$, it is possible to rewrite the preceding equation in terms of i only. The resulting equation is known as a differential equation of the second order. There are simple direct methods for solving such equations which the student will study after completing his course in calculus. An understanding of the details of the solution provides deeper physical insight into the behavior of alternating-current circuits, but the student will have to do without this insight at this point.

The solution consists of the sum of a *steady-state* current and a *transient* current. The transient current dies out exponentially, like the charging current of a capacitor, and while in practice transient currents and potential differences may be of importance, we shall consider only the steady-state solution, which is

$$i = \frac{V_m}{\sqrt{R^2 + [\omega L - (1/\omega C)]^2}} \sin(\omega t - \phi),$$

where

$$\phi = \tan^{-1} \frac{\omega L - (1/\omega C)}{R}.$$

The steady-state current, like the terminal voltage, is seen to vary sinusoidally with the time. Its maximum value is

$$I_m = \frac{V_m}{\sqrt{R^2 + [\omega L - (1/\omega C)]^2}}.$$

The steady-state current may hence be written

$$i = I_m \sin(\omega t - \phi). \qquad (37\text{–}2)$$

The frequency of the current is therefore the same as that of the voltage, but the two differ in phase, or are out of phase, by the angle ϕ. Let us introduce the following abbreviations:

$$\omega L = X_L, \qquad \frac{1}{\omega C} = X_C,$$

$$\omega L - \frac{1}{\omega C} = X_L - X_C = X,$$

$$\sqrt{R^2 + X^2} = Z.$$

Then

$$I_m = \frac{V_m}{\sqrt{R^2 + (X_L - X_C)^2}} = \frac{V_m}{\sqrt{R^2 + X^2}} = \frac{V_m}{Z}, \qquad (37\text{–}3)$$

$$\phi = \tan^{-1} \frac{X}{R}. \qquad (37\text{–}4)$$

The quantity Z is called the *impedance* of the cricuit; X, the *reactance;* and X_L and X_C, the *inductive reactance* and *capacitive reactance* respectively. Impedances and reactances are expressed in ohms. The general term for a device possessing reactance is a *reactor*.

The maximum current is seen to be related to the maximum potential difference by an equation having the same form as Ohm's law for steady currents, impedance Z corresponding to resistance R.

Let us consider next the factors which determine the resistance, reactance, and impedance of a circuit. In the first place, the resistance of a conductor carrying an alternating current may not be the same as the resistance of the same conductor when carrying a steady current. The difference arises from the fact that the current density in a wire carrying alternating current is not uniform over the cross section of the wire, but is greater near the surface, a phenomenon known as "skin effect." The effective cross section of the conductor is therefore reduced and its resist-

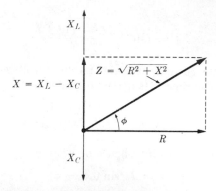

FIG. 37–3. Vector impedance diagram for the series circuit of Fig. 37–2.

ance increased. Skin effect is brought about by self-induced emf's set up by the variations in the internal flux in a conductor and is greater the higher the frequency. While an important factor at radio frequencies, it can usually be neglected at a frequency of 60 cycles/sec. The actual resistance of a conductor at any frequency is called its *effective resistance* at that frequency. Unless explicitly stated otherwise, we shall ignore skin effects and assume the resistance of a conductor to be independent of frequency.

The reactance of an inductor, $X_L = \omega L$, is proportional both to its inductance and to the frequency. If there is any iron associated with the inductor then the self-inductance is not a constant, but again for simplicity we shall ignore this variation.

Capacitive reactance, $X_C = 1/\omega C$, is inversely proportional both to the capacitance and the frequency.

The relation between the impedance Z of a series circuit, and the values of R, X_L, and X_C may be represented graphically by treating all these quantities as vectors. The resistance R is represented by a vector along the positive x-axis, and the reactances X_L and X_C by vectors along the positive and negative y-axes respectively. The impedance Z is the vector sum or resultant of these three vectors. See Fig. 37–3, which is called the *vector impedance diagram* of the circuit. Figure 37–3 has been drawn for the case where $X_L > X_C$ and X is positive. If $X_L < X_C$, X is negative and extends downward rather than upward.

EXAMPLE. A 1000-ohm resistor is in series with an 0.5-henry inductor and an 0.2-μf capacitor. Compute the impedance of the circuit and draw the vector impedance diagram (a) at an angular frequency $\omega = 2\pi f = 2000$ rad/sec, (b) at an angular frequency $\omega = 5000$ rad/sec.

(a) When $\omega = 2000$ rad/sec,

$$X_L = \omega L = 2000 \frac{\text{rad}}{\text{sec}} \times 0.5 \frac{\text{volt}}{\text{amp/sec}} = 1000 \text{ ohms},$$

$$X_C = \frac{1}{\omega C} = \frac{1}{2000 \text{ rad/sec} \times 0.2 \times 10^{-6} \text{ volt/coul}} = 2500 \text{ ohms},$$

$$X = X_L - X_C = 1000 \text{ ohms} - 2500 \text{ ohms} = -1500 \text{ ohms},$$

$$Z = \sqrt{R^2 + X^2} = \sqrt{(1000 \text{ ohms})^2 + (-1500 \text{ ohms})^2} = 1800 \text{ ohms}.$$

[See Fig. 37–5(a).]

(b) When $\omega = 5000$ rad/sec,

$$X_L = \omega L = 5000 \frac{\text{rad}}{\text{sec}} \times 0.5 \frac{\text{volt}}{\text{amp/sec}} = 2500 \text{ ohms},$$

$$X_C = \frac{1}{\omega C} = \frac{1}{5000 \text{ rad/sec} \times 0.2 \times 10^{-6} \text{ volt/coul}} = 1000 \text{ ohms},$$

$$X = X_L - X_C = 2500 \text{ ohms} - 1000 \text{ ohms} = 1500 \text{ ohms},$$

$$Z = \sqrt{R^2 + X^2} = \sqrt{(1000 \text{ ohms})^2 + (1500 \text{ ohms})^2} = 1800 \text{ ohms}.$$

[See Fig. 37–5(b).]

37–2 Effective values. The instantaneous value of an alternating current, emf, or potential difference varies continuously from a maximum in one direction through zero to a maximum in the opposite direction, and so on. The behavior of a simple series circuit as given by Eq. (37–3) is expressed in terms of maximum values I_m and V_m. It is found more convenient to describe alternating currents and voltages by their effective values than by their maximum values. The effective value of a varying current is defined as that steady current which would develop the same quantity of heat in the same time in the same resistance.

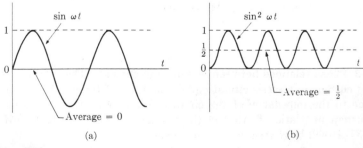

Fig. 37–4. (a) The average value of $\sin \omega t$ is zero. (b) The average value of $\sin^2 \omega t$ is $\frac{1}{2}$.

The rate of development of heat in a resistance R, carrying a sinusoidal alternating current $i = I_m \sin \omega t$, is

$$i^2 R = I_m^2 (\sin^2 \omega t) R.$$

Therefore

$$(i^2 R)_{avg} = I_m^2 R (\sin^2 \omega t)_{avg}.$$

It may be seen from Fig. 37–4(b) that the average value of $\sin^2 \omega t$ is $\frac{1}{2}$. Hence the average rate of heating is $\frac{1}{2} I_m^2 R$. If I_{eff} is that steady current which would produce the same rate of heating, then

$$I_{eff}^2 R = \frac{1}{2} I_m^2 R$$

or

$$I_{eff} = \frac{I_m}{\sqrt{2}}.$$

Hence, *if a current varies sinusoidally*, its effective value is $1/\sqrt{2} = 0.707$ times its maximum value. Similarly, the effective value of a sinusoidally varying voltage is $1/\sqrt{2}$ times its maximum value. For example, when it is stated that the alternating potential difference between the supply mains of a household power line is 110 volts, this means that the effective potential difference is 110 volts, and hence the maximum potential difference is $110 \times \sqrt{2} = 155$ volts.

When the first and last terms of Eq. (37–3) are divided by $\sqrt{2}$, we obtain

$$\frac{I_m}{\sqrt{2}} = \frac{V_m/\sqrt{2}}{Z},$$

or

$$I_{eff} = \frac{V_{eff}}{Z}. \tag{37–5}$$

It will be understood from now on that the letters I, $\mathcal{E}$, or V, without subscripts, refer to the effective values of the corresponding quantities. Equation (37–5) will therefore be written

$$I = \frac{V}{Z}.$$

37–3 Phase relations between voltage and current. The effective alternating current in a series circuit equals the ratio of the effective terminal voltage to the impedance of the circuit. We now consider the *phase* of the current in relation to that of the voltage. Equations (37–1), (37–2), and (37–4) will be rewritten for convenience.

$$v = V_m \sin \omega t, \qquad i = I_m \sin (\omega t - \phi), \qquad \phi = \tan^{-1} \frac{X}{R}.$$

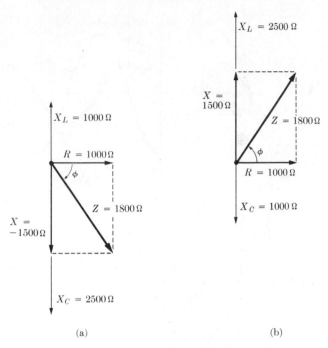

(a)   (b)

FIG. 37–5. Vector impedance diagrams for Example in Section 37–1. (a) $\omega = 2\pi f = 2000$ rad/sec, (b) $\omega = 2\pi f = 5000$ rad/sec.

The product ωt represents an angle (in radians) and its magnitude at any time t is called the *phase angle* or simply the *phase* of the voltage. Similarly, the quantity $(\omega t - \phi)$ is the phase angle or the phase of the current. The current is said to *differ in phase* from the voltage, or to be *out of phase* with the voltage, by an angle ϕ. Since the reactance X may be either positive or negative, the same is true of the angle ϕ. If $X_L > X_C$, as in Fig. 37–5(b), then X is positive, ϕ is positive, and the current maxima, minima, etc., occur at later times than do those of the voltage. The current is said to *lag* the voltage. On the other hand, if $X_L < X_C$, as in Fig. 37–5(a), X is negative, ϕ is negative also, and the current *leads* the voltage.

The angle ϕ can be found at once from the vector impedance diagram, since $\tan \phi = X/R$. See Figs. 37–5(a) and 37–5(b).

As special cases it is evident that if a circuit consists of a pure resistance connected to an alternating potential difference,

$$X = 0, \qquad Z = R, \qquad \phi = 0,$$

and the current and voltage are *in phase*, as in Fig. 37–6(a).

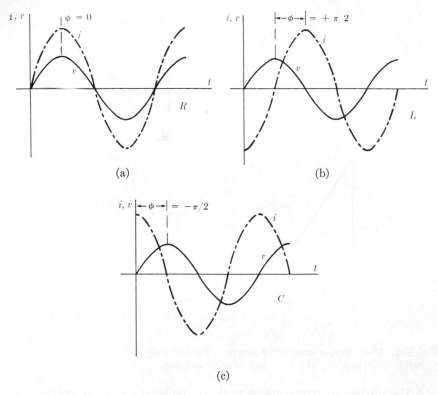

Fig. 37–6.   Phase relations between potential difference and current in special circuits. (a) Resistance only. (b) Inductance only. (c) Capacitance only.

If the circuit consists of a pure inductance,

$$R = 0, \qquad Z = X_L, \qquad \phi = +\frac{\pi}{2},$$

and the current lags the voltage by $\pi/2$ radians or 90°, as in Fig. 37–6(b).
    If the circuit contains capacitance only,

$$R = 0, \qquad Z = X_C, \qquad \phi = -\frac{\pi}{2},$$

and the current leads the voltage by 90°, as in Fig. 37–6(c).
    The *current* in all parts of a series circuit is in the same phase. That is, it is a maximum in the resistor, the inductor, and the capacitor at the same instant, zero in all three at a later instant, a maximum in the opposite direction at a still later instant, and so on.

37–4 Potential difference between points of an a-c circuit. The effective potential difference between any two points of a series circuit equals the product of the current and impedance of the circuit between the two points, provided there is no seat of emf in the path between the points.

$$V_{ab} = IZ_{ab}.$$

The phase angle ϕ between V_{ab} and I is

$$\phi = \tan^{-1} \frac{X_{ab}}{R_{ab}}.$$

In Fig. 37–7, the impedance Z_{ab} between a and b equals R, since there are no other circuit elements between these points. Hence, $V_{ab} = IR$ and $\phi = \tan^{-1} 0 = 0$. That is, *the potential difference between the terminals of a pure resistance is in phase with the current in the resistance.*

Between points b and c, $Z_{bc} = X_L$, $V_{bc} = IX_L$, $\phi = \tan^{-1} \infty = +\pi/2$. *The potential difference between the terminals of a pure inductance leads the current in the inductance by 90°.*

Between points c and d, $Z_{cd} = X_C$, $V_{cd} = IX_C$, $\phi = \tan^{-1}(-\infty) = -\pi/2$. *The potential difference between the terminals of a capacitor lags the current in the capacitor by 90°.*

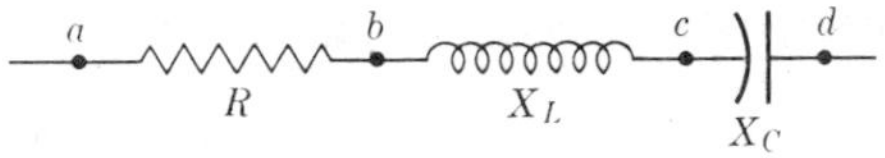

Fig. 37–7. The effective potential difference V_{ad} across the circuit is *not* equal to the arithmetic sum of the effective potential differences V_{ab}, V_{bc}, V_{cd}.

As a numerical example, if the current I in Fig. 37–7 is 5 amp, $R = 8$ ohms, $X_L = 6$ ohms, $X_C = 12$ ohms, we have

$$V_{ab} = IR = 5 \text{ amp} \times 8 \text{ ohms}$$
$$= 40 \text{ volts, } v_{ab} \text{ and } i \text{ in phase,}$$

$$V_{bc} = IX_L = 5 \text{ amp} \times 6 \text{ ohms}$$
$$= 30 \text{ volts, } v_{bc} \text{ leads } i \text{ by 90°,}$$

$$V_{cd} = IX_C = 5 \text{ amp} \times 12 \text{ ohms}$$
$$= 60 \text{ volts, } v_{cd} \text{ lags } i \text{ by 90°.}$$

The impedance of the entire circuit, Z_{ad}, is

$$\sqrt{(8 \text{ ohms})^2 + (6 \text{ ohms} - 12 \text{ ohms})^2} = 10 \text{ ohms,}$$

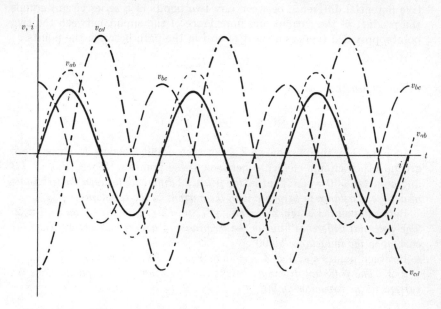

FIG. 37–8. Phase relations between v_{ab}, v_{bc}, v_{cd}, and i for the circuit of Fig. 37–7.

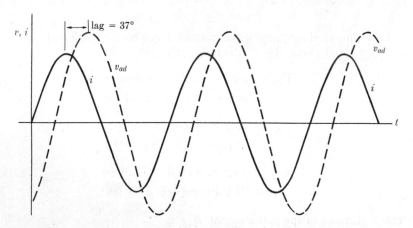

FIG. 37–9. Instantaneous potential difference v_{ad} and current i for the circuit of Fig. 37–7.

and the effective potential difference across the circuit, V_{ad}, is

$$V_{ad} = IZ_{ad} = 5 \text{ amp} \times 10 \text{ ohms} = 50 \text{ volts},$$

although

$$V_{ab} + V_{bc} + V_{cd} = 130 \text{ volts}.$$

This example illustrates one of the unexpected situations which arise in alternating-current circuits, namely, that the sum of the (effective) potential differences across a number of circuit elements in series does *not* equal the (effective) potential difference between the terminals of the group as a whole. This anomaly is readily explained, however, when the phase relations between the individual potential differences are taken into account.

Figure 37–8 should be studied carefully. The full line represents the instantaneous current, the same at each instant in each part of the circuit, and having a maximum value of $5\sqrt{2}$ amperes. The other three curves represent instantaneous potential differences between a and b, b and c, and c and d, having maximum values of $40\sqrt{2}$, $30\sqrt{2}$, and $60\sqrt{2}$ volts respectively, and bearing the phase relations to i as shown.

The *instantaneous* potential difference v_{ad} is equal to the sum of the instantaneous potential differences v_{ab}, v_{bc}, and v_{cd}. If the three dotted curves are added, the curve obtained will therefore represent the instantaneous potential difference between a and d. This curve is shown in Fig. 37–9. Its maximum value is $50\sqrt{2}$ volts, and its effective value 50 volts, as it should be. It lags the current by 37°, which agrees with the value of ϕ as computed from

$$\tan \phi = \frac{X_L - X_C}{R} = \frac{(6 - 12) \text{ ohms}}{8 \text{ ohms}} = -0.75, \quad \text{whence } \phi = -37°.$$

37–5 Resonance. The impedance of an a-c series L–R–C circuit depends on the frequency, since the inductive reactance is directly, and the capacitive reactance is inversely, proportional to the frequency. This dependence is illustrated in Fig. 37–10, where a logarithmic frequency scale has been used because of the wide range of frequencies covered. Figure 37–10(a) shows X_L, X_C, X, R, and Z as functions of frequency. Notice that there is one particular frequency at which X_L and X_C are numerically equal. At this frequency, $X = X_L - X_C$ is zero. Hence the impedance Z, equal to $\sqrt{R^2 + X^2}$, is a minimum at this frequency, and is equal to the resistance R.

If a generator of constant terminal voltage but variable frequency is connected across the circuit, the current I varies with frequency, as shown in Fig. 37–10(b), and is a maximum at the frequency at which the impedance Z is a minimum. The same diagram also shows the phase dif-

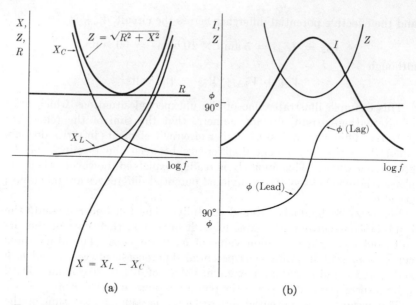

Fig. 37–10. (a) Reactance, resistance, and impedance as functions of frequency (logarithmic frequency scale). (b) Impedance, current, and phase angle as functions of frequency (logarithmic frequency scale).

ference ϕ as a function of frequency. At low frequencies, where capacitive reactance X_C is the predominating factor, the current leads the voltage. At the frequency where $X = 0$, the current and voltage are in phase, and at high frequencies, where inductive reactance X_L predominates, the current lags the voltage.

This behavior of the current in an a-c series circuit as the generator frequency is varied is exactly analogous to the response of a mechanical spring-mass system as the frequency of the driving force is varied. The frequency at which the current is a maximum is called the *resonant* frequency f_0, and is easily computed from the fact that at this frequency $X_L = X_C$.

$$X_L = X_C,$$

$$2\pi f_0 L = \frac{1}{2\pi f_0 C},$$

$$f_0 = \frac{1}{2\pi} \sqrt{\frac{1}{LC}}. \tag{37-6}$$

Note that this is equal to the natural frequency of oscillation of an L–C circuit, as derived in Section 36–7.

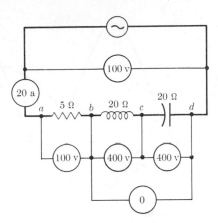

Fig. 37–11. Series resonant circuit.

As an example, consider the series circuit in Fig. 37–11, connected to a generator of constant terminal voltage 100 volts and of such frequency that X_L and X_C are equal. Let $X_L = 20$ ohms, $X_C = 20$ ohms, $R = 5$ ohms. The impedance Z is then equal to the resistance R and the current is

$$I = \frac{V}{Z} = \frac{V}{R} = \frac{100 \text{ volts}}{5 \text{ ohms}} = 20 \text{ amp.}$$

The potential difference across the resistor is

$$V = IR = 20 \text{ amps} \times 5 \text{ ohms} = 100 \text{ volts.}$$

The potential difference across the inductor is

$$V = IX_L = 20 \text{ amps} \times 20 \text{ ohms} = 400 \text{ volts.}$$

The potential difference across the capacitor is

$$V = IX_C = 20 \text{ amps} \times 20 \text{ ohms} = 400 \text{ volts.}$$

The potential difference across the inductor-capacitor combination (V_{bd}) is

$$V = IX = 0.$$

It will be seen that the instantaneous potential differences across the inductor and capacitor are 180° out of phase, and while the effective values of each may be large, their resultant at each instant is zero. Hence a voltmeter across b and d, Fig. 37–11, reads zero.

If the self-inductance L or the capacitance C of a circuit can be varied, the resonant frequency can be varied also. This is the procedure by which a radio receiving set may be "tuned" to the desired station.

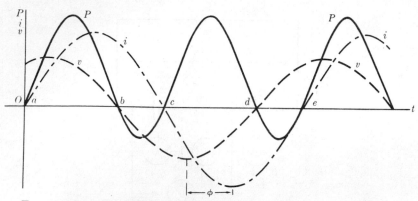

FIG. 37–12. The instantaneous power P is the product of the instantaneous potential difference and the instantaneous current.

37–6 Power in a-c circuits. The instantaneous rate at which energy is supplied to an electrical device in which there is an alternating current is equal to the product of the instantaneous potential difference between the terminals of the device and the instantaneous current. The instantaneous power P fluctuates as shown in Fig. 37–12, where the power curve is obtained by multiplying together the curves representing v and i.

$$P = vi \text{ (instantaneous values)}.$$

It has been shown that energy is supplied to an electrical device when the direction of the current in the device is from the high to the low potential terminal. If the direction of the current is from the low to the high potential terminal, the device is supplying energy to the circuit. Between points a and b of Fig. 37–12, where the v and i curves are both positive, the former is the case and energy is supplied to the device. Between points b and c, the potential difference is reversed, the direction of the current remaining unchanged. Hence during this interval the device returns energy to the circuit. Between c and d, both v and i are reversed and energy is again supplied to the device. Where the power curve is positive, then, as between a and b, or c and d, energy is supplied to the device (at a rate equal to the ordinate of the power curve) and where the power curve is negative, as between b and c, energy is returned to the circuit.

The total amount of energy supplied in a time t is represented graphically by the *net* area under the power curve during that time, and the average power equals the total energy supplied divided by the time.

When one speaks of "the" power supplied to a device in an a-c circuit, the average power is meant. The "effective" power has no significance. In general, v and i are out of phase by an angle ϕ. That is,

$$v = V_m \sin \omega t, \qquad i = I_m \sin (\omega t - \phi).$$

If the product of v and i is formed and then averaged over a time interval of one period, the average power P is found to be

$$\boxed{P = VI \cos \phi.} \qquad (37\text{–}7)$$

That is, the average power supplied to a device in an a-c circuit equals the product of the effective potential difference, the effective current, and the cosine of the angle of lag or lead. The quantity $\cos \phi$ is called the *power factor* of the device. Depending on the nature of the device, the power factor can have any value between zero (when $\phi = 90°$) and unity (when $\phi = 0°$).

A power factor of zero means that the device consists of a pure react-ance, inductive or capacitive. From Eq. (37–7), the average power sup-plied to such a device is zero, which is evidently correct, since the energy input to a capacitor or inductor goes into building up an electric or mag-netic field, and all of this energy is recovered when the field later decreases to zero.* During those parts of the cycle when the field is decreasing, the reactor returns energy to the circuit and helps run the generator.

A low power factor (large angle of lag or lead) is undesirable in power circuits because, for a given potential difference, a large current is needed to supply a given amount of power with correspondingly large heat losses in the transmission lines. Since many types of a-c machinery draw a lagging current, this situation is likely to arise. It can be corrected by connecting a capacitor in parallel with the load. The leading current drawn by the capacitor compensates for the lagging current in the other branch of the circuit. The capacitor itself takes no net power from the line.

The power supplied to (or by) a device in a d-c circuit may be meas-ured either by an ammeter-voltmeter or by a wattmeter. In an a-c circuit the power cannot be measured by an ammeter and voltmeter, since each indicates effective values only and takes no account of phase relations or power factor. A dynamometer type wattmeter, however, automatically includes the correction for power factor and indicates the true power supplied. The same type of wattmeter is used for both d-c and a-c meas-urements.

---

* Exceptions: (a) If hysteresis is present, all of the energy supplied to the circuit is not recovered. (b) At high frequencies energy is *radiated* from the circuit as electromagnetic waves.

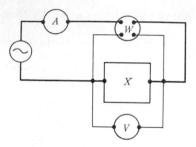

FIG. 37–13. Measurement of the power factor of a circuit by use of a-c ammeter, voltmeter, and wattmeter simultaneously.

If an a-c ammeter, voltmeter, and a wattmeter are simultaneously connected as in Fig. 37–13, V, I, and P may all be measured independently. This is an experimental method by which the power factor of a device may be measured.

37–7 The transformer. For reasons of efficiency it is desirable to transmit electrical power at high voltages and small currents, with consequent reduction of I^2R heating in the transmission line. On the other hand, considerations of safety and of insulation of moving parts require relatively low voltages in generating equipment and in motors and household appliances. One of the most useful features of a-c circuits is the ease and efficiency with which voltages (and currents) may be changed from one value to another by means of transformers.

In principle, the transformer consists of two coils electrically insulated from each other and wound on the same iron core (Fig. 37–14). An alternating current in one winding sets up an alternating magnetic flux in the core. Most of this flux links with the other winding and induces in it an alternating emf. Power is thus transferred from one winding to the other via the flux in the core. The winding to which power is supplied is called the *primary*, that from which power is delivered is called the *secondary*. Either winding may be used as the primary. The symbol for an iron-core transformer is ⧢⧣

In any actual transformer the flux lines are not confined entirely to the iron but some of them return through the air, as indicated in Fig. 37–14. That part of the flux which links both the primary and secondary windings is called the *mutual* flux. The part linking the primary only is the *primary leakage flux* and the part linking the secondary only is the *secondary leakage flux*.

The power output of a transformer is necessarily less than the power input because of unavoidable losses in the form of heat. These losses consist of I^2R heating in the primary and secondary windings (the

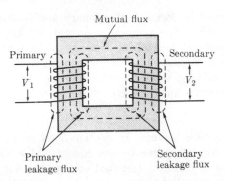

Fig. 37–14. An iron-core transformer.

copper losses) and hysteresis and eddy current heating in the core (the core losses). Hysteresis is minimized by the use of iron having a narrow hysteresis loop, and eddy currents are minimized by laminating the core. In spite of these losses, transformer efficiencies are usually well over 90% and in large installations may reach 99%.

For simplicity, we shall consider an idealized transformer in which there are no losses and no leakage flux. Let the secondary circuit be open. The primary winding then functions merely as an inductor. The primary current, which is small, lags the primary voltage by 90° and is called the *magnetizing* current. The power input to the transformer is zero. The core flux is in phase with the primary current. Since the same flux links both primary and secondary, the induced emf *per turn* is the same in each. The ratio of primary to secondary induced emf is therefore equal to the ratio of primary to secondary turns, or

$$\frac{\mathcal{E}_2}{\mathcal{E}_1} = \frac{N_2}{N_1}.$$

In the idealized case assumed, the induced emf's $\mathcal{E}_1$ and $\mathcal{E}_2$ are numerically equal to the corresponding terminal voltages V_1 and V_2. Hence by properly choosing the turn ratio N_2/N_1, any desired secondary voltage may be obtained from a given primary voltage. If $V_2 > V_1$, we have a *step-up* transformer; if $V_2 < V_1$, a *step-down* transformer.

Consider next the effect of closing the secondary circuit. The secondary current I_2 and its phase angle ϕ_2 will, of course, depend on the nature of the secondary circuit. As soon as the secondary circuit is closed, some power must be delivered by the secondary (except when $\phi_2 = 90°$) and from energy considerations an equal amount of power must be supplied to the primary. The process by which the transformer is enabled to draw the requisite amount of power is as follows. When the secondary circuit is open, the core flux is produced by the primary current only. But when the secondary circuit is closed, both primary and secondary currents set up a flux in the core. The secondary current, by Lenz's law, tends to weaken the core flux and therefore to decrease the back emf in the primary. But (in the absence of losses) the back emf in the primary must equal the primary terminal voltage, which is assumed to be fixed. The primary current therefore increases until the core flux is restored to its original no-load magnitude.

37–8 Electromagnetic waves. In Section 36–8 we discussed the problem of a long transmission line to one end of which was suddenly connected a generator of constant terminal voltage V. Suppose that after a time $T/2$ the polarity of the generator is reversed, that it is connected with the reversed polarity for a time T, then reversed again for a time T, etc. The time T is the *period* of the reversals. Figure 37–15 shows the distribution of current and charge along the line after a few such reversals (compare Fig. 36–13).

The boundary plane AA continues to advance toward the right with velocity c, as in Fig. 36–13. At the instant the polarity was first reversed, the currents in both conductors, at the left end of the line, reversed also, and a new boundary plane BB was established which also traveled to the right with velocity c. The next reversal established the plane CC, and so on. The situation is closely analogous to that in a tube containing a fluid when a plunger at the left end is moved alternately back and forth with a constant speed v between reversals. Note that the current is not the same at all points of the conductors in Fig. 37–15, but is alternately to the left and to the right in adjacent regions.

If instead of reversing a d-c generator we connected an a-c generator at the left end of the line in Fig. 37–15, the only difference would be that the voltage would reverse gradually and sinusoidally, instead of suddenly. If the first connections were made when the upper terminal of the gen-

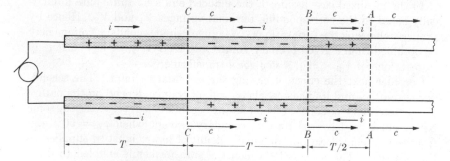

FIG. 37–15. Propagation of a series of disturbances along a transmission line when the polarity of the generator is reversed periodically.

erator was at its maximum positive potential V_m, the potential difference would decrease sinusoidally (or cosinusoidally) from a value V_m at AA to zero at BB. It would then increase to a maximum V_m in the opposite direction at a point midway between BB and CC, decrease to zero at CC, and so on. Similarly, the current in the upper conductor would be a maximum toward the right at AA, would be zero at BB, a maximum toward the left midway between BB and CC, and so on. We would then have sinusoidal waves of current and voltage traveling along the line from left to right.

For a situation like that in Fig. 37–15 to exist, it is necessary that the length of the line shall be long in comparison with the distance traveled by a wave in a time of one period.

For a 60-cycle/sec generator, this would require a very long line, but if the frequency is, say, 100 megacycles/sec or 10^8 cycles/sec, the distance traveled in a time of one period (or the wavelength λ of the wave) is

$$\lambda = cT = \frac{c}{f} = \frac{3 \times 10^8 \text{ m/sec}}{10^8 \text{ sec}^{-1}} = 3 \text{ m}.$$

At sufficiently high frequencies, therefore, a line of moderate length can accommodate a large number of waves.

The waves along a transmission line have been described above in terms of currents and potential differences. Let us now consider the electric and magnetic fields associated with the wave. Figure 37–16 shows the electric intensity **E** and the magnetic intensity **H** over a plane perpendicular to the transmission line between the sections AA and BB in Fig. 37–15, as seen from the generator, looking along the line. Part (a) refers to an open two-wire line and part (b) to a coaxial cable with center conductor positive. A region such as this, in which both electric and magnetic fields exist, is

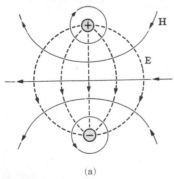

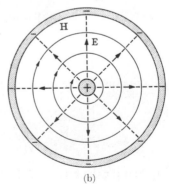

(a)   (b)

FIG. 37–16. (a) Electric intensity **E** and magnetic intensity **H** at a portion of the two-wire line of Fig. 37–15 between AA and BB as seen looking along the line from the generator. (b) A similar diagram for a coaxial cable.

called an *electromagnetic* field, and if, as in this case, the entire pattern of electric and magnetic fields is moving, we say that we have an *electromagnetic wave*. Electromagnetic waves in free space, such as light waves and radio waves, do not differ at all in nature from the waves surrounding a transmission line like that in Fig. 37–15 with an alternating voltage maintained across one end. The only difference is that in free space the waves spread out in all directions, whereas here they are guided by the transmission line.

Many of the important features of all electromagnetic waves can be deduced from a study of Fig. 37–16. First, we see that the waves are *transverse*, since the direction of propagation in these diagrams is away from the reader, while the electric and magnetic fields lie in a plane perpendicular to this direction.

Second, the electric and magnetic intensities are perpendicular to each other at every point, as well as being perpendicular to the direction of travel.

Third, the two fields are in phase with each other. (From the preceding description of a sinusoidal wave we saw that the maximum and minimum values of both current and potential difference occurred at the same point. The magnetic field is a maximum where the current is a maximum, and the electric field is a maximum where the potential difference is a maximum.)

Finally, the electric and magnetic fields always stand in the same ratio to each other. To compute this ratio, we recall (see Problem 25–20) that the electric intensity E at a radial distance r from the axis of a coaxial cable is

$$E = \frac{\lambda}{2\pi\epsilon_0 r},$$

where λ is the charge per unit length, and that

$$H = \frac{i}{2\pi r}.$$

Making use of the following relations,

$$\lambda = C'V,$$

$$\frac{V}{i} = \sqrt{\frac{L'}{C'}}, \qquad c = \sqrt{\frac{1}{L'C'}} = \sqrt{\frac{1}{\mu_0\epsilon_0}},$$

we find for the ratio of E to H at any point

$$\frac{E}{H} = \sqrt{\frac{\mu_0}{\epsilon_0}}.$$

37–9 Radiation of electromagnetic waves. When electromagnetic waves are established on a coaxial cable by an a-c generator connected to one of its ends, there is a flow of energy along the cable, but energy does not flow outward from the cable into the surrounding space. At the far end of the cable, if it is open, the situation is different. Most of the energy in the original wave will be reflected, but some will leave the cable and flow out into space, or will be *radiated*. A tube with an oscillating plunger or a loud-speaker at one end provides a good analogy. When sound waves travel along the tube from the speaker, most of the sound energy is reflected at the far end, but if this end is open, some sound is radiated out into space.

The effectiveness of a circuit as a radiator depends to a great extent on its geometry. If the electric field is localized, as between a pair of closely spaced wires, the rate of radiation of energy is relatively small. As the wires are separated and the field between them has an appreciable magnitude throughout a larger volume, the efficiency of the circuit as a radiator increases. The limiting case is reached when the circuit has been reduced to that of Fig. 37–17—a straight conductor with an alternator of some sort at its center. The electric field at some instant has the general shape shown by the broken lines. As the polarity of the alternator reverses, this field reverses also. Since charge flows along the conductor with each reversal, the conductor is also surrounded by a magnetic field shown by solid lines which are circles concentric with the conductor. The mag-

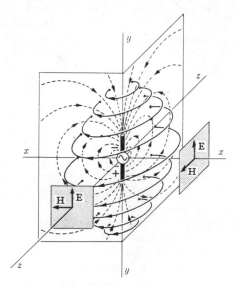

FIGURE 37–17

netic field also reverses with reversal of current. The electric field around the conductor is similar to that around an electric dipole, and the combined electric and magnetic field is like that which would result if the electric moment of the dipole alternated sinusoidally in magnitude. Hence the conductor is often referred to as an *oscillating dipole*. The antenna of a radio broadcasting station is a large oscillating dipole.

If one looks at the conductor along the x-axis in Fig. 37–17, the electric and magnetic fields within a small area (shown shaded) are at right angles to each other. The lines of electric intensity, **E**, are vertical or parallel to the y-axis; the lines of magnetic intensity, **H**, are parallel to the z-axis. Close to the conductor these fields are 90° out of phase, since at the instant when the capacitor is fully charged and the electric field a maximum, the current and the magnetic field are both zero. Further from the conductor, and for reasons which are too complex to go into here, the phase relation changes and the fields are in phase with each other. Their spatial relation remains the same, however, with the electric field parallel to the conductor and the magnetic field perpendicular to it.

A *wave front* is defined as a surface at all points of which the vector **E** (or **H**) is in the same phase. A line in the direction of propagation, perpendicular to the wave front, is called a *ray*. At a sufficient distance from the conductor the wave fronts may be considered planes. Figure 37–18(a) shows a portion of the x-axis at a considerable distance from the conductor. The waves are advancing along this axis toward the right. The magnitude and direction of both the electric and the magnetic intensities are represented as a function of x *at a particular instant*. What is represented is therefore the *wave form*. Where the electric and magnetic lines are close together, the fields are strong; where they are far apart, the fields are weak. Their directions are shown by arrows and by the usual dots and crosses. A more conventional diagram of the wave form at the same instant is shown in Fig. 37–18(b).

While an oscillating dipole like that shown in Fig. 37–17 sends out electromagnetic waves in all directions, the amplitude of the waves is different in different directions. The amplitude is the same, and is a maximum, for all directions in the xz-plane in Fig. 37–17. In directions approaching that of the y-axis, the amplitude decreases and becomes zero along the y-axis. That is, the dipole does not emit any radiant energy in the direction of its own length.

The wavelength of light waves is of the order of 5×10^{-5} cm. Wave~ in the broadcast band are of the order of 100 meters. Thus the ~re very much shorter than the dimensions of most optical appa~ ~ile the latter are much longer than the dimensions of ordinary ~. The development in recent years of apparatus capable of ~ultra-high-frequency electromagnetic waves whose wavelength

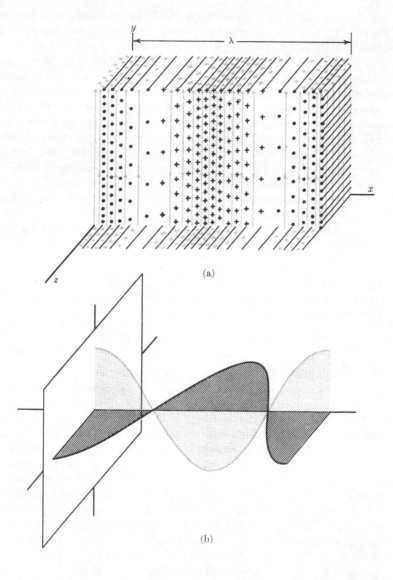

FIG. 37–18. (a) Electric and magnetic field distribution of a plane electro-magnetic wave at any one instant. The electrostatic lines of force have been screened, so that they appear lighter than the magnetic lines of force. (b) A conventionalized diagram of the wave form at the same instant. (Reprinted from *Ultra-High-Frequency Radio Engineering* by W. L. Emery, by permission of The Macmillan Company.)

is a few centimeters has opened up a wholly new field of research in which for the first time the dimensions of one's apparatus are of the same order of magnitude as the wavelength of the generated or received waves.

It turns out that when wavelengths (or frequencies) in this range are involved, many concepts such as resistance and impedance, which are entirely adequate for handling direct currents, or alternating currents at a frequency of 60 cycles/sec, lose much of their significance. The emphasis shifts from a consideration of the motion of charges in conductors to the variations in the electric and magnetic intensities in the space outside of or enclosed by conductors. While conductors are still used to convey energy from one point to another, the conductor is considered merely as a guide for the electromagnetic waves, and is called a *wave guide*.

The crowning achievement of electromagnetic theory was the prediction by Maxwell in 1864 that an oscillating circuit should be the source of electromagnetic waves which should travel with a speed given by the expression

$$u = \sqrt{1/\mu\epsilon}, \tag{37-8}$$

where μ and ϵ are, respectively, the permeability and permittivity of the medium. In free space, $\mu = \mu_0$, $\epsilon = \epsilon_0$, and the equation reduces to the special case derived by simple means in Section 36-8,

$$c = \sqrt{1/\mu_0\epsilon_0} = 3 \times 10^8 \frac{\text{m}}{\text{sec}}.$$

The close agreement between this theoretical value and the measured value of the speed of light constituted a strong indication that light was an electromagnetic wave, but it was by no means a complete verification of Maxwell's theory. It remained for Heinrich Hertz more than twenty years later, in 1887, to produce electromagnetic waves with the aid of oscillating circuits and to receive the waves with resonators of the same frequency. Hertz then produced stationary electromagnetic waves and measured the distance between adjacent nodes, in order to measure the wavelength. Knowing the frequency of his resonators, he then found the velocity of electromagnetic waves from the fundamental wave equation $c = f\lambda$, and directly verified Maxwell's theoretical value.

It is rather interesting that the possibility of future practical use of electromagnetic waves for purposes of long-distance communication did not seem to have occurred to Hertz. Due to the enthusiasm and energy of Marconi and others, "wireless telegraphy," or, as it was later called, "radio" became a familiar household phenomenon.

PROBLEMS

37–1. (a) At what frequency would a 5-henry inductor have a reactance of 4000 ohms? (b) At what frequency would a 5-μf capacitor have the same reactance?

37–2. What is the reactance of an 0.015-μf capacitor at (a) 1 cycle/sec? (b) 5 kilocycles/sec? (c) 2 megacycles/sec?

37–3. (a) What is the reactance of a 1-henry inductor at a frequency of 60 cycles/sec? (b) What is the inductance of an inductor whose reactance is 1 ohm at 60 cycles/sec? (c) What is the reactance of a 1-μf capacitor at a frequency of 60 cycles/sec? (d) What is the capacitance of a capacitor whose reactance is 1 ohm at 60 cycles/sec?

37–4. (a) Compute the reactance of a 10-henry inductor at frequencies of 60 cycles/sec and 600 cycles/sec. (b) Compute the reactance of a 10-μf capacitor at the same frequencies. (c) At what frequency is the reactance of a 10-henry inductor equal to that of a 10-μf capacitor?

37–5. A series circuit consists of a 25-ohm resistor, a 10-μf capacitor, and an inductor having a resistance of 12 ohms and inductance 0.1 henry. Determine for frequencies of 100 cycles/sec and 1000 cycles/sec (a) the impedance of the circuit, (b) the impedance of the inductor.

37–6. A capacitor has a reactance of 40 ohms at 60 cycles/sec. What percentage change in frequency will cause an increase of 20% in the reactance?

37–7. A resistanceless inductor of reactance 10 ohms and a capacitor of reactance 25 ohms (both measured at 60 cycles/sec) are connected in series with a 10-ohm resistor across a 100-volt, 60-cycle a-c line. Find the voltage across each part of the circuit.

37–8. In Fig. 37–19, $I = 5$ amp, $R = 8$ ohms, $X_L = 6$ ohms, $X_C = 12$ ohms. Compute V_{ab}, V_{bc}, V_{cd}, V_{ad}, and the phase angle between line current and line voltage.

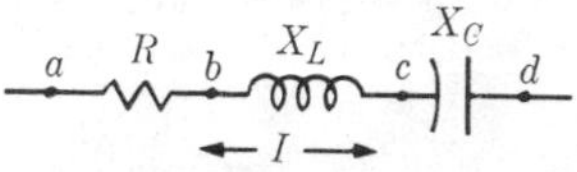

FIGURE 37–19

37–9. A tone control circuit consists of a 100-ohm resistor in series with a capacitor. The circuit is designed to have twice the impedance at 100 cycles/sec that it has at 300 cycles/sec. What size capacitor is required?

37–10. A length of wire bent in the form of a narrow U carries a current whose frequency is 60 cycles/sec. What is the frequency of vibration of the sides of the U? What is the cause of the vibration of loose laminations in the core of a transformer?

37–11. A 400-ohm resistor is in series with a 0.1-henry inductor and a 0.5-μf capacitor. Compute the impedance of the circuit and draw the vector impedance diagram (a) at a frequency of 500 cycles/sec, and (b) at a frequency of 1000 cycles/sec. Compute in each case the phase angle between line current and line voltage, and state whether the current lags or leads.

37–12. (a) A pure resistance and a pure inductance are in series across a 100-volt a-c line. An a-c voltmeter gives the same reading whether connected across the resistance or the inductance. What does it read? (b) The magnitudes of the resistance and inductance in part (a) are altered so that a voltmeter across the inductance reads 50 volts. What will the voltmeter read when connected across the resistance?

37-13. (a) What is the impedance of the circuit shown in Fig. 37-20 at a frequency of 60 cycles/sec? If V_{ac} is 220 volts, determine (b) V_{ad}, (c) V_{bd}.

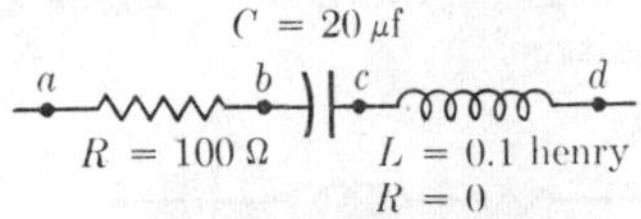

$$C = 20\,\mu f$$

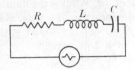

$$R = 100\,\Omega \qquad L = 0.1 \text{ henry} \\ R = 0$$

FIGURE 37-20

37-14. An 0.2-henry pure inductor in series with a capacitor carries a current of 3 amp when the combination is placed across a 120-volt, 50-cycle line. (a) What is the reactance of the capacitor? (b) What is the voltage across the inductor?

37-15. The terminal voltage of an a-c generator is 100 volts and the so-called angular frequency $\omega = 2\pi f$ is 500 rad/sec. In series across the generator are a 3-ohm resistor, a 50-μf capacitor, and an inductor whose inductance can be varied from 10 to 80 millihenrys. The peak voltage (V_{max}) across the capacitor should not exceed 1200 volts. (a) What is the maximum allowable current in the series circuit? (b) To what value can the inductance be safely increased?

37-16. A coil whose resistance is 10 ohms and whose inductance is 15 millihenrys is in series with a 12-ohm resistor and a 200-μf capacitor across a 100-volt, 60-cycle a-c line. Find the voltage across the terminals of the coil.

37-17. For the circuit of Problem 37-13 draw the following curves, using the same set of axes, over a frequency range from 50 to 200 cycles/sec: (a) reactance vs. frequency for the capacitor, (b) reactance vs. frequency for the inductor, (c) resistance vs. frequency for the resistor. (d) Construct $X_L - X_C$ graphically by subtracting ordi-

nates. Indicate the parts of this curve where voltage leads and voltage lags, and the point of resonance.

37-18. In Fig. 37-21, the resistance of R is 250 ohms, L has an inductance of 0.5 henry and zero resistance, and C has a capacitance of 0.02 μf. (a) What is the resonant frequency of the circuit? (b) The capacitor can withstand a peak voltage of 350 volts. What maximum effective terminal voltage may the generator have at resonant frequency?

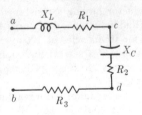

FIGURE 37-21

37-19. Points a and b in Fig. 37-22 are the terminals of a 60-cycle a-c line. The rms voltage between a and b is 130 volts. If $R_1 = 6$ ohms, $R_2 = R_3 = 3$ ohms, $X_C = 3$ ohms, $X_L = 8$ ohms, compute (a) the current in the circuit; (b) the voltage between a and c; (c) the voltage between c and d.

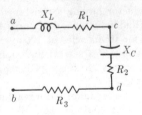

FIGURE 37-22

37-20. If the reactances X_L and X_C in Problem 37-8 are for a frequency of 60 cycles/sec, find the frequency at which the circuit would be in resonance.

37-21. The graphs in Fig. 37-10 were constructed for a series L-R-C circuit with $R = 5000$ ohms, $L = 0.5$ h, $C = 0.2 \times 10^{-6}$ f, and they cover a range of angular frequencies from $\omega = 100$ rad/sec to $\omega = 20,000$ rad/sec. Suppose the resistance R is (a) reduced to 1000 ohms, (b) increased to 10,000 ohms. Let the circuit be connected to the terminals of a generator of constant terminal voltage 1000 volts and controllable frequency. Construct graphs of I vs. ω, when $R = 1000$ ohms and when $R = 10,000$ ohms, over the angular frequency range from 100 to 20,000 rad/sec, using a logarithmic frequency scale, as in Fig. 37–10. Compare the "sharpness" of the resonance curves with each other and with that in Fig. 37–10(b). (A sufficient number of points for plotting can be obtained by computing the currents at 10,000 and 20,000 rad/sec, and at the resonant frequency.)

37–22. A coil has a resistance of 20 ohms. At a frequency of 100 cycles/sec the voltage across the coil leads the current in it by 30°. Determine the inductance of the coil.

37–23. The terminal voltage of the a-c generator in Fig. 37–23 is 150 volts, and $R = 10$ ohms, $X_L = 50$ ohms, $X_C = 50$ ohms. Find the current in the circuit, and V_{ab}, V_{bc}, V_{cd}, V_{bd}, V_{ad}.

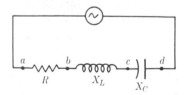

FIGURE 37–23

37–24. A 2-μf capacitor, a 2-henry inductor, and a resistor of resistance R are in series across an a-c generator of terminal voltage 100 volts. Compute the current in the circuit for the following values of angular frequency $\omega = 2\pi f$: 0, 200, 400, 500, 600, 800 rad/sec, (a) when $R = 100$ ohms, (b) when $R = 500$ ohms. Construct graphs of the results, plotting I vertically and ω horizontally.

37–25. A $6\frac{2}{3}$-μf capacitor is connected in series with a coil to an a-c supply of 1.2 volts and of controllable frequency. By adjusting the frequency it is observed that the current reaches its largest effective value of 0.2 amp when the angular frequency $\omega = 2\pi f$ is 50,000 rad/sec. (a) Find the resistance and inductance of the coil. (b) What is the current when $\omega = 150,000$ rad/sec? (c) What is the peak voltage across the capacitor at this frequency?

37–26. The capacitance C in Fig. 36–12 is 300 $\mu\mu$f. What should be the inductance L if the resonant frequency of the circuit is 1 megacycle/sec (10^6 cycles/sec)?

37–27. An inductor having a reactance of 25 ohms gives off heat at the rate of 2.39 cal/sec when it carries a current of 0.5 amp. What is the impedance of the inductor?

37–28. The circuit of Problem 37–5 carries a current of 0.25 amp whose frequency is 100 cycles/sec. (a) What power is consumed in the circuit? (b) in the resistor? (c) in the capacitor? (d) in the inductor? (e) What is the power factor of the circuit?

37–29. A series circuit has a resistance of 75 ohms and an impedance of 150 ohms. What power is consumed in the circuit when a potential difference of 120 volts is impressed across it?

37–30. Compute the power supplied to the circuits in Problems 37–7 and 37–8, using both the equations $P = I^2 R$ and $P = VI \cos \theta$.

37–31. A circuit draws 330 watts from a 110-volt 60-cycle a-c line. The power factor is 0.6 and the current lags the voltage. (a) Find the capacitance of the series capacitor that will result in a power factor of unity. (b) What power will then be drawn from the supply line?

37–32. A series circuit has an impedance of 50 ohms and a power factor of 0.6 at 60 cycles/sec, the voltage lagging the current. (a) Should an inductor or a capacitor be placed in series with the circuit to raise its power factor? (b) What size element will raise the power factor to unity?

37–33. The efficiency of a transformer is 92%. When 150 volts is impressed across the primary winding it carries a current of 2 amp. What is the voltage across the secondary winding when 0.1 amp is drawn from it?

37–34. The range of wavelengths allocated to the "broadcast band" is from about 190 m to 556 m. A given station operates within a channel 10 kilocycles wide. What is the maximum number of stations that may operate in this band if no overlapping of wavelengths is to take place?

37–35. What is the frequency of electromagnetic waves (in free space) of the following wavelengths: 10^{-8} cm (x-rays); 5×10^{-5} cm (yellow light); 10 cm (microwaves); 300 m (broadcast band)?

CHAPTER 38

ELECTRONICS

38-1 Vacuum pumps. Many of the devices of modern life consist of glass or metal tubes from which practically all the air has been exhausted. Among these are, for example, electric light bulbs, radio tubes, cathode-ray oscilloscopes, photoelectric cells, x-ray tubes, and many others. These devices could not have been developed if means had not been available for producing high vacua. It is therefore important, before we study these tubes, to learn how pressures as low as 10^{-8} mm of mercury are obtained. Of all the pumps that have been developed, two are particularly important in physics laboratories: the rotary oil pump for pressures as low as 10^{-4} mm of mercury, and the mercury or oil diffusion pump for pressures as low as 10^{-8} mm of mercury.

In Fig. 38-1 is depicted schematically a type of rotary oil pump known as the Cenco "hyvac" pump. Larger sizes known as "megavac" and "hypervac" pumps are available but the principle is the same. The vessel to be exhausted is connected to the tube A which communicates directly with the space marked B. As an eccentric cylinder C rotates in the direction shown, the point of contact between it and the inner walls of the stationary cylinder moves around in a clockwise direction, thereby trapping some air in the space marked E. The sliding vane D is kept in contact with the rotating cylinder by the pressure of the rod F. When the air in E is compressed enough to increase the pressure slightly above atmospheric, the valve G opens and the air bubbles through the oil and leaves through an opening H in the upper plate. The cylinder is caused to rotate by means of a small electric motor.

To reduce the pressure below about 10^{-3} or 10^{-4} mm of mercury, a diffusion pump is usually employed. In this pump a rapidly moving jet of mercury or of a special oil of extremely low vapor pressure

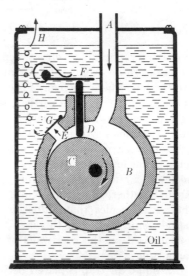

Fig. 38-1. The Cenco "hyvac" rotary oil pump.

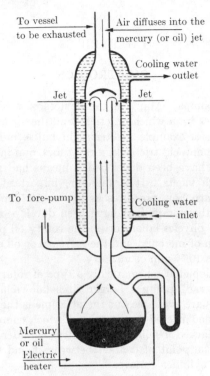

FIG. 38–2. The diffusion pump.

(octoil, butyl phthallate, etc.) sweeps or pushes the air molecules away from the vessel to be exhausted. Air molecules from the vessel keep diffusing into the jet. There are many types and sizes on the market, some of glass and some of metal; some vertical, some horizontal; some with water cooling and some with air cooling; some with one jet and some with multiple jets. A common type is depicted in Fig. 38–2.

A rotary oil pump is used to reduce the pressure within the diffusion pump to the low value necessary to ensure a well-defined jet in which there are fewer air molecules per unit of volume than in the vessel to be exhausted. Otherwise, air molecules might diffuse from the jet to the vessel. The air molecules that diffuse into the jet are eventually removed by the oil pump (called in this case the fore-pump) and the mercury or oil is condensed on the cool walls of the pump and returns to the well at the bottom.

If a liquid air trap is placed between the diffusion pump and the vessel to be exhausted to condense water vapor and other undesirable vapors, and the walls of the vessel are heated to drive out adsorbed gas (outgassing

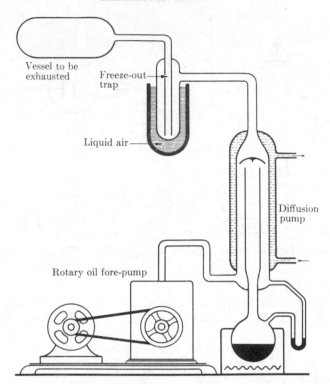

Vessel to be
exhausted   Freeze-out
              trap

Liquid air

Diffusion
pump

Rotary oil fore-pump

FIG. 38–3. Typical pumping assembly for the production of a high vacuum.

operation), the pressure in the vessel may be reduced to a value as low as 10^{-8} mm of mercury. A typical pumping assembly is depicted in Fig. 38–3.

38–2 Thermionic emission. During the course of his experiments on electric light bulbs, Thomas Edison, in 1883, observed a phenomenon which is fundamental to the science known today as *electronics*. A glass-blower had sealed into the bulb of an ordinary filament lamp an extra metal electrode or plate, shown in Fig. 38–4. The glass bulb was then exhausted and the filament was heated as usual. When the plate was connected through a galvanometer to the positive terminal of the 110-volt d-c source, a galvanometer deflection indicated the existence of a current, whereas no appreciable current existed when the plate was connected to the negative terminal. Edison merely noted these results but engaged in no further investigation.

The explanation of the Edison effect is as follows. Electrons are liberated (or evaporated) from the hot filament and are attracted to a positively charged plate, but repelled by a negatively charged one. The lib-

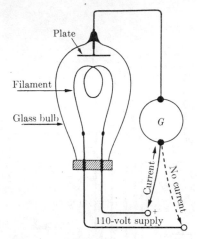

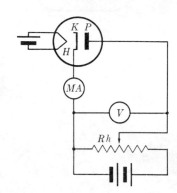

Fig. 38–4. Edison's original experiment.

Fig. 38–5. Circuit for measuring plate current and plate voltage in a vacuum diode.

eration of electrons from a hot wire is called *thermionic emission* or the *thermionic effect*. There is a certain minimum energy, different for different metals, which an electron must have in order to be able to get out of the metal. At low temperatures very few electrons have this amount of energy, but as the temperature is raised the energies of the electrons increase and the number capable of escaping increases rapidly.

The escape of electrons from the surface of an isolated metallic conductor leaves the conductor positively charged. The electrons which have escaped are therefore attracted by the conductor and form a "cloud" of negative charge outside its surface. This cloud is called a *space charge*. If a second nearby conductor is at a higher potential than the first, the electrons in the cloud are attracted to it, and as long as the potential difference between the conductors is maintained there will be a steady drift of electrons from the emitter or *cathode* to the other body, which is called the plate or *anode*.

In the common thermionic tube the cathode and anode (and often other electrodes as well) are enclosed within an evacuated glass or metal container, leads to the various electrodes being brought out through the base or walls of the tube. We shall first describe the characteristics of a simple thermionic tube in which the only electrodes are the cathode and anode. Such a tube is called a *diode*.

The diode is shown schematically in Fig. 38–5. The cathode and plate are represented by K and P. The cathode is often in the form of a hollow cylinder, which is heated by a fine resistance wire H within it. Electrons emitted from the outer surface of the cathode are attracted to the plate, which is a larger cylinder surrounding the cathode and coaxial with it. The electron current to the plate is read on the milliammeter MA. The potential difference between plate and cathode can be controlled by the slide wire and read on voltmeter V.

If the potential difference between cathode and anode is small (a few volts), only a few of the emitted electrons reach the plate, the majority penetrating a short distance into the cloud of space charge and then returning to the cathode. As the plate potential is increased, more and more electrons are drawn to it, and with sufficiently high potentials (of the order of a hundred volts) all of the emitted electrons arrive at the plate. Further increase of plate potential does not increase the plate current, which is then said to become *saturated*.

A graph of plate current, I_p, vs. plate potential V_p is shown in Fig. 38–6(a). Notice that I_p is not zero even when V_p is zero. This is because the electrons leave the cathode with an initial velocity and the more rapidly moving ones may penetrate the cloud of space charge and reach the plate even with no accelerating field. In fact, a *retarding* field is necessary to prevent their reaching the plate, an effect which may be used to measure their velocities of emission.

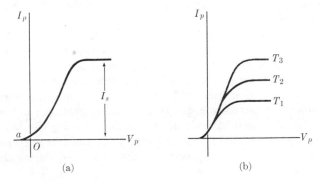

FIG. 38–6. (a) Plate current-plate voltage characteristic of a diode. (b) Plate current curves at three different cathode temperatures. $T_3 > T_2 > T_1$.

The saturation current I_s in Fig. 38–6(a) is equal to the current from the cathode, and for a given tube its magnitude depends markedly on the cathode temperature. Figure 38–6(b) shows three plate current curves at three different temperatures, where $T_3 > T_2 > T_1$. The relation between saturation current and temperature was first derived by O. E. Richardson and later in a slightly different form by S. Dushman. The Dushman equation is

$$J_s = AT^2 e^{-\phi/kT}, \tag{38-1}$$

where J_s is the saturation current density at the cathode surface, A is a constant characteristic of the emitting surface, T is the kelvin temperature of the emitter, k is the Boltzmann constant, and ϕ is the *work function* of the surface, a quantity related to the energy required for an electron to leave the surface.

The work function ϕ of a surface may be considerably reduced by the presence of impurities. A small amount of thorium, for example, reduces the work function of pure tungsten by about 50%. Since the smaller the work function the larger the current density at a given temperature (or the lower the temperature at which a given emission can be attained), most vacuum tubes now use cathodes having composite surfaces.

38–3 Rectification. There are some crystalline materials whose electrical conductivity in one direction is much greater than in the opposite direction. An alternating potential difference applied across two wires touching the crystal at appropriate points gives rise to a current much larger in one direction than in the other. The current is said to be *rectified*, and any device for accomplishing this result is called a *rectifier*. Since electrons can flow through a diode only from cathode to plate (corresponding to a conventional current from plate to cathode), the diode may be used as a rectifier.

The circuit shown in Fig. 38–7 is commonly used to rectify half of the alternating-current cycle, that is, to produce *half-wave rectification*. In this diagram and in others to follow, the connections to the cathode heater are not shown. So far as the operation of a tube is concerned, it is a matter of indifference what heating device is used. T is a transformer with the secondary connected to apply an alternating potential difference V_{ab} between the plate and cathode of the diode. During the half-cycle in which the plate is positive with respect to the cathode a current exists in the load resistance R_L. No current exists, however, during the following half-cycle, as shown in Fig. 38–7(b).

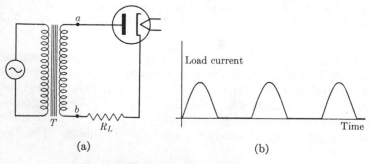

FIG. 38–7. Half-wave rectification.

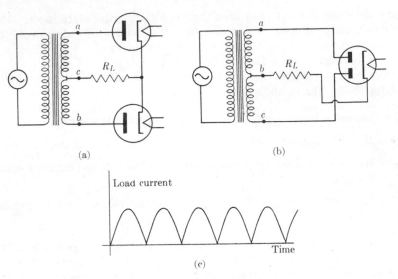

(a)   (b)

Load current

Time

(c)

FIG. 38–8. Full-wave rectification.

For *full-wave rectification*, two separate diodes, as in Fig. 38–8(a), or, what amounts to the same thing, a vacuum tube equipped with two plates as shown in Fig. 38–8(b) may be used. The secondary of the transformer is tapped at the center c, giving rise to two alternating potential differences V_{ac} and V_{bc} which are 180° out of phase. During one half-cycle one tube conducts and the other does not. This is reversed during the next half-cycle, so that a current exists in the load R_L during each half-cycle, as shown in Fig. 38–8(c).

38–4 The triode. Lee de Forest, in 1907, discovered that if a third electrode, called a *grid*, is inserted between the cathode and plate of a thermionic tube, the potential of this electrode exerts much more control

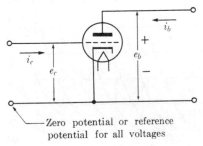

Zero potential or reference potential for all voltages

FIG. 38–9. Arbitrarily chosen positive directions for currents and voltages in a triode.

over the plate current than does the potential of the plate itself. The grid is usually an open mesh or a helix of fine wire which allows most of the electrons to pass through its openings. In the symbol for a triode the grid is represented by a dashed line, as shown in Fig. 38–9.

The various voltages and currents in a triode are shown schematically in Fig. 38–9. The symbols mean the following:

e_c = the instantaneous total voltage rise from cathode to grid,

e_b = the instantaneous total voltage rise from cathode to plate,

i_c = the instantaneous total current through the external circuit toward the grid,

i_b = the instantaneous total current through the external circuit toward the plate.

Commercial tubes are invariably operated at potentials much lower than would be required to draw saturation current. The currents to various electrodes cannot be represented by any simple equation and are best expressed by graphs. In particular, the current to an electrode is rarely a linear function of the potential of that electrode. The vacuum tube therefore does not obey Ohm's law and is a *nonlinear* circuit element.

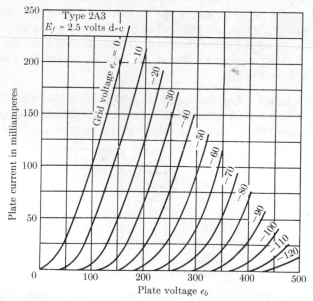

FIG. 38–10. Average plate characteristics of a 2A3 triode.

The plate current i_b, in a triode, depends both on the plate potential e_b and the control grid potential e_c, both measured relative to the cathode. In Fig. 38–10, plate current is plotted vertically and plate voltage horizontally. The curves give plate current as functions of plate voltage when the control grid voltage is kept constant at the values shown. For example, when the grid voltage is −40 volts and the plate voltage is 250 volts, the plate current is 75 milliamperes. If the negative grid voltage is reduced, say to −30 volts, the plate voltage remaining approximately the same, it can be seen from Fig. 38–10 that the plate current will increase to 150 milliamperes. A change of grid voltage of 10 volts therefore causes an increase in plate current of 75 milliamperes. In general, small variations in grid potential produce relatively large variations in plate current. It is this property of the triode which is used in vacuum tube relays, amplifiers, and oscillators.

38–5 Vacuum-tube relay. A relay is a device to close or open a local circuit which may be used to accomplish some useful purpose, such as to open or close doors, ring an alarm, light a lamp, etc. If a current is maintained in an electromagnet such as A in Fig. 38–11(a), the iron armature B is attracted and the local circuit is open, so that the device C (lamp, motor, bell, etc.) is not actuated. Should the current in A, however, be reduced to a value insufficient to attract the armature B, the armature will spring back and close the local circuit. There are various ways of reducing the current in A. In Fig. 38–11(a), the electromagnet is in

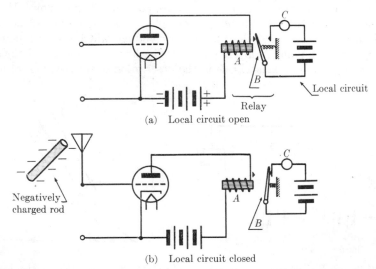

(a)　Local circuit open

(b)　Local circuit closed

FIG. 38–11. Principle of the vacuum-tube relay.

series with the plate circuit of a triode. The grid is not connected to any external device (it is said to be "floating"), but has acquired a small negative charge by picking up some of the electrons on their way from the filament to the plate. This small negative potential of the grid is not sufficient to lower the current in A appreciably. If, as in Fig. 38–11(b), the grid is connected to an antenna and a negatively charged rod is brought near the antenna, the grid will be rendered much more negative and the plate current will be reduced to a small enough value to actuate the relay.

38–6 Elementary principles of amplification. The circuit diagram of a simple single-stage amplifier is given in Fig. 38–12. When the input terminals a and b are unconnected as shown, the grid potential e_c remains at the value $-E$ (known as a negative grid bias), since the grid is directly connected to the biasing battery through the grid resistor. If a sinusoidal alternating voltage of amplitude ΔE is connected between a and b, this voltage is superposed on the constant grid bias $-E$, which then fluctuates between $-(E - \Delta E)$ and $-(E + \Delta E)$.

Corresponding to any grid voltage there will be a plate current i_b, and consequently an "iR" drop in the load. The plate potential therefore will not equal the full voltage of the plate battery (or "B" battery) but will be equal to the B-battery voltage minus the iR drop in the load. As the grid is made less negative, the plate current increases, the iR drop in the load increases, and the plate potential decreases. If the plate current is large enough to make the iR drop in the load equal to the B-battery voltage, then the plate voltage will be zero, corresponding to point M in Fig. 38–13. On the other hand, at zero plate current, there will be no iR drop in the load, and the full battery voltage will be on the plate, corresponding to point N in Fig. 38–13. The line MN is called the *load line* and plays a fundamental role in the description of the behavior of an amplifier.

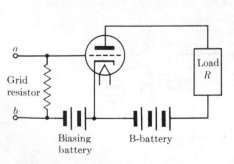

FIG. 38–12. Simple single-stage amplifier.

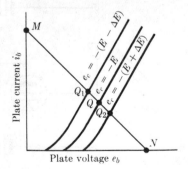

FIG. 38–13. Line MN is the load line.

In general, the potential difference e_b between the cathode and the plate is equal to the B-battery voltage E_{bb} minus the iR drop in the load, neglecting the internal resistance of the battery. Thus

$$e_b = E_{bb} - i_b R.$$

Since E_{bb} and R are constant, this is the equation of the load line MN of Fig. 38–13. This equation (independent of the properties of the tube) must be satisfied along with the relations between e_b and i_b which describe the static characteristics of the tube. Therefore, *only the points of inter-section* of the characteristic curves and the load line are significant in the operation of the tube.

Point Q, in Fig. 38–13, is the operating point of the tube when the grid voltage $e_c = -E$. As the grid voltage fluctuates between the limits of $-(E - \Delta E)$ and $-(E + \Delta E)$, the corresponding changes of plate current and plate voltage are given by points on the load line between the limiting points Q_1 and Q_2. It follows therefore that an alternating grid voltage varying sinusoidally from $-(E - \Delta E)$ to $-(E + \Delta E)$ will set up an alternating plate current and an alternating plate voltage whose variations are also sinusoidal, provided the points Q_1, Q, and Q_2 lie on straight-line portions of their respective curves. These changes are shown in Figs. 38–14 and 38–15. Notice that e_b and e_c are 180° out of phase.

To produce the sinusoidal variations of e_c very little power is needed, since the grid current is exceedingly small at all times because of the negative grid bias, and because the grid resistor has a very high resistance.

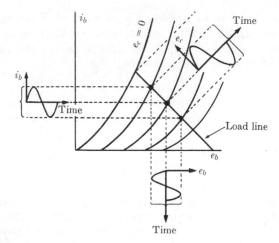

FIG. 38–14. Sinusoidal variations of grid voltage produce sinusoidal variations of plate current and plate voltage.

The power output in the plate circuit, however, may be considerable. In this respect the tube differs from a step-up transformer, which is merely a voltage multiplier and in which the power output is at most equal to the power input. The increase in power produced by a vacuum tube amplifier is supplied by the B-battery. The tube therefore is a device for releasing power from the plate battery in a form which is the exact replica of the power supplied to the input circuit.

The variations in grid voltage need not be sinusoidal. They may correspond to speech or music, in which case the amplifier may be used in a public address system. Since speech or music represents frequencies in the range from 20 to 20,000 cycles per second, the amplifier should be able to amplify all these frequencies equally well. The design of such amplifiers is an important part of the subject of applied electronics.

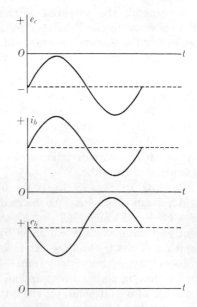

FIG. 38–15. Graphs of e_c, i_b, and e_b as functions of time. Output and input voltages are 180° out of phase.

Usually, the signal to be amplified is so weak that several stages of amplification are needed. This is accomplished by utilizing the variations of potential in the plate circuit of one tube to supply the variations of grid potential of the next tube, and so on.

38–7 Elementary principles of oscillation. It was shown in the preceding chapter that the discharge of a capacitor C through an inductor L is oscillatory, with a frequency

$$= \frac{1}{2\pi} \sqrt{\frac{1}{LC}}. \qquad (38\text{–}2)$$

The oscillations, however, die out quickly because of the resistance of the circuit. The greater the resistance the more rapidly are the oscillations damped. An undamped or continuous oscillation can be produced only if energy is supplied to an oscillating circuit at the same rate as that at which it is dissipated.

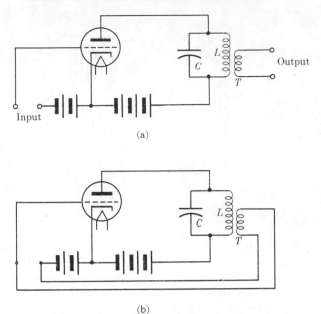

(a)

(b)

Fig. 38–16. Essentials of an oscillator. (a) Amplifier. (b) Feedback from output to input.

Consider the amplifying circuit shown in Fig. 38–16(a). A sinusoidal variation in potential between cathode and grid (input) produces, as we have seen before, an amplified sinusoidal potential variation in the plate circuit, part of which may be taken off by the step-down transformer labeled T. Suppose the turn ratio of this transformer is chosen so that the output voltage has the same magnitude as the input voltage. In general, for any arbitrary frequency of the input voltage, there is a difference of phase between it and the output voltage. However, there is one particular frequency such that the phases of the output and input voltages are the same. Then if the output is connected directly to the input, as shown in Fig. 38–16(b), sinusoidal variations of voltage at this frequency will be self-maintaining, and the tube acts as an oscillator. The frequency of oscillation is very nearly that given by Eq. (38–2). No energy supply from the outside is necessary to start the oscillation. Closing the battery switch or producing any sudden change in the electrical or mechanical constants of the circuit will start a voltage pulse which rapidly builds up to a steady oscillation.

Circuits of this type may be constructed to yield undamped oscillations of very high frequency and very high power. The greatest use for such circuits is in the field of radio, radar, and television.

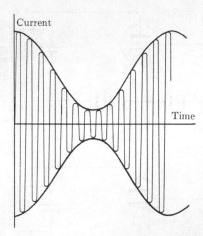

FIG. 38–17. Amplitude modulated wave with sinusoidal modulation.

38–8 Amplitude modulation. An alternating current of constant frequency whose magnitude varies with the time is said to be *amplitude modulated*. Figure 38–17 is a graph of a high-frequency alternating current which is modulated with a sinusoidal modulation. If the high frequency (or radiofrequency) oscillation is used to give rise to radio waves, the wave is called the *carrier wave*. In radio, the low-frequency modulation is the audiofrequency corresponding to speech or music.

A basic circuit to produce a low-frequency modulation of a high-frequency oscillation is shown in Fig. 38–18. An exciting source of high frequency f_1 is permanently connected in the grid circuit of a triode. By means of a coupling transformer, a voltage of lower frequency can be added to the first. This voltage might result from sound waves impinging on a telephone transmitter, as shown in the diagram, but for simplicity we shall assume it to consist of a single frequency f_2, lower than f_1.

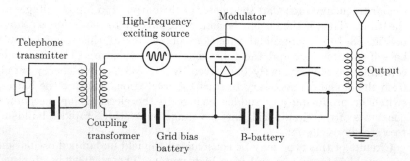

FIG. 38–18. Basic circuit for grid-bias modulation.

The vacuum tube must be operated on the curved portion of its characteristic curve, or as a nonlinear circuit element. The plate current in the output circuit, unlike that in the output of an amplifier, is therefore not an exact replica of the input to the grid, but consists of a complex mixture of different frequencies. One of these has the form shown in Fig. 38–17, consisting of an oscillation at the high frequency f_1 whose amplitude fluctuates at the low frequency f_2. The antenna coupled to the plate circuit then transmits radiation of the same wave form. The unwanted components of frequencies other than f_1 are eliminated by filter circuits not shown in the diagram.

38–9 Demodulation or detection. A *demodulator* or *detector* is a device to separate the modulation or intelligence-carrying frequencies from the radiofrequency carrier. The demodulation is usually carried out by a process of rectification using some form of nonlinear circuit element. The simple diode circuit of Fig. 38–19 is often used. If the diode were a perfect detector, the capacitor C would become charged to the peak of the input wave during each carrier frequency cycle and then there would be sufficient current drain through the resistor R to cause the output voltage to decrease as rapidly as does the envelope of the modulated input voltage. In these circumstances, the output voltage would have the same wave form as the envelope of the modulated wave.

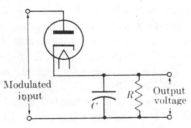

Fig. 38–19. Diode detector.

These ideal conditions cannot be achieved in practice. The actual behavior of the circuit is shown in Fig. 38–20. The voltage drop in the tube itself prevents the voltage of the capacitor from actually reaching the peak value. When the input voltage drops below the capacitor voltage, the tube ceases to conduct and the capacitor slowly discharges through the resistor until the next positive peak of input voltage occurs and recharges it. The resulting form of the output voltage is therefore somewhat jagged, although not as exaggeratedly so as in Fig. 38–20.

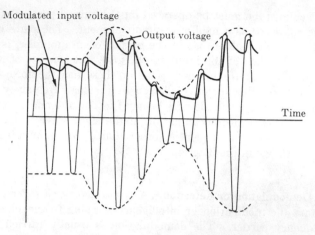

Modulated input voltage

Output voltage

Time

Fig. 38–20. Action of the diode detector of Fig. 38–19. The irregularities in the output wave form are greatly exaggerated, since ordinarily there would be many more cycles of the high frequency during a cycle of the envelope than are shown.

38–10 The radio receiver. Almost all modern radio sets make use of the superheterodyne principle. There are as many variations of this circuit as there are manufacturers of radios. We shall limit ourselves in this section to the principle itself without going into details of design.

It was pointed out in Section 23–7 that two tones of different frequencies give rise in the ear to combination tones consisting of a beat frequency equal to the difference of the two frequencies, and a summation tone equal to the sum of the two frequencies. Thus, if an 1800-cycle note and a 1000-cycle note are played simultaneously, the ear hears four separate frequencies: 1800, 1000, 800, and 2800.

Now suppose a radio set receives a modulated signal of 1000 kilocycles per second (1000 kc) and it is desired to transform it into a 100-kc signal. A local oscillator is used whose frequency is either 1100 kc or 900 kc. If these two signals are then put into a tube called a *mixing tube,* and the output of this tube is passed through a special circuit called a *filter circuit* which cuts off everything but the 100-kc signal (the intermediate frequency), the resulting oscillation is a 100-kc signal *with the same modulations* as the original 1000-kc signal. This is now sent through an *intermediate frequency* amplifier. After sufficient amplification, the signal is sent through a detector and the audiofrequencies corresponding to the speech or music are obtained. These frequencies are then amplified by an audiofrequency amplifier, and the output is sent to a loud-speaker. A block diagram of the system is shown in Fig. 38–21.

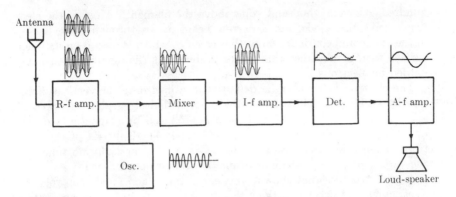

Loud-speaker

FIG. 38–21. Block diagram representation of a typical radio-broadcast receiver. R-f amp. is radiofrequency amplifier; Osc. is oscillator; I-f amp. is intermediate-frequency amplifier; Det. is detector; A-f amp. is audiofrequency amplifier.

When we "tune" a radio to a particular station, we vary the constants of the oscillating circuit to provide a frequency which, when combined with the frequency of the waves broadcast by the desired station, will always give rise to the same intermediate frequency for which the rest of the set is tuned. The intermediate frequency is usually set at 460 kc. The advantages of the superheterodyne circuit are that it avoids the necessity of tuning many stages simultaneously, and also that the intermediate frequency is invariably lower than the incoming frequency and therefore easier to amplify.

38–11 The cathode-ray tube.   One of the most useful of recent electronic developments is the cathode-ray tube, whose essential features are illustrated in Fig. 38–22. The tube itself is of glass and is highly evacuated. Electrons (cathode rays) are emitted by a heated filament K and accelerated toward an anode P maintained at a potential of from several

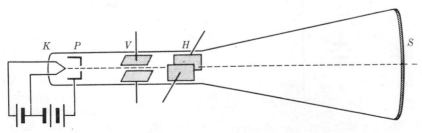

FIG. 38–22. Simplified drawing of a cathode-ray tube.

hundred to several thousand volts above the filament. Most of the electrons strike the anode, but a narrow beam passes through a small hole in the anode and continues on to the screen S, which is coated on its inner surface with a substance that emits visible light (fluoresces) when bombarded by electrons.

The electron beam may be deflected in a horizontal or vertical direction by an electric field between the pairs of deflecting plates marked H and V. (In some tubes the deflection is produced by magnetic fields set up by coils outside the tube.) The extremely small inertia of the electrons enables the electron stream to follow, with practically no time lag, the variations in the electric or magnetic fields which deflect it.

A grid structure (not shown) between cathode and anode controls the electron current and hence the intensity of the spot on the screen. When the tube is used as a television receiver the spot is caused to sweep rapidly over the screen, while its intensity is controlled by the grid in accordance with variations in brightness of points in the object being televised. Persistence of vision (and a small persistence of screen fluorescence) creates the illusion of an image.

38–12 The photoelectric effect. In the thermionic emission of electrons from metals, the energy needed by an electron to escape from the metal surface is furnished by the energy of thermal agitation. Electrons may also acquire enough energy to escape from a metal, even at low temperatures, if the metal is illuminated by light of sufficiently short wavelength. This phenomenon is called the *photoelectric effect*. It was first observed by Heinrich Hertz in 1887, who noticed that a spark would jump more readily between two spheres when their surfaces were illuminated by the light from another spark. Hall-wachs investigated the effect more fully the following year, and it is usually known by his name.

A modern type phototube is shown schematically in Fig. 38–23. A beam of light, indicated by the arrows, falls on a photosensitive surface S. Electrons emitted by the surface are drawn to the collector C, normally maintained at a positive potential with respect to the emitter. Emitter and collector are enclosed in an evacuated container. The photoelectric current can be read on the galvanometer G.

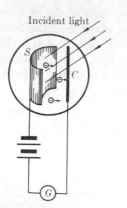

FIG. 38–23. Schematic diagram of photocell circuit.

It is found that with a given material as emitter, the wavelength of the light must be shorter than a critical value, different for different surfaces, in order that any photoelectrons at all may be emitted. This critical wavelength, or the corresponding frequency, is called the *threshold frequency* of the particular surface. The threshold frequency for most metals is in the ultraviolet (critical wavelength 200 to 300×10^{-7} cm), but for potassium and caesium oxide it lies in the visible spectrum (400 to 700×10^{-7} cm).

Just as in the case of thermionic emission, the photoelectrons form a cloud of space charge around the emitter S. That some of the electrons are emitted with an initial velocity is shown by the fact that even with no emf in the external circuit a few electrons penetrate the cloud of space charge and reach the collector, causing a small current in the external circuit. The velocity of the most rapidly moving electrons can be deduced by measuring the reversed voltage (negative potential of collector) which is required to reduce the current to zero.

A remarkable feature of photoelectric emission is the relation between the number and maximum velocity of escaping electrons on one hand, and the intensity and wavelength of the incident light on the other. Surprisingly enough, it is found that the maximum velocity of emission is *independent of the intensity* of the light, but does depend on its wavelength. It is true that the photoelectric current increases as the light intensity is increased, but only because more electrons are emitted. With light of a given wavelength, no matter how feeble it may be, the maximum velocity of the photoelectrons from a given surface is always the same, provided, of course, that the frequency is above the threshold frequency.

The explanation of the photoelectric effect was given by Einstein in 1905, although his theory was so radical that it was not generally accepted until 1916, when it was confirmed by experiments performed by Millikan. Extending a proposal made two years earlier by Planck, Einstein postulated that a beam of light consisted of small bundles of energy which are now called *light quanta* or *photons*. The energy W of a photon is proportional to its frequency f, or is equal to its frequency multiplied by a constant. That is,

$$W = hf,$$

where h is a universal constant called Planck's constant whose value is 6.63×10^{-27} erg·sec. When a photon collides with an electron at or just within the surface of a metal, it may transfer its energy to the electron. This transfer is an "all-or-none" process, the electron getting all the photon's energy or none at all. The photon then simply drops out of existence. The energy acquired by the electron may enable it to escape from the surface of the metal if it is moving in the right direction.

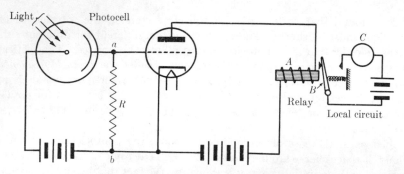

Fig. 38–24. Principle of the photoelectric relay.

In leaving the surface of the metal the electron loses energy in amount ϕ (the work function of the surface). Some electrons may lose more than this if they start at some distance below the metal surface, but the maximum energy with which an electron can emerge is the energy gained from a photon minus the work function. Hence the maximum kinetic energy of the photoelectrons ejected by light of frequency f is

$$\tfrac{1}{2}mv_{\max}^2 = hf - \phi. \tag{38–3}$$

This is Einstein's photoelectric equation, and it was in exact agreement with Millikan's experimental results.

The currents obtainable with vacuum phototubes are extremely small, of the order of a few microamperes per lumen of light flux. These currents may be increased by a factor of 5 to 10 if a small quantity of gas is left in the tube. The electrons ionize the gas and more current-carriers are available.

One of the most important uses of the photoelectric cell is to operate a relay which opens or closes a local circuit to accomplish some useful purpose. In this connection the photocell is called an *electric eye*. A simple photoelectric relay circuit is shown in Fig. 38–24. While the light is incident upon the photoelectric surface a photoelectric current exists in the resistor R and the potential of point a is the potential of point b plus the "iR" drop in the resistor R. The grid of the vacuum tube, which is connected to a, is therefore only slightly negative, and the plate current is sufficient to actuate the electromagnet A, thereby attracting the armature B and keeping the local circuit open. When the light is cut off, the point a (and therefore the grid) becomes more negative in the absence of an iR drop in R and the plate current is reduced. The armature then springs back and closes the local circuit. A wide variety of industrial operations are performed in this way.

Photosensitive surface

FIG. 38–25. Photronic cell.

Figure 38–25 is a photograph of another type of photoelectric cell, called a barrier-layer or photronic cell. A layer of copper oxide is deposited on a copper disk, with an extremely thin layer of metal on top of the oxide. Light passing through the thin metal layer drives electrons from the oxide into this layer, producing between the copper disk and the metal layer a potential difference which depends upon the amount of light striking the cell.

38–13 The x-ray tube. X-rays are produced when rapidly moving electrons, which have been accelerated through potential differences of some tens or hundreds of thousands of volts, are allowed to strike a metal target. They were first observed by Wilhelm K. Roentgen (1845–1923) in 1895, and are also called "Roentgen rays."

X-rays are of the same nature as light or any other electromagnetic wave and, like light waves, they are governed by quantum relations in their interaction with matter. One may hence speak of x-ray photons or quanta, the energy of such a photon being given by the familiar relation

$$W = hf.$$

Wavelengths of x-rays range from 10^{-10} to 10^{-6} cm.

At present, practically all x-ray tubes are of the Coolidge type, invented by W. D. Coolidge of the General Electric laboratories in 1913. A diagram of a Coolidge tube is given in Fig. 38–26. A thermionic cathode and an anode are enclosed in a glass tube which has been pumped down to an extremely low pressure, so that electrons emitted from the

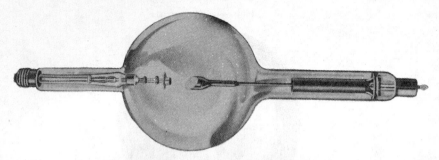

FIG. 38–26. Coolidge-type x-ray tube.

cathode can travel directly to the anode with only a small probability of a collision on the way, reaching the anode with a speed corresponding to the full potential difference across the tube. X-radiation is emitted from the anode surface as a consequence of its bombardment by the electron stream.

It will be seen that x-ray production is an inverse phenomenon to photo-electric emission. In the latter, electrons acquire kinetic energy from light waves or photons. In the former, x-ray waves or photons are produced at the expense of electronic kinetic energy.

There appear to be two distinct processes going on when x-rays are emitted. Some of the electrons are stopped by the target and their kinetic energy is converted directly to x-radiation. Others transfer their energy in whole or in part to the atoms of the target, which retain it temporarily as "energy or excitation" but very shortly emit it as x-radiation. The latter is characteristic of the material of the target, while the former is not.

38–14 Conduction in gases. Unlike a metal or an electrolyte, a gas free from external influences contains no free charges to serve as carriers in an electric field. Gases may be rendered conducting, however, in a variety of ways, in all of which some of the molecules become ionized by the detachment of one or more of their outer electrons. Some of these electrons may then attach themselves to neutral molecules, forming negative ions, so that in an ionized gas both positive and negative ions and free electrons are usually present.

In order to ionize a molecule, energy must be supplied to it in some way. This may come about as a result of a collision with a rapidly moving molecule, ion, or electron, or by interaction with a quantum of radiation (a photon). Some common ionizing agents are cosmic rays, radioactive emanations, photons, x-rays, electrons, positive ions, and high-speed atoms.

Ionization by collision is the chief means of producing ions in most instances of gaseous conduction. Positive and negative ions and electrons

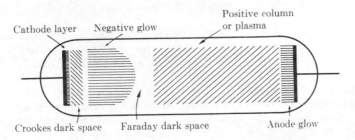

Fig. 38–27. Schematic diagram of gas discharge.

are accelerated by the electric field in the gas and may acquire sufficient energy to ionize a neutral molecule when a collision takes place. A current in a gas is referred to as a *discharge.*

The type of discharge in a neon sign and a fluorescent lamp is called a *glow discharge.* Glow discharges take place at pressures of a few millimeters of mercury. Figure 38–27 represents a tube with electrodes sealed in at its ends and containing a gas at low pressure. Because of the few ions formed by cosmic rays or other means, the gas will be very slightly conducting even at low voltages. When the critical voltage is reached, the current increases very rapidly and the gas in the tube becomes luminous, whence the term "glow discharge."

A marked difference in the appearance of the gas near the cathode and anode will be noted after the glow discharge sets in. The surface of the cathode is covered with a thin layer of luminous gas called the *cathode layer.* Immediately beyond it is a relatively nonluminous region called the *Crookes dark space* (after Sir William Crookes, one of the early workers in this field). Beyond the Crookes dark space is a second luminous region, blue if the discharge is in air, called the *negative glow.* Following this is another relatively dark region, the *Faraday dark space,* and beyond this is the *positive column* or *plasma* which occupies the remainder of the tube. The positive column is often broken up into alternate luminous and nonluminous portions called *striations.*

Most of the light emitted by the gas comes from the positive column. Light is emitted by a gas molecule on returning to its normal state after one of its outer electrons has been removed or raised to a higher "energy level." This light is characteristic of the gas in the tube, and in general much of it lies in the ultraviolet. Fluorescent lamps are gaseous discharge tubes whose inner walls are covered with a material which absorbs ultraviolet light and re-emits light in the visible spectrum. The luminous efficiency of such lamps is considerably greater than that of incandescent lamps.

Problems

Planck's constant $h = 6.63 \times 10^{-27}$ erg·sec $= 6.63 \times 10^{-34}$ joule·sec.
Speed of light $c = 3.00 \times 10^{10}$ cm/sec $= 3.00 \times 10^{8}$ m/sec.
1 electron volt $= 1.60 \times 10^{-22}$ erg $= 1.60 \times 10^{-19}$ joule.

38–1. In the photoelectric effect, what is the relation between the threshold frequency f_0 and the work function ϕ?

38–2. The photoelectric threshold wavelength of tungsten is 2.73×10^{-5} cm. Calculate the maximum kinetic energy of the electrons ejected from a tungsten surface by ultraviolet radiation of wavelength 1.80×10^{-5} cm. (Express the answer in electron volts.)

38–3. A photoelectric surface has a work function of 4.00 electron volts. What is the maximum velocity of the photoelectrons emitted by light of frequency 3×10^{15} sec^{-1}?

38–4. When ultraviolet light of wavelength 2.54×10^{-5} cm from a mercury arc falls upon a clean copper surface, the retarding potential necessary to stop the emission of photoelectrons is 0.59 volt. What is the photoelectric threshold wavelength for copper?

CHAPTER 39

THE NATURE AND PROPAGATION OF LIGHT

39–1 The nature of light. Until about the middle of the 17th century, it was generally believed that light consisted of a stream of corpuscles. These corpuscles were emitted by light sources, such as the sun or a candle flame, and traveled outward from the source in straight lines. They could penetrate transparent materials and were reflected from the surfaces of opaque materials. When the corpuscles entered the eye, the sense of sight was stimulated.

By the middle of the 17th century, while most workers in the field of optics accepted the corpuscular theory, the idea had begun to develop that light might be a wave motion of some sort. Christian Huygens, in 1670, showed that the laws of reflection and refraction could be explained on the basis of a wave theory and that such a theory furnished a simple explanation of the recently discovered phenomenon of double refraction. The wave theory failed of immediate acceptance, however. For one thing, it was objected that if light were a wave motion one should be able to see around corners, since waves can bend around obstacles in their path. We know now that the wavelengths of light waves are so short that the bending, while it does actually take place, is so small that it is not ordinarily observed. As a matter of fact, the bending of a light wave around the edges of an object, a phenomenon known as diffraction, was noted by Grimaldi before 1663 and interpreted by Hooke in 1665 in terms of a wave picture, but the significance of Grimaldi's observations was not recognized by most physicists at that time.

It was not until 1827 that the experiments of Thomas Young and Augustin Fresnel, on interference, and the measurements of the velocity of light in liquids by Leon Foucault at a somewhat later date, demonstrated the existence of optical phenomena for whose explanation a corpuscular theory was inadequate. The phenomena of interference and diffraction will be discussed further in Chapter 46, where it will be shown that they are only what would be expected if light is a wave motion. Young's experiments enabled him to measure the wavelength of the waves, and Fresnel showed that the rectilinear propagation of light, as well as the diffraction effects observed by Grimaldi and others, could be accounted for by the behavior of waves of short wavelength.

The next great forward step in the theory of light was the work of the Scottish scientist James Clerk Maxwell. In 1873, Maxwell showed that an oscillating electrical circuit should radiate electromagnetic waves. The velocity of propagation of the waves could be computed from purely electrical and magnetic measurements, and it turned out to be very nearly 3×10^8 m/sec. Within the limits of experimental error, this was equal to the measured velocity of propagation of light. The evidence seemed inescapable that light consisted of electromagnetic waves of extremely short wavelength. Fifteen years after this discovery by Maxwell, Heinrich Hertz, using an oscillating circuit of small dimensions, succeeded in producing short wavelength waves (we would speak of them today as microwaves) of undoubted electromagnetic origin and showed that they possessed all the properties of light waves. They could be reflected, refracted, focused by a lens, polarized, and so on, just as could waves of light. Maxwell's electromagnetic theory of light and its experimental justification by Hertz constituted one of the triumphs of physical science. By the end of the 19th century it was the general belief that little, if anything, would be added in the future to our knowledge of the nature of light. Such was not to be the case.

The classical electromagnetic theory failed to account for the phenomenon of photoelectric emission, that is, the ejection of electrons from a conductor by light incident on its surface. In 1905, Einstein extended an idea proposed five years earlier by Planck and postulated that the energy in a light beam, instead of being distributed through space in the electric and magnetic fields of an electromagnetic wave, was concentrated in small packets or *photons*. A vestige of the wave picture was retained, in that a photon was still considered to have a frequency and the energy of a photon was proportional to its frequency. The mechanism of the photoelectric effect consisted in the transfer of energy from a photon to an electron. Experiments by Millikan showed that the kinetic energies of photoelectrons were in exact agreement with the formula proposed by Einstein.

Still another striking confirmation of the photon nature of light is the Compton effect. A. H. Compton, in 1921, succeeded in determining the motion of a photon and a single electron, both before and after a "collision" between them, and found that they behaved like material bodies having kinetic energy and momentum, both of which were conserved in the collision. The photoelectric effect and the Compton effect, then, both seem to demand a return to a corpuscular theory of light.

The present standpoint of physicists, in the face of apparently contradictory experiments, is to accept the fact that light appears to be dualistic in nature. The phenomena of light propagation may best be explained by the electromagnetic wave theory, while the interaction of light with matter, in the processes of emission and absorption, is a corpuscular phenomenon.

39-2 Waves and rays. Most of our work in optics will have to do with the propagation of light and the formation of images by mirrors and lenses. All these effects can be interpreted in terms of a wave theory. When waves spread out from a small source in a uniform medium, the wave fronts are spheres concentric with the source. At large distances from the source, the radii of the spheres become so large that the wave fronts can be considered plane. Figure 37–17 is a diagram of the electromagnetic fields in a plane electromagnetic wave. Such a diagram can be simplified by drawing only those wave fronts in which the electric and magnetic intensities are a maximum in one direction or the other, and which are therefore separated from one another by one-half a wavelength.

A train of light waves may be represented even more simply by *rays* than by wave fronts. In a corpuscular theory a ray is simply the path followed by a light corpuscle. From the wave viewpoint, a ray is an imaginary line drawn in the direction in which the wave is traveling. Thus in Fig. 37–17 the rays are straight lines perpendicular to the wave fronts and parallel to the x-axis. At a boundary surface between two substances, such as the surface between a glass plate and the air outside it, the direction of a ray may change suddenly, but it is a straight line both in the air and in the glass. If a substance is not homogeneous the rays, in general, are curved but are still normal to the wave fronts. This is the case in the earth's atmosphere, where the density of the air, and hence the velocity, vary with elevation.

The wavelength of electromagnetic waves capable of affecting the sense of sight lies between 0.00004 cm and 0.00007 cm. Because these wavelengths are so small, it is convenient to express them in terms of a small unit of length.

Three such units are commonly used, the *micron*, the *millimicron*, and the Angstrom. One micron $(1\,\mu)$ is a millionth of a meter, one millimicron $(1\,m\mu)$ is one one-thousandth of a micron, and one Angstrom $(1\,A)$ is one ten-thousandth of a micron.

$$1\,\mu = 10^{-6}\,\text{m} = 10^{-4}\,\text{cm}.$$

$$1\,m\mu = 10^{-9}\,\text{m} = 10^{-7}\,\text{cm}.$$

$$1\,A = 10^{-10}\,\text{m} = 10^{-8}\,\text{cm}.$$

Most workers in the fields of optical instrument design, color, and physiological optics express wavelengths in *millimicrons*. For example, the wavelength of the yellow light from a sodium flame is 0.0000589 cm or 589 mμ.

Figure 39–1 is a chart of the electromagnetic spectrum. Although waves of different wavelengths must be excited by different methods, all are

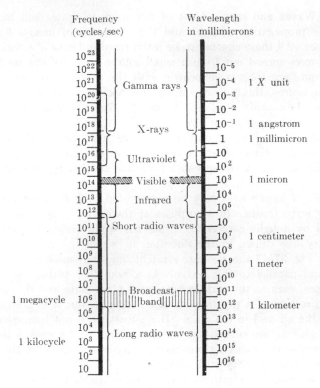

FIG. 39–1. A chart of the electromagnetic spectrum.

alike as far as their fundamental nature is concerned. Note the relatively small portion occupied by the visible spectrum.

39–3 Shadows. Probably one of the first optical phenomena to be noted was that the shadow of an object illuminated by a source of small dimensions has the same shape as the object and that the edges of the shadow are extensions of straight lines from the source, tangent to the edges of the object. Point O in Fig. 39–2(a) represents a *point source* of light. That is, the dimensions of the source are small in comparison with other distances involved. S is a screen, and P is a circular obstacle between source and screen. The portion of the screen bounded by rays from the source tangent to the edges of the obstacle is called the *geometrical shadow* of the obstacle.

If the source is not sufficiently small to be considered a point, the shadow consists of two portions as in Fig. 39–2(b). The inner portion, which receives no light from the source, is called the *umbra*. Surrounding the umbra is the *penumbra*, within which a part of the source is screened

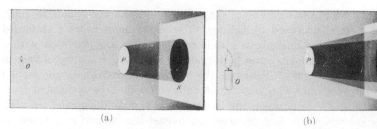

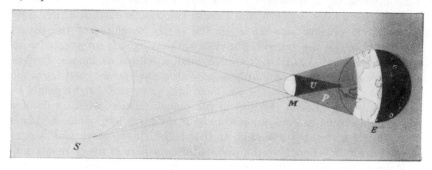

FIG. 39–2. (a) A point source of light casts a sharply defined shadow. (b) If the source is not a point, the shadow consists of a central umbra surrounded by a penumbra.

FIG. 39–3. A solar eclipse. The eclipse is total for an observer within the umbra, partial for one within the penumbra.

by the obstacle. An observer within the umbra cannot see any part of the source; one within the penumbra can see a portion of the source; while from points outside the penumbra the entire source can be seen.

The phenomenon of a partial or total solar eclipse occurs when a portion of the earth's surface moves into the penumbra or umbra of the shadow of the moon cast by the sun. In Fig. 39–3 (obviously not to scale) S, M, and E represent the sun, moon, and earth. The moon's shadow in space consists of a conical umbra, U, surrounded by a penumbra, P. When this shadow sweeps over the earth's surface, the solar eclipse is total for all observers within the umbra. Within a band on either side lying within the penumbra, the eclipse is a partial one. Eclipses of the moon arise in a similar manner when the relative positions of sun, earth, and moon are such that the moon lies within the shadow of the earth.

39–4 The velocity of light. The velocity of light in free space is one of the fundamental constants of nature. Its magnitude is so great (about 186,000 mi/sec or 3×10^8 m/sec) that it evaded experimental measurement until 1675. Up to that time it was generally believed that light traveled with an infinite velocity.

The first attempts to measure the velocity of light were made in 1667, using a method proposed by Galileo. Two experimenters were stationed on the tops of two hills about a mile apart. Each was provided with a lantern, the experiment being performed at night. One man was first to uncover his lantern and, observing the light from this lantern, the second was to uncover his. The velocity of light could then be computed from the known distance between the lanterns and the time elapsing between the instant when the first observer uncovered his lantern and when he observed the light from the second. While the experiment was entirely correct in principle, we know now that the velocity is too great for the time interval to be measured in this way with any degree of precision.

Eight years later, in 1675, the Danish astronomer Olaf Roemer, from astronomical observations made on one of the satellites of the planet Jupiter, obtained the first definite evidence that light is propagated with a finite velocity. Jupiter has twelve small satellites or moons, four of which are sufficiently bright to be seen with a moderately good telescope or a pair of field glasses. The satellites appear as tiny bright points at one side or the other of the disk of the planet. These satellites revolve about Jupiter just as does our moon about the earth and, since the plane of their orbits is nearly the same as that in which the earth and Jupiter revolve, each is eclipsed by the planet during a part of every revolution.

Roemer was engaged in measuring the time of revolution of one of the satellites by taking the time interval between consecutive eclipses (about 42 hrs). He found, by a comparison of results over a long period of time, that while the earth was receding from Jupiter the periodic times were all somewhat longer than the average, and that while it was approaching Jupiter the times were all somewhat shorter. He concluded rightly that

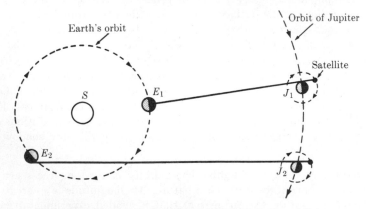

FIG. 39–4. Roemer's method of deducing the velocity of light.

the cause of these variations was the varying distance between Jupiter and the earth.

Figure 39–4, not to scale, illustrates the case.   Let observations be started when the earth and Jupiter are in the positions E_1 and J_1.   Since Jupiter requires about 12 years to make one revolution in its orbit, then by the time the earth has moved to E_2 (about five months later) Jupiter has moved only to J_2.   During this interval the distance between the planets has been continually increasing.   Hence at each eclipse, the light from the satellite must travel a slightly greater distance than at the preceding eclipse, and the observed time of revolution is slightly larger than the true time.

Roemer concluded from his observations that a time of about 22 minutes was required for light to travel a distance equal to the diameter of the earth's orbit.   The best figure for this distance, in Roemer's time, was about 172,000,000 miles.   Although there is no record that Roemer actually made the computation, had he used the data above he would have found a velocity of about 130,000 mi/sec or 2.1×10^8 m/sec.

The first successful determination of the velocity of light from purely terrestrial measurements was made by the French scientist Fizeau in 1849.   A schematic diagram of his apparatus is given in Fig. 39–5.   Lens L_1 forms an image of the light source S at a point near the rim of a toothed wheel T, which can be set into rapid rotation. G is an inclined plate of clear glass.   Suppose first that the wheel is stationary and the light passes through one of the openings between the teeth.   Lenses L_2 and L_3, which are separated by about 8.6 km, form a second image on the mirror M. The light is reflected from M, retraces its path, and is in part reflected from the glass plate G through the lens L_4 into the eye of an observer at E.

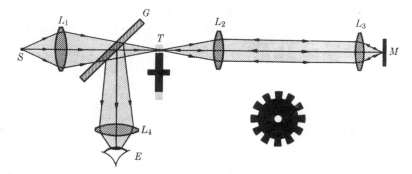

FIG. 39–5.   Fizeau's toothed wheel method for measuring the velocity of light. S is a light source, L_1, L_2, L_3, and L_4 are lenses, T is the toothed wheel, M is a mirror, and G is a glass plate.

If the wheel T is set in rotation, the light from S is "chopped up" into a succession of wave trains of limited length. If the speed of rotation is such that by the time the front of one wave train has traveled to the mirror and returned, an opaque segment of the wheel has moved into the position formerly occupied by an open portion, no reflected light will reach the observer E. At twice this angular velocity, the light transmitted through any one opening will return through the next and an image of S will again be observed. From a knowledge of the angular velocity and radius of the wheel, the distance between openings, and the distance from wheel to mirror, the velocity of light may be computed. Fizeau's measurements were not of high precision. He obtained a value of 3.15×10^8 m/sec.

Fizeau's apparatus was modified by Foucault, who replaced the toothed wheel with a rotating mirror. By introducing between the wheel and the mirror a tube filled with water, he proved that the velocity of light in water is less than in air. A corpuscular theory demands that it shall be greater, and at the time these measurements were made they were taken as conclusive proof that a corpuscular theory was untenable.

The most precise measurements by the Foucault method were made by the American physicist Albert A. Michelson (1852–1931). His first experiments were performed in 1878 while he was on the staff of the Naval Academy at Annapolis. The latest, which were under way at the time of his death, were completed in 1935 by Pease and Pearson.

In an analysis of all measurements up to 1953, DuMond and Cohen report that the best value is

$$c = 2.997929 \times 10^8 \text{ m/sec},$$

which they believe correct within $\pm 0.000008 \times 10^8$ m/sec.

The most accurate direct experimental determination of ϵ_0 was made by Rosa and Dorsey at the United States National Bureau of Standards. Using the equation derived in Section 36–8,

$$c = \sqrt{1/\epsilon_0 \mu_0},$$

they obtained the value

$$c = (2.9979 \pm 0.0001) \times 10^8 \text{ m/sec},$$

which is seen to be in excellent agreement with the value reported by DuMond and Cohen.

39–5 Index of refraction. With a few exceptions, the velocity of light in a material substance, which we shall represent by v, is less than the velocity in free space. Furthermore, while light of all wavelengths travels with the same velocity in empty space, the velocity in material sub-

TABLE 39–1

INDEX OF REFRACTION FOR YELLOW SODIUM LIGHT

($\lambda = 589$ mμ)

Substance	Index of refraction
Solids:	
Ice (H_2O)	1.309
Fluorite (CaF_2)	1.434
Rock salt ($NaCl$)	1.544
Quartz (SiO_2)	1.544
Zircon ($ZrO_2 \cdot SiO_2$)	1.923
Diamond (C)	2.417
Fabulite ($SrTiO_3$)	2.409
Rutile (TiO_2)	$\begin{cases} 2.616 \\ 2.903 \end{cases}$
Liquids at 20°C:	
Methyl alcohol (CH_3OH)	1.3290
Water (H_2O)	1.3330
Ethyl alcohol (C_2H_5OH)	1.3618
Carbon tetrachloride (CCl_4)	1.4607
Turpentine	1.4721
Glycerine	1.4730
Benzene	1.5012
Carbon disulfide (CS_2)	1.6276

stances is different for different wavelengths. This effect is known as *dispersion*. The ratio of the velocity of light in a vacuum to the velocity of light of a particular wavelength in any substance is called the *index of refraction* of the substance for light of that particular wavelength. We shall designate index of refraction by n, stating, if necessary, the particular wavelength to which it refers. If no wavelength is stated, the index is usually assumed to be that corresponding to the yellow light from a sodium flame, of wavelength 589 mμ. Index of refraction is evidently a pure number (the ratio of two velocities) and in most instances is numerically greater than unity.

$$n = \frac{c}{v} \cdot$$

(39–1)

The velocity of light in a gas is nearly equal to its velocity in free space and the dispersion is small. For example, the index of refraction of air at standard conditions, for violet light of wavelength 436 mμ, is 1.0002957, while for red light of wavelength 656 mμ, the index is 1.0002914. It follows that for most purposes the velocity of light in air can be assumed equal to its velocity in free space and the index of refraction of air can be assumed unity. The index of refraction of a gas increases uniformly as the density of the gas is increased.

The index of refraction of most of the common glasses used in optical instruments lies between 1.46 and 1.96. The values for a number of solids and liquids are given in Table 39–1.

39–6 Huygens' principle. Huygens' principle is a geometrical method for finding, from the known shape of a wave front at some instant, what the shape will be at some later instant. The principle states that every point of a wave front may be considered the source of small secondary wavelets, which spread out in all directions with a velocity equal to the velocity of propagation of the waves. The new wave front is then found by constructing a surface tangent to the secondary wavelets or, as it is called, the *envelope* of the wavelets. If the velocity of propagation is not the same at all portions of the wave front, the appropriate velocity must be used for the various wavelets.

Fig. 39–6. Huygens' principle.

Huygens' principle is illustrated in Fig. 39–6. The original wave front, AA', is traveling as indicated by the small arrows. We wish to find the shape of the wave front after a time interval t. Let v represent the velocity of propagation. Construct a number of circles (traces of spherical wavelets) of radius $r = vt$, with centers along AA'. The trace of the envelope of these wavelets, which is the new wave front, is the curve BB'. The velocity v has been assumed the same at all points and in all directions.

39–7 Atmospheric refraction. The density of the earth's atmosphere is greatest at the surface of the earth and decreases with increasing elevation. As a result of this, light rays entering the earth's atmosphere from the sun or the stars are continuously deviated so as to follow a

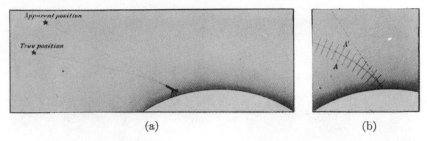

(a)   (b)

FIG. 39–7. Deviation of a ray by the earth's atmosphere.

curved path, as is shown in Fig. 39–7(a). The cause of the deviation may
be seen by considering the wave fronts, which, if coming from astronomical
objects, may be assumed plane when reaching the earth. The lower
portion of a wave front such as AA', Fig. 39–7(b), is always traveling in
air of a greater density than the upper portion A'. Greater density means
greater index of refraction or smaller velocity. Hence the lower portion
of the wave always travels more slowly than the upper portion, and
Huygens' construction leads to the shift in the direction of the wave front
as shown. An observer at the earth's surface sees the light source in the
direction of the tangent to the rays when they reach the earth and con-
cludes that the object is nearer the zenith than its true position.

Rays entering the earth's atmosphere horizontally are "lifted" by atmospheric refraction through about 0.5°. This is very nearly equal to
the angle subtended by the sun's disk, so that when the sun appears
to be just above the horizon at sunrise or sunset, it is, geometrically,
just below it. Furthermore, since the sun requires about two minutes to
move (apparently) a distance equal to its own diameter, the day (at the
equator) is lengthened by about two minutes at both sunrise and sunset.
At higher latitudes the increase is even greater. The necessary correction for atmospheric refraction must be made by every navigator in the
process of "shooting" the sun or any other heavenly body.

The deviation of light by atmospheric refraction decreases with increasing angle of elevation of the light above horizontal, falling to zero
for light incident normally on the earth's surface. Since rays from the
upper portion of the sun's disk are incident at a slightly greater angle than
those from the lower part, they are refracted to a smaller extent. This
accounts for the slightly flattened appearance of the sun at sunset or
sunrise, the lower portion being lifted more than the upper.

Another phenomenon produced by atmospheric refraction is the mirage,
illustrated in Fig. 39–8. The conditions necessary for its production
require that the air nearer the surface of the ground shall be less dense
than that above, a situation which is sometimes found over an area

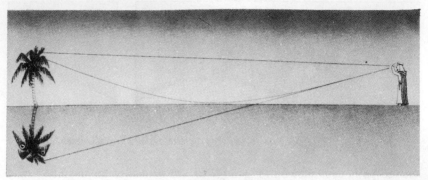

FIG. 39–8. The mirage.

intensely heated by the sun's rays. Light from the upper portion of an object may reach the eye of an observer by the two paths shown in the figure, with the result that the object is seen in its actual position, together with its inverted image below it, as though a reflecting surface lay between the object and observer. The weary traveler in the desert interprets the reflecting surface as a body of water. This same phenomenon accounts for the "wet" appearance of the surface of a smooth highway under a hot sun, when it is seen at a glancing angle.

PROBLEMS

39–1. What is the wavelength in meters, microns, millimicrons, and Angstrom units of (a) soft x-rays of frequency 2×10^{17} cycles/sec? (b) green light of frequency 5.6×10^{14} cycles/sec?

39–2. The visible spectrum includes a wavelength range from about 400 mμ to about 700 mμ. Express these wavelengths in inches.

39–3. The diameters of the sun, earth, and moon are respectively 864,000 mi, 7920 mi, and 2160 mi. The distances from the earth to the sun and to the moon vary somewhat, but suppose an eclipse of the sun takes place when the distance from earth to sun is 92,900,000 mi and the distance from earth to moon is 226,000 mi. Compute the length of the conical umbra of the moon's shadow and compare with the distance from the moon to the earth's surface.

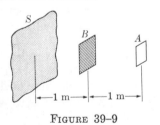

FIGURE 39–9

39–4. In Fig. 39–9, A is an extended light source in the form of a square 2 cm on a side. B is an opaque square sheet parallel to A, and 3 cm on a side. (a) What is the area of the umbra of the shadow of B on screen S? (b) What is the area of the penumbra on S?

39–5. Repeat Problem 39–4 when A is replaced by a point source of light at its center.

39–6. (a) What is the velocity of light of wavelength 500 mμ (in vacuum), in glass whose index at this wavelength is 1.50? (b) What is the wavelength of these waves in the glass?

39–7. A glass plate 3 mm thick, of index 1.50, is placed between a point source of light of wavelength 600 mμ (in vacuum) and a screen. The distance from source to screen is 3 cm. How many waves are there between source and screen?

39–8. The velocity of light of wavelength 656 mμ in heavy flint glass is 1.60×10^8 m/sec. What is the index of refraction of this glass?

39–9. The dielectric coefficient of benzene is 2.3 and its relative permeability may be assumed to equal unity. (a) Using Eq. (37–8), determine the velocity of light in benzene. (b) Using this value of velocity, calculate the index of refraction of benzene. Compare this with the experimentally determined value of 1.501.

39–10. Light of a certain frequency has a wavelength in water of 442 mμ. What is the wavelength of this light when it passes into carbon disulfide?

39–11. Assuming the radius of the earth's orbit to be 92,900,000 miles, and taking the best value of the velocity of light, compute the time required for light to travel a distance equal to the diameter of the earth's orbit. Compare with Roemer's value of 22 minutes.

39–12. Fizeau's measurements of the velocity of light were continued by Cornu, using Fizeau's apparatus but with the distance between mirrors increased to 22.9 km. One of the toothed wheels used was 40 mm in diameter and had 180 teeth. Find the angular velocity at which it should rotate so that light transmitted through one opening will return through the next.

CHAPTER 40

REFLECTION AND REFRACTION AT PLANE SURFACES

40–1 Reflection of a plane wave at a plane surface. Consider the trace of a plane wave surface AA' (Fig. 40–1) which is just making contact with the reflecting surface MM' along a line through A perpendicular to the plane of the diagram. The planes of the wave surface and the reflecting surface are also normal to the plane of the figure. The position of the wave surface after a time interval t may be found by applying Huygens' principle. With points on AA' as centers, draw a number of secondary wavelets of radius vt, where v is the velocity of propagation in the medium above the surface. Those wavelets originating near the upper end of AA' spread out unhindered, and their envelope gives that portion of the new wave surface OB'. The wavelets originating near the lower end of AA', however, strike the reflecting surface. If the latter had not been there, they would have occupied the positions shown by the dotted circular arcs. The effect of the reflecting surface is to reverse the direction of travel of those wavelets which strike it, so that that part of a wavelet which would have penetrated below the surface actually lies above it, as shown by the full lines. The envelope of these reflected wavelets is then that portion of the wave surface OB. The trace of the entire wave surface at this instant is the broken line BOB'. A similar construction gives the line CPC' for the wave surface after another interval t.

The angle ϕ between the incident wave and the surface is called the *angle of incidence;* that between the reflected wave and the surface, r, is called the *angle of reflection.* To find the relation between these angles,

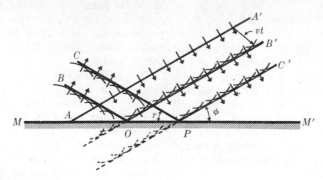

Fig. 40–1. Successive positions of a plane wave AA' as it is reflected from a plane surface.

consider Fig. 40–2, which is the same
as a portion of Fig. 40–1. From O,
draw $OP = vt$, perpendicular to
AA'. Now OB, by construction, is
tangent to a circle of radius vt with
center at A. Hence if AQ is drawn
from A to the point of tangency, the
triangles APO and AQO are equal.
(Right triangles with the side AO in
common and with $AQ = OP$.) The
angle ϕ therefore equals the angle r,

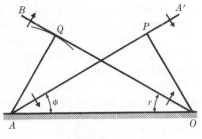

FIGURE 40–2

and we have the *law of reflection: A plane wave is reflected from a plane
surface with the angle of reflection equal to the angle of incidence.*

40–2 Refraction of a plane wave at a plane surface. Whenever a train
of light waves, traveling in one transparent medium, strikes the surface of
a second transparent medium whose index differs from that of the first
(that is, in which the velocity differs from that in the first), two new
wave trains are found to originate at the interface. One, the reflected
wave, travels back into the original medium, while the other, called the
refracted wave, is propagated into the second medium. The direction of
the reflected wave is given by the law of reflection deduced in Section 40–1.
We now proceed to find the direction of trav⸱⸱ ⸱f the refracted wave.

Consider the trace of a plane wave surface AA' (Fig. 40–3) which is
just making contact with the surface MM' along a line through A perpendicular to the plane of the diagram. MM' represents a boundary

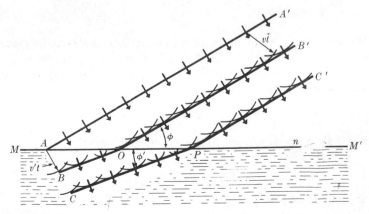

FIG. 40–3. Successive positions of a plane wave front AA' as it is refracted
by a plane surface.

surface between two transparent media of different indices of refraction. Let n be the index of the medium above MM', and n' that of the medium below. Assume that $n' > n$. The reflected waves are not shown in the figure, as they proceed exactly as in Fig. 40–1. Let us apply Huygens' principle to find the position of the refracted wave surface after a time t.

With points on AA' as centers, draw a number of secondary wavelets. Those originating near the upper end of AA' travel with velocity $v = c/n$ and after a time interval t are spherical surfaces of radius vt. The wavelet originating at point A, however, is traveling in the lower medium with speed $v' = c/n'$ and in time t is a spherical surface of radius $v't$. The envelope of the wavelets from the original wave surface is the plane whose trace is the broken line BOB'. A similar construction leads to the trace CPC' after a second interval t.

The angles ϕ and ϕ' between the surface and the incident and refracted wave surfaces are called respectively the *angle of incidence* and the *angle of refraction*. To find the relation between these angles refer to Fig. 40–4, which is the same as a portion of Fig. 40–3. Draw $OQ = vt$, perpendicular to AQ, and draw $AB = v't$, perpendicular to BO. From the right triangle AOQ,

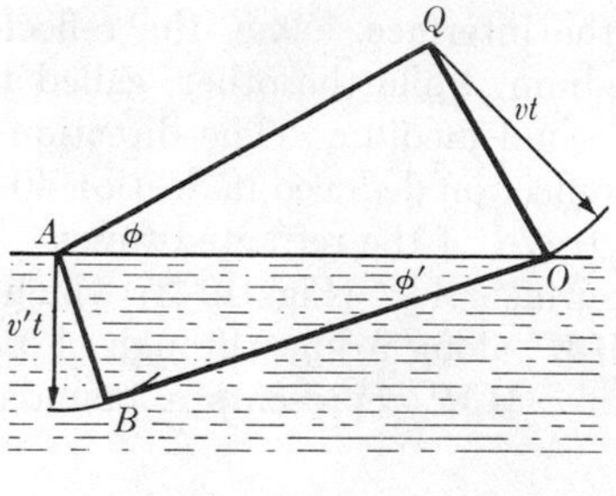

$$\sin \phi = \frac{vt}{AO},$$

and from the right triangle AOB,

$$\sin \phi' = \frac{v't}{AO}.$$

Hence

$$\frac{\sin \phi}{\sin \phi'} = \frac{v}{v'}. \qquad (40\text{–}1)$$

FIGURE 40–4

That is, when a train of plane waves strikes the boundary surface between two transparent media, *the ratio of the sine of the angle of incidence to the sine of the angle of refraction is equal to the ratio of the velocities in the two media.* Since by definition

$$n = \frac{c}{v} \qquad \text{and} \qquad n' = \frac{c}{v'},$$

where c is the velocity of light in free space, it follows that

$$\frac{v}{v'} = \frac{n'}{n},$$

and Eq. (40–1) may be written

$$\frac{\sin \phi}{\sin \phi'} = \frac{n'}{n},$$

or

$$n \sin \phi = n' \sin \phi'. \qquad (40\text{--}2)$$

This equation is more useful than Eq. (40–1), since the index of refraction of a substance is the property which is usually tabulated, rather than the velocity of light in that substance. Since for any given pair of substances the ratio n'/n is a constant, Eq. (40–2) is equivalent to

$$\frac{\sin \phi}{\sin \phi'} = \text{constant}.$$

The discovery that the sines of the angles of incidence and refraction stand in a constant ratio to each other is usually credited to Willebrord Snell, in 1621, although there seems to be some doubt whether the discovery was actually made by him. In accord with common usage, however, we shall refer to Eq. (40–2) as *Snell's law*.

40–3 Ray treatment of reflection and refraction. It is possible to analyze the passage of light through any optical system by successive applications of Huygens' principle to the wave surfaces, as was done in the preceding section at a single surface. However, it is often much simpler to trace a few rays through the system. The wave surfaces may then be constructed at right angles to the rays.

The simple case of reflection and refraction of plane waves at a plane surface is illustrated in Fig. 40–5. In Fig. 40–5(a) there is shown a train of plane waves incident on a plane boundary surface, together with the reflected and refracted waves. In Fig. 40–5(b) the same wave trains are represented by rays. Figure 40–5(c) shows a single incident ray together with the refracted ray and the reflected ray. The angle between any *wave surface* and the *reflecting surface* is equal to the angle between the corresponding *ray* and the *normal* to the reflecting surface, since the sides of the angles are mutually perpendicular. Thus in Fig. 40–5(c), ϕ is equal to the angle of incidence, ϕ' is equal to the angle of refraction, and r is equal to the angle of reflection. The planes of the incident and refracted waves and the plane of the boundary surface are all perpendicular to the plane of the diagram. It follows that the corresponding rays and the surface normal, which are perpendicular to these planes, *all lie in the same plane*, that is, the plane of the diagram. In general, the plane determined by an incident ray and the normal to the surface at the point of incidence is called the *plane of incidence*.

It is evident from Snell's law that the angle of refraction is always less than the angle of incidence for a ray passing from a medium of smaller into one of larger index, as from air into glass. In such a case the ray is

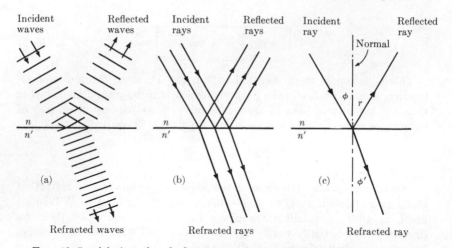

FIG. 40–5. (a) A train of plane waves is in part reflected and in part re-fracted at the boundary between two media. (b) The waves in (a) are represented by rays. (c) For simplicity, only a single incident, reflected, and refracted ray are drawn.

bent *toward* the normal. If the light is traveling in the opposite direction, the reverse is true and the ray is bent *away from* the normal.

To summarize the laws of reflection and refraction in terms of rays:

When a ray of light is reflected, the angle of reflection is equal to the angle of incidence. The incident ray, the reflected ray, and the normal to the surface at the point of incidence, all lie in the same plane.

When a ray of light is refracted, n sin φ = n′ sin φ′. The incident ray, the refracted ray, and the normal to the surface at the point of incidence, all lie in the same plane.

40–4 Total internal reflection. Figure 40–6 shows a number of rays diverging from a point source P in a medium of index n and striking the surface of a second medium of index n', where $n > n'$. From Snell's law,

$$\sin \phi' = \frac{n}{n'} \sin \phi.$$

Since n/n' is greater than unity, $\sin \phi'$ is larger than $\sin \phi$ and evidently equals unity (i.e., $\phi' = 90°$) for some angle ϕ less than 90°. This is illustrated by ray 3 in the diagram, which emerges just grazing the surface at an angle of refraction of 90°. The angle of incidence for which the refracted ray emerges tangent to the surface is called the *critical angle* and is designated by ϕ_c in the diagram. If the angle of incidence is greater than the critical angle, the sine of the angle of refraction, as computed by Snell's law, is greater than unity. This may be interpreted to mean that beyond the critical angle the ray does not pass into the upper medium but is *totally internally reflected* at the boundary surface. Total internal reflection can occur only when a ray is incident on the surface of a medium whose index is *smaller* than that of the medium in which the ray is traveling.

The critical angle for two given substances may be found by setting $\phi' = 90°$ or $\sin \phi' = 1$ in Snell's law. We then have

$$\sin \phi_c = \frac{n'}{n}.$$ (40–3)

The critical angle of an air-glass surface, taking 1.50 as a typical index of refraction of glass, is

$$\sin \phi_c = \frac{1}{1.50} = 0.67, \qquad \phi_c = 42°.$$

This angle, very conveniently, is slightly less than 45°, which makes possible the use in many optical instruments of prisms of angles 45°–45°–90° as totally reflecting surfaces. The advantages of totally reflecting prisms over metallic surfaces as reflectors are, first, that the light is *totally* reflected, while no metallic surface reflects 100% of the light incident on it, and second, the reflecting properties are permanent and not affected by tarnishing. Offsetting these is the fact that there is some loss of light by reflection at the surfaces where light enters and leaves the prism, although recently discovered methods of coating the surfaces with so-called "non-reflecting" films can reduce this loss considerably.

The simplest type of reflecting prism is shown in Fig. 40–7. Its angles are 45°–45°–90°. Light incident normally on one of the shorter faces

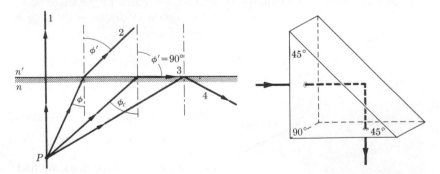

FIG. 40–6. Total internal reflection. The angle of incidence ϕ_c, for which the angle of refraction is 90°, is called the critical angle.

FIG. 40–7. A totally reflecting prism.

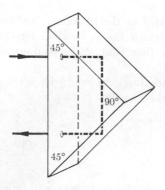

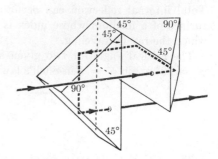

FIG. 40–8. The Porro prism.   FIG. 40–9. A combination of two
Porro prisms.

strikes the inclined face at an angle of incidence of 45°. This is greater
than the critical angle, so the light is totally internally reflected and
emerges from the second of the shorter faces after undergoing a deviation
of 90°.

A 45°–45°–90° prism, used as in Fig. 40–8, is called a *Porro* prism.
Light enters and leaves at right angles to the hypotenuse and is reflected
at each of the shorter faces. The deviation is 180°. Two Porro prisms
are often combined as in Fig. 40–9.

40–5 Refraction by a plane parallel plate. Suppose light is incident at
an angle ϕ_1 (as in Fig. 40–10) on the upper surface of a transparent plate,
the surfaces of the plate being plane and parallel to one another. Let ϕ_1'
be the angle of refraction at the upper surface, and ϕ_2 and ϕ_2' the angles of
incidence and refraction at the lower surface. Let n be the index of the
medium on either side of the plate, and let the index of the plate be n'.

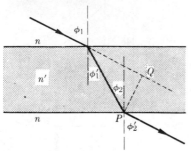

FIG. 40–10. Refraction by a parallel plate.

The figure is drawn with $n' > n$.
From Snell's law,

$$n \sin \phi_1 = n' \sin \phi_1',$$

$$n' \sin \phi_2 = n \sin \phi_2'.$$

But as is evident from the diagram,

$$\phi_1' = \phi_2.$$

Combining these relations, we find

$$\phi_1 = \phi_2'.$$

That is, the emergent ray is parallel to the incident ray. It is not deviated in passing through the plate but is *displaced* by the distance *PQ*. It will be left as an exercise to show that a ray of light passing through any number of plane parallel plates of different index is not deviated but only displaced from its original path, provided it emerges into a medium of the same index as that in which it was originally traveling.

40–6 Refraction by a prism. The prism, in one or another of its many forms, is second only to the lens as the most useful piece of optical apparatus. Totally reflecting prisms have been mentioned briefly. We consider now the *deviation* and the *dispersion* produced by a prism.

Consider a light ray incident at an angle ϕ on one face of a prism, as in Fig. 40–11(a). Let the index of the prism be n, the included angle at the apex be A, and let the medium on either side of the prism be air. It is desired to find the *angle of deviation*, δ. This is a straightforward problem in surveying. One has only to apply Snell's law at the first surface, compute the angle of refraction, then by geometry find the angle of incidence at the second surface, and from a second application of Snell's law find the angle of refraction at the second surface. The direction of the emergent ray is then known and the angle of deviation may be found.

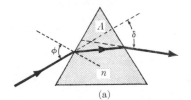 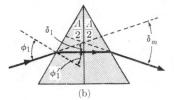

(a)   (b)

FIG. 40–11. (a) Deviation by a prism. (b) The deviation is a minimum when the ray passes through the prism symmetrically.

While the method is simple enough, the expression for the angle δ turns out in the general case to be rather complicated. However, as the angle of incidence is, say, decreased from a large value, the angle of deviation decreases at first and then increases, and is a minimum when the ray passes through the prism symmetrically as in Fig. 40–11(b). The angle δ_m is then called the angle of *minimum deviation* and in this special case it is related to the angle of the prism and its index by the equation

$$n = \frac{\sin (A + \delta_m)/2}{\sin A/2}. \tag{40–4}$$

To derive Eq. (40–4), we have from Fig. 40–11(b),

$$\phi_1' = \frac{A}{2} \text{ (sides mutually perpendicular)},$$

$$\delta_1 = \frac{\delta_m}{2} \text{ (half the deviation takes place at each surface)},$$

$$\phi_1 = \phi_1' + \delta_1 = \frac{A}{2} + \frac{\delta_m}{2} = \frac{A + \delta_m}{2},$$

$$\sin \phi_1 = n \sin \phi_1',$$

$$\therefore \sin \frac{A + \delta_m}{2} = n \sin \frac{A}{2}, \text{ which is Eq. (40–4).}$$

The index of refraction of a transparent solid may be measured, making use of the equation derived above. The specimen whose index is desired is ground into the form of a prism. The angle of the prism A and the angle of minimum deviation δ_m are measured with the aid of a spectrometer. Since these angles may be determined with a high degree of precision, this method is an extremely accurate one and by means of it indices of refraction may be measured to the sixth place of decimals.

If the angle of the prism is small, the angle of minimum deviation is small also and we may replace the sines of the angles by the angles. One then obtains

$$n = \frac{A + \delta_m}{A},$$

or

$$\delta_m = (n - 1)A, \tag{40–5}$$

a useful approximate relation.

40–7 Dispersion.   Most light beams are a mixture of waves whose wavelengths extend throughout the visible spectrum. While the velocity of light waves in a vacuum is the same for all wavelengths, the velocity in a material substance is different for different wavelengths. Hence the index of refraction of a substance is a function of wavelength. A substance in which the velocity of a wave varies with wavelength is said to exhibit *dispersion*. Figure 40–12 is a diagram showing the variation of index of refraction with wavelength for a number of the more common optical materials.

Consider a ray of white light, a mixture of all visible wavelengths, incident on a prism as in Fig. 40–13. Since the deviation produced by the prism increases with increasing index of refraction, violet light is deviated most and red least, with other colors occupying intermediate positions.

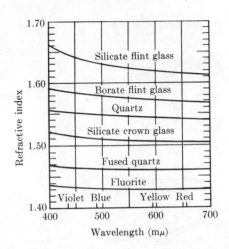

FIG. 40–12. Variation of index with wavelength.

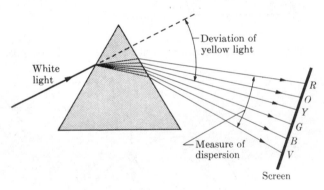

FIG. 40–13. Dispersion by a prism. The band of colors on the screen is called a spectrum.

On emerging from the prism, the light is spread out into a fan-shaped beam as shown. The light is said to be *dispersed* into a spectrum.

When white light is dispersed by a prism, it can be seen from Fig. 40–13 that the whole fan-shaped beam is deviated from the incident direction. A convenient measure of this deviation is provided by the angle of deviation of yellow light, since yellow is roughly midway between red and violet. A simple measure of the dispersion is provided by the angular separation of the red and violet rays. Since deviation and index of refraction are related, the deviation of the entire spectrum is controlled by the index of refraction for yellow light, whereas the dispersion depends on the difference between the index for violet light and that for red light.

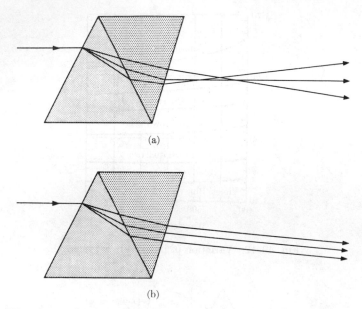

(a)

(b)

FIG. 40–14. (a) A direct-vision prism. (b) An achromatic prism.

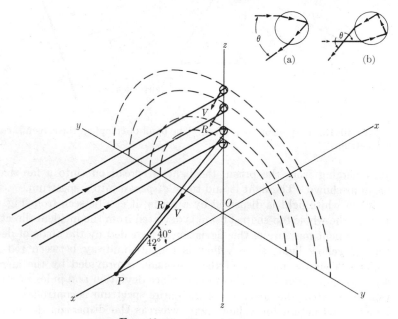

FIG. 40–15. The rainbow.

From the graphs of Fig. 40–12 it can be seen that for a substance like fluorite, whose index for yellow light is small, the difference between the indices for red and violet is also small. On the other hand, in the case of silicate flint glass, both the index for yellow light and the difference between extreme indices are large. In other words, for most transparent materials the greater the deviation, the greater the dispersion.

The brilliance of diamond is due in part to its large dispersion. In recent years synthetic crystals of titanium dioxide and of strontium titanate, with about eight times the dispersion of diamond, have been produced.

Because of the shape of the curves in Fig. 40–12, the dispersions produced by two prisms of equal angles are not exactly proportional to the mean deviations. It is therefore possible to combine two (or more) prisms of different materials in such a way that there is no net deviation of a ray of some chosen wavelength, while there remains an outstanding dispersion of the spectrum as a whole. Such a device, illustrated in Fig. 40–14(a), is known as a *direct-vision prism*. Two prisms may also be designed so that the dispersion of one is offset by the dispersion of the other, although the deviation is not. A compound prism of this sort is called *achromatic* (without color). See Fig. 40–14(b).

40–8 The rainbow. The rainbow is produced by the combined effects of refraction, dispersion, and internal reflection of sunlight by drops of rain. When conditions for its observation are favorable two bows may be seen, the inner being called the primary bow and the outer the secondary bow. The inner bow, which is the brighter, is red on the outside and violet on the inside, while in the more faint outer bow the colors are reversed. The primary bow is produced in the following manner. Assume that the sun's rays are horizontal, and consider a ray striking a raindrop as in Fig. 40–15(a). This ray is refracted at the first surface and is in part reflected at the second surface, passing out again at the front surface as shown. The French scientist Descartes computed the paths of some thousands of rays incident at different points on the surface of a raindrop and showed that if a ray of any given color were incident at such a point that its deviation was a maximum, all other rays of the same color which struck the surface of the drop in the immediate neighborhood of this point would be reflected in a direction very close to that of the first. Hence each color is strongly reflected in the direction of maximum deviation of that particular color. The angle of maximum deviation of red light is 138°, or the angle θ in Fig. 40–15 is 180° − 138° = 42°. The corresponding angle for violet light is 40°, while that for other colors lies between these.

Consider now an observer at P, Fig. 40–15. The xy-plane is horizontal and sunlight is coming from the left parallel to the x-axis. All drops which lie on a circle subtending an angle of 42° at P, and with the center at O, will reflect red light strongly to P. All those on a circle subtending 40° at P will reflect violet light strongly, while those occupying intermediate positions will reflect the intermediate colors of the spectrum.

The point O, the center of the circular arc of the bow, may be considered the shadow of P on the yz-plane. As the sun rises above the horizon the point O moves down, and hence with increasing elevation of the sun a smaller and smaller part of the bow is visible. Evidently an observer at ground level cannot see the primary bow when the sun is more than 42° above the horizon. If the observer is in an elevated position, however, the point O moves up and more and more of the bow may be seen. In fact, it is not uncommon for a complete circular rainbow to be seen from an airplane.

The secondary bow is produced by two internal reflections, as shown in Fig. 40–15(b). As before, the light which is reflected in any particular direction consists largely of the color for which that direction is the angle of maximum deviation. Since the angle of deviation is here the angle θ, and since the violet is deviated more than the red, the violet rays in the secondary bow are deflected down at a steeper angle than the red and the secondary bow is red on the inside and violet on the outside edge. The corresponding angles are 50.5° for red and 54° for violet.

The preceding discussion applies when the drops producing a rainbow are relatively large. When the drops are small, diffraction plays just as important a role as dispersion and reflection, and red light, for example, is received in appreciable amounts from drops lying on circles other than those subtending an angle of 42°. The bow is then a complicated mixture of colors and its appearance depends on the size of the drops.

PROBLEMS

40–1. Prove that a ray of light reflected from a plane mirror rotates through an angle 2θ when the mirror rotates through an angle θ about an axis perpendicular to the plane of incidence.

40–2. Prove that a ray of light travels the shortest possible distance in going from point A to point B after reflection from the plane mirror M in Fig. 40–16. (*Hint:* Draw a straight line connecting B and the image of A.)

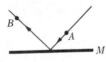

FIGURE 40–16

40–3. A parallel beam of light makes an angle of 30° with the surface of a glass plate having a refractive index of 1.50. (a) What is the angle between the refracted beam and the surface of the glass? (b) What should be the angle of incidence ϕ with this plate for the angle of refraction to be $\phi/2$?

40–4. Light strikes a glass plate at an angle of incidence of 60°, part of the beam being reflected and part refracted. It is observed that the reflected and refracted portions make an angle of 90° with each other. What is the index of refraction of the glass?

40–5. A ray of light is incident on a plane surface separating two transparent substances of indices 1.60 and 1.40. The angle of incidence is 30° and the ray originates in the medium of higher index. Compute the angle of refraction.

40–6. A point light source is 2 inches below a water-air surface. Compute the angles of refraction of rays from the source making angles with the normal of 10°, 20°, 30°, and 40°, and show these rays in a carefully drawn full-size diagram.

40–7. A parallel-sided plate of glass having a refractive index of 1.60 is held on the surface of water in a tank. A ray coming from above makes an angle of incidence of 45° with the top surface of the glass. (a) What angle does the ray make with the normal in the water? (b) How does this angle vary with the refractive index of the glass?

40–8. A glass cube in air has a refractive index of 1.50. Parallel rays of light enter the top obliquely and then strike a side of the cube. Is it possible for the rays to emerge from this side?

40–9. A point source of light is 8 inches below the surface of a body of water. Find the diameter of the largest circle at the surface through which light can emerge from the water.

40–10. The index of refraction of the prism shown in Fig. 40–17 is 1.56. A ray of light enters the prism at point a and follows in the prism the path ab which is parallel to the line cd. (a) Sketch carefully the path of the ray from a point outside the prism at the left, through the glass, and out some distance into the air again. (b) Compute the angle between the original and final directions in air. (Dotted lines are construction lines only.)

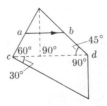

FIGURE 40–17

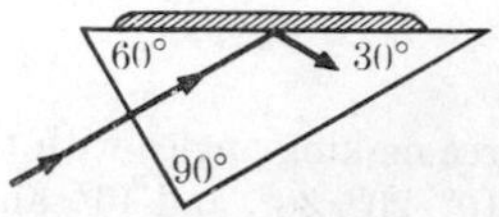

60°   30°

90°

FIGURE 40–18

40–11. Light is incident normally on the short face of a 30°-60°-90° prism as in Fig. 40–18. A drop of liquid is placed on the hypotenuse of the prism. If the index of the prism is 1.50, find the maximum index the liquid may have if the light is to be totally reflected.

40–12. A 45°-45°-90° prism is immersed in water. What is the minimum index of refraction the prism may have if it is to reflect totally a ray incident normally on one of its shorter faces?

40–13. A light ray strikes a parallel-sided glass plate of thickness t at an angle of incidence ϕ. Show that the lateral displacement D of the emergent beam is given by the relation

$$D = t \, \frac{\sin (\phi - \phi')}{\cos \phi'},$$

where ϕ' is the angle of refraction of the ray within the glass.

40–14. A ray of light is incident at an angle of 60° on one surface of a glass plate 2 cm thick, of index 1.50. The medium on either side of the plate is air. Find the transverse displacement between the incident and emergent rays.

40–15. The prism of Fig. 40–19 has a refractive index of 1.414, and the angles A are 30°. Two light rays m and n are parallel as they enter the prism. What is the angle between them after they emerge?

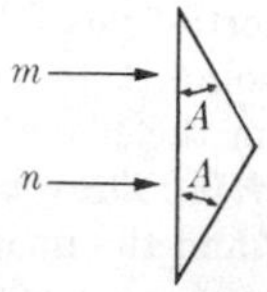

m ——

n ——

A
A

FIGURE 40–19

40–16. What is the angle of minimum deviation of an equiangular prism having a refractive index of 1.414?

40–17. An equiangular prism is constructed of the silicate flint glass whose index of refraction is given in Fig. 40–12. Find the angles of minimum deviation for light of wavelength 400 mμ and 700 mμ.

40–18. A silicate crown prism of apex angle 15° is to be combined with a prism of silicate flint so as to result in no net deviation of light of wavelength 550 mμ. (See Fig. 40–12 for indices of refraction.) Find the angle of the flint prism. Assume that light passes through both prisms at the angle of minimum deviation.

CHAPTER 41

REFLECTION AND REFRACTION AT A SINGLE SURFACE

41–1 Introduction. In the preceding chapter we discussed the reflection and refraction of rays of light at a surface separating two substances of different index, but considered only a single ray or bundles of parallel rays. We now take up the problem of tracing the paths of a large number of rays, all of which diverge from some one point of an object which is either self-luminous or has a rough surface capable of reflecting light in all directions. Such a point is represented by P in Fig. 41–1. At the right of P is a plane surface like that of a block of glass. A ray incident on any point of the surface is in part transmitted and in part reflected. The direction of the reflected ray is given by the law of reflection and that of the transmitted or refracted ray by Snell's law. These two principles suffice to determine the directions of all rays after they encounter a surface of any shape. We shall first consider the reflected rays only, from both plane and spherical surfaces, and then discuss refraction at plane and spherical surfaces. Surfaces other than plane and spherical are used only rarely in optical instruments, since these are the only shapes that can be produced by machine methods at reasonable cost.

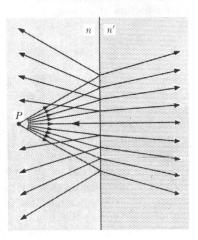

Fig. 41–1. Reflection and refraction of rays at a plane surface.

41–2 Reflection at a plane mirror. While some light is reflected at any surface separating two substances of different index, it is often desirable that the fraction reflected shall be as large as possible. By making the surface of highly polished metal, or by applying a thin metallic coat to a polished surface, the fraction of the light reflected can be made nearly 100%. A highly reflecting smooth surface is called a *mirror*, and we shall speak of the reflecting surfaces in the sections to follow as mirrors, although the equations to be derived will apply also to smooth surfaces from which the light is only partially reflected, such as the surface of a pane of window glass, or that of a lens.

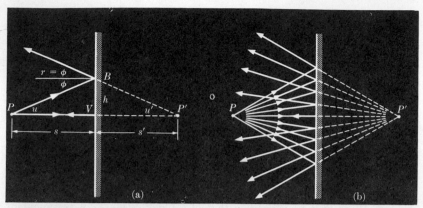

Fig. 41–2. Rays diverging from point P appear to diverge from point P' after reflection at a plane surface.

Figure 41–2(a) shows two rays diverging from a point P at a distance s at the left of a plane mirror. We call P the *object point* and s the *object distance*. In measuring the object distance we shall always *start at the reflecting surface and proceed toward the object point. If this direction is opposite the direction of the oncoming light, the object distance s is positive.* In Fig. 41–2(a) it is evident that s is positive. The ray PV, incident normally on the mirror, returns along its original path. The ray PB, making an arbitrary angle u with PV, strikes the mirror at an angle of incidence $\phi = u$ and is reflected at an angle $r = \phi = u$.

Extend the reflected rays by dotted lines at the right of the mirror, as shown. These dotted lines intersect at P', at a distance s' to the right of the mirror. We shall prove in a moment that *all* rays diverging from P will give rise to reflected rays which, when prolonged backwards into the region behind the mirror, intersect at the point P', as shown in Fig. 41–2(b). If one looks toward the mirror from the left, his eye treats the diverging reflected rays as if they had actually originated at the point P'. We say that P' is the *image* of point P and we call s' the *image distance*. In measuring the image distance we shall always *start at the reflecting surface and proceed toward the image point. If this direction is the same as that of the ongoing (reflected) light, the image distance s' is positive.*

In Fig. 41–2(a) it is evident that s' is negative. The angle u' is equal to r and hence is equal to u. Let h represent the distance VB. Then from the triangles PBV and $P'BV$,

$$\tan u = \frac{h}{s}, \qquad \tan u' = \frac{h}{-s'},$$

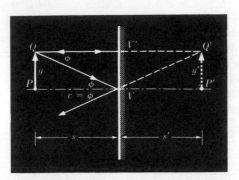

FIG. 41–3. Construction for determining the height of an image formed by reflection at a plane surface.

and since $u = u'$, it follows that

$$s = -s'. \tag{41-1}$$

This result is true whatever the value of the angle u. For the special case of a plane mirror, we see that the image of an object point lies on the extension of the normal from the object point to the mirror, and that the object distance and image distance are equal in absolute value.

Now consider an object of finite size and parallel to the mirror, represented by the arrow PQ in Fig. 41–3. Point P', the image of P, is found as in Fig. 41–2(a). Two of the rays from Q are shown in Fig. 41–3, and all rays from Q appear to diverge from its image Q' after reflection. Other points of the object PQ are imaged between P' and Q'. Let y and y' represent the lengths of object and image, respectively. These lengths are *measured from the axis PP', and are positive when this direction is up.* The ratio y'/y is called the *magnification m.*

$$m = \frac{y'}{y}.$$

From the triangles PQV and $P'Q'V$,

$$\tan \phi = \frac{y}{s} = \frac{y'}{-s'},$$

and since $s = -s'$, it follows that $y' = y$ and hence for a plane mirror the magnification is unity.

The image $P'Q'$ in Fig. 41–3 is called *virtual,* meaning that the reflected rays *appear* to diverge from the image, although they do not actually do so. Virtual images are represented by dashed lines.

The three-dimensional virtual image of a three-dimensional object, formed by a plane mirror, is shown in Fig. 41–1. The image of every object point lies on the normal from that point to the mirror, and the distances from object and image to the mirror are equal. Thus while the images $P'Q'$ and $P'S'$ are parallel to their objects, $P'R'$ is reversed relative to PR. The object and its image are related in the same way as are a left hand and a right hand. To verify this, point your thumbs along

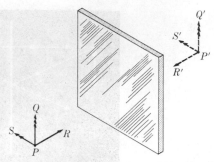

Fig. 41–4. A plane mirror forms a three-dimensional perverted image of a three-dimensional object.

PR and $P'R'$, your forefingers along PQ and $P'Q'$, and your middle fingers along PS and $P'S'$. When an object and image are related in this way the image is called *perverted*. When the transverse dimensions of object and image are in the same direction, the image is *erect*. Thus a plane mirror forms an erect but perverted image.

41–3 Reflection at a spherical mirror. Figure 41–5 shows a spherical mirror of radius of curvature R, with its concave side toward the left. The center of curvature of the surface is at C. In measuring the radius of curvature we shall always *start at the reflecting surface and proceed toward the center of curvature. If this direction is the same as that of the ongoing (reflected) light, the radius of curvature is positive.* In Fig. 41–5, R is positive. Point P is an object point. Since the direction from the mirror to P is opposite that for the oncoming light, the object distance s is positive. The ray PV, passing through C, strikes the mirror normally and is reflected back along itself. Point V is called the *vertex*, and the line PCV the *axis*.

Ray PB, at an arbitrary angle u with the axis, strikes the surface at B, where the angle of incidence is ϕ and the angle of reflection is $r = \phi$. The rays reflected at V and B intersect at the image point P' at a distance s' from the mirror. Since the direction from the mirror to P' is the same as that of the ongoing light, s' is positive. We wish to derive an expression for s'.

Making use of the fact that an exterior angle of a triangle equals the sum of the two opposite interior angles, and considering the triangles PBC and $P'BC$ of Fig. 41–5, we have

$$\theta = u + \phi, \qquad u' = \theta + \phi.$$

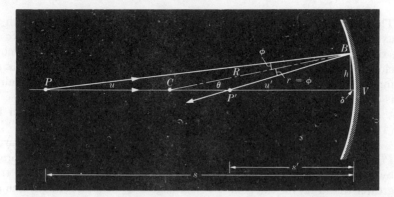

FIG. 41–5. Construction for finding the position of the image P' of a point object P, formed by a concave spherical mirror.

Eliminating ϕ between these equations gives

$$u + u' = 2\theta. \tag{41-2}$$

Let h represent the height of B above the axis, and δ the short distance from V to the foot of this vertical line. Now write the expressions for the tangents of u, u', and θ:

$$\tan u = \frac{h}{s + \delta}, \qquad \tan u' = \frac{h}{s' - \delta}, \qquad \tan \theta = \frac{h}{R - \delta}.$$

Evidently, these trigonometric equations cannot be solved as simply as the corresponding equations for a plane mirror. However, if the angle u is small, the angles u' and θ will be small also. Since the tangent of a small angle is nearly equal to the angle (in radians), we can replace $\tan u'$ by u', etc., in the equations above. Also, if u is small, the distance δ can be neglected compared with s', s, and R. Hence *approximately, for small angles,*

$$u = \frac{h}{s}, \qquad u' = \frac{h}{s'}, \qquad \theta = \frac{h}{R}.$$

Substituting in Eq. (41–2) and canceling h, we get

$$\boxed{\frac{1}{s} + \frac{1}{s'} = \frac{2}{R},} \tag{41-3}$$

as a general relation among the three quantities s, s', and R. The significant feature of the equation above is that *it does not contain the angle u.*

This means that *all* rays from P making sufficiently small angles with the axis will, after reflection, intersect at P'. Such rays, nearly parallel to the axis, are called *paraxial* rays. As the angle increases, the point P' moves closer to the vertex and a spherical mirror, unlike a plane mirror, does not form a point image of a point object. This property of a spherical mirror is called *spherical aberration*.

If $R = \infty$ the mirror becomes plane and Eq. (41-3) reduces to Eq. (41-1), previously derived for this special case.

Now suppose we have an object of finite size, represented by the arrow PQ in Fig. 41-6, perpendicular to the axis PV. The image of P formed by paraxial rays is at P'. Since the object distance for point Q is a trifle greater than that for the point P, the image $P'Q'$ is not a straight line but is curved, another aberration of spherical surfaces called *curvature of field*. However, if the height PQ is not too great, the image is nearly straight and perpendicular to the axis, and we shall assume this to be the case.

We now compute the magnification m. The ray QCQ', incident normally, is reflected back on itself. The ray QV makes an angle of incidence ϕ and an angle of reflection $r = \phi$. From the triangles PQV and $P'Q'V$,

$$\tan \phi = \frac{y}{s} = \frac{-y'}{s'}.$$

Hence

$$m = \frac{y'}{y} = -\frac{s'}{s}. \qquad (41\text{-}4)$$

For a plane mirror, $s = -s'$ and hence $y' = y$, as we have already shown.

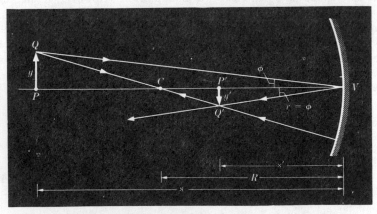

Fig. 41-6. Construction for determining the height of an image formed by a concave spherical mirror.

41–4 Sign conventions. In the sections to follow we shall see that in general an object point may lie on either side of a reflecting or refracting surface. The same is true of an image point, and of the center of curvature of a spherical surface. (If the latter lies at the left of the surface, the concave side of the surface faces toward the left.) Also, objects and images of finite size may extend either above or below the axis of a surface. By adopting a convention of algebraic signs for s, s', R, y, and y', it becomes unnecessary to derive special formulas for a large number of special cases. A single formula can cover all cases and the algebraic sign of a quantity will tell us whether it lies at the right or left of a surface, etc. Many sign conventions are in common use. The one that we have been using is due to R. E. Worley and applies equally well to reflecting and refracting surfaces, giving rise to the same relation between s and s' for both a mirror and a lens. Summarizing:

1. All distances are measured along the axis *from* the reflecting or refracting surface to the point in question.
2. An object distance (from the surface to the object) against the oncoming light is positive.
3. An image distance (from the surface to the image) with the ongoing light is positive.
4. A radius of curvature (from the surface to the center of curvature) with the ongoing light is positive.
5. An object or image dimension above the axis is positive.

To illustrate the use of these conventions, let us derive for a convex mirror the relation between object and image distance, and the expression

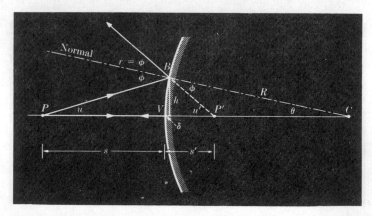

Fig. 41–7. Construction for finding the position of the image P' of a point object P, formed by a convex spherical mirror.

for the magnification. In Fig. 41–7 we make use of the triangles PBC and $P'BC$ and get

$$\phi = u + \theta, \quad u' = \phi + \theta$$

or

$$u - u' = -2\theta. \tag{41–5}$$

Also

$$\tan u = \frac{h}{s + \delta}, \quad \tan u' = \frac{h}{-s' - \delta}, \quad \tan \theta = \frac{h}{-R - \delta}.$$

Assuming the angles u, u', and θ to be small (rays are paraxial) and that δ is very small compared with s, s', and R, the preceding equations become

$$u = \frac{h}{s}, \quad u' = \frac{h}{-s'}, \quad \theta = \frac{h}{-R},$$

and when these are substituted into Eq. (41–5), we get

$$\frac{1}{s} + \frac{1}{s'} = \frac{2}{R},$$

which is exactly the same formula as that obtained for a concave mirror (Eq. 41–3).

Figure 41–8 shows the image of a finite object formed by a convex mirror. From the triangles PQV and $P'Q'V$,

$$\tan \phi = \frac{y}{s} = \frac{y'}{-s'}.$$

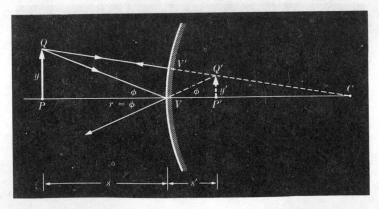

FIG. 41–8. Construction for determining the height of an image formed by a convex spherical mirror.

Hence, just as for a concave mirror (Eq. 41-4),

$$m = \frac{y'}{y} = -\frac{s'}{s}.$$

The image $P'Q'$ formed by the concave mirror in Fig. 41-6 is determined by actual rays of light that intersect at all the points lying between P' and Q'. Such an image is a *real image* and may be formed on a screen. In Fig. 41-8, however, the image formed by the convex mirror consists of points from which the reflected rays of light appear to be coming. Actually no real light exists in the space behind the mirror. This image is therefore a *virtual image*.

EXAMPLE 1. (a) What type of mirror is required to form an image, on a wall 3 m from the mirror, of the filament of a headlight lamp 10 cm in front of the mirror? (b) What is the height of the image if the height of the object is 5 mm?

(a) $s = 10$ cm, $s' = 300$ cm.

$$\frac{1}{10 \text{ cm}} + \frac{1}{300 \text{ cm}} = \frac{2}{R},$$

$$R = 19.4 \text{ cm}.$$

Since the radius is positive, a concave mirror is required.

(b) $m = -\frac{s'}{s} = -\frac{300 \text{ cm}}{10 \text{ cm}} = -30.$

The image is therefore inverted (m is negative) and is 30 times the height of the object or $30 \times 5 = 150$ mm.

EXAMPLE 2. A small object lies 4 in. to the left of the vertex of a concave mirror of radius of curvature 12 in. Find the position and magnification of the image.

$$s = 4 \text{ in.}, \qquad R = 12 \text{ in.},$$

$$\frac{1}{4 \text{ in.}} + \frac{1}{s'} = \frac{2}{12 \text{ in.}},$$

$$s' = -12 \text{ in.},$$

$$m = -\frac{s'}{s} = -\frac{-12 \text{ in.}}{4 \text{ in.}} = 3.$$

The image is therefore 12 in. to the right of the vertex (s' is negative), is virtual (s' is negative), erect (m is positive), and 3 times the height of the object. See Fig. 41-9.

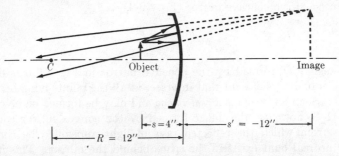

FIGURE 41–9

41–5 Focal point and focal length. When an object point is at a very large distance from a mirror, all rays from that point that strike the mirror are parallel to one another. The object distance $s = \infty$, and from Eq. (41–3)

$$\frac{1}{\infty} + \frac{1}{s'} = \frac{2}{R}, \qquad s' = \frac{R}{2}.$$

The image distance s' then equals one-half the radius of curvature and has the same sign as R. This means that if R is positive, as in Fig. 41–10(a), the image point F lies to the left of the mirror and is real, while if R is negative, as in (b), the image point F lies at the right of the mirror and is virtual.

Conversely, if the image distance s' is very large, the object distance s is

$$\frac{1}{s} + \frac{1}{\infty} = \frac{2}{R}, \qquad s = \frac{R}{2}.$$

The object distance then equals half the radius of curvature. If R is positive, as in Fig. 41–11(a), s is positive. If R is negative, as in Fig. 41–11(b), s is negative and the *object is behind* the mirror. That is, rays previously made converging by some other surface are converging toward F.

The point F in Figs. 41–10 and 41–11 is called the *focal point* of the mirror. It may be considered either as the image point of an infinitely distant object point on the mirror axis, or as the object point of an infinitely distant image point. Thus the mirror of an astronomical telescope forms at its focal point an image of a star on the axis of the mirror.

The distance between the vertex of a mirror and the focal point is called the *focal length* of the mirror and is represented by f. The magnitude of the focal length, from the preceding discussion, equals one-half the radius of curvature. We shall see in the next chapter that a lens also has a focal length, and that the focal length of a lens which *converges* parallel rays to a real image is also a positive quantity. A concave mirror, which

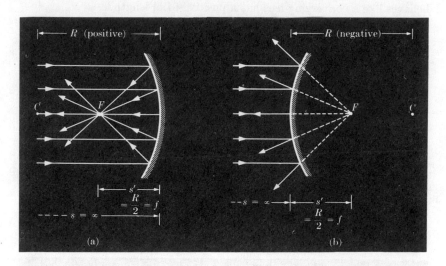

FIG. 41–10. Incident rays parallel to the axis (a) converge to the focal point F of a concave mirror, (b) diverge as though coming from the focal point F of a convex mirror.

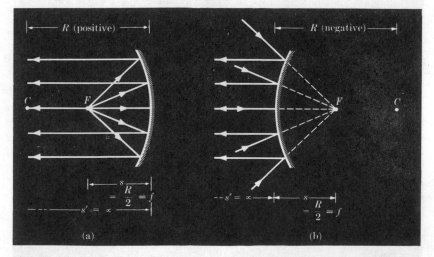

FIG. 41–11. Rays from a point object at the focal point of a spherical mirror are parallel to the axis after reflection. The object in part (b) is virtual.

behaves like a converging lens has a positive focal length.

$$f = \frac{R}{2}.$$

(41–6)

The relation between object and image distances for a mirror may now be written

$$\frac{1}{s} + \frac{1}{s'} = \frac{1}{f}.$$

(41–7)

41–6 Graphical methods. The position and size of the image formed by a mirror may be found by a simple graphical method. This method consists of finding the point of intersection, after reflection from the mirror, of a few rays diverging from some point of the object *not* on the mirror axis. Then (neglecting aberrations) *all* rays from this point which strike

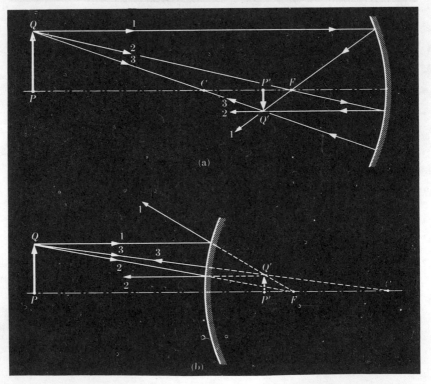

FIG. 41–12. Rays used in the graphical method of locating an image.

the mirror will intersect at the same point. Three rays whose paths may readily be traced are shown in Fig. 41–12.

1. *A ray parallel to the axis.* After reflection, this ray passes through the focal point of a concave mirror or appears to come from the focal point of a convex mirror.

2. *A ray from (or proceeding toward) the focal point.* This ray is reflected parallel to the axis.

3. *A ray along the radius* (extended if necessary). This ray intersects the surface normally and is reflected back along its original path.

Having found the position of the image point by means of the intersection of any two of the rays 1, 2, 3, the paths of all other rays from the same point may be drawn.

EXAMPLE. A concave mirror has a radius of curvature of magnitude 20 inches. Find graphically the image of an object in the form of an arrow perpendicular to the axis of the mirror and at the following object distances: 30 inches, 20 inches, 10 inches, 5 inches. Check the construction by computing the size and magnification of the image.

The graphical construction is indicated in the four parts of Fig. 41–13. [Note that in (b) and (c) only two of the three rays can be used.] The calculations are given below.

The radius of curvature is $R = 20$ inches, and the focal length $f = R/2 = 10$ inches. Hence

$$\frac{1}{s} + \frac{1}{s'} = \frac{1}{f} = \frac{1}{10 \text{ in.}}.$$

(a)
$$\frac{1}{30 \text{ in.}} + \frac{1}{s'} = \frac{1}{10 \text{ in.}}, \qquad s' = 15 \text{ in.},$$

$$m = -\frac{s'}{s} = -\frac{15 \text{ in.}}{30 \text{ in.}} = -\frac{1}{2}.$$

(b)
$$\frac{1}{20 \text{ in.}} + \frac{1}{s'} = \frac{1}{10 \text{ in.}}, \qquad s' = 20 \text{ in.},$$

$$m = -\frac{s'}{s} = -\frac{20 \text{ in.}}{20 \text{ in.}} = -1.$$

(c)
$$\frac{1}{10 \text{ in.}} + \frac{1}{s'} = \frac{1}{10 \text{ in.}}, \qquad s' = \infty,$$

$$m = -\frac{s'}{s} = -\frac{\infty}{10 \text{ in.}} = -\infty.$$

(d)
$$\frac{1}{5 \text{ in.}} + \frac{1}{s'} = \frac{1}{10 \text{ in.}}, \qquad s' = -10 \text{ in.},$$

$$m = -\frac{s'}{s} = -\frac{-10 \text{ in.}}{5 \text{ in.}} = 2.$$

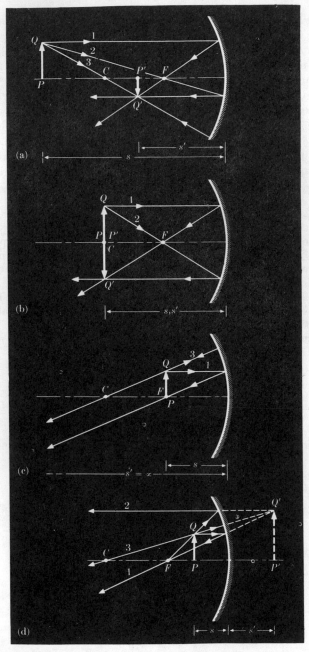

FIG. 41–13. Image of an object at various distances from a concave mirror.

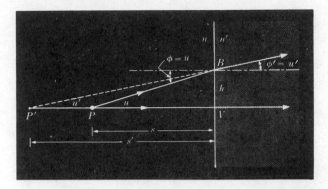

Fig. 41-14. Construction for finding the position of the image P' of a point object P, formed by refraction at a plane surface.

41-7 Refraction at a plane surface. The method of finding the image of a point object formed by rays refracted at a plane or spherical surface is essentially the same as for reflection, the only difference being that Snell's law replaces the law of reflection. In every case, we let n represent the index of the medium at the left of the surface and n' that of the medium at the right. The same convention of signs is used as in reflection.

Consider first a plane surface, shown in Fig. 41-14, and assume $n' > n$. A ray from the object point P toward the vertex V is incident normally and passes into the second medium without deviation. A ray making an angle u with the axis is incident at B with an angle of incidence $\phi = u$. The angle of refraction, ϕ', is found from Snell's law,

$$n \sin \phi = n' \sin \phi'.$$

The two rays both appear to come from point P' after refraction. From the triangles PVB and $P'VB$,

$$\tan \phi = \frac{h}{s}, \qquad \tan \phi' = \frac{h}{-s'}. \qquad (41\text{-}8)$$

(We must write $-s'$, since this quantity is negative in the diagram.)

If the angle u is small, the angles ϕ, u', and ϕ' are small also, and therefore, approximately,

$$\tan \phi = \sin \phi, \qquad \tan \phi' = \sin \phi'.$$

Then Snell's law can be written

$$n \tan \phi = n' \tan \phi',$$

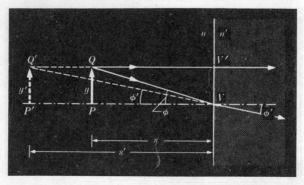

FIG. 41–15. Construction for determining the height of an image formed by refraction at a plane surface.

and from Eq. (41–8), after canceling h,

$$\frac{n}{s} = -\frac{n'}{s'},$$

or

$$\frac{s'}{s} = -\frac{n'}{n}. \tag{41–9}$$

This is an *approximate* relation, *good for paraxial rays only*. That is, a plane refracting surface does *not* image all rays from a point object at the same image point.

Consider next the image of a finite object, as in Fig. 41–15. The two rays shown diverging from point Q appear to diverge from its image Q' after refraction. From the triangles PQV and $P'Q'V$,

$$\tan \phi = \frac{y}{s}, \qquad \tan \phi' = \frac{y'}{-s'}.$$

Combining with Snell's law and using the small-angle approximation, $\sin \phi = \tan \phi$, $\sin \phi' = \tan \phi'$, we get

$$\frac{ny}{s} = -\frac{n'y'}{s'},$$

and hence

$$m = \frac{y'}{y} = -\frac{ns'}{n's}. \tag{41–10}$$

However, from Eq. (41–9), $ns' = -n's$, so

$$m = \frac{y'}{y} = 1 \quad \text{(plane refracting surface)},$$

in agreement with Fig. 41–15. The image distance is greater than the object distance, but image and object are the same size.

A common example of refraction at a plane surface is afforded by looking vertically downward into the quiet water of a pond or a swimming pool; the apparent depth is less than the actual depth. Figure 41–16 illustrates this case. Two rays are shown diverging from a point Q at a distance s below the surface. Here, n' (air) is less than n (water) and the ray incident at V is deviated *away from* the normal. The rays after re-

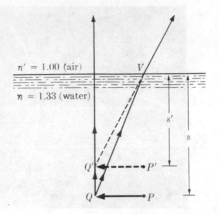

Fig. 41–16. Arrow $P'Q'$ is the image of the underwater object PQ.

fraction appear to diverge from Q', and the arrow PQ, to an observer looking vertically downward, appears lifted to the position $P'Q'$. From Eq. (41–9),

$$s' = -\frac{n'}{n}\, s = -\frac{1.00}{4/3}\, s = -\frac{3}{4}\, s.$$

The apparent depth s' is therefore only three-fourths of the actual depth s. The same phenomenon accounts for the apparent sharp bend in an oar when a portion of it extends below a water surface. The submerged portion appears lifted above its actual position.

41–8 Refraction at a spherical surface.

Finally, we consider refraction at a spherical surface. In Fig. 41–17, P is an object point at a distance s to the left of a spherical surface of radius R. The indices at the left and right of the surface are n and n', respectively. Ray PV, incident normally, passes into the second medium without deviation. Ray PB, making an angle u with the axis, is incident at an angle ϕ with the normal and is refracted at an angle ϕ'. These rays intersect at P' at a distance s' to the right of the vertex. From the triangles PBC and $P'BC$,

$$\phi = \theta + u, \qquad \theta = u' + \phi'. \qquad (41\text{–}11)$$

From Snell's law,

$$n \sin \phi = n' \sin \phi'.$$

Also, the tangents of u, u', and θ are

$$\tan u = \frac{h}{s + \delta}, \qquad \tan u' = \frac{h}{s' - \delta}, \qquad \tan \theta = \frac{h}{R - \delta}. \qquad (41\text{–}12)$$

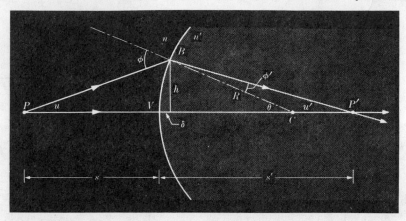

FIG. 41–17. Construction for finding the position of the image P' of a point object P, formed by refraction at a spherical surface.

For paraxial rays we may approximate both the sine and tangent of an angle by the angle itself, and neglect the small distance δ. Snell's law then becomes

$$n\phi = n'\phi',$$

and combining with the first of Eqs. (41–11), we get

$$\phi' = \frac{n}{n'}(u + \theta).$$

Substituting this in the second of Eqs. (41–11) gives

$$nu + n'u' = (n' - n)\theta.$$

Using the small-angle approximations of Eqs. (41–12) and canceling h, this becomes

$$\frac{n}{s} + \frac{n'}{s'} = \frac{n' - n}{R}. \tag{41–13}$$

If $R = \infty$ and the surface is plane, this equation reduces to Eq. (41–9), already derived for the special case of a plane surface.

The magnification is found from the construction in Fig. 41–18. From point Q draw two rays, one through the center of curvature C and the other incident at the vertex V. From the triangles PQV and $P'Q'V$,

$$\tan \phi = \frac{y}{s}, \qquad \tan \phi' = \frac{-y'}{s'},$$

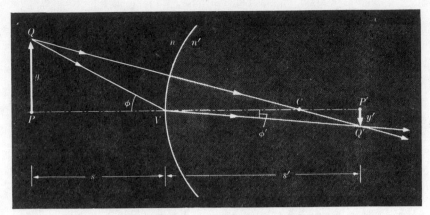

Fig. 41–18. Construction for determining the height of an image formed by refraction at a spherical surface.

and from Snell's law,

$$n \sin \phi = n' \sin \phi'.$$

For small angles,

$$\tan \phi = \sin \phi, \qquad \tan \phi' = \sin \phi',$$

and hence

$$\frac{ny}{s} = -\frac{n'y'}{s'},$$

or

$$m = \frac{y'}{y} = -\frac{ns'}{n's}, \tag{41–14}$$

which agrees with the relation previously derived for a plane surface.

Equations (41–13) and (41–14) can be applied to both convex and concave refracting surfaces when a consistent sign convention is used, and they apply whether n' is greater or less than n. The reader should construct diagrams like Figs. 41–17 and 41–18, when R is negative and $n' < n$, and use them to derive Eqs. (41–13) and (41–14).

The concepts of focal point and focal length can also be applied to a refracting surface. Such a surface is found to have two focal points. The first is the object point when the image is at infinity, the second is the image point of an infinitely distant object. These points lie on opposite sides of the surface and at different distances from it, so that a single refracting surface has two focal lengths. The positions of the focal points can readily be found from Eq. (41–13) by setting s or s' equal to infinity.

41-9 Summary. The results of this chapter are conveniently summarized in Table 41–1. Note that the equation for a plane surface follows immediately from the appropriate equation for a curved surface by letting $R = \infty$.

TABLE 41-1

	Plane mirror	Curved mirror	Plane refracting surface	Curved refracting surface
Object and image distances	$\dfrac{1}{s} + \dfrac{1}{s'} = 0$	$\dfrac{1}{s} + \dfrac{1}{s'} = \dfrac{2}{R} = \dfrac{1}{f}$	$\dfrac{n}{s} + \dfrac{n'}{s'} = 0$	$\dfrac{n}{s} + \dfrac{n'}{s'} = \dfrac{n' - n}{R}$
Magnification	$m = -\dfrac{s'}{s} = 1$	$m = -\dfrac{s'}{s}$	$m = -\dfrac{ns'}{n's} = 1$	$m = -\dfrac{ns'}{n's}$

EXAMPLE 1. One end of a cylindrical glass rod (Fig. 41–19) is ground to a hemispherical surface of radius $R = 20$ mm. Find the image distance of a point object on the axis of the rod, 80 mm to the left of the vertex. The rod is in air.

$$n = 1, \qquad n' = 1.5, \qquad R = +20 \text{ mm}, \qquad s = +80 \text{ mm}.$$

$$\frac{1}{80 \text{ mm}} + \frac{1.5}{s'} = \frac{1.5 - 1}{+20 \text{ mm}},$$

$$s' = +120 \text{ mm}.$$

The image is therefore formed at the right of the vertex (s' is positive) and at a distance of 120 mm from it. Suppose that the object is an arrow 1 mm high, perpendicular to the axis. Then

$$n = 1, \qquad n' = 1.5, \qquad s = +80 \text{ mm}, \qquad s' = +120 \text{ mm}.$$

Hence

$$m = -\frac{ns'}{n's} = -\frac{1 \times 120 \text{ mm}}{1.5 \times 80 \text{ mm}} = -1.$$

That is, the image is the same height as the object, but is inverted.

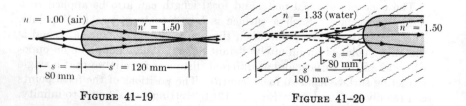

FIGURE 41-19   FIGURE 41-20

EXAMPLE 2. Let the same rod be immersed in water of index 1.33, the other quantities having the same values as before. Find the image distance (Fig. 41–20).

$$\frac{1.33}{80 \text{ mm}} + \frac{1.5}{s'} = \frac{1.5 - 1.33}{+20 \text{ mm}},$$

$$s' = -180 \text{ mm}.$$

The fact that s' is a negative quantity means that the rays, after refraction by the surface, are not converging but appear to diverge from a point 180 mm to the left of the vertex. We have met a similar case before in the refraction of spherical waves by a plane surface and have called the point a *virtual image*. In this example, then, the surface forms a virtual image 180 mm to the left of the vertex.

PROBLEMS

41–1. What is the size of the smallest vertical plane mirror in which an observer standing erect can see his full length image?

41–2. The image of a tree just covers the length of a 2-inch plane mirror when the mirror is held one foot from the eye. The tree is 300 ft from the mirror. What is its height?

41–3. An object is placed between two mirrors arranged at right angles to each other. (a) Locate all of the images of the object. (b) Draw the paths of rays from the object to the eye of an observer.

41–4. An object 1 cm high is 20 cm from the vertex of a concave spherical mirror whose radius of curvature is 50 cm. Compute the position and size of the image. Is it real or virtual? Erect or inverted?

41–5. A concave mirror is to form an image of the filament of a headlight lamp on a screen 4 m from the mirror. The filament is 5 mm high, and the image is to be 40 cm high. (a) What should be the radius of curvature of the mirror? (b) How far in front of the vertex of the mirror should the filament be placed?

41–6. The diameter of the moon is 2160 mi and its distance from the earth is 240,000 mi. Find the diameter of the image of the moon formed by a spherical concave telescope mirror of focal length 12 ft.

41–7. A spherical concave shaving mirror has a radius of curvature of 1 ft. What is the magnification when the face is 4 in. from the vertex of the mirror?

41–8. A concave spherical mirror has a radius of curvature of 10 cm. Make a diagram of the mirror to scale, and show rays incident on it parallel to the axis and at distances of 1, 2, 3, 4, and 5 cm from it. Using a protractor, construct the reflected rays and indicate the points at which they cross the axis.

41–9. An object is 6 inches from the center of a silvered spherical glass Christmas tree ornament 3 inches in diameter. What is the position and magnification of its image?

41–10. A tank whose bottom is a mirror is filled with water to a depth of 20 cm. A small object hangs motionless 8 cm under the surface of the water. What is the apparent depth of its image when viewed at normal incidence?

41–11. A ray of light in air makes an angle of incidence of 45° at the surface of a sheet of ice. The ray is refracted within the ice at an angle of 30°. (a) What is the critical angle for the ice? (b) A speck of dirt is embedded $\frac{3}{4}$ in. below the surface of the ice. What is its apparent depth when viewed at normal incidence?

41–12. A microscope is focused on the upper surface of a glass plate. A second plate is then placed over the first. In order to focus on the bottom surface of the second plate, the microscope must be raised 1 mm. In order to focus on the upper surface it must be raised 2 mm *further*. Find the index of refraction of the second plate. (This problem illustrates one method of measuring index of refraction.)

41–13. A layer of ether ($n = 1.36$) 2 cm deep floats on water ($n = 1.33$) 4 cm deep. What is the apparent distance from the ether surface to the bottom of the water layer, when viewed at normal incidence?

41–14. A long glass rod 8 cm in diameter has a hemispherical surface at the end 4 cm in radius. The refractive index of the glass is 1.50. Determine each position of the image if an object is placed on the axis of the rod at the following distances from its end: (a) infinitely far, (b) 16 cm, (c) 4 cm.

41–15. The rod of Problem 41–14 is immersed in a liquid. An object 60 cm from the end of the rod and on its axis is imaged at a point 100 cm inside the rod. What is the refractive index of the liquid?

41–16. What should be the index of refraction of a transparent sphere in order that paraxial rays from an infinitely distant object will be brought to a focus at the vertex of the second surface?

41–17. The left end of a long glass rod 10 cm in diameter, of index 1.50, is ground and polished to a convex hemispherical surface of radius 5 cm. An object in the form of an arrow 1 mm long, at right angles to the axis of the rod, is located on the axis 20 cm to the left of the vertex of the convex surface. Find the position and magnification of the image of the arrow formed by paraxial rays incident on the convex surface.

41–18. A transparent rod 40 cm long is cut flat at one end and rounded to a hemispherical surface of 12 cm radius at the other end. A small object is embedded within the rod along its axis and halfway between its ends. When viewed from the flat end of the rod the apparent depth of the object is 12.5 cm. What is its apparent depth when viewed from the curved end?

41–19. A solid glass hemisphere having a radius of 10 cm and a refractive index of 1.50 is placed with its flat face downward on a table. A parallel beam of light of circular cross section 1 cm in diameter travels directly downward and enters the hemisphere along its diameter. What is the diameter of the circle of light formed on the table?

CHAPTER 42

LENSES AND LENS ABERRATIONS

42-1 Images as objects. Most optical systems include more than one reflecting or refracting surface. The image formed by the first surface serves as the object for the second; the image formed by the second surface serves as the object for the third; etc. Figure 42-1 illustrates the various situations which may arise, and the following discussion of them should be thoroughly understood.

In Fig. 42-1, the arrow at point O represents a small object at right angles to the axis. A narrow cone of rays diverging from the head of the arrow is traced through the system. Surface 1 forms a real image of the arrow at point P. Distance V_1O is the object distance for the first surface and distance V_1P is the image distance. Both of these are positive.

The image at P, formed by surface 1, serves as the object for surface 2. The object distance is V_2P and is positive, since the direction from V_2 to P is opposite that of the oncoming light. The second surface forms a virtual image at point Q. The image distance is V_2Q and is negative because the direction from V_2 to Q is opposite that of the ongoing light.

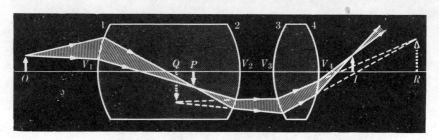

Fig. 42-1. The object for each surface, after the first, is the image formed by the preceding surface.

The image at Q, formed by surface 2, serves as the object for surface 3. The object distance is V_3Q and is positive. The image at Q, although virtual, constitutes a real object as far as surface 3 is concerned. The rays incident on surface 3 are rendered converging and, except for the interposition of surface 4, would converge to a real image at point R. Even though this image is never formed, distance V_3R is the image distance for surface 3 and is positive.

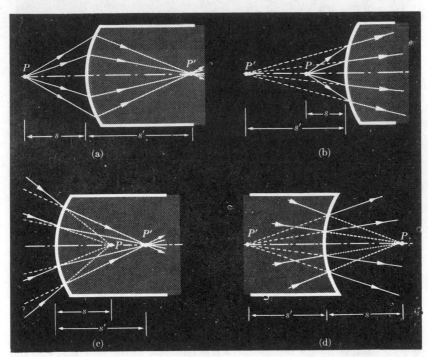

Fig. 42-2. (a) A real image of a real object. (b) A virtual image of a real object. (c) A real image of a virtual object. (d) A virtual image of a virtual object.

The rays incident on surfaces 1, 2, and 3 have all been diverging and the object distance has been the distance from the vertex of the surface to the point from which the rays were actually or apparently diverging. The rays incident on surface 4, however, are *converging* and there is no point at the left of the vertex from which they diverge or appear to diverge. *The image at R, toward which the rays are converging*, is the object for surface 4, and since this image is reached by proceeding in the direction of the oncoming light, the object distance V_4R is negative. The image at R is called a *virtual object* for surface 4. In general, whenever a *converging* cone of rays is incident on a surface, the point toward which the rays are converging serves as the object, the object distance is negative, and the point is called a virtual object.

Finally, surface 4 forms a real image at I, the image distance being V_4I and positive.

The meaning of virtual object and of virtual image are further exemplified by Fig. 42-2.

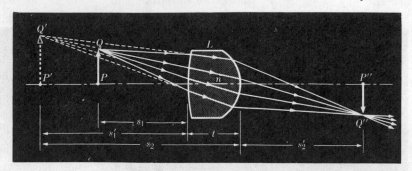

FIG. 42–3. The image formed by the first surface of a lens serves as the object for the second surface.

42–2 The thin lens. A lens is an optical system bounded by two refracting surfaces having a common axis. The general problem of refraction by a lens is solved by applying the methods of Section 42–1 to each surface in turn, the object for the second surface being the image formed by the first. Figure 42–3 shows a pencil of rays diverging from point Q of an object PQ. The first surface of lens L forms a virtual image of Q at Q'. This virtual image serves as a real object for the second surface of the lens, which forms a real image of Q' at Q''. Distance s_1 is the object distance for the first surface; s_1' is the corresponding image distance. The object distance for the second surface is s_2, equal to the sum of s_1' and the lens thickness t, and s_2' is the image distance for the second surface.

If, as is often the case, the lens is so thin that its thickness t is negligible in comparison with the distances s_1, s_1', s_2, and s_2', we may assume that s_1' equals s_2, and measure object and image distances from either vertex of the lens. We shall also assume the medium on both sides of the lens to be air, with index of refraction 1.00. For the first refraction, Eq. (41–13) becomes

$$\frac{1}{s_1} + \frac{n}{s_1'} = \frac{n-1}{R_1}.$$

Refraction at the second surface yields

$$\frac{n}{s_2} + \frac{1}{s_2'} = \frac{1-n}{R_2}.$$

Adding these two equations, and remembering that the lens is so thin that $s_2 = -s_1'$, we get

$$\frac{1}{s_1} + \frac{1}{s_2'} = (n-1)\left(\frac{1}{R_1} - \frac{1}{R_2}\right).$$

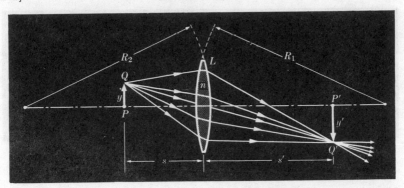

FIG. 42–4. A thin lens.

Since s_1 is the object distance for the thin lens and s_2' is the image distance, the subscripts may be omitted, and we get finally

$$\frac{1}{s} + \frac{1}{s'} = (n-1)\left(\frac{1}{R_1} - \frac{1}{R_2}\right).$$
(42–1)

The usual sign conventions apply to this equation. Thus, in Fig. 42–4, s, s', and R_1 are positive quantities, but R_2 is negative.

The *focal length f* of a thin lens may be defined either as (a) the object distance of a point object on the lens axis whose image is at infinity, or (b) the image distance of a point object on the lens axis at an infinite distance from the lens. When we set either s or s' equal to infinity in Eq. (42–1) we find for the focal length

$$\frac{1}{f} = (n-1)\left(\frac{1}{R_1} - \frac{1}{R_2}\right),$$
(42–2)

which is known as the *lensmaker's equation*.

Substituting Eq. (42–2) in Eq. (42–1), the thin lens equation becomes

$$\frac{1}{s} + \frac{1}{s'} = \frac{1}{f}.$$
(42–3)

This is known as the *Gaussian* form of the thin lens equation, after the mathematician, Karl F. Gauss. Notice that it has exactly the same form as the equation for a spherical mirror.

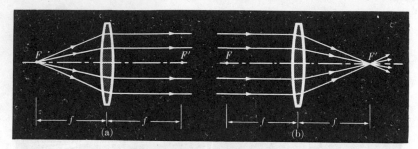

FIG. 42–5. First and second focal points of a thin lens.

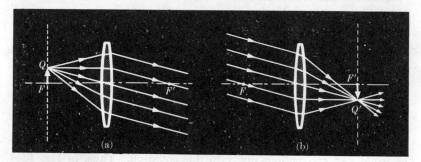

FIG. 42–6. Planes through the focal points of a lens are called *focal planes*.

The object point for which the image is at infinity is called the *first focal point* of the lens and is lettered F in Fig. 42–5(a). The image point for an infinitely distant object is called the *second focal point* and is lettered F' in Fig. 42–5(b). The focal points of a thin lens lie on opposite sides of the lens at a distance from it equal to its focal length.

Figure 42–6 corresponds to Fig. 42–5, except that it is drawn for object and image points not on the axis of the lens. Planes through the first and second focal points of a lens, perpendicular to the axis, are called the first and second *focal planes*. Paraxial rays from point Q in Fig. 42–6(a), in the first focal plane of the lens, are parallel to one another after refraction. In other words, they converge to an infinitely distant image of point Q. In Fig. 42–6(b) a bundle of parallel rays from an infinitely distant point, not on the lens axis, converges to an image Q' lying in the second focal plane of the lens.

The three-dimensional image of a three-dimensional object, formed by a lens, is shown in Fig. 42–7. Since point R is nearer the lens than point P, its image, from Eq. (42–3), is farther from the lens than is point P' and

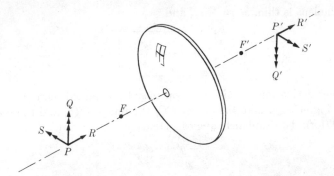

FIG. 42–7. A lens forms a three-dimensional image of a three-dimensional object.

the image $P'R'$ points in the same direction as the object PR. Arrows $P'S'$ and $P'Q'$ are reversed in space, relative to PS and PQ. Although we speak of the image as "inverted," only its transverse dimensions are reversed.

Figure 42–7 should be compared with Fig. 41–4, showing the image formed by a plane mirror. Note that the image formed by a lens, although it is inverted, is not perverted. That is, if the object is a left hand, its image is a left hand also. This may be verified by pointing the left thumb along PR, the left forefinger along PQ, and the left middle finger along PS. A rotation of 180° about the thumb as an axis then brings the fingers into coincidence with $P'Q'$ and $P'S'$. In other words, inversion of an image is equivalent to a rotation of 180° about the lens axis.

The magnification produced by a lens is the product of the magnification at each of its surfaces. The magnification due to the first refraction is, from Eq. (41–14),

$$m_1 = -\frac{1 \times s'_1}{ns_1},$$

and that due to the second refraction is

$$m_2 = -\frac{ns'_2}{1 \times s_2}.$$

The over-all magnification m of the lens is therefore

$$m = \left(-\frac{1 \times s'_1}{ns_1}\right)\left(-\frac{ns'_2}{1 \times s_2}\right).$$

Since the lens is thin, $s_2 = -s_1'$, and

$$m = -\frac{s'}{s}. \tag{42-4}$$

A simpler derivation of this equation may be obtained merely by inspection of Fig. 42–4, where the object PQ, the image $P'Q'$, and the lines PP' and QQ' form two similar triangles. Hence

$$\frac{-y'}{y} = \frac{s'}{s},$$

and since m, as usual, is y'/y, we get

$$m = -\frac{s'}{s},$$

in agreement with Eq. (42–4).

Although Eqs. (42–3) and (42–4) were derived for the special case of rays making small angles with the axis and, in general, do not apply to rays making large angles, they may be used for any lens which has been corrected so that all rays are imaged at the same point. They are therefore two of the most important equations in geometrical optics.

42–3 The Newtonian form of the thin lens equation. Figure 42–8 shows an object O and its image I formed by a thin lens L. The object and image distances, measured from the lens, are s and s' respectively. Let x and x' represent the distances of object and image *measured from the corresponding focal points F and F'*. Then

$$s = x + f, \quad s' = x' + f.$$

When these expressions for s and s' are inserted in Eq. (42–3), we get

$$\frac{1}{x+f} + \frac{1}{x'+f} = \frac{1}{f},$$

which reduces to the simple equation

$$xx' = f^2. \tag{42-5}$$

This is known as the *Newtonian* form of the thin lens equation. The sign of x is positive if the object lies at the left of the first focal point F, as in Fig. 42–8, negative if it lies at the right. The sign of x' is positive if the image lies at the right of the second focal point F', negative if it lies at the left.

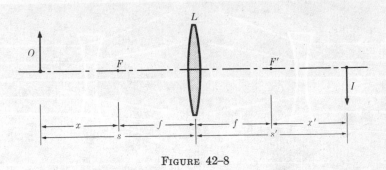

FIGURE 42–8

The magnification of the lens may be expressed in terms of x or of x', as follows:

$$m = -\frac{s'}{s} = -\frac{x'+f}{x+f}.$$

Multiplying numerator and denominator by x, and using Eq. (42–5), we get

$$m = -\frac{xx'+xf}{x^2+xf} = -\frac{f^2+xf}{x^2+xf} = -\frac{f(f+x)}{x(f+x)} = -\frac{f}{x}.$$

Multiplying numerator and denominator by x', we get

$$m = -\frac{x'^2+x'f}{xx'+x'f} = -\frac{x'^2+x'f}{f^2+x'f} = -\frac{x'(f+x')}{f(f+x')} = -\frac{x'}{f}.$$

We have, therefore,

$$\boxed{m = -\frac{f}{x} = -\frac{x'}{f}.} \qquad (42\text{–}6)$$

The Newtonian form of the lens equation is simpler algebraically than Eq. (42–3) and it has the advantage of being applicable to any lens, whether thin or thick, or to any combination of lenses. However complex a lens or lens system may be, the positions of its focal points can always be readily found by finding the position of the image of a distant object. The focal length, although it is not measurable without special equipment, is usually stamped by the manufacturer on the lens mounting.

The Gaussian form of the lens equation can also be used for any lens, thick or thin, provided the object and image distances are measured from the proper reference points, known as the *principal points* of the lens. A more advanced text should be consulted for the method of locating the principal points.

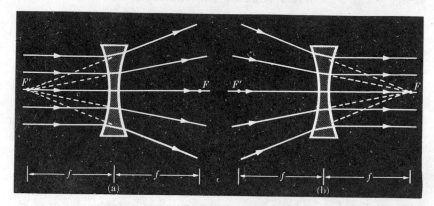

FIG. 42–9. Focal points of a diverging lens.

42–4 Diverging lenses. A bundle of parallel rays incident on the lens shown in Figs. 42–5 and 42–6 converges to a real image after passing through the lens. The lens is called a *converging lens*. Its focal length, as computed from Eq. (42–2), is a positive quantity and it is also called a *positive lens*.

A bundle of parallel rays incident on the lens in Fig. 42–9 becomes diverging after refraction and the lens is called a *diverging lens*. Its focal length, computed by Eq. (42–2), is a negative quantity and it is also called a *negative lens*. The focal points of a negative lens are reversed, relative to those of a positive lens. The second focal point, F', of a negative lens is the point from which rays, originally parallel to the axis, appear to diverge after refraction, as in Fig. 42–9(a). Incident rays converging toward the first focal point F, as in Fig. 42–9(b), emerge from the lens parallel to its axis. That is, just as for a positive lens, the second focal point is the (virtual) image of an infinitely distant object on the axis of the lens, while the first focal point is the object point (a virtual object if the lens is diverging) for which an image is formed at infinity. Equations (42–2)

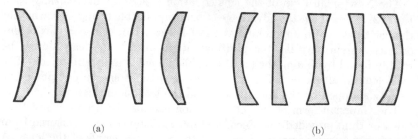

(a)   (b)

FIG. 42–10.   (a) Meniscus, plano-convex, and double-convex converging lenses.   (b) Meniscus, plano-concave, and double-concave diverging lenses.

to (42–6) apply both to negative and
to positive lenses. Various types of
lenses, both converging and diverging,
are illustrated in Fig. 42–10.

In addition to lenses having spherical surfaces, use is frequently made
of *cylindrical* lenses, particularly in
spectacles, to correct a defect of vision
known as *astigmatism*. One or both

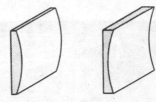

FIG. 42–11. Cylindrical lenses.

surfaces of a cylindrical lens are portions of cylinders (Fig. 42–11).
Since defects of vision other than astigmatism are frequently present
also, a spectacle lens may be cylindrical at one surface and spherical at
the other, or one of its surfaces may be a combined sphere and cylinder.

42–5 Graphical methods. The position and size of the image of an
object formed by a thin lens may be found by a simple graphical method.
This method consists of finding the point of intersection, after passing
through the lens, of a few rays diverging from some chosen point of the
object. Then (neglecting lens aberrations) all rays from this point which
pass through the lens will intersect at the same point. In using the
graphical method, the entire deviation of any ray is assumed to take

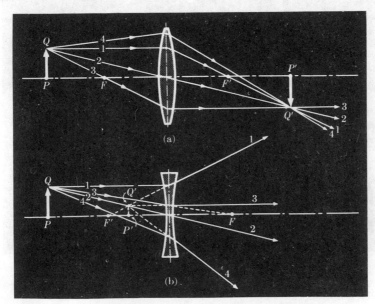

FIG. 42–12. Graphical method of locating an image.

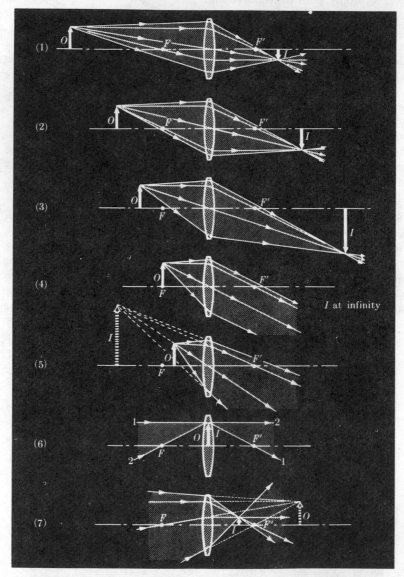

Fig. 42–13. Formation of an image by a thin lens.

place at a plane through the center of the lens. Three rays whose paths may readily be traced are shown in Fig. 42–12:

1. *A ray parallel to the axis.* After refraction by the lens, this ray passes through the second focal point of a converging lens, or appears to come from the second focal point of a diverging lens.

2. *A ray through the center of the lens.* This ray is not appreciably deviated, since the two lens surfaces through which the central ray passes are very nearly parallel if the lens is thin. We have seen that a ray passing through a plate with parallel faces is not deviated, but only displaced. For a thin lens, the displacement may be neglected.

3. *A ray through (or proceeding toward) the first focal point.* This ray emerges parallel to the axis.

Having found the position of the image point by means of the intersection of any two of the rays 1, 2, 3, the paths of all other rays from the same point, such as ray 4 in Fig. 42–12, may be drawn. A few examples of this procedure are given in Fig. 42–13.

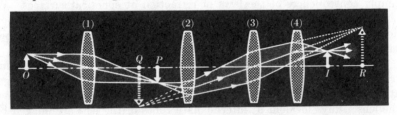

Fig. 42–14. The object for each lens, after the first, is the image formed by the preceding lens.

42–6 Images as objects. It was shown in Section 42–1 and Fig. 42–1 how the image formed by any one *surface* in an optical system serves as the object for the next surface. In the majority of optical systems employing lenses, more than one lens is used and the image formed by any one *lens* serves as the object for the next lens. Figure 42–14 illustrates the various possibilities. Lens 1 forms a real image at P of a real object at O. This real image serves as a real object for lens 2. The virtual image at Q formed by lens 2 is a real object for lens 3. If lens 4 were not present, lens 3 would form a real image at R. Although this image is never formed, it serves as a virtual object for lens 4, which forms a final real image at I.

42–7 Lens aberrations. The relatively simple equations we have derived connecting object and image distances, focal lengths, radii of curvature, etc., were based upon the approximation that all rays made small angles with the axis. In general, however, a lens is called upon to image not only points on its axis, but points which lie off the axis as well. Furthermore, because of the finite size of the lens, the cone of rays which forms the image of any point is of finite size. Nonparaxial rays proceeding from a given object point do not, in general, all intersect at the same point after refraction by a lens. Consequently, the image formed by these rays is not a sharp one. Furthermore, the focal length of a lens depends upon its index of refraction, which varies with wavelength. Therefore, if the light proceeding from an object is not monochromatic, a lens forms a number of colored images which lie in different positions and are of different sizes, even if formed by paraxial rays.

The departures of an actual image from the predictions of simple theory are called *aberrations*. Those caused by the variation of index with wavelength are the *chromatic aberrations*. The others, which would arise even if the light were monochromatic, are the *monochromatic aberrations*. Lens aberrations are not caused by any faulty construction of the lens, such as the failure of its surfaces to conform to a truly spherical shape, but are simply consequences of the laws of refraction at spherical surfaces. We now examine the aberrations of a single thin lens in somewhat more detail, taking up first the monochromatic and then the chromatic aberrations.

Spherical aberration. The effect known as spherical aberration is illustrated in Fig. 42–15. Paraxial rays from an axial point P are imaged at P'. Rays incident on the lens near its rim are imaged at P'', closer to the lens. Rays incident at intermediate zones of the lens are imaged between P' and P''. There is evidently no plane in which a sharp image of P is formed. If a screen is placed perpendicular to the axis at P', the position of the image formed by paraxial rays, the image on the screen consists of a circular disk whose outline is the intersection with the screen of the outer cone of rays refracted by the lens. The refracted beam is everywhere of circular cross section and it will be seen from the figure that there is one plane, CC, at which the cross section of the beam is smallest. This smallest cross section is known as the *circle of least confusion* and the best image will be secured if the screen is placed at this point.

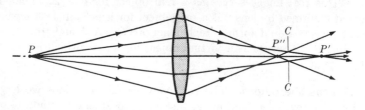

Fig. 42–15. Spherical aberration.

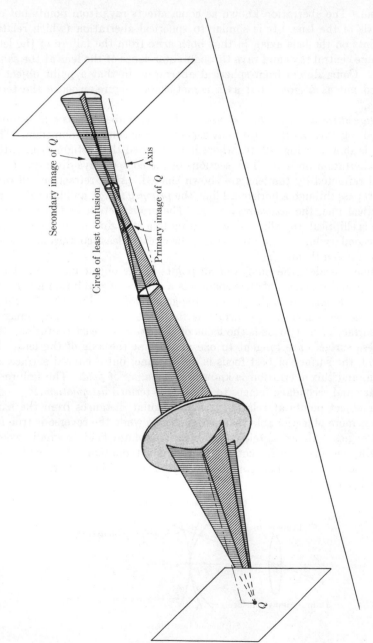

Fig. 42–16. Astigmatism.

Coma. The aberration known as coma affects rays from points not on the axis of the lens. It is similar to spherical aberration (which relates to points on the lens axis), in that both arise from the failure of the lens to image central rays and rays through outer zones of the lens at the same point. Coma differs from spherical aberration in that a point object is imaged not as a circle, but as a comet-shaped figure, whence the term "coma."

Astigmatism and curvature of field. These two aberrations will be considered together, as they are joint aspects of the same phenomenon. The effect is shown in Fig. 42–16, where it is assumed that astigmatism is the only aberration present. Two sections of the cone of rays diverging from Q and refracted by the lens are shown shaded. After refraction, all rays from Q pass through a horizontal line, the *primary image*, and later through a vertical line, the *secondary image*. The cross section of the refracted beam is elliptical, the ellipse degenerating to a straight line at the primary and secondary images, and to a circle, the circle of least confusion, at some point between them.

If one considers the images of all points in the object plane, the locus of the primary images of these points is a surface of revolution about the lens axis, designated as the primary image surface (see Fig. 42–17). Similarly, the secondary image surface is the locus of the secondary images. The surface of best focus is the locus of the circles of least confusion. All of these surfaces are tangent to one another at the axis of the lens. In general, the surface of best focus is not a plane, but a curved surface, as shown, and this aberration is known as *curvature of field*. The failure of primary and secondary images to coincide is termed *astigmatism*.

For object points at relatively small angular distances from the axis, coma is more objectionable than astigmatism, while the reverse is true for large angles. Hence a telescope objective, whose field is small, would probably be corrected for coma rather than astigmatism. In a wide-field camera lens, on the other hand, some correction would necessarily be made for astigmatism.

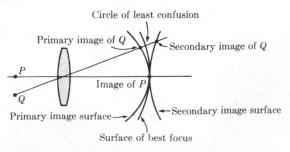

FIG. 42–17. Curvature of field.

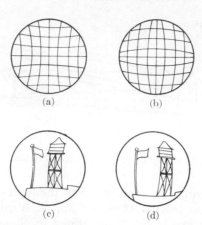

FIG. 42–18. (a) and (c) illustrate pincushion distortion. (b) and (d) show barrel distortion.

Distortion. Spherical aberration, coma, and astigmatism refer to the failure of a lens to form a point image of a point object. *Distortion* is an aberration arising not from a lack of sharpness of the image, but from a variation of magnification with distance from the axis. If the magnification increases with increasing distance, the outer parts of the field are disproportionately magnified. A square network then appears, like Fig. 42–18(a). This effect is referred to as "pincushion" distortion. If the magnification decreases with increasing distance, the opposite effect, known as "barrel" distortion, is obtained [Fig. 42–18 (b)]. A moderate amount of distortion is not objectionable in an instrument intended solely for visual use, but it must evidently be eliminated from a camera lens used for aerial mapping or for copying drawings, where straight lines must be imaged as straight lines.

The chromatic aberrations. The focal length of a lens is a function of the index of refraction of the material of which the lens is composed. Since the index of refraction of all optical substances varies with wavelength, the focal length of a lens is different for different colors. As a consequence, a single lens forms not merely one image of an object, but a series of images at varying distances from the lens, one for each color present in the incident light. Furthermore, since the magnification depends upon the focal length, these images are of different sizes. The variation of image distance with index of refraction is called *axial* or *longitudinal chromatic aberration* and the variation of image size is called *lateral chromatic aberration.*

These aberrations are illustrated in Fig. 42–19, which is much exaggerated for the sake of clearness. (The monochromatic aberrations are

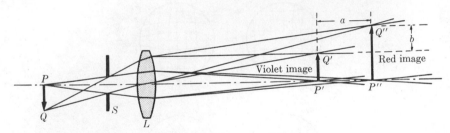

FIG. 42–19. Chromatic aberration.

assumed to be absent.) PQ is an object in the form of an arrow. It is imaged by a lens L, in front of which is a stop S. A cone of rays is shown diverging from each end of the arrow. Since the index is larger for the shorter wavelengths, the focal length is smaller for these wavelengths. The violet rays are therefore imaged nearest the lens and form the smallest image. The red rays are imaged farthest from the lens and form the largest image. The violet image is shown at $P'Q'$ and the red image at $P''Q''$. Images formed by other colors (not shown) lie at intermediate points and are of intermediate sizes. The axial chromatic aberration is measured by the distance a and the lateral chromatic aberration by the distance b. It will be seen that there is no one plane in which all images are simultaneously in sharp focus.

It is not possible to eliminate all of the seven aberrations from a single thin lens. However, by constructing a compound lens of a number of individual lenses, it is possible to balance the aberrations of one part of the system against those of another. The greater the number of elements, the greater the degree of correction which may be secured. Hence all high quality lenses are compound lenses. Even then, no lens system ever contains a sufficient number of refracting surfaces to permit the complete elimination of all five monochromatic aberrations and the two chromatic aberrations. As a consequence, a lens designer is forced to select the aberrations most detrimental to the purpose for which the lens is destined and reduce these aberrations to negligible amounts. Thus in a telescope objective, which is required to cover only a small angular field, spherical aberration, coma, and axial chromatism are the most important. On the other hand, in a photographic objective (which must ordinarily cover a large field), only partial correction of these aberrations is possible because of the necessity of producing some degree of correction for such aberrations as astigmatism, curvature of field, and distortion. As a general rule, systems that need be corrected only for a small field or for a small aperture produce images of higher quality than systems with either a large field or a large aperture.

PROBLEMS

42-1. A thin-walled glass sphere of radius R is filled with water. An object is placed a distance $3R$ from the surface of the sphere. Determine the position of the final image. The effect of the glass wall may be neglected.

42-2. A transparent rod 40 cm long is cut flat at one end and rounded to a hemispherical surface of 12 cm radius at the other end. An object is placed on the axis of the rod and 10 cm from the hemispherical end. (a) What is the position of the final image? (b) What is its magnification? Assume the refractive index to be 1.50.

42-3. Both ends of a glass rod 10 cm in diameter, of index 1.50, are ground and polished to convex hemispherical surfaces of radius 5 cm at the left end and radius 10 cm at the right end. The length of the rod between vertices is 60 cm. An arrow 1 mm long, at right angles to the axis and 20 cm to the left of the first vertex, constitutes the object for the first surface. (a) What constitutes the object for the second surface? (b) What is the object distance for the second surface? (c) Is the object real or virtual? (d) What is the position of the image formed by the second surface? (e) What is the height of the final image?

42-4. The same rod as in Problem 42-3 is now shortened to a distance of 10 cm between its vertices, the curvatures of its ends remaining the same. (a) What is the object distance for the second surface? (b) Is the object real or virtual? (c) What is the position of the image formed by the second surface? (d) Is the image real or virtual? Erect or inverted, with respect to the original object? (e) What is the height of the final image?

42-5. A glass rod of refractive index 1.50 is ground and polished at both ends to hemispherical surfaces of 5 cm radius. When an object is placed on the axis of the rod and 20 cm from one end the final image is formed 40 cm from the opposite end. What is the length of the rod?

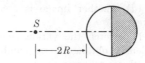

FIGURE 42-20

42-6. A solid glass sphere of radius R and index 1.50 is silvered over one hemisphere, as in Fig. 42-20. A small object is located on the axis of the sphere at a distance $2R$ from the pole of the unsilvered hemisphere. Find the position of the final image after all refractions and reflections have taken place.

42-7. A narrow beam of parallel rays enters a solid glass sphere in a radial direction. At what point outside the sphere are these rays brought to a focus? The radius of the sphere is 3 cm and its index is 1.50.

42-8. A glass plate 1 inch thick, of index 1.50, having plane parallel faces, is held with its faces horizontal and its lower face 4 inches above a printed page. Find the position of the image of the page, formed by rays making a small angle with the normal to the plate.

42-9. (a) Show that the equation $(1/s) + (1/s') = 1/f$ is that of an equilateral hyperbola having as asymptotes the lines $x = f$ and $y = f$. (b) Construct a graph with object distance (s) as abscissa, and image distance (s') as ordinate, for a lens of focal length f, and for object distances from 0 to ∞. (c) On the same set of axes construct a graph of magnification (ordinate) vs. object distance.

42–10. A converging lens has a focal length of 10 cm. For object distances of 30 cm, 20 cm, 15 cm, and 5 cm determine (a) image position, (b) magnification, (c) whether image is real or virtual, (d) whether image is erect or inverted.

42–11. Sketch the various possible thin lenses obtainable by combining two surfaces whose radii of curvature are, in absolute magnitude, 10 cm and 20 cm. Which are converging and which are diverging? Find the focal length of each lens if made of glass of index 1.50.

42–12. The radii of curvature of the surfaces of a thin lens are +10 cm and +30 cm. The index is 1.50. (a) Compute the position and size of the image of an object in the form of an arrow 1 cm high, perpendicular to the lens axis, 40 cm to the left of the lens. (b) A second similar lens is placed 160 cm to the right of the first. Find the position of the final image. (c) Same as (b) except the second lens is 40 cm to the right of the first. (d) Same as (c) except the second lens is diverging, of focal length −40 cm.

42–13. An object is placed 18 cm from a screen. (a) At what points between object and screen may a lens of 4 cm focal length be placed to obtain an image on the screen? (b) What is the magnification of the image for these positions of the lens?

42–14. An object is imaged by a lens on a screen placed 12 cm from the lens. When the lens is moved 2 cm farther from the object the screen must be moved 2 cm closer to the object to refocus it. What is the focal length of the lens?

42–15. Three thin lenses, each of focal length 20 cm, are aligned on a common axis and are separated by 30 cm. Find the position of the image of a small object on the axis, 60 cm to the left of the first lens.

42–16. An equiconvex thin lens made of glass of index 1.50 has a focal length in air of 30 cm. The lens is sealed into an opening in one end of a tank filled with water (index = 1.33). At the end of the tank opposite the lens is a plane mirror, 80 cm distant from the lens. Find the position of the image formed by the lens, water, mirror system, of a small object outside the tank on the lens axis and 90 cm to the left of the lens. Is the image real or virtual? Erect or inverted?

42–17. For a thin converging lens (a) what is the minimum distance between an object and its image if the image is real? (b) What is the minimum distance if the image is virtual?

42–18. A diverging meniscus lens of 1.48 refractive index has spherical surfaces whose radii are 2.5 and 4 cm. What would be the position of the image if an object were placed 15 cm in front of the lens?

42–19. A plano-convex lens has a thickness along its axis of 2 cm. The refractive index is 1.50 and the radius of curvature of the convex surface is 10 cm. The convex surface faces toward the left. (a) Find the distance from the first focal point to the vertex of the convex surface. (b) Find the distance from the vertex of the plane surface to the second focal point.

42–20. When an object is placed at the proper distance in front of a converging lens, the image falls on a screen 20 cm from the lens. A diverging lens

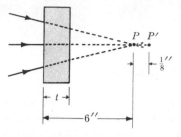

FIGURE 42–21

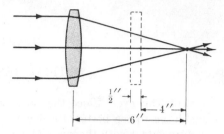

FIGURE 42–22

is now placed halfway between the converging lens and the screen, and it is found that the screen must be moved 20 cm farther away from the lens to obtain a clear image. What is the focal length of the diverging lens?

42–21. (a) Prove that when two thin lenses of focal lengths f_1 and f_2 are placed *in contact*, the focal length f of the combination is given by the relation

$$1/f = (1/f_1) + (1/f_2).$$

(b) A converging meniscus lens has an index of refraction of 1.50 and the radii of its surfaces are 5 and 10 cm. The concave surface is placed upward and filled with water. What is the focal length of the water-glass combination?

42–22. Two thin lenses, both of 10 cm focal length, the first converging, the second diverging, are placed 5 cm apart. An object is placed 20 cm in front of the first (converging) lens. (a) How far from this lens will the image be formed? (b) Is the image real or virtual?

42–23. Rays from a lens are converging toward a point image P as in Fig. 42–21. What thickness t of glass of

index 1.50 must be interposed as in the figure in order that the image shall be formed at P'?

42–24. An object 10 ft in front of a camera lens is sharply imaged on a photographic film 6 inches behind the lens. A glass plate 0.5 inch thick, of index 1.50, having plane parallel faces, is interposed between lens and plate as shown in Fig. 42–22. (a) Find the new position of the image. (b) At what distance in front of the lens will an object be in sharp focus on the film with the plate in place, the distance from lens to film remaining 6 inches? Consider the lens as a simple thin lens.

42–25. A narrow beam of white light is incident on a double convex lens of silicate flint glass whose surfaces are each of radius 20 cm. Making use of Fig. 40–12, determine the distance between the points at which the red (700 mμ wavelength) and violet (400 mμ wavelength) components cross the axis of the lens.

42–26. An ocular consists of two similar positive thin lenses having focal lengths of 2 inches, separated by a distance of 1 inch. Where are the focal points of the ocular?

CHAPTER 43

OPTICAL INSTRUMENTS

43–1 The eye. Since the purpose of most optical instruments is to enable us to see better, the logical place to begin a discussion of such instruments is with the eye. The essential parts of the eye, considered as an optical system, are shown in Fig. 43–1.

The eye is very nearly spherical in shape, and about an inch in diameter. The front portion is somewhat more sharply curved, and is covered by a tough, transparent membrane C, called the *cornea*. The region behind the cornea contains a liquid A called the *aqueous humor*. Next comes the *crystalline lens*, L, a capsule containing a fibrous jelly hard at the center and progressively softer at the outer portions. The crystalline lens is held in place by ligaments which attach it to the ciliary muscle M. Behind the lens, the eye is filled with a thin jelly V consisting largely of water, called the *vitreous humor*. The indices of refraction of both the aqueous humor and the vitreous humor are nearly equal to that of water, about 1.336. The crystalline lens, while not homogeneous, has an "average" index of 1.437. This is not very different from the indices of the aqueous and vitreous humors, so that most of the refraction of light entering the eye is produced at the cornea.

A large part of the inner surface of the eye is covered with a delicate film of nerve fibers, R, called the *retina*. A cross section of the retina is shown in Fig. 43–2. Nerve fibers branching out from the *optic nerve* O terminate in minute structures called rods and cones. The rods and cones, together with a bluish liquid called the visual purple, which circulates among them, receive the optical image and transmit it along the optic nerve to the brain. There is a slight depression in the retina at Y called the yellow spot or macula. At its center is a minute region, about 0.25 mm in diameter, called the *fovea centralis*, which contains cones exclusively. Vision is much more acute at the fovea than at other portions of

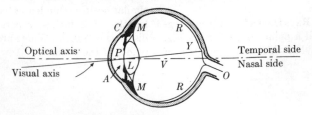

FIG. 43–1. The eye.

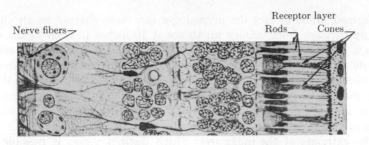

Fig. 43-2. Section of the human retina (500×). Light is incident from the left.

the retina, and the muscles controlling the eye always rotate the eyeball until the image of the object toward which attention is directed falls on the fovea. The outer portion of the retina merely serves to give a general picture of the field of view. The fovea is so small that motion of the eye is necessary to focus distinctly two points as close together as the dots in a colon (:).

There are no rods or cones at the point where the optic nerve enters the eye and an image formed at this point cannot be seen. This region is called the *blind spot*. The existence of the blind spot can be demonstrated by closing the left eye and looking with the right eye at the cross in Fig. 43-3. When the diagram is about 10 inches from the eye, the square disappears. At a smaller distance, the square reappears while the circle disappears. At a still smaller distance, the circle again appears.

FIGURE 43-3

In front of the crystalline lens is the iris, at the center of which is an opening P called the *pupil*. The function of the pupil is to regulate the quantity of light entering the eye, the pupil automatically dilating if the brightness of the field is low, and contracting if the brightness is increased. This process is known as *adaptation*. However, the range of pupillary diameter is only about fourfold (hence the range in area is about sixteenfold) over a range of brightness which is 100,000 fold. The relatively enormous variation in light entering the eye is far from compensated by the change in size of the pupil, the receptive mechanism of the retina being able to adapt itself to large differences in quantity of light.

To see an object distinctly, a sharp image of it must be formed on the retina. If all the elements of the eye were rigidly fixed in position there would be but one object distance for which a sharp retinal image would be formed, while in fact the normal eye can focus sharply on an object at any distance from infinity up to about 10 inches in front of the eye. This is made possible by the action of the crystalline lens and the ciliary muscle to which it is attached. When relaxed, the normal eye is focused on objects at infinity, i.e., the second focal point is at the retina. When it is desired to view an object nearer than infinity, the ciliary muscle tenses and the crystalline lens assumes a more nearly spherical shape. This process is called *accommodation*.

The extremes of the range over which distinct vision is possible are known as the *far point* and the *near point* of the eye. The far point of a normal eye is at infinity. The position of the near point evidently depends on the extent to which the curvature of the crystalline lens may be increased in accommodation. The range of accommodation gradually diminishes with age as the crystalline lens loses its flexibility. For this reason the near point gradually recedes as one grows older. This recession of the near point with age is called *presbyopia*, and should not be considered a defect of vision, since it proceeds at about the same rate in all normal eyes. A table of the approximate position of the near point at various ages is given below.

Age (years)	Near point (cm)
10	7
20	10
30	14
40	22
50	40
60	200

43–2 Defects of vision. There are a number of common defects of vision which have to do simply with an incorrect relation between the various parts of the eye considered as an optical system. A normal eye forms an image on the retina of an object at infinity when the eye is relaxed, and is called *emmetropic*. If the far point of an eye is not at infinity, the eye is *ametropic*. The two simplest forms of ametropia are *myopia* (nearsightedness), and *hyperopia* (farsightedness). These are illustrated in Fig. 43–4(b) and (c).

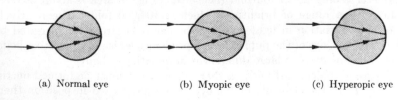

(a) Normal eye   (b) Myopic eye   (c) Hyperopic eye

FIGURE 43–4

In the myopic eye, the eyeball is too long in comparison with the radius of curvature of the cornea, and rays from an object at infinity are focused in front of the retina. The most distant object for which an image can be formed on the retina is then nearer than infinity, or the far point is nearer than infinity. On the other hand, the near point of a myopic eye, if the accommodation is normal, is even closer to the eye than is that of a person with normal vision.

In the hyperopic eye, the eyeball is too short and the image of an infinitely distant object would be formed behind the retina. By accommodation, these parallel rays may be made to converge on the retina, but evidently, if the range of accommodation is normal, the near point will be more distant than that of an emmetropic eye. These defects may be stated in a somewhat different way. The myopic eye produces too much convergence in a parallel bundle of rays for an image to be formed on the retina; the hyperopic eye, not enough.

Astigmatism refers to a defect in which the surface of the cornea is not spherical, but is more sharply curved in one plane than another. (It should not be confused with the lens aberration of the same name, which applies to the behavior, after passing through a lens having spherical surfaces, of rays making a large angle with the axis.) Astigmatism makes it impossible, for example, to focus clearly on the horizontal and vertical bars of a window at the same time.

All of the types of defective vision mentioned above may be corrected by the use of spectacles. We shall illustrate with the aid of numerical examples.

Presbyopia and hyperopia. The near point of either a presbyopic or a hyperopic eye is farther from the eye than normal. To see clearly an object at normal reading distance (this distance is usually assumed to be 25 cm, or 10 inches) we must place in front of the eye a lens of such focal length that it forms an image of the object at or beyond the near point. Thus the function of the lens is not to make the object appear larger, but in effect to move the object farther away from the eye to a point where a sharp retinal image can be formed.

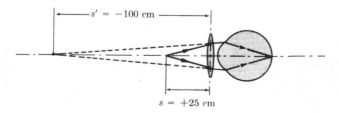

FIGURE 43–5

EXAMPLE. The near point of a certain eye is 100 cm in front of the eye. What lens should be used to see clearly an object 25 cm in front of the eye? (See Fig. 43-5.)

We have

$$s = +25 \text{ cm}, \qquad s' = -100 \text{ cm},$$

$$\frac{1}{f} = \frac{1}{s} + \frac{1}{s'} = \frac{1}{+25 \text{ cm}} + \frac{1}{-100 \text{ cm}},$$

$$f = +33 \text{ cm}.$$

That is, a converging lens of focal length 33 cm is required.

Myopia. The far point of a myopic eye is nearer than infinity. To see clearly objects beyond the far point, a lens must be used which will form an image of such objects, not farther from the eye than the far point.

EXAMPLE. The far point of a certain eye is 1 meter in front of the eye. What lens should be used to see clearly an object at infinity?

Assume the image to be formed at the far point. Then

$$s = \infty, \qquad s' = -100 \text{ cm},$$

$$\frac{1}{f} = \frac{1}{s} + \frac{1}{s'} = \frac{1}{\infty} + \frac{1}{-100 \text{ cm}},$$

$$f = -100 \text{ cm}.$$

A diverging lens of focal length 100 cm is required, as in Fig. 43-6.

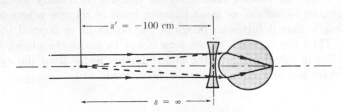

FIGURE 43-6

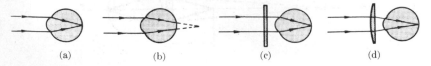

| (a) | (b) | (c) | (d) |

FIG. 43-7. Correction of astigmatism by a cylindrical lens.

Astigmatism. The correction of astigmatism by means of a cylindrical lens is illustrated in Fig. 43-7, in which (a) and (b) represent the top and side views respectively of an astigmatic eye. The curvature of the cornea in a horizontal plane, as seen in (a), has the proper value such that rays from infinity are focused on the retina. In the vertical plane, however, as seen in (b), the curvature is not sufficient to form a sharp retinal image.

By placing before the eye a cylindrical lens with axis horizontal, as in (c) and (d), the rays in a horizontal plane are unaffected, while the additional convergence of the rays in a vertical plane, shown in (d), now causes these to be sharply imaged on the retina.

The optometrist describes the converging or diverging effect of spectacle lenses in terms, not of the focal length, but of its reciprocal. The reciprocal of the focal length of a lens is called its *power*, and if the focal length is in meters the power is in *diopters*. Thus the power of a positive lens whose focal length is 1 meter is 1 diopter; if the focal length is 2 meters the power is 0.5 diopter and so on. If the focal length is negative, the power is negative also. For example, a lens of power -0.5 diopter is a diverging lens of focal length -2 meters.

43-3 The magnifier. The apparent size of an object is determined by the size of its retinal image, which, in turn, if the eye is unaided, depends upon the angle subtended by the object at the eye. When one wishes to examine a small object in detail one brings it close to the eye, in order that the angle subtended and the retinal image may be as large as possible. Since the eye cannot focus sharply on objects closer than the near point, a given object subtends the maximum possible angle at an unaided eye when placed at this point. (We shall assume hereafter that the near point is 25 cm from the eye.) By placing a converging lens in front of the eye,

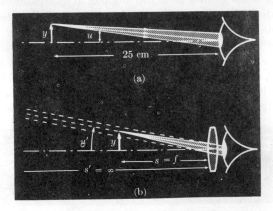

Fig. 43-8. A simple magnifier.

the accommodation may, in effect, be increased. The object may then be brought closer to the eye than the near point and will subtend a correspondingly larger angle. A lens used for this purpose is called a *magnifying glass, a simple microscope,* or a *magnifier.* The magnifier forms a virtual image of the object and the eye "looks at" this virtual image. Since a (normal) eye can focus sharply on an object anywhere between the near point and infinity, the image can be seen equally clearly if it is formed anywhere within this range. We shall assume that the image is formed at infinity.

The magnifier is illustrated in Fig. 43-8. In (a), the object is at the near point, where it subtends an angle u at the eye. In (b), a magnifier in front of the eye forms an image at infinity, and the angle subtended at the magnifier is u'. The *angular magnification M* (not to be confused with the *lateral magnification m*) is defined as the ratio of the angle u' to the angle u. The value of M may be found as follows:

From Fig. 43-8(a),
$$u = \frac{y}{25} \text{ (approximately).}$$

From Fig. 43-8(b),
$$u' = \frac{y}{f} \text{ (approximately).}$$

Hence
$$M = \frac{u'}{u} = \frac{y/f}{y/25}$$

and
$$\boxed{M = \frac{25}{f} \quad (f \text{ in centimeters).}} \tag{43-1}$$

While it appears at first as if the angular magnification may be made as large as desired by decreasing the focal length f, the aberrations of a simple double convex lens set a limit to M of about 2× or 3×. If these aberrations are corrected, the magnification may be carried as high as 20×.

An *ocular* or *eyepiece* is a magnifier used for viewing an image formed by a lens or lenses preceding it in an optical system. The Ramsden ocular is illustrated in Fig. 43-9. It is constructed of two plano-convex lenses of equal focal length, separated by a distance of about $\frac{2}{3}$ of this length.

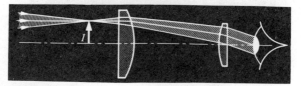

FIG. 43-9. The Ramsden ocular.

The image to be examined is shown at I; the final image is at infinity. Since four refracting surfaces are available, the aberrations of a simple magnifier can be greatly reduced.

43-4 The microscope. When an angular magnification higher than that attainable with a simple magnifier is desired, it is necessary to use a *compound microscope*, usually called merely a *microscope*. The essential elements of a microscope are illustrated in Fig. 43–10. The object O to be examined is placed just beyond the first focal point F of the *objective* lens, which forms a real and enlarged image I. This image lies just within the first focal point F_1 of the ocular, which forms a virtual image of I at I'.

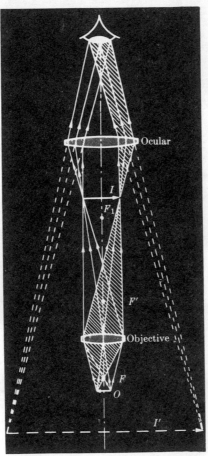

Fig. 43–10. The microscope.

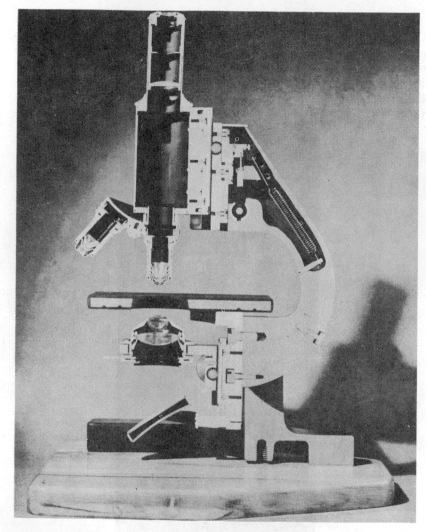

FIG. 43–11. Sectional view of a modern microscope. (Courtesy of Bausch & Lomb Optical Co.)

As was stated earlier, the position of I' may be anywhere between the near and far points of the eye. While both the objective and ocular of an actual microscope are highly corrected compound lenses, they are shown as simple thin lenses for simplicity.

Since the objective merely forms an enlarged real image which is examined by the ocular, the over-all magnification M of the compound microscope is the product of the lateral magnification m_1 of the objective and the angular magnification M_2 of the ocular. It will be recalled that

$$m_1 = -\frac{x'}{f_1},$$

where f_1 is the focal length of the objective and x' is the image distance measured from its second focal point. The angular magnification of the ocular (considered as a simple lens) is $M_2 = 25/f_2$ where f_2 is the focal length of the ocular. Hence the over-all magnification M of the compound microscope is

$$M = m_1 \times M_2 = -\frac{x'}{f_1} \times \frac{25}{f_2} \quad (x', f_1, f_2, \text{ in cm}). \qquad (43\text{–}2)$$

It has become customary among microscope manufacturers to specify the values of m_1 and M_2, rather than the focal lengths of objective and ocular.

Figure 43–11 is a cutaway view of a modern microscope. The instrument is provided with a rotating nosepiece to which are permanently attached three objectives of different magnifications. This construction makes possible a rapid and convenient exchange of one objective for another. Cross sections of three modern microscope objectives are shown in Fig. 43–12.

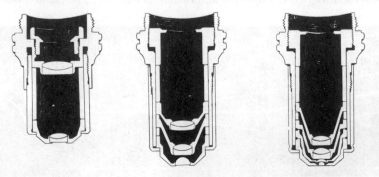

FIG. 43–12. Sectional views of three modern microscope objectives. (Courtesy of Bausch & Lomb Optical Co.)

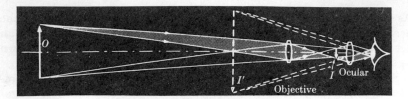

FIG. 43–13. The astronomical telescope.

43–5 Telescopes. The optical system of a refracting telescope is essentially the same as that of a compound microscope. In both instruments, the image formed by an objective is viewed through an ocular. The difference is that the telescope is used to examine large objects at large distances and the microscope to examine small objects close at hand.

The *astronomical* telescope is illustrated in Fig. 43–13. The objective lens forms a real, reduced image I of the object O. I' is the virtual image of I formed by the ocular. As with the microscope, the image I' may be formed anywhere between the near and far points of the eye.

In practice, the objects examined by a telescope are at such large distances from the instrument that the image I is formed very nearly at the second focal point of the objective. Furthermore, if the image I' is at infinity, the image I is at the first focal point of the ocular. (This is not the case in Fig. 43–13, which has been drawn to show all the essential elements in a finite diagram.) The distance between objective and ocular, or the length of the telescope, is therefore the sum of the focal lengths of objective and ocular, $f_1 + f_2$.

The angular magnification of a telescope is defined as the ratio of the angle subtended at the eye by the final image I', to the angle subtended at the (unaided) eye by the object. This ratio may be expressed in terms of the focal lengths of objective and ocular as follows. The shaded bundle

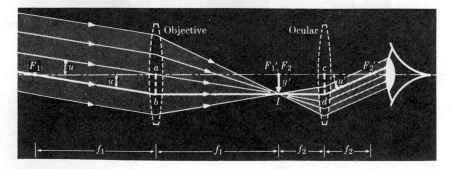

FIG. 43–14. Telescope, final image at infinity.

of rays in Fig. 43–14 corresponds to that in Fig. 43–13, except that the object and the final image are both at infinity. The ray passing through F_1, the first focal point of the objective, and through F'_2, the second focal point of the ocular, has been emphasized. The object (not shown) subtends an angle u at the objective and would subtend essentially the same angle at the unaided eye. Also, since the observer's eye is placed just to the right of the focal point F'_2, the angle subtended at the eye by the final image is very nearly equal to the angle u'. The distances ab and cd are evidently equal to one another and to the height y' of the image I. Since both u and u' are small, they may be approximated by their tangents. From the right triangles F_1ab and F'_2cd, $u = -y'/f_1$, $u' = y'/f_2$. Hence

$$M = \frac{u'}{u} = -\frac{y'/f_2}{y'/f_1} = -\frac{f_1}{f_2}. \tag{43–3}$$

The angular magnification of a telescope is therefore equal to the ratio of the focal length of the objective to that of the ocular. The minus sign denotes an inverted image. While an inverted image is not a disadvantage if the instrument is to be used for astronomical observations, it is desirable

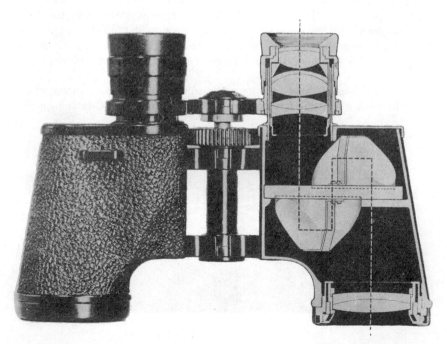

FIG. 43–15. The prism binocular. (Courtesy of Bausch & Lomb Optical Co.)

that a *terrestrial telescope* shall form an erect image. This may be accomplished by the insertion of an erecting lens or lens system between the objective and ocular. The erecting lens simply serves to invert the image formed by the objective. This is the optical system of the "spyglass." It has the disadvantage of requiring an unduly long tube, since four times the focal length of the erecting lens must be added to the sum of focal lengths of objective and ocular.

The long draw tube of the terrestrial telescope is avoided in the *prism binocular*, of which Fig. 43–15 is a cutaway view. A pair of 45°–45°–90° totally reflecting prisms, arranged as in Fig. 40–9, are inserted between objective and ocular and the image is inverted by the four reflections from the inclined faces of the prisms.

Most astronomical observations today are made not visually but photographically. By exposing a photographic plate for a long period of time, objects too faint ever to be seen can be recorded in a photograph. Hence the modern astronomical telescope is more accurately described as a camera than as a telescope.

Although the term "astronomical telescope" is applied to the type of instrument described earlier in this section, most telescopes used today for astronomical purposes make use of a concave mirror, rather than a lens, as the objective. The optical system of a reflecting telescope for visual use is essentially the same as that of an astronomical refracting telescope, the real image formed by the objective being examined by an ocular. When used as a camera, the real image is allowed to fall on a photographic plate.

The *Galilean telescope* owes its name to Galileo, who constructed one of the first telescopes of this type in 1609. A diverging rather than a con-

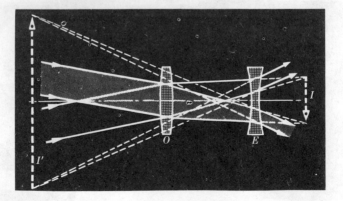

Fig. 43–16. The Galilean telescope.

verging lens is used as an ocular. The optical system is illustrated in Fig. 43–16. Rays from a distant object (not shown) are made converging by the objective O. The image I serves as a virtual object for the ocular E. The final image I' is virtual and erect, as indicated. The angular magnification of this telescope is also given by

$$ M = -\frac{f_1}{f_2}, $$

but since f_2 is negative, M is a positive quantity and the image is erect. The distance between objective and ocular is the difference between (the absolute values of) their focal lengths. Consequently, this instrument may be made much more compact than the astronomical type. Its chief disadvantage is that it cannot cover as wide a field of view without the use of objectives of unduly large diameter. The "opera glass" is a Galilean telescope.

43–6 The camera. The essential elements of a camera are a lens, a light-tight box, and a sensitized plate or film for receiving the image. In contrast with a telescope objective, for which the field of view is limited to a range of about 6°, a photographic objective is called upon to cover a field of 50° or even more. Furthermore, the aperture of the lens must be large, in order that it may collect sufficient light to permit of short exposures. The combination of wide field and large aperture makes the problem of correcting a photographic lens a difficult one. Nevertheless, even the simplest lenses, such as those used in Brownie cameras, are corrected for chromatic aberration and curvature of field. Most modern high-speed, short-focal length lenses are modifications of the Zeiss "Tessar" lens, illustrated in Fig. 43–17.

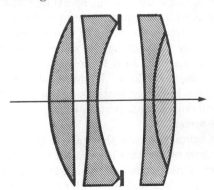

FIG. 43–17. Zeiss "Tessar" lens.

The light-gathering power of a photographic objective is usually stated in terms of its f/-number, which is determined by the focal length of the lens and by its diameter or the diameter of the aperture which effectively determines the lens area. Thus the notation $f/4.5$ means that the focal length of the lens is 4.5 times its effective diameter. The smaller the f/-number, the larger the lens diameter for a given focal length, and the greater the light-gathering power or "speed" of the lens. Extremely fast lenses may have f/-numbers as small as $f/1.9$ or $f/1.5$. That of the Brownie lens is approximately $f/11$. The required time of exposure increases with the square of the f/-number.

For a given position of the photographic plate, only those objects lying in the plane conjugate to that of the plate are sharply focused upon it, objects at a greater or less distance appearing somewhat blurred. However, because of lens aberrations, a point of a given object will be imaged as a small circle, called the *circle of confusion*, even with the best focusing. The circles of confusion of points at other distances will be larger. If extremely sharp definition of the image is not essential, there is evidently a certain range of object distances, called the *depth of field*, such that all objects within this range are simultaneously "in focus" on the plate. That is, the circles of confusion of points within this range are not so large that the image is unsatisfactory. The so-called *fixed-focus* camera is one with a large depth of field, so that all objects beyond a certain distance are simultaneously in satisfactory focus.

43–7 The projector. The optical system of the projection lantern, or the motion picture projector, is illustrated in Fig. 43–18. The arrow at the left represents the light source (for example, the filament of a projection lamp). For simplicity, the slide to be projected is represented as opaque except for a single transparent aperture.

Of course, light is emitted from all points of the source and in all directions. The diagram traces the paths of three pencils of rays originating at the ends and at the midpoint of the source. The function of the condensing lens is to deviate the light from the source inward, so that it can pass through the projecting lens. If the condensing lens were omitted, light passing through the outer portions of the slide would not strike the projecting lens and only a small portion of the slide near its center would be imaged on the screen.

A study of the figure will show that (a) for the three selected points of the source, only those rays within the shaded pencils can pass through the aperture, all others striking the condensing lens being intercepted by the opaque portions of the slide, and (b) similar pencils of rays could be drawn from every other point of the source.

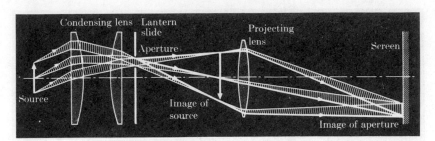

FIG. 43–18. The projection lantern.

Each of these pencils converges, after passing through the aperture, to form an image of its point of origin just to the left of the projecting lens. In practice, this image would be formed *at* the projecting lens, but for clarity in the diagram the image and the lens have been displaced slightly. The focal length of the condensing lens should be such that the image of the source just fills the projecting lens. If the image of the source is larger than the projecting lens, some of the light passing through the slide is wasted. If it is smaller, the area of the projecting lens is not being fully utilized. Thus, in the diagram, the outer portions of the projecting lens serve no useful purpose.

Three rays tangent to the upper edge of the aperture have been emphasized in the figure. These rays originate at *different* points of the source. Hence, although they intersect at the edge of the aperture, this point of intersection does not constitute an image of any point of the source. But these three rays diverge from a common point of the lantern slide, and therefore this point of the slide is imaged as shown on the screen. Similarly, rays tangent to any point of the edge of the aperture are imaged at a conjugate point on the screen. Thus if the aperture is circular, a circular spot of light appears on the screen.

Note that light from *all* points of the source illuminates *every* point of the image of the aperture, and would do the same were the aperture at any other point of the slide.

The preceding discussion has explained the conditions that determine the *focal length* of the condensing lens and the *diameter* of the projecting lens (the image of the source formed by the condensing lens should just fill the projecting lens). The *diameter* of the condensing lens must evidently be at least as great as the diagonal of the largest slide to be projected, while the *focal length* of the projecting lens is determined by the magnification desired between the slide and its image, and the distance of the lantern from the screen.

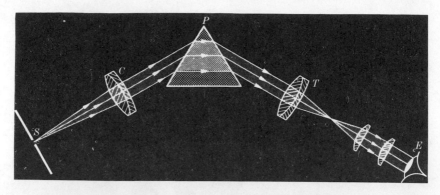

FIG. 43–19. Principle of the prism spectrometer.

43–8 The prism spectrometer. Optical instruments may be grouped into two general classes, *image-forming* instruments and *analyzing* instruments. Instruments of the former class, such as those we have been discussing, serve to form the image of some given object; those of the latter class are used to determine the composition, intensity, or state of polarization of a beam of light. We shall consider next the prism spectrometer. This is an analyzing instrument, used primarily to discover what wavelengths are present in a given light beam.

The essential elements of a prism spectrometer are illustrated in Fig. 43–19. A narrow slit S, illuminated by the light to be analyzed, is located at the first focal point of the achromatic lens C, called the *collimator*. The parallel beam of light emerging from the collimator falls on the prism P, is deviated, and the emergent light examined by the telescope T. Since, as we have seen, the index of refraction of optical materials varies with wavelength, the various wavelengths present in the light are deviated by different angles.

The observer E sees a number of images of the slit side by side, each formed by light of a particular wavelength. If the source emits light of all wavelengths, the images form a continuous succession, called a *continuous spectrum*. If the source emits only a few definite wavelengths, the images of the slit are separated from one another and appear as a series of bright lines, each the color of the light producing it. The spectrum is then called a *line spectrum*.

PROBLEMS

43-1. When two thin lenses are closely spaced, the power of the combination is the sum of the powers of the individual lenses. Two thin lenses of 25 cm and 40 cm focal length are in contact. What is the power of the combination?

43-2. What is the power of the spectacles required (a) by a hyperopic eye whose near point is 125 cm? (b) by a myopic eye whose far point is 50 cm?

43-3. What spectacles are required for reading purposes by a person whose near point is at 200 cm? (b) The far point of a myopic eye is at 30 cm. What spectacles are required for distant vision?

43-4. (a) Where is the near point of an eye for which a spectacle lens of power $+2$ diopters is prescribed? (b) Where is the far point of an eye for which a spectacle lens of power -0.5 diopter is prescribed for distant vision?

43-5. A person with myopia is prescribed spectacles of -1.50 diopters. (a) What is the far point of the myopic eyes? (b) If the person wore spectacles of -1.00 diopter, what would be his greatest distance of distinct vision?

43-6. A person with normal vision has a range of accommodation from 25 cm to infinity. Over what range would he be able to see objects distinctly when wearing the spectacles of a friend whose correction is $+4$ diopters?

43-7. A thin lens of 10 diopters power is used as a simple magnifier. (a) What angular magnification is obtainable with the lens? (b) What is the closest that an object may be brought to the eye when examined through the lens?

43-8. The focal length of a simple magnifier is 10 cm. (a) How far in front of the magnifier should an object to be examined be placed if the image is formed at the observer's near point, 25 cm in front of his eye? (b) If the object is 1 mm high, what is the height of its image formed by the magnifier? Assume the magnifier to be a thin lens.

43-9. The image formed by a microscope objective of focal length 4 mm is 180 mm from its second focal point. The ocular has a focal length of 31.25 mm. (a) What is the magnification of the microscope? (b) The unaided eye can distinguish two points as separate if they are about 0.1 mm apart. What is the minimum separation, using this microscope?

43-10. A certain microscope is provided with objectives of focal lengths 16 mm, 4 mm, and 1.9 mm, and with oculars of angular magnifications 5$\times$ and 10$\times$. What is (a) the largest, (b) the least over-all magnification obtainable? Each objective forms an image 160 mm beyond its second focal point.

43-11. The focal length of the ocular of a certain microscope is 2.5 cm. The focal length of the objective is 16 mm. The distance between objective and ocular is 22.1 cm. The final image formed by the ocular is at infinity. Treat all lenses as thin. (a) What should be the distance from the objective to the object viewed? (b) What is the linear magnification produced by the objective? (c) What is the over-all magnification of the microscope?

43-12. A microscope with an objective of focal length 9 mm and an ocular of focal length 5 cm is used to project an image on a screen 1 m from the ocular. What is the lateral magnification of the image? Let $x' = 18$ cm.

43-13. The moon subtends an angle at the earth of approximately $\frac{1}{2}°$. What is the diameter of the image of the moon produced by the objective of the Lick Observatory telescope, a refractor having a focal length of 58 ft?

43–14. The ocular of a telescope has a focal length of 10 cm. The distance between objective and ocular is 2.1 m. What is the angular magnification of the telescope?

43–15. A crude telescope is constructed of two spectacle lenses of focal lengths 100 cm and 20 cm respectively. (a) Find its angular magnification. (b) Find the height of the image formed by the objective of a building 200 ft high and distant one mile.

43–16. A Galilean telescope is to be constructed, using the same objective as in Problem 43–15. (a) What type and focal length lens should be used as an ocular if the telescopes are to have the same magnification? (b) Compare the lengths of the telescopes.

43–17. A camera lens is focused on a distant point source of light, the image forming on a screen at *a* (Fig. 43–20). When the screen is moved backward a distance of 2 cm to *b*, the circle of light on the screen has a diameter of

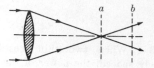

FIGURE 43–20

4 mm. What is the $f/$-number of the lens?

43–18. Camera *A*, having an $f/8$ lens 2.5 cm in diameter, photographs an object using the correct exposure of 1/100 sec. What exposure should camera *B* use in photographing the same object if it has an $f/4$ lens 5 cm in diameter?

43–19. The focal length of an $f/2.8$ camera lens is 8 cm. (a) What is the diameter of the lens? (b) If the correct exposure of a certain scene is 1/200 sec at $f/2.8$, what would be the correct exposure at $f/5.6$?

43–20. The dimensions of a lantern slide are $3'' \times 4''$. It is desired to project an image of the slide, enlarged to $6' \times 8'$, on a screen 30 ft from the projection lens. (a) What should be the focal length of the projection lens? (b) Where should the slide be placed?

CHAPTER 44

ILLUMINATION

44-1 Sources of light. It was pointed out in Section 17-4 that the energy of electromagnetic radiation, or *radiant energy*, emitted per unit time, depends upon the temperature and the nature of the surface of a body. This radiation is a mixture of different wavelengths. At a temperature of 300°C the most intense of these waves has a wavelength of 5000×10^{-9} m or 5000 mμ (read *millimicrons*, one micron $= 10^{-6}$ m), which is in the *infrared* region. At a temperature of 800°C a body emits enough visible radiant energy to be self-luminous and appears "red hot." By far the larger part of the energy emitted, however, is still carried by infrared waves. At 3000°C, which is about the temperature of an incandescent lamp filament, the radiant energy contains enough of the "visible" wavelengths, between 400 mμ and about 700 mμ, so that the body appears nearly "white hot."

In modern incandescent lamps, the filament is a coil of fine tungsten wire. An inert gas such as argon is introduced to reduce evaporation of the filament. Incandescent lamps vary in size from one no larger than a grain of wheat to one with a power input of 5000 watts, used for illuminating airfields.

The brightest source of light is the *carbon arc*. Rods of carbon from 6 to 12 inches in length and from $\frac{1}{4}$ to $\frac{1}{2}$ inch in diameter are placed either horizontally, as shown in Fig. 44-1(a), or at an angle, as shown in Fig. 44-1(b). Sometimes the carbon rods are copper coated to improve electrical conductivity. To start a carbon arc, the two carbons are connected to a 110-volt or 220-volt d-c source, are allowed to touch momentarily, and are then withdrawn. Intense electron bombardment of the positive carbon causes an extremely hot crater to form at the end of the positive carbon. This end, at a temperature of about 4000°C, is the source of light. An electric motor or a clockwork mechanism is used to keep the carbons close to each other as they burn away. Carbon arcs are used in all motion picture theaters, where they operate on from 50 to several hundred amperes.

A common laboratory source of light is provided by a mercury arc. A glass or quartz tube has tungsten electrodes sealed in each end. A pool of mercury surrounds the negative electrode. A difference of potential is established across the electrodes and the tube is tilted until the mercury makes contact between the two electrodes. Some mercury is vaporized, and when the tube is restored to its vertical position an electric

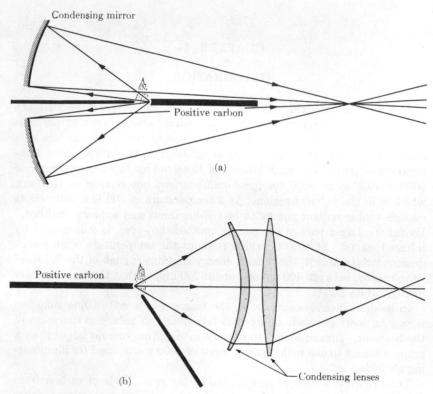

FIG. 44–1. Two types of carbon arcs. (a) With condensing mirror, for moderately sized motion picture theaters. (b) With condensing lenses, for large motion picture theaters.

discharge is maintained by electrons and positive mercury ions. When the mercury is at low pressure the mercury atoms emit a characteristic light consisting of only yellow, green, blue, and violet. A didymium filter may be used to absorb the yellow, and a yellow glass filter to absorb the blue and violet, leaving an intense green light consisting of a very small band of wavelengths whose average value is 546 mμ. Low-pressure mercury arcs containing only one isotope of mercury, of atomic weight 198, are obtainable from the United States National Bureau of Standards. The green light from these lamps consists of an extremely narrow band of wavelengths, and is the nearest approach to *monochromatic* light.

If the current through a quartz mercury arc lamp is allowed to increase, the temperature rises greatly and the vapor pressure of the mercury rises to between 50 and 100 atmospheres. Such a lamp requires water cooling, and when operating is a very intense source of white light.

An intense source of yellow light of average wavelength 589.3 mμ is provided by a sodium arc lamp. This is usually made of a special kind of glass that is not attacked by sodium and into which electrodes are sealed. Each electrode is a filament for providing electrons to maintain an electric discharge through an inert gas. After the inert gas discharge has taken place for a few minutes, the temperature rises to a value at which the vapor pressure of the sodium is great enough to provide sufficient sodium atoms to emit the characteristic yellow sodium light. Sodium lamps are often used for street lighting because of their economy and because great visual acuity results from the absence of chromatic aberration of the eye when almost monochromatic light is used.

A very important development in illumination engineering is provided by the fluorescent lamp. This consists of a glass tube containing argon and a small droplet of mercury. The electrodes consist of tungsten filaments. When an electric discharge takes place in the mercury-argon mixture, only a small amount of visible light is emitted by the mercury and argon atoms. There is, however, considerable *ultraviolet* light (light of wavelength shorter than that of visible violet). This ultraviolet light is absorbed in a thin layer of material, called a *phosphor*, with which the interior walls of the glass tube are coated. The phosphor has the property of *fluorescence*, which means that it emits visible light when illuminated by light of shorter wavelength. Lamps may be obtained which will fluoresce with any desired color, depending on the nature of the phosphor. Phosphors commonly used are cadmium borate for pink, zinc silicate for green, calcium tungstate for blue, and mixture for white.

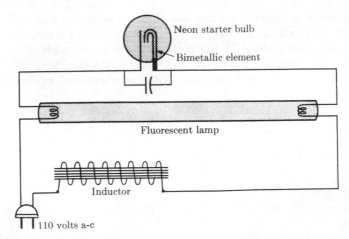

FIG. 44–2. Circuit consisting of a neon starter bulb and a series inductor for starting a fluorescent lamp.

The method commonly employed to start a fluorescent lamp embodies some interesting physical principles. Consider, for example, the fluorescent lamp depicted in Fig. 44–2. When 110 volts a-c are established across the lamp, the full line voltage exists across the electrodes of a small neon starter bulb which is usually mounted in the base of the lamp. The neon glows and warms up the electrodes, one of which is a bimetallic element. The bimetal expands and touches the other electrode, thereby short-circuiting the neon lamp and causing an appreciable current to exist in the two filaments of the fluorescent lamp. In a short time the filaments get hot and the neon lamp cools off. Then the bimetal contracts and breaks the circuit in the neon lamp, creating a voltage surge in the line because of the presence of an inductor. This momentary increase of voltage causes an electric discharge to take place in the mercury-argon mixture between the two filaments. Once this discharge is maintained, the potential difference across the fluorescent lamp, which is the same as the potential difference across the neon starter bulb, is too small to create a discharge in the neon bulb itself.

44–2 Luminous flux. In all the lamps described in the preceding section, electrical power is supplied and radiation is emitted. The radiant energy emitted per unit of time is called *radiant power* or *radiant flux*. Not all the electrical power is converted into radiant flux; some is lost by heat conduction, heat convection, and absorption. Of the remaining radiant flux, only a small fraction lies within the wavelength interval (400 mμ to 700 mμ) which evokes the visual sensation in the normal eye. That part of the radiant flux which affects the eye is called *luminous flux*. The situation is depicted by the flow diagram shown in Fig. 44–3. We shall be concerned in this chapter with the theory and measurements of the luminous flux emitted by sources and incident upon surfaces.

The visual sensation produced by luminous flux has three attributes, *hue, saturation,* and *brightness.* Hue is the attribute that enables one to

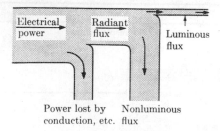

FIG. 44–3. Conversion of electrical power into luminous flux and nonluminous flux.

Fig. 44–4. A scale of grays to illustrate the sensation of brightness. The greatest brightness sensation is evoked by the rectangle at the left, the least by that at the right.

classify the sensation as red, green, blue, etc. Saturation describes the extent to which the sensation departs from a neutral gray. Hue and saturation will be discussed fully in the next chapter.

The sensation of brightness is illustrated by Fig. 44–4, which shows a series of rectangles printed in neutral gray, ranging from white at one end of the scale to black at the other. The white rectangle evokes the greatest sensation of brightness, the black rectangle the least, while intermediate sensations of brightness are evoked by intermediate rectangles. A colored sample of luminous flux may be compared with the gray scale with the aid of an instrument called a *flicker photometer*. The theory of this instrument will be discussed later. Let it be accepted at present that we can compare the brightness produced by equal amounts of different colored lights. It is an important experimental fact that *equal amounts of radiant flux of different wavelengths do not produce visual sensations of equal brightness*. A lamp emitting, say, one-thousandth of a watt of green light would appear to an observer to be bright, whereas a lamp emitting one-thousandth of a watt of blue light would appear dim. Furthermore, a lamp emitting only radiation of wavelength greater than 700 mμ or shorter than 400 mμ would appear black. Evidently, the watt is not a suitable unit for measuring luminous flux. What is needed is a unit which expresses the ability of radiation to evoke the sensation of brightness. This unit is the *lumen*, but before we can define the lumen, we must first describe the international standard source, and then explain what is meant by the steradian measure of a solid angle.

44–3 The standard source and the lumen. The photometric standard for many years was an actual candle constructed according to definite specifications. This standard was later replaced by a number of carbon filament lamps. The need for a more permanent standard that could be reproduced at will led to the adoption, by international agreement, of a standard source, depicted in Fig. 44–5. A cylindrical tube of a refractory (that is, a material such as fused thoria, with a very high melting point) is surrounded by pure platinum (which does not oxidize, combine chemically with thoria, or corrode). The tube widens out at the open end, and when the platinum is at its normal melting point, the light emitted from the open end is a very good experimental approximation of blackbody

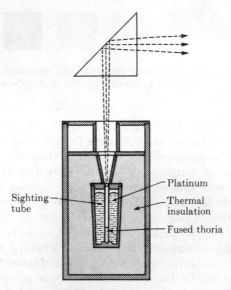

FIG. 44–5. International standard source of light.

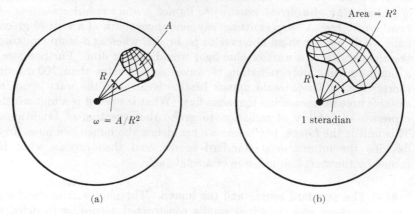

FIG. 44–6. Definition of the steradian measure of a solid angle.

radiation. The luminous flux emitted by this *standard source* depends on the area of the opening and upon the size of the cone of radiation, that is, the *solid angle*.

A set of lines radiating from a point are said to define a solid angle at that point. With this point as center, and with any distance R as radius, imagine a spherical surface to be constructed. The set of lines emanating from the center of this sphere cuts off on the surface of the sphere an area A. The *steradian* measure of the solid angle ω is defined as the ratio

$$\omega = \frac{A}{R^2},$$

as shown in Fig. 44–6(a). If the area A is exactly equal to R^2, then the solid angle is one steradian, as shown in part (b) of the figure. Since the total area of a sphere is $4\pi R^2$, the total solid angle subtended at a point is

$$\omega \text{ (total)} = \frac{4\pi R^2}{R^2} = 4\pi \text{ steradians.}$$

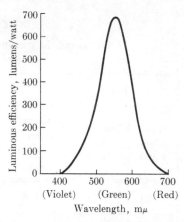

FIG. 44–7. Luminous efficiency of monochromatic radiant flux as a function of wavelength.

We are now in a position to define the unit of luminous flux, the *lumen*.

A lumen is the luminous flux issuing from one-sixtieth of a square centimeter of opening of a standard source, and included within a solid angle of one steradian. When the area is two-sixtieths of a square centimeter, the luminous flux is two lumens, and so on.

With the aid of a flicker photometer, we may now compare the brightness sensation evoked by a standard source with that evoked, say, by one watt of light of any color. In other words, we may measure the luminous flux, in lumens, of one watt of colored light. Experiment shows that one watt of green light of wavelength 555 mμ has a luminous flux of 680 lumens, whereas one watt of yellow light of wavelength 600 mμ has a luminous flux of 411 lumens. The ratio of the luminous flux to the radiant flux is defined as the *luminous efficiency*, and is measured in lumens per watt. The graph of Fig. 44–7 is the result of a series of very careful experiments, and is known as the *standard luminosity curve*. It is clear from this curve that the eye is most sensitive to green light, of wavelength 555 mμ.

Luminous efficiency expresses a property of a sample of radiant flux. The same term is also applied to a light source such as an incandescent or fluorescent lamp, but with a somewhat different meaning which is better described as an "over-all" luminous efficiency. The latter is defined as the ratio of the luminous flux output of the source to the *total electrical* power input. Since most light sources do not, in the first place, convert all the power supplied to them into radiant flux, and since, in the second place, much of the radiant flux they do emit is at wavelengths where the relative luminosity is small or even zero, the over-all luminous efficiency of light sources is much less than 680 lumens/watt. For example, the over-all

TABLE 44–1

OVER-ALL LUMINOUS EFFICIENCY OF TUNGSTEN AND FLUORESCENT LAMPS

Tungsten lamps			Fluorescent lamps			
Input power, watts	Luminous flux, lumens	Over-all efficiency, $\frac{\text{lumens}}{\text{watt}}$	Input power, watts	Length, inches	Luminous flux, lumens	Over-all efficiency, $\frac{\text{lumens}}{\text{watt}}$
10	78	7.8	4	6	73	18.2
25	260	10.4	6	9	210	35.0
40	465	11.7	8	12	330	41.2
60	835	13.9	14	15	490	35.0
100	1630	16.3	20	24	960	48.0
200	3650	18.3	30	36	1500	50.0
500	9950	19.9	40	48	2320	58.0
1000	21500	21.5	100	60	4400	44.0

luminous efficiency of a 40-watt tungsten lamp is about 12 lumens/watt and that of a 40-watt white fluorescent lamp is about 58 lumens/watt.

The over-all luminous efficiency of tungsten and fluorescent lamps, as measured by Weitz and Reinhardt, is given in Table 44–1, where it may be seen that a 40-watt fluorescent lamp gives five times as much light as a 40-watt incandescent lamp.

44–4 Illuminance. When luminous flux strikes a surface, we say that the surface is *illuminated*. This familiar concept is defined quantitatively as follows. At any point of the surface we construct a small area ΔA, as in Fig. 44–8, and let ΔF represent the luminous flux incident on this area. The *illuminance* E at the point is defined as the ratio of ΔF to ΔA.

$$E = \frac{\Delta F}{\Delta A}. \tag{44–1}$$

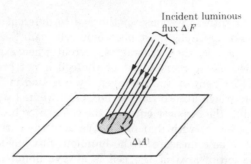

FIG. 44–8. Illuminance is luminous flux incident per unit area.

That is, *illuminance* is *luminous flux incident per unit area.* In modern illuminating engineering practice, illuminance is expressed in *lumens per square meter.* An older unit, the lumen per square foot, or footcandle, is rapidly becoming obsolete.

If the illuminance is the same at all points of a surface of finite area A, and if F is the total luminous flux incident on the surface, Eq. (44–1) becomes

$$E = \frac{F}{A} \cdot \tag{44-2}$$

The illuminance on a surface can be measured, with an accuracy that is sufficient for most purposes, by a photronic type of photoelectric cell, described in Section 38–12. This cell generates a current when radiant flux is incident on its surface. The relative amount of current generated by radiant flux of different wavelengths is, unfortunately, not the same as

TABLE 44–2

TYPICAL VALUES OF ILLUMINANCE

Mode of illumination	Illuminance†, lumens/m²
Sunlight plus skylight (maximum)	100,000
Sunlight plus skylight (overcast day)	10,000
Interiors near window—daylight	1,000
Minimum recommended for close work—artificial light	100
Full moonlight	0.2
Starlight	0.0003

† Representative values.

the relative brightness response of the eye to different wavelengths (see Fig. 44–7). For example, most photronic cells can "see" radiant flux in the infrared, that is, they generate a current when exposed to infrared waves. Hence the current output of the cell is not proportional to the *luminous* flux incident on it. However, by inserting in front of the cell a filter or filters which absorb radiant flux of unwanted wavelengths in the desired amount, the response curve of the cell can be brought into reasonably good agreement with that of the eye, and the current generated by it can be taken as a measure of the luminous flux incident on it. Then, provided the entire area of the cell is always illuminated, the current output is proportional to the incident flux per unit area, or the illuminance, and the scale on the meter can be calibrated to read lumens/m^2.

44–5 Luminous intensity of a point source. Consider the point source of light S in Fig. 44–9. Let ΔF represent the luminous flux crossing any section of a narrow cone of solid angle $\Delta\omega$ steradians whose apex is at the source. The *luminous intensity* of the source, in the direction of the cone, is defined as the ratio of the flux ΔF to the solid angle $\Delta\omega$, or as the *flux emitted per unit solid angle*. Luminous intensity is represented by I.

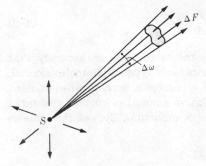

$$I = \frac{\Delta F}{\Delta\omega}. \qquad (44\text{--}3)$$

The unit of intensity is *one lumen per steradian*. This unit is also called *one candle*. The common expression "candlepower" should be avoided, since luminous intensity is not power. It follows from the definition of the lumen that the luminous intensity of one-sixtieth

FIG. 44–9. The intensity of a point source is the flux emitted per unit solid angle.

of a square centimeter of opening of a standard source, in a direction perpendicular to the plane of the opening, is one candle.

Most sources do not emit equal quantities of flux per unit solid angle in all directions, so in general the intensity of a source is different in different directions. The common incandescent lamp, for instance, cannot emit any flux in the direction of its base, and its intensity in that direction is zero. An idealized point source that emits uniformly in all directions is called a *uniform point source*. Since the total solid angle subtended at a point is 4π steradians, a source whose intensity in all directions is I candles, or I lumens/steradian, emits a total of $4\pi I$ lumens.

44-6 Illuminance produced by a point source. Let ΔA in Fig. 44–10 be an element of surface whose normal makes an angle θ with the distance r to a point source S. Let I represent the intensity of the source in the direction of the element ΔA. The solid angle subtended by ΔA at the source is

$$\Delta \omega = \frac{\Delta A \cos \theta}{r^2}, \tag{44-4}$$

and since by definition the intensity I of the source is

$$I = \frac{\Delta F}{\Delta \omega},$$

the flux ΔF in the solid angle $\Delta \omega$ is

$$\Delta F = I \, \Delta \omega = \frac{I \, \Delta A \cos \theta}{r^2}.$$

All of this flux is incident on the area ΔA, and hence the illuminance of ΔA is

$$E = \frac{\Delta F}{\Delta A} = \frac{I \cos \theta}{r^2}. \tag{44-5}$$

That is, the illuminance of an element of surface by a point source is inversely proportional to the square of the distance of the element from the source and directly proportional to the intensity of the source and the cosine of the angle between the normal to the element and the line joining element and source.

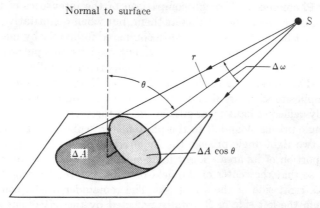

Fig. 44–10. Illuminance of a surface by a point source.

When a surface element is illuminated by more than one source, the total illuminance is the arithmetic sum of the illuminances produced by the individual sources.

EXAMPLE. A point source of light is 2 m from a screen in which there is a circular hole 10 cm in diameter. The screen is at right angles to the line joining the center of the hole and the source. It is found that 0.05 lumen of luminous flux from the source passes through the hole. (a) What is the solid angle, in steradians, subtended by the hole at the source? (b) What is the intensity of the source in the direction of the hole? (c) If the source emits uniformly in all directions, find the total number of lumens it emits. (d) The over-all luminous efficiency of the source is 20 lumens/watt. What is the power input to the source?

(a) $$\Delta\omega = \frac{\Delta A \cos\theta}{R^2} \quad \frac{(\pi/4)(10^2) \text{ cm}^2}{(200)^2 \text{ cm}^2}$$

$$= 0.00197 \text{ steradian.}$$

(b) $$I = \frac{\Delta F}{\Delta\omega} = \frac{0.05 \text{ lumen}}{0.00197 \text{ steradian}} = 25.4 \frac{\text{lumens}}{\text{steradian}}$$

$$= 25.4 \text{ candles.}$$

(c) $$F \text{ (total)} = 4\pi I$$

$$= 319 \text{ lumens.}$$

(d) Power input $$= \frac{319 \text{ lumens}}{20 \text{ lumens/w}}$$

$$= 16.0 \text{ watts.}$$

44–7 Photometry. A rough comparison of the intensities of two point sources may be made by looking at them, but when quantitative measurements must be made, the sources are compared indirectly by means of the illuminance they produce. The instrument used for this purpose is called a Lummer-Brodhun photometer and its construction is illustrated in Fig. 44–11. The screen S is a sheet of plaster of Paris or magnesium oxide, whose opposite sides are illuminated by the two sources to be compared. Diffusely reflected light from either side of the screen is reflected by the right-angle prisms A and B to the photometer "cube" C. The latter consists of two right-angle prisms, the hypotenuse of one being ground away over a portion of its area. Light incident on the area in contact is transmitted, so that the center of the field of view receives only light reflected from the right side of the screen S. The remainder of the field receives light from the left side of S, totally reflected by the left prism at regions where the two prisms are not in contact. The screen S and the reflecting

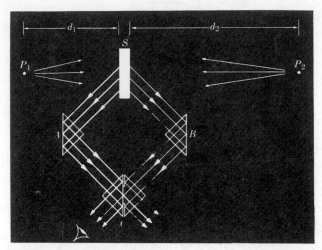

Fig. 44–11. Principle of the Lummer-Brodhun photometer.

prisms in Fig. 44–11 are enclosed within a protecting case, not shown in the diagram.

The position of the photometer may be adjusted along a line between the two sources until the field of view of the observer appears of uniform brightness. When this is the case, both faces of the screen S are equally illuminated. The distances d_1 and d_2 from the screen to the sources are then measured and, from Eq. (44–5),

$$\frac{I_1}{d_1^2} = \frac{I_2}{d_2^2},$$

where I_1 and I_2 are the intensities of the sources in the direction of the screen. If the intensity of either source is known, that of the other can be computed.

The Lummer-Brodhun photometer works well when the two sources to be compared are of the same hue. If the two sources are widely different in hue, no photometric balance can be attained with a photometer of the Lummer-Brodhun type, and one must have recourse to a *flicker photometer*. In the flicker photometer, the screen seen by the observer is illuminated alternately by light from the two sources. If the frequency of alternation is varied, a frequency will be found at which the hue difference disappears, because of persistence of vision. Then by varying the source distances, a brightness match may be achieved.

In many instances it is sufficient to know the total luminous flux output of a light source, in lumens, and it is not necessary to measure the

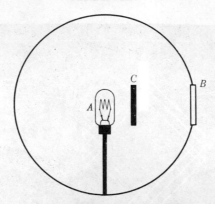

FIG. 44-12. Principle of the sphere photometer.

intensity, or the number of lumens per steradian, in any specified direction or directions. The total flux can be measured with a *sphere photometer*, illustrated in Fig. 44–12. The inner surface of a hollow sphere is coated with a diffusely reflecting white paint. The sphere must be large in comparison with the dimensions of the light source. (This may require the construction of a sphere 10 ft or more in diameter.) The light source A is mounted at the center of the sphere. Reflections and re-reflections from the sphere walls result in a uniform illuminance on them at all points, proportional to the total luminous flux output of the source. A small disk of diffusely transmitting opal glass B is set in the sphere wall and the light from its outer surface is compared with that from a standard lamp by a photometer, or a photronic cell is set in the wall and its current output read on a galvanometer. An opaque shield C prevents direct light from the source from reaching the opal glass or the photronic cell.

44–8 Extended sources. Luminance. Candles, kerosene lamps, and bare incandescent lamps are approximately point sources. At the time these were in common use the concept of intensity, in candles, together with the inverse square law (Eq. 44–5) sufficed for most calculations of the illumination produced by artificial light sources. Since the advent of frosted bulbs, diffusing shades, fluorescent lamps, and the general introduction of indirect lighting, most light sources are extended sources rather than points, and a property of such sources known as their *luminance* has come to be of increasing importance. The luminance of an extended source is defined as the luminous intensity per unit area, and is measured in candles per square meter. Representative values of the luminance of a number of extended sources are given in Table 44–3.

TABLE 44–3

TYPICAL VALUES OF LUMINANCE

Source	Luminance, candles/m^2
Surface of sun	2×10^9
Tungsten filament at 2700°K	10^7
Standard source	**600,000**
White paper in sunlight	25,000
Fluorescent lamp	6,000
Candle flame	5,000
Clear sky	3,200
Surface of moon	2,900
White paper in moonlight	0.03

Summary

Radiant flux means the quantity of energy per unit time that arrives at or is emitted from any surface by means of electromagnetic waves. Radiant flux is expressed in *watts*.

Brightness is that attribute of any color sensation which permits it to be classified as equivalent to the sensation produced by some member of a series of neutral grays.

Luminous flux is radiant flux evaluated with respect to its capacity to evoke the sensation of brightness. Luminous flux is expressed in *lumens*.

The *illuminance* on a surface is the luminous flux incident per unit area, and is expressed in *lumens per square meter*.

The *luminous intensity* of a point source is the luminous flux emitted

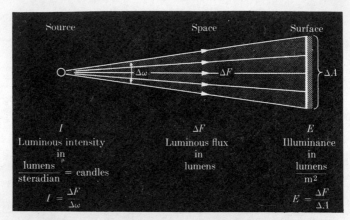

FIG. 44–13. Summary of terms in illumination engineering.

per unit solid angle. The unit is *one lumen per steradian*, also called *one candle*.

The *luminance* of an extended source is the intensity per unit area of the source, and is expressed in *candles per square meter*.

Some of these terms are represented in Fig. 44–13.

PROBLEMS

44–1. A source emits light of 600 mμ wavelength. What is the luminous flux passing through an aperture near the source if the radiant flux through the aperture is 2.5 watts?

44–2. A source emits light of two wavelengths, 500 mμ and 555 mμ. The total radiant flux is 20 watts and the total luminous flux 8900 lumens. (a) What is the luminous efficiency of the source? (b) How much radiant flux does each wavelength contribute?

44–3. A sample of radiant flux consists of 10 watts of monochromatic light of wavelength 450 mμ and 20 watts of monochromatic light of wavelength 600 mμ. (a) What is the radiant flux in the sample? (b) What is the luminous flux in the sample? (c) What is the luminous efficiency of the sample?

44–4. A point source of light is 2 m from a screen in which there is a circular hole 10 cm in diameter. The screen is at right angles to the line joining the center of the hole and the source. It is found that 0.05 lumen of luminous flux from the source passes through the hole. (a) What is the solid angle, in steradians, subtended by the hole at the source? (b) What is the intensity of the source in the direction of the hole? (c) If the source emits uniformly in all directions, find the total number of lumens it emits. (d) The over-all luminous efficiency of the source is 20 lumens/watt. What is the power input to the source?

44–5. A lamp has a luminous intensity of 50 candles and an over-all luminous efficiency of 12 lumens/watt. How many watts are supplied to the lamp?

44–6. In Fig. 44–14, the lens L has a diameter of 10 cm and is placed 50 cm from the source A, of 100 candles intensity. (a) What is the solid angle subtended by the lens at the source? (b) How many lumens enter the lens? (c) After passing through the lens the light from A just covers a screen S, 5 cm in diameter. What is the illuminance of the screen?

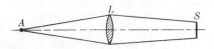

FIGURE 44–14

44–7. (a) A lamp whose luminous intensity is 100 candles is placed one meter above a horizontal table. What is the illuminance of a point on the table directly under the lamp? (b) How far must the lamp be moved in a horizontal direction to reduce the illuminance at the point to $\frac{1}{2}$ of this value?

44–8. In Fig. 44–15, the mirror M and screen S are parallel and 50 cm apart. Lamp A, having an intensity of 75 candles, is placed midway between them. What is the illuminance on the screen at P?

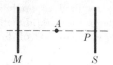

FIGURE 44–15

44–9. A uniform point source is suspended 4 m above a desk. The illuminance of the desk at a point directly below the source is 100 lumens/m^2. (a) What is the illuminance on the desk at a point 3 m from the first point? (b) At what distance from the first point is the illuminance 20 lumens/m^2?

44-10. The standard photometer bar is 3 m long. A lamp whose intensity in the direction of the photometer is known to be 30 candles is set up at one end of the bar, and a lamp of unknown intensity at the other end. The field of view of a Lummer-Brodhun photometer appears of uniform brightness when it is 80 cm from the 30-candle lamp. What is the intensity of the other lamp, in the direction of the photometer?

44-11. A photoflash lamp has a luminous intensity of about 5 million candles. How far from a surface must such a lamp be placed to produce an illuminance equal to that of maximum sunlight plus skylight?

44-12. A 45-candle standard lamp is 135 cm from the screen of a Lummer-Brodhun photometer. The field of view of the photometer is of uniform brightness when a second lamp is 65 cm from the screen. What is the intensity of this lamp?

44-13. Suppose a uniform point source of any desired intensity could be constructed with an over-all luminous efficiency of 20 lumens/watt. If such a source were suspended 3 m above a desk, what power input to the source would be required to produce an illuminance on the desk, directly below the lamp, equal to that of direct sunlight?

44-14. The over-all luminous efficiency of a street lamp is 30 lumens/watt. Assume the lamp to emit like a uniform point source. (a) If the lamp is 8 m above the street, what power input is required to produce an illuminance, at a point directly below the lamp, equal to that of full moonlight? (b) What is the illuminance at a point 6 m away from the first point?

44-15. Two lamps, of 25 and 50 candles, are 100 cm apart. At what point between them will a screen be equally illuminated on both sides?

44-16. A relay is to be controlled by a vacuum photocell, actuated by the light passing through an aperture measuring 15 mm by 40 mm. At least 0.2 lumen must strike the photocell to operate the relay. What is the maximum permissible distance from the aperture to a uniform point source of intensity 50 candles, if the light from the source is to operate the relay?

44-17. A certain baseball field is in the shape of a square, 140 m on a side. The field is to be illuminated for night games by six towers supporting banks of 1000-watt incandescent lamps, each with an over-all luminous efficiency of 30 lumens/watt. The illuminance desired on the playing field is 200 lumens/m^2. Assume that 50% of the luminous flux emitted by the lamps reaches the field. (a) How many lamps are needed in each tower? (b) Compare the power input to each tower with the power developed by a modern automobile engine.

CHAPTER 45

COLOR

45–1 Colorimetry. A modern magazine with its wealth of illustrations in color, color photography for the amateur as well as the professional, colored plastics, goods in colored packages, all testify to the increasing importance of color in our daily lives. Color has become the concern not only of the artist, but of the physicist and chemist and of the engineer and industrialist as well.

The following statement of Lord Kelvin was quoted in Chapter 1 of this book and it is appropriate to repeat it here. "I often say that when you can measure what you are speaking about, and express it in numbers, you know something about it; but when you cannot express it in numbers, your knowledge is of a meagre and unsatisfactory kind; it may be the beginning of knowledge, but you have scarcely, in your thoughts, advanced to the stage of *Science*, whatever the matter may be." We have today a science of color; color is something that can be measured and expressed in numbers. The science of color measurement is called *colorimetry*.

The word color is commonly used in several different senses. The psychologist uses the word with reference to the *sensation in the consciousness of a human observer* when the retina of his eye is stimulated by radiant energy. In an entirely different sense, the term is used to specify a *property of an object*, as, for example, when we say that the color of a book is red. The Committee on Colorimetry of the Optical Society of America has recommended the following definition: *"Color consists of the characteristics of light* other than spatial and temporal inhomogeneities; light being that aspect of radiant energy of which a human observer is aware through the ·visual sensations which arise from the stimulation of the retina of the eye."

The "characteristics of light" referred to in this definition are threefold. The first is *luminous flux,* which is a measure of the effectiveness of the light in evoking the sensation of brightness, and which was discussed in the preceding chapter. The other two characteristics, which are referred to jointly as the *chromaticity* of the light, are ·*dominant wavelength* and *purity.* Methods for determining dominant wavelength and purity will be described in this chapter. The former corresponds to the attribute of *color sensation* called *hue,* the latter to the attribute called *saturation.*

885

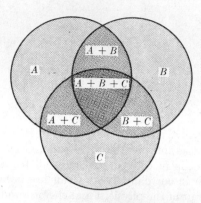

Fᴵɢ. 45–1. Additive color mixtures.

45–2 Additive color mixture. Suppose that three projection lanterns, A, B, and C, are set up so as to project onto a screen three overlapping circular patches of light, each of a different color, as in Fig. 45–1. The light from each lantern is referred to as a *component*. The regions lettered A, B, C in Fig. 45–1 are illuminated by a single component. The regions lettered $A + B$, $B + C$, and $A + C$ are illuminated by two components, while all three components illuminate the central region lettered $A + B + C$. The light reflected from a region illuminated by more than one component is called a *color mixture*. The mixture is additive, because the reflected light is made up of the fraction of component A reflected by the screen, plus the fraction of component B reflected, plus the fraction of component C reflected.

It is well known that each of the mixtures differs from the others in color, as well as differing from each of the three components. Furthermore, it is not possible to detect in any mixture the colors of the components of which it is composed. In this respect the eye differs from the ear. If two notes of different pitch are struck simultaneously on a piano, the resulting sensation is not that of a single pitch intermediate between the two, but both notes can be distinguished. Our sense of hearing is analytical, while our color sense is not.

Let us now adjust the projection lanterns A, B, and C so that all three circles coincide, as in Fig. 45–2, and with a fourth lantern X project onto the screen a second circle illuminated by light of any arbitrary color. If lanterns A, B, and C are each provided with a device for controlling the quantity of luminous flux emitted (for example, a rheostat in series with the projection lamp) it is found that a wide gamut of colors at X can be matched by additive mixtures of the components A, B, and C in the proper proportions.

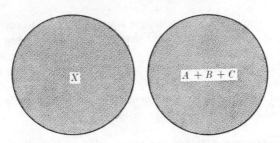

Fig. 45–2. An additive mixture of three components A, B, and C matches the color X.

When used in this way, the apparatus constitutes one form of *colorimeter*. We can say that the color at X has been measured, in the sense that it can be specified by three numbers representing the quantities of the three components that are required for a color match.

Although a wide gamut of colors at X can be matched by the additive mixture of any three arbitrary components, it is not possible to match all colors. This is not because of a faulty choice of components. A second set of components, different from the first, could be combined to match some colors which the first set could not, but it would then be found that other colors, which could be matched by mixing the first set, could not be matched by the second. To extend the number of components to four or more would widen the gamut to some extent, but unless the number of components were infinite there would still be some colors for which a match could not be secured.

When a color at X cannot be matched by an additive mixture of three components, a color match may be secured between a mixture of the unknown and one of the components, on one hand, and a mixture of the other two components on the other. For example, a mixture of X and A might be matched by a mixture of B and C. In some cases, it is necessary to add two of the components to the color at X, and match this mixture with the third component. Thus even if it is not possible to *match* the original color with but three components, it is nevertheless possible to *specify* it by stating the quantity of the component (or components) which, when added to it, will result in a match with stated amounts of the remaining components. Thus *all colors can be measured in terms of any three components*, and the results of the measurement expressed by three numbers. Quantities of any component that must be added to a given color to secure a match are considered negative.

We see, therefore, that the common belief that *all* colors can be matched by a mixture of three properly chosen "primary colors" is incorrect, unless the concept of "matching" is extended in the sense described above.

Furthermore, there are no three unique components that *must* be used for color matching. We shall show later that red, green, and blue components permit matching the widest gamut of colors without using negative quantities of a component, and in this sense red, green, and blue can be considered as the "primary colors."

Notice that the preceding statements are experimental facts, and are independent of any theories of color vision.

45–3 Color mixture data for spectrum colors. It is not necessary to set up a colorimeter and match a given color in order to know the amounts of three given components that would be required for a match. Careful experiments have been made to determine the amounts of three components needed to match all the *spectrum* colors. Then, since any color is a mixture of spectrum colors, the amounts of the components required to match a given color can be calculated from the data above if the radiant flux in the given color is known at each wavelength.

Figure 45–3 shows, for one particular set of components, the amounts of each that must be added to match a spectrum color at any wavelength. These components are themselves spectrum colors; a red of wavelength 650 mμ, a green of wavelength 530 mμ, and a blue of wavelength 425 mμ.

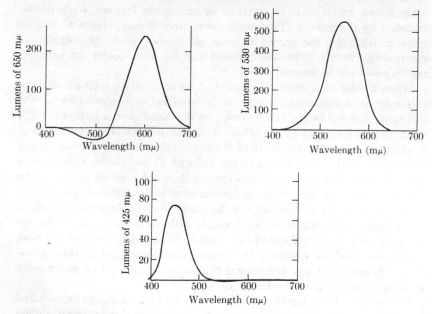

Fig. 45–3. Number of lumens of each of three monochromatic components required to match 1 watt of monochromatic radiant flux.

The ordinates of the three curves give the number of lumens of each component such that an additive mixture matches one watt of radiant flux at the indicated wavelength.

If other components had been used, a different set of curves would have been obtained. It is possible, however, to compute what the curves would be for any other set of components, so experiments need be performed with one set of components only. The International Commission on Illumination (the I.C.I.) in 1931 agreed to express all color mixture data in terms of three components so chosen that the curves corresponding to those in Fig. 45–3 were everywhere above the x-axis. This avoids the use of negative numbers in calculations. The standard I.C.I components lie outside the realm of real colors, but this is not of importance, since the amounts of the components that would be required for a match are found by mathematical methods. As long as we agree to specify colors in terms of the same set of components, one set is as good as another.

45–4 The chromaticity diagram. Let A, B, and C represent the amounts of the three I.C.I. components needed to match a spectrum color. For convenience, three new quantities x, y, and z are now defined by the equations

$$x = \frac{A}{A + B + C}, \quad y = \frac{B}{A + B + C}, \quad z = \frac{C}{A + B + C}. \quad (45\text{--}1)$$

Evidently, $x + y + z = 1$, so that any two of these quantities are sufficient to define a color. This makes it possible to represent colors in

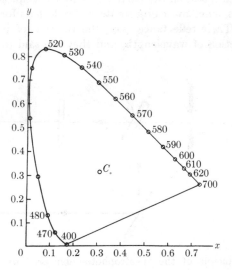

Fig. 45–4. Chromaticity diagram showing spectrum locus and illuminant C.

a two-dimensional diagram. The quantities x and y are the ones plotted. When the procedure above is carried out for spectrum colors one obtains the tongue-shaped curve in Fig. 45–4, called the *spectrum locus*. The numbers on the curve are wavelengths in millimicrons. The ends of the curve, at 400 mμ and 700 mμ, are connected by a straight line. The figure is called a *chromaticity diagram*.

The amounts of the I.C.I. components needed to match *any arbitrary color* (that is, a mixture of light of many different wavelengths) can be found by an integration process. The values of x and y for the arbitrary color are then computed by Eq. (45–1) and the point representing this color can then be plotted in the chromaticity diagram.

Point C in Fig. 45–4 is plotted from the values of x and y obtained when the procedure above is carried out for the light from a certain standard source known as "illuminant C" and which is a good approximation to average daylight or "white light." (There is no unique definition of "white light." Average daylight, sunlight, and skylight may all be considered "white," although the radiant flux at each wavelength is widely different in the three. In the absence of an accepted definition, we shall consider the light from illuminant C as "white.") Point C is called the "white point."

45–5 Spectrophotometry. We see objects by means of the light they reflect. (For simplicity, the discussion will be limited to opaque, nonself-luminous objects.) The color of the reflected light depends on the color of the incident light, and on the particular way the color is modified in the reflection process, since most objects do not reflect uniformly throughout the spectrum. Their reflectance (i.e., the fraction of incident light reflected) is a function of wavelength, and they are said to exhibit *selective reflection*.

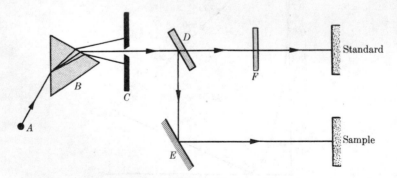

FIG. 45–5. Principle of the spectrophotometer used to measure spectral reflectance.

The methods of measuring the reflectance of an object at each wavelength constitute one branch of the science of *spectrophotometry*. The principle of one type of spectrophotometer is shown in Fig. 45–5. Light from a source A is dispersed by prism B, and a narrow range of wavelengths is isolated by slit C. The beam passing through the slit is divided at D into two beams of equal intensity by a half-silvered mirror or its equivalent. The transmitted beam strikes a standard white surface of magnesium oxide, while the reflected beam, after reflection from mirror E, strikes the surface of the sample. The latter, in general, has a lower reflectance than the standard white, so it appears less bright than the standard. The quantity of light striking the standard may be reduced by a device shown schematically at F, until sample and standard appear equally bright. If, for example, the light incident on the standard must be reduced by 50% to secure a brightness match, the reflectance of the sample at this wavelength is 50%. By repeating the measurement at other wavelengths, the complete reflectance curve of the sample may be obtained.

Figure 45–6 is a photograph of an automatic recording photoelectric spectrophotometer developed by Professor A. C. Hardy of M. I. T. In this instrument the standard and sample are viewed by a photoelectric cell, the amplified current from which is used to adjust the light beams until equal quantities of light are reflected from standard and sample. The reflectance curve is drawn automatically on a sheet of coordinate paper. The color version of Fig. 45–7 given in the frontispiece shows six colored rectangles. Beside each is its reflectance curve, re-plotted on a smaller scale from the curve drawn by the recording spectrophotometer. Notice carefully that each sample reflects to some extent throughout the entire spectrum. That is, it is not true that the yellow sample reflects only yellow, the green sample only green, etc.

The reflectance curve of a material tells us only how the material modifies the light incident on it. The exact nature of the reflected light depends on the nature of the incident light as well. If the six samples in Fig. 45–7 are all illuminated by monochromatic light, say a green of wavelength 500 mμ, all will look green, but with a brightness that depends on their individual reflectances at this wavelength. Hence to specify the colors of the samples we must also specify the kind of light by which they are illuminated. If we specify illuminant C (average daylight) then the nature of the reflected light is perfectly definite and the values of x and y for the reflected light can be computed. When this is done, one obtains the points represented by the small circles in the chromaticity diagrams opposite each sample. Thus not only the pure spectrum colors and the "white" point, but all possible colors, can be plotted in the diagram.

Fig. 45–6. Automatic recording photoelectric spectrophotometer. The sample and the standard white can be seen in the foreground, and a portion of the reflectance curve on the cylinder at the left. (Courtesy of General Electric Co.)

FIGURE 45–7

The following two pages show reflectance curves and chromaticities for six color samples. This figure is shown in color in the frontispiece.

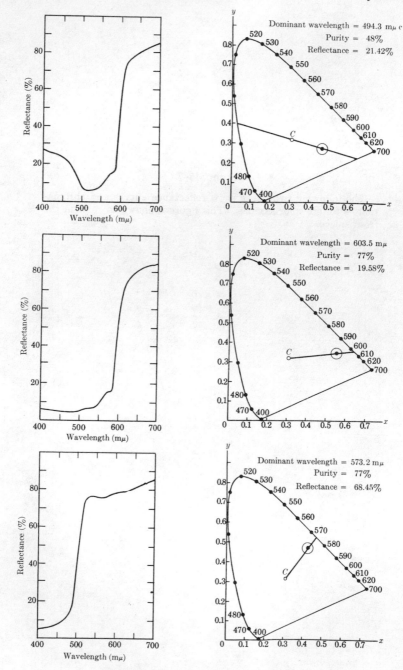

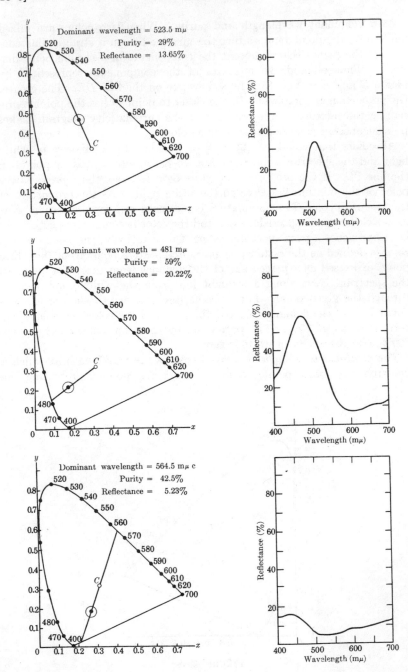

45–6 Dominant wavelength and purity. When two colors are mixed additively, the point representing the mixture lies on a straight line connecting the points that represent the components in a chromaticity diagram. Thus all additive mixtures of the components represented by points D and E in Fig. 45–8 lie somewhere on the line DE. The greater the proportion of component D, the closer to point D lies the point representing the mixture. This property of the chromaticity diagram makes possible another means of specifying a color.

All colors that could be obtained or matched by a mixture of white light and the spectrum color G, in Fig. 45–8, are represented by points on the line CG. If the proportion of white light is large, the representative point of the mixture lies close to the white point. As the proportion of the spectrum color G in the mixture is increased, the representative point moves closer to the spectrum locus and the color becomes more saturated, i.e., approaches a pure spectrum color. Quantitatively, the *purity* of any color is defined as the distance of its representative point from the white point, expressed as a percentage of the distance from the white point to the spectrum locus along a straight line from the white point passing through the given point. For example, the distance CF in Fig. 45–8 is about 75% of the distance CG, and the purity of the color represented by point F is about 75%. The purity of any spectrum color is, of course, 100%, and the purity of white is zero.

The *dominant wavelength* of a given color is the wavelength at which a line from the white point, passing through the point representing the

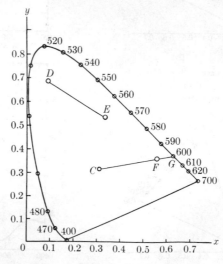

FIGURE 45–8

color, intersects the spectrum locus. The dominant wavelength of color
F in Fig. 45-8 is 600 mμ. The specification of a color in terms of dominant
wavelength and purity enables the appearance of the color to be visualized more readily than does its description in terms of the amounts of
three components required for a match. The dominant wavelengths and
purities of the samples in Fig. 45-7 are indicated on their respective
chromaticity diagrams.

One other property of a sample such as those in Fig. 45-7 must be specified. If the reflectance of a sample were to be increased or decreased at
each wavelength in correct proportion, the dominant wavelength and
purity would remain unchanged, but the brightness of the sample (with a
constant illumination) would be different. Hence the samples are not
completely described by their dominant wavelength and purity, but the
value of their *average reflectance* must be included also. This is computed
from the reflectance curve, weighted by the standard luminosity curve of
Fig. 44-7.

The "color of an object" is understood to include a statement of its
average reflectance, together with the dominant wavelength and purity
of the light it reflects, all with reference to a stated illuminant. For example, the green sample in Fig. 45-7 has an average reflectance of 13.7%,
a dominant wavelength of 523.5 mμ, and a purity of 29%, all referred to
illuminant C.

The dominant wavelength of a color, although it is not the same thing
as the sensation of hue evoked by the color, does correspond to hue in

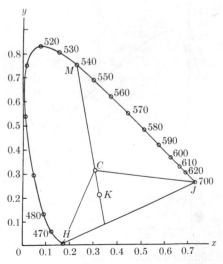

Fig. 45-9. The color at K is a purple, complementary to the spectrum at M.

somewhat the same way that the wavelength of a sound wave corresponds
to the sensation of pitch evoked by the wave. Similarly, the purity of a
color corresponds to the sensation of saturation.

Colors having representative points within the triangle HCJ in Fig. 45–9
are described as purples or magentas. Since lines from the white point
through points in this triangle do not intersect the spectrum locus, purples
cannot be matched by a mixture of white and a spectrum color. They
are called *nonspectral* colors. The dominant wavelength of a purple is
obtained by extending a line from its representative point through the
white point until it intersects the spectrum locus. The dominant wavelength of the color at K, in Fig. 45–9, is that of the spectrum color at
point M. Purple samples reflect more strongly in the red and blue, and
less so in the green, and may be described as "minus greens." From the
properties of the chromaticity diagram it can be seen that the purple at
K, in Fig. 45–9, and the spectrum color at M, could be combined in proper
proportions to match illuminant C, or white light. When two colors can
be added to obtain white they are called *complementary*. The spectrum
color at M is a green, and is complementary to the purple or minus green
at K. This is indicated by the suffix c following a statement of the wavelength of the spectrum color at M. (See Fig. 45–7.)

The purity of a color in the region HCJ in Fig. 45–9 is defined as the
distance of its representative point from the white point, expressed as a
percentage of the distance from the white point to the line HJ joining the

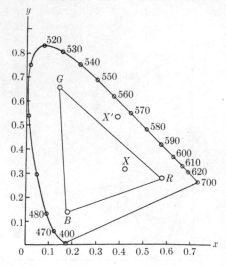

Fig. 45–10. All additive mixtures of components R, G, and B are represented
by points within the triangle RGB.

extremities of the spectrum locus. The purity of the color at K in Fig. 45–9 is about 45%.

Any real color can be considered an additive mixture of spectrum colors. It follows that the representative point of any real color must lie somewhere within the region bounded by the spectrum locus and the straight line joining its extremities. This region is called the *locus of real colors*.

It can now be understood why a wide gamut of colors, but not all colors, can be matched by an additive mixture of three properly chosen (real) components. Suppose the three components are represented by points R, G, and B in Fig. 45–10. All additive mixtures of B and G lie on the line BG. By adding component R to one of these mixtures, any color, such as X within the triangle RGB can be matched. A color such as X' could not be matched by mixtures of R, G, and B, but if B were added to X' in such proportions that the mixture were represented by a point on the line RG, this color could then be matched by a mixture of R and G.

It will also be seen that there is no set of real primaries such that the triangle of which they form the corners will include all real colors, but that the widest gamut of colors can be matched if the components are a highly saturated (or a spectrum) red, green, and blue.

45–7 The subtractive method of color mixing. Curves A and B, Fig. 45–11, are the transmittance curves of a blue and yellow filter respectively. Suppose the two filters are placed in contact, and inserted in a beam of white light from a projection lantern. We wish to find the color of the transmitted light.

Let the light pass first through the blue and then through the yellow filter. At each wavelength, curve A gives the fraction of the incident light transmitted by the blue filter, and curve B gives the *fraction of this fraction* transmitted by the yellow filter. Thus at 500 mμ, 69% of the incident light is transmitted by the blue filter, and 58% of 69%, or 40%, is transmitted through the yellow filter. Hence the transmittance of the combination is found by multiplying the transmittance curves of the filters together, wavelength by wavelength. The resulting curve is C, Fig. 45–11. Evidently the final result is the same if the light passes first through the yellow and then through the blue filter. The transmittance curve has a maximum in the central portion of the spectrum, and the hue of the transmitted light will be green. Since each filter subtracts some energy from the light incident upon it, this method of mixing colors is called a *subtractive* process.

The colors obtained by mixing paints and inks are produced by a subtractive process. In the first place, let us consider an opaque white

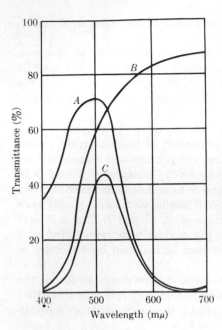

FIG. 45–11. Subtractive color mixing.

paint or ink. Its base is a liquid "vehicle," usually linseed oil. The vehicle is quite colorless and transparent. Suspended in it are tiny particles of equally colorless and transparent material, such as an oxide of lead, zinc, or titanium. The index of refraction of the suspended material must be as different as possible from that of the vehicle. We have seen that whenever light is incident on a surface bounding two media of different indices of refraction, some of the light is reflected at the surface. Consider a ray striking the surface of the white paint, Fig. 45–12. Some light will be reflected at the air-vehicle surface, since there is a change in index at this surface. The remainder penetrates into the paint and strikes a boundary between vehicle and suspended particle, where again a portion is reflected. The reflected part returns through the surface, and the part remaining penetrates further, a portion being reflected at each boundary surface which it crosses. Since reflection occurs whatever the wavelength of the incident light, the paint reflects uniformly throughout the spectrum or, in other words, it is "white." Note that its white "color" is not produced by suspending white particles in the vehicle, but is due simply to a difference in index between particle and vehicle, both of which are transparent.

If a colored paint or ink is desired, the suspended particles are dyed the desired color, or other dyed particles are added to the white paint. The dyed particles then behave like tiny filters in the path of the light rays in the paint. The light reflected back out of the paint must pass through many of these filters on its way in and out, each filter absorbing some of the light incident upon it. The spectral distribution of the incident light is modified by this absorption, and we say that the paint is colored.

Suppose that a blue and a yellow paint are mixed. Then the light rays in the paint will pass through both blue and yellow filters before making their way out of the surface (Fig. 45–13). The effect is the same as that produced when a blue and yellow filter are placed "in series" in

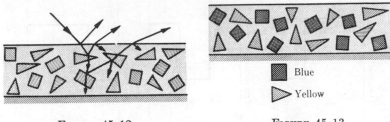

FIGURE 45-12   FIGURE 45-13

the path of a light beam. If the paint mixture is illuminated by white light, then green will predominate in the reflected light, and the hue of a mixture of blue and yellow pigments is green.

In three-color printing processes, where one ink is printed over another, it is necessary that the inks be transparent. That is, only a small portion of the light should be reflected, and most of it transmitted. This result is secured by using suspended particles whose index is nearly the same as that of the vehicle. The inks are printed one over the other on white paper, and the incident light passes through them, is reflected from the white paper, and passes through the inks again on its way out.

45-8 Subtractive "primaries." As explained in Section 45-6, a wide gamut of colors can be matched by *additive* mixtures of a red, a green, and a blue component. The amounts of each component in the mixture are controlled, say, by rheostats in the circuit of each of three projection lanterns. When colors are reproduced by printing inks, or by the dyes in a color photograph, the mixture is *subtractive* and control is obtained by varying the density with which each ink is printed, or the concentration of each dye.

The particular portion of the spectrum that each ink or dye controls is that portion in which it *absorbs*. The greater the density or concentration, the more light is absorbed; the smaller the concentration, the less light is absorbed.

The widest gamut of colors can be secured in a three-color subtractive process, i.e., one using three inks or dyes, if the same colors are *controlled* that give the widest gamut in an additive process, namely, a red, a green, and a blue. Note carefully that this does not imply that the inks or dyes are red, green, and blue. The ideal dyes would have transmittances as shown in Fig. 45-14, which apply to one particular concentration. The dye in Fig. 45-14(a) absorbs only in the red, that in (b) absorbs only in the green, that in (c) absorbs only in the blue. If the concentrations were greater, less light would be transmitted (or more absorbed) in the red, green, and blue respectively. If the concentrations were less, less

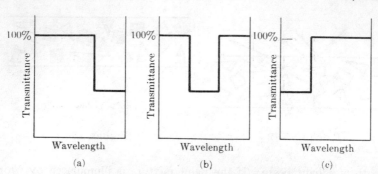

FIG. 45-14. Transmittance curves of ideal dyes for a three-color subtractive process.

light would be absorbed and more transmitted. Dyes or inks having the ideally sharp cut-offs of Fig. 45-14 are not available. Transmittance curves of the dyes used in the Eastman "wash-off relief" process for making color prints are shown in Fig. 45-15. It will be seen that they approximate the idealized curves. The three dyes in Fig. 45-15 can be described as a "minus-red," a "minus-green," and a "minus-blue." The hue of the "minus-red" dye, when printed on a white surface and viewed by white light, is blue. The hue of the "minus-green" is a reddish purple or magenta. That of the "minus-blue" is yellow. The "minus-green" or magenta is usually (but erroneously) described as "red."

There is a common belief that "the primary colors are red, yellow, and blue." This mistaken impression comes about in part as a result of the incorrect description of the magenta dye or ink used in color reproduction as "red," and in part because of the failure to appreciate the nature of the subtractive process, i.e., each dye or ink controls the particular region of the spectrum in which it absorbs. The three colors *controlled* by the three dyes in Fig. 45-15 are the same as those that would give a wide gamut of colors in an additive process, namely, red, green, and blue. The blue, or "minus-red" dye, controls the red; the magenta, or "minus-green" dye, controls the green; the yellow, or "minus-blue" dye, controls the blue.

Because the actual inks used in color printing, even when printed in maximum concentration, do not absorb to a sufficient extent to give good blacks, a fourth plate is usually used to accentuate the blacks. Hence the process is referred to as a "four-color process."

Three of the colored rectangles in Fig. 45-7 are printed with the "primary" inks of a four-color process. These are the magenta at the upper left (minus green), the yellow at the lower left (minus blue), and the blue or cyan at the center right (minus red). The orange at the center left is obtained by printing the magenta ink over the yellow ink, the

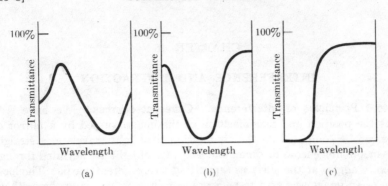

Fig. 45–15.   Transmittance curves of the three dyes used in the Eastman "wash-off relief" process.

green at the upper right by printing the yellow over the blue, and the purple at the lower right by printing the magenta over the blue. The reader will find it instructive to trace the reflectance curves for the yellow and blue inks on tracing paper and to place this composite curve over the reflectance curve of the green sample.

CHAPTER 46

INTERFERENCE AND DIFFRACTION

46–1 Principles of interference. Coherent sources. We have seen that the position and magnification of the image formed by a mirror or lens can be computed on the assumption that light travels in a straight line in a homogeneous medium, and that rays of light are deviated through definite angles at the surfaces separating two different media. The location of an image was seen to be a problem in geometry, and the methods used are those of *geometrical optics*.

In this chapter we shall discuss the phenomena of interference and diffraction, for whose understanding the principles of geometrical optics do not suffice. Instead, we must return to the more fundamental point of view that light is a wave motion, and that the effect of a number of wave trains arriving at one point on a screen depends upon the phases of the waves as well as upon their amplitudes. This part of the subject is called *physical optics*.

At any point where two or more trains of waves cross one another they are said to *interfere*. This does not mean that any wave train is impeded by the presence of the others, but refers to the combined effect for them all at the point in question. The *principle of superposition* states that the resultant displacement at any point and at any instant may be found by adding the instantaneous displacements that would be produced at the point by the individual wave trains if each were present alone. The term "displacement" as used here is a general one. If one is considering surface ripples on a liquid, the displacement means the actual displacement of the surface above or below its normal level. If the waves are sound waves, the term refers to the excess or deficiency of pressure. If the waves are electromagnetic, the displacement means the magnitude of the electric or magnetic field intensity.

The fundamental problem under consideration is the effect at one point on a screen when light waves coming from different sources arrive at this point. Suppose, for the sake of simplicity, we have two sources. If the waves leaving these sources start in phase, travel different paths, and then come together on a screen, they *may* arrive in phase. If this is the case, they will reinforce each other. But this reinforcement may last only a very short time, for one of the sources may undergo a sudden phase shift, after which the two wave trains from the two sources will not start in phase. When these new waves arrive together at the screen, they may not reinforce. It is a fundamental property of the atoms or molecules of

904

a source of light that they are continually undergoing transitions which produce frequent haphazard phase changes in the light which they emit.

To produce observable interference effects, *it is necessary to have two sources emitting light waves which, at the start, are always in phase. This can never be accomplished with two separate sources.* Even if the light waves from separate sources were in phase at one moment, they would shortly get out of phase. To ensure the existence of two light waves leaving two points always in phase, *it is necessary to start with only one light wave* and to split this wave into two parts, each of which travels a different path, the two waves eventually meeting at the same point on a screen. In these circumstances, any haphazard changes of phase which the original light wave undergoes are shared by the two parts, which therefore leave their respective starting points always in phase. Two points of this sort are called *coherent sources.*

Let S_2 and S_3 in Fig. 46-1 represent two coherent *point* sources on the line xO, and P a point in a vertical plane for which the path difference $PS_2 - PS_3$ is some whole number of wavelengths $m\lambda$. The vibrations at P due to the two waves will therefore be in phase and the two waves will reinforce each other at this point. Reinforcement will also take place at point P' in a horizontal plane if $P'S_2 = PS_2$ and $P'S_3 = PS_3$. In fact, at all points of the circle through P and P', with center at O, the

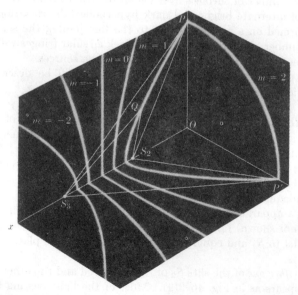

Fig. 46-1. Curves of maximum intensity in the interference pattern of two monochromatic point sources.

waves from the two sources will reinforce, and a bright circular *interference fringe* will appear on a vertical screen through P and P', perpendicular to the line xO.

Point Q in Fig. 46–1 is another point for which the path difference $QS_2 - QS_3$ is also $m\lambda$, and the curve passing through P and Q is the locus of all such points in the vertical plane. This curve is a hyperbola, a curve which has the property that the difference between the distances from any point on it to two fixed points is a constant. If we imagine this hyperbola to be rotated about the line xO as an axis, it sweeps out a surface called a *hyperboloid*, and we see that the waves from S_2 and S_3 will arrive at *all* points of this surface so as to reinforce one another.

The diagram of Fig. 46–1 has been drawn for the simple case where the distance from S_2 to S_3 is 3λ, and where the path difference $PS_2 - PS_3$ $= 2\lambda$ ($m = 2$). The hyperbola lettered $m = 1$ is the locus of points in a vertical plane for which the path difference is λ. The locus of all points for which the path difference is zero ($m = 0$) is a line passing through the midpoint of S_2S_3. Hyperbolas for which $m = -1$ and $m = -2$ are also shown. Rotation of these curves about xO gives rise, in this case, to five hyperboloids. Bright lines will appear on a screen in any position, along those curves where the hyperboloids intersect the screen.

If the distance between the sources is many wavelengths, there will be a large number of surfaces over which the waves reinforce, and a large number of alternate bright and dark hyperbolic (almost straight) fringes will be formed on a screen parallel to the line joining the sources. Also, a great number of alternate bright and dark circular fringes will be formed on a screen perpendicular to the line joining the sources.

The experimental realization of these ideas will be described in the next section.

46–2 Young's experiment and Pohl's experiment. One of the earliest demonstrations of the fact that light can produce interference effects was performed in 1800 by the English scientist Thomas Young. The experiment was a crucial one at the time, since it added further evidence to the growing belief in the wave nature of light. A corpuscular theory was quite inadequate to account for the effects observed.

Young's apparatus is shown in Fig. 46–2(a). Light from a source at the left (not shown) falls on a narrow slit S_1. Two more slits, S_2 and S_3, are parallel to S_1 and equidistant from it. A screen is placed at the right of the slits.

When *either one* of the slits S_2 or S_3 is covered and the other is open, the screen appears as in Fig. 46–3(a). Most of the light passing through the slit falls in the central bright band, but some is "bent" outward to form the fainter bands on each side of the center. This effect is called *diffraction* and is discussed in Section 46–7.

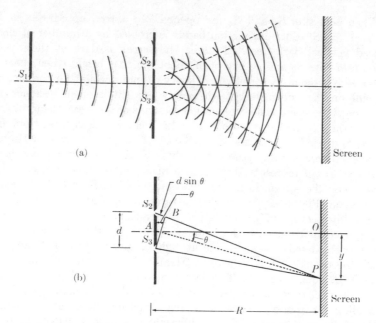

(a)

Screen

(b)

Screen

FIG. 46–2. Interference of light waves passing through two slits. Young's experiment.

(a)

(b)

FIG. 46–3. (a) Diffraction bands produced by light passing through a single narrow slit.   (b) Interference bands or fringes produced when light passes simultaneously through two closely spaced parallel slits.

When *both* slits S_2 and S_3 are opened, the screen appears as in Fig. 46–3(b). Each of the diffraction bands is crossed by a number of closely spaced vertical dark lines. That is, the screen is dark at these points when *both* slits S_2 and S_3 are open, although it is bright when *either one* of the slits is open. A corpuscular theory cannot account for the fact that a point on the screen, bright when only one slit is open, becomes dark when both are open. The explanation in terms of the wave theory follows.

According to Huygens' principle, cylindrical wavelets spread out from slit S_1 and reach slits S_2 and S_3 at the same instant. A train of Huygens wavelets diverges from both of these slits, which therefore act as coherent sources. Let d represent the distance between the slits, and consider a point P on the screen, in a direction making an angle θ with the axis of the system [Fig. 46–2(b)]. With P as a center and PS_3 as radius, strike an arc intersecting PS_2 at B. If the distance R from slits to screen is large in comparison with the distance d between the slits, the arc S_3B can be considered a straight line at right angles to PS_3, PA, and PS_2. Then the triangle BS_2S_3 is a right triangle, similar to POA, and the distance S_2B equals $d \sin \theta$. This latter distance is the difference in path length between the waves reaching P from the two slits. The waves spreading out from S_2 and S_3 necessarily start in phase, but they will not be in phase at P because of this difference in length of path. According to the principles discussed in the preceding section, complete reinforcement will take place at the point P, that is, P will lie at the center of a bright interference fringe when the path difference $d \sin \theta$ is some integral number of wavelengths, say $m\lambda$ ($m = 0,1,2,3$, etc.). Thus

$$d \sin \theta = m\lambda,$$

or

$$\sin \theta = \frac{m\lambda}{d}.$$

Now λ is of the order 5×10^{-5} cm, while d cannot be made much smaller than about 10^{-2} cm. As a rule, only the first five to ten fringes are bright enough to be seen, so that m is at most, say, 10. Therefore, the very largest value of $\sin \theta$ is

$$\sin \theta \text{ (maximum)} = \frac{10 \times 5 \times 10^{-5} \text{ cm}}{10^{-2} \text{ cm}} = 0.05,$$

which corresponds to an angle of only 3°.

The central bright fringe at point O, or zeroth fringe ($m = 0$), corresponds to zero path difference, or $\sin \theta = 0$. If point P is at the center of the mth fringe, the distance y from the zeroth to the mth fringe is, from Fig. 46–2(b),

$$y = R \tan \theta.$$

Since, however, the angle θ for all values of m is extremely small,

$$y = R \sin \theta.$$

Therefore

$$y = R \frac{m\lambda}{d},$$

and

$$\lambda = \frac{yd}{mR}. \qquad (46\text{–}1)$$

Hence by measuring the distance between the slits, the distance to the screen, and the distance from the central fringe to some fringe on either side, the wavelength of the light producing the interference pattern may be computed.

EXAMPLE. With two slits spaced 0.2 mm apart, and a screen at a distance of one meter, the third bright fringe is found to be displaced 7.5 mm from the central fringe. Find the wavelength of the light used.

Let λ be the unknown wavelength in centimeters. Then

$$\lambda = \frac{yd}{mR} = \frac{0.75 \text{ cm} \times 0.02 \text{ cm}}{3 \times 100 \text{ cm}} = 5 \times 10^{-5} \text{ cm} = 500 \text{ m}\mu.$$

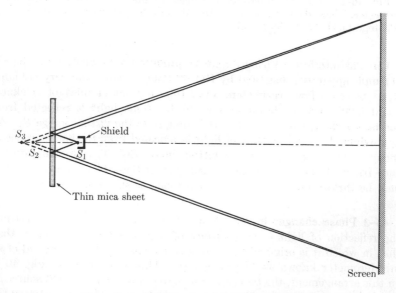

FIG. 46–4. Pohl's mica sheet interferometer.

FIG. 46–5.   Circular interference fringes produced by Pohl's mica interferometer.   The dark rectangle is the shadow of the mercury arc housing. (Photographed by I. Antman.)

Circular interference fringes may be produced very easily with the aid of simple apparatus suggested by Robert Pohl. A small mercury arc lamp S_1 is placed a few centimeters away from a sheet of mica of thickness about 0.002 inch, as shown in Fig. 46–4. Some light is reflected from the first surface, as though it were issuing from the virtual image S_2. An approximately equal amount of light is reflected from the back surface as though it were coming from the virtual image S_3. The circular interference fringes formed by the light issuing from these two coherent sources may be thrown on the entire wall of a room, as shown in Fig. 46–5.

46–3 Phase changes in reflection. A very important fact concerning the reflection of light from a surface of higher index of refraction than that in which it is originally traveling is demonstrated with the aid of an interferometer known as *Lloyd's mirror*. This is depicted in Fig. 46–6. In this arrangement, the two coherent sources are the actual slit source S_1 and its virtual image S_2. The fringes formed by interference between the

FIG. 46-6. Lloyd's mirror. When the ocular is focused on the edge B of the glass block, the fringe nearest the edge is black.

light waves from these coherent sources may be viewed on a ground glass screen placed anywhere beyond the mirror. If, instead of viewing the fringes on a screen, an ocular is used to view the fringes that form in space in a plane passing through the edge B, the fringe nearest this edge is seen to be black. This is the fringe corresponding to zero path difference, and if the two wave trains giving rise to this fringe had both traveled in air or had both been reflected from glass, this fringe would have been bright. The zeroth fringe, however, was formed by two wave trains, one of which had undergone reflection from the glass and one of which had proceeded directly from S_1. The fact that the zeroth fringe is black indicates that *the waves reflected from glass have undergone a phase shift of* 180°. In other words, the wave train has gained (or lost) half a wavelength in the process of reflection.

46-4 Interference in thin films. The brilliant colors that are often seen when light is reflected from a soap bubble or from a thin layer of oil floating on water are produced by interference effects between the two trains of light waves reflected at opposite surfaces of the thin films of soap solution or of oil. In Fig. 46-7, the line ab is one ray in a beam of mono-chromatic light incident on the upper surface of a thin film. The lines at right angles to ab indicate the wave surfaces in the incident beam.

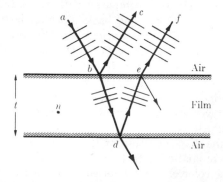

FIG. 46-7. Interference between light waves reflected from the upper and lower surfaces of a thin film.

A part of the incident light is reflected at the first surface, as indicated by ray *bc*, and a part, represented by *bd*, is transmitted. At the second surface a part is again reflected and of this a part emerges as represented by ray *ef*. Lines at right angles to *bc* and *ef* represent wave surfaces. If the beam has appreciable width, the wave surfaces will overlap and the reflected wave trains can produce interference effects.

For simplicity, we shall assume that light is incident at right angles to the film. Let t represent the thickness of the film and n its index of refraction. If λ is the wavelength of the light waves in air, the wavelength in the film is λ/n, and the number of waves contained in the path length through the film and back, or $2t$, is $2t/(\lambda/n)$. Suppose this is some integral number. Then a wave surface in the light that has traveled through the film and back emerges from the film at the same time that a wave surface in the incident wave train arrives at and is reflected from the film. If no other considerations were involved, the waves reflected from the two surfaces would be in the correct relation to interfere *constructively*, that is, their displacements would add. However, at the upper surface the light is reflected from a medium of index greater than that in which it is traveling, while the reverse is true at the lower surface. As was shown with Lloyd's mirror, when a train of waves is reflected at the surface of a medium of higher index, the reflected wave train loses (or gains) half a wavelength. Hence the waves that have traveled through the film and back are exactly out of phase with the waves reflected at the upper surface and the wave trains interfere *destructively*. In other words, if the path length through the film and back contains an integral number of waves, no light is reflected. It can be seen without further detailed explanation that if the path length through the film and back contains some integral number of waves *plus half a wave*, conditions are right for constructive interference and there will be strong reflection.

If the film is extremely thin compared with the wavelength of light, the path length through the film and back is negligible and the only outstanding effect is the loss of half a wavelength in the waves reflected at the first surface. Then, regardless of wavelength, the waves reflected from the two surfaces are out of step and destroy one another. Hence no light is reflected and the film appears black by reflected light. (There is no violation of the principle of conservation of energy in destructive interference, since whatever energy is absent in the reflected light is found in the transmitted light.)

If the film is in the shape of a thin wedge of narrow angle, and is viewed by reflected monochromatic light, it will appear to be crossed by parallel bright bands of the color of the light used, separated by dark bands. At the apex, the film will be dark. At a distance from the apex such that the film thickness is one-quarter of a wavelength, it will be bright. Where the thickness equals one-half a wavelength it will be dark, and so on. If the film is illuminated first by blue, then by red light, the spacing of the red bands is greater than that of the blue, as is to be expected from the greater wavelength of the red light. The bands produced by intermediate wavelengths occupy intermediate positions. If the film is illuminated by white light, its color at any point is that due to the mixture of those colors which may be reflected at that point, while the colors for which the thickness is such as to result in destructive interference are absent. Just those colors which are absent in the reflected light, however, are found to predominate in the transmitted light. At any point, the color of the film by reflected light is complementary to its color by transmitted light.

The frontispiece is reproduced from a Kodachrome photograph of the light reflected from a thin film of soap solution. The film is formed on a glass ring and mounted in a vertical plane. As a result of drainage of the liquid in a downward direction, the thickness of the film increases from top to bottom. The black section at the top indicates that the thickness in this region is less than one-quarter of the wavelength of light.

The phenomenon of interference is utilized in the production of so-called "nonreflecting" glass. A thin layer or film of transparent material is deposited on the surface of the glass, as in Fig. 46–8. If the index of this material is properly chosen at some value intermediate between that of air and the glass, equal quantities of light will be reflected from its outer surface, and from the boundary surface between it and the glass. Furthermore, since in both reflections the light is reflected from a medium of greater index than that in which it is traveling, the same phase change occurs in each reflection. It follows that if the film thickness is one-quarter wavelength (normal incidence is assumed), the light reflected from the first surface will be 180° out of phase with that reflected from the second, and complete destructive interference will result.

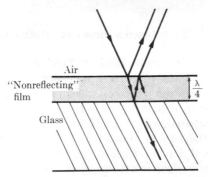

Fig. 46–8. Destructive interference results when the film thickness is one-quarter of a wavelength.

The thickness can, of course, be one-quarter wavelength for one particular wavelength only. This is usually chosen in the yellow-green portion of the spectrum, where the eye is most sensitive. Some reflection then takes place at both longer and shorter wavelengths and the reflected light has a purple hue. The over-all reflection from a lens or prism surface can be reduced in this way from 4 or 5 percent to a fraction of 1 percent. The treatment is highly effective in eliminating stray reflected light and increasing the contrast in an image formed by highly corrected lenses having a large number of air-glass surfaces.

46–5 Newton's rings. If the convex surface of a lens is placed in contact with a plane glass plate, as in Fig. 46–9, a thin film of air is formed between the two surfaces. The thickness of this film is very small at the point of contact, gradually increasing as one proceeds outward. The loci of points of equal thickness are circles concentric with the point of contact. Such a film is found to exhibit interference colors, produced in the same way as the colors in a thin soap film. The interference bands are circular, concentric with the point of contact. When viewed by reflected light, the center of the pattern is black, as is a thin soap film. Note that in this case there is no phase reversal of the light reflected from the upper surface of the film (which here is of smaller index than that of the medium in which the light is traveling before reflection), but the phase of the wave reflected from the lower surface is reversed. When viewed by transmitted light, the center of the pattern is bright. If white light is used, the color of the light reflected from the film at any point is complementary to the color transmitted.

Fig. 46–9. Air film between a convex and a plane surface.

These interference bands were studied by Newton, and are called after him, *Newton's rings*. Figure 46–10 is a photograph of Newton's rings, formed by the air film between a convex and a plane surface.

The surface of an optical part which is being ground to some desired curvature may be compared with that of another surface, known to be correct, by bringing the two in contact and observing the interference fringes. For example, if a plane surface (an "optical flat") is desired, a glass plate whose lower surface is accurately plane is placed over the surface to be tested. If both surfaces are accurately plane, and if contact between them is made at one edge, a series of straight interference fringes,

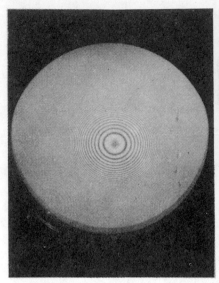

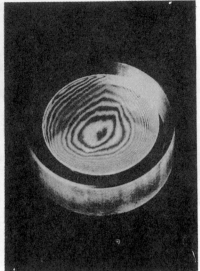

Fig. 46–10. Newton's rings formed by interference in the air film between a convex and a plane surface. (Courtesy of Bausch & Lomb Optical Co.)

Fig. 46–11. The surface of a telescope objective under inspection during manufacture. (Courtesy of Bausch & Lomb Optical Co.)

parallel to the line of contact, will be observed. If the surface being ground is not plane, the interference bands will be curved. By noting the shape and separation of the fringes, the departure of the surface from the desired form may be determined.

Figure 46–11 is a photograph made at one stage of the process of manufacturing a telescope objective. The lower, larger diameter, thicker disk is the master. The smaller upper disk is the objective under test. The "contour lines" are Newton's interference fringes, and each one indicates an additional departure of the specimen from the master of one-half a wavelength of light. That is, at 10 lines from the center spot the space between the specimen and master is 5 wavelengths, or about 0.0001 inch. This specimen is very poor.

46–6 Diffraction. According to geometrical optics, if an opaque object is placed between a point light source and a screen, as in Fig. 46–12, the edges of the object will cast a sharp shadow on the screen (the penumbra will be negligible if the source is sufficiently small). No light will reach the screen at points within the geometrical shadow, while outside the shadow the screen will be uniformly illuminated. The photograph repro-

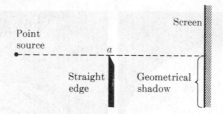

FIG. 46–12. Geometrical shadow of a straight edge.

duced in Fig. 46–13 was made by placing a razor blade halfway between a pinhole illuminated by monochromatic light and a photographic film, so that the film made a record of the shadow cast by the blade. Figure 46–14 is an enlargement of a region near the shadow of an edge of the blade. The boundary of the *geometrical* shadow is indicated by the short arrows. Notice that a small amount of light has "bent" around the edge, into the geometrical shadow, which is bordered by alternate bright and dark bands. Note also that in the first bright band, just outside the geometrical shadow, the illumination is actually greater than in the region of uniform illumination at the extreme left.

This simple experimental setup serves to give some idea of the true complexity of what is often considered the most elementary of optical phenomena, the shadow cast by a small source of light.

The reason that a diffraction pattern like that of Fig. 46–13 is not commonly observed in the shadow of an object is merely that most light sources are not point sources. If a shadow of a razor blade is cast by a frosted bulb incandescent lamp, for example, the light from every point of the surface of the lamp forms its own diffraction pattern, but these overlap to such an extent that no individual pattern can be observed.

The term *diffraction* is applied to problems in which one is concerned with *the resultant effect produced by a limited portion of a wave surface.* Since in most diffraction problems some light is found within the region of geometrical shadow, diffraction is sometimes defined as "the bending of light around an obstacle." It should be emphasized, however, that the process by which diffraction effects are produced is going on continuously in the propagation of every wave. Only if a part of the wave is cut off by some obstacle are the effects commonly called "diffraction effects" observed. But since every optical instrument does in fact make use of only a limited portion of a wave (a telescope, for example, utilizes only that portion of a wave admitted by the objective lens), it is evident that a clear comprehension of the nature of diffraction is essential for a complete understanding of practically all optical phenomena.

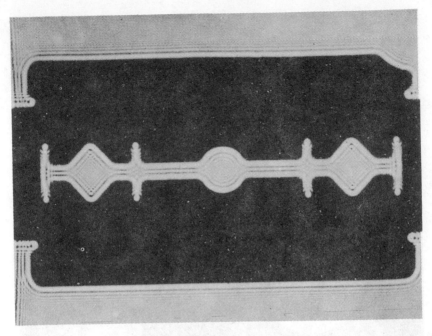

Fig. 46–13. Shadow of a razor blade.

Fig. 46–14. Shadow of a straight edge.

The main features observed in diffraction effects can be predicted with
the help of Huygens' principle, according to which every point of a wave
surface can be considered the source of a secondary wavelet which spreads
out in all directions. However, instead of finding the new wave surface
by the simple process of constructing the envelope of all the secondary

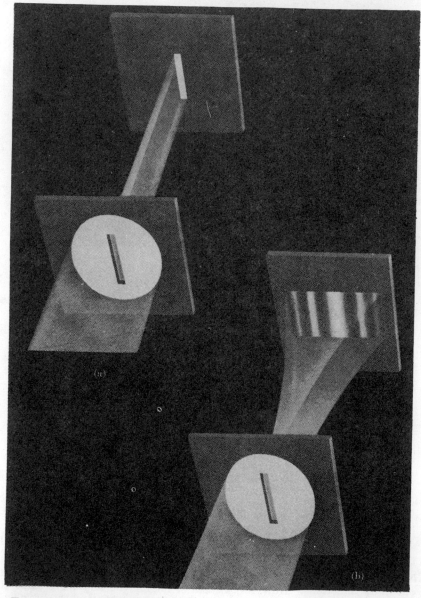

FIG. 46-15. (a) Geometrical "shadow" of a slit. (b) Diffraction pattern of a slit. The slit width has been greatly exaggerated.

wavelets, we must combine these wavelets according to the principles of interference. That is, at every point we must combine the displacements that would be produced by the secondary wavelets, taking into account their amplitudes and relative phases. The mathematical operations required are not simple (one must find the combined effect of an infinite number of infinitesimal wavelets) and it must suffice to indicate the only general ideas involved, and describe the results.

46–7 Fraunhofer diffraction by a single slit. In the drawing of Fig. 46–15, a beam of parallel monochromatic light is incident from the left on an opaque plate in which there is a narrow horizontal slit. According to the principles of geometrical optics, the transmitted beam would have the same cross section as the slit, and a screen in the path of the beam would be illuminated uniformly over an area of the same size and shape as the slit, as in part (a) of the figure. Actually, what one observes on the screen is the diffraction pattern shown in part (b). The beam spreads out vertically after passing through the slit, and the diffraction pattern consists of a central bright band, which may be much wider than the slit width, bordered by alternating dark bands and bright bands of decreasing intensity. A diffraction pattern of this nature can readily be observed by looking at a point source such as a distant street light through a narrow slit formed between two fingers in front of the eye. The retina of the eye then corresponds to the screen in Fig. 46–15.

The width of the slit in Fig. 46–15 has been greatly exaggerated for clarity. To obtain a vertical spread having the proportions shown in the figure, the slit width would have to be of the order of 5 wavelengths of light. There is also a small horizontal spreading of the beam, which has been omitted in the diagram for simplicity.

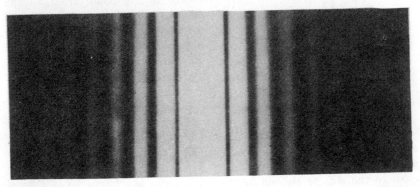

Fig. 46–16. Diffraction pattern of a single slit.

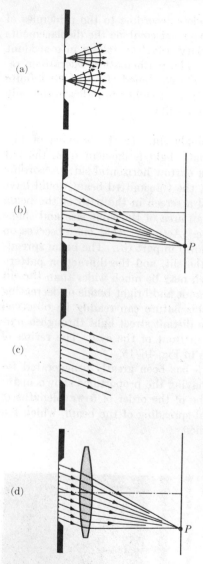

(a)

(b)

(c)

(d)

FIG. 46–17. Diffraction by a slit.

Figure 46–16 is an enlargement of a photograph made by placing a photographic film in the plane of the screen in a setup like that in Fig. 46–15.

Let us now apply Huygens' principle to compute the distribution of light on the screen. Small elements of area are obtained by subdividing the wave surface passing through the slit into narrow strips, parallel to the long edges of the slit. A section through the slit is shown in Fig. 46–17(a). The division of the wave surface into narrow strips, which are seen end on, is indicated by the short lines across the wave surface. From each of these strips, secondary wavelets spread out in all directions, as shown.

In Fig. 46–17(b), a screen is placed at the right of the slit and P is one point on a line in the screen, the line being parallel to the long edges of the slit and perpendicular to the plane of the diagram. The light reaching a point on the line is calculated by applying the principle of superposition to all the wavelets arriving at the point, from all the elementary strips of the original wave surface. Because of the varying distances to the point, and the varying angles with the original direction of the light, the amplitudes and phases of the wavelets at the point will be different.

The problem is greatly simplified when the screen is sufficiently distant, or the slit sufficiently narrow, so that all rays from the slit to a point on the screen can be considered parallel, as in Fig. 46–17(c). The former case, where the screen is relatively close to the slit (or the slit is relatively wide) is referred to as *Fresnel* diffraction, the latter as *Fraunhofer* diffraction. There is, of course, no difference in the nature of the diffraction process in the two cases, and Fresnel diffraction merges gradually into Fraunhofer diffraction as the screen is moved away from the slit, or as the slit width is decreased.

Fraunhofer diffraction occurs also if a lens is placed just beyond the slit as in Fig. 46–17(d), since the lens brings to a focus in its second focal plane all light traveling in a specified direction. That is, the lens forms in its focal plane a reduced image of the pattern that would appear on an infinitely distant screen in the absence of the lens.

The photograph in Fig. 46–16 is a Fraunhofer diffraction pattern.

Some of the important aspects of Fraunhofer diffraction by a slit can be deduced very easily. Consider the two extremely narrow strips in the wave passing through a slit, one just below the upper edge of the slit and the other just below its center line, as in Fig. 46–18, and the wavelets from these strips that travel in a direction making an angle α with the direction of the incident light. The two wave trains start out from the plane of the original wave surface in phase, but the upper one has to travel a greater distance than the lower before reaching the screen. This additional distance, from Fig. 46–18, is

$$D/2 \sin \alpha,$$

where D is the slit width.

For those points on the screen that lie on a line through O, opposite the center of the slit, the angle α is zero and the path difference is zero. The wavelets from *all* strips on the transmitted wave surface therefore reach points on this line in phase with one another, their amplitudes add, and the center of the diffraction pattern is bright. As we consider points

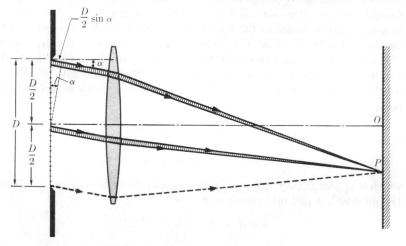

FIG. 46–18. Diffraction by a single slit.

farther and farther out from the center, the angle α increases and the path difference increases. When the path difference has become equal to one-half a wavelength, the wavelets from the two strips in Fig. 46–18 reach the screen out of phase and complete destructive interference results. The path difference between the wavelets from the two strips next below those in Fig. 46–18 is also one-half wavelength, so that these two wavelets cancel each other also. Proceeding in this way, it is seen that the light from each element in the upper half of the slit is canceled by the light from the corresponding element in the lower half. Hence no light reaches the screen at points along a line, the direction to which lies at an angle α above or below the original direction of the light, provided that

$$\frac{D}{2} \sin \alpha = \frac{\lambda}{2},$$

or

$$\sin \alpha = \frac{\lambda}{D}.$$

By dividing the slit into quarters, sixths, etc., one can show by similar reasoning that the screen is again dark when

$$\sin \alpha = \frac{2\lambda}{D}, \quad \frac{3\lambda}{D}, \text{ etc.} \qquad (46\text{–}2)$$

The angle corresponding to the first minimum at either side of the center is called the *half-angular breadth* of the central band. The angular breadth of the entire central band is twice as great. The half-angular breadth is proportional to the wavelength λ and inversely proportional to the slit width D. It was stated earlier that in order to obtain a divergence of the diffracted beam like that shown in Fig. 46–15, the slit width should be about 5 wavelengths. We can now justify this statement. If the slit width D equals 5 wavelengths, the half-angular breadth of the central band is

$$\sin \alpha = \frac{\lambda}{D} = \frac{\lambda}{5\lambda} = 0.20,$$

$$\alpha = 12° \text{ (very nearly)},$$

which is approximately the angular divergence shown in Fig. 46–15. When the slit width is just one wavelength,

$$\sin \alpha = 1, \quad \alpha = 90°,$$

and the central band spreads out over an angle of 180°.

46–8 The plane diffraction grating. Suppose that instead of a single slit, or two slits side by side as in Young's experiment, we have a very large number of parallel slits all of the same width, and spaced at regular intervals. Such an arrangement, known as a *diffraction grating*, was first constructed by Joseph Fraunhofer (1787–1826). The earliest gratings were of fine wires, 0.04 mm to 0.6 mm in diameter, spaced at intervals of from 0.0528 mm to 0.6866 mm. Gratings are now made by ruling, with a diamond point, a large number of equidistant grooves on a glass or metal surface.

Let GG, in Fig. 46–19, represent the grating, the slits of which are perpendicular to the plane of the paper. While only five slits are shown in the diagram, an actual grating contains several thousand, with a grating spacing d of the order of one ten-thousandth of an inch. Let a train of plane waves be incident normally on the grating from the left. The problem of finding the intensity of the light transmitted by the grating then combines the principles of interference and diffraction. That is, each slit gives rise to a diffracted beam whose nature, as we have seen, depends on the slit width. These diffracted beams then interfere with one another to produce the final pattern.

Let us assume that the slits are so narrow that the diffracted beam from each spreads out over a sufficiently wide angle for it to interfere with all the other diffracted beams. Consider first the light proceeding from elements of infinitesimal width at the lower edges of each opening, and traveling in a direction making an angle θ with that of the incident beam, as in Fig. 46–19. A lens at the right of the grating forms in its focal plane a diffraction pattern similar to that which would appear on a screen at infinity.

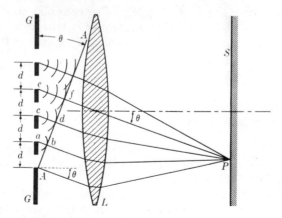

Fig. 46–19. The plane diffraction grating.

Suppose the angle θ in Fig. 46–19 is taken so that the distance $ab = \lambda$, the wavelength of the incident light. Then $cd = 2\lambda$, $ef = 3\lambda$, etc. The waves from all of these elements, since they are in phase at the plane of the grating, are also in phase along the plane AA and therefore reach the point P in phase. The same holds true for any set of elements in corresponding positions in the various slits.

If the angle θ is increased slightly, the disturbances from the grating elements no longer arrive at AA in phase with one another, and even an extremely small change in angle results in almost complete destructive interference between them, provided there are a large number of slits in the grating. Hence the maximum at the angle θ is an extremely sharp one, differing from the rather broad maxima and minima which result from interference or diffraction effects with a small number of openings.

As the angle θ is still further increased, a position is eventually reached in which the distance ab in Fig. 46–19 becomes equal to 2λ. Then cd equals 4λ, cf equals 6λ, and so on. The disturbances at AA are again all in phase, the path difference between them now being 2λ, and another maximum results. Evidently still others will appear when $ab = 3\lambda$, $4\lambda, \ldots$. Maxima will also be observed at corresponding angles on the opposite side of the grating normal, as well as along the normal itself, since in the latter position the phase difference between disturbances reaching AA is zero.

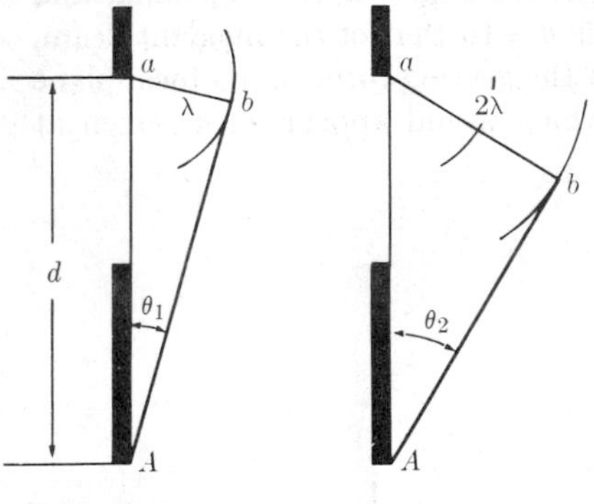

The angles of deviation for which the maxima occur may readily be found from Fig. 46–20. Consider the right triangle Aba. Let d be the distance between successive grating elements, called the "grating spacing." The necessary condition for a maximum is that $ab = m\lambda$, where $m = 0, 1, 2, 3$, etc. It follows that

FIG. 46–20. First order maximum when $ab = \lambda$, second order when $ab = 2\lambda$.

$$\sin \theta = m \frac{\lambda}{d} \qquad (46\text{–}3)$$

is the necessary condition for a maximum. The angle θ is also the angle by which the rays corresponding to the maxima have been *deviated* from the direction of the incident light.

In practice, the parallel beam incident on the grating is usually produced by a lens at the first focal point of which is a narrow illuminated slit. Each of the maxima is then a sharp image of the slit, of the same color as that of the light illuminating the slit, assumed thus far to be monochromatic. If the slit is illuminated by light consisting of a mixture of wavelengths, the lens L will form a number of images of the slit in different positions, every wavelength in the original light giving rise to a set of slit images deviated by the appropriate angles. If the slit is illuminated with white light, a continuous group of images is formed side by side or, in other words, the white light is dispersed into continuous spectra. In contrast with the single spectrum produced by a prism, a grating forms a number of spectra on either side of the normal. Those which correspond to $m = 1$ in Eq. (46–3) are called *first order*, those which correspond to $m = 2$ are called *second order*, and so on. Since for $m = 0$ the deviation is zero, all colors combine to produce a white image of the slit in the direction of the incident beam.

In order that an appreciable deviation of the light may be produced, it is necessary that the grating spacing shall be of the same order of magnitude as the wavelength of light. Gratings for use in or near the visible spectrum are ruled with from 10,000 to 30,000 lines per inch.

The diffraction grating is widely used in spectroscopy instead of a prism as a means of dispersing a light beam into spectra. If the grating spacing is known, then from a measurement of the angle of deviation of any wavelength, the value of this wavelength may be computed. In the case of a prism this is not so; the angles of deviation are not related in any simple way to the wavelengths but depend on the characteristics of the material of which the prism is constructed. Since the index of refraction of optical glass varies more rapidly at the violet than at the red end of the spectrum, the spectrum formed by a prism is always spread out more at the violet end than it is at the red. Also, while a prism deviates red light the least and violet the most, the reverse is true of a grating, since in the latter case the deviation increases with increasing wavelength.

EXAMPLE 1. The limits of the visible spectrum are approximately 400 mμ to 700 mμ. Find the angular breadth of the first order visible spectrum produced by a plane grating having 15,000 lines per inch, when light is incident normally on the grating.

The grating spacing, d, in centimeters, is

$$d = \frac{2.54 \text{ cm/in.}}{15,000 \text{ lines/in.}} = 1.69 \times 10^{-4} \text{ cm.}$$

The angular deviation of the violet is

$$\sin \theta = \frac{4 \times 10^{-5} \text{ cm}}{1.69 \times 10^{-4} \text{ cm}} = 0.237,$$

$$\theta = 13° 40'.$$

The angular deviation of the red is

$$\sin \theta = \frac{7 \times 10^{-5} \text{ cm}}{1.69 \times 10^{-4} \text{ cm}} = 0.415,$$

$$\theta = 24° \, 30'.$$

Hence the first order visible spectrum includes an angle of

$$24° \, 30' - 13° \, 40' = 10° \, 50'.$$

EXAMPLE 2. Show that the violet of the third order visible spectrum overlaps the red of the second order.

The angular deviation of the third order violet is

$$\sin \theta = \frac{3 \times (4 \times 10^{-5} \text{ cm})}{d}$$

and of the second order red it is

$$\sin \theta = \frac{2 \times (7 \times 10^{-5} \text{ cm})}{d}.$$

Since the first angle is smaller than the second, whatever the grating spacing, the third order will always overlap the second.

46–9 Fresnel diffraction due to a circular obstacle. A circular *opening* in an opaque screen transmits only a small circular patch of a wave surface; the remainder of the wave is obscured. An interesting effect is observed if we reverse this procedure and insert a small circular *obstacle* in the light from a distant point source. A small circular patch of the wave is then obscured, while the remainder is allowed to proceed. Figure 46–21 is a photograph of the shadow of a small ball bearing, supported from the tip of a magnetized sewing needle. Constructive interference of the wavelets from the unobstructed portion of the incident wave results in the small bright spot at the center of the geometrical shadow.

46–10 Diffraction of x-rays by a crystal. Although x-rays were discovered by Roentgen in 1895, it was not until 1913 that x-ray wavelengths were measured with any degree of precision. Experiments had indicated that these wavelengths might be of the order of 10^{-8} cm, which is about the same as the interatomic spacing in a solid. It occurred to Laue in 1913 that if the atoms in a crystal were arranged in a regular way, a crystal might serve as a three-dimensional diffraction grating for x-rays. The experiment was performed by Friederich and Knipping and it succeeded, thus verifying in a single stroke both the hypothesis that x-rays *are* waves (or at any rate wavelike in some of their properties) and that the atoms in a crystal are arranged in a regular manner. Since that time, the phe-

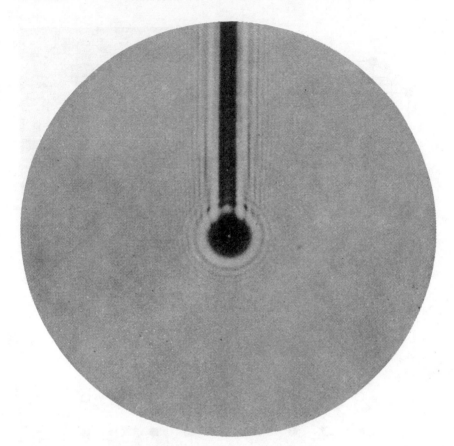

Fig. 46–21. Shadow of a ball bearing.

nomenon of x-ray diffraction by a crystal has proved an invaluable tool of the physicist, both as a method of measuring x-ray wavelengths and of studying the structure of crystals.

Figure 46–22 is a diagram of a simple type of crystal, that of sodium chloride (NaCl). The black circles represent the sodium, and the open circles the chlorine ions. Figure 46–23 is a diagram of a section through the crystal. Planes such as those parallel to *aa*, *bb*, *cc*, etc., can be constructed through the crystal in such a way that they pass through relatively large numbers of atoms. These sets of equidistant planes correspond to the lines in a plane grating.

Figure 46–24 is a photograph made by directing a narrow beam of x-rays at a thin section of a crystal of quartz and allowing the diffracted

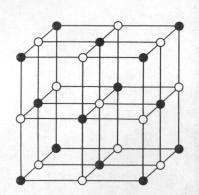

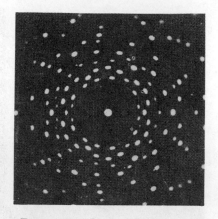

FIG. 46–22. Model of arrangement of ions in a crystal of NaCl. Black circles, Na; open circles, Cl.

FIG. 46–24. Laue diffraction pattern formed by directing a beam of x-rays at a thin section of quartz crystal. (Courtesy of Dr. B. E. Warren.)

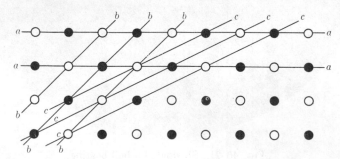

FIG. 46–23. Crystal planes such as aa, bb, and cc serve as a three-dimensional diffraction grating for x-rays.

beams to strike a photographic plate. Each spot corresponds to the diffraction by a particular set of crystal planes.

46–11 The resolving power of optical instruments. It will be recalled that the expressions for the magnification of a telescope or a microscope, derived in Chapter 43, involved (except for certain numerical factors) only the focal lengths of the lenses making up the optical system of the instrument. It appears at first sight as though any desired magnification might be attained by a proper choice of these focal lengths. Beyond a certain point, however, while the image formed by the instrument becomes larger (or subtends a larger angle) it does not gain in detail, even though all lens aberrations have been corrected. This limit to the useful magnification is set by the fact that light is a wave motion and the laws of geometrical optics do not hold strictly for a wave surface of limited extent. Physically, the image of a point source is not the intersection of *rays* from the source, but the diffraction pattern of those *waves* from the source that pass through the lens system.

It is an important experimental fact that the light from a point source, diffracted by a circular opening, is focused by a lens, not as a geometrical point, but as a disk of finite radius surrounded by dark and bright rings. The larger the wave surface admitted (i.e., the larger the lenses or diaphragms in an optical system), the smaller the diffraction pattern of a point source and the closer together may two point sources be before their diffraction disks overlap and become indistinguishable. An optical system is said to be able to *resolve* two point sources if the corresponding diffraction patterns are sufficiently small or sufficiently separated to be distinguished. The numerical measure of the ability of the system to resolve two such points is called its *resolving power*.

Figure 46–25(a) is a photograph of four point sources made with the camera lens "stopped down" to an extremely small aperture. The nature of the diffraction patterns is clearly evident and it is obvious that further magnification, or enlargement of the picture, would not aid in resolving the sources. What is necessary is not to make the image *larger*, but to make the diffraction patterns *smaller*. Figures 46–25(b) and (c) show how the resolving power of the lens is increased by increasing its aperture. In (b) the diffraction patterns are sufficiently small for all four sources to be distinguished. In (c) the full aperture of the lens was utilized.

An arbitrary criterion proposed by Lord Rayleigh is that two point sources are just resolvable if the central maximum of the diffraction pattern of one source just coincides with the first minimum of the other. Let P_1 and P_2 in Fig. 46–26 be two point objects and let P'_1 and P'_2 be the centers of their diffraction patterns, formed by some optical instrument such as a microscope or telescope and which for simplicity is represented in the diagram as a single lens. If the images are just resolved, that is, if according to Rayleigh's criterion the first minimum of one pattern coincides with the center of the other, the separation of the centers of the patterns equals the radius of the central bright disk. From a knowledge of the focal lengths and separations of the lenses in any particular instrument, one can compute the corresponding distance between the two point objects. This distance, the minimum separation of two points that can just be resolved, is called the *limit of resolution* of the instrument. The smaller this distance, the greater is said to be the *resolving power*. The resolving power increases with the solid angle of the cone of rays intercepted by the instrument and is inversely proportional to the wavelength

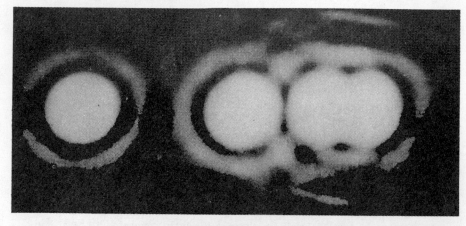

(a)

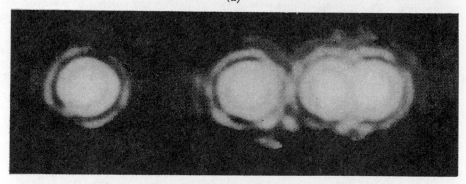

(b)

(c)

FIG. 46–25. Diffraction patterns of four "point" sources, with a circular opening in front of the lens. In (a), the opening is so small that the patterns at the right are just resolved by Rayleigh's criterion. Increasing the aperture decreases the size of the diffraction patterns, as in (b) and (c).

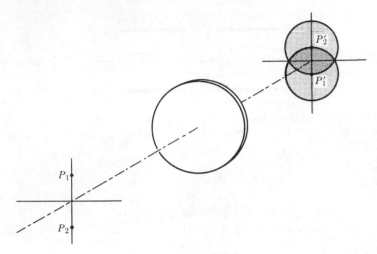

Fig. 46–26. Two point sources are just resolvable if the first minimum of the diffraction pattern of one coincides with the center of the other.

of the light used. It is as if the light waves were the "tools" with which our optical system is provided, and the smaller the tools the finer the work which the system can do.

46–12 The electron microscope. The shorter the wavelength, the smaller is the limit of resolution of a microscope. Modern physical theories indicate that a moving electron can, for some purposes, be considered as a wave, and the wavelengths of electron waves can easily be made very much shorter than the wavelengths of visible light. Hence the limit of resolution of a microscope may be extended to a value several hundred times smaller than that obtainable with an optical instrument by using electrons, rather than light waves, to form an image of the object being examined.

A beam of electrons can be focused either by a magnetic or an electric field of the proper configuration, and both types are used in electron microscopes. Figure 46–27 illustrates an electrostatic lens. Two hollow cylinders are maintained at different potentials. A few of the equipotentials are indicated, and the trajectories of a beam of electrons traveling from left to right are shown by the dashed lines. The optical analog of this electrostatic lens is shown in Fig. 46–28. It will be evident without going into further details that by the proper design of such lenses the elements of an optical microscope such as its condensing lens, objective, and ocular can all be duplicated electronically.

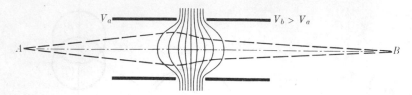

FIG. 46–27. An electrostatic electron lens. The cylinders are at different potentials, V_a and V_b. A beam of electrons diverging from point A is focused at point B.

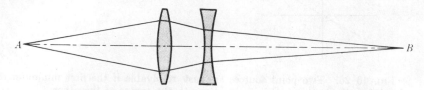

FIG. 46–28. Optical analog of the electron lens in Fig. 46–27.

FIG. 46–29. Electron micrograph of aluminum oxide, magnified 53,500 times. (Courtesy of Radio Corporation of America.)

The source of electrons in an electron microscope is a heated filament. Electrons emitted by the filament are accelerated by an electron gun and strike the object to be examined. This must necessarily be a thin section so that some of the electrons can pass through it. The thicker portions of the section absorb more of the electron stream than do the thinner portions, just as would a lantern slide in a projection lantern. Needless to say, the entire apparatus must be evacuated.

The final image may be formed on a photographic plate, or on a fluorescent screen which can be examined visually or photographed with a still further gain in magnification. Commercial electron microscopes give satisfactory definition at an over-all magnification, electronic followed by photographic, as great as 50,000×. Figure 46–29 is an electron micrograph of aluminum oxide, magnified 53,500 times.

It should be pointed out that the ability of the electron microscope to form an image does not depend on the wave properties of the electrons; their trajectories can be computed by treating them as charged particles, deflected by the electric or magnetic fields through which they move. It is only when considerations of resolving power arise that the electron wavelengths come into the picture. The situation is analogous to that in the optical microscope. The paths of light rays through an optical microscope can be computed by the principles of geometrical optics, but the resolving power of the microscope is determined by the wavelength of the light used.

PROBLEMS

46–1. Two slits are spaced 0.3 mm apart and are placed 50 cm from a screen. What is the distance between the second and third dark lines of the interference pattern when the slits are illuminated with light of 600 mμ wavelength?

46–2. Light of wavelength 500 mμ is incident perpendicularly from air on a film 10^{-4} cm thick and of 1.375 refractive index. Part of the light enters the film and is reflected back at the second face. (a) How many waves are contained along the path of this light in the film? (b) What is the phase difference between these waves as they leave the film and as they enter it?

46–3. A glass plate 0.40 micron thick is illuminated by a beam of white light normal to the plate. The index of refraction of the glass is 1.50. What wavelengths within the limits of the visible spectrum ($\lambda = 40 \times 10^{-6}$ cm to $\lambda = 70 \times 10^{-6}$ cm) will be intensified in the reflected beam?

46–4. Two rectangular pieces of plane glass are laid one upon the other on a table. A thin strip of paper is placed between them at one edge so that a very thin wedge of air is formed. The plates are illuminated by a beam of sodium light at normal incidence. Bright and dark interference bands are formed, there being ten of each per centimeter length of wedge measured normal to the edges in contact. Find the angle of the wedge.

46–5. What is the thinnest film of 1.40 refractive index in which destructive interference of the violet component (400 mμ) of an incident white beam in air can take place by reflection? What is then the residual color of the beam?

46–6. A sheet of glass 10 cm long is placed in contact with a second sheet, and is held at a small angle with it by a metal strip 0.1 mm thick placed under one end. The glass is illuminated from above with light of 546 mμ wavelength. How many dark interference fringes are observed per cm in the reflected light?

46–7. The surfaces of a prism of index 1.52 are to be made "nonreflecting" by coating them with a thin layer of transparent material of index 1.30. The thickness of the layer is such that at a wavelength of 500 mμ (in vacuum), light reflected from the first surface is one-half a wavelength out of phase with that reflected from the second surface. Find the thickness of the layer.

46–8. The radius of curvature of the convex surface of a plano-convex lens is 30 cm. The lens is placed convex side down on a plane glass plate, and illuminated from above with red light of wavelength 650 mμ. Find the diameter of the third bright ring in the interference pattern.

46–9. A slit of width D was placed in front of a lens of focal length 80 cm. The slit was illuminated by light of wavelength 600 mμ and the diffraction pattern of Fig. 46–16 was formed on a screen in the second focal plane of the lens. If the photograph of Fig. 46–16 represents an enlargement to twice the actual size, what was the slit width?

46–10. Plane monochromatic waves of wavelength 600 mμ are incident normally on a plane transmission grating having 500 lines/mm. Find the angles of deviation in the first, second, and third orders.

46–11. A plane transmission grating is ruled with 4000 lines/cm. Compute

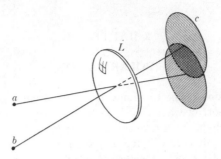

FIGURE 46-30

the angular separation in degrees, in the second order spectrum, between the α and δ lines of atomic hydrogen, whose wavelengths are respectively 656 mμ and 410 mμ.

46-12. (a) What is the wavelength of light which is deviated in the first order through an angle of 20° by a transmission grating having 6000 lines/cm? (b) What is the second order deviation of this wavelength?

46-13. What is the longest wavelength that can be observed in the fourth order for a transmission grating having 5000 lines/cm?

46-14. In Fig. 46-30, two point sources of light a and b, at a distance of 50 m from lens L and 6 mm apart, produce images at c which are just resolved by Rayleigh's criterion. The focal length of the lens is 20 cm. What is the diameter of the diffraction circles at c?

CHAPTER 47

POLARIZATION

47-1 Polarization. The phenomena of interference and diffraction can occur with any sort of waves, such as sound waves or surface waves on a liquid. In this chapter we consider some optical phenomena that depend not merely on the fact that light is a wave motion, but that the waves are *transverse*. These are called *polarization* effects. They can be observed only with transverse waves and cannot be duplicated with sound waves because the latter are longitudinal.

Let us recall for a moment the nature of the electromagnetic waves radiated by a radio antenna, as described in Section 37–9. Suppose the antenna is vertical, and we consider a portion of a wave front in a vertical plane and not too near the antenna, as in Fig. 47–1. The electric field intensity **E** at all points of this wave front is in a vertical direction, as indicated. If in the wave front in the diagram the electric intensity is a maximum in the upward direction, then in wave fronts one-half a wavelength ahead of or behind this one the intensity is a maximum in a downward direction. At all points of any plane fixed in space, the electric vector oscillates up and down along a vertical line and the wave is said to be *linearly* polarized. (Waves of this sort are also described as plane polarized, or merely as polarized.)

To avoid confusion, the magnetic intensity **H** is not shown in Fig. 47–1. It is always at right angles to the electric intensity **E**.

The "antennas" that radiate light waves are the molecules of which light sources are composed. The electrically charged particles in the molecules acquire energy in some way, and radiate this energy as electromagnetic waves of short wavelength. Presumably the waves from any

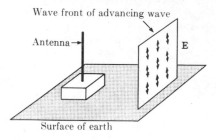

FIG. 47–1. The electromagnetic waves radiated by an antenna are linearly polarized.

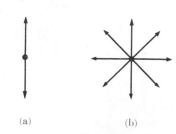

(a) (b)

FIG. 47–2. Schematic diagrams of (a) linearly polarized light, and (b) ordinary light.

936

one molecule are linearly polarized, like those from a radio antenna. But since any actual light source contains a tremendous number of molecules, oriented at random, the light emitted is a mixture of waves linearly polarized in all possible transverse directions. Let the plane of the diagram in Fig. 47–2(a) represent a wave front in a beam of light advancing toward the reader, and the dot an end view of one ray in this beam. A linearly polarized light wave is represented schematically by the double arrow, which indicates that the electric field oscillates in the vertical direction only. A beam of natural light is represented as in part (b), in which the arrows indicate a mixture of waves, linearly polarized in all possible transverse directions.

47–2 Polarization by reflection. There are a number of methods by which the vibrations in one particular direction can be "sorted out," in whole or in part, from a beam of natural light. One of these is the familiar process of reflection. When natural light strikes a reflecting surface, there is found to be a preferential reflection for those waves in which the electric vector is vibrating perpendicular to the plane of incidence. (The plane of incidence is the plane containing the incident ray and the normal to the surface. See Fig. 47–3.) An exception is that at normal incidence all directions of polarization are reflected equally. At one particular angle of

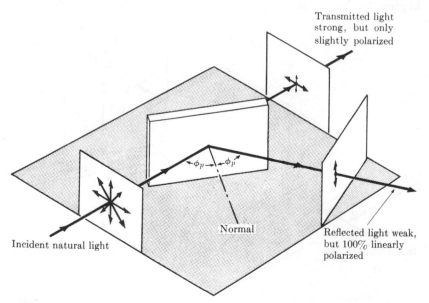

FIG. 47–3. When light is incident at the polarizing angle, the reflected light is linearly polarized.

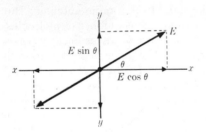

FIG. 47–4. Linearly polarized light resolved into two linearly polarized components.

incidence, known as the *polarizing angle*, no light whatever is reflected except that in which the electric vector is perpendicular to the plane of incidence. This case is illustrated in Fig. 47–3.

The situation depicted in Fig. 47–3 calls for somewhat more explanation. The heavy double arrow lettered E in Fig. 47–4 represents the amplitude of the electric field in a linearly polarized wave advancing toward the reader, the direction of vibration making an angle θ with the x-axis. This wave can be resolved into two component waves (that is, it is equivalent to these two waves) linearly polarized along the x- and y-axes, and of amplitudes $E \cos \theta$ and $E \sin \theta$. In the same way, each linearly polarized component in the incident beam of natural light in Fig. 47–3, as represented by the "star" of vectors, can be resolved into two components, one perpendicular and the other parallel to the plane of incidence.

We can describe the reflection of light at the surface by stating what happens to each component of an arbitrary linearly polarized wave in the

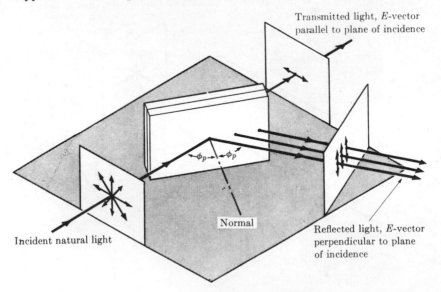

FIG. 47–5. Separation of natural light into two beams of linear light by reflection from a pile of plates.

incident light. When incident at the polarizing angle, *none* of the components parallel to the plane of incidence are reflected; that is, they are 100% transmitted in the *refracted* beam. Of the components perpendicular to the plane of incidence, about 15% are reflected if the reflecting surface is glass. (The fraction reflected depends on the index of the reflecting material.) Hence the *reflected* light is weak and *completely* linearly polarized. The *refracted* light is a mixture of the parallel components, all of which are refracted, and the remaining 85% of the perpendicular component. It is therefore strong, but only *partially* polarized.

At angles of incidence other than the polarizing angle some of the components parallel to the plane of incidence are reflected, so that except at the polarizing angle the reflected light is not completely linearly polarized.

To increase the intensity of the reflected light, a pile of thin glass plates is often used, as shown in Fig. 47–5. Due to the many rays reflected at the polarizing angle from the various surfaces, there is not only an increase in intensity of the reflected light, but also an increase in the polarization of the transmitted light, which now contains much less of the perpendicular component.

If n is the index of the material in which the light is traveling before reflection, and n' is the index of the reflecting material, the polarizing angle ϕ_p is given by

$$\tan \phi_p = \frac{n'}{n}. \qquad (47\text{–}1)$$

This equation is known as *Brewster's law*, after Sir David Brewster, who discovered it experimentally in 1812.

47–3 Double refraction. The progress of a wave train through a homogeneous isotropic medium, such as glass, may be determined graphically by Huygens' construction. The secondary wavelets in such a medium are spherical surfaces. There exist, however, many transparent crystalline substances which, while homogeneous, are *anisotropic*. That is, the velocity of a light wave in them is not the same in all directions. Crystals having this property are said to be *doubly refracting*, or *birefringent*. Two sets of Huygens wavelets propagate from every wave surface in such a crystal, one set being spherical and the other ellipsoidal. The two sets are tangent to each other in one direction, called the *optic axis* of the crystal.

Figure 47–6(a) shows the traces of the Huygens wavelets from a point source within a doubly refracting crystal. The complete wave surfaces are obtained by rotating the diagram about axis AA. The direction of line AOA is the optic axis. (The optic axis is a *direction* in the crystal, not just one line. Any other line parallel to AOA is also an optic axis.)

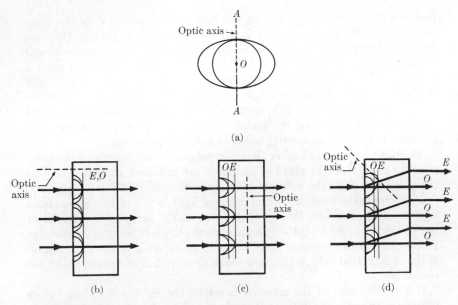

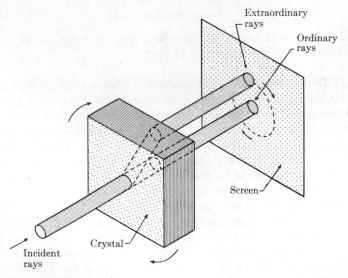

FIG. 47-6. (a) Spherical and ellipsoidal waves diverge from point O in a doubly refracting crystal. (b) Light traveling in the direction of the optic axis, (c) perpendicular to the optic axis, and (d) at an arbitrary angle to the optic axis.

FIG. 47-7. A narrow beam of natural light can be split into two beams by a doubly refracting crystal.

Parts (b), (c), and (d) of Fig. 47–6 show the wave fronts in three sections cut from the crystal in different directions, when light is incident normally on the surface of the section. It will be seen that two sets of waves travel through the crystal, one formed by the tangents to the spheres and the other by the tangents to the ellipsoids.

It may be seen in Fig. 47–6(d) that a ray incident normally is broken up into two rays in traversing the crystal. The ray which corresponds to wave surfaces tangent to the spherical wavelets is undeviated and is called the *ordinary ray*. The ray corresponding to the wave surfaces tangent to the ellipsoids is deviated even though the incident ray is normal to the surface, and is called the *extraordinary ray*. If the crystal is rotated about the incident ray as an axis, the ordinary ray remains fixed but the extraordinary ray revolves around it, as shown in Fig. 47–7. Furthermore, for angles of incidence other than 0°, Snell's law (i.e., $\sin \phi / \sin \phi' =$ constant) holds for the ordinary but not for the extraordinary ray, since evidently the velocity of the latter is different in different directions.

The index of refraction for the extraordinary ray is therefore a function of direction. It is customary to state the index for the direction at right angles to the optic axis, in which the velocity is a maximum or a minimum. Some values of n_O and n_E, the indices for the ordinary and extraordinary rays, are listed in Table 47–1.

Figure 47–6 is drawn for a crystal in which the velocity of the ellipsoidal waves is greater than that of the spherical waves, except in the direction of the optic axis. In some crystals the velocity of the ellipsoidal waves is less than that of the spherical waves, except along the optic axis where the two are equal. Both this type of crystal and that described above are called *uniaxial*. In some crystals there are two different directions in which the velocities are equal. These crystals are called *biaxial*, but since all of the doubly refracting crystals used in optical instruments (chiefly quartz and calcite) are uniaxial, we shall consider only this type.

TABLE 47–1

INDICES OF REFRACTION OF DOUBLY REFRACTING CRYSTALS
(For light of wavelength 589 mμ)

Material	n_O	n_E
Calcite	1.6583	1.4864
Quartz	1.544	1.553
Tourmaline	1.64	1.62
Ice	1.306	1.307

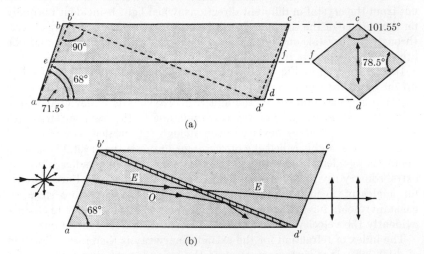

FIG. 47-8. (a) Natural crystal of Iceland spar. (b) A Nicol prism.

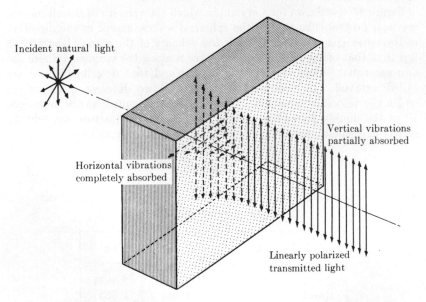

FIG. 47-9. Linearly polarized light transmitted by a dichroic crystal.

47-4 Polarization by double refraction. Experiment shows that the ordinary and extraordinary waves in a doubly refracting crystal are linearly polarized in mutually perpendicular directions. Consequently, if some means can be found to separate one wave from the other, a doubly refracting crystal may be used to obtain linearly polarized light from natural light. There are a number of ways in which this separation may be accomplished.

One method of separating the two components is by means of a *Nicol prism* or one of its modifications. The Nicol prism is a crystal of Iceland spar or calcite ($CaCO_3$), whose natural shape is shown by the full lines in Fig. 47-8(a). To make a Nicol prism, the end faces of the crystal are cut at a more obtuse angle, as shown by the dotted lines. The crystal is then cut along the shorter diagonal $b'd'$ and cemented together again with Canada balsam. The index of Canada balsam has such a value that the ordinary ray is totally reflected, while the extraordinary ray is transmitted as in Fig. 47-8(b).

Certain doubly refracting crystals exhibit *dichroism;* that is, one of the polarized components is absorbed much more strongly than the other. Hence if the crystal is cut of the proper thickness, one of the components is practically extinguished by absorption, while the other is transmitted in appreciable amount, as indicated in Fig. 47-9. Tourmaline is one example of such a dichroic crystal.

A recent development in polarizing materials is polaroid, one type of which consists of a thin layer of tiny needlelike dichroic crystals of herapathite (iodoquinine sulfate), in parallel orientation, embedded in a plastic matrix and enclosed for protection between two transparent plates. This method of construction makes possible the manufacture of polarizing plates or sheets of large area. While the transmitted light is slightly colored and not completely polarized, the large area of such plates and their moderate cost has already opened up many new applications of polarized light.

47-5 Percentage polarization. Malus' law. When light is incident on a polarizer, as in Fig. 47-10, linear light only is transmitted. The polarizer may be a pile of plates, a Nicol prism, or a sheet of polaroid. It is represented as a polaroid disk in Fig. 47-10. The dotted line across the polarizer indicates the direction of the electric vector in the transmitted light. The transmitted light falls on a photocell, and the current in a microammeter connected to the cell is proportional to the quantity of light incident on it.

If the incident light is unpolarized, then as the polarizer is rotated about the incident ray as an axis, the reading of the microammeter remains constant. The polarizer transmits the components of the incident

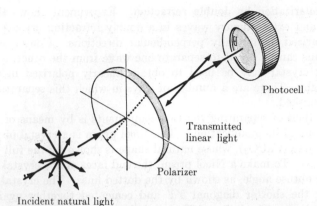

Fig. 47–10. The intensity of the transmitted linear light is the same at all azimuths of the polarizer.

waves in which the E-vector is parallel to the transmission direction of the polarizer, and by symmetry the components are equal for all azimuths.

If there is any variation in the meter reading as the polarizer is rotated, the incident light is not natural light and is said to be *partially* polarized. (But just what kind of light it is cannot be determined from this experiment alone.) Suppose the meter reading does vary. Let I_{max} and I_{min} represent the maximum and minimum values of the quantity of light incident on the photocell, or the maximum and minimum meter readings, since the two are proportional. The *percentage polarization* of the incident light is defined as

$$\text{Percent polarization} = \frac{I_{max} - I_{min}}{I_{max} + I_{min}} \times 100. \qquad (47\text{--}2)$$

Suppose now that a second polaroid is inserted in the light between polarizer and photocell, as in Fig. 47–11. Let the transmission direction of the second polaroid, or *analyzer*, be vertical, and let that of the polarizer make an angle θ with the vertical. The linear light transmitted by the polarizer may be resolved into two components as shown, one parallel and the other perpendicular to the transmission direction of the analyzer. Evidently only the parallel component, of amplitude $E \cos \theta$, will be transmitted by the analyzer. The transmitted light is a maximum when $\theta = 0$, and is zero when $\theta = 90°$, or when polarizer and analyzer are *crossed*. At intermediate angles, since the quantity of energy is proportional to the square of the amplitude (see Section 23–2), we have

$$\boxed{I = I_{max} \cos^2 \theta,} \qquad (47\text{--}3)$$

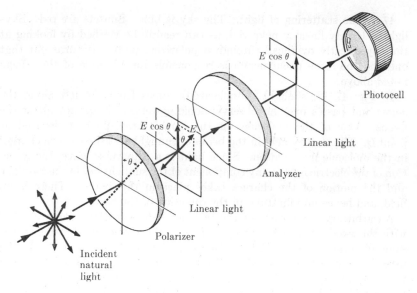

FIG. 47–11. The analyzer transmits only that component of the linear light parallel to its transmission direction.

where I_{max} is the maximum amount of light transmitted and I is the amount transmitted at the angle θ. This relation, which was discovered experimentally by Etienne Louis Malus in 1809, is called *Malus' law.*

Evidently, the significance of the angle θ, in general, is the angle between the transmission directions of polarizer and analyzer. If either the analyzer or the polarizer is rotated, the amplitude of the transmitted beam varies in the same way with the angle between them.

Polaroid is now widely used in "sun glasses" where, from the standpoint of its polarizing properties, it plays the role of the analyzer in Fig. 47–11. We have seen that when unpolarized light is reflected, there is a preferential reflection for light polarized perpendicular to the plane of incidence. When sunlight is reflected from a horizontal surface, the plane of incidence is vertical. Hence in the reflected light there is a preponderance of light polarized in the horizontal direction, the proportion being greater the nearer the angle of incidence is to the polarizing angle. The transmission direction of the polaroid in the sun glasses is vertical, so none of the horizontally polarized light is transmitted.

Apart from this polarizing feature, these glasses serve the same purpose as any dark glasses absorbing 50% of the incident light, since even in an unpolarized beam, half the light can be considered as polarized horizontally and half vertically. Only the vertically polarized light is transmitted.

47–6 The scattering of light. The sky is blue. Sunsets are red. Sky-light is largely linearly polarized, as can readily be verified by looking at the sky directly overhead through a polarizing plate. It turns out that one and the same phenomenon is responsible for all three of the effects noted above.

In Fig. 47–12, sunlight (unpolarized) comes from the left along the z-axis and passes over an observer looking vertically upward along the y-axis. One of the molecules of the earth's atmosphere is located at point O. The electric field in the beam of sunlight sets the electric charges in the molecule in vibration. Since light is a transverse wave, the direction of the electric field in any component of the sunlight lies in the xy-plane and the motion of the charges takes place in this plane. There is no field, and hence no vibration, in the direction of the z-axis.

An arbitrary component of the incident light, vibrating at an angle θ with the x-axis, sets the electric charges in the molecule vibrating in the same direction, as indicated by the heavy line through point O. In the usual way, we can resolve this vibration into two, one along the x- and the other along the y-axis. The result, then, is that each component in the incident light produces the equivalent of two molecular "antennas," oscillating with the frequency of the incident light, and lying along the x- and y-axes.

It has been explained in Section 37–9 that an antenna does not radiate in the direction of its own length. Hence the antenna along the y-axis

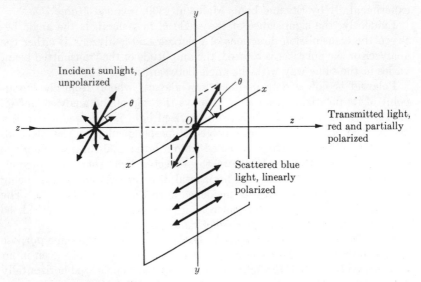

FIG. 47–12. Scattered light is linearly polarized.

does not send any light to the observer directly below it. It does, of course, send out light in other directions. The only light reaching the observer comes from the component of vibration along the x-axis and, as is the case with the waves from any antenna, this light is linearly polarized with the electric field parallel to the antenna. The vectors on the y-axis below point O show the direction of vibration of the light reaching the observer.

The process described above is called *scattering*. The energy of the scattered light is abstracted from the original beam, which becomes weakened in the process.

The vibration of the charges in the molecule is a *forced* vibration, like the vibration of a mass on a spring when the upper end of the spring is moved up and down with simple harmonic motion. It is well known that the amplitude of the forced vibrations is greater, the closer the driving frequency approaches the natural frequency of vibration of the spring-mass system. Now the natural frequency of the electric charges in a molecule is the same as that of wavelengths in the ultraviolet. The frequencies of the waves in visible light are less than the natural frequency, but the higher their frequency, or the shorter their wavelength, the closer is the driving frequency to the natural frequency, the greater the amplitude of vibration, and the greater the intensity of the scattered light. In other words, blue light is scattered more than red, with the result that the hue of the scattered light is blue.

Toward evening, when sunlight has to travel a large distance through the earth's atmosphere to reach a point over or nearly over an observer, a large proportion of the blue light in sunlight is removed from it by scattering. White light minus blue light is yellow or red in hue. Thus when sunlight, with the blue component removed, is incident on a cloud, the light reflected from the cloud to the observer has the yellow or red hue so commonly seen at sunset.

From the explanation above, it follows that if the earth had no atmosphere we would receive no skylight at the earth's surface, and the sky would appear as black in the daytime as it does at night. This conclusion is borne out by observations at high altitudes, where there is less atmosphere above the observer.

47–7 Circular and elliptic polarization. Linearly polarized light represents a special and relatively simple type of polarization. When the ordinary and extraordinary rays in a doubly refracting crystal are separated, each ray taken alone is linearly polarized, but with the directions of vibration at right angles. When, however, the crystal is cut with its faces parallel to the optic axis, so that light, incident normally on one of its faces, traverses the crystal in a direction perpendicular to the optic

FIG. 47–13. Vibrations which result from the combination of a horizontal and a vertical simple harmonic motion of the same frequency and the same amplitude, for various values of the phase difference.

axis, as shown in Fig. 47–6(c), the ordinary and extraordinary rays are not separated. *They traverse the same path, but with different speeds.* Upon emerging from the second face of the crystal, the ordinary and extraordinary rays are out of phase with each other and give rise to either elliptically polarized, circularly polarized, or linearly polarized light, depending upon a number of factors which we shall proceed to discuss now.

Since in the ordinary ray the direction of vibration is perpendicular to that in the extraordinary ray, we have to consider a fundamental problem which, for the sake of simplicity, may be discussed in mechanical terms: What sort of vibration results from the combination of two simple harmonic vibrations at right angles to each other and differing in phase? The solution may be reached in a variety of ways: (1) with the aid of mechanical equipment, (2) by using two circles of reference for plotting two simple harmonic motions at right angles, and (3) by establishing alternating potential differences on the horizontal and vertical plates of a cathode-ray oscilloscope.

In Fig. 47–13 are shown the results obtained by combining a horizontal and a vertical simple harmonic motion of the same frequency and the same amplitude, for nine different phase differences. It is at once evident that *two simple harmonic motions at right angles to each other never produce destructive interference, no matter what the phase difference.*

1. When the phase difference is 0, 2π, or any even multiple of π, the result is a linear vibration at 45° to both original vibrations.

2. When the phase difference is π, 3π, or any odd multiple of π, the result is also a linear vibration, but at right angles to those corresponding to even multiples of π.

3. When the phase difference is $\pi/2$, $3\pi/2$, or any odd multiple of $\pi/2$, the resulting vibration is a circle.

4. At all other phase differences, the resulting vibration is an ellipse.

With these facts in mind, consider the optical apparatus shown in Fig. 47–14. After unpolarized light traverses the polarizer, it is linearly polarized, with the vibration direction along the dotted line drawn on the polarizer. This linear light then enters a crystal plate cut so that the light travels in a direction perpendicular to the optic axis. The crystal plate has been rotated about the light beam until the optic axis makes

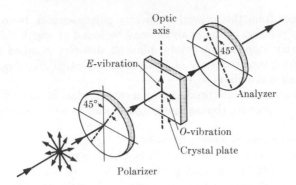

FIG. 47–14. Crystal plate between crossed polaroids. Since the optic axis makes an angle of 45° to the vibration direction of the linearly polarized light transmitted by the polarizer, the amplitudes of the O- and E-vibrations in the crystal are equal.

an angle of 45° with the direction of vibration of the linear light incident upon it. Since the E-vibration is, in this case, parallel to the optic axis, and the O-vibration is perpendicular to it, it follows that the amplitudes of the E and O beams are identical. The E and O beams travel through the crystal along the same path but with different speeds and, as they are about to emerge from the second crystal face, they combine to form one of the vibrations depicted in Fig. 47–13, depending on the phase difference.

The phase difference between the E- and O-vibrations at the second face of the crystal depends on the following: (1) the frequency of the light, (2) the indices of refraction of the crystal for E and O light, (3) the thickness of the crystal.

If a given crystal has such a thickness as to give rise to a phase difference of $\pi/2$ for a given frequency, then, according to Fig. 47–13, a circular vibration results and the light emerging from this crystal is said to be *circularly polarized light*. The crystal itself is called a *quarter-wave plate*. If the crystal plate shown in Fig. 47–14 is a quarter-wave plate, the intensity of light transmitted by the analyzer will remain unvaried as the analyzer is rotated. In other words, if an analyzer alone is used to analyze circularly polarized light, it will give the same result as when used to analyze unpolarized light.

A quarter-wave plate for, say, green light, is not a quarter-wave plate for any other color. Other colors have different frequencies, and since the E and O indices are different for these frequencies the phase difference would not be $\pi/2$.

If the crystal has such a thickness as to give rise to a phase difference of π for a given frequency, then, according to Fig. 47–13, a linear vibration perpendicular to the incident vibration direction results. The light that emerges from this crystal is linearly polarized and, by rotating the analyzer, a position of the analyzer may be found at which this light will be completely stopped. A crystal plate of this sort is called a *half-wave plate* for the given frequency of light. For any other frequency it would not be a half-wave plate.

If the phase difference produced by a crystal plate is such as to produce an elliptical vibration, the emerging light is said to be *elliptically polarized*.

47–8 Production of colors by polarized light. Consider, for the sake of definiteness, a crystal plate which is a half-wave plate for red light. If red light, linearly polarized at 45° to the optic axis, is allowed to traverse the plate, it will emerge from the plate as linearly polarized light with the vibration direction perpendicular to that of the incident light. An analyzer which is crossed with the polarizer will therefore transmit this red light.

Now suppose the incident radiation is *white* light. Only the red component of the white light will emerge from the half-wave plate as linearly polarized light. All the other wavelengths will emerge as either elliptically or circularly polarized light. When the analyzer is in a position to transmit the red, linearly polarized light completely, it will cut out a small amount of all the other wavelengths. The light transmitted by the analyzer will therefore predominate in red, and will have a pinkish hue. When the analyzer is rotated through 90°, so as to cut the red light out completely, the other wavelengths will be transmitted to some extent and the resulting hue will be the complement of pink, that is, a pale green.

Now suppose that we have a crystal plate of nonuniform thickness, such as a rough strip of selenite (gypsum). A small piece of the strip may have the proper thickness to act as a half-wave plate for red light, another piece may serve as a half-wave plate for yellow light, and so on. When a projecting lens is used to project an image of the selenite on a screen, the rest of the apparatus being the same as that in Fig. 47–14, the image will show patches of different colors, corresponding to regions of different thickness. These colors will change into the complementary values when the analyzer is rotated through 90°.

Ordinary cellophane, such as that used for wrapping cigarette packages, is doubly refracting. Striking color effects can be obtained by inserting various thicknesses of cellophane, or a crumpled ball of the material, between a polarizer and an analyzer.

47–9 Optical stress analysis. When a polarizer and an analyzer are mounted in the "crossed" position, i.e., with their transmission directions at right angles to each other, no light is transmitted through the combination. But if a doubly refracting crystal is inserted between polarizer and analyzer, the light after passing through the crystal is, in general, elliptically polarized, and some light will be transmitted by the analyzer. Thus the field of view, dark in the absence of the crystal, becomes light when the crystal is inserted.

Some substances, such as glass, celluloid, and bakelite, while not normally doubly refracting, become so when subjected to mechanical stress. From a study of the specimen between "crossed Nicols" much information regarding the stresses can be obtained. Improperly annealed glass, for example, may be internally stressed to an extent which might cause it later to develop cracks. It is evidently important that optical glass should be free from such a condition before it is subjected to expensive grinding and polishing. Hence such glass is always examined between crossed Nicols before grinding operations are begun.

Fig. 47–15. Photoelastic stress analysis. (Courtesy of Dr. W. M. Murray, M.I.T.)

The double refraction produced by stress is the basis of the science of *photoelasticity.* The stresses in opaque engineering materials such as girders, boiler plates, gear teeth, etc., can be analyzed by constructing a transparent model of the object, usually of bakelite, and examining it between crossed Nicols. Very complicated stress distributions such as those around a hole or a gear tooth, which it would be practically impossible to analyze mathematically, may thus be studied by optical methods. Figure 47–15 is a photograph of a photoelastic model under stress.

Liquids are not normally doubly refracting, but some become so when an electric field is established within them. This phenomenon is known as the *Kerr effect.* The existence of the Kerr effect makes it possible to construct an electrically controlled "light valve." A cell with transparent walls contains the liquid between a pair of parallel plates. The cell is inserted between crossed Nicols. Light is transmitted when an electric field is set up between the plates and is cut off when the field is removed.

47–10 Study of crystals by convergent polarized light. Polarized light is used extensively in the field of mineralogy. A transparent specimen of rock or crystal is cut into a thin plate and mounted on the stage of a *polarizing microscope,* which has a polarizer below the substage condenser and an analyzer above the objective lens. The substage condenser serves to converge the polarized light onto the specimen, from which it diverges to the objective lens. When monochromatic light is used, the image formed in the focal plane of the objective is found to have a pattern which indicates whether (a) the crystal is uniaxial or biaxial, (b) if uniaxial, where the optic axis is, and (c) if biaxial, the angle between the optic axes. Some of the polarization figures obtained with convergent polarized light are shown in Fig. 47–16. If white light is used, these patterns are brilliantly colored.

The figure obtained with a uniaxial crystal cut with its faces perpendicular to the optic axis consists of concentric colored rings, and when the polarizer and analyzer are crossed, there is a black cross superimposed on the rings. The elements of the black cross are called brushes. When circularly polarized light is used, the cross may be eliminated.

Polarizing ring sights are constructed from a plate of crystal, two polaroids, two quarter-wave plates, and two protecting plates of glass. When mounted on a gun perpendicular to the barrel and viewed with the eye, colored rings appear in space and move with the gun. Aiming the gun is accomplished by getting the target within the center of the ring system.

47–11 Optical activity. When a beam of linearly polarized light is sent through certain types of crystals and certain liquids, the direction of

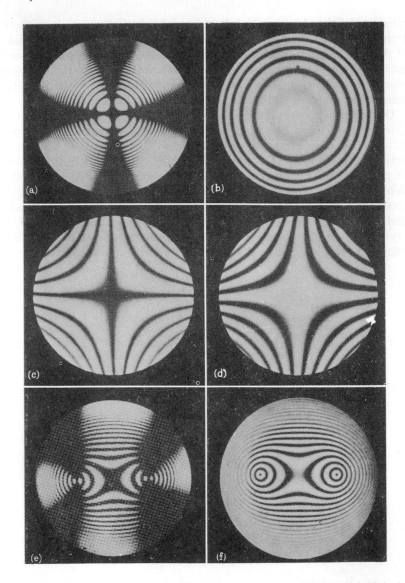

FIG. 47–16. Figures obtained with convergent polarized light. (a) Uniaxial crystal cut perpendicular to the optic axis, crossed polaroids. (b) Same crystal, parallel polaroids, with quarter-wave plates to eliminate brushes. (c) Uniaxial crystal cut parallel to the optic axis, crossed polaroids. (d) Same crystal, parallel polaroids. (e) Biaxial crystal, crossed polaroids. (f) Same crystal with quarter-wave plates to eliminate brushes. (Photographed by H. Hauswaldt, Magdeburg, 1902.)

vibration of the emerging linearly polarized light is found to be different from the original direction. This phenomenon is called *rotation of the plane of polarization,* and substances which exhibit the effect are called *optically active.* Those which rotate the plane of polarization to the right, looking along the advancing beam, are called dextrorotatory or right-handed; those which rotate it to the left, laevorotatory or left-handed.

Optical activity may be due to an asymmetry of the molecules of a substance, or it may be a property of a crystal as a whole. For example, solutions of cane sugar are dextrorotatory, indicating that the optical activity is a property of the sugar molecule. The rotation of the plane of polarization by a sugar solution is used commercially as a method of determining the proportion of cane sugar in a given sample. Crystalline quartz is also optically active, some natural crystals being right-handed and others left-handed. Here the optical activity is a consequence of the crystalline structure, since it disappears when the quartz is melted and allowed to resolidify into a glassy noncrystalline state called fused quartz.

PROBLEMS

47-1. A beam of light is incident on a liquid of 1.40 refractive index. The reflected rays are completely polarized. What is the angle of refraction of the beam?

47-2. The critical angle of light in a certain substance is 45°. What is the polarizing angle?

47-3. (a) At what angle above the horizontal must the sun be in order that sunlight reflected from the surface of a calm body of water shall be completely polarized? (b) What is the plane of the E-vector in the reflected light?

47-4. A parallel beam of "natural" light is incident at an angle of 58° on a plane glass surface. The reflected beam is completely linearly polarized. (a) What is the angle of refraction of the transmitted beam? (b) What is the refractive index of the glass?

47-5. Canada balsam has a refractive index of 1.528. What is the minimum angle of incidence that the ordinary ray may make with the Canada balsam layer of a Nicol prism to be totally reflected at this layer?

47-6. A parallel beam of linearly polarized light of wavelength 589 mμ (in vacuum) is incident on a calcite crystal as in Fig. 47-6(c). Find the wavelengths of the ordinary and extraordinary waves in the crystal.

47-7. A polarizer and an analyzer are oriented so that the maximum amount of light is transmitted. To what fraction of its maximum value is the intensity of the transmitted light reduced when the analyzer is rotated through (a) 30°, (b) 45°, (c) 60°?

47-8. A beam of linearly polarized light strikes a calcite crystal, the direction of the electric vector making an angle of 60° with the optic axis. (a) What is the ratio of the amplitude of the two refracted beams? (b) What is the ratio of their intensities?

47-9. A beam of light, after passing through the Nicol prism N_1 in Fig. 47-17, traverses a cell containing a scattering medium. The cell is observed at right angles through another Nicol N_2. Originally, the Nicols are oriented until the brightness of the field seen by the observer is a maximum. (a) Prism N_2 is rotated through 90°. Is extinction produced? (b) Prism N_1 is now rotated through 90°. Is the field bright or dark? (c) Prism N_2 is then restored to its original position. Is the field bright or dark?

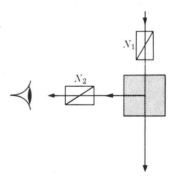

FIGURE 47-17

47-10. In Fig. 47-18, A and C are sheets of polaroid whose transmission directions are as indicated. B is a sheet of doubly refractive material whose optic axis is vertical. All three sheets are parallel. Unpolarized light enters from the left. Discuss the state of polarization of the light at points 2, 3, and 4.

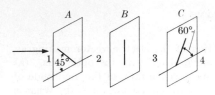

FIGURE 47–18

47–11. The phase difference δ between the E and O rays after traversing a crystal plate such as that in Fig. 47–14 is given by

$$\delta = \frac{2\pi}{\lambda} t(n_O - n_E),$$

where λ is the wavelength in air and t is the thickness of the crystal. (a) Show that the minimum thickness of a quarter-wave plate is given by $t = \lambda/4(n_O - n_E)$. (b) What is this minimum thickness for a quarter-wave calcite plate and light of 400 mμ wavelength?

47–12. What is the state of polarization of the light transmitted by a quarter-wave plate when the electric vector of the incident linearly polarized light makes an angle of 30° with the optic axis?

47–13. Assume the values of n_O and n_E for quartz to be independent of wavelength. A certain quartz-crystal is a quarter-wave plate for light of wavelength 800 mμ (in vacuum). What is the state of polarization of the transmitted light when linearly polarized light of wavelength 400 mμ (in vacuum) is incident on the crystal, the direction of polarization making an angle of 45° with the optic axis?

CHAPTER 48

SPECTRA AND ATOMIC PHYSICS

48–1 Line spectra. We have seen how a prism or grating spectrograph functions to disperse a beam of light into a spectrum. If the light source is an incandescent solid or liquid, the spectrum is *continuous;* that is, light of all wavelengths is present. If, however, the source is a gas through which an electrical discharge is passing, or a flame into which a volatile salt has been introduced, the spectrum is of an entirely different character. Instead of a continuous band of color, only a few colors appear, in the form of isolated parallel lines. (Each "line" is an image of the spectrograph slit, deviated through an angle dependent on the frequency of the light forming the image.) A spectrum of this sort is termed a *line spectrum.* The wavelengths of the lines are characteristic of the element emitting the light. That is, hydrogen always gives a set of lines in the same position, sodium another set, iron still another, and so on. The line structure of the spectrum extends both into the ultraviolet and infrared regions, where photographic or other means are required for its detection.

The positions of some of the more prominent lines of a number of elements are illustrated in Fig. 48–1.

It might be expected that the frequencies of the light emitted by a particular element would be arranged in some regular way. For instance, a radiating atom might be analogous to a vibrating string, emitting a fundamental frequency and its harmonics. At first sight there does not seem to be any semblance of order or regularity in the lines in Fig. 48–1, and for many years unsuccessful attempts were made to correlate the observed frequencies with those of a fundamental and its overtones. Finally, in 1885, Johann Jakob Balmer (1825–1898) found a simple formula which gave the frequencies of a group of lines emitted by atomic hydrogen. Since the spectrum of this element is relatively simple, and fairly typical of a number of others, we shall consider it in more detail in the next section.

48–2 Spectral series. Under the proper conditions of excitation, atomic hydrogen may be caused to emit the sequence of lines illustrated in Fig. 48–2. This sequence is called a *series*. There is evidently a certain order in this spectrum, the lines becoming crowded more and more closely together as the limit of the series is approached. The line of longest wavelength or lowest frequency, in the red, is known as H_α, the next, in the blue-green, as H_β, the third as H_γ and so on. Balmer found that the

957

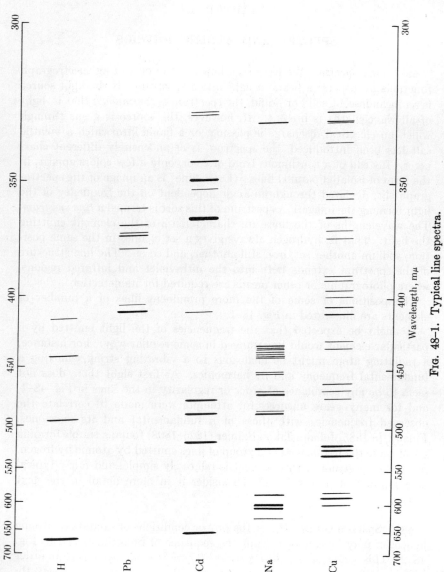

FIG. 48–1. Typical line spectra.

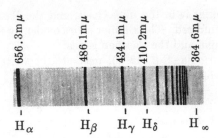

FIG. 48–2. The Balmer series of atomic hydrogen. (Reproduced by permission from *Atomic Spectra and Atomic Structures* by Gerhard Herzberg. Copyright 1937 by Prentice-Hall, Inc.)

wavelengths of these lines were given accurately by the simple formula,

$$\frac{1}{\lambda} = R\left(\frac{1}{2^2} - \frac{1}{n^2}\right), \qquad (48\text{–}1)$$

where λ is the wavelength, R is a constant called the Rydberg constant, and n may have the integral values 3, 4, 5, etc. If λ is in meters,

$$R = 1.097 \times 10^7 \text{ m}^{-1}.$$

Letting $n = 3$ in Eq. (48–1), one obtains the wavelength of the H_α line.

$$1/\lambda = 1.097 \times 10^7 \text{ m}^{-1} \left(\tfrac{1}{4} - \tfrac{1}{9}\right) = 1.522 \times 10^6 \text{ m}^{-1},$$

whence

$$\lambda = 656.3 \text{ m}\mu.$$

If $n = 4$, one obtains the wavelength of the H_β line, etc. For $n = \infty$, one obtains the limit of the series, at $\lambda = 364.6 \text{ m}\mu$. This is the shortest wavelength in the series.

Still other series spectra for hydrogen have since been discovered. These are known, after their discoverers, as the Lyman, Paschen, and Brackett series. The formulas for these are

$$\text{Lyman series:} \quad \frac{1}{\lambda} = R\left(\frac{1}{1^2} - \frac{1}{n^2}\right), \qquad n = 2, 3, \ldots$$

$$\text{Paschen series:} \quad \frac{1}{\lambda} = R\left(\frac{1}{3^2} - \frac{1}{n^2}\right), \qquad n = 4, 5, \ldots$$

$$\text{Brackett series:} \quad \frac{1}{\lambda} = R\left(\frac{1}{4^2} - \frac{1}{n^2}\right), \qquad n = 5, 6, \ldots$$

The Lyman series is in the ultraviolet, and the Paschen and Brackett series are in the infrared. The Balmer series evidently fits into the scheme between the Lyman and the Paschen series.

The Balmer formula, Eq. (48–1), may also be written in terms of the frequency of the light, recalling that

$$c = f\lambda \quad \text{or} \quad \frac{1}{\lambda} = \frac{f}{c}.$$

Thus Eq. (48–1) becomes

$$f = Rc\left(\frac{1}{2^2} - \frac{1}{n^2}\right) \tag{48-2}$$

or

$$f = \frac{Rc}{2^2} - \frac{Rc}{n^2}. \tag{48-3}$$

Each of the fractions on the right side of Eq. (48–3) is called a *term*, and the frequency of every line in the series is given by the difference between two terms.

There are only a few elements (hydrogen, singly ionized helium, doubly ionized lithium) whose spectra can be represented by a simple formula of the Balmer type. Nevertheless, it is possible to separate the more complicated spectra of other elements into series, and to express the frequency of each line in the series as the difference of two terms. The first term is constant for any one series, while the various values of the second term are found by assigning successive integral values to a quantity corresponding to n in Eq. (48–3), which appears in the (somewhat more complicated) expression for this term.

48–3 The Bohr atom. Einstein invoked the concept of light quanta, or photons, to account for the experimental facts of photoelectric emission. We shall now see how the Danish physicist Niels Bohr, in 1913, first applied the same ideas to the emission of light by atoms.

Experiments on the scattering of alpha particles by thin metallic foils were performed by Rutherford and his co-workers about 1906. These led to the hypothesis that atoms consisted of a relatively massive, positively charged nucleus, surrounded by a swarm of electrons. To account for the fact that the electrons in an atom remained at relatively large distances from the nucleus, in spite of the electrostatic force of attraction of the nucleus for them, Rutherford postulated that the electrons revolved about the nucleus, the force of attraction providing the requisite centripetal force to retain them in their orbits. This assumption, however, has an unfortunate consequence. A body moving in a circle is continuously accelerated toward the center of the circle, and according to classical electromagnetic theory an accelerated electron radiates energy. The total energy of the electrons would therefore gradually decrease, their orbits would become

Interference colors in the light reflected
from a thin soap film.

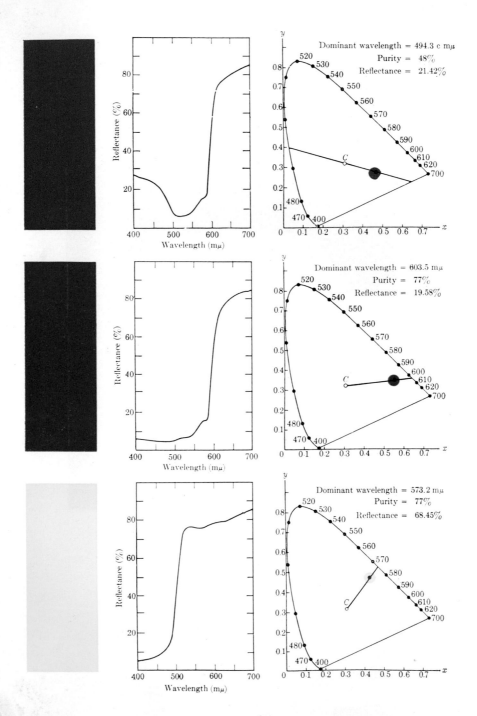

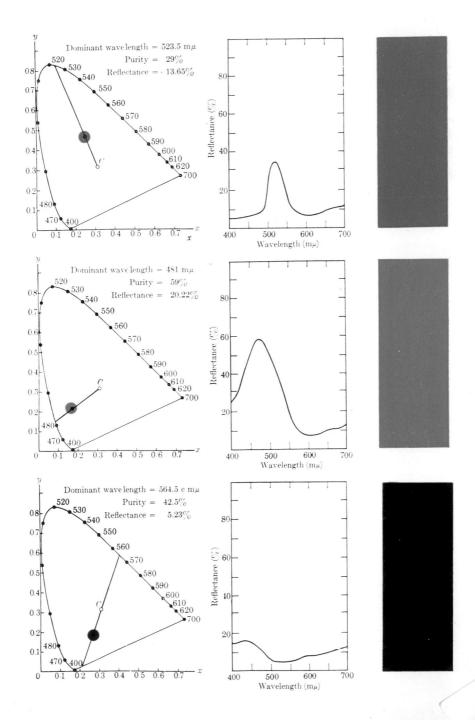

smaller and smaller, and eventually they would spiral into the nucleus and come to rest. Furthermore, according to classical theory, the frequency of the electromagnetic waves emitted by a revolving electron is equal to the frequency of revolution. As the electrons radiated energy their angular velocities would change continuously and they would emit a continuous spectrum (a mixture of all frequencies), in contradiction to the line spectrum which is observed.

Faced with the dilemma that electromagnetic theory predicted an unstable atom emitting radiant energy of all frequencies, while observation showed stable atoms emitting only a few frequencies, Bohr concluded that in spite of the success of electromagnetic theory in explaining large-scale phenomena, it could not be applied to processes on an atomic scale. Bohr's *first postulate*, therefore, was that *an electron in an atom can revolve in certain specified orbits without the emission of radiant energy*, contrary to the predictions of the classical electromagnetic theory. The first postulate therefore "explained" the stability of the atom.

A completely stable atom, however, is as unsatisfactory as an unstable one, since atoms *do* emit radiant energy. Bohr's *second postulate* incorporated into atomic theory the quantum concepts that had been developed by Planck and applied by Einstein to the photoelectric effect. The second postulate was that *an electron may suddenly "jump" from one of its specified nonradiating orbits to another of lower energy. When it does so, a single photon is emitted whose energy equals the energy difference between the initial and final states, and whose frequency f is given by the relation*

$$hf = W_1 - W_2, \qquad (48\text{--}4)$$

where h is Planck's constant and W_1 and W_2 are the initial and final energies.

It remained to specify the radii of the nonradiating orbits. Bohr found that the frequencies of the spectral lines of atomic hydrogen, as computed from Eq. (48–4), were in agreement with observation provided the electron was permitted to rotate about the nucleus *only in those orbits for which the angular momentum is some integral multiple of $h/2\pi$*. It will be recalled that the angular momentum of a particle of mass m, moving with tangential velocity v in a circle of radius r, is mvr. Hence the quantum condition above may be stated

$$mvr = n\,\frac{h}{2\pi}, \qquad (48\text{--}5)$$

where $n = 1, 2, 3$, etc.

The hydrogen atom consists of a single electron of charge $-e$, rotating about a single proton of charge $+e$. The electrostatic force of attraction between the charges,

$$F = \frac{1}{4\pi\epsilon_0} \frac{e^2}{r^2},$$

provides the centripetal force and, from Newton's second law,

$$\frac{1}{4\pi\epsilon_0} \frac{e^2}{r^2} = \frac{mv^2}{r}. \tag{48-6}$$

When Eqs. (48-5) and (48-6) are solved simultaneously for r and v, we obtain

$$r = \epsilon_0 \frac{n^2 h^2}{\pi m e^2}, \tag{48-7}$$

$$v = \frac{1}{\epsilon_0} \frac{e^2}{2nh}.$$

Let

$$\epsilon_0 \frac{h^2}{\pi m e^2} = r_0. \tag{48-8}$$

Then Eq. (48-7) becomes

$$r = n^2 r_0,$$

and the permitted, nonradiating orbits are of radii r_0, $4r_0$, $9r_0$, etc.

The appropriate value of n is called the *quantum number* of the orbit.

The numerical values of the quantities on the left side of Eq. (48-8) are:

$$\epsilon_0 = 8.85 \times 10^{-12} \frac{\text{coul}^2}{\text{newton·m}^2},$$

$$h = 6.62 \times 10^{-34} \text{ joule·sec},$$

$$m = 9.11 \times 10^{-31} \text{ kgm},$$

$$e = 1.60 \times 10^{-19} \text{ coul}.$$

Hence r_0, the radius of the first Bohr orbit, is

$$r_0 = \frac{8.85 \times 10^{-12} \, (\text{coul}^2/\text{n·m}^2) \times (6.62 \times 10^{-34} \text{ joule·sec})^2}{3.14 \times 9.11 \times 10^{-31} \text{ kgm} \times (1.60 \times 10^{-19} \text{ coul})^2}$$

$$= 5.3 \times 10^{-11} \text{ m} = 0.53 \times 10^{-8} \text{ cm}.$$

This is in good agreement with atomic diameters as estimated by other methods, namely, about 10^{-8} cm.

The kinetic energy of the electron in any orbit is

$$E_k = \tfrac{1}{2}mv^2 = \frac{1}{\epsilon_0^2}\frac{me^4}{8n^2h^2},$$

and the potential energy is

$$E_p = -\frac{1}{4\pi\epsilon_0}\frac{e^2}{r} = -\frac{1}{\epsilon_0^2}\frac{me^4}{4n^2h^2}.$$

The total energy, W, is therefore

$$W = E_k + E_p = -\frac{1}{\epsilon_0^2}\frac{me^4}{8n^2h^2}. \tag{48-9}$$

The total energy has a negative sign because the reference level of potential energy is taken with the electron at an infinite distance from the nucleus. Since we are interested only in energy differences, this is not of importance.

The energy of the atom is least when its electron is revolving in the orbit for which $n = 1$, for then W has its largest negative value. For $n = 2, 3, \ldots$ the absolute value of W is smaller, hence the energy is progressively larger in the outer orbits. The *normal state* of the atom is that of lowest energy, with the electron revolving in the orbit of smallest radius, r_0. As a result of collisions with rapidly moving electrons in an electrical discharge, or for other causes, the atom may temporarily acquire sufficient energy to raise the electron to some outer orbit. The atom is then said to be in an *excited state*. This state is an unstable one, and the electron soon falls or "jumps" back to a state of lower energy, emitting a photon in the process.

Let n be the quantum number of some excited state, and l the quantum number of the lower state to which the electron returns after the emission process. Then W_1, the initial energy, is

$$W_1 = -\frac{1}{\epsilon_0^2}\frac{me^4}{8n^2h^2},$$

and W_2, the final energy, is

$$W_2 = -\frac{1}{\epsilon_0^2}\frac{me^4}{8l^2h^2}.$$

The decrease in energy, $W_1 - W_2$, which we place equal to the energy hf of the emitted photon, is

$$W_1 - W_2 = hf = -\frac{1}{\epsilon_0^2}\frac{me^4}{8n^2h^2} + \frac{1}{\epsilon_0^2}\frac{me^4}{8l^2h^2},$$

or

$$f = \frac{1}{\epsilon_0^2} \frac{me^4}{8h^3} \left(\frac{1}{l^2} - \frac{1}{n^2} \right). \tag{48--10}$$

This equation is of precisely the same form as the Balmer formula (Eq. 48–2) for the frequencies in the hydrogen spectrum if we place

$$\frac{1}{\epsilon_0^2} \frac{me^4}{8h^3} = Rc, \tag{48--11}$$

and let $l = 1$ for the Lyman series, $l = 2$ for the Balmer series, etc. The Lyman series is therefore the group of lines emitted by electrons returning from some excited state to the normal state. The Balmer series is the group emitted by electrons returning from some higher state, but which stop in the second orbit instead of falling at once to that of lowest energy. That is, an electron returning from the third orbit ($n = 3$) to the second orbit ($l = 2$) emits the H_α line. One returning from the fourth orbit ($n = 4$) to the second ($l = 2$) emits the H_β line, etc. (See Fig. 48–3.)

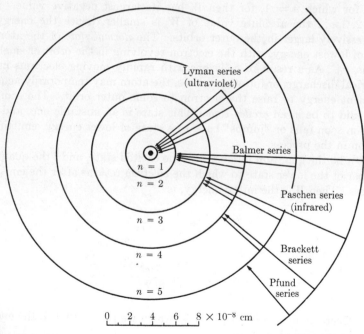

FIG. 48–3. "Permitted" orbits of an electron in the Bohr model of a hydrogen atom. The transitions or "jumps" responsible for some of the lines of the various series are indicated by arrows.

The question naturally arises as to whether or not Eq. (48–11) is true, since every quantity in it may be determined quite independently of the Bohr theory, and apart from this theory we have no reason to expect these quantities to be related in this particular way. The quantities m and e, for instance, are found from experiments on free electrons, h may be found from the photoelectric effect, R by measurements of wavelengths, while c is the velocity of light. However, if we substitute in Eq. (48–11) the values of these quantities, obtained by such diverse means, we find that it does hold exactly, within the limits of experimental error.

48–4 Deuterium. The discovery of deuterium constitutes another triumph of Bohr's theory of the hydrogen atom. According to Bohr, an electron revolving about a stationary nucleus in an orbit characterized by the quantum number n has an energy given by Eq. (48–9), thus

$$W = -\frac{1}{\epsilon_0^2}\frac{me^4}{8n^2h^2}.$$

The nucleus of a hydrogen atom, a proton, has a mass 1840 times that of an electron, and therefore the assumption that the proton remains stationary while the electron revolves around it is a fair one if great accuracy is not desired. In devising a theory to explain spectral lines, however, the utmost refinements must be introduced because measurements of the wavelengths of spectral lines are among the most precise in all experimental physics. It is natural, therefore, to take into account the fact that both the electron and proton revolve about their common center of gravity. When this is done, the energy of an electron becomes

$$W = -\frac{1}{\epsilon_0^2}\frac{m}{1+m/M}\frac{e^4}{8n^2h^2},$$

where M is the mass of the nucleus.

It was suspected in 1931 that ordinary hydrogen was a mixture of two isotopes, one isotope consisting of an electron revolving about a proton, and the other consisting of an electron revolving about a nucleus of mass twice that of the proton.

If all of these atoms are excited in an electric discharge and the Balmer lines are measured carefully, the frequency of, say, the second Balmer line (H_β) would be slightly different for the two different hydrogens. Thus

$$f_1 = \frac{1}{\epsilon_0^2}\frac{m}{1+m/M_1}\frac{e^4}{8h^3}\left(\frac{1}{2^2}-\frac{1}{4^2}\right)\binom{\text{for a nucleus}}{\text{of mass }M_1},$$

and

$$f_2 = \frac{1}{\epsilon_0^2} \frac{m}{1 + m/M_2} \frac{e^4}{8h^3} \left(\frac{1}{2^2} - \frac{1}{4^2}\right) \binom{\text{for a nucleus}}{\text{of mass } M_2},$$

where $m/M_1 = 1/1840$ and $m/M_2 = 1/3680$. The two different H_β's would be very close together because the wavelength difference corresponding to the frequency difference $f_1 - f_2$ is only 1.3 angstroms. Furthermore, the H_β line corresponding to the heavy isotope would be very much fainter than the other because in any ordinary sample of hydrogen, there is presumably only a small percentage of heavy hydrogen.

In spite of these difficulties, Urey, Murphy, and Brickwedde, in 1932, undertook the task of determining whether the heavy isotope of hydrogen existed. With the aid of a diffraction grating spectrograph they found the blue H_β line to consist of a very strong line and a faint companion. They then proceeded to prepare hydrogen with a higher percentage of the heavy isotope by allowing liquid hydrogen to evaporate and retaining the residue. With this residue in the discharge tube, the companion line was much stronger and its displacement from the other H_β line was in agreement with the value predicted by the Bohr theory. They called the heavier isotope *deuterium*.

48-5 Wave mechanics. The Bohr model of the atom was successful in explaining the observed spectra of atomic hydrogen and of a few other elements, but for atoms having a large number of orbital electrons, and for molecules, the theory was not as satisfactory. Furthermore, there seemed to be no good justification, except that it led to the right answer, for the hypothesis that only those orbits are permitted for which the angular momentum is equal to some integral multiple of $h/2\pi$. The next advance in atom-building, which followed the theory of Bohr by about ten years, was a suggestion by de Broglie that since light appeared to be dualistic in nature, behaving in some aspects like waves and in others like corpuscles, the same might be true of matter. That is, electrons and protons, which until that time had been thought to be purely corpuscular, might in some circumstances behave like waves. The rapid development of this idea in the hands of Heisenberg, Schroedinger, and many others, led to the so-called *wave mechanics* or *quantum mechanics*, which has placed atomic theory on what we believe to be a secure foundation.

A single section on "wave mechanics" cannot, of course, give the reader any adequate comprehension of this complex and highly mathematical subject, any more than the whole field of "Newtonian mechanics" could be covered in the same amount of space. We can only point out the main lines of thought in a nonmathematical way, describe some of the experimental evidence for the wave nature of material particles, and show how the quantum numbers that were introduced in such an artificial way by Bohr now enter naturally into the problem of atomic structure.

The essential feature of the new wave mechanics, as we have said, is that particles of matter are also endowed with wavelike properties. An electron, then, must be considered as some sort of wave, more or less spread out through space and not simply localized at a point. The idea that the electrons in an atom move in definite Bohr orbits such as those in Fig. 48–3 has been abandoned. Instead, the new theory specifies merely that there are certain *regions* in which an electron is more or less likely to be found. The orbits themselves, however, were never an essential part of Bohr's theory, since the only quantities that determined the frequencies of the emitted photons were the *energies* corresponding to the orbits. The new theory still assigns definite energy states to an atom. In the hydrogen atom the energies are the same as those given by Bohr's theory; in more complicated atoms where the Bohr theory did not work, the wave mechanical picture is in excellent agreement with observation.

We shall illustrate how quantization arises in atomic structure by an analogy with the classical mechanical problem of a vibrating string fixed at its ends. When the string vibrates, the ends must be nodes, but nodes may occur at other points also, and the general requirement is that the length of the string shall equal some integral number of half-wave lengths. The point of interest is that the solution of the problem of the vibrating string leads to the appearance of *integral numbers*.

In a similar way, the principles of quantum mechanics lead to a wave equation (Schroedinger's equation) that must be satisfied by an electron in an atom, subject also to certain boundary conditions. Let us think of an electron as a wave extending in a circle around the nucleus. In order that the wave may "come out even," the circumference of this circle must include some *integral number* of wavelengths. The wavelength of a particle of mass m, moving with a velocity v, is given according to wave mechanics by the equation

$$\lambda = \frac{h}{mv}, \qquad (48\text{--}12)$$

where λ is the wavelength and h is Planck's constant. Then if r is the radius and $2\pi r$ the circumference of the circle occupied by the wave, we must have

$$2\pi r = n\lambda,$$

where $n = 1, 2, 3$, etc.

Since $\lambda = h/mv$, this equation becomes

$$2\pi r = n \frac{h}{mv},$$

or

$$mvr = n \frac{h}{2\pi}.$$

But mvr is the angular momentum of the electron, and we see that the wave mechanical picture leads naturally to Bohr's postulate that the angular momentum equals some integral multiple of $h/2\pi$.

There is even more direct experimental evidence of the wavelike nature of electrons. We have described in Chapter 46 how the layers of atoms in a crystal serve as a diffraction grating for x-rays. An x-ray beam is strongly reflected when it strikes a crystal at such an angle that the waves reflected from the atomic layers combine to reinforce one another. The point of importance here is that the existence of these strong reflections is evidence of the wave nature of x-rays.

In 1927, Davisson and Germer, working in the Bell Telephone Laboratories, were studying the nature of the surface of a crystal of nickel by directing a beam of electrons at the surface and observing the electrons reflected at various angles. It might be expected that even the smoothest surface attainable would still look rough to an electron, and that the electron beam would therefore be diffusely reflected. But Davisson and Germer found that the electrons were reflected in almost the same way that x-rays would be reflected from the same crystal. The wavelengths of the electrons in the beam were computed from their known velocity, with the help of Eq. (48–12), and the angles at which strong reflection took place were found to be the same as those at which x-rays of the same wavelength would be reflected.

48–6 Absorption spectra. Although the precise picture of electronic orbits about the nucleus of an atom has been abandoned in modern physics, the concept of energy levels still remains. The fundamental problem of the spectroscopist is to determine the energy levels of an atom from the measured values of the wavelengths of the spectral lines emitted when the atom proceeds from one set of energy levels to another. In the case of complicated spectra emitted by the heavier atoms this is a task requiring tremendous ingenuity. Nevertheless, almost all spectra have been analyzed, and the resulting energy levels have been tabulated or plotted with the aid of diagrams similar to the one shown for sodium in Fig. 48–4.

The lowest energy level of the atom is called the *normal state*, and all higher levels are called *excited states*. As we have seen, a spectral line is emitted when an atom proceeds from an excited state to a lower state. The only means discussed so far for raising the atom from the normal state to an excited state has been with the aid of an electric discharge. Let us consider now another method involving the absorption of radiant energy.

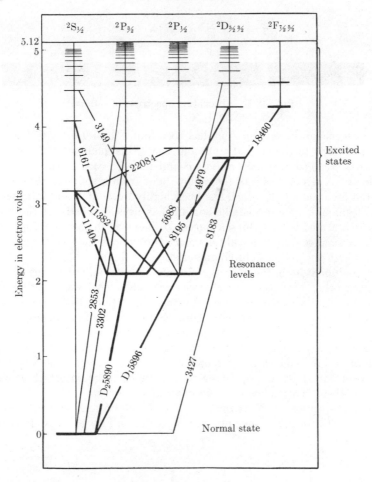

FIG. 48–4. Energy levels of the sodium atom. Numbers on the lines between levels are wavelengths in angstroms.

From Fig. 48–4 it may be seen that a sodium atom emits the characteristic yellow light of wavelengths 5890 and 5896 angstroms (the D_1 and D_2 lines) when it undergoes the transitions from the two levels marked *resonance levels* to the normal state. Suppose a sodium atom in the normal state were to absorb a quantum of radiant energy of wavelength 5890 or 5896 angstroms. It would then undergo a transition in the opposite direction and be raised to one of the resonance levels. After a short time, known as the *lifetime* of the excited state (which in the case of the reso-

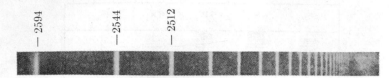

FIG. 48–5. Absorption spectrum of sodium.

nance levels of the sodium atom has been found to be 1.6×10^{-8} sec), the atom returns to the normal state and emits this quantum. The emission process is called *resonance radiation* and may be easily demonstrated as follows. A strong beam of the yellow light from a sodium arc is concentrated on a glass bulb which has been highly evacuated and into which a small amount of pure metallic sodium has been distilled. If the bulb is gently warmed with a Bunsen burner to increase the sodium vapor pressure, resonance radiation will take place throughout the whole bulb, which glows with the yellow light characteristic of sodium.

A sodium atom in the normal state may absorb radiant energy of wavelengths other than the yellow resonance lines. All wavelengths corresponding to spectral lines emitted when the sodium atom returns to its normal state may be absorbed. Thus, from Fig. 48–4, wavelengths 3302, 2853, etc., may be absorbed by a normal sodium atom. If, therefore, the light from a carbon arc is sent through an absorption tube containing sodium vapor, and then examined with a spectroscope, there will be a series of dark lines corresponding to the wavelengths absorbed, as shown in Fig. 48–5. This is known as an *absorption spectrum*.

The absorption of the resonance lines of sodium may be easily demonstrated with the aid of the apparatus depicted in Fig. 48–6. A large chunk

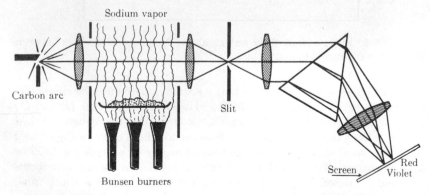

FIG. 48–6. Apparatus for observing the absorption spectrum of sodium vapor.

of metallic sodium placed in an iron boat and heated with a battery of large Bunsen burners supplies sufficient concentration of sodium atoms to absorb the yellow light and create a thick dark line in the yellow part of the continuous spectrum. The slit of the spectroscope is usually too wide to show the presence of two dark lines close together.

The sun's spectrum is an absorption spectrum. The main body of the sun emits a continuous spectrum, whereas the cooler vapors in the sun's atmosphere emit line spectra corresponding to all the elements present. When the intense light from the main body of the sun passes through the cooler vapors the lines of these elements are absorbed. The light emitted by the cooler vapors is so small compared with the unabsorbed continuous spectrum, that the continuous spectrum appears to be crossed by a myriad of faint dark lines. These were first observed by Fraunhofer and are therefore called *Fraunhofer lines*. They may be observed with any student spectroscope pointed toward any part of the sky.

48–7 Band spectra. Up to this point we have confined our attention to spectra emitted by individual atoms. Many gases, however, have molecules consisting of two or more atoms held more or less tightly together. Thus hydrogen, oxygen, nitrogen, carbon monoxide, etc., are diatomic gases with molecules composed of two atoms each. To obtain the spectrum of atomic hydrogen or atomic oxygen, a heavy electric discharge is needed to dissociate some of the molecules into atoms. If no dissociation takes place, the molecules themselves emit light which when analyzed with a spectroscope shows an enormous number of lines spaced so close together that they form what appear roughly to be bands. Hence the term *band spectrum*. Typical band spectra are shown in Fig. 48–7.

FIG. 48–7. Typical band spectrum. (Courtesy of R. C. Herman.)

Each line in a band spectrum is the result of a transition between two energy levels of the molecule. The energy levels of molecules are much more numerous and much more complicated than those of atoms. They arise not only from different electron "orbits" but also from different energies of rotation and vibration. A whole set of bands corresponds to an electronic transition, a single band to a vibrational transition, and a single line in a band to a rotational transition.

48–8 X-Ray spectra. The elements of the periodic system may be arranged in sequence according to *atomic number,* that is, according to the number of electrons which surround the nucleus of the atom. The electrons group themselves in various "shells" about the nucleus. Each shell seems able to hold a certain maximum number of electrons. As we consider atoms of larger and larger atomic number, first the inner shell fills up to its maximum number, then the second shell, then the third, and so on. (This order is not exactly followed in all cases, but is nearly so.) The innermost shell, known as the K-shell, can contain at the most two electrons. The next outer shell, the L-shell, can contain eight. The third, the M-shell, has a capacity for 18 electrons, while the N-shell may hold 32. The sodium atom, for example, which contains 11 electrons, has two in the K-shell, eight in the L-shell, and a single electron in the M-shell. Molybdenum, with 42 electrons, has two in the K-shell, eight in the L-shell, 18 in the M-shell, and 14 in the N-shell.

The outer electrons of an atom, as the M electron of sodium, are the ones responsible for the optical spectra of the elements. Relatively small amounts of energy suffice to remove these to excited states, and on their return to their normal states wavelengths in or near the visible region are emitted. The inner electrons, such as those in the K-shell, require much more energy to displace them from their normal levels. As a result, we would expect a photon of much larger energy, and hence much higher frequency, to be emitted when the atom returns to its normal state after the displacement of an inner electron. This is in fact the case, and it is the displacement of the inner electrons which gives rise to the emission of x-rays.

The usual method of producing x-rays is to bombard the atoms of an element with rapidly moving electrons or cathode rays. The substance to be bombarded is made the anode in an evacuated tube, the cathode

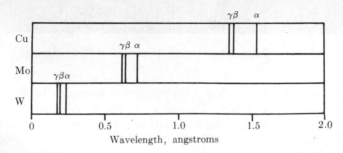

Fig. 48–8. Wavelengths of the K_α, K_β, and K_γ lines of copper, molybdenum, and tungsten.

being an incandescent tungsten filament. Electrons emitted thermioni-
cally by the filament are accelerated by a high potential difference between
cathode and anode. On colliding with the atoms of the anode, or *target*,
some of these electrons, provided they have acquired sufficient energy,
will dislodge one of the inner electrons of a target atom, say one of the
K electrons. This leaves a vacant space in the K-shell, which is immediately filled by an electron from either the L-, M-, or N-shells. The read-
justment of the electrons is accompanied by a decrease in the energy of
the atom, and an x-ray photon is emitted with energy just equal to this
decrease. Since the energy change is perfectly definite for atoms of a
given element, we can predict definite frequencies for the emitted x-rays
or, in other words, the x-ray spectrum should be a line spectrum also.
We can predict further that there should be just three lines in the series,
corresponding to the three possibilities that the vacant space may have
been filled by an L, M, or N electron.

This is precisely what is observed. Figure 48–8 illustrates the so-called
K-series of the elements tungsten, molybdenum, and copper. Each series
consists of three lines, known as the K_α, K_β, and K_γ lines. The K_α line
is produced by the transition of an L electron to the vacated space in the
K-shell, the K_β line by an M electron, and the K_γ line by an N electron.

In addition to the K-series, there are other series known as the L-,
M-, and N-series, produced by the ejection of electrons from the L-, M-,
and N-shells rather than the K-shell. As would be expected, the electrons
in these outer shells, being farther away from the nucleus, are not held
as firmly as those in the K-shell. Consequently, the other series may be
excited by more slowly moving electrons, and the photons emitted are of
lower energy and longer wavelength.

In addition to the x-ray *line* spectrum there is a background of *continuous* x-radiation from the target of an x-ray tube. This is due to the
sudden deceleration of those cathode rays which do not happen to eject
an electron. The remarkable feature of the continuous spectrum is that
while it extends indefinitely toward the long wavelength end, it is cut off
very sharply at the short wavelength end. Again the quantum theory
furnishes a satisfactory explanation of the short-wave limit of the continuous x-ray spectrum.

A bombarding electron may be brought to rest in a single process if
the electron happens to collide head-on with an atom of the target, or it
may make a number of collisions before coming to rest, giving up part of
its energy each time. If we assume that the energy lost at each collision
is radiated as an x-ray photon, these photons may be of any energy up to
a certain maximum, namely, that of an electron which gives up all of its
energy in a single collision. Hence there will be a short-wave limit to the

spectrum. The frequency of this limit is found as usual by setting the energy of the electron equal to the energy of the x-ray photon.

$$hf = \tfrac{1}{2}mv^2. \qquad (48\text{-}13)$$

This is precisely the same equation as that for the photoelectric effect except for the work function term, which is negligible here since the energies of the x-ray photons are so large. In fact, the emission of x-rays may be described as an *inverse photoelectric effect*. In photoelectric emission the energy of a photon is transformed into kinetic energy of an electron; here, the kinetic energy of an electron is transformed into that of a photon.

EXAMPLE. Compute the potential difference through which an electron must be accelerated in order that the short-wave limit of the continuous x-ray spectrum shall be exactly 1 angstrom.

The frequency corresponding to 1 angstrom (10^{-10} m) is given by

$$f = \frac{c}{\lambda} = \frac{3 \times 10^8 \text{ m/sec}}{10^{-10} \text{ m}} = 3 \times 10^{18} \text{ sec}^{-1}.$$

The energy of the photon is

$$hf = 6.62 \times 10^{-34} \text{ joule·sec} \times 3 \times 10^{18} \text{ sec}^{-1} = 19.9 \times 10^{-16} \text{ joule}.$$

This must equal the kinetic energy of the electron, $\tfrac{1}{2}mv^2$, which is also equal to the product of the electronic charge and the accelerating voltage, V.

$$\tfrac{1}{2}mv^2 = eV = 19.9 \times 10^{-16} \text{ joule}.$$

Since

$$e = 1.60 \times 10^{-19} \text{ coulomb},$$

$$V = \frac{19.9 \times 10^{-16} \text{ joule}}{1.60 \times 10^{-19} \text{ coul}} = 12,400 \text{ volts}.$$

CHAPTER 49

RADIOACTIVITY AND NUCLEAR PHYSICS

49-1 Natural radioactivity. In studying the fluorescence and phosphorescence of compounds irradiated with visible light, Becquerel, in 1896, performed a crucial experiment which led to a deeper understanding of the properties of the nucleus of an atom. After illuminating some pieces of uranium-potassium sulfate with visible light, Becquerel wrapped them in black paper and separated the package from a photographic plate by a piece of silver. After several hours' exposure the photographic plate was developed and showed a blackening due to something that must have been emitted from the compound and was able to penetrate both the black paper and the silver.

Rutherford showed later that the emanations given off by uranium sulfate were capable of ionizing the air in the space between two oppositely charged metallic plates (an ionization chamber). The current registered by a galvanometer in series with the circuit was taken to be a measure of the "activity" of the compound.

A systematic study of the activity of various elements and compounds led Mme. Curie to the conclusion that it was an atomic phenomenon, and by the methods of chemical analysis, she and her husband, Pierre Curie, found that "ionizing ability" or "activity" was associated not only with uranium but with two other elements that they discovered, radium and polonium. The activity of radium was found to be more than a million times that of uranium. Since the pioneer days of the Curies, many more radioactive substances have been discovered.

The activity of radioactive material may be easily shown to be the result of three different kinds of emanations. A small piece of radioactive material is placed at the bottom of a long groove in a lead block, as shown in Fig. 49-1. Some distance above the lead block a photographic plate is placed, and the whole apparatus is highly evacuated. A strong magnetic field is applied at right angles to the plane of the diagram. After developing the plate, three distinct spots are found, one in the direct line of the groove in the lead block, one deflected to one side, and one to the other side. From a knowledge of the direction of the magnetic field, it is concluded that one of the emanations is positively charged (alpha particles), one is negatively charged (beta particles), and one is neutral (gamma rays).

Further investigation showed that all three emanations are not emitted simultaneously by all radioactive substances. Some elements emit alpha

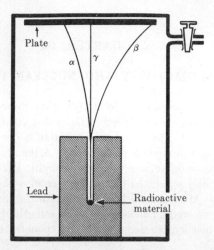

FIG. 49–1.   The three emanations from a radioactive material and their paths in a magnetic field perpendicular to the plane of the diagram.

particles, others emit beta particles, while gamma rays sometimes accompany one and sometimes the other.   Furthermore, no simple macroscopic physical or chemical process, such as raising or lowering the temperature, chemical combination with other nonradioactive substances, etc., could change or affect in any way the activity of a given sample.   As a result, it was suspected from the beginning that radioactivity is a *nuclear* process and that the emission of a charged particle from the nucleus of an atom results in leaving behind a different atom, occupying a different place in the periodic table.   In other words, radioactivity involves the transmutation of elements.

49–2 Alpha particles.   In the preceding section it was shown that alpha particles are positively charged.   To determine the magnitude of the charge, experiments were first performed to determine the number of alpha particles emitted per second per unit mass of radioactive material. This was accomplished with the aid of a device called a *Geiger counter*, one of the most important instruments of modern physics.

As shown in Fig. 49–2, a Geiger counter consists of a metal cylinder and a wire along the axis.   The cylinder contains a gas such as air or argon at a pressure of from 50 to 100 mm of mercury.   A difference of potential slightly less than that necessary to produce a discharge is maintained between the wire and the cylinder wall.   Alpha particles (or, for that matter, any particles to be studied) can enter through a thin glass or mica window.   The particle entering the counter produces ionization of the gas

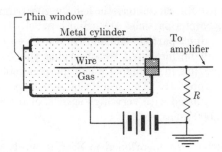

FIG. 49–2. Schematic diagram of a Geiger counter.

molecules. These ions are accelerated by the electric field and produce more ions by collisions, causing the ionization current to build up rapidly. The current, however, decays rapidly since the circuit has a small time constant. There is therefore a momentary surge of current or a momentary potential surge across R which may be amplified and made to actuate a relay to advance a mechanical counter, or to produce a click in a loudspeaker.

Placing a known mass of radium a known distance from the window of a Geiger counter, Rutherford and Geiger counted the number of alpha particles emitted in a known time interval. They found that 3.57×10^{10} alpha particles were emitted per second per gram of radium. They then allowed the alpha particles from the same source to fall upon a plate and measured its rate of increase of charge. Dividing the rate of increase of charge by the number emitted per second, Rutherford and Geiger determined the charge on an alpha particle to be 3.19×10^{-19} coulomb, or practically twice the charge on an electron, but opposite in sign.

The next problem was to determine the mass of an alpha particle. This was accomplished by measuring first the ratio of charge to mass by the electric and magnetic deflection method described in Chapter 31. The ratio was found by Rutherford and Robinson to be 4.82×10^{7} coulombs per kilogram. Combining this result with the charge of an alpha particle, the mass was found to be 6.62×10^{-27} kgm, almost exactly four times the mass of a hydrogen atom.

Since a helium atom has a mass four times that of a hydrogen atom and, stripped of its two outer electrons (as a bare nucleus), has a charge equal in magnitude and opposite in sign to two electrons, it seemed certain that alpha particles were helium nuclei. To make the identification certain, however, Rutherford and Royds collected the alpha particles in a glass discharge tube over a period of about six days and then established an electric discharge in the tube. Examining the spectrum of the emitted light, they identified the characteristic helium spectrum and established without doubt that alpha particles are helium nuclei.

The speed of an alpha particle emitted from a given radioactive source such as radium may be measured by observing the radius of the circle traversed by the particle in a magnetic field perpendicular to the motion, as explained in Chapter 31. The results of such experiments show that alpha particles are emitted with very high speeds, of the order of 1.6×10^7 m/sec or about 10,000 miles/sec.

49-3 Beta particles. As mentioned in Section 49–1, beta particles are negatively charged and are therefore deflected in an electric or magnetic field. Deflection experiments similar to those described in Chapter 31 prove conclusively that beta particles have the same charge and mass as electrons. They are emitted with tremendous speeds, some reaching a value of 0.9995 that of light.

According to Einstein's special theory of relativity, the mass of a particle should depend upon its speed according to the equation

$$m = \frac{m_0}{\sqrt{1 - v^2/c^2}},$$

where m_0 is the mass at zero speed (rest mass), v is the speed of the particle, and c is the speed of light. Assuming the charge to remain constant, the ratio of the charge e to the mass m of a beta particle should vary as follows:

$$\frac{e}{m} = \frac{e}{m_0} \sqrt{1 - v^2/c^2},$$

and therefore the value of e/m measured by deflection methods should depart considerably from the value e/m_0, since the values of v for beta particles approach so closely the value of c. Experiments to test these relativistic equations have been performed on the beta particles emitted by radium, and complete confirmation obtained.

Unlike alpha particles, which are emitted from a given nucleus with one or a few definite velocities, beta particles are emitted with a continuous range of velocities, from zero up to a maximum which depends on the nature of the emitting nucleus. If the principles of conservation of energy and of momentum are to hold in nuclear processes, it is necessary to assume that the emission of a beta particle is accompanied by the emission of another particle of negligible rest mass and with no charge. This particle, called the *neutrino*, is believed to have zero rest mass and zero charge and therefore, even in traversing the densest matter, would be expected to produce very little measurable effect. In spite of this, Reines and Corvan, in 1953 and again in 1956, succeeded in detecting its existence in a series of extraordinary experiments.

49–4 Gamma rays. Since gamma rays are not deflected by a magnetic field, they cannot consist of charged particles. They are, however, diffracted at the surface of a crystal in a manner similar to that of x-rays but with extremely small angles of diffraction. Experiments of this sort lead to the conclusion that "gamma rays" are actually electromagnetic waves of extremely short wavelength, about 1/100 that of x-rays.

The gamma-ray spectrum of any one element is a line spectrum, suggesting that a gamma-ray photon is emitted when a nucleus proceeds from a state of higher to a state of lower energy. This view is substantiated in the case of radium by the following facts. When alpha particles are emitted from radium they are found to consist of two groups, those with a kinetic energy of 48.79×10^5 electron volts and those with an energy of 46.95×10^5 electron volts. When a radium atom emits an alpha particle of the smaller energy, the resulting nucleus (which corresponds to the element *radon*) has a greater amount of energy than if the higher speed alpha particle had been emitted. This represents an excited state of the radon nucleus. If now the radon nucleus undergoes a transition from this excited state to the lower energy state, a gamma-ray photon of energy $(48.79 - 46.95) \times 10^5 = 1.84 \times 10^5$ electron volts should be emitted. The measured energy of the gamma-ray photon emitted by radium is 1.89×10^5 electron volts, in excellent agreement.

Thus, by correlating alpha-particle energies and gamma-ray energies, it is possible in some cases to construct nuclear energy level diagrams similar to x-ray energy level diagrams.

49–5 Radioactive transformations. Every atom is specified with the aid of three numbers:

1. The *atomic number Z*, or the positive charge of the nucleus, expressed as a multiple of the electronic charge.

2. The *atomic mass*, or the mass of the atom expressed in atomic mass units (abbreviated amu) which are of such magnitude that the atomic mass of the most abundant isotope of oxygen is taken arbitrarily to be exactly 16 amu.

3. The *mass number A*, or the nearest whole number to the actual atomic mass.

These numbers are given for a few of the light elements in Table 49–1.

When a radioactive atom emits an alpha particle, the atomic number is reduced by 2 and the mass number reduced by 4, since an alpha particle is a helium nucleus with a charge of 2 units and a mass number 4. On the other hand, when a beta particle is emitted, the atomic number is increased by 1 but the mass number remains the same, since a beta particle is an electron with a charge of $-e$ and a negligible mass. The emission of gamma rays leaves both the atomic number and the mass number un-

TABLE 49-1

ATOMIC DATA

Element		Atomic number Z	Atomic mass in amu	Mass number A
Hydrogen	H	1	1.00813	1
Deuterium	D	1	2.01473	2
Helium	He	2	3.01688	3
Helium	He	2	4.00389	4
Lithium	Li	3	6.01682	6
Lithium	Li	3	7.01784	7
Beryllium	Be	4	8.00766	8
Beryllium	Be	4	9.01486	9
Boron	B	5	10.01631	10
Boron	B	5	11.01292	11
Carbon	C	6	12.00386	12
Carbon	C	6	13.00761	13

altered. In natural radioactivity either an alpha particle or a beta particle is emitted, and gamma rays may accompany either process.

Suppose a convenient mass of radioactive material is isolated by chemical methods, and its activity is measured as a function of the time. In all cases the "decay" curve has the appearance of the graph in Fig. 49-3. It is an exponential decay curve similar to that representing the discharge of a capacitor through a resistor. The fact that such a curve represents the activity of all known radioactive materials is interpreted as follows. The emission of an alpha or beta particle from a nucleus is a haphazard event, so that when a very large number of nuclei are present, the emission obeys the laws of probability. If it takes a time T for half the original nuclei to disintegrate, then in the next interval T, half of those remaining will disintegrate, and so on. The time for half the original atoms to undergo radioactive transformation is called the *half-life* of the atom, and it is one of the important constants to be measured. It is not necessary to wait till half of the sample has disintegrated in order to measure the half-life. If the logarithm of the activity is plotted as a func-

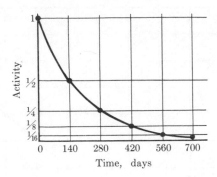

Fig. 49-3. Decay curve for the radioactive element polonium. Polonium has a half-life of 140 days.

tion of the time (on semilog paper), the resulting graph will be found to be a straight line, from whose slope the half-life may be obtained.

In studying radioactivity the following questions must be answered:

1. What is the parent nucleus?
2. What particle is emitted from this nucleus?
3. What is the half-life of the parent nucleus?
4. What is the resulting nucleus (called the product nucleus)?
5. Is the product nucleus radioactive and if so, what are the answers to questions 2, 3, and 4 for this nucleus, and so on?

Exhaustive investigations have been carried on in the last fifty years, and these questions have been answered for many nuclei. The results are most conveniently expressed on a diagram such as that shown in Fig. 49-4. The mass number (the nearest whole number to the atomic mass) is plotted along the y-axis, and the atomic number (positive nuclear charge) along the x-axis. Unit increase of atomic number without change of mass number indicates emission of a beta particle; decrease of two in atomic number accompanied by a decrease of four in mass number indicates emission of an alpha particle. The half-lives are given either in years (y), days (d), hours (h), minutes (m), or seconds (s). Figure 49-4, representing the uranium series of radioactive elements, is only one of three such series that exist.

49-6 Artificial nuclear disintegration. The nuclear disintegrations that have been described up to this point have consisted exclusively of a natural, uncontrolled emission of either an alpha or beta particle. Nothing was done to initiate the nuclear explosion, and nothing could be done to stop it. It occurred to Rutherford in 1919 that it ought to be possible to penetrate a nucleus with a massive high-speed particle such as an alpha particle and thereby either produce a nucleus with greater atomic number

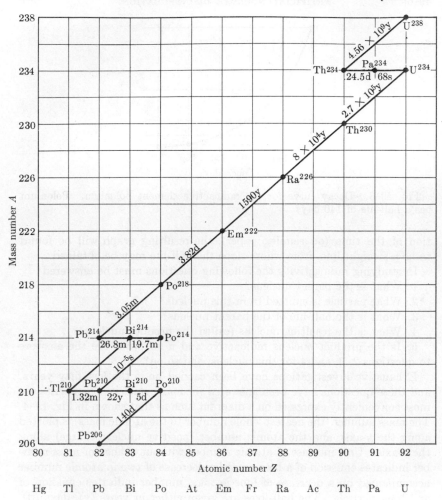

FIG. 49–4. The uranium series of radioactive elements.

and mass number or induce an artificial nuclear explosion. Rutherford was successful in bombarding nitrogen with alpha particles and obtaining as a result an oxygen nucleus and a proton, according to the reaction

$$_2\text{He}^4 + _7\text{N}^{14} \rightarrow _8\text{O}^{17} + _1\text{H}^1. \tag{49–1}$$

In this symbolism, the number at the lower left corner represents the atomic number, and the upper right number represents the mass number. Thus, $_2\text{He}^4$ is an alpha particle and $_1\text{H}^1$ is a proton. Notice that the sum of the initial atomic numbers is equal to the sum of the final atomic numbers, a condition imposed by the conservation of charge. The sum of the initial mass numbers is also equal to the sum of the final mass numbers, but the initial rest mass is not equal to the final rest mass. The difference between the rest masses is equal to the *nuclear reaction energy*, using Einstein's equation expressing the equivalence of mass and energy,

$$W = mc^2.$$

If the sum of the final rest masses exceeds the sum of the initial rest masses, energy is absorbed in the reaction. Conversely, if the final sum is less than the initial sum, energy is released in the form of kinetic energy of the final particles.

For example, in the case of the nuclear reaction represented by Eq. (49–1), the rest masses of the various particles, in amu, are as follows:

$$_2He^4 = \ 4.00389 \text{ amu} \qquad _8O^{17} = 17.00450 \text{ amu}$$
$$_7N^{14} = 14.00750 \text{ amu} \qquad _1H^1 \ = \ 1.00813 \text{ amu}$$
$$\overline{\qquad 18.01139 \text{ amu} \qquad} \qquad \overline{\qquad 18.01263 \text{ amu}}$$

The rest mass of the final products exceeds that of the initial particles by 0.00124 atomic mass unit. From Einstein's equation, this is equivalent to 1.155 million electron volts. This amount of energy is absorbed in the reaction. If the initial particles did not have this much kinetic energy, the reaction would not have taken place.

The reaction discussed in Section 7–12 is the proton bombardment of lithium and consequent formation of two alpha particles, thus

$$_1H^1 + {}_3Li^7 \rightarrow {}_2He^4 + {}_2He^4.$$

In this reaction, the sum of the final rest masses is smaller than the sum of the initial rest masses. Energy, therefore, is liberated, and appears as kinetic energy of the two separating alpha particles.

Alpha particles and protons are not the only particles used to instigate artificial nuclear disintegration. With the aid of the cyclotron, the nucleus of a deuterium atom, known as the *deuteron* and represented by the symbol $_1D^2$, may be speeded up tremendously. At high speed the deuteron is a very effective "atom smasher." In order that positively charged particles such as the alpha particle, the proton, and the deuteron can be used to penetrate the nuclei of other atoms, they must travel with very high speeds to avoid being repelled or deflected by the positive charge of the nucleus they are approaching. Obviously, the ideal bombarding particle is one which, besides being massive, has no charge and is therefore not affected by the electric field around a nucleus. A discussion of this particle, called a *neutron*, will be given in Section 49–8.

49-7 Cosmic rays. The positron and meson. If a charged electroscope is left standing, it will eventually lose its charge no matter how well it is insulated. Evidently the air is slightly ionized at all times, even in the absence of obvious causes of ionization such as x-rays, ultraviolet light, and radioactivity. Ionization of air inside a vessel is decreased slightly if the vessel is lowered into a lake, but increases considerably if the vessel is transported in a balloon high into the stratosphere. Hess suggested that the ionization is due to some kind of penetrating waves or particles from outer space, and called them *cosmic rays*. It is fairly certain that cosmic rays consist largely of high-speed protons with energies of the order of billions of electron volts. A collision between such a proton and the nucleus of a nitrogen or oxygen atom in the upper atmosphere gives rise to so many interesting secondary phenomena that the study of cosmic rays has become one of the richest sources of knowledge of the structure and properties of the nucleus.

At this point it is worth while to describe an instrument devised by C. T. R. Wilson, called a *cloud chamber*, which is used extensively not only to study cosmic rays, but also to render visible the paths of the particles engaging in artificially produced nuclear reactions.

The principle of the cloud chamber is illustrated in Fig. 49-5. The space above the water, called the expansion chamber, contains saturated water vapor. If this vapor is slightly compressed by squeezing the rubber bulb, and then allowed to expand quickly (adiabatically), water droplets will condense on any particles which serve as nuclei of condensation. A massive particle moving rapidly in the water vapor creates many ions

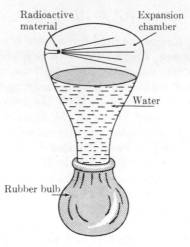

Fig. 49-5. Principle of the Wilson cloud chamber.

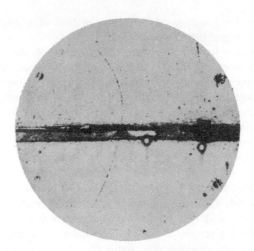

FIG. 49–6. Track of a positive electron traversing a lead plate 6 mm thick. (Photograph by C. D. Anderson.)

and electrons in its path.   Water droplets condense on these ions and electrons and thus make visible the path of the ionizing particle.   Cloud chambers are sometimes made several feet in diameter, and when illuminated on the side, are photographed from above, at times with the aid of two cameras in order to obtain stereoscopic pictures.   Very often the cloud chamber is placed in a magnetic field so that the ionizing particle travels perpendicular to the field.   If the ionizing particle is charged, it will be deflected, and by measuring the radius of curvature of the path its momentum may be determined, provided the charge is known.

The positive electron was first observed during the course of an investigation of cosmic rays by Dr. Carl D. Anderson in 1932, in the cloud chamber photograph reproduced in Fig. 49–6.   The photograph was made with the cloud chamber in a magnetic field perpendicular to the plane of the paper.   A lead plate crosses the chamber and evidently the particle has passed through it.   Since the curvature of the track is greater above the plate than below it, the velocity is less above than below and the inference is that the particle was moving upward, since it is difficult to see how it could have gained energy going through the lead.

The density of droplets along the path is what would be expected if the particle were an electron.   But the direction of the magnetic field and the direction of motion are consistent only with a particle of positive sign. Hence Anderson concluded the track had been made by a positive electron or *positron*.   Since the time of this discovery many thousands of such tracks have been photographed and the positron's existence is now definitely established. Its mass is the same as that of a negative electron and its charge is equal but of opposite sign.

Positive electrons have only a transitory existence and do not form a part of ordinary matter. There are two known processes which result in positive electrons. They are ejected from the nuclei of certain artificially radioactive materials, and they spring into existence (along with a negative electron) in a process known as "pair production" in which a γ-ray is simultaneously annihilated. Charge is conserved in the process, since the particles have charges of opposite sign.

The meson was first observed in 1936 by Anderson and Neddermeyer, as a component of cosmic radiation, although such a particle had been predicted theoretically by Yukawa in 1935. Our knowledge of mesons is much less clear-cut than that of other elementary particles. There are positive, negative, and neutral mesons. Their masses are of the order of a few hundred electron masses. The mass of a π-meson is about 280 times that of an electron; the mass of a μ-meson, about 210 times. π-mesons are found in the fragments of nuclear explosions and have now been produced in the laboratory by bombarding light nuclei with 400-Mev α-particles. A π-meson is a short-lived particle, decaying in about 10^{-8} sec to a μ-meson and probably a neutral meson. The average life of a μ-meson is about 10^{-6} sec and its decay products have not been definitely established. Most of the mesons in cosmic rays in the lower atmosphere, including the one first observed by Anderson and Neddermeyer, are μ-mesons. It is believed that π-mesons play an important part in the mechanism of nuclear binding.

49–8 The neutron. In 1930, Bothe and Becker in Germany observed that when beryllium, boron, or lithium was bombarded by fast alpha particles, the bombarded material emitted something, either particles or electromagnetic waves, of much greater penetrating power than the original alpha particles. Further experiments in 1932 by Curie and Joliot in Paris confirmed these results, but all attempts to explain them in terms of γ-rays were unsuccessful. Chadwick in England repeated the experiments and found that they could be satisfactorily interpreted on the assumption that *uncharged* particles of mass approximately equal to that of a proton were emitted from the nuclei of the bombarded material. He called the particles *neutrons*. The emission of a neutron from a beryllium nucleus takes place according to the reaction

$$_2He^4 + {}_4Be^9 \rightarrow {}_6C^{12} + {}_0n^1,$$

where $_0n^1$ is the symbol for a neutron.

Since neutrons have no charge, they produce no ionization in their passage through gases. They are not deflected by the electric field around

TABLE 49–2

NUCLEAR PARTICLES

Nucleus	Mass number (total number of nuclear particles) A	Atomic number (number of protons) Z	Number of neutrons $A - Z$
$_1H^1$	1	1	0
$_1D^2$	2	1	1
$_2He^4$	4	2	2
$_3Li^6$	6	3	3
$_3Li^7$	7	3	4
$_4Be^9$	9	4	5
$_5B^{10}$	10	5	5
$_5B^{11}$	11	5	6
$_6C^{12}$	12	6	6
$_6C^{13}$	13	6	7
$_7N^{14}$	14	7	7
$_8O^{16}$	16	8	8
$_{11}Na^{23}$	23	11	12
$_{29}Cu^{65}$	65	29	36
$_{80}Hg^{200}$	200	80	120
$_{92}U^{235}$	235	92	143
$_{92}U^{238}$	238	92	146

a nucleus and can be stopped only by colliding with a nucleus in a direct hit, in which case they may either undergo an elastic impact or penetrate the nucleus. If an elastic body strikes a motionless elastic body of the same mass, the first is stopped and the second moves off with the same speed as the first. Since the proton and neutron masses are almost the same, it follows that fast neutrons may be slowed down by performing collisions with the hydrogen atoms in hydrogenous materials like water or paraffin. The usual laboratory method of obtaining slow neutrons is to surround the fast neutron source with water or blocks of paraffin.

Once the neutrons are moving slowly, they may be detected by means of the alpha particles they eject from the nucleus of a boron atom, according to the reaction

$$_0n^1 + _5B^{10} \rightarrow _3Li^7 + _2He^4.$$

The ejected alpha particle then produces ionization which may be detected in a Geiger counter or an ionization chamber.

The discovery of the neutron gave the first real clue to the structure of the nucleus. Heretofore it had been thought that the total mass of a nucleus was due to protons only. Now it is believed that a nucleus consists of both protons and neutrons (except hydrogen, whose nucleus consists only of one proton) and that (1) the mass number equals the total number of nuclear particles, and (2) the atomic number equals the number of protons only.

The number of neutrons in a nucleus is therefore the difference between the mass number and the atomic number, as shown in Table 49–2, where a few representative elements are listed.

49–9 Nuclear fission.   Up to this point, all nuclear reactions considered have involved the ejection of relatively light particles, such as alpha particles, beta particles, protons, or neutrons. That this is not always the case was discovered by Hahn and Strassman in Germany in 1939. These scientists bombarded uranium ($Z = 92$) with neutrons, and after a careful chemical analysis discovered barium ($Z = 56$) and krypton ($Z = 36$) among the products. Cloud-chamber photographs showed the two heavy particles traveling in opposite directions with tremendous speed. The uranium is said to undergo *fission*. Measurement showed that an enormous amount of energy, 200 million electron volts, is released when uranium splits up in this way. Since the rest mass of a uranium atom exceeds the sum of the rest masses of the fission products, it follows from the Einstein mass-energy relation that the extra energy released during fission is transformed into kinetic energy of the fission fragments. Uranium fission may be accomplished by either fast or slow neutrons. Of the two most abundant isotopes of uranium, $_{92}U^{238}$ and $_{92}U^{235}$, both may be split by a fast neutron, whereas only $_{92}U^{235}$ is split by a slow neutron.

When uranium undergoes fission, barium and krypton are not the only products. Over 100 different isotopes of more than 20 different elements have been detected among fission products. All of these atoms are, however, in the middle of the periodic table, with atomic numbers ranging from 34 to 58.

Discovery of the fact that 200 million electron volts of energy were released when uranium underwent fission, although of great interest to physicists, appeared to be of little importance in everyday life. The phenomenon took on a different aspect when it was discovered that during fission other neutrons were liberated from the uranium nucleus. This immediately suggested the possibility of a chain reaction, that is, a self-sustaining series of events which, once started, will continue until all the uranium in a given sample is used up (provided the sample stays together). In the case of a uranium chain reaction, a neutron causes one uranium atom to undergo fission, during which a large amount of energy and several neutrons are emitted. These neutrons then cause fission in neighboring uranium nuclei which also give out energy and more neutrons. The chain reaction may be made to proceed slowly and in a controlled manner, and the device for accomplishing this is called an *atomic pile* or a *nuclear reactor*. If the chain reaction is fast and uncontrolled, the device is a bomb (called an *atomic bomb*), whose destructive ability is many thousands of times that of previously existing bombs.

The first experiments on an atomic pile were performed at Columbia University by Fermi, Szilard, and Zinn. The work was then continued in Chicago, where these physicists succeeded in establishing a controlled chain reaction in a huge structure composed of graphite in which rods of uranium were embedded. The principles of pile construction, operation, and control constitute a fascinating branch of modern applied physics. It would take too much space to go into details, but it is worth while to list the important uses for an atomic pile:

1. To produce the element plutonium from $_{92}U^{238}$ for explosive purposes.

2. To produce a neutron beam of high intensity for nuclear bombardment studies.

3. To produce artificially radioactive isotopes for medical use and for biological research.

4. To generate power for the propulsion of ships, submarines, and possibly aircraft.

49–10 Thermonuclear reactions. There are two types of nuclear reactions in which large amounts of energy may be liberated. In both types, the rest mass of the products is less than the original rest mass. The fission of uranium, already described, is an example of one type. The other involves the combination of two light nuclei to form a nucleus which is more complex but whose rest mass is less than the sum of the rest masses of the original nuclei. Examples of such energy-liberating reactions are as follows:

$$_1H^1 + {}_1H^1 \rightarrow {}_1H^2 + {}_1e^0,$$

$$_1H^2 + {}_1H^1 \rightarrow {}_2He^3 + \gamma\text{-radiation},$$

$$_2He^3 + {}_2He^3 \rightarrow {}_2He^4 + {}_1H^1 + {}_1H^1.$$

In the first, two protons combine to form a deuteron and a positron. In the second, a proton and a deuteron unite to form the light isotope of helium. For the third reaction to occur, the first two reactions must occur twice, in which case two nuclei of light helium unite to form ordinary helium. These reactions, known as the *proton-proton chain*, are believed to take place in the interior of the sun and also in many other stars which are known to be composed mainly of hydrogen.

The positrons produced during the first step of the proton-proton chain collide with electrons; annihilation takes place, and their energy is converted into γ-radiation. The net effect of the chain, therefore, is the combination of four hydrogen nuclei into a helium nucleus and γ-radiation. The net amount of energy released may be calculated from the mass balance as follows:

Rest mass of 4 hydrogen atoms	$= 4.03258$ amu
Rest mass of 1 helium atom	$= 4.00387$ amu
Difference in mass	$= 0.02871$ amu
	$= 26.7 \times 10^6$ electron volts

In the case of the sun, a gram of its mass contains about 2×10^{23} protons. Hence, if all of these protons were consumed, the energy released would be about 55,000 kwh. If the sun were to continue to radiate at its present rate, it would take about 30 billion years to exhaust its supply of protons.

Temperatures of millions of degrees are necessary to initiate the proton-proton chain. A star may achieve such a high temperature by contracting and consequently liberating a large amount of gravitational potential energy. When the temperature gets high enough the reactions occur, more energy is liberated, and the pressure of the resulting radiation prevents further contraction. Only after most of the hydrogen has been converted into helium will further contraction and an accompanying increase of temperature result. Conditions are then suitable for the formation of heavier elements.

Temperatures and pressures similar to those in the interior of stars may be achieved on earth at the moment of explosion of a uranium or plutonium fission bomb. If the fission bomb is surrounded by proper proportions of the hydrogen isotopes, these may be caused to combine into helium and liberate still more energy. This combination of uranium and hydrogen is called a "hydrogen bomb."

Attempts are being made at this time all over the world to control the fusion of hydrogen isotopes and to utilize the resulting energy for peaceful purposes. The reactions whose control is being studied are the following:

$$_1H^2 + {_1H^2} \rightarrow {_1H^3} + {_1H^1} + 4 \text{ Mev}, \tag{1}$$

$$_1H^3 + {_1H^2} \rightarrow {_2He^4} + {_0n^1} + 17.6 \text{ Mev}, \tag{2}$$

$$_1\text{H}^2 + {_1}\text{H}^2 \rightarrow {_2}\text{He}^3 + {_0}\text{n}^1 + 3.3 \text{ Mev,} \tag{3}$$

$$_2\text{He}^3 + {_1}\text{H}^2 \rightarrow {_2}\text{He}^4 + {_1}\text{H}^1 + 18.3 \text{ Mev.} \tag{4}$$

In the first, two deuterons combine to form tritium and a proton. In the second, the tritium nucleus combines with another deuteron to form helium and a neutron. The result of both of these reactions is the liberation of 21.6 Mev of energy. Reactions (3) and (4) represent another pair that is about equal in probability to reactions (1) and (2) and which would be attended by the liberation of the same amount of energy. No one has as yet succeeded in producing these reactions under controlled laboratory conditions. The story of the attempt is told in a fascinating book, *Project Sherwood*, by A. S. Bishop, Addison-Wesley Publishing Company, 1958.

ANSWERS TO ODD-NUMBERED PROBLEMS

CHAPTER 1

1-1. 25.7 lb, 30.6 lb

1-3. (a) 18.5 lb (b) 9.2 lb

1-7. (a) 19.3 lb in a direction midway between the 10-lb forces (b) 8.46 lb in a direction midway between the 10-lb forces

1-9. 308 lb, 25° above the x-axis

1-11. (a) 2 in. (b) 3.46 in.

1-13. (a) 7 lb, 2.9 lb (b) 7.6 lb (c) 11 lb

1-15. $R = 0$

CHAPTER 2

2-3. (a) 10 lb (b) 20 lb

2-5. (a) 150 lb(A), 180 lb(B), 200 lb(C)
(b) 200 lb(A), 280 lb(B), 200 lb(C)
(c) 550 lb(A), 670 lb(B), 200 lb(C)
(d) 167 lb(A), 58 lb(B), 125 lb(C)

2-7. (a) Parts (b) and (c) can be solved
(b) In part (a) another side or angle is needed

2-9. 630 lb

2-11. (a) 20 lb (b) 30 lb

2-13. (a) $F = w/2 \sin \theta$
(b) $T = w/2 \tan \theta$

2-17. 22 lb (normal force does *not* equal weight)

2-19. (a) 76 lb (b) 24 lb
(c) from 15.4 to 84.6 lb

2-21. (a) Pulled up
(b) 145 lb

2-23. (a) 3 lb (b) 4 lb (c) 5 lb

2-25. (b) 10 lb (c) 30 lb

CHAPTER 3

3-3. (a) 20 lb (b) 30 lb

3-5. (a) -6 lb, 10 lb (b) $\frac{5}{3}$
(c) 12 lb (d) 2 ft from right end of bar

3-7. 722 lb, 722 lb, 1500 lb

3-9. (a) 69.4 lb (b) 212 lb, 19° above the horizontal

3-11. 2 weights

3-13. 81.5 lb, 78° above the horizontal

3-15. 19.3 ft

3-17. (a) 54 lb (b) 24 lb

3-19. 15 lb each

3-21. (a) 20 lb on A, 140 lb on B
(b) 4 ft

3-23. 32.5 lb and 13 lb on each front leg, 17.5 lb and 7 lb on each rear leg

3-25. (a) 15 lb (b) 5 lb on each front leg, 20 lb on each rear leg
(c) 8.75 lb on each front leg, 16.25 lb on each rear leg
(d) 3.33 ft above floor

3-27. On the perpendicular bisector of the line joining the 9 and 12 lb weights, at a distance of 0.6 ft from this line.

3-29. 7.4 inches from the large end

3-31. 4 inches to the right and 2.5 inches up from the lower left-hand corner

CHAPTER 4

4-1. (a) 15 mi/hr
(b) 22 ft/sec
(c) 672 cm/sec

4-3. 61 cm/sec, 60.1 cm/sec,
60.01 cm/sec, 60 cm/sec

4-5. (a) 0 (b) 6.3 ft/sec^2
(c) -11 ft/sec^2 (d) 100 ft
(e) 230 ft (f) 320 ft

4-7. 4 ft/sec^2, 620 ft

4-9. (a) 2.67 mi/hr·sec, 3.92 ft/sec^2
(b) 7.5 sec (c) 441 ft, 550 ft
between 15 sec and 22.5 sec

4-11. (a) 12.5 cm/sec^2 (b) 7840 cm

4-13. (a) 300 ft (b) 60 ft/sec

4-15. (a) 24 ft/sec, 29 ft/sec,
34 ft/sec
(b) 2.5 ft/sec^2
(c) 21.5 ft/sec (d) 8.6 sec
(e) 23 ft (f) 1 sec
(g) 24 ft/sec

4-17. (a) 32 ft/sec (b) 2.83 sec
(c) 16 ft (d) 22.6 ft/sec
(e) 16 ft/sec

4-19. (a) 8.7 sec (b) 75 ft
(c) $v_A = 52$ ft/sec,
$v_T = 35$ ft/sec

4-21. (a) 94 ft/sec (b) 124 ft
(c) 53 ft/sec (d) 150 ft/sec^2
(e) 1.96 sec (f) 93 ft/sec

4-23. 39.4 ft

4-25. (a) 48 ft/sec (b) 36 ft
(c) 80 ft/sec

4-27. (a) 32 ft (b) 13 ft/sec, -32
ft/sec^2
(c) -51 ft/sec, -32 ft/sec^2
(d) 37 ft/sec

4-29. (a) 36 ft (b) 0.5 sec
(c) 32 ft/sec, -32 ft/sec^2,
-16 ft/sec, -32 ft/sec^2

4-31. (a) 4 m/sec^2 (b) 6 m/sec
(c) 4.5 m

4-33. 6.55 knots

4-35. (a) 50 mi/hr, 53° S of W
(b) 60° S of W

4-37. (a) 5 mi/hr, 53° E of N
(b) 0.75 mi (c) 15 min

CHAPTER 5

5-1. (a) 400 lb (b) 12,800 dynes
(c) 12,800 n

5-3. (a) 2 m/sec^2 (b) 100 m
(c) 20 m/sec

5-7. (a) 0.5 slug (b) 500 ft

5-9. (a) 1.62×10^{-10} dyne
(b) 3.33×10^{-9} sec
(c) 1.8×10^{17} cm/sec^2

5-11. (a) 19.6 n (b) 2.55 sec

5-13. (a) 4 lb (b) 128 ft

5-15. 48 ft/sec^2

5-17. (a) 40 lb (b) 4 ft/sec^2 down
(c) zero

5-19. 240 ft

5-21. (a) 12 sec after force is applied
(b) 8 ft/sec^2

5-23. $W = 2wa/(g + a)$

5-25. (a) 37° (b) 6.4 ft/sec^2
(c) 2.5 sec

5-27. (a) 6 lb, (b) 8 ft/sec^2

5-29. (a) 2 lb (b) 1.9 lb

5-31. (a) 196 cm/sec^2
(b) 314,000 dynes

5-33. (a) to left (b) 2.13 ft/sec^2
(c) 43.3 lb

5-35. 1.33 lb

5-37. 4 lb

5-39.

	a_1	a_2
(a)	0	0
(b)	0	0
(c)	0	16 ft/sec^2
(d)	4 ft/sec^2	28 ft/sec^2
(e)	16 ft/sec^2	48 ft/sec^2

5-41. (a) 4.4 ft/sec^2
(b) 1.2 lb

5-43. 127.5 lb

5-45. 6.2×10^{27} gm

5-47. 6.32 ft/sec^2

CHAPTER 6

6-1. 10 ft/sec

6-3. (a) 20 sec (b) 6000 ft
(c) $v_x = 300$ ft/sec,
$v_y = 640$ ft/sec

6-5. (a) 100 ft (b) 200 ft
(c) $v_x = 80$ ft/sec,
$v_y = 80$ ft/sec
$v = 113$ ft/sec at 45° below
horizontal

6-7. (a) 0.56 mi (b) 296 mi/hr at 47°
below horizontal
(c) 10 sec

6-9. (a) 40 sec (b) 55°

6-11. (a) 121 ft/sec (b) 57.2 ft
(c) 3.8 sec

6-13. 100 ft

6-15. Yes. Ball clears fence by 10 ft

6-17. (a) 67 ft/sec (b) 39 ft/sec at 31°
below horizontal

6-19. 1.98 sec, 157 sec

6-21. 1300 ft

6-23. 22°

6-27. (a) 32 ft/sec (b) 1 sec
(c) 54 ft

6-29. (a) 66,700 mi/hr
(b) 0.0193 ft/sec^2

6-31. 0.5

6-33. (a) 38.2 rev/min
(b) 5 lb

6-35. (a) 0.27 (b) 15°

6-37. (a) 198 cm/sec
(b) 29.5×10^4 dynes

6-39. (a) 128 ft/sec^2 (b) 480 lb
(c) 480 lb (d) 16 ft/sec

6-41. $\cos^2 \theta$

6-43. 36,000 km above earth

6-45. 16,900 mi/hr

CHAPTER 7

7-1. 63.4×10^6 ft·lb

7-3. 9850 ft·lb

7-5. (a) 55,000 ft·lb (b) 4 times

7-7. 4.5×10^{-10} erg

7-9. 9.8 joules

7-11. (a) 5 lb, 10 lb, 20 lb
(b) 1.3 ft·lb, 5 ft·lb, 20 ft·lb

7-13. (a) 33 ft·lb
(b) about 15 ft·lb

7-15. (a) 160 ft·lb (b) 160 ft·lb

7-17. (a) 3300 ft·lb (b) 1300 ft·lb
(c) 1500 ft·lb (d) 500 ft·lb
Goes into heat.
(e) $b + c + d = a$

7-19. (a) 42 lb (b) 105 ft·lb

7-21. (a) 40 ft/sec (b) 20 ft/sec

7-23. 10 cm

7-25. (a) 0.25 (b) 3.5 ft·lb

7-29. 1.81 m/sec

7-31. 0.655 hp, 489 watts, 0.489 kw

7-33. 154 hp

7-35. $1.29

7-37. (a) 250 lb (b) 5 hp (c) 80 hp

7-39. (a) 8200 joules (b) 8200 joules
(c) 0.55 hp

7-41. (a) 6300 lb (b) 30 ft/sec
(c) 68,000 ft·lb (d) 220,000 ft·lb
(e) 250 hp

7-43. (a) 55,000 dynes (b) 1.3
(c) 1.7 (d) 79%

7-45. 12,000 lb

7-51. (a) 18×10^{20} ergs
(b) 18×10^{26} ergs/sec
(c) 1.2×10^{13} gm (about 3 billion gallons)

CHAPTER 8

8-1. (a) 28,000 slug·ft/sec
(b) 60 mi/hr (c) 43 mi/hr

8-3. (a) 8×10^5 m/sec^2
(b) 4×10^4 n (c) 5×10^{-4} sec
(d) 20 n·sec

8-5. 1.5 ft/sec

8-7. 0.65 mi/hr

8-9. 17 mi/hr 53° E of S

8-13. (a) 10 cm/sec (b) 0.14 joule
(c) −70 cm/sec, 80 cm/sec

8–15. (a) 100 gm (b) 16 cm/sec
8–17. 58,700 ft
8–19. 1.82 ft/sec
8–21. (a) 149° from direction of
electron
(b) 10.6×10^{-16} gm·cm/sec
(c) 14.5×10^{-10} erg
8–23. (a) 41 cm, $100(0.64)^n$, 10
(b) 0.71 sec, $0.9 \times (0.8)^n$ sec
(c) 0.8

8–25. 7.2 ft below starting point
8–27. 280 m/sec
8–29. (a) 0.16 (b) 240 joules
(c) 0.32 joule
8–31. 596 m/sec
8–33. (a) 0.19 ft/sec (b) 1.3 lb
8–35. (a) 4 ft/sec (b) 2 lb
(c) 25,000 ft·lb for bullets,
40 ft·lb for man

CHAPTER 9

9–1. (a) 1.5 rad (b) 1.6 rad, 90°
(c) 120 cm, 120 ft
9–3. (a) 20 ft/sec (b) 230 rev/min
9–5. 5 rad/sec², 1000 rad
9–7. 20 rad/sec²
9–11. (a) At the bottom of the wheel
(b) 360 ft/sec at 3° from the
vertical
9–13. (a) 135°
(b) 2.36 ft/sec², 11.03 ft/sec²
9–15. 164,000 rev/min
9–17. (a) 2.67 kgm·m²
(b) 10.7 kgm·m²
(c) 1.6×10^{-3} kgm·m²
9–19. (a) A smallest (b) D largest
9–21. (a) 2.56×10^{28} slug·mi²
(b) 2530 mi
9–23. (a) 278 ft·lb (b) 70 ft
9–25. 1.1 slug·ft²
9–27. (a) 2×10^7 joules (b) 18 min
9–29. (a) 4 rad/sec² (b) 14 rad/sec²
(c) 32,000 ft·lb
9–31. 0.47

9–33. (a) 10 rad/sec² (b) 200 ft·lb
(c) 6.15 rad/sec²
9–35. (a) 21.3 lb (b) 52.3 ft/sec
(c) 2.45 sec
9–37. (a) 10.7 ft/sec², 0, 5.33 lb
(b) 4.57 ft/sec², 9.14 rad/sec²,
6.86 lb, 4.57 lb
9–39. (a) 240 cm/sec, 320 cm/sec
(b) 5×10^5 gm·cm²
(c) 1600 cm/sec²
(d) 780 cm/sec²
(e) 51,000 dynes, tension
9–41. (a) 2m/sec² (b) 9.8 newtons
9–43. (a) 12 rad/sec (b) 0.027 joule
9–45. $(mg \pm \mu Mg)/M\omega^2$
9–47. 0.08 rev/sec
9–49. (a) -0.04 rad/sec
(b) 60 deg (c) 72 deg
9–51. (a) 2 slug·ft²
(b) 2620 ft·lb
9–53. (a) 180,000 dynes
(b) 4300 rev/min

CHAPTER 10

10–1. 25×10^6 lb/in²
10–3. (b) 14×10^6 lb/in²
(c) 0.016×10^6 lb/in²
10–5. (a) 27.5 lb (b) 0.028 ft
10–7. 0.0253 in.
10–9. (a) 1.8 ft (b) 30,000 lb/in² in
steel, 12,000 lb/in² in copper (c) 0.001 in steel,
0.0006 in copper

10–13. 2000 lb
10–15. Steel, 0.64×10^{-6} atm⁻¹
Water, 50×10^{-6} atm⁻¹
Water is 78 times more compressible
10–17. (a) $(E \cos^2 \theta)/A$
(b) $(F \sin 2\theta)/2A$
(c) 0° (d) 45°

CHAPTER 11

11-1. (a) 9470 cm/sec^2, 377 cm/sec
     (b) 5680 cm/sec^2, 301 cm/sec
     (c) 0.0368 sec

11-3. (a) 2400π^2 ft/sec^2
     (b) 740 lb (c) 43 mi/hr

11-5. 23 lb

11-7. 6.20 cm

11-9. (a) $\frac{1}{2}mv^2 + \frac{1}{2}kx^2$
     (b) $\frac{1}{2}kA^2$

11-11. (a) $L_1 = 35$ cm, $L_2 = 25$ cm
     (c) 1 sec

11-13. (a) 9 vib/sec
     (b) 20×10^6 lb/in^2

11-15. (a) 2 ft/sec
     (b) 4 ft/sec^2

11-17. 979.78 cm/sec^2

11-19. (a) 40 rad/sec (b) 34 rad/sec
     (c) 120 rad/sec^2

11-21. 67 cm

CHAPTER 12

12-1. 21 lb/in^2

12-3. 120 lb/in^2, 18,000 lb/ft^2

12-5. 34.8 ft^2

12-7. 270,000 ft^3, 9.3 tons lift, using helium

12-9. (a) 5 cm (b) 4900 dynes/cm^2

12-11. (a) 100 lb/ft^3 (b) E will read 5 lb, D will read 15 lb

12-15. (a) 4500 lb (b) 10,000 lb
     (c) 230 lb

12-17. 100.87 gm

12-19. (b) 4 lb (c) 1 ft^3

12-21. 0.781 gm/cm^3

CHAPTER 13

13-3. 13,720 dynes/cm^2

13-5. (a) 70.7 cm of Hg
     (b) 71.2 cm of Hg
     (c) 11 cm

13-7. 4.3 cm

CHAPTER 14

14-1. (a) 36 ft/sec (b) 0.2 ft^3/sec

14-3. 39.6 ft/sec

14-5. (a) 0.056 ft^3/sec (b) 3 ft

14-7. (a) 16 ft/sec (b) 0.79 ft^3/sec

14-9. (a) 0.2 ft^3/sec (b) 4.7 ft
     (c) 3 ft

14-11. (a) 12 lb/in^2 (b) 12 ft^3/sec

14-13. 50 hp

14-15. (a) 2.5 sec (b) 44 lb/in^2
     (c) 33 lb/in^2

14-17. 12 ft^3/min

14-19. 27 ft^3/sec

14-21. 325 ft/sec

14-23. (a) 6.4 ft^3/sec
     (b) 6.02 lb/in^2

14-25. (a) 1500 (b) laminar flow
     (c) 0.043 (d) 18.2 cm of water

14-27. (a) 30.4 cm/sec (b) turbulent flow (c) 53.8 liters/sec

14-29. (a) 0.77 cm/sec
     (b) 1.89 cm/sec

CHAPTER 15

15-3. 1.6 ft

15-5. 0.03 cm

15-7. 1.0×10^{-5} (C°)$^{-1}$

15-9. (a) 13×10^{-6} (C°)$^{-1}$
     (b) 19×10^4 lb/in^2

15-11. (a) 76°C (b) −63.3°C

15–13. Period decreases, 1.8×10^{-4}

15–15. 270,000 lb

15–17. 460 atm

15–19. 72,000 lb/in², assuming length of brass is constant

15–21. 9.35×10^8 dynes/cm²

CHAPTER 16

16–1. 74 ft³

16–3. 4.0 Btu

16–5. Assuming a heat of combustion of 11,000 Btu/lb
  (a) 18.7×10^7 Btu
  (b) 42.2 ft

16–7. (a) 80.5% (b) 330 Btu

16–9. 370 years

16–11. 0.1 Btu/lb·F°

16–13. 1.00, 0.827, 0.35

16–15. (a) 0.092 cal/gm·C°
  (b) 27.6 gm

16–17. 725 cal

16–19. It melts the ice

16–21. 0°C with 0.2 gm of ice left

16–23. 539 cal/gm

16–25. 24°C

16–27. 40°C

16–29. 1.84 kgm

16–31. 17,100 cm

16–33. 445 cal/gm

CHAPTER 17

17–1. 86,400 cal/day

17–3. (a) 1.8 cal/sec (b) 20 cm

17–5. (a) 40°C (b) 2.4 cal/sec

17–7. 1.15×10^{-3} cal/sec·cm·C°

17–9. 110°C

17–11. 84.2 C°

17–13. 4.54×10^5 cal

17–15. 1.78 watts

17–17. 20.03°K

CHAPTER 18

18–1. 6.6×10^4 ft·lb

18–3. (a) Yes (b) No
  (c) Negative

18–5. (a) No (b) Yes (c) Yes
  (d) Work done on the resistor = heat transferred to the water

18–7. 10.8 ft³

18–11. $U_1 = U_2$

18–13. (a) 60 Btu (b) liberate 70 Btu
  (c) 50 Btu; −10 Btu

CHAPTER 19

19–1. 3.6 lb/in²

19–3. (a) 0.75 atm (b) 2 gm

19–5. 3.25

19–7. (a) 927°C (b) 0.325 gm

19–9. Adiabatic expansion

19–11. 16 liter·atm

19–13. When the piston has descended 13.12 in.

19–15. 0.0023 gm

19–17. (b) 600°K (c) 4 atm

19–19. (a) When piston is 3.13 inches from bottom (b) 477°K

19–27. 16%

19–29. (a) 12°C (b) 10 gm/cm³

19–31. 1.3 lb/hr

19–33. (a) About 3×10^{-7} cm
  (b) About 10 times as great

19–35. 1700 ft/sec

19–37. 4800°K

CHAPTER 20

20-1. 4

20-3. 93 C°

20-5. 15%

20-7. (a) 2 atm, 5 liters;
1 atm, 5 liters;

1 atm, 3 liters;
2 atm, 3 liters;
(b) 2 liter·atm

20-9. (a) 6.6 (b) 0.64 kwh
(c) 3¢

CHAPTER 21

21-1. 316 m/sec

21-3. 6320 cm/sec

21-5. 0.164 sec

21-7. 48×10^{-6} atm^{-1}

21-9. 322 m/sec, 1320 m/sec,
347 m/sec

21-11. (a) 132 cy/sec (b) 1320 cy/sec
(c) 13,200 cy/sec

CHAPTER 22

22-3. (a) 200 cy/sec
(b) 49th overtone

22-5. (a) 3600 cm/sec
(b) 6.5×10^6 dynes

22-7. 1.28

22-9. (a) 5000 m/sec
(b) 340 m/sec

22-11. Diatomic

22-13. (a) 1140, 2280, 3420, 4560,
5700 cy/sec
(b) 570, 1710, 2850, 3990,
5130 cy/sec (c) 16, 17

22-15. (a) 420 cy/sec (b) 415 cy/sec

CHAPTER 23

23-1. (a) 9 times (b) 4 times

23-3. (a) 60 db (b) 77 db

23-5. (a) π rad (b) Due to A:
4×10^{-10} watt/cm^2. Due
to B: 12×10^{-10} watt/
cm^2 (c) 2.1×10^{-10} watt/
cm^2, 63.2 db

23-7. 10^{-6} watt

23-9. (a) 454 cy/sec (b) 462 cy/sec
(c) 8 cy/sec

23-11. (a) 1090 cy/sec
(b) 1100 cy/sec

23-13. (a) 11 ft (b) 1 ft
(c) Almost 15 waves
(d) 1100 ft/sec (e) 0.49 ft

CHAPTER 24

24-1. (a) 8 dynes attraction
(b) 12 dynes toward negative
charge
(c) Along line connecting
charges and 14.5 cm from
negative charge

24-3. (a) 192 dynes (b) 120 dynes

24-5. 24 and 2 statcoul

24-7. 11.9 cm

24-9. 58 tons

24-11. 2.2×10^{-9} coul

24-13. 2.16×10^{-7} n

CHAPTER 25

25-1. (a) 4 n/coul upward
(b) 12.8×10^{-19} n down

25-3. (a) 4.8×10^{-15} n
(b) 5.3×10^{15} m/sec^2

25-5. (a) 0.704 cm
(b) arc tan (7.04/20)
(c) 4.92 cm

26-7. (a) 1.42 cm (b) 9.8 cm

25–9. -25×10^{-9} coul

25–11. (a) 1.8×10^4 n/coul,
neg. x-dir.
(b) 8×10^3 n/coul, pos. x-dir.
(c) 3.3×10^3 n/coul,
70° 2nd quad.
(d) 6.4×10^3 n/coul,
neg. x-dir.

25–13. 2.12×10^{-10} line

25–15. (a) 1.14×10^{21} n/coul
5.17×10^{11} n/coul

25–17. 3 m

25–19. 41°

25–23. Two electrons

CHAPTER 26

26–1. $V_{ba} = 5000$ volts
26–3. (b) 6.67×10^{-4} m
26–5. 951 volts
26–7. (a) 2.17×10^{-3} cm
(b) $v_e/v_p = 42.8$
(c) Energies are equal
26–9. (a) Zero (b) 1.44×10^{-6} joule

26–11. (a) 3 m (b) 2×10^{-7} coul
26–13. (a) 5×10^4 volts
(b) 2.19×10^6 m/sec
26–15. (a) 1800 volts (b) 0
(c) 450 ergs
26–17. (b) 2.30×10^6 m/sec

CHAPTER 27

27–1. 4.25×10^{-4} coul
27–3. (a) $5 \, \mu f$ (b) 64 volts
27–5. (a) 0.02 coul (b) 800 volts
(c) 8 joules (b) 2 joules
27–7. (a) 1.2×10^{-3} coul,
2.4×10^{-3} coul, 1200 volts
(b) 4×10^{-4} coul,
8×10^{-4} coul, 400 volts
27–9. (a) 3.8×10^{-7} coul
(b) 7600 volts

(c) 1.43×10^{-3} joule
(d) 1.35×10^{-3} joule
27–11. (a) 16.5 (b) infinity
27–13. 7.08×10^{-7} coul/m^2
27–15. 1.7 m^2
27–17. (a) 2.66×10^{-5} coul/m^2
(b) 1.77×10^{-5} coul/m^2

CHAPTER 28

28–1. (a) 20 ma
(b) 2.75×10^{-6} m/sec
28–3. 1.3×10^5 electrons/mm^3
28–5. 0.96 ma
28–7. (a) Yes; 4.36 ohms
(b) No; R varies with i
28–9. 53.5 volts

28–13. (b) 99.52 ohms
(c) 0.0148 ohm
28–15. 286°C
28–17. 84.3%
28–19. (a) 22 ohms (b) 5.5 amp
(c) 157 cal/sec (d) 550 watts

CHAPTER 29

29–1. (a) 0.05 ohm (b) 0.15 ohm
(c) 0.006 ohm
29–3. Switch open: (a) 12 volts
(b) 0 (c) 12 volts
Switch closed: (a) 11.1 volts
(b) 11.1 volts (c) 0
29–7. (a) 16.7 ohms (b) 150 watts

29–9. (a) 10 volts (b) 3 ohms
(c) 14.0 volts, opposing 18 volt
battery
29–11. (a) -3.3 volts (b) -3.6 volts
(c) -8.8 volts
29–13. (a) -3.75 volts (b) 3.75 volts
(c) 4.1 volts

29–15. (a) 230 volts (b) 5 volts
    (c) 225 volts (d) 5 volts
    (e) 220 volts (g) 11.5 kw,
    0.5 kw, 11 kw (h) 11.1 kw,
    0.13 kw

29–17. 1.52 volts, 0.1 ohm

29–19. R_{ab} = 55 ohms

29–21. (a) 8 ohms (b) 12 volts

29–23. 27 watts

29–25. 90 watts

29–27. (a) 2.7 ohms (b) 1 amp,
    4 volts

29–29. (a) 2 amp

    (b) 2 amp through 1 ohm
    resistor
    1 amp through 8 ohm
    resistor
    0.67 amp through 6 ohm
    resistor
    0.33 amp through 12 ohm
    resistor
    (c) 6 volts

29–31. 397 ohms

29–33. $\mathcal{E}_1$ = 18 volts
    $\mathcal{E}_2$ = 7 volts
    V_{ab} = 13 volts

CHAPTER 30

30–1. 11.1 amp

30–3. 5 faradays

30–5. 151 sec

30–7. 1.19 gm

30–9. 16.3 gm

30–11. 5.11×10^{-4} cm

30–13. -1.42 mv

CHAPTER 31

31–1. (a) 0.24 weber, 24×10^6 maxwells (b) Zero
    (c) 0.24 weber

31–3. (a) 1.7×10^{-8}

31–5. (a) 2.9×10^7 m/sec
    (b) 4.3×10^{-8} sec
    (c) 8.7×10^6 volts

31–7. 0.5 w/m^2 downward
    $\parallel$ to y-axis

31–9. 3640

31–11. (a) 1.7×10^8 m/sec
    (c) 0.48 m

31–13. 0.0213 m

31–15. F_{ab} = 1.20 n in neg. z-dir.
    F_{bc} = 1.20 n in neg. y-dir.
    F_{cd} = 1.70 n, 45° up, $\parallel$ to
    y-z plane
    F_{de} = 1.20 n, in neg. y-dir.

31–17. (a) 16,000 dynes,
    83,000 dyne·cm
    (b) 16,000 dynes,
    48,000 dyne·cm
    (c) Same torque

31–19. 3.6×10^{-6} n·m

CHAPTER 32

32–1. (a) 0.0331 ohm for 1 amp range,
    0.00331 ohm for 10 amp
    range
    (b) 0.033 watt for 1 amp shunt,
    0.33 watt for 10 amp shunt

32–3. 30°

32–5. R_1 = 0.00802 ohm
    R_2 = 0.0324 ohm
    R_3 = 0.404 ohm

32–7. 2985 ohms, 12,000 ohms,
    135,000 ohms;
    3000 ohms, 15,000 ohms,
    150,000 ohms

32–9. (a) 23.3 ohms
    (b) 116.5 volts

32–11. 4.97 ohms

32–13. 20 volts

32–15. (a) 1200 ohms (b) 30 volts

32–17. 2.5 μf

32–19. (a) 150 ohms, 300 ohms

(b) 1.55 volts, 13.2 ohms

32–21. (a) 1000 ohms

(b) 13.6 watts

32–23. 90%

32–25. (a) 213 volts

(b) 11.7 cal/sec

32–27. (a) 780 watts (b) 562 watts

(c) 1980 rev/min

CHAPTER 33

33–1. (a) 20×10^{-6} w/m^2

(b) 7.1×10^{-6} w/m^2

(c) 20×10^{-6} w/m^2

(d) Zero

(e) 5.4×10^{-6} w/m^2

33–3. (a) Zero

(b) 1.41×10^{-6} w/m^2 $\angle 45°$

(c) 3×10^{-6} w/m^2 in pos. x-dir.

33–5. (a) 2 amp out of diagram

(b) 2.13×10^{-5} w/m^2

(c) 1.64×10^{-5} w/m^2

33–7. 238 amp

33–9. 72×10^{-5} n

33–11. 2.51×10^{-3} w/m^2

33–13. 3.42×10^{-3} w/m^2

33–15. 6.00×10^{-4} w/m^2

CHAPTER 34

34–1. $\mathcal{E}_A = 0$, $\mathcal{E}_C = 0.0707$ volt, $\mathcal{E}_D = 0.10$ volt

34–3. (a) 1 volt from B to A

(b) 1.25 n (c) 5 watts

34–5. 8.79 volts

34–7. (a) 0.885 rev/sec

(b) Zero

34–9. 9×10^{-6} volt

34–11. (a) $B = mv/qR$

(b) $\mathcal{E} = A\,\Delta B/\Delta t$

34–13. (a) 2080 rev/min

(b) 157 volts

34–15. (a) 1.19 volts

(b) 0.59 volt

34–17. 0.05 w/m^2

34–19. 2.7×10^{-4} coul

CHAPTER 35

35–1. (a) 0.300 w/m^2

(b) 398 amp·turns/m

(c) 99.83%

35–3. (a) 7.5 amp·m^2

(b) 7.5×10^{-3} newt·m

(c) 1.8% of H_c

35–5. 8 amp

35–7. 58.7 amp·turns/m, 7.35×10^{-5} w/m^2

35–9. 8×10^{-4} n·m

35–11. 424 amp·turns/m

35–13. 13.6 amp·turns/m

35–15. 0.14 sec

35–17. (a) 0.045 amp

(b) 0.012 amp

(c) 0.15 amp, 0.23 amp

CHAPTER 36

36–3. (a) 12 μsec

(b) 2.53 volts

36–5. (a) 0.05 amp (b) 1 amp/sec

(c) 0.5 amp/sec (d) 0.23 sec

(e) 1.97×10^{-2} amp

3.17×10^{-2} amp

3.89×10^{-2} amp

4.33×10^{-2} amp

36–7. 0.326 amp to right

36–9. (a) q (μcoul): 0, 400, 630, 870, 1000

(b) i (μa): 100, 60, 37, 14, 0

(c) 10 sec

(d) 6.9 sec

CHAPTER 37

37–1. (a) 127 cy/sec
(b) 7.97 cy/sec

37–3. (a) 377 ohms (b) 2.65 mh
(c) 2650 ohms
(d) 2650 μf

37–5. (a) 103.5 ohms, 613 ohms
(b) 63.9 ohms, 628 ohms

37–7. 56 v, 139 v, 56 v

37–9. 6.85 μf

37–11. (a) 515 ohms, 39°, i leads
(b) 505 ohms, 38°, i lags

37–13. (a) 138 ohms (b) 181 v
(c) 125 v

37–15. (a) 21 amp (b) 73 mh

37–19. (a) 10 amp (b) 100 v
(c) 42 v

37–23. 15 amp; 150 v, 750 v, 750 v,
zero, 150 v

37–25. (a) 6 ohms; 6×10^{-5} h
(b) 0.12 amp (c) 0.17 v

37–27. 47.2 ohms

37–29. 48 watts

37–31. (a) 150 μf
(b) 917 watts

37–33. 2760 v

37–35. 3×10^{18} cy/sec
6×10^{14} cy/sec
3×10^{9} cy/sec
10^{6} cy/sec

CHAPTER 38

38–1. $hf_0 = \phi$

38–3. 1.72×10^{8} cm/sec

CHAPTER 39

39–1. (a) 1.5×10^{-9} m,
1.5×10^{-3} μ,
1.5 mμ, 15 A .
(b) 5.37×10^{-7} m, 0.537 μ,
537 mμ, 5370 A

39–3. 232,000 mi

39–5. (a) 36 cm^2 (b) 0

39–7. 52,500 waves

39–9. (a) 1.98×10^{8} m/sec
(b) 1.515

39–11. 16.6 min

CHAPTER 40

40–3. (a) 54° 46′
(b) 82° 50′

40–5. 34° 50′

40–7. (a) 26° 14′
(b) Does not depend on it

40–9. 18.2 in.

40–11. 1.30

40–15. 30°

40–17. 52.3° for 400 mμ
47.4° for 700 mμ

CHAPTER 41

41–1. Half the observer's height

41–5. 9.88 cm, 5 cm

41–7. 3

41–9. 0.643 in., 0.143

41–11. (a) 45° (b) 0.53 in.

41–13. 3.0 cm

41–15. 1.35

41–17. $s' = 30$ cm, $m = -1$

41–19. 0.667 cm

CHAPTER 42

42–1. $4R$ from center of sphere
42–3. (a) The first image
(b) 30 cm (c) Real (d) At ∞
(e) Infinite
42–5. 50 cm
42–7. 1.5 cm
42–11.

R_1	R_2	f
10 cm	20 cm	40 cm
10 cm	−20 cm	13.3 cm
−10 cm	20 cm	−13.3 cm
−10 cm	−20 cm	−40 cm

42–13. (a) 6 cm and 12 cm from the object
(b) −2, −0.5
42–15. 60 cm to right of third lens
42–17. (a) 4f (b) 0
42–19. (a) 20.0 cm (b) 18.7 cm
42–21. (b) 12 cm
42–23. $t = 0.375$ in.
42–25. 1.23 cm

CHAPTER 43

43–1. 6.5 diopters
43–3. (a) 3.5 diopters
(b) −3.33 diopters
43–5. (a) 66.7 cm (b) 200 cm
43–7. (a) 2.5 (b) 7.14 cm
43–9. (a) 361×
(b) 2.77 × 10⁻⁵ cm

43–11. (a) 1.74 cm (b) −11.25×
(c) −112.5×
43–13. 0.506 ft
43–15. (a) −5 (b) 3.79 cm
43–17. $f/5$
43–19. (a) 2.86 cm
(b) 0.02 sec

CHAPTER 44

44–1. 1125 lumens
44–3. (a) 30 watts (b) 8700 lumens
(c) 290 lumens/watt
44–5. 52.3 watts
44–7. (a) 100 lumens/m²
(b) 0.762 m
44–9. (a) 51.2 lumens/m²
(b) 5.56 m

44–11. 7.08 m
44–13. 5.65 × 10⁵ watts
44–15. 41.5 cm from 25 candle lamp
44–17. (a) 44 lamps
(b) 44 kw = 59 hp

CHAPTER 46

46–1. 1 mm
46–3. 480 mμ
46–5. 0.71 × 10⁻⁵ cm
46–7. 106 mμ

46–9. 0.014 cm
46–11. 12.5°
46–13. 500 mμ

CHAPTER 47

47–1. 35° 32′
47–3. (a) 37° (b) Horizontal
47–5. 67° 22′

47–7. (a) 0.75 (b) 0.50 (c) 0.25
47–11. (b) 5.82 × 10⁻⁵ cm
47–13. Linearly polarized, rotated 90°

CONVERSION FACTORS

LENGTH:

$1 \text{ m} = 100 \text{ cm} = 1000 \text{ mm}$
$1 \text{ km} = 1000 \text{ m} = 0.6214 \text{ mile}$
$1 \text{ m} = 39.37 \text{ in.}; 1 \text{ cm} = 0.3937 \text{ in.}$
$1 \text{ ft} = 30.48 \text{ cm}; 1 \text{ in.} = 2.540 \text{ cm}$
$1 \text{ mi} = 5{,}280 \text{ ft} = 1.609 \text{ km}$
$1 \text{ A} = 10^{-8} \text{ cm}; 1\mu \text{ (micron)} = 10^{-4} \text{ cm}$

AREA:

$1 \text{ cm}^2 = 0.155 \text{ in.}^2; 1 \text{ m}^2 = 10^4 \text{ cm}^2 = 10.76 \text{ ft}^2$
$1 \text{ in.}^2 = 6.452 \text{ cm}^2; 1 \text{ ft}^2 = 144 \text{ in.}^2 = 0.0929 \text{ m}^2$

VOLUME:

$1 \text{ liter} = 1000 \text{ cm}^2 = 10^{-3} \text{ m}^3 = 0.0351 \text{ ft}^3 = 61 \text{ in.}^3$
$1 \text{ ft}^3 = 0.0283 \text{ m}^3 = 28.32 \text{ liters}; 1 \text{ in.}^3 = 16.39 \text{ cm}^3 = 7.5 \text{ gal}$

VELOCITY:

$1 \text{ cm/sec} = 0.03281 \text{ ft/sec}; 1 \text{ ft/sec} = 30.48 \text{ cm/sec}$
$1 \text{ mile/min} = 60 \text{ mi/hr} = 88 \text{ ft/sec}$

ACCELERATION:

$1 \text{ cm/sec}^2 = 0.03281 \text{ ft/sec}^2 = 0.01 \text{ m/sec}^2$
$30.48 \text{ cm/sec}^2 = 1 \text{ ft/sec}^2 = 0.3048 \text{ m/sec}^2$
$100 \text{ cm/sec}^2 = 3.281 \text{ ft/sec}^2 = 1 \text{ m/sec}^2$

FORCE:

$1 \text{ dyne} = 2.247 \times 10^{-6} \text{ lb} = 10^{-5} \text{ newton}$
$1.383 \times 10^4 \text{ dynes} = 0.0311 \text{ lb} = 0.1383 \text{ newton}$
$4.45 \times 10^5 \text{ dynes} = 1 \text{ lb} = 4.45 \text{ newtons}$
$10^5 \text{ dynes} = 0.2247 \text{ lb} = 1 \text{ newton}$

MASS:

$1 \text{ gm} = 6.85 \times 10^{-5} \text{ slug} = 10^{-3} \text{ kgm}$
$453.6 \text{ gm} = 0.0311 \text{ slug} = 0.4536 \text{ kgm}$
$1.459 \times 10^4 \text{ gm} = 1 \text{ slug} = 14.59 \text{ kgm}$
$10^3 \text{ gm} = 0.0685 \text{ slug} = 1 \text{ kgm}$

PRESSURE:

$1 \text{ atm} = 14.7 \text{ lb/in.}^2 = 1.013 \times 10^6 \text{ dynes/cm}^2$

ENERGY:

$1 \text{ joule} = 10^7 \text{ ergs} = 0.239 \text{ cal}; 1 \text{ cal} = 4.18 \text{ joule}$
$1 \text{ ev} = 10^{-6} \text{ Mev} = 1.60 \times 10^{-12} \text{ erg} = 1.07 \times 10^{-9} \text{ amu}$
$1 \text{ amu} = 1.66 \times 10^{-24} \text{ gm} = 1.49 \times 10^{-3} \text{ erg} = 931 \text{ Mev}$

COMMON LOGARITHMS

N	0	1	2	3	4	5	6	7	8	9
0	....	0000	3010	4771	6021	6990	7782	8451	9031	9542
1	0000	0414	0792	1139	1461	1761	2041	2304	2553	2788
2	3010	3222	3424	3617	3802	3979	4150	4314	4472	4624
3	4771	4914	5051	5185	5315	5441	5563	5682	5798	5911
4	6021	6128	6232	6335	6435	6532	6628	6721	6812	6902
5	6990	7076	7160	7243	7324	7404	7482	7559	7634	7709
6	7782	7853	7924	7993	8062	8129	8195	8261	8325	8388
7	8451	8513	8573	8633	8692	8751	8808	8865	8921	8976
8	9031	9085	9138	9191	9243	9294	9345	9395	9445	9494
9	9542	9590	9638	9685	9731	9777	9823	9868	9912	9956
10	0000	0043	0086	0128	0170	0212	0253	0294	0334	0374
11	0414	0453	0492	0531	0569	0607	0645	0682	0719	0755
12	0792	0828	0864	0899	0934	0969	1004	1038	1072	1106
13	1139	1173	1206	1239	1271	1303	1335	1367	1399	1430
14	1461	1492	1523	1553	1584	1614	1644	1673	1703	1732
15	1761	1790	1818	1847	1875	1903	1931	1959	1987	2014
16	2041	2068	2095	2122	2148	2175	2201	2227	2253	2279
17	2304	2330	2355	2380	2405	2430	2455	2480	2504	2529
18	2553	2577	2601	2625	2648	2672	2695	2718	2742	2765
19	2788	2810	2833	2856	2878	2900	2923	2945	2967	2989
20	3010	3032	3054	3075	3096	3118	3139	3160	3181	3201
21	3222	3243	3263	3284	3304	3324	3345	3365	3385	3404
22	3424	3444	3464	3483	3502	3522	3541	3560	3579	3598
23	3617	3636	3655	3674	3692	3711	3729	3747	3766	3784
24	3802	3820	3838	3856	3874	3892	3909	3927	3945	3962
25	3979	3997	4014	4031	4048	4065	4082	4099	4116	4133
26	4150	4166	4183	4200	4216	4232	4249	4265	4281	4298
27	4314	4330	4346	4362	4378	4393	4409	4425	4440	4456
28	4472	4487	4502	4518	4533	4548	4564	4579	4594	4609
29	4624	4639	4654	4669	4683	4698	4713	4728	4742	4757
30	4771	4786	4800	4814	4829	4843	4857	4871	4886	4900
31	4914	4928	4942	4955	4969	4983	4997	5011	5024	5038
32	5051	5065	5079	5092	5105	5119	5132	5145	5159	5172
33	5185	5198	5211	5224	5237	5250	5263	5276	5289	5302
34	5315	5328	5340	5353	5366	5378	5391	5403	5416	5428
35	5441	5453	5465	5478	5490	5502	5514	5527	5539	5551
36	5563	5575	5587	5599	5611	5623	5635	5647	5658	5670
37	5682	5694	5705	5717	5729	5740	5752	5763	5775	5786
38	5798	5809	5821	5832	5843	5855	5866	5877	5888	5899
39	5911	5922	5933	5944	5955	5966	5977	5988	5999	6010
40	6021	6031	6042	6053	6064	6075	6085	6096	6107	6117
41	6128	6138	6149	6160	6170	6180	6191	6201	6212	6222
42	6232	6243	6253	6263	6274	6284	6294	6304	6314	6325
43	6335	6345	6355	6365	6375	6385	6395	6405	6415	6425
44	6435	6444	6454	6464	6474	6484	6493	6503	6513	6522
45	6532	6542	6551	6561	6571	6580	6590	6599	6609	6618
46	6628	6637	6646	6656	6665	6675	6684	6693	6702	6712
47	6721	6730	6739	6749	6758	6767	6776	6785	6794	6803
48	6812	6821	6830	6839	6848	6857	6866	6875	6884	6893
49	6902	6911	6920	6928	6937	6946	6955	6964	6972	6981
50	6990	6998	7007	7016	7024	7033	7042	7050	7059	7067
N	0	1	2	3	4	5	6	7	8	9

COMMON LOGARITHMS

N	0	1	2	3	4	5	6	7	8	9
50	6990	6998	7007	7016	7024	7033	7042	7050	7059	7067
51	7076	7084	7093	7101	7110	7118	7126	7135	7143	7152
52	7160	7168	7177	7185	7193	7202	7210	7218	7226	7235
53	7243	7251	7259	7267	7275	7284	7292	7300	7308	7316
54	7324	7332	7340	7348	7356	7364	7372	7380	7388	7396
55	7404	7412	7419	7427	7435	7443	7451	7459	7466	7474
56	7482	7490	7497	7505	7513	7520	7528	7536	7543	7551
57	7559	7566	7574	7582	7589	7597	7604	7612	7619	7627
58	7634	7642	7649	7657	7664	7672	7679	7686	7694	7701
59	7709	7716	7723	7731	7738	7745	7752	7760	7767	7774
60	7782	7789	7796	7803	7810	7818	7825	7832	7839	7846
61	7853	7860	7868	7875	7882	7889	7896	7903	7910	7917
62	7924	7931	7938	7945	7952	7959	7966	7973	7980	7987
63	7993	8000	8007	8014	8021	8028	8035	8041	8048	8055
64	8062	8069	8075	8082	8089	8096	8102	8109	8116	8122
65	8129	8136	8142	8149	8156	8162	8169	8176	8182	8189
66	8195	8202	8209	8215	8222	8228	8235	8241	8248	8254
67	8261	8267	8274	8280	8287	8293	8299	8306	8312	8319
68	8325	8331	8338	8344	8351	8357	8363	8370	8376	8382
69	8388	8395	8401	8407	8414	8420	8426	8432	8439	8445
70	8451	8457	8463	8470	8476	8482	8488	8494	8500	8506
71	8513	8519	8525	8531	8537	8543	8549	8555	8561	8567
72	8573	8579	8585	8591	8597	8603	8609	8615	8621	8627
73	8633	8639	8645	8651	8657	8663	8669	8675	8681	8686
74	8692	8698	8704	8710	8716	8722	8727	8733	8739	8745
75	8751	8756	8762	8768	8774	8779	8785	8791	8797	8802
76	8808	8814	8820	8825	8831	8837	8842	8848	8854	8859
77	8865	8871	8876	8882	8887	8893	8899	8904	8910	8915
78	8921	8927	8932	8938	8943	8949	8954	8960	8965	8971
79	8976	8982	8987	8993	8998	9004	9009	9015	9020	9025
80	9031	9036	9042	9047	9053	9058	9063	9069	9074	9079
81	9085	9090	9096	9101	9106	9112	9117	9122	9128	9133
82	9138	9143	9149	9154	9159	9165	9170	9175	9180	9186
83	9191	9196	9201	9206	9212	9217	9222	9227	9232	9238
84	9243	9248	9253	9258	9263	9269	9274	9279	9284	9289
85	9294	9299	9304	9309	9315	9320	9325	9330	9335	9340
86	9345	9350	9355	9360	9365	9370	9375	9380	9385	9390
87	9395	9400	9405	9410	9415	9420	9425	9430	9435	9440
88	9445	9450	9455	9460	9465	9469	9474	9479	9484	9489
89	9494	9499	9504	9509	9513	9518	9523	9528	9533	9538
90	9542	9547	9552	9557	9562	9566	9571	9576	9581	9586
91	9590	9595	9600	9605	9609	9614	9619	9624	9628	9633
92	9638	9643	9647	9652	9657	9661	9666	9671	9675	9680
93	9685	8689	9694	9699	9703	9708	9713	9717	9722	9727
94	9731	9736	9741	9745	9750	9754	9759	9763	9768	9773
95	9777	9782	9786	9791	9795	9800	9805	9809	9814	9818
96	9823	9827	9832	9836	9841	9845	9850	9854	9859	9863
97	9868	9872	9877	9881	9886	9890	9894	9899	9903	9908
98	9912	9917	9921	9926	9930	9934	9939	9943	9948	9952
99	9956	9961	9965	9969	9974	9978	9983	9987	9991	9996
100	0000	0004	0009	0013	0017	0022	0026	0030	0035	0039
N	0	1	2	3	4	5	6	7	8	9

NATURAL TRIGONOMETRIC FUNCTIONS

Angle					Angle				
De-gree	Ra-dian	Sine	Co-sine	Tan-gent	De-gree	Ra-dian	Sine	Co-sine	Tan-gent
0°	.000	0.000	1.000	0.000					
1°	.017	.018	1.000	.018	46°	0.803	0.719	0.695	1.036
2°	.035	.035	0.999	.035	47°	.820	.731	.682	1.072
3°	.052	.052	.999	.052	48°	.838	.743	.669	1.111
4°	.070	.070	.998	.070	49°	.855	.755	.656	1.150
5°	.087	.087	.996	.088	50°	.873	.766	.643	1.192
6°	.105	.105	.995	.105	51°	.890	.777	.629	1.235
7°	.122	.122	.993	.123	52°	.908	.788	.616	1.280
8°	.140	.139	.990	.141	53°	.925	.799	.602	1.327
9°	.157	.156	.988	.158	54°	.942	.809	.588	1.376
10°	.175	.174	.985	.176	55°	.960	.819	.574	1.428
11°	.192	.191	.982	.194	56°	.977	.829	.559	1.483
12°	.209	.208	.978	.213	57°	.995	.839	.545	1.540
13°	.227	.225	.974	.231	58°	1.012	.848	.530	1.600
14°	.244	.242	.970	.249	59°	1.030	.857	.515	1.664
15°	.262	.259	.966	.268	60°	1.047	.866	.500	1.732
16°	.279	.276	.961	.287	61°	1.065	.875	.485	1.804
17°	.297	.292	.956	.306	62°	1.082	.883	.470	1.881
18°	.314	.309	.951	.325	63°	1.100	.891	.454	1.963
19°	.332	.326	.946	.344	64°	1.117	.899	.438	2.050
20°	.349	.342	.940	.364	65°	1.134	.906	.423	2.145
21°	.367	.358	.934	.384	66°	1.152	.914	.407	2.246
22°	.384	.375	.927	.404	67°	1.169	.921	.391	2.356
23°	.401	.391	.921	.425	68°	1.187	.927	.375	2.475
24°	.419	.407	.914	.445	69°	1.204	.934	.358	2.605
25°	.436	.423	.906	.466	70°	1.222	.940	.342	2.747
26°	.454	.438	.899	.488	71°	1.239	.946	.326	2.904
27°	.471	.454	.891	.510	72°	1.257	.951	.309	3.078
28°	.489	.470	.883	.532	73°	1.274	.956	.292	3.271
29°	.506	.485	.875	.554	74°	1.292	.961	.276	3.487
30°	.524	.500	.866	.577	75°	1.309	.966	.259	3.732
31°	.541	.515	.857	.601	76°	1.326	.970	.242	4.011
32°	.559	.530	.848	.625	77°	1.344	.974	.225	4.331
33°	.576	.545	.839	.649	78°	1.361	.978	.208	4.705
34°	.593	.559	.829	.675	79°	1.379	.982	.191	5.145
35°	.611	.574	.819	.700	80°	1.396	.985	.174	5.671
36°	.628	.588	.809	.727	81°	1.414	.988	.156	6.314
37°	.646	.602	.799	.754	82°	1.431	.990	.139	7.115
38°	.663	.616	.788	.781	83°	1.449	.993	.122	8.144
39°	.681	.629	.777	.810	84°	1.466	.995	.105	9.514
40°	.698	.643	.766	.839	85°	1.484	.996	.087	11.43
41°	.716	.658	.755	.869	86°	1.501	.998	.070	14.30
42°	.733	.669	.743	.900	87°	1.518	.999	.052	19.08
43°	.751	.682	.731	.933	88°	1.536	.999	.035	28.64
44°	.768	.695	.719	.966	89°	1.553	1.000	.018	57.29
45°	.785	.707	.707	1.000	90°	1.571	1.000	.000	∞

PERIODIC TABLE OF THE ELEMENTS

Atomic weights are based on the most recent values adopted by the International Union of Chemistry. (For artificially produced elements, the approximate atomic weight of the most stable isotope is given in brackets.)

Period	Series	I	II	III	IV	V	VI	VII	VIII			O
1	1	1 H 1.0080										2 He 4.003
2	2	3 Li 6.940	4 Be 9.013	5 B 10.82	6 C 12.011	7 N 14.008	8 O 16.0000	9 F 19.00				10 Ne 20.183
3	3	11 Na 22.991	12 Mg 24.32	13 Al 26.98	14 Si 28.09	15 P 30.975	16 S 32.066	17 Cl 35.457				18 A 39.944
4	4	19 K 39.100	20 Ca 40.08	21 Sc 44.96	22 Ti 47.90	23 V 50.95	24 Cr 52.01	25 Mn 54.94	26 Fe 55.85	27 Co 58.94	28 Ni 58.71	
	5	29 Cu 63.54	30 Zn 65.38	31 Ga 69.72	32 Ge 72.60	33 As 74.91	34 Se 78.96	35 Br 79.916				36 Kr 83.80
5	6	37 Rb 85.48	38 Sr 87.63	39 Y 88.92	40 Zr 91.22	41 Nb 92.91	42 Mo 95.95	43 Tc [99]	44 Ru 101.1	45 Rh 102.91	46 Pd 106.4	
	7	47 Ag 107.880	48 Cd 112.41	49 In 114.82	50 Sn 118.70	51 Sb 121.76	52 Te 127.61	53 I 126.91				54 Xe 131.30
6	8	55 Cs 132.91	56 Ba 137.36	57–71 Lanthanide series*	72 Hf 178.50	73 Ta 180.95	74 W 183.86	75 Re 186.22	76 Os 190.2	77 Ir 192.2	78 Pt 195.09	
	9	79 Au 197.0	80 Hg 200.61	81 Tl 204.39	82 Pb 207.21	83 Bi 209.00	84 Po 210	85 At [210]				86 Rn 222
7	10	87 Fr [223]	88 Ra 226.05	89– Actinide series**								

*Lanthanide series: 57 La 138.92 | 58 Ce 140.13 | 59 Pr 140.92 | 60 Nd 144.27 | 61 Pm [147] | 62 Sm 150.35 | 63 Eu 152.0 | 64 Gd 157.26 | 65 Tb 158.93 | 66 Dy 162.51 | 67 Ho 164.94 | 68 Er 167.27 | 69 Tm 168.94 | 70 Yb 173.04 | 71 Lu 174.99

**Actinide series: 89 Ac 227 | 90 Th 232.05 | 91 Pa 231 | 92 U 238.07 | 93 Np [237] | 94 Pu [242] | 95 Am [243] | 96 Cm [245] | 97 Bk [249] | 98 Cf [249] | 99 E [253] | 100 Fm [255] | 101 Md [256] | 102 No | 103

FUNDAMENTAL CONSTANTS

Largely based on values in the *American Institute of Physics Handbook* (1957). The probable error for each value has been omitted here; it should properly be considered part of the datum.

Name of Quantity	Symbol	Value
Velocity of light in vacuum	c	2.9979×10^8 m/sec
Charge of electron	q_e	-1.602×10^{-19} coul = -4.803×10^{-10} statcoul
Rest mass of electron	m_e	9.108×10^{-31} kgm
Ratio of charge to mass of electron	q_e/m_e	1.759×10^{11} coul/kgm = 5.273×10^7 statcoul/gm
Planck's constant	h	6.625×10^{-34} j·sec
Boltzmann's constant	k	1.380×10^{-23} j/°K
Avogadro's number (chemical scale)	N_0	6.023×10^{23} molecules/mole
Universal gas constant (chemical scale)	R	8.314 j/mole·°K
Mechanical equivalent of heat	J	4.185×10^3 j/kcal
Standard atmospheric pressure	1 atm	1.013×10^5 new/m^2
Volume of ideal gas at 0°C and 1 atm (chemical scale)		22.415 liter/mole
Absolute zero of temperature	0°K	-273.16°C
Acceleration due to gravity (sea level, at equator)		9.78049 m/sec^2
Universal gravitational constant	G	6.673×10^{-11} new·m^2/kgm^2
Mass of earth	m_E	5.975×10^{24} kgm
Mean radius of earth		6.371×10^6 m = 3959 mi
Equatorial radius of earth		6.378×10^6 m = 3963 mi
Mean distance from earth to sun	1 AU	1.49×10^{11} m = 9.29×10^7 mi
Eccentricity of earth's orbit		0.0167
Mean distance from earth to moon		3.84×10^8 m $\doteq$ 60 earth radii
Diameter of sun		1.39×10^9 m = 8.64×10^5 mi
Mass of sun	m_S	1.99×10^{30} kgm = 333,000 × mass of earth
Coulomb's law constant	C	8.98×10^9 new·m^2/coul^2
Faraday's constant (1 faraday)	F	96,500 coul/mole
Mass of neutral hydrogen atom	m_{H^1}	1.008142 amu
Mass of proton	m_p	1.007593 amu
Mass of neutron	m_n	1.008982 amu

FUNDAMENTAL CONSTANTS—*Continued*

Name of Quantity	Symbol	Value
Mass of electron	m_e	5.488×10^{-4} amu
Ratio of mass of proton to mass of electron	m_p/m_e	1836.12
Rydberg constant for nucleus of infinite mass	R_∞	109,737 cm^{-1}
Rydberg constant for hydrogen	R_H	109,678 cm^{-1}
Wien displacement law constant		0.2898 cm·°K

Numerical constants: $\pi = 3.142$; $e = 2.718$; $\sqrt{2} = 1.414$; $\sqrt{3} = 1.732$

GREEK ALPHABET

A	α	Alpha	N	ν	Nu
B	β	Beta	Ξ	ξ	Xi
Γ	γ	Gamma	O	o	Omicron
Δ	δ	Delta	Π	π	Pi
E	ϵ	Epsilon	P	ρ	Rho
Z	ζ	Zeta	Σ	σ	Sigma
H	η	Eta	T	τ	Tau
Θ	θ	Theta	Υ	υ	Upsilon
I	ι	Iota	Φ	ϕ	Phi
K	κ	Kappa	X	χ	Chi
Λ	λ	Lambda	Ψ	ψ	Psi
M	μ	Mu	Ω	ω	Omega

INDEX

INDEX

Printed in Japan
Tokyo